TRADE UNIONISM AND LABOR PROBLEMS

Also published in

REPRINTS OF ECONOMIC CLASSICS

BY JOHN R. COMMONS

THE DISTRIBUTION OF WEALTH [1893]
LABOR AND ADMINISTRATION [1913]
PROPORTIONAL REPRESENTATION [1907]
RACES AND IMMIGRANTS IN AMERICA [1924]
SOCIAL REFORM AND THE CHURCH [1894]
THE SOCIOLOGICAL THEORY OF SOVEREIGNTY [1899-1900]
TRADE UNIONISM AND LABOR PROBLEMS
Second Series [1921]

JOHN R. COMMONS & JOHN B. ANDREWS

PRINCIPLES OF LABOR LEGISLATION 4TH EDITION [1936]

JOHN R. COMMONS *Et Al*

HISTORY OF LABOR IN THE UNITED STATES,
4 VOLS. [1918, 1935]

TRADE UNIONISM AND LABOR PROBLEMS

EDITED

WITH AN INTRODUCTION

BY

JOHN R. COMMONS

PROFESSOR OF POLITICAL ECONOMY, UNIVERSITY OF WISCONSIN

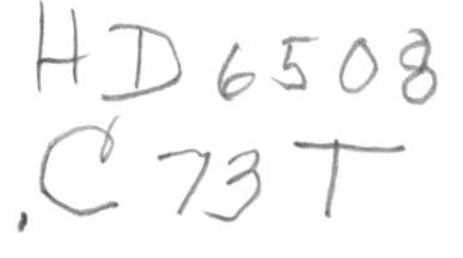

REPRINTS OF ECONOMIC CLASSICS

AUGUSTUS M. KELLEY · PUBLISHERS

NEW YORK · 1967

First Edition 1905
(Boston: Ginn & Co., 1905)

Reprinted 1967 by

Augustus M. Kelley · Publishers

Library of Congress Catalogue Card Number
66-21664

Printed in the United States of America
by Sentry Press, New York, N. Y. 10019

PREFACE

This book is intended to do for the study of labor unions and labor problems what Ripley's "Trusts, Pools and Corporations" has done for the study of capital and its organization; and the preface to Dr. Ripley's book states the purpose of this book. It is "intended to be more than a mere collection of economic reprints," and is "planned for use specifically as a text-book; not merely as a handy volume for reference, or as a collection of original documents. . . . It denotes a deliberate attempt at the application to the teaching of economics of the *case system*, so long successful in our law schools. With this end in view, each chapter is intended to illustrate a single, definite, typical phase of the general subject. The primary motive is to further the interests of sound economic teaching, with especial reference to the study of concrete problems of great public and private interest. A difficulty in the substitution of present-day social and economic studies for the good old-fashioned linguistic ones, or for the modern sciences, — a difficulty especially peculiar to descriptive economics as differentiated from economic theory, — has always been to secure data sufficiently concrete, definite, and convenient to form a basis for analysis, discussion, and criticism. . . . The first requisite, therefore, for the successful conduct of economic instruction in the descriptive field is to provide raw material; which in discussion, supplementary to the general lectures, may be worked over in detail in the class room."

Selected, as these chapters are, mainly from the economic journals, it has not always been possible to restrict each chapter to a case illustrating a single phase or topic of the general subject. It has therefore been necessary to furnish in the Introduction and the Index a set of cross references by which the student may bring together the several illustrations of each phase. In this way it is hoped that two objects may be secured: first, that of viewing each industry and its labor conditions as a unit, wherein the several topics, such as division of labor, apprenticeship, minimum wage, "closed shop," and so forth, shall appear in their relations to the whole; and, second, that of furnishing the data for such general statements or conclusions regarding these topics as will make due allowance for the variety of attendant circumstances under which they are exhibited. The latter is properly the case method of study, as will be appreciated from the two chapters devoted to the decisions of courts.

Since the volume is made up of selected cases illustrating a branch of political economy of world-wide variety and profound importance, it is intended to be looked upon as supplementary to a treatise like Adams and Sumner's "Labor Problems," or to the more general works on political economy, or to a lecture course. For the general public it makes available the contributions of many original investigators, scattered through the economic and trade journals, which otherwise would be restricted to those who have access to the great libraries of the country.

I wish to express my great indebtedness to Professor W. Z. Ripley, the editor of this series, for his assistance and criticisms in the process of making selections and otherwise; and to the authors of the several papers for permission to reprint. It is also a privilege to be able to acknowledge the willing coöperation of the editors of the *Political Science Quarterly*, the *Quarterly Journal of Economics*, the *Yale Review*, the *Economic Journal*, the *Annals of the American Academy of Political and Social Science*, the *Review of Reviews*, the *Columbia University Studies in History, Economics, and Public Law*, the *Engineering Magazine*, the *Sibley Journal of Mechanical Engineering*, the *Atlanta University Press*, the *National Civic Federation Review*, and *Charities*.

My colleagues, Professor T. S. Adams and Professor E. A. Gilmore, have given me aid which I heartily appreciate, and I have been fortunate in the assistance rendered by Miss Helen L. Sumner of the Wisconsin University Graduate School.

JOHN R. COMMONS.

CONTENTS

INTRODUCTION

Though organized for contest and marked by a history of struggle, the goal of trade unionism is the trade agreement.[1] This implies the equal organization of employers and the settlement of a wage scale and conditions of work through conferences of representatives. The trade agreement must be distinguished from "arbitration," which, properly speaking, is the reference of disputes to an umpire. Far from being a simple solution of that kind, it is a form of constitutional government, with its legislative, executive, and judicial branches, its common law and statute law, its penalties and sanctions. As an economic organization its object is, on the one hand, to change the status of labor from one of caprice and uncertainty to one of definiteness, and, on the other, to equalize competitive conditions among employers so far as their labor costs are concerned.

That the trade agreement is subject to abuse and may become a conspiracy of employers and unions against the public is intimated in two or three chapters.[2] Where such is the case the agreement has passed beyond its legitimate scope of protecting labor and equalizing the competitive labor conditions of employers. It will be noticed, however, that in such agreements the union may become the cat's-paw of an association, usually of small employers or contractors, and may subject its officers to corruption and itself to internal dissensions.

Labor unions differ among themselves in their internal organization, the principal distinction among American unions being that of "industrial" and "trade" unions. The miners' union[3] is the most prominent example of the industrial union, by which is meant the inclusion in one organization of all employees in an establishment. Another example is that of

[1] Pages 1, 65, 154. [2] Pages 39, 57, 74, 94. [3] Page 13.

the butcher workmen.[1] The "trade" union, or the union including only workmen of a single craft, is seen in its typical form in the several unions of the building trades,[2] but it will be noticed that, through the practice of the sympathetic strike under the control of a "building trades council," or a "board of delegates," the several trade unions working on a building are able to combine their strength in a way similar to that of an industrial union. The teamsters' union[3] is peculiar in that, while all of its members follow the same craft, yet they work under very different conditions in different industries. Each industry, therefore, has its own craft union, but the several unions in a city are united in a joint council controlled by the same international organization. The same is true of the joint council of the packing trades,[4] and herein they differ from the building trades councils, the separate unions of which are subject to separate national trade unions.

Typical cases of the conflicts between employers and unions by way of strikes, lockouts, and boycotts are deserving of close analysis.[5] They are often described in the decisions of courts,[6] in some cases leading to trade agreements, in others to the destruction of the labor union. Where the trade agreement has broken down generally, as in New Zealand and Australia, through the defeat of the unions in strikes or lockouts, industrial peace has been sought through compulsory, or rather state, arbitration, and it is a significant fact that a similar result is reached by state regulation of the minimum wage.[7] In the United States the much greater strength of organized labor in several industries is reflected in the trend of thought and practical interest away from state adjustment of the economic demands of unions and towards the restraint and control of the unions themselves by the state. This is seen in the discussion of measures designed to impose greater responsibility on unions, illustrated by the demand for incorporation.[8] The discussion

[1] Page 222.
[2] Pages 65, 87.
[3] Page 36.
[4] Page 223.
[5] Pages 65, 87, 222.
[6] Page 156.
[7] Page 195.
[8] Page 137.

of this subject brings out more clearly than has been done before the legal nature of these organizations. Here the attitude of the courts becomes of paramount importance, and certain illustrative cases have been selected, showing the grounds on which judges assert the jurisdiction of courts of equity in labor disputes through the writ of injunction, as well as conflicting decisions in different jurisdictions on the boycott and discriminations against nonunionists.[1] On the latter subject will be found a concise statement of the present position of American law in the several states.[2]

Underlying the organization of labor are the economic conditions and issues that provoke it into existence. Two industries which offer examples of division of labor not associated with machinery are slaughtering and meat packing[3] and the factory system in clothing manufacture;[4] and the articles on these industries reveal the two supreme advantages of a minute division of labor, namely, increased speed of the workman and openings for the cheap labor of immigrants, women, and children. The chapter on the introduction of the linotype[5] is selected, not because it is typical of the effects on labor of the introduction of machinery, but because it presents the exceptionally wise policy of an intelligent labor organization in welcoming the machine and sharing its gains with the employer, the inventor, and the public. In other industries machinery has often displaced the union of skilled labor, and the resulting effects through division of labor should be looked for rather in the articles on slaughtering and meat packing and clothing manufacture.

Division of labor and machinery make possible the substitution of payment by the piece in place of payment by the day or hour, since the workman is specialized on simple and uniform operations, whose quality can readily be inspected. But that which is nominally day work becomes actually piecework when a certain output or task is required. This transition from real

[1] Page 156.
[2] Page 183.
[3] Page 222.
[4] Page 316.
[5] Page 250.

day wages to nominal day wages but actual piece wages is seen in the clothing trade and in slaughtering.[1] The object and effect of piece wages are greatly to increase the speed of the workman, with the result that the higher earnings tempt, and through competition, even force the employer to "cut" the piece rates, so that the workman is earning no more by his intense speed than he did when he took his time. The same result is reached on day wages when a foreman or a contractor is remunerated according to his success in reducing costs.[2] One object of labor organizations is to check this intense speed, sometimes by placing an absolute limit on the amount of work permitted to be done in a given time,[3] sometimes by reducing the task,[4] and sometimes by prohibiting piecework, bonus, and task systems.[5] This is usually denounced by employers as restriction of output, and denied by the unions, but the distinction should clearly be made between the *fact* of restriction and the *justification*. Advanced as a measure of protection to health and to the older men, a restriction of this kind is, in principle, justifiable, and the only question is that of drawing the line between what is a fair output and what is excessive. Restriction is also justified as a protective measure in cases where the employer takes advantage of increased earnings to cut the piece rate.

The matter of restriction of output has attracted larger attention in Great Britain than in the United States, and the value of the "case method" could not better be illustrated than in the article by the manager of the *Manchester Guardian*.[6] The simple question, "Do unions restrict output?" cannot receive a truthful general answer. Each allegation must be investigated with reference to all the circumstances, including the attitude of employers.[7] That this involves technical and detailed knowledge of the business, such as that displayed by the writer

[1] Pages 225, 324.
[2] Pages 236, 326.
[3] Pages 107, 227.
[4] Page 328.
[5] Page 268.
[6] Page 289.
[7] See also Special Report of the U. S. Bureau of Labor, Department of Commerce and Labor, on "Regulation and Restriction of Output." It may be obtained through congressmen.

of the chapter in question, should raise a warning to those who without such knowledge accept the *ex parte* statements of the parties to this acute and invidious dispute.

That restriction of output is sometimes a protective measure is now recognized by thoughtful employers, as is seen in their increasing approval of the "premium system," which is designed to meet that objection.[1] The unions also naturally look with suspicion on this system for reasons not fully brought out in the chapter on this subject, because in the hands of a driving foreman or superintendent it tends to become a task system under the form of a so-called "time base." This becomes a "dead line," since the employee who is not able to earn a premium is discharged, and if, in addition, the employer cuts the time base, he thereby increases the task, and the effect is the same as when he cuts the piece rate. The virtue of the premium system is that it automatically cuts the piece rates when the output is increased and thereby lessens the temptation of the employer arbitrarily to cut them. If once either the premium rate or, more important, the time base is cut, the system breaks down and reverts to the evils of piecework which it is designed to obviate.

A mark of trade-union policy under the day-wage system as distinguished from piecework is the minimum wage. That this is not a uniform wage is seen in different chapters. The significance of the minimum wage in protecting the union appears in the policy of the butcher workmen[2] and the coal miners,[3] where it operates to give a preference to members of the union, while its operation on a large scale, covering many industries under legislative enactment, shows itself as a substitute for compulsory arbitration.[4] The theory of the minimum wage is accepted by employers when they adopt the premium system,[5] although they add to that theory a device for speeding up the workmen which is objectionable from the standpoint of a union like that of the printers.[6]

[1] Page 274.
[2] Page 244.
[3] Page 345.
[4] Page 207.
[5] Page 278.
[6] Page 268.

Owing to minute division of labor and specialization of work American industry has failed to train up the all-round mechanic, and this failure has been seriously felt during the recent rapid expansion of trade. Many large establishments[1] have begun systematically to provide this training, the object being mainly to secure men for the leading positions, such as foremen, superintendents, and gang leaders, to supervise and direct the relatively unskilled and specialized machine hands and piece workers. The apprentice system, therefore, applies to scarcely more than 5 or 10 per cent of the positions in such an establishment, reliance still being placed on the general labor market for supplying the mass of their workmen. On the part of smaller establishments which cannot afford the expense of an apprenticeship system the subject has been taken up by associations of manufacturers, and efforts are being made in many parts of the country to establish technical and industrial schools supported by private endowment or by state and municipal aid. The important distinction between practical shop work and technical school work is touched upon in the chapter dealing with this subject, showing the correlation between the two that is sought to be maintained in the modern as distinguished from the old system of apprenticeship.

The characteristic feature of American labor problems is that of the many nationalities and races working together under the same management. Several of the chapters in this volume, while dealing with other topics, reveal this great underlying social fact. The displacement of earlier nationalities by newer types of immigrants with lower standards of living appears at many points, and at the same time the resistance to this displacement through the "closed shop" and preference to union men is apparent. The industrial and social characteristics of various peoples afford a field of study in themselves, but the issues produced by this competition of races appear in their extreme form in the chapter on the Negro artisan.[2]

[1] Page 304.

[2] Page 349. See also pages 23, 241, 245, 317, 336, 379, 424, 491.

The chapter on the employment of women in the clothing trade[1] is in part a sequel to that on the sweating system. While the latter shows the modern development of that system, influenced by the immigration of Russian Jews, the former shows the protective barriers which the garment workers' union has been able to throw about one branch of the trade through the use of the union label. On account of the limited constituency appealed to through the label, the position of women in that industry is not typical of their employment in general, as can be seen in the statistical chapter on women's wages in manual work[2] and in the work of women in meat packing.[3] The subject of child labor, for reasons stated in the chapter illustrative of that subject,[4] has its greatest interest and social importance in the employment of girls.

Of equal significance with the matter of wages and methods of payment are those questions that deal with the social consequences of American industry. Foremost is that of health in occupations, with its related subject, temperance. That there is both an industrial and an individual side to this question is brought out by the writer on the printer's health.[5] The reduction in the hours of labor[6] is the most demonstrable fruit of labor unions, but the fact that it must be accompanied by a better use of the leisure gained is also made plain by the same writer.

The activities of unions in reducing the daily period of work is all the more important on account of the obstacles in the way of state regulation in the United States. These obstacles are found more in our form of government than in our economic conditions. The leading state in this line of protecting employees' welfare[7] is handicapped by the lack of uniformity consequent upon our federal system, while the constitutions of the states and the nation, under the often diverse decisions of the courts, prevent the legislatures from doing what in other countries is

[1] Page 371.
[2] Page 396.
[3] Page 238.
[4] Page 423. See also pages 242, 345.
[5] Page 436.
[6] Page 454.
[7] Page 482.

solely a matter of legislative discretion.[1] Though the courts are clear and united on the principles underlying their decisions, they differ widely in their estimate of the facts set forth in any particular case as a justification of the legislative act. Even an amendment to a state constitution is not enough to remove this subject from judicial discretion, since the Supreme Court of the United States, under the fourteenth amendment, has shown its determination to restrain state enactments wherever its judgment does not approve the necessity of such legislation. These principles appear in the decisions in the case of *Holden* v. *Hardy* and *Lochner* v. *New York*.[1]

Unquestionably the most advanced act of government in caring for the welfare of working people is found in the movement away from employers' liability under the common law to workmen's compensation and compulsory insurance under statute law.[2] That this movement is as yet confined to foreign countries renders it no less interesting by way of comparison with American practice, as pointed out in Chapter XXV.

More perplexing than all labor problems is that of irregular and uncertain employment. The cycles of prosperity and depression affect both capital and labor alike and obstruct the best intentioned efforts of employers, unions, and legislatures. An idea of the significance of this distressing problem may be seen in the slaughtering and meat-packing industry,[3] and its influence is sometimes seen in the policy of restricting output in order to "make work" or "spread out work." Attempts to lighten the evils of unemployment are seen in the out-of-work benefits of the cigar makers,[4] in the efforts of Swiss cantons to provide relief by way of insurance,[5] and in the public employment offices of the United States and Germany.[6]

JOHN R. COMMONS.

[1] Page 509.
[2] Pages 546, 574.
[3] Page 229.
[4] Page 527.
[5] Page 589.
[6] Page 603.

TRADE UNIONISM AND LABOR PROBLEMS

I

TRADE AGREEMENTS[1]

Philanthropists have long been dreaming of the time when capital and labor should lay aside the strike and boycott and should resort to arbitration. By arbitration they understand the submission of differences to a disinterested third party. But the philanthropists have overlooked a point. Arbitration is never accepted until each party to a dispute is equally afraid of the other; and when they have reached that point, they can adopt something better than arbitration, — namely, negotiation. This distinction was clearly brought out at the notable conference on arbitration held at Chicago in December, 1900, under the auspices of the National Civic Federation. All the speakers were men of practical experience, and they agreed that arbitration is impossible without organization, and that two equally powerful organizations can negotiate as well as arbitrate. This higher form of industrial peace—negotiation—has now reached a formal stage in a half dozen large industries in the United States, which, owing to its remarkable likeness to parliamentary government in the country of its origin, England, may well be called constitutional government in industry.

The longshoremen and the dock managers of the Great Lakes now meet twice a year in a grand parliament of two houses, — the House of Lords and the House of Commons. The House of Lords is a primary assembly of all the dock managers along

[1] From the *Review of Reviews*, March, 1901.

the lakes, each firm or corporation appearing in its primary right of ownership. The House of Commons is a representative assembly of two delegates from each local union of longshoremen. The dock managers, to the number of twenty or thirty, meet in their house on one side of the street; the longshoremen, to the number of sixty or more, meet in another house on the other side. Each house appoints a conference committee of four or five members, including its president and secretary. These committees receive proper instructions from their constituent bodies. They meet in joint sessions, where they present their demands and counter-demands. They are referred back to the respective houses for discussion and further instructions. In this way, for ten or fifteen days, they higgle and bluff and parry until they can agree on a scale of wages and conditions of labor for every port and every kind of traffic under their joint jurisdiction. There is no arbitration; nothing is submitted to a disinterested third party. Each house has a veto on the other. The legislation adopted must be such that each independently consents to it; not that each is fully satisfied with it, but that each is convinced that nothing better can be secured without civil war, i.e. a strike or lockout. In this way, some twenty dock companies and several thousand dock laborers have created the highest form of industrial peace, — constitutional government.

The bituminous mine operators and the bituminous mine workers of the four great states of Illinois, Indiana, Ohio, and Pennsylvania have essentially the same constitution, except that the two houses meet at times upon the same floor. This annual interstate conference of the bituminous coal industry is the most picturesque and inspiring event in the modern world of business. Here is an industry where, for many years, industrial war was chronic, bloodshed frequent, distrust, hatred, and poverty universal. To-day the leaders of the two sides come together for a two weeks' parliament, face to face, with plain speaking, without politics, religion, or demagogy; and there they legislate for an industry that sends upon the market annually $200,000,000 of product. At the annual joint conference of 1900 — the third in the history of their constitution — there were presented the credentials of 195 operators and 450 miners. The operators, like the dock managers, were there, each in his own right, as owners of coal mines in the four states. The miners were there as the elected representatives of 110,000 mine workers in the employment of these same operators. Here were more than 600 men, sitting on the same floor, the employers on the right side, the employees on the left side, each subdivided in four groups, according to their four states, as follows:

Operators	States	Miners
72	Illinois	235
60	Indiana (Dists. 8 and 11)	60
50	Ohio	90
13	Pennsylvania (Dist. 5 and Central Field)	65
195	Total	450

Plainly, if the two sides of this conference are to be placed on an equality, the 450 miners cannot be permitted to outvote the 195 operators. At the same time, it is an advantage for them to meet and vote together, instead of separately, as is done by the longshoremen and dock managers. This obstacle is overcome by giving to the operators 16 votes and the miners 16 votes, subdivided into 4 votes for each state. Thus the 235 miners of Illinois have the same number of votes as the 13 operators of Pennsylvania, and so on. Their votes are cast by the chairman of each delegation. Finally, and most significant of all, while a majority vote decides all questions of procedure, a *unanimous* vote is required on all "main and principal questions," i.e. questions affecting the proposed scale of wages and trade agreement. The theory is that there are just two parties to the bargain, — the employer and the workman. And, like any voluntary purchase and sale, each party must consent to all the terms. This unanimous vote is brought about in the following way. Of course, six hundred men cannot "get down to business." Not only is the opportunity too great for cheap and loud talk, but the main discussion is being continually thrown off the track by subordinate topics. Consequently, the joint conference appoints a "joint scale committee" of thirty-two, including four operators from each state and four miners from each state, each selected by their respective caucuses. But this committee of thirty-two finds itself also too large. It therefore appoints from its own number a "subscale committee" of sixteen, which reports its conclusions back to the separate houses.

The most comforting feature of these negotiations is the matter-of-fact way in which each side takes the other. There is none of that old-time hypocrisy on the part of the employers, that their great interest in life is to shower blessings upon their hands; and there is none of that ranting demagogy on the part of the workmen about the dignity of labor and the iniquity of capital. On the contrary, each side frankly admits that its ruling motive is self-interest; that it is trying to get as much as it can and to give as little as it must; and that the only sanction which compels them to come together, and to stay together until they reach a unanimous vote, is the positive knowledge that otherwise the mines will shut down and neither the miner will earn wages nor the operator reap profits. It is simply wholesome fear that backs their discussions; the capitalist knows that there are no other laborers in the world whom he can import as "scabs" to take the places of those whose representatives face him in this conference and this scale committee, and he knows, too, from a severe experience, that every one of these 110,000 miners will obey as one man the voice of these their chosen representatives. The miners know, also, that these capitalists with whom they are negotiating are the very ones who control their only opportunities for earning the wages that feed themselves and their families. Consequently, everybody knows that an agreement must be reached before adjournment, or else the industry will be reduced to anarchy, and their wages and profits, to say nothing of lives, will be destroyed.

The above statement as to the unanimous vote needs qualification. The method of voting is rather that of the *unit rule*, combined with *unanimous vote of the units*. It will be noticed from what was said that there are 8 units, 4 for the operators and 4 for the miners, each casting 4 votes. Now, each unit makes up its vote by a majority vote of the individuals within the unit. Indeed, it sometimes occurs that after a so-called unanimous vote an individual operator rises to protest against it. But, as a rule, by caucusing and conferring, the operators vote solidly together and the miners solidly together. The two sides are brought together only through the services of the scale committee, as follows:

In every trade agreement there are usually two large and distinct questions on which the parties differ, namely, wages and methods of managing employees. The labor side wants higher wages (including short hours) and restrictions on bosses and foremen. The employer side wants low wages and a free hand for the boss. Each side thereupon comes to the joint conference with demands more extreme than it expects to see granted. At the conference of 1900 the operators offered an advance of 9 cents per ton and the miners demanded an advance of 20 cents. The operators wished to retain the system of paying for the screened coal only, and not for the slack and waste; but the miners demanded payment on the basis of the "run-of-the-mine," i.e. of all coal brought to the surface, before it is run over the screens. The miners asked also 7 cents differential between pick and machine mining, but the operators wanted 12 cents differential.

These opposing propositions had been formulated in separate conventions and conferences by the opposing sides. The operators' position was presented to the joint conference and received the unanimous "aye" of the operators and the unanimous "no" of the miners. The miners' proposition was then presented, and received the unanimous "aye" of the miners and the unanimous "no" of the operators. The two sides then began their parrying. Mr. Mitchell accused the operators of "joking." The operators accused the miners of absurdity. Several days were spent in these tilts. An operator acted as chairman, with eminent fairness; a miner acted as secretary. Finally, when the occasion seemed desperate and everybody had threshed out his opinions and proclaimed his unalterable determination never to yield, the scale committee held its private sessions for a day and a half. Concessions were made on both sides. Certain matters were left undecided or referred back to the state conferences. The committee reported a unanimous agreement, and the joint conference adopted it unanimously. It gave an advance of 14 cents in some districts, and 9 cents in others. It permitted the "mine-run" standard in certain districts, and the "screened" standard in other districts, and a "double standard" in yet a third group of districts, but regulated the size of the screen and fixed a wide differential between "mine-run" and "regulation screen." Similar compromises were made on the machine scale, day labor, and all along the line. Nobody was satisfied, yet everybody was satisfied. It was the best they could do, and it saved the business from paralysis. "A failure to agree," said President Mitchell in his closing speech, "would not only have ruined the homes of the miners, but would have ruined the business of the operators." And though the miners did not get what they expected, yet, said Mitchell, "there has never been a time in the history of mining, even within the recollection of the oldest one among you, when an advance so great as this, and applied to so great a number of men, was secured."

This remarkable form of constitutional government is not the creation of any single intellect, nor of any constitutional convention. It did not spring self-created from the theories of economists or publicists. It "just growed," like Topsy and the British constitution. Indeed, it has not yet finished growing. No man can be found who can tell who it was that first suggested this or that feature of their constitution. For more than twenty-five years the miners and operators have held joint conferences off and on in scattered districts. A temporary union of miners would spring up, the operators would organize to meet it, formal or informal conferences would result, but always heretofore there have been two radical defects in enforcing their agreements: first, the miners' organization did not control the entire competitive field; second, the constitution had developed only a legislative branch of government, but not a judicial branch. Neither of these defects have even yet been entirely overcome.

The first defect just mentioned was overcome in 1897, as far as the favorable conditions of existing prosperity demanded, when the miners' union conquered the state of Illinois. Prior to that time it controlled only the northern district of Illinois, and every effort to establish uniform wages and conditions over the interstate field was undermined by the cutthroat competition of the southern districts. But in 1897 the miners inaugurated a notable strike, beginning with less than 1000 members in that state and no money, and ending in a complete victory, with 35,000 members and a full treasury. Immediately the first interstate joint conference was called at Chicago, in January, 1898, and a scale and an agreement were adopted for the four states. These were successfully enforced everywhere for the succeeding year. This inspired confidence on the part of the operators. The second conference was held at Pittsburg, in January, 1899, and others annually.

The success of each conference depends directly upon the enforcement of the legislation of the preceding conference. Curiously enough, this enforcement falls solely upon the miners' organization. The operators, indeed, have their several state associations, but no national nor interstate association like that of the miners. Moreover, the operators are loosely organized. They can bring only moral suasion to bear upon the recalcitrant operator who rebels at their national decrees. But the miners can do more; they not only can suspend their own local unions which violate the agreement, but they can shut down the mine of the rebellious operator and drive him out of business. The operators understand this, and they know that their own protection against the cutthroat operator depends solely on the Miners' Union. President Mitchell, of the union, at the close of the Indianapolis conference, significantly accepted his office of joint executive in what might be called his inaugural. He said: "I will give notice to the operators now that, when they go home, unless they keep the agreement inviolate, we will call the men out; and I will serve notice on the miners that, unless they keep the laws of the organization, we will suspend them from the organization."

Plainly this amazing inaugural as executive over a grand national industry — a pledge of an *imperium in imperio* — depends for its validity on the control of the entire competitive field. Just as southern Illinois prior to 1897 could break down the executive by sending its labor-exploited coal to the common markets, so now there is danger in the unorganized regions of West Virginia, with their negroes and Italians and poor whites. The output of these unorganized miners is a growing menace, and when business depression returns will be an imminent peril. There is also an ever-present irritation in the hundreds of small mines operated by farmers and others, and their sons, at odd times and between jobs. In Illinois there are some 900 mines of which only 200 are represented in the state association; the other 700 produce only 10 per cent of the product. These small concerns are locally troublesome and may become dangerous.

The second defect in the constitutional government of the bituminous industry is the absence of a judiciary. The joint conference is the legislative branch; the president of the miners' unions is the executive branch; but there is no judicial branch. If the reader noticed the quotation above from President Mitchell's inaugural, he will have observed that Mr. Mitchell himself expects not only to execute the law upon the operator, but also to decide first whether the operator has violated it. Now this is plainly a matter for judicial determination. The interstate agreement has never provided for a jury nor a judicial hearing. Here is the next line of growth. And indeed growth has already begun in this direction. The latest and extremely significant development in this phase of industrial evolution is the creation, during the year 1900, by the Illinois Coal Operators' Association, of the office of

"Commissioner."[1] This commissioner bears the same relation to the state operators' association that the president of the state miners' association bears to that organization. He lacks, of course, equal executive power, because his organization does not hold the whip. But he consults with the miners' executive in every case of local dispute. A complaint, for example, comes to Mr. Justi — "the commissioner" — from an operator somewhere in the state to the effect that the local union has ordered its members out on a strike. Mr. Justi at once telephones to Mr. Ryan, the state secretary of the miners. Mr. Ryan forthwith orders the local union to return to work pending investigation. Then both Mr. Justi and Mr. Ryan proceed to the point of disturbance. They hear both sides. They reach a common interpretation of the interstate agreement as applied to this particular dispute. The local operator and the local miners are then informed of the decision and the necessary orders are given. The case is settled, not by the sole dictum of the miners' executive, but by the joint decision of the two executives of the miners and operators. The first year's trial of this innovation has demonstrated its value and has given to it an indispensable place in the frame of government. It only remains for other states to create a similar office, and then for an interstate association of coal operators to create the same officer to meet the national president of the mine workers' union. It should be added that in the longshoremen's agreement these local differences and interpretations of the general trade agreement are submitted to arbitration, provided the two executives cannot agree.

Other industries with powerful labor unions have reached results similar to those of the longshoremen and coal miners, but by less bulky methods. The conference between the Stove Founders' National Defense Association and the Iron Molders' Union was not only among the first to substitute negotiation for arbitration as a basis of agreement, but also the first to create the double executive and judiciary. The employers had

[1] Other state and local associations of operators have commissioners, and in 1905 they formed an association for the discussion of common questions.

organized their association in 1886 for defense against the powerful molders' union, which, they felt, was tyrannizing their business. In a fiercely fought strike the molders were defeated, but the employers suffered so seriously that they consented to discuss plans for future trade agreements. In 1891 five representatives of each organization met in a constitutional convention. Here, unlike the miners, they created outright a brand-new form of government. The representatives of the molders urged the strict arbitration plan. The manufacturers, says President Castle, of their organization, "refused to enter into an agreement that would obligate them in advance to submit important questions affecting their business to the decision of an odd, disinterested man, who had no knowledge of the business and who might be biased. Arguments upon this question were earnest and extended. It was contended extremely difficult to secure the services of such a man. Extravagant, unjust, and ridiculous demands would be made by the molders because there would be a chance to gain through the odd man, while there could not possibly be a loss. The employer would not stand an even chance with the employee, aside from the merits of the situation, in an average number of arbitrations, because public sympathy is with the workman; they have the votes; they have patronage to bestow upon every business and profession, and they know how to use this influence to the best advantage."

It was finally agreed to create a conference committee of six members, three from each organization. This committee meets every year in March or April and establishes a general piece-rate scale of prices for the year. There is no concurrent conference of the two organizations on the large scale existing in the wharfage and coal-mining industries. All local disputes concerning the interpretation of the national agreement are settled locally if possible; if not, then by the two presidents of the national associations; but if these disagree, then by the original conference committee of six, wherein a majority vote decides. In nine years this conference committee has been called together only once, so successful have been the presidents in settling every dispute. During these nine years there has not been a general strike, and no local strike or lockout has lasted more than one or two days. During the depression there was no reduction in wages, but in 1899 there was an advance of 10 per cent, and in 1900 an advance of 5 per cent. The total advances to 1902 were 20 per cent. Other industries might be mentioned, but these illustrate the principles.

First, the employer must recognize the union. This does not necessarily mean unionizing his place. Here is an interesting phase of these national trade agreements. The employers who enter into them make a distinction, as already stated, between the question of wages and the question of control over their own business. They are willing to pay high wages if all their competitors pay the same wages. It is not high wages that they dread, but secret and unfair cutting of wages. This is also exactly what the laborers resist. The joint state or national agreements place all competitors on the same basis in the same market. Indeed, in the coal trade the scale is nicely adjusted so that the districts with the better quality of coal and the lower railway charges are required to pay enough higher wages than other districts to counterbalance their superior natural advantages. On this basis, so far as the union enforces the agreement every operator knows exactly what his competitor's coal is costing ; there is no secret cutting ; and the trade is not brought down to the level of the few unscrupulous and oppressive operators who grind down their laborers. For this reason the bulk of employers who have had experience with these joint agreements are heartily in favor of them.

But the case is different with the restrictive rules of the unions. Formerly an operator dreaded most of all the "pit committee" of the local union. This committee corresponds to the walking delegate. The "pit committee" would often dispute with the foreman or boss as to authority over the men, and would order miners to do this or that and forbid them to do other things, in contradiction to the orders of the foreman. Consequently, when the mine-workers' union demanded in their first interstate agreement that only union men be employed, the operators refused, and that question is still a draw. But it has practically solved itself. Since there is no interstate legislation on the subject, the local unions are free to take the matter into their own hands; and they have done this effectually by refusing to work with nonunion men. And the local operators have everywhere quietly conceded the point, because they no longer are subject to the "pit committee." If they have any trouble now with that committee, they call in the two executive and judicial officers of the two state or national associations and these decide the issue between the "pit committee" and the operator.

This matter works out in the same way in the stove trade. The employers jealously refused to unionize their shops, but they found when their national agreements got in working order that a "union" shop is just as free as an "independent" shop. The case is different with the longshoremen, the boot and shoe workers, and the Typographical Union, where local disputes are submitted to an outside arbitrator. In these agreements the factories and shops are required to be unionized. The unions claim that otherwise they cannot enforce upon their own locals the arbitration awards.

The most important result of these trade agreements is the new feeling of equality and mutual respect which springs up in both employer and employee. After all has been said in press and pulpit about the "dignity of labor," the only "dignity" that really commands respect is the bald necessity of dealing with labor on equal terms. With scarcely an exception the capitalist officials who make these agreements with the labor officials of these powerful unions testify to their shrewdness, their firmness, their temperance, their integrity, and their faithfulness to contracts. Magnificent generalship is shown in combining under one leadership the miscellaneous races, religions, and politics that compose the miners or the dock laborers of America. The labor movement of no other country has faced such a problem.

J. R. COMMONS.

II

THE MINERS' UNION: ITS BUSINESS MANAGEMENT[1]

The United Mine Workers of America has a total membership in the United States exceeding 300,000. Its officials claim for it the distinction of being the strongest and largest single trade union in the world. It is well organized in at least ten of the twenty-seven coal-producing states, and is gradually extending its power into all of the twenty-seven. About 75 per cent of all the coal mine employees in the country are at present members of the union; more than 85 per cent of the total of 486,000 are governed by the union's scales and work under its conditions of employment; and, the officials of the union claim, fully 90 per cent of all coal mine workers in the United States would go out on a strike if a national suspension of coal mining is ever found to be necessary by the union.

The general scheme of organization of the United Mine Workers bears a close resemblance in many of its features to that of our political organization. It is composed of national, district, subdistrict, and local unions. The jurisdiction of the national union is intended to cover the entire coal-producing area of the country. At present it is effective in Ohio, Indiana, Illinois, Kansas, Iowa, Missouri, Kentucky, Tennessee, Alabama, the hard-coal fields of Pennsylvania, and in portions of the central and western bituminous coal fields of that state. It also extends into Maryland, Virginia, West Virginia, Michigan, Arkansas, Indian Territory, Colorado, New Mexico, Montana, and Texas.

[1] From *Annals, American Academy of Political Science*, Vol. XXV, 1905, pp. 67–86. See also Report Anthracite Coal Strike Commission, Bulletin No. 46, U. S. Bureau of Labor; John Mitchell, Organized Labor, chapters 40 to 45.

Subject to the constitution of the national union and the legislation of the national convention the district union generally has jurisdiction over a particular state. This is due to the convenience of state line divisions. There are exceptions, however. In Pennsylvania, for example, owing to the unusual prominence of the coal-producing area of that state, there are six districts: Districts 1, 7, and 9 in the anthracite region; District 2 in the Clearfield or central soft coal field; District 5 in the Pittsburg or western bituminous coal field; and District 16, which also includes Maryland. In Indiana District 8 covers the block coal field and District 11 the bituminous coal territory of that state. In a few cases one district extends over more than one state, — District 17 includes Virginia as well as West Virginia and District 21 takes in Arkansas and Indian Territory. Under the constitution and legislation of the district union are the subdistrict unions. These subdistrict unions have been made a feature of the organization in order that special regulation may be secured in particular cases for widely varying conditions, which prevail in almost every state, without placing the whole district in jeopardy when only small areas are affected. Within the jurisdiction of the subdistrict are the local unions, — the units making up the district and national unions. The local union is the smallest of the four unions. It usually has jurisdiction over the mine workers at a particular colliery or mine. It must have at least ten members. The constitution and legislation of the national union and the agreement of the Interstate Joint Conference, which latter is entered into between representatives of operators and mine workers, take precedence and are supreme over all the unions. The district exercises authority and governing surveillance over the subdistricts, and the subdistrict over the locals. Each union, however, has its own constitution and by-laws, its own officers and conventions, and it legislates for its own particular area within the authority granted to it.

The United Mine Workers of America is one of the most democratic organizations in the world, but has the possibility of becoming all at once one of the most autocratic. It is democratic in the sense that in the final analysis its policy and management is in the hands of its members. All power vests with them in their collective capacity. To them in their local unions every great question affecting the national union is referred sooner or later, and from the local unions come the final decisions on all such questions. They nominate and elect by direct vote of the members the president, vice president, and secretary-treasurer; indirectly through their particular districts they elect the members of the national executive board; they choose the delegates that make up the national convention; they send instructions to this convention; upon most of the recommendations made to this convention by the president they instruct their delegates before the convention assembles how they are to vote; they not only choose the national and their own local officers, but through regularly elected delegates they compose the subdistricts and districts and through these determine the policy that is to be adopted in any particular instance.

Once a year representatives of the local unions meet in regular convention as the national union, usually at Indianapolis, beginning the third Monday in January, and for ten days or two weeks outline the policy of the national union for the ensuing year. This convention possesses absolute power; there is nothing affecting the organization it cannot do even to altering or amending its fundamental law, the constitution. It can even abrogate, if it so chooses, the agreement of the Interstate Joint Conference. The representatives to this convention are elected directly by the local unions on the basis of one vote in the convention for each one hundred members (or less), and an additional vote for each additional one hundred members or majority fraction thereof. No representative, however, can cast more than five votes on any question. The representative must be "a miner or mine worker or employed by the organization" and a member in good standing of a local union in the district where he resides.[1] The constitution of the national union interprets the term "miner or mine worker" as meaning "any one working in or around the mines *and a member of a local union.*"

[1] Section 2, Article V, of the constitution.

No member of the United Mine Workers occupying a position other than that of miner or mine worker, excepting those holding positions with the organization, is eligible as representative to any subdistrict, district, or national convention. Special conventions, the delegates to which must possess the above qualifications, are provided for by the constitution.

The purpose of the national convention is to legislate on any question pertaining to the objects of the organization. These objects are expressed in the preamble to the constitution. "There is no fact more generally known or more widely believed," says this preamble, "than that without coal there would not have been any such grand achievements, privileges and blessings as those which characterize the twentieth-century civilization, and believing as we do, that those whose lot it is to daily toil in the recesses of the earth, mining and putting out this coal which makes these blessings possible, are entitled to a fair and equitable share of the same: therefore, we have formed 'The United Mine Workers of America,' for the purpose of the more readily securing the objects sought by educating all mine workers in America to realize the necessity of unity of action and purpose, in demanding and securing by lawful means the just fruits of our toil." The objects of the organization are declared to be:

First. To secure an earning fully compatible with the dangers of our calling and the labor performed.

Second. To establish as speedily as possible, and forever, our right to receive pay for labor performed, in lawful money, and to rid ourselves of the iniquitous system of spending our money wherever our employers see fit to designate.

Third. To secure the introduction of any and all well-defined and established appliances for the preservation of life, health and limbs of all mine employees.

Fourth. To reduce to the lowest possible minimum the awful catastrophes which have been sweeping our fellow-craftsmen to untimely graves by the thousands; by securing legislation looking to the most perfect system of ventilation, drainage, etc.

Fifth. To enforce existing laws; and where none exist, enact and enforce them; calling for a plentiful supply of suitable timber for supporting the roof, pillars, etc., and to have all working places rendered as free from water and impure air and poisonous gases as possible.

Sixth. To uncompromisingly demand that eight hours shall constitute a day's work, and that not more than eight hours shall be worked in any one day by any mine worker. The very nature of our employment, shut out from the sunlight and pure air, working by the aid of artificial light (in no instance to exceed one candle power), would, in itself, strongly indicate that, of all men, a coal miner has the most righteous claim to an eight-hour day.

Seventh. To provide for the education of our children by lawfully prohibiting their employment until they have attained a reasonably satisfactory education, and in every case until they have attained fourteen years of age.

Eighth. To abrogate all laws which enable coal operators to cheat the miners, and to substitute laws which enable the miner, under the protection and majesty of the state, to have his coal properly weighed or measured, as the case may be.

Ninth. To secure, by legislation, weekly payments in lawful money.

Tenth. To render it impossible, by legislative enactment in every state, for coal operators or corporations to employ Pinkerton detectives or guards, or other forces (except the ordinary forces of the state) to take armed possession of the mines in cases of strikes or lockouts.

Eleventh. To use all honorable means to maintain peace between ourselves and employers; adjusting all differences, so far as possible, by arbitration and conciliation, that strikes may become unnecessary.

The means for obtaining these ends are declared to be conciliation, arbitration, or strikes. All three methods have been employed in the course of the union's existence.

In order to carry out the policy of the national convention, to enforce the constitution, and for the conduct of the business of the national union, there are a president, a vice president, a secretary-treasurer and an executive board, whose terms of office are from April 1 of one year to March 31 of the next. These officials, with the exception of the executive board, are nominated by the local unions (a candidate must be nominated by at least three locals), and they are elected during the first week in

December of each year by a majority of the popular vote of the members voting who are in good standing at that time in the national, district, or local unions. Any member in good standing in the organization is eligible to hold office in the national union, provided he is not at the same time a salaried officer of a district and has been a member of a local union for one year preceding his election. The nominations are made by the locals on specially prepared blanks two months before the annual national convention. Every candidate thus nominated must be notified and his consent secured before his name is placed on the ballots. These are then sent to the locals from the national offices not later than six weeks before the convention is to assemble. Each member present in his local union meeting at the time of the election has one vote for each officer to be chosen. Severe penalties are attached to the violation by any officer or local union of the constitutional provisions governing the election. Not later than twenty days prior to the national convention the ballot of each local must be sent in special envelopes, sealed, and marked "election returns," addressed to the national secretary-treasurer, and by this officer deposited in an unopened ballot box. Only the national auditors, or their alternates, who are also selected by popular vote, are to open this box. The result of this election as canvassed by them is reported to the national convention, which declares elected to the respective offices those candidates receiving the majority of the votes cast. In case there is no election under this provision, the convention chooses the national officers, each delegate casting by ballot the number of votes for which his local has paid per capita tax.

This referendum plan for selecting the officers of the national union became effective for the first time in 1902 and is still to be regarded in its experimental stage. It has not given satisfaction, as recent elections have demonstrated that the rank and file take very little interest in balloting for the candidates except in those districts where strikes are in progress, or have just been closed, or are about to be inaugurated. A scheme is now under advisement to make participation in the annual election for national officers compulsory by fining members who do not vote unless a sufficient excuse can be given. Formerly the election of national officers was by delegates to the national convention. Under this plan it was possible to elect a national officer by less than a majority of the votes of the members of the local unions. It was also possible for officers or candidates to manipulate the election or to form a combination to control the affairs of the organization and perpetuate themselves in power. The plan of election by popular vote was designed to obviate these defects.

When the national convention is not in session all power under its legislation and the constitution of the national union is vested in the national officers. During this time, which is for all but about two weeks of the year, supreme authority is, in the final analysis, in the hands of one man, the national president. In case of conflict of policy the decision of the president is final. He has power to suspend or remove any national officer "for insubordination or just and sufficient cause";[1] he temporarily fills all vacancies in the national offices. The constitution provides that in the exercise of the power of removal and appointment he shall have the consent of the executive board, but he can suspend or remove the members of this board. He has strong influence over them in still another way: as members of the board these officers receive no salary, but nearly all of them are paid $4 a day and expenses as organizers. Their positions as organizers depend entirely upon appointment by the president. Moreover, the president with the vice president and the secretary-treasurer are members of the board. It convenes at his call and is presided over by him. He decides all questions of dispute concerning the meaning of the constitution; he signs all bills and official documents; he determines the salaries of all employees with $3.50 or less a day and who are not elected by the national convention; he presides at all national conventions, both regular and special; usually he presents an address to these gatherings, reviewing the work of the national union and recommending whatever

[1] Section 2, Article II, of the constitution.

action he deems best upon any question before the organization. His recommendations are generally adopted. He calls special national conventions when instructed by the executive board or requested by five districts. He also summons conventions of two or more districts. He may at any time, in person or through a national officer, visit local unions, district or subdistrict conventions, and any other places connected with the organization; he may appoint representatives to examine the financial accounts of any local union and instruct its officers in their duties; in brief, he exercises general supervision over the workings of all the unions — local, subdistrict, district, as well as national. In 1902 he was paid a salary of $1800. This amount has since been increased to $3000. He is required to devote his time and attention to the organization.

No strike can be ordered by any district nor can final action be taken upon any questions directly or indirectly affecting the interests of the mine workers of another district until the approval of the national president is secured in writing, or, if he disapproves, until favorable action upon an appeal from his decision has been taken by the executive board. An exception to this, of course, occurs in case the strike or action has been ordered by the national convention. Local strikes are under the jurisdiction of the district officers. Together with the other national officers the president has the power to order a suspension of mining operations by members of the union in any district or districts where such action is deemed advisable for the settlement of a strike in another district or for the good of the union. The national officers form districts and assign to them the number of men and the extent of territory they are to have jurisdiction over; and they may at any time change the boundary and jurisdiction of any district.

The vesting of such great power by the United Mine Workers of America in the hands of one man is due primarily to the exigencies of strike times when for all practical purposes the union becomes a military organization in the control of which there must not be the least possibility of divided leadership. Labor unions have been taught through sad experience, and none more so than the United Mine Workers, that an industrial army moving for higher wages and better conditions of employment must have but one commander in chief if the possibility of defeat is to be reduced to a minimum.

Next in importance to the president in the conduct of the national union is the executive board. This board is in a sense the organization's board of directors. It is composed of one member from each district. Unlike the selection of the president, the members of this board are not chosen directly by the local unions, but by the district conventions made up of delegates elected by the locals—somewhat like the choosing of United States senators by state legislatures. At the present time there are twenty-three members, one each from the twenty districts throughout the country, and the president, vice president, and secretary-treasurer who are members *ex officio*. This makes the board too large and unwieldy for expediting business and recently, with the rapid spread of the union and the consequent increase in the number of districts, this question has come to be a very serious one to the officers of the organization. It is more than probable that before long some other plan for selecting the board members will be substituted. Formerly the national convention elected the six or eight members of the board. Another objection to the board as at present constituted is that each member has one vote in its deliberations. This gives to a district having only 2000 members (such as District 16 in Maryland) as much voting influence as a district having 75,000 mine workers (such as District 1 in the anthracite region of Pennsylvania). This makes it possible for board members representing but 20 per cent of the total membership to determine the policy of the national union when the convention is not in session. The evil of this defect is somewhat lessened in its scope by the constitutional provision making necessary a vote of two thirds of the members of the board before a general strike or national suspension order can be issued, and by the power of suspension and removal lodged with the president. The evil of this inequality in the voting strength of the districts in the board has been made still less serious as a result of the anthracite strike in 1902. In the convention of 1903 following that memorable struggle, President Mitchell in his annual address said on this point: "Our membership in the anthracite fields represents practically 40 per cent of the total membership of the organization, while the voting strength of the three members of the national executive board from the anthracite field is only about 15 per cent of the voting strength of the national organization on the executive board." He stated that he did not believe any advantage would be taken of this disproportionate representation, "but in order to overcome what appears to be a plausible objection on the part of the anthracite railway presidents to recognition of our union, I should recommend that upon the question of inaugurating a strike in the anthracite field the anthracite members of the national executive board be given equal voting power with the members of the executive board from the bituminous fields. Upon all other questions the voting strength of the members of the board may remain as at present." This recommendation of the president was adopted by the convention in passing an amendment to the constitution providing that each member in the executive board, in voting on the question of a general strike or suspension, "shall have one vote, and one additional vote for every 5000 members in good standing they represent, or a majority fraction thereof."

This executive board, including the president, wields power next in importance to that of the national convention; in fact, it executes the orders of the national convention and between conventions exercises full power to direct the workings of the national union, including the levying and collecting of assessments. Not only does it have the power to order a general strike or suspension, but it can overrule upon appeal the decisions of district officers upon questions affecting strikes within the district. It is also a court of appeal upon questions affecting the interests of two or more districts, excepting in those cases where the national convention has taken action. The board convenes upon the order of the president, its presiding officer or chairman, or of the secretary-treasurer at the request of eleven of its members. It may at any time instruct the president to call a special national convention. It holds in trust for the national union all moneys in the treasury over $15,000. Among its other duties is that of a national board of conciliation and arbitration.

Nearly all the members of the executive board are employed by the president as national organizers. As such they receive $4 a day and expenses. These are the "walking delegates." They bear the brunt of the fight, are always to be found in the thickest of it, and generally constitute the advance guard of the field force of the organization when an invasion of territory heretofore unorganized is decided upon. They are the missionaries of the new doctrine as to the rights of man; they usually are compelled to blaze it forth to their kind in a wilderness of conflicting passions and class hatreds; they are met with suspicion and bitter antagonism even from those they would save from industrial servitude. These organizers are of many tongues; they go among strange peoples from many climes. They teach their doctrine of unionism alike to the Negro, the Slav, the Lithuanian, the Greek, the German, the Englishman, and the American. Through months and even years of bitter antagonism, of almost crushing opposition, they work patiently at their tasks to bring the many nationalities into the organization and to mold the heterogeneous mass into unity of belief and action. Fearless and undaunted they bear persecution and suffer imprisonment and even death for the faith that is in them. However far apart one's views may be from the ends and objects professed by these organizers, if he could but see the spirit of martyrdom often exhibited by them, he would believe, as the writer does, that they are performing a real and a lasting work as pioneers in the formation of our industrial state.

These organizers, going into coal fields whose mine workers are outside the national union, begin their task by getting into personal touch with the men. They stop them on the street corners, visit the places in which they are in the habit of congregating, distribute among them tracts containing information about the organization, and in various other ways plant the idea of unionism in the minds of a few of the men. From these few it spreads, at first almost unobservably, until gradually more and more of the workers begin talking about "the union," and by degrees nearly all the employees of the mine, or where the mines are in close proximity the employees of a number of mines, are discussing the objects and benefits of organization. When he thinks the time opportune the organizer calls a meeting of those he believes interested in the movement and organizes them into a local union. They secure a charter and other supplies from the national headquarters for $15 and are assigned a number by which the local is to be officially known. In some cases the jurisdiction of a local extends to two or more collieries or mines, but as a rule it is confined to the employees of a single mine. Where a mining plant employs several thousand men they are organized into a number of locals, usually according to nationality or language, or, in case they are scattered in nearby mining towns, to place of residence.

Once the national union gains a foothold in a coal field its spread is rapid or slow, depending upon the particular conditions encountered. Miners, mine laborers, and other workmen, skilled and unskilled, employed in and about the mine, excepting the mine manager and the top boss, may join its ranks. No one is excluded because of race, color, or nationality. Each member is expected to pay twenty-five cents a month as dues and whatever assessments are levied. He is provided with a "due card" upon which the amounts paid by him are entered. This card is his evidence of membership. (In some coal fields, — in the anthracite region of Pennsylvania for example, — where the union is not recognized by the operators, the members wear buttons in the lapels of their coats as indicating membership in the organization.) Provision is made for issuing transfer cards when members go from one mine to another. Local unions are compelled to accept all properly made out transfer cards and must admit the holder to membership provided he has been a member of the organization for at least three months. No member in good standing who holds a due or transfer card "shall be debarred or hindered from obtaining work on account of race, creed, or nationality."[1] When any member is suspended or discharged from his place at the mine a committee of the local (the mine committee) makes an investigation, and if it finds that the member is not guilty of an offense justifying his discharge, the grievance is reported in writing to the subdistrict and district presidents; if these upon investigation find the report of the committee to be correct, it is made their duty to insist upon the reinstatement of the suspended or discharged member. Members of the locals elect their own officers every six months and legislate for their own particular area, subject to the constitutions of the national, district, and subdistrict unions. Each local is compelled to become a part of the subdistrict located within its district and to contribute to it before the local can secure representation in either the district or the national union, and to secure the benefits of the national union the local must at all times be in good standing with the national, district, and subdistrict unions. All locals three months or more in arrears for dues or assessments are published each month by the national secretary-treasurer. This is called the "unfair list" by the locals in good standing.

It is in the local union that strikes usually have their origin. Its members are the workers in and about the mines and are the first to feel the effects of the adverse conditions of employment which give rise to grievances. Whenever any difference arises between the members of a local and their employers it is made the duty of the officers of that local to endeavor to effect an amicable adjustment, and failing in this to notify the officers of the district having jurisdiction over the particular local. If the district officers after an investigation of the cause of the complaint fail to effect a peaceable settlement "on a basis that would be fair and just to aggrieved members,"[2] and find that a strike would best serve the interests of the particular locality, they may order the inauguration of a strike. The local has the right of appeal from the decision of the district officers to the

[1] Section 3, Article VII, of the constitution.

[2] Section 1, Article X, of the constitution.

national executive board. Local strikes not approved by the district officers or the national executive board are not supported by the district, and any local union striking in violation of these provisions may be refused recognition by the national officers. In fact, such unauthorized action on the part of a local union has resulted in its being deprived of its charter. Suspension of local unions has occurred on several occasions during the past five or six years. The charter of a local union at Salineville, Ohio, was revoked in 1902 because it engaged in a strike disapproved by the national officers.

No district can take final action upon questions that directly or indirectly affect the interests of the mine workers of another district or that require a strike to determine until the president and secretary of the aggrieved district "shall jointly prepare, sign, and forward to the national president a written statement setting forth the grievances complained of, the action contemplated by the district, together with the reasons therefor, and the national president shall, within five days after the receipt of such statement, either approve or disapprove of the action contemplated by the aggrieved district, and such approval or disapproval, together with the reasons therefor, shall be made in writing, and a copy forwarded to the secretary of the complaining district. Should the action contemplated by the aggrieved district receive the approval of the national president, the district shall be free to act, but should the national president disapprove the action contemplated, the district may appeal to the National Executive Board, which shall be convened to consider such appeal within five days after its receipt by the national secretary. Until the national president has approved, or the National Executive Board has sustained the appeal, no district shall be free to enter upon a strike unless it shall have been ordered by a national convention."[1] . . . "The national officers shall, at any time they deem it to the best interest of mine workers in a district that is idle, for just and sufficient reasons, order a suspension in any other district or districts that would in any way impede the settlement of the

[1] Section 2, Article X, of the constitution.

district affected: provided, that such action would conserve to the best interest of the United Mine Workers of America."[1]

As the machinery for the inauguration of a strike is first put in motion by the local union, so does the success of the strike depend to a large degree upon the support given by the locals, not only by those whose members happen to be on strike but by those in other fields whose members remain at work. The members of the locals constitute the rank and file of the organization: they are the privates, corporals, and sergeants of the great army of mine workers moving toward an improvement in the conditions of their employment. In peace times they prepare the organization for strikes by contributing in dues and assessments to the district and national unions besides providing for their own local treasuries. So well did they do this in 1902 that immediately upon the special national convention issuing its appeal for relief to carry on the anthracite mine workers' strike, District 12 (Illinois) contributed $50,000 from its treasury, District 8 (Indiana) $10,000, District 11 (Indiana) $8000, District 13 (Iowa) $5000, District 2 (Central Pennsylvania) $3,259.50, and Districts 25 (Missouri) and 20 (Alabama) $1000 each. Only a month before this appeal was issued District 12 (Illinois) had contributed $50,000 for the conduct of the strike in the two Virginias, making $100,000 from one district alone within two months for carrying on strikes. Besides the districts the subdistricts and locals in all the organized coal producing states contributed in the aggregate a large sum from their respective treasuries to prosecute the strike of the anthracite miners.

Under the constitution every local union is required to pay into the national treasury a per capita tax of ten cents a month for each member and such additional assessments as may be levied by the national executive board. Boys under sixteen years of age are regarded as half members and pay one half as much tax and assessment as full members. In the deliberations of the local each boy member has one half a vote. These dues and assessments from the locals form the principal sources of

[1] Section 3, Article X, of the constitution.

income for the national union. When a strike of unusual proportions is in progress contributions from other labor organizations and from the general public increase the funds in the national treasury. The important part these play in the conduct of the organization was shown during the six months' strike in the anthracite region of Pennsylvania in 1902. To carry on that struggle alone, not including the expenses accompanying the strike of mine workers in progress at the same time in the Virginias, the various unions of the United Mine Workers of America voluntarily donated $258,344 and the members of the organization paid in special assessments $1,967,026, a total of $2,225,370. This is more impressive when it is remembered that more than one half of the members of the union, including the 147,000 anthracite mine workers, were on strike, and in consequence made no contributions to the defense fund. From the trade unions and the general public $419,954 was contributed. The total amount paid by the United Mine Workers for strike purposes from January 1 to December 31, 1902, was $1,889,202. This included the cost of smaller strikes in seven districts besides the ones in the three anthracite districts of Pennsylvania and the district covering the two Virginias. A total of 184,000 mine workers in the United States were on strike for two months and 160,000 for five months during 1902. In that year the total income of the United Mine Workers of America was $3,010,877.82, and the total expenditures $2,080,805.44. At the beginning of 1903 there was a balance in the national treasury of the union of $1,027,120.29.[1]

All this indicates the importance of the financial organization of the United Mine Workers of America. This constitutes one of the strongest features of the national union. At its head is the secretary-treasurer, nominated and elected directly by the vote of the members of the local unions. He conducts all the business of the organization concerning the management of national headquarters, having charge of all books, documents, and effects; supervises the *Mine Workers' Journal*, the official

[1] Report national secretary-treasurer, 1903.

weekly organ of the union ; receives all moneys and pays all bills, excepting when the president orders otherwise and providing that not over $15,000 is subject to the secretary-treasurer's order at any one time. All sums over this amount are deposited by him to the credit of the executive board, and to draw upon these a written order of two thirds of the board members is necessary. He is required to give a bond of $25,000. His yearly salary in 1902 was $1500 and expenses, but it has since been increased to $2500 and expenses. As a rule he reports quarterly to the locals the condition of the national treasury.

Over all the sources of revenue and expenditure the national secretary-treasurer enforces strict discipline with severe penalties for violations of the rules. Each secretary of a local is required by the national constitution to fill out and forward to the national and district secretary-treasurers before the twenty-fifth of each month a report of all members in good standing in that local on the first day of that month, together with all taxes and assessments due from it to the national and district officers. For a violation of this provision a local union is subject to suspension from all privileges or benefits until the deficiency is made good. To keep a check on these reports the local secretary must inform the national office of the amount of money paid and the number of members reported to the district secretary, and must send the same statement to the district office. He is required to certify that such report is for the full number of members in good standing in the local. Despite these constitutional provisions not a few of the locals fail to report the full number of members in good standing, excepting about the time of the national convention, and they do it then in order to secure in the convention as large a voting representation as possible. The reason for their not making the full report is generally traced to the desire of the locals to have their own treasuries well filled in order to meet their own particular wants. Some of the locals have in this way succeeded in purchasing ground and erecting a building for their headquarters. All financial officers of the local unions are required to give a bond "for the faithful performance of their duties."

It sometimes happens, however, that officers prove faithless to their trust and abscond with the moneys. The national union makes efforts to have them arrested and punished, but it does not always succeed.

If the members of a local are idle for one month or more, they are exonerated from the payment of the per capita tax and assessments until they resume work. This condition may occur through a mine being abandoned or idle for repairs, by reason of a strike, or other causes. But to secure such exoneration a request, signed by the president, secretary, and mine committee, must be approved by the district and national secretaries each month, in place of the regular monthly financial report, as long as the members are idle. In case the local union is in arrears for two months preceding the one in which the convention is held, or has not in every particular complied with the constitution of its district, or has less than ten members, it is not entitled to representation in the national convention.

So well organized are the financial features of the United Mine Workers of America that the national union was able to carry on a widespread system of relief to the needy anthracite mine workers during the closing two months of the 1902 strike. In this relief work no distinction was made between union and nonunion men. In fact, the testimony of many witnesses is to the effect that aid was furnished as freely to the nonunion as to the union mine workers. For this relief work the members of the locals were organized into committees of various kinds. Applications for relief were investigated by one of these committees, and if conditions were found as represented, orders for merchandise on local grocers were furnished. On the face of the order was stated the amount for which it was drawn; on the reverse side were blanks for the dates, name, quantity, and price of the articles purchased. Both the merchant and purchaser signed the order when goods to its face value had been bought, and then returned it to the committee, which presented it to the district secretary-treasurer for payment. This officer then secured direct from national headquarters the necessary amount to pay the bills. In some parts of the Schuylkill field it was found necessary for the union to establish commissaries and furnish the needy with food direct from its own supplies. In some parts of the West Virginia field, while the strike there was in progress, scores of tents were erected in the woods for sheltering strikers who were driven from their homes. Food and clothing bought in carload lots by the national union were shipped from the large cities to the disturbed districts and distributed among the strikers.

Not only does the financial feature of the organization indicate that the United Mine Workers is founded upon business principles, but there is still another phase of the work of the national union which more strongly emphasizes this statement. This is the holding of an annual joint conference with representatives of the operators and coal mining companies of Ohio, Indiana, Illinois, and the Pittsburg field of Pennsylvania. In these conferences labor is regarded as a commodity, and the possessor of this labor — the mine worker — is accorded the right through representatives of the union to "bargain" with representatives of the purchasers of that labor — the coal-mining companies — for the price of his labor and the conditions under which it is to be sold. This joint-conference movement in these four states dates its beginning in 1885, although there have been periods since then when it was inoperative.[1] The periods when it was not in force were years of depression in the coal trade, accompanying general industrial paralysis. The United Mine Workers of America had come into existence at Columbus, Ohio, January, 1890, by the amalgamation of the Progressive Union and the National Trades Assembly, No. 135, Knights of Labor, both of which organizations had claimed jurisdiction over the mine workers of the country and between whom there had been bitter and open hostility. To this division in the ranks of the mine workers and to the fact that the young organization was for a time too weak and adverse

[1] For a complete and detailed account of the origin and operation of the Interstate Joint Conference the reader is referred to the author's article, "The Union Movement among Coal Mine Workers," *Bulletin of the Bureau of Labor, Department of Commerce and Labor*, March, 1904, No. 51.

conditions were too strong is partly due the failure to hold the joint conferences at intervals preceding 1898. They were restored after the general suspension of soft-coal mining in eight of the states in 1897 and have been held annually since then. In Iowa, Kansas, Missouri, Kentucky, Tennessee, and Alabama annual joint agreements are also signed between representatives of the mine workers and of the operators in each state. The conferences in the six last-named states are held separately and are not a part of the so-called interstate agreement of the central competitive district. The agreements entered into, however, cover in general the same specific points, stating the wages that are to prevail along with specified conditions of employment.

Through these contracts and agreements not a few of the objects of the national union have been attained and undoubtedly better conditions of employment have been secured for the mine workers in the states where they are in effect. Since the great strike of 1897 the United Mine Workers has extended the eight-hour workday into the mines of Iowa, Missouri, Kansas, Michigan, Kentucky, and parts of Tennessee, and has secured for the mine employees of those states increases in wages ranging from 13 to over 30 per cent. Increases in the wages of mine workers in other states have also been secured through joint conventions with the operators, and increases in wages with improved conditions of employment were forced from the railroad mining companies and independent operators in the three hard-coal fields of Pennsylvania in 1900 and 1902. Arbitration of the questions in dispute between the anthracite mine workers and the operators by a commission appointed by the President of the United States was also forced upon the hard-coal mining interests. Since 1898 the membership of the national union has increased from 43,000 to nearly 300,000. Of this total membership about 185,000 mine employees, producing annually 125,000,000 tons of bituminous coal, or over one third of the total coal production of the United States, now work under agreements. Many of the 147,000 anthracite mine workers are strongly organized in the national union, but as yet they have been unable to secure agreements from the coal-hauling railroads which virtually control the mining operations. These hard-coal miners produce annually about 60,000,000 tons. The remaining 115,000 mine workers of the country, producing annually about 100,000,000 tons of bituminous coal and employed principally in the states west of the Mississippi and in West Virginia, Virginia, Michigan, Maryland, and in central and western Pennsylvania, are as yet unorganized in the United Mine Workers and have no agreements with their employers.

Enough has been said to show that the management of the United Mine Workers of America is as much of a business as is the conduct of any of the great industrial or commercial enterprises of the present day. It directs its strength against those forces tending to keep down the price of its commodity, mine labor, with as much regard for its own particular interests and in disregard of the interests of others where and when these conflict as does any of the industrial or other trusts. In order to control the price of mine labor it aims to prevent mine workers from selling their labor at a lower price than that set by the union. It does this by taking them into the organization and persuading them to sell their labor at union prices, or by driving them out of the industry, just as the great steel trust endeavors to absorb or destroy the independent steel manufacturer, or as the sugar trust attempts to control or drive out the independent refiner. The mine worker, refusing from one cause or another to be governed by the union in the sale of his labor, is the independent producer of mine labor, or the nonunion man. In driving out the commodity he has to sell, the union is forced to attack the individual, as it is impossible to dissociate the one from the other. In consequence violence and bloodshed result. Not only does the union attempt in various ways to control this independent producer of mine labor in the selling of his commodity, but, not unlike the so-called trusts, in fixing the price of this labor and the conditions under which it is to be sold, if it feels itself strong enough it brooks no interference from other organizations which have mine labor to sell. This is well illustrated by the United Mine Workers practically driving out of the anthracite fields of Pennsylvania the separate organizations of blacksmiths, engineers, carpenters, and firemen which existed in one or more of the three fields prior to the recent strikes. We see it again in the union's steady absorption of the mine employees in the coal-producing states west of the Mississippi river, most of whom have been under the jurisdiction of the Western Federation of Miners, an organization composed principally of quartz miners, and the Western Labor Union. If it ever becomes necessary in order to attain its objects, or once attained, to prevent these objects being lost, the same absorption by the United Mine Workers of the coal miners of Canada and Nova Scotia may be looked for.

Trade unionism under the stimulus of the United Mine Workers of America has come to be a business operation on a large scale. As a business its success depends upon the close observance of market conditions and the obeying of laws governing those conditions. Most trusts deal with material commodities — goods that have no feeling or mode of independent action. They are thus able usually not only to increase the price of their particular commodity on a rising market, but, if they so wish, to reduce prices on a falling market. With the trade union the difference is that it deals with a commodity possessed by an individual with feelings and sympathies and modes of independent action. The general experience has been that when a period of falling prices sets in the possessor of mine labor objects strongly to reducing the price of his labor. The past teaches us that he persists stubbornly, even against the advice of the leader of his union, in his refusal to reduce his wages and will go to the extent of striking against such reduction. The trade union also confronts great difficulties in raising the price of its commodity on rising markets, largely due to the fact that the consumers of labor, unlike the consumers of most trust commodities, are strongly organized. The part of the intelligent labor leader (of the business manager of labor) is closely to observe the conditions of the labor and general markets and all factors likely to affect the wages of the worker (the price of labor) and to direct his organization along the lines they indicate as the proper course. A study of such conditions is provided for in the constitution of the United Mine Workers by giving to the president, with the consent of the executive board, the power to appoint a man whose duty it is to collect and compile statistics on production, distribution, consumption, freight rates, market conditions, and any other matter of interest connected with the coal trade likely to affect wages.

FRANK JULIAN WARNE.

[A remarkable and very unusual instance of the intelligent labor leadership called for in the concluding paragraph of the foregoing article was the reduction of wages in the bituminous field accepted by referendum vote of the union in 1904. On account of falling markets the operators had demanded a reduction of 10 per cent in the prices for mining, but after prolonged conference they agreed to accept a reduction of 5½ per cent. The union throughout the country was obstinately opposed to any reduction, and the revulsion against the action of their president in recommending and urging the acceptance of the operators' proposition showed itself in bitter and outspoken denunciation. Throughout his home town and elsewhere his picture was turned to the wall. But he and the executive board carried through their campaign of education, and finally the referendum vote sustained their position, and thus saved the industry from a general strike. This unusual evidence of business sagacity on the part of a union adds interest to the detailed account of its business management as well as the trade-agreement system which made such an outcome possible. — ED.]

III

THE TEAMSTERS OF CHICAGO[1]

Only since the year 1902 have the teamsters of Chicago discovered their power. They have always been classed as unskilled labor, and the old-line trade unionist ridiculed and discouraged the organizers who ventured to create a teamsters' union. The skilled unions saw the strategic position of the teamster, and the brewery workers made some of the brewery drivers a part of their "industrial" union. But the driver felt that they wanted him, not to help him, but to help themselves. Only when he broke away and organized his own teamsters' union did he get enthusiasm for union principles.

Again, the teamster had never been clearly distinguished from the team owner. The oldest so-called union was that of the hack drivers, organized in 1867. But that was a union of hack owners as much as hack drivers, since the majority owned the rigs they drove. Consequently their interest lay rather in holding up the fares charged to the public than the wages earned by the driver. Their organization was never influential and often comatose. Not until 1902 did they take in the livery drivers employed by the great companies and thereby become a labor union as well as a guild. Their history since then is similar to that of other teamsters and drivers.

The laws of the former International Team Drivers' Union, chartered by the American Federation of Labor in 1899, admitted to membership a team owner if he operated not more than five teams. This threw the unions, the conventions, and the laws into the hands of the owners, and prices were more prominent than wages. Such a union was inherently weak. While the larger team owners were formally excluded, yet their

[1] From the *Quarterly Journal of Economics*, Vol. XIX, 1905, pp. 400–433.

teamsters were not attracted to a union whose views respecting wages were those of small team owners. The first object necessary to form an effective union was community of interest, and this required separation from employers. The Chicago teamsters, in defiance of their international organization, refused to admit owners; and finally, in 1902, they seceded, and formed a new national union, including only teamsters and helpers. They admitted the driver who owned the team he operated, but excluded him if he owned a team driven by some one else.

Even this differentiation was not enough. Teamsters are employed in every industry. No craft is so necessary and universal. But teaming in one industry is distinct from teaming in another. The laundry driver has little in common with the coal teamster, except horses and streets. His problems of unionism, such as methods of payment, hours, and discipline, are different. In 1894 coal teamsters, truck drivers, and others were in a general union, just as they are to-day in smaller towns. But that union quickly disappeared. In 1886 something similar had occurred under the Knights of Labor. But in 1902 each industry was organized separately in its own "local." Though each is called a local union, it is more than local in the geographical sense. Each local is a distinct craft, with jurisdiction over the entire city for all workmen of its craft, and the principle recognized for all is the same as that explicitly stated by the Ice Wagon Drivers: "Our Local Union has the powers of self-government, known as Local Autonomy, and, if deemed advisable, to make such by-laws that will be beneficent to the local organization, such as admitting persons who own and operate one team, regulating initiation fees or dues, honorable withdrawal cards, trials, fines, suspensions and expulsions in conformity with the general laws." There are, of course, many cases where locals overlap; and, in order to avoid conflict of jurisdiction, each stable is assigned to the local to which 51 per cent or more of its work belongs.

Thus the teamsters of Chicago were the first to establish two principles new to the occupation, — craft autonomy and wage unionism. Starting with these principles, within two years there were organized 47 locals, from the Truck Drivers with over 5000 members to the Dye House Drivers with 46. Afterwards this differentiation was found too fine, and some of the smaller locals were merged into others. Nearly all were organized during the first year. They created a joint executive council of seven delegates from each local, with power over strikes, and in 1903 they amalgamated with the International Team Drivers, which meanwhile had changed its constitution to exclude employers. The organization is now known as the International Brotherhood of Teamsters, with 821 locals in some 300 cities.

Such sudden and precipitate organization was accomplished and recognized with scarcely a half dozen strikes. This was owing partly to the secrecy maintained, but mainly to an early demonstration of power and a sympathetic interest on the part of one class of team owners. This second factor is explained by the peculiar nature of the business.

The two classes of team owners are those who follow teaming for a living and those whose teaming is an adjunct to their general business. The latter include the department stores, the meat packers, grocers and meat markets, the brewers, the largest manufacturers, the milk dealers, lumber dealers, railway express companies, ice companies, some of the wholesale merchants, and others. The former include truck owners, expressmen and van owners, liverymen, the commission team owners, and, to a lesser degree, coal team owners, ice wagon owners, and similar teaming contractors. The significance of this distinction lies in the fact that many of the manufacturers and most of the wholesale merchants and commission houses do their teaming through contractors. With the manufacturers and wholesale merchants the teamsters' wages are but a small part of their total expenses. With the retail merchants the proportion is larger, the largest being that of the milk dealers, — 15 per cent or less. But with the contracting team owners the wages of teamsters and helpers are 50 to 75 per cent of their total expenses. Consequently, while competition of manufacturers and merchants is but slightly affected by the teamsters' wages, competition of team owners is mainly a question of the wages and hours of their competitors. The manufacturer and wholesale merchant are interested in keeping wages low, but the team owner is interested in keeping them equal. The team owner has therefore welcomed and encouraged the organization of the teamsters, notwithstanding an extraordinary increase in the rates of wages, because the union equalized competition. In taking this attitude his position has not been the same as that of the merchant or manufacturer, whose cost of trucking was increased whether done directly or by contract. One consequence is that the team owners — by which will be meant those with whom teaming is their business and not an adjunct — have organized associations, not only as employers to negotiate with the unions, but also as contractors to regulate rates of cartage and livery. The principal associations of this kind are the Chicago Team Owners, dealing with the truck drivers; the Furniture Movers and Expressmen's Association, dealing with the van teamsters and helpers and the baggage and parcel delivery drivers and helpers; the Commission Team Owners, dealing with the commission drivers; and four liverymen's associations, dealing with the hack, coupé, and livery drivers. These associations determine by joint agreements the rates of wages and the hours and conditions of labor, and the scales thus determined are the union scales paid also by merchants and manufacturers not members of the association to their teamsters employed directly. Many of the other teamsters' unions have joint agreements with employers' associations; but such associations being composed of merchants or manufacturers are loose and informal, while the associations named above are compact and permanent, some of them with bonds and forfeits binding them not only to the scale of wages but also to the scale of prices.

The Coal Team Owners and their drivers deserve special mention by reason of their early leadership and their peculiar methods. The drivers were organized in the fall of 1900 and secured individual agreements during 1901. They made further demands in the winter of 1901–1902, which, added to those already secured, doubled the cost of teaming. For a two-horse wagon they formerly received 50 cents a load of 4 or 5 tons, and for a three-horse wagon 65 cents a load of 6 or 7 tons, regardless of distance. At these rates the labor cost of cartage was about 10 cents a ton, and the teamster earned $8 to $12 a week of indefinite hours. The scale finally agreed upon substitutes weekly and overtime rates for the former piece rates. The two-horse driver receives $15 and the three-horse driver $18 for a week of 66 hours, and 35 cents and 40 cents an hour overtime, respectively. At these rates the labor cost was raised to about 20 cents a ton.

In order to pay these higher wages the coal dealers contended that they must get higher prices for cartage. The anti-trust law of Illinois, as amended in 1897, made an exception in favor of any article "the cost of which is mainly made up of wages."[1] To avail themselves of this exception the coal dealers separated their *cartage* from their *coal* and organized, not a dealers' association, but a Coal Team Owners' Association, since the cost of cartage, but not the cost of coal, is "mainly made up of wages," and since a team owner does not have title in the property he delivers and is therefore not responsible for its price to the public. There is also a considerable amount of coal hauled by contract, and contracting team owners who are not dealers are also members of the association. The rates charged for cartage had formerly been 22 to 27 cents a ton. The association adopted and issued a schedule setting the rates at 50 cents a ton for manufacturing and steam use and 60 cents a ton for domestic use within two and one half miles from the point of loading; for each additional mile or fraction thereof 10 cents a ton. Thus the rates for cartage were doubled when the teamsters' wages were doubled. But since they started on different bases it is also true that the absolute increase in cartage was twice as great as the increase in wages, namely 20 to 25 cents a ton when wages were increased 10 cents a ton. There are, of course, other expenses besides wages,

[1] This exception was afterwards declared unconstitutional, as being an unlawful discrimination. See *People* v. *Butler Street Foundry Co.*, 201 Ill. 236.

mainly, feed and care of horses; and these are offered as a justification for the disproportionate advance, though the occasion thereof was the advance in wages. At the same time, since the dealers mainly own their teams and their prices for coal include delivery, their ability to maintain the rate of cartage really depends on their ability to maintain the price of coal. This they have not been able to do on bituminous coal on account of the many sources of supply, while they have thoroughly succeeded on anthracite coal on account of the centralized control of supply.

However this may be, the coal dealers at first relied upon the teamsters to control the market and even to create one. They made a provisional agreement in January, 1902, to take effect the following May and to continue for five years, if the teamsters meanwhile could demonstrate their power. The agreement provided that none but members of the union should be employed and that the teamsters should work for none but members of the association. With this understanding the agent of the teamsters stopped the delivery of coal to the great firm of Marshall Field & Co. for a few hours in winter until that firm signed a two-year contract with the union to use coal instead of natural gas during the summer. This spectacular demonstration had two results. The managers of other stores and office buildings, who also had made the mistake of building sky scrapers without coal bunkers, signed a similar contract when requested; and nearly all of the teamsters in Chicago joined the union. The astute agent of the coal team owners, John C. Driscoll by name, who had engineered this *coup*, proceeded on his part to organize the team owners in other branches, and eventually became secretary of five such associations. In each case agreements similar to the original one were made with the new teamsters' locals. These and other locals were organized without general strikes, except those of the packing house and department store teamsters in June. Yet, while they had but few strikes on their own account, the teamsters in the first flush of enthusiasm stopped work in sympathy with strikers on the inside; and this in the case of the freight handlers in July was the most destructive since 1894. That disaster sobered the teamster, but it showed him his power.

Springing from these sympathetic strikes came the most remarkable board of arbitration known to industrial disputes. Seven of the largest employers of teamsters and seven agents of the teamsters' unions constituted themselves for one year the industrial umpires of Chicago. Practically all the strikes of new unions during that period came before this board. The older unions, such as the building trades, disdained this upstart jurisprudence and refused to submit their disputes. But it happened that most of the strikes of that period were those of new unions. The board's powers were quasi compulsory, since the employer who would not submit to arbitration could not get teamsters, and the strikers who would not submit could not get the help of the teamsters. Many of the strikes were handled by Driscoll, the agent of the teaming employers, without bringing them before the board of arbitration, and had it not been for his unscrupulous use of money in bribing the leaders of the unions, the board might have continued. But his corruption was finally exposed, the teamsters withdrew their representatives, and eventually deposed the officers who had been on friendly terms with him. The board of arbitration was dissolved. Employers, also, who were willing that Driscoll should use their money to "buy off" the leaders of troublesome strikes, became distrustful when they learned that he secretly fomented strikes to be bought off. He lost his position in all but the Coal Team Owners' Association, and the others substituted men of a different type. Since this reform movement of 1903 the teaming industry can be studied as an economic rather than as a criminal phenomenon.

Hours and Wages

The change most impressive brought about by the unions is that from indefinite hours and wages to definite wages and pay for overtime. The teamsters' occupation is peculiar in that it has carried over and retained in industry the practices of agriculture. The teamster has always been expected to "care for his stock" as well as to drive his wagon. Even where a teaming contractor's business had grown so large as to require the services of stablemen, the teamster was expected to be at the stable before working time and to remain at the stable after working time long enough to feed and curry his horses, clean their stalls, grease and repair his wagon, hitch up and unhitch, and keep his harness clean and the brass polished. This required also several hours on Sunday. For such work he was not supposed to be paid, — it was the necessary preparation for work, not the real productive effort that brought him wages. This continues to hold good under the union agreements, so that, while the teamster says that he now has a ten-hour working day, the day lasts nearly always from six o'clock in the morning to six or half past six in the evening, with one hour for dinner. Consequently, the actual working time for which his stipulated day's wages is paid is 11 or 11½ hours. This enables the truck driver to back his wagon up to the platform for his first load at seven o'clock, the time when the inside workers begin, and to get his last load in time to return to the stable and leave for home at about six in the evening. Formerly he might not get his last load till the inside workers quit, and this might keep him at the barn till eight or nine o'clock and even later. In some lines of teaming not depending on factories and warehouses, such as furniture moving, groceries, markets, and commission driving, he was called out much earlier in the morning or kept later at night according to the amount of work the team owner could find for him to do. The van teamster who took out a sleighing party was not paid for it, because that was night work. Often he and others reported at the stable at three, four, or five o'clock in the morning and left the stable at eight, nine, or ten at night. On this account it is impossible to know the number of hours most of the teamsters formerly worked. As they were not paid for overtime, their former earnings give no indication of the hours employed. In general, they ranged from 70 to 100 hours a week, according to seasons and kinds of teaming.

These hours have been reduced in two ways: first, by cutting out Sunday work, or stipulating that it shall be paid at one and one half or double rates; and second, by stipulating a rate per hour for overtime before six A.M. and after six P.M. Under these conditions the larger team owners employ stablemen to do much of the work formerly done by the teamsters, and in order to avoid the higher rates for overtime, they try to arrange their work to bring it within the regular time. The wholesale merchant who kept his truck driver hauling to the railways during the day and then gave him a city load late in the afternoon now concentrates his schedule of trips. Nevertheless, in some lines the teamster continues to make a large amount of overtime. It is not unusual for the coal teamster, at $18 a week and 40 cents overtime, to earn $20 or $24 a week. In other branches overtime varies greatly according to the business. Consequently, in this industry the policy of reducing the hours of labor is necessarily often a policy of merely getting pay for overtime and so greatly increasing the earnings. The driver must finish his trip and return his team to the stable; and while overtime cannot always be abolished, it can be paid for.

Again, there are some lines in which very little change in the hours, except Sunday relief, has occurred. The railway express drivers never had the care of their horses, and their reduction in hours has been but three or four a week. The laundry and bakery drivers have about the same hours as formerly. The routes of the keg beer drivers had always been equalized, so that they could finish their work in the morning; but they were kept around the barn indefinitely for extra jobs and errands. These extras have been cut off.

The action of the milk wagon drivers deserves special mention. They directed their efforts at first not to the rates of wages, but to the hours of work. Formerly they started out in the summer at from one to four o'clock in the morning, made a delivery of milk in the forenoon and a second delivery in the afternoon, returned at four or five o'clock, spent one or two hours in balancing their books, and got away at six or seven in the evening, making 12 to 18 hours a day. Then they worked 10 hours on Sunday, delivering milk and caring for their horses and wagons, altogether 100 hours a week for $10 or $12. In the winter they began at six A.M., making 80 hours a week.

Their first step after organizing in January, 1903, was to cut out the second delivery, to fix their hours in winter from 8 to 5, and to decide that in summer no delivery should be made in the afternoon and "all wagons must be off the street by one P.M." This brought the hours to about 52 a week, including 4 hours on Sunday, — a reduction of nearly 50 hours in summer and 30 hours in winter. Within the past three years their wages have advanced to $45 and $60 a month, so that the rate of pay per hour has more than doubled. These are minimum rates. There are also "route men," whose commissions on sales bring their total earnings to $70 or $80 a month.

Public amazement and invective followed the "one-daily-delivery" system. The rule was adopted in January and did not attract attention until warm weather. Then the newspapers, with several columns daily, attacked the union. Early in June the commissioner of health stated in his weekly bulletin: "The 'one-daily-delivery' of milk has begun to reap its harvest. Even in well-to-do families this thirty-six to sixty hours' old milk cannot be kept from souring from one delivery to the next. Herod was more merciful in the method he used in his slaughter of the innocents."

Now that two summers have passed a somewhat cooler estimate can be made of the drivers' action.[1] In fact, the change to the "one-daily-delivery" of milk could have but little direct effect on the death rate of children. The milk formerly

[1] At the close of the first season the health commissioner's statistics showed that the number of deaths of children under five years of age during the three summer months (July, August, and September) was ten less than that of the preceding year, and at the close of the second season (1904) his figures for the same months showed a still further decrease of 388 deaths. The death rate of children under five for the twelve months remained stationary the first year and fell from 39.39 per 1000 living to 32.64 the second year, and the number of deaths in the three summer months, which had been 30.4 per cent of the year's total in 1902, fell to 26.6 per cent of the smaller year's total in 1904.

delivered in the afternoon was from exactly the same milking as that delivered in the forenoon, the only difference being that the driver carried a part or all of it around in his wagon all day instead of leaving it at the house in the morning. The morning deliveries are always, with the unimportant exception noted below, at least twenty-four and thirty-six hours old, having been drawn the morning of the day before and the evening of the second day before. Furthermore, in the poorer sections of the city, where home refrigerators are scarce, a large part of the milk has always been bought at groceries or depots conveniently located in nearly every block. In 1904 there were issued 2424 milk licenses for such stores against 2516 for wagons. Both drivers and dealers state that almost their only afternoon customers were in the wealthier sections of the city, and the amount taken was small, being only what the mistress wished for an unexpected guest or an extra function. On the whole, it appears that the afternoon delivery was a needless waste, imposed by the thoughtlessness of housewives. The fifty hours saved each week to the drivers have not laid any hardship on the public.

While not directly affecting the death rate, the revolt of the drivers indirectly reduced it by awakening public conscience and bringing about reforms in the municipal health department. The Children's Hospital Society created a Milk Commission, including physicians, bacteriologists, and representatives of the Women's Club, established a laboratory, and by special arrangement sent out in bottles milk fourteen hours old to sick children of the congested districts and the hospitals. The Civic Federation employed the biological department of the University of Chicago to test some three hundred samples of milk from various sources. Their report reflected unfavorably upon the inspection of the Municipal Department of Health, and finally led in 1904 to the appointment of an additional force of milk inspectors, including four country inspectors to visit farms; and all inspectors were instructed to pay special attention to the sanitary condition of dairies and utensils. In that year for the first time the department's bacteriologist made a systematic examination of the city's market milk. Considerable amounts of milk were condemned, nineteen milk peddlers' premises were abolished, several hundred dealers were notified to place and keep their depots in sanitary condition. An ordinance was adopted requiring metal seals to cans, by means of which responsibility can be fixed on the shipper, the railway employee, or the dealer. This has reduced milk watering 50 per cent. The railroads were induced to furnish better facilities for handling.[1] Coupled with a cool summer in 1904 and the completion of sewer systems and the drainage canal, the death rate of all ages declined somewhat, and the death rate of children declined still more, as stated above. On the whole, the stand taken by the milk wagon drivers diverted attention from a false security on two deliveries of milk a day to the real source of danger, — an inadequate milk inspection.

Earnings

The wages formerly earned were as indefinite as the hours. While the books of the team owners, if examined, would throw no light on the former rates of pay per hour, they would show the earnings by the week or month. In lieu of such an examination the testimony of employers and men has been found to agree remarkably in some lines and fairly well in others. Apparent disagreements are explained by the existence of exceptionally high or exceptionally low wages. The policy of the unions has been to establish a minimum rate of pay, and then to stipulate that no employee receiving more than the scale shall suffer a reduction. Consequently, exceptional men, especially in those lines where commissions are paid, have not gained an increase in weekly earnings, though the reduction in hours has increased their hourly rates; while the lowest paid positions have been substantially increased by the week and amazingly increased by the hour. Looking at the position of the average teamster without special abilities or disabilities, it may be said that for 70 to 100 hours' work his earnings before

[1] Report of Bacteriologist and Director of the Municipal Laboratory, 1904 (MS.).

organization were $8 to $12 a week. Some grocery drivers, garbage collectors, beer wagon helpers, and many boys got as little as $4.50 and $6, while men on commission got as much as $25 or $30; but the prevailing testimony sets the bulk of the earnings at $9. Since organization the minimum rates per week have been raised, so that they range from $10 for retail grocery drivers to $18 for a three-horse coal team driver; the standard towards which all are aiming being $15 a week of six days, and the rate that the largest number have reached is somewhat less. The advances made for helpers are relatively greater than those for drivers, bringing the two closer together, and both to a higher level.

While these increases are large, they nearly always exaggerate the increased labor cost to the employers. Often the highest paid men were not affected, and the better paid men were already close to the new minimum. In some lines, like department stores and railway express, only one company was paying the extremely low rates, and that usually to boys. In other lines this proportion was larger. The boys have been discharged and men have taken their places; and their greater efficiency somewhat offsets the apparent increase in pay. Furthermore, from the teamster's standpoint the reduction in hours, which has so enormously increased his hourly rate, has often been in the hours uselessly spent in waiting or doing uneconomical work in order to be on hand when wanted. Such wasted hours the employer did not count, and their reduction does not increase proportionately his hourly cost, because now he keeps the teamster busy every minute while on duty. Consequently, the team owner's increased labor cost is not to be measured by the teamster's extraordinary gain by the hour, as would naturally be supposed, but rather by his more moderate gain by the week.

Commissions

In several lines the teamster is more than a driver: he is a solicitor or order clerk, and can build up or break down his employer's business. In some cases the companies have regular solicitors who are not drivers, but even then the driver must be relied upon to "hold his trade." This takes an extreme form in the laundry business, where in a union of 700 members there are 200 drivers, known as "commission men," who own each a horse and wagon and "control their trade." Some of these men have agencies at hotels, news stands, and so on, where orders may be left. They can transfer their business from one laundry to another, and their commission is 40 per cent. At such rates the most successful driver makes as much as $100 a week. Naturally, the laundrymen objected to this power of transferring business, and they began to require contracts preventing a man on leaving their employment from going into the laundry business for two years thereafter. The courts refused to sustain such contracts, but afterwards, when they were modified so as to limit their operation to a designated territory, they were sustained. The union met the policy of the laundrymen by a clause in their agreements stipulating that drivers owning their own wagon and known as "commission men" should receive not less than 40 per cent of the gross amount of work, and that "no driver shall be requested to sign any contract conflicting with this agreement." Evidently, a union of solicitors owning their places of business, protecting their commissions, and maintaining their power to throw business from one employer to another partakes more of the nature of a merchants' guild than a labor union. In the case of laundry drivers not owning their wagons the union agreement provides a minimum salary of $15 a week, which is an advance of something like 50 per cent on their former wages. In addition, many of them get a commission on business beyond a certain amount. The rule of a minimum salary holds for drivers in all other lines where commissions are paid, the laundrymen owning their wagons being the only class paid solely by commissions without a minimum guaranty.

In the case of the bakery drivers the guaranty is $14 a week, which would be useful only in the out districts where business is light, but where the union does not yet control. The valuable advances are in the rates of commission, and these apply to the large bakeries supplying the down-town district. Here the minimum of $14 is significant, not as a true minimum, but as a basis on which to compute the commissions. For example, the best paying company in the city, which formerly paid $14 a week and 6 per cent on sales above $250 now pays $14 a week and 1½ per cent on business up to $150, 3 per cent on the excess to $250, and 7 per cent on the excess above $250. Consequently, a driver who formerly received $17 on a week's business of $300 now gets $22.75. The larger his business, the larger has been the rate of increase in his earnings, a few getting as much as $40 a week and none less than $16.

The commission scheme of the beer drivers is suggestive. The bottle beer driver, more than the keg beer driver, is expected to "hold his trade." In both cases the commission is paid, not on the sales, but on the "empties" returned; and in both cases the commission has always been looked upon as spending-money. The bottle beer driver joins many lodges to which bartenders belong. He seldom sees the saloon proprietor, for his visits are made early in the morning. His persuasiveness is exerted on the bartender. To prevent him from transferring his trade from one brewery to another, the brewers have a strong association and an agreement not to take another brewer's driver. The agreement is enforced by a clearing house, organized as follows. The driver does not get all of the "empties." Many of them are thrown in the alleys and back yards, and come into the hands of junk dealers. These sell them to the clearing house of the brewers' association. The brewer who does not abide by the rules of the association cannot get back his junk bottles through the clearing house until his fine is paid. This is one of the means that hold the brewers together in fixing prices and resisting organized labor. Lacking such a clearing house, the laundrymen have not been able as effectively to resist the "commission men."

The keg beer driver gets his salary of $80 a month and 4 cents additional on empty kegs returned. Before organization his salary was $60 to $80 and his commission was 8 cents, but out of this he paid his helper $20 to $35 a month. Now the helper gets $55 a month paid by the brewer, and the driver tries to keep his commission through a clause in the agreement providing that "peddlers, helpers, and extra drivers shall not be required to spend any money with customers on their routes, and their not spending any money shall not be cause for any complaint or discharge." Under this arrangement the majority "take home" more than their salary, and the best men with the best routes are said to earn, net, as much as $30 or $35 a week.

The milk wagon driver's commission is computed on the basis of "1 cent to the point," a point being the unit of each article sold, as a quart of milk, a half pint of cream, or a pound of butter. This figures out about 14 per cent on sales; but he is usually paid a minimum of $60 a month, if his sales do not yield so much, and one half cent a point on sales above the amount necessary to compute the minimum at 1 cent. The best man earns $100, and the majority in the service of the "big firms" earn $65. The commission is optional, and very few of the small dealers pay it. The union demands for 1905 would make it compulsory, would raise it to 1 1/5 cent, and would for the first time establish a minimum wage of $17.50 per week instead of the fluctuating minima ranging from $45 paid by the small dealer to $60 paid by the large dealer.

The commission system fades into the graded salary system in the case of the yeast wagon drivers (belonging to the bakery drivers' local). The union has changed the grading and promotions from the basis of individual bargaining to the basis of seniority, the driver beginning at $15 and advancing $1 at the end of the first year, and then $1 at two-year intervals, until at the end of the seventh year he reaches $19. Since the starting point was formerly $12 and seniority was counted back for those in the service at the time when the change was made, some of the best men received no advance, while others long in the service but not hitherto preferred by employers were advanced at once from $12 a week to $18 and $19.

In the case of the grocery and market drivers the range of wages was formerly extreme, since experienced men were rare and unsuitable men abundant. The best commanded $25 or $30 a week, and the poorest $5 a week. The union did not attempt to grade all the men according to seniority, but contented itself with grading the order clerks, or "those controlling their own trade," in three classes of $12, $13, and $14 for the first three six-month periods and leaving further promotions to the employer. For other classes of drivers they simply raised the minimum from, say, $11 a week for those in the wholesale trade to $15, and from $5 a week for retail drivers to $10.

The same distinction appears among the railway express drivers. The union grades the "conductor" on a double wagon, since he is a solicitor and the responsible man under bonds, at $62.50 the first three months, $67.50 after three months, and $70 after six months, but fixes a flat rate for the driver. Apart from these three grades, promotions to higher pay are at the discretion of the six companies, among whom competition is keen and the best solicitors eagerly sought.

In these cases we can see the transition to the ordinary teamster, who does not "control his trade." This is the situation with the great bulk of teaming, such as that of the truck driver, coal teamster, building-material driver, and so on. In general, wherever the commission or premium system on sales is possible the union prefers it, and even requires it; but where the commission cannot be definitely measured because the traffic is miscellaneous, the union tries to substitute grading according to seniority. And, finally, where the teamster is only a driver and not a solicitor the union establishes simply a flat minimum. There is one exception to the last statement. This is in the loading, unloading, and hauling of common brick from the cars, employing about 200 men in a union of 700. The price was formerly 36 cents per 1000, raised by agreement with the union to 40 cents, at which the driver earns $3 to $4 a day as against a day rate of $2.25 in the same local union. With this exception the ordinary driver in the different locals is paid by the week or month.

Besides wages and hours the unions have secured relief from exactions which the members consider important. The department store drivers and the livery drivers no longer purchase their uniforms at company prices. The expense of securing bonds, formerly amounting to $5 a year, required of many classes of teamsters, is now borne by the employer. The grocery and market wagon drivers are no longer responsible for goods stolen off their wagons or spoiled by kerosene; and they, as well as the department store and other classes of retail-delivery drivers, are protected against losses for which they are not responsible on C.O.D. packages and on goods returned. The agreements in all cases contain an arbitration clause whereby an umpire decides if employer and employee cannot agree.

Strikes

The experience of the unions has led to a decided change in the matter of strikes. Sympathetic strikes seem to have been eliminated during the past two years, except where a sister local of teamsters was involved. As far as other industries are concerned, the teamsters have endeavored to adopt the let-alone policy of the railway brotherhoods, although within the past few weeks they have listened to the appeals of the garment workers and violated this policy as well as their agreements.[1] All of their agreements require work to be continued pending arbitration.[2] A vote to strike must be taken on paper ballots,

[1] See P.S., note following this chapter, p. 64.

[2] The truck drivers, like others, issue a card to their stewards, as follows:

Advice to Stewards

1. Become acquainted with the laws of the I. B. of T. and of your Local Union.
2. Become acquainted with the agreement of your Local and the Employers'.
3. Examine the Due Books of every member working in the barn in which you are Steward no later than the 10th of each month.
4. When a new man is employed, ask him for his Due Book. If he is not a member of Local 705, or he is three months in arrears (and a member of Local 705 in good standing can be had), object to him going to work.
5. When a member has a complaint, he must report it to the Steward, whose duty it is to take the member to the employer, hear both sides of the case, and, if the employer is right, tell the member so. If he is not satisfied, send him to the officials of the Local. If the employer refuses to comply with the Steward's decision, notify the officials at once.
6. Stewards must not call a strike unless authorized by the Local through its officers.
7. Stewards should use their influence to prevent a strike until the officers have had a chance to adjust the difference.
8. Stewards should attend as many meetings as they possibly can.

and must have a two-thirds majority of the local. It must then go to the joint executive council. If approved, it is referred to the general executive board of the international organization. That body is prohibited from approving "unless there is sufficient funds on hand in the International Union to pay strike benefits" of $5 a week. If it decides to sustain the local, it sends a representative to take charge of the negotiations and, if he deems it advisable, to order a strike. A local striking without such approval receives no support.

The controlling influence of the International is strengthened by the system of finance. Out of the local dues of 50 cents a month, 15 cents are paid to the International treasury, whose funds are said to be large (no figures are published). The locals have moderate treasuries, mainly for insurance benefits, and the International is expected after the first week to support the strikes it approves. Nearly all of the locals pay death benefits of $100, adding $10 for flowers. The coal teamsters tried sick benefits for a while, but stopped the experiment because "too many got sick."

The initiation fees of several locals are $5.25; but the coal, truck, ice, van, railway express, and a few other locals have advanced the fee to $15. For a time the truck drivers placed theirs at $25, but they reduced it to $15, which seems to be the figure towards which all are tending. Usually the fee is paid in installments extending over five or six weeks after the novitiate has gone to work. Certain ice companies "check off" the fee from wages and pay it over to the union treasury, but this practice is an exception.

THE "CLOSED AND OPEN STABLE"

There is a wide diversity among the agreements respecting the employment of union members. Some of them, like those of the railway express drivers and department store drivers, simply say, "There shall be no discrimination against union drivers." The majority are similar to the truck drivers' agreement, which reads, "Party of the first part agrees to employ members of the Truck Drivers' Union, Local 705, when in their power to do so." The furniture drivers' agreement formerly read as follows: "Party of the first part agrees to employ members of the Furniture Drivers' and Helpers' Local No. 722, or those who will make application within twelve hours after receiving employment and become a member at the next regular meeting of the organization. In hiring men, the union men to have the preference." This is also the form of several other agreements, such as that of the grocery and market wagon drivers. It amounted to an open-shop agreement, and, because advantage had been taken of it to weaken the union, the Furniture Drivers' Local went on strike at its termination in October, 1904, to secure a closed-shop agreement. A compromise was finally made, and this clause was changed to read: "There shall be no discrimination against union drivers or helpers. In hiring men, party of the first part agrees to give preference to members of Local 722." In practice this new agreement makes the union headquarters the employment office of the wholesale furniture dealers.

The commission team owners agree likewise "to employ none but members of Commission Drivers' Union, Local No. 3, in good standing and carrying the regular working card of the organization, if such drivers can be supplied by the business agent of Local No. 3, or competent men who are willing to become members of said Local No. 3." Besides that of the coal teamsters, already cited, the van teamsters' agreement is strictly closed shop, as follows: "Party of the first part agrees to employ none but members of the Van Teamsters and Helpers Union, Local 711, I. B. of T., in good standing and carrying the regular working card of the organization."

Whatever the form of these agreements they operate to give members of the unions steady employment as against the introduction of outsiders. Yet, except in the two or three strictly closed-shop agreements, the team owners say that they can employ any man they see fit, whether union member or not, provided they pay the scale and he joins the union. They discharge him, however, if the union brings charges against him and does not admit him. The high scale of wages makes it to their interest to employ experienced men who know the depots and routes. Hence in the case of the team owners' associations the open-shop question has never come up. In others it causes friction and sometimes strikes. This is especially true of the laundry business, where the only prolonged strike (which has lasted since June, 1904) turns on the clause of the former agreement conceding tc the laundrymen the right to hire nonmembers. In some cases the union cannot furnish members when called upon, notably the ice wagon drivers and helpers, more than one half of whose members leave the city during the winter. On this account they take in some 300 new members each season in a total membership of 1800. Their agreement reads: "We concede the employer the right to hire all Ice Wagon Drivers and Helpers, providing he notifies the officials of the Ice Wagon Drivers and Helpers Local Union No. 2 within twelve hours after employing said Drivers and Helpers; and, if there are any charges against said Driver or Helper, the employer on his part agrees to discharge said Driver or Helper within twelve hours after receiving due notice from the officials of the Ice Wagon Drivers and Helpers Local Union No. 2. In hiring men, the Union men to have preference." The above twelve-hour clause is found in most of the open-shop agreements.

In these and all other cases more reliance is placed on the daily attitude of the employers and their representatives than on the wording of the agreements. The unions stand ready to strike on evidence of persistent discrimination, by which is sometimes meant the employment of nonmembers when members are unemployed. The employers on their side, with the exceptions mentioned, practice conciliation, and realize that if they kept nonunion men in their employment they could destroy the unions. Furthermore, the teamster's occupation is more exposed than that of any other craftsman. Each driver is an establishment in himself. In the crowded streets, with 30,000 teamsters organized, there is not much room for the unorganized. Actual or expected violence is looked upon by employers and teamsters as a matter of course. Blockades and obstruction, as well as violence, are effective, and all union drivers are expected to do what the truck drivers explicitly command in their by-laws: "All members of this local shall at all times while on duty wear his union button in plain sight, so it can be seen by any one. Any member failing to do so shall be subject to a fine of not less than $1 for each offense."

It will thus be seen that the agreements, whether "closed-shop" or "open-shop" in form, are "union-shop" in practice. On the other hand, the reciprocal feature of the coal teamsters' provisional agreement, which forbade union drivers to work for employers not members of the team owners' association, has been eliminated. In its place the following was substituted: "The organization agrees on its part to do all in its power to further the interests of said Association." The commission drivers made the same agreement with the Commission Team Owners' Association. The van teamsters and truck drivers agree not to further the interests of the associations of team owners, but simply to "further the interests of their employer." These peculiar clauses do not mean that the drivers will work only for members of those associations, since there are drivers working for nonmembers. They simply mean that the drivers will not work for nonmembers on terms more favorable than those granted to members. The object is not that of an exclusive agreement, but to equalize competitive conditions. One result undoubtedly is to strengthen the team owners' associations, and to enable them better to maintain their official scales of cartage. Prior to the organization of the unions the owners' associations were weak and ineffective. Their official scales were cut by destructive competition. Now they include nearly all the team owners, who seek the cover of the association for protection against the union. The prices for cartage have in most cases been raised, but it is impossible to know how much. The official cartage scales have been advanced 20 to 40 per cent, but this is not decisive, for they were not enforced, whereas the present scales are fairly well enforced. The double wagon, which the truck owners' scale formerly set at $24 a week with driver and which was actually hired by the merchant at $22 to $26, is now hired at a minimum of $31. The single wagon has advanced from a nominal rate of $18 and an actual one of $15 or $20 to an official $22 a week. The carriage to a cemetery, for which $5 was formerly charged, now costs $7. The official scale of the commission team owners was always charged like a uniform freight rate by the commission dealer to the shipper, even when less than that scale was paid by the dealer to the team owner. In this case the new scale was made by agreement between the team owners and the dealers, and cartage charges were raised 10 to 100 per cent, the average on the bulk of the business being about 30 per cent.

This scale and all others are placed at such figures that the team owner, whether member or nonmember, who pays the union scale of wages cannot make a profit if he cuts the scale of cartage. The scale cannot be exorbitant compared with the wages, since merchants and manufacturers have the option of hiring their teamsters directly for the same wages and hours and running their own stables; many of them do so, while others prefer to sell their horses and wagons and let out their teaming to contractors at the official scale. It must be remembered that a teaming contractor assumes the liabilities of a common carrier, and a single accident to his cargo or to a pedestrian may wipe off the profits of a year, or even his entire capital. In the former period of reckless competition no margin was allowed for insurance against such catastrophes, and the wholesale merchant, who now pays the increased cartage to a teaming contractor, pays for the assumption of a risk that formerly cost him nothing, and is usually overlooked, when he does his own trucking, until the accident occurs.

In the case of fares and charges where the general public is concerned, such as those for cabs and express and furniture moving, the maximum scale is usually fixed by municipal ordinance; the changed conditions simply mean that the legal prices are charged, whereas formerly they were undercut. In the case of the charge of Parmelee (the railway baggage express) of 50 cents on trunks from stations, there has been no increase, since that was fixed by agreement with the railway companies. Other expressmen have advanced their 25-cent charges to 35 cents and their 35-cent charges to 50 cents. The municipal ordinance which formerly fixed the hire of cabs at 25 cents per passenger per mile now fixes it at 50 cents per trip per mile, whether one passenger or two.

The economic basis which supports these official scales of cartage in competitive lines may be illustrated by the case of the furniture movers. The van teamsters reported at the barn not later than half past four in the morning, and went home at night when their work was finished. The employer, not paying them for overtime, and being at liberty to keep them as late at night as he pleased without extra cost, often figured on doing a cheap job if the customer would delay the beginning until late in the afternoon, finishing late at night. The labor cost for such a job was practically nothing, and hence there was no bottom to prices. One team owner could not tell how low his competitors would be willing to go, nor could he tell how low he himself could afford to go. Even his horses, skeletonized by overtime, did not set a certain minimum. On two or three occasions the owners had attempted to form an association and to agree on a minimum scale of charges, but their agreements were always broken by the temptation so easily offered to get the teamster's work for nothing, and to give the customer the benefit of the exploitation. When the teamsters organized and reduced their indefinite hours of 90 or more a week to a definite 60, with 25 cents an hour for overtime, then the employer could see a solid foundation on which to maintain the prices agreed upon. The result has been that the unscrupulous team owner who beat his competitors by cheating and overworking his teamsters has not been able to continue in the business; and the other class of owners, who regretted, but could not remedy what some of them now describe as the "actual slavery" of the teamster, are more prosperous than ever before. Their horses and equipment are better cared for, and their services to the public better performed. True, the "public" pay higher charges for cartage than before, but the complaint from that source has partly subsided. In view of the facts their grievance is like that of the Roman populace when the gladiatorial combats were stopped.

The one-team owner who drives his wagon has a peculiar and dubious place in this business. He is the connecting link, as it were, between the ancient guild and the modern organizations of employers and workmen on class lines. He is eligible either to the teamsters' union or the team owners' association. As a member of the owners' association he is expected to observe the scale of cartage, and as a member of the union the owners ask that he be made to observe it. The policy of the unions on this point is to have less and less to do with regulating prices, and therefore to leave the one-team owner free to do as he pleases, unless he employs a helper. Of course, he needs a button or a card in order to travel uninterrupted, and this fact induces him to join one of the associations. If he joins the truck owners, he gets an association button which the teamsters recognize. If he is an ice wagon driver, he requires a helper, and so is not eligible to the union; but he is given a card certifying that he employs a union helper and is "entitled to all courtesies and respect of members of the I. B. of T." One of the locals, the express drivers, is composed solely of these one-team owners. Their charges are regulated by municipal ordinance on work done by the trip. A wagon and driver are hired by the week at $24. They can work as many hours a day as they please, since each is his own "employer."

The interests of these small proprietors lead them into a field foreign to that of the ordinary labor union, as may be seen in the legal activities of the hack, coupé, and cab drivers. Since 1896 this local has expended $7000 in securing certain rights of common carriers. Formerly abutting property owners, including the railway companies, leased the right to stand on the street in front of their property; and the revenues of hotels from this seizure of the public highway amounted to $50 or $60, and in one case $200, a month. The cab drivers won a suit in the criminal court [1] and another in the Supreme Court of

[1] *City of Chicago* v. *Wilson*, *Chicago Legal News*, August 16, 1902.

Illinois[1]; and now any driver can stand on the streets at any place designated by police authorities. Next they contested the right to solicit passengers inside the depots and to stand on the line designated by the railroad authorities for Parmelee's drivers. A railroad company secured an injunction in the United States Circuit Court, and the union carried it to the Circuit Court of Appeals[2] and then to the United States Supreme Court, whence a decision is now awaited.

An interesting outcome of the change from indefinite to definite hours and wages, as well as of the separation of classes, has been the breakdown of the "fatherly feeling" which some of the team owners say they formerly had for some of their teamsters. They learned to feel an interest in the men who had been in their service for many years and to share their sorrows and joys. Though such a man was unfitted for other branches of work, he was satisfactory in his old position, if he would accept a lower rate of pay and make himself generally useful. Or the owner employed a boy at $1 a day out of regard for his widowed mother. Now the union comes between the owner and his teamster. It compels the owner to advance his pay by $3 or $6 a week to a minimum rate. It requires a higher rate for that overtime in which the teamster had shown his general usefulness. The teamster takes his orders from the union and becomes a party to the coercion. Estrangement follows. The owner cannot afford to keep the man or boy at the higher rates of pay. He must have vigorous young men. He has discharged the boys. A large manufacturer has cut off the two weeks' vacation on full pay which he formerly gave to his teamsters. The bargain has lost its indefinite, easy, fatherly relation of "give-and-take," and has become a close calculation.

A similar estrangement occurs between the team owner and his customers, "the public." The merchant or manufacturer was formerly willing to let the truck owner send an old man or a boy with the team, which he got for a dollar or two less a week on that account. The small team owner, with inferior

[1] *Pennsylvania R. R.* v. *City of Chicago*, 181 Ill. 289.

[2] *Donovan et al.* v. *The Pennsylvania Co.*, 116 Fed. 907, 120 Fed. 215 (1903).

equipment, formerly secured trade by making concessions in price. Now he must have just as good a team, just as large a wagon, or just as attractive a van as his wealthy competitor in order to get the trade. The public has lost its desire to help out the poor team owner. Its friendly feeling, like the fatherly feeling of the team owner, disappears when no longer paid for. Thus has the cash *nexus* of unionism uncovered and dislodged a certain amount of unconscious hypocrisy.

Naturally, at first, the team owners were at sea in dealing with the new situation. Having lost the personal control of their teamsters, it seemed to them that they must control the organization that had come between them. But these organizations in turn seemed to be simply the union leaders and officers. Consequently, an era of corruption was ushered in, the employers turning over their funds to Driscoll, a "labor expert," but not a team owner, who knew how to handle the leaders. This continued, as described above, until the unions had time to learn self-government and depose the leaders who assumed to sell and deliver them. They also took from the business agents their votes, though not their seats, in the joint teamsters' council. The team owners then, perforce, changed their policy. They deposed Driscoll, and elected plain business men, team owners like themselves. The policy of these men is what they describe as "fair dealing." They try to remedy every grievance, open and aboveboard, on its merits. They realize that the team owner who, by a corrupt bargain with the union agent, is not compelled to remedy the grievance of his teamster has thereby an advantage over his competitors. Equal treatment is as necessary to preserve the team owners' association as it is to preserve the teamsters' union. In this way they cultivate what they call a "friendly feeling" with the teamsters in place of the former paternal feeling.

This new kind of friendly feeling, while severe on individuals here and there, accords with the teamster's view of himself. From what has already been said of his work and wages it follows that he is more than the mere unskilled laborer, as is generally assumed. He is sometimes a traveling salesman and at least a traveling representative. Even the ordinary teamster looks upon his occupation as a craft, and the object of his union is to have it recognized as such. He, like the salesman, is really a man of the world, — comes in contact with many classes of people and learns to deal with men as well as to handle material. His work is a constant adaptation of means to ends in a struggle for business, without the aid of a foreman to do his thinking. He must know the depots, the streets, and the best routes. He is intrusted with his employer's property and with his employer's responsibilities as a common carrier for goods hauled and for pedestrians injured. He often requires special attributes of carefulness and promptness. The van teamster cites with professional pride the expensive furniture moved from a fashionable dwelling without a scratch. The commission team driver feels his responsibility for perishable goods and for prompt and careful handling. The garbage collector calls himself the sanitary teamster. The helpers of the machinery-moving and safe-moving teamsters are millwrights.

Now the efforts of the teamsters to have these qualities recognized as distinguishing a craft and not common to the mere laborer are seen in some of their policies. First, there is the enforcement of weekly salaries, as far as possible, instead of payment by the load or laying a man off when work is interrupted. This policy leads the employer to "bunch" his work better, — to keep a man steadily employed in place of letting him "hang around," waiting for work. Of course, trade in some lines is seasonal, and allowance for this is made by classifying employees as "steady men" and "extra drivers and helpers." The latter in some cases are paid by the hour; the livery "tripper," by 25 per cent of the liveryman's charge. They are considered as serving a kind of apprenticeship, while for the "steady men" in slack times the old employee is to have the preference, being the last laid off and the first taken on. The closed-shop policy, also, is justified as the protection of their craft against the "farmer" or the "hobo," who can drive a wagon but is not a teamster. As long, too, as the minimum wage can be maintained, the team owner is not inclined to employ these inexperienced and less reliable drivers. That the hope of the teamster to make his calling a craft is being realized is borne out by the witness of team owners, who speak sometimes with enthusiasm of the superior character of the men who have come to the front. The "bums" are gradually weeded out by the employers themselves. Men of integrity and self-respect secure the offices, and the worldly wisdom of the teamster makes him amenable to reason and fair dealing. He harbors no resentment on account of his former treatment, for he acknowledges that the team owners were themselves victims of destructive competition.

Yet the employers do not feel that their sailing is smooth or the future certain. The former defeated corruptionist and a few adroit employers, still seeking to "tie up" a competitor in business, are able to foment occasional petty strikes and violations of agreements. Equally serious are the enormous advances in wages and the self-confident demands of the unions for more and still more, and most serious of all is the prospect of sympathetic strikes on behalf of other unions unable to win on their own account. It is evident that employers are understanding each other better and are preparing for united action. Many of them consider the teamster as the keystone of Chicago unionism. The freight tunnel, now completed under all the down-town streets, is expected to free them from an event like the freight handlers' strike. But prediction would be vain.

J. R. COMMONS.

P.S. — Even before the publication of the foregoing article in the *Quarterly Journal of Economics* in May, 1905, a sympathetic strike was "called" by the teamsters in behalf of the garment workers, and is now in progress (July). This strike was a violation of their agreements with the team owners, and it has been accompanied with the importation of Negro strike breakers, with street riots and blockades, with violence upon scores of persons, with the loss of several lives, with heavy damage to many lines of business, and with large expenditures for additional police protection. A grand jury has been summoned to investigate the charges of corruption in this and earlier strikes of the teamsters and to return indictments for conspiracy, assault, and murder.

J. R. C.

IV

THE NEW YORK BUILDING TRADES[1]

The employers and work people in New York who have been familiar with the building trades during the year 1903 universally agree that never in their experience have they met so tangled a situation. A succession of strikes, lockouts, and criminal prosecutions of walking delegates, growing out of trade jurisdiction, rival organizations, and union misrule, and ending in the organization of the employers and a reorganization of the industry with a joint arbitration board, make this a significant and interesting labor dispute of the year 1903.

The storm center of the disturbance was the United Board of Building Trades, familiarly known as the "Board of Delegates." When this board was created in March, 1902, it was confidently expected that the former anarchy of jurisdictional strikes and dual unions would be remedied; and the board was organized under the advice and even the pressure of several influential contractors who had suffered from fights between the unions. But the organization, while it remedied in part the evils of disunion, brought forth the new evil of "graft."

The first Board of Delegates in the building trades was started in 1884 by the walking delegates of the only four unions that had such officers at that time. These delegates met first in a spirit of fun and sociability and without authority from their unions. The board was extraconstitutional. It did not realize its possibilities. The delegate was merely the business agent of the union, selected to carry its messages, but without authority to change or enlarge his instructions. But there was one circumstance in the building trades that served to give this extraconstitutional body unexpected but useful

[1] From the *Quarterly Journal of Economics*, Vol. XVIII, 1904, pp. 409–437.

power. This was the necessity of prompt action in dealing with contractors. The building industry in New York, as well as elsewhere in the United States, unlike that in England and Europe, is conducted on a system of subcontracting. The mason builder, or general contractor, secures the contract from the owner, or "client," and generally puts up the brickwork; but he submits by competitive bidding all the other work to as many contractors as there are kinds of work. This system enables the contractor to enter the field with little or no capital, since it is usually arranged that partial payments shall be made by the owner to the general contractor, and by him to the subcontractors, as the work progresses. A subcontractor may have but a few days' work on a job; and if he violates his agreement with the union or any of the rules the union is striving to enforce, his work may be finished and his men discharged before the union can hold a meeting and call a strike. Consequently, in the building trades the unions have given their walking delegates authority to call a strike at the moment when they are satisfied a rule is violated. This usually occurs when the delegate finds a nonunion man on the job, since a nonunion man is not supposed to observe the rules or wage scale of the union. The delegate then reports his action to the union meeting, where he is generally sustained as a matter of course.

But a strike of a single union on a job may not be effective. Then the delegate must bring the matter home, if possible, to the general contractor. The other unions are working for other contractors, and in order to hold the general contractor responsible, the entire construction must be tied up. The unions have provided for this in advance by a clause inserted when they make an agreement, which reads, "A sympathetic strike shall not be a violation of this agreement." With this in mind the delegate invites the other delegates whose men are on the job to meet him at the place, and he endeavors to satisfy them that his grievance is real and cannot be remedied unless they also "pull" their men. Here is the occasion for the Board of Delegates. They meet two or three times a week to advise one another of their grievances and to make appointments to meet on the jobs. If the Board of Delegates is recognized anywhere in the union constitution, it is informally recognized in this provision for sympathetic strikes.

It is a significant fact that the only union of the building trades which does not permit the sympathetic strike is that of the bricklayers, who are employed by the general contractor, while the unions employed by subcontractors hold that the sympathetic strike is indispensable. Naturally the bricklayers' delegate has never been a member of the Board of Delegates.

To return to the origin of the United Board. The sociable board of four delegates inaugurated in 1884, not realizing its possibilities, felt its way only by gradual steps to joint action. The unions when they acted in sympathy had done so hitherto through the Central Labor Union, a representative assembly of all trades in the city, meeting once a week. But little by little the Board of Delegates took independent action, and so prompt and satisfactory were the results that the unions quietly accepted their usurpations and other unions elected delegates who joined the board. In 1890 the board had become entirely independent and dominant in the building trades.

But their supremacy did not long continue. Internal factions and conflicts arose, mainly on personal grounds; and in 1894 the board divided. For six years two hostile boards were in the field, the Board of Delegates and the Building Trades Council. In some trades there were two unions claiming the same work, one in the board and the other in the council. In other trades the unions attempted to enlarge their jurisdiction to cover a different trade in the opposing board. Each board acted as a unit, employing the sympathetic strike against the other. Employers who hired men from one board could not get men of other trades from the other board. Building construction was continually interrupted, not on account of lockouts, low wages, or even employment of nonunion men, but on account of fights between the unions. The friendly employer who hired only union men and also the unfriendly employer were used as clubs to hit the opposing union. And the friendly employer suffered more than the unfriendly.

No doubt the merging of the two boards into the United Board of Building Trades in March, 1902, was welcomed by employers and workmen. The board included all the strong unions except the bricklayers. Delegates were admitted on credentials signed by the officers of the union, and thus the board was officially recognized. Its objects were "to secure harmony and unity of action" and "to stop internal warfare." It provided arbitration of disputes between unions, and a penalty of suspension for the union failing to obey a decision. Some fifteen jurisdictional disputes were thus decided during the life of the board. In but one case was a decision defied; and this one defiance began the movement that wrecked the board, as will soon appear.

The United Board adopted simple and effective rules for sympathetic strikes. A union might act independently, but if it did it forfeited support. When a delegate brought in his grievance it became the "property of the board." All of the delegates having men on the job, said the rules, "shall be ordered to investigate the grievance and, if deemed necessary, shall have power to order a strike, provided two thirds of the committee favor said strike." Members of the committee were fined $3 if thirty minutes late at the place appointed. If they failed to agree, the delegate had an appeal to the board, where a majority decided, and a final appeal to the president of the board, whose decision was binding on him and the delegate refusing to strike in sympathy.

With the employers unorganized this sympathetic strike was irresistible. Soon rumors of "graft" and "hold-up" began to circulate. One firm was said to have paid $2000 to have a strike "called off." Statements were made of smaller amounts paid over. It was declared that some of these payments went, in whole or in part, to members of the union as compensation for "waiting time," that is, time lost while on strike. Like the Germans in the war with France, the unions compelled the conquered to pay the cost of the conquest. This indemnity policy was praised as a peace measure, and, indeed, such it was in a small way; but the defective bookkeeping and accounting of the unions left opportunities for delegates to pocket unknown sums for themselves.

Probably the most amazing act of the board during its brief career was the "hold-up" of the Association of Interior Decorators and Cabinet Makers and the "sell-out" of the Amalgamated Painters. The latter organization was a partner in the board at its origin and objected to the admission of the local branch of the International Brotherhood of Painters, which at that time had but a few hundred members. The international organization struck against the employers on their work outside New York, and thus won from them a contract to employ only Brotherhood men in New York. The Amalgamated Painters had the support of the Board of Delegates, and the board called out the other trades where Brotherhood men were employed. But the ring in control of the board offered to seat the Brotherhood on payment of a large sum of money. Not being able to get this from the union, they demanded it from the employers, who contributed $400 each to the fund. The board then seated the Brotherhood and remained "neutral" in the fight between the two unions.

How extensive was this blackmail on employers or on each other is not publicly known, but it seems to have centered in a ring headed by the leading spirit and organizer of the board, Sam Parks, business agent of the Structural Iron Workers. More serious than blackmail was the alleged partnership of Parks and the board with the largest firm of builders, the George A. Fuller Company. This company operates on a large scale throughout the United States, and it had introduced a system of direct employment in place of the contract system of other builders. By dispensing with subcontractors and doing all its construction through its own departments, thereby more easily keeping on friendly terms with the Board of Delegates, it was able to complete a building in much less time than other builders, — an item of money value to its clients. It is known that this company paid considerable sums to delegates for services, such as going to other localities to use their good offices. In various ways it had the friendship and confidence of the delegates. On the other hand, mechanics preferred to work for it, since its construction was on such a large scale that their employment was steadier ; and workmen in the building trades always spoke highly of its treatment of the men, its prompt payment of wages, protection of life and limb, and readiness to remedy grievances. It is certainly true that the Fuller company suffered little or nothing from strikes during the reign of the United Board, while other builders were continually troubled.

These things might have continued longer than they actually did, had it not been for two weaknesses of the board, — secession of the carpenters and accession of the team drivers. One was a weakness of discipline, the other a weakness of expansion. They opened the way for employers to organize.

Between the local branch of the old English organization, known as the Amalgamated Society of Carpenters and Joiners, and the American Brotherhood of Carpenters there was a long-standing feud. The Amalgamated was a small but sturdy organization of 700 members ; the Brotherhood claimed 10,000 members. Both went into the United Board in March, 1902. The Brotherhood had a contract with the Fuller company to employ only Brotherhood men. It demanded similar agreements with other builders and was extending its control at the expense of its diminutive rival. It finally demanded the dissolution of the Amalgamated. This the board rejected. The Brotherhood withdrew in July, 1902. From that time until April, 1903, the board permitted Brotherhood carpenters, although outside the board, to work with other unions, and tried to remain neutral. But the Brotherhood was aggressive. On certain jobs it refused to work if Amalgamated men were employed. The board stood by the Amalgamated and refused to work on those particular jobs with the Brotherhood. The Brotherhood decided to fight the board. The national officers took the matter up, came on the ground with their treasury, and on April 7, without warning, 10,000 Brotherhood carpenters began an amazingly suicidal strike throughout the city. They struck not only in the shops where Amalgamated men were employed, but they struck in shops where they had contracts for the exclusive employment of their own members. The motives and logic of this self-destruction are explained on the ground that the Brotherhood throughout the country had grown so rapidly that its officers had "lost their heads." At any rate, all buildings were tied up. The Fuller company by a quick stroke of generalship secured nearly all of the Amalgamated men in town the day after its Brotherhood men quit work and so was not seriously affected. At this point a meeting was called by a committee of the Building Trades Club, a semi-business organization, and the Building Trades Employers' Association was started.

But the carpenters' strike, big as it was, was soon eclipsed. A small union of building material drivers had been admitted to the Board of Delegates; and the board saw in that union a hope of controlling the entire building industry by the easy means, first, of shutting off the material of any "unfair" contractor, and, next, of unionizing the lumber and material yards. The drivers represented that they controlled the bulk of the teamsters in the lumber and material line, and the board indorsed their proposed demand that none but union teamsters be employed. Here the board overreached itself, and its venture in the line of expansion brought it to an unknown continent where the employers were organized. The Association of Lumber Dealers and the Association of Brick and Material Handlers are close organizations of fifteen years' successful operation, controlling all of the yards and acting together under a joint secretary. In the year 1891 they had disastrously defeated a union of teamsters, and they had maintained their organization intact from that time as an exchange, a credit association, a social club, and an employers' association. The drivers now began by presenting their demands to one yard at a time; they had gone as far as five yards when, without warning, every yard in Manhattan shut its gates. The secretary of the two associations notified the board through the daily press that the shut-down would continue until the board revoked its indorsement of the teamsters' demand. The carpenters' strike laid off 10,000 men, but the material men's shut-down laid off 70,000. It continued four weeks and split the board. The board at this time contained thirty-seven unions, of which twenty-two belonged to the skilled trades and fifteen to unskilled occupations, the teamsters among the latter. The housesmiths, led by Sam Parks, went with the unskilled unions, and took enough other trades to make a majority of one, each union having a single vote. The skilled trades forthwith seceded, formed a new Board of Skilled Mechanics, revoked the indorsement of the teamsters, and the dealers immediately opened their yards.

But now it was the turn of the material dealers to be surprised. They had deprived the builders of material, and now the builders were ready to deprive them of a market. Two years before there had been a vigorous effort to organize the builders and contractors. Each trade for many years had had its separate organization, but it had not been possible at that time to create a central body. The conflicting interests were too great, the plan of organization was crude, and, more than all, the unions themselves were not yet centralized. But the material dealers' shut-down furnished the opportunity. While it continued, the builders completed their organization. As soon as the shut-down was declared off, they declared a lockout. A week later they offered to the unions a plan of arbitration.

Unlike the former plan to organize the employers, this association was built on existing foundations. There were in existence thirty associations of employers and contractors in the thirty different trades of the building industry. While in the former attempt at organization each contractor joined the central association as an individual, regardless of the trade association to which he owed allegiance, in the present association the existing trade associations enter as units under a constitution binding each association, while its individual members are required to be also members of the general association. The autonomy of the several associations is left untouched except at points of conflict or at points where united action is necessary in dealing with the unions. In other words, the

Building Trades Employers' Association is a federal government like the United States, in which the individual is a member both of the general association and of his trade association, the general association possessing such powers as are delegated to it, and all other powers being reserved to the original trade associations. But these delegated powers are broad, for they include the power "generally to determine, regulate, and control the conduct of the members of this association and the employers' associations represented on the board in all matters pertaining to their relation with their employees." Any action dealing with prices or restricting competition is especially excluded. Every member of a trade association becomes thereby a member of the general association. There are also "individual" and "associate" members, but these have no voice in the Board of Governors. A member's dues are $40, which are paid for him by his trade association. But he is personally required to give bond ranging from $500 to $2500, with a surety company, "to insure compliance with and obedience to the decisions, orders, prohibitions, and regulations of the Board of Governors." The amount of the bond is made payable on the mere formal notice of the Board of Governors, and is stipulated as liquidated damages and not as a penalty. Latterly the association recommended to its members a form of contract containing a lockout clause exempting the contractor from damages where such lockout is ordered by the Building Trades Employers' Association. The bonding provision of the constitution, enforced by the additional clause that a member cannot resign "during a temporary suspension of business," is counted as the most essential and effective feature of the organization. Taken with another clause of the constitution, it amounts to compulsory membership in the association, — the parallel to the unions' "closed shop." This other clause reads, "To promote and maintain harmony between the different trades, it is recommended that the members of the association shall place all orders for work requiring labor at the building in any trade represented on the Board of Governors with members of this association." Since the

Mason Builders' Association has taken the lead in the movement, this section of the constitution, although a recommendation, is practically a pledge on the part of the general contractors that they will sublet their work only to members of the federated associations. Thus have the employers found it necessary to bind themselves to each other after the manner of the unions with which they are dealing.

At the same time the practice of making exclusive agreements within each trade seems in a fair way to be broken up by this larger association of all the employers in the industry. The Stone Trade Association has not been admitted, since it has an agreement by which members of the Stonecutters' Union work only for members of the employers' association, the union treasury receiving a bonus of 10 per cent on all contracts. This has led to a system of "cooked" bidding on contracts. The arrangement is already crumbling, and two or three stone trade employers have broken away and have applied for admission to the Building Trades Employers' Association as associate members. Four associations of employers which have exclusive agreements, yet without the obnoxious bonus or bidding features of the stone trade, are represented in the Board of Governors. These are the plumbers, the steam and hot-water fitters, the marble dealers, and the tile dealers.

The Board of Governors is made up of three representatives for each trade association. At the time of its inauguration twenty associations took part through their executive committees. Soon thereafter thirty associations were represented on the Board of Governors. The unit rule prevails, but each delegate counts one vote for every five members. Thus the three representatives of the mason builders with 108 members cast as a unit 21 votes out of a total of 160 votes. A quorum to order a "cessation or resumption of work by any or all of the members of the association" must include three fourths of the associations, and the affirmative must cast four fifths of the votes. The Board of Governors meets once a month or on twenty-four hours' notice. The association meets semiannually or on request either of twenty-five members or of the Board of Governors.

There were three evils which the new association determined to drive from the building industry, namely, sympathetic strikes, jurisdictional strikes, and the power of the walking delegate to call a strike. The Board of Governors drafted a plan of arbitration designed to overcome these evils. Since the walking delegates were the objects of attack, the plan was not submitted to the Board of Delegates, but was addressed to the secretaries of the unions and to individual members. The unions were requested to meet and act upon it. The communication contained the following:

For the last few years the conditions in our industry have been steadily growing worse until they culminated in the present cessation of work. As you can see from our platform and plan of arbitration, we have but one object in view, namely, to conduct our business relations in a fair, honest, and American way, and we want *you* to help us. . . . No doubt our actions, our motives, and our plans will be attacked by those representatives of labor who are unwilling to be deprived of any powers which have been given to them or have been *assumed by them*. . . . We refuse to believe that the rank and file of labor is acquainted with many of the acts of these representatives and of the conditions which exist in some of the trades, but how grievous they were is proven by the present standstill and the fact that within three weeks nearly thirty employers' associations of our industry have become a unit, as a living protest against oppression and extortion. We therefore call upon every conservative and thinking mechanic to attend the meeting of his union and register his vote against the un-American methods that have crept into the trade, and to insist upon the plan of arbitration as suggested. . . .

Unfortunately, the communication to the unions did not contain an invitation to appoint representatives to confer upon amendments to the plan; and since the employers declined to meet the walking delegates who had hitherto conducted such negotiations, nearly all of the members looked on the plan as an ultimatum. This interpretation was afterwards disavowed by the Board of Governors. At any rate, with unimportant exceptions the unions ignored it, and in many cases the secretaries did not even read it at the meetings, explaining that it did not bear the union printers' label. The communication was sent only to the unions of skilled mechanics and helpers and not to the unions of laborers.

A deadlock ensued, and continued for three weeks. Meantime the New York Civic Federation addressed an invitation to the unions of mechanics and to the Board of Governors, proposing a joint conference to discuss the employers' plan of arbitration. The Board of Governors accepted the invitation, and the labor members of the Civic Federation went to the meetings of several unions to urge its acceptance. The officers of three or four unions prevented them from getting a hearing, but in every case where they were given the privilege of the floor the union voted to send a committee. It was privately arranged with the walking delegates that they would not seek appointment on these committees; and in the conference that followed there was present but one such delegate, who took no part in the discussion and whose presence was not objected to. The conference met with sixty members of the Board of Governors, and with fifteen unions represented officially and three unions represented unofficially. It was called to order by the chairman of the conciliation committee of the Civic Federation, representing employers, and a report on credentials was made by the secretary of the same committee, representing trade unions. After brief speeches counseling moderation, these intermediaries withdrew, and the conference proceeded to elect as its chairman the chairman of the Board of Governors, and as secretary the president of the Tile Layers' Union. The conference began at two o'clock on July 3 and held continuous session until three o'clock of the morning of July 4. Amendments were adopted, and the amended plan was signed by all of the conferees. An adjournment was taken until July 9, when three "explanatory clauses" were added. In this final form it was printed, and submitted to all the unions. Within three weeks two thirds of the unions signed and returned to work, and within four weeks the General Arbitration Board was organized and had adopted its rules of procedure. With those unions which did not sign negotiations were conducted; and in a few cases where these negotiations were unsuccessful "scab" unions were organized, with which the members of the signatory unions worked on buildings without protest.

In its framework the arbitration plan is identical with that originally submitted by the employers, but certain amendments were added at the conference. It provides that unions and employers in each trade shall decide all questions affecting only their particular trade. If they cannot decide and cannot agree on an umpire, they must select an arbitration board outside the trade from the list of general arbitrators. The General Arbitration Board is composed of two arbitrators elected by each employers' association and two elected by each union, the union arbitrators not to be walking delegates. No strike can be ordered by a union or a walking delegate, and no lockout by an employer or an association before the matter in dispute is brought before the General Arbitration Board and settled. This includes specifically jurisdictional disputes and sympathetic strikes, as well as appeals on matters which cannot be settled by the employers and unions within a trade. The following items were added in the conferences with the unions, — only members of the unions party to the agreement are to be employed, and the employers' association agrees to enforce this clause on all contractors. If the union is unable to provide sufficient workmen, any employer may bring the matter before the General Arbitration Board, which has power to authorize him to employ nonmembers. Unskilled trades, not being parties to the agreement, are represented through mechanics of that trade.

The notable fact which the conferences developed was the willingness of the employers to add the items which the unions requested and the willingness of the unions to accept the framework which the employers proposed. In fact, the conferences resolved themselves mainly into explanations of misunderstandings. So impressive is this fact that to an outsider it might seem that the lockout could have been avoided, had the employers in the first place simply asked the unions to send representatives to a conference. But it must be remembered that the conference excluded walking delegates, who might have been less conciliatory, since it was for the purpose of clipping their powers that the conference assembled; and, moreover, the walking delegates could doubtless have prevented the unions from electing as representatives any but themselves, had not two or three weeks of idleness compelled them to realize the strength of the new organization of employers.

However this may be, at the very beginning of the first conference the union representatives proposed that all lockouts and strikes be declared off, that work be resumed, and that thereupon the plan of arbitration be taken up. Several unions stated that the lockout was a violation of existing agreements with their employers, and this was peculiarly true of the bricklayers, whose arbitration agreement with the mason builders had not once been violated in eighteen years. Now they were locked out through no fault of their own, in order to compel them to accept an additional agreement which had not been offered to them in the regular course. The bricklayers, indeed, on this account refused to send representatives to the conference. Several other unions filed the same grievance; and this violation of existing agreements was the argument of greatest force played upon by those who were able afterwards to prevent various unions from accepting the amended plan, satisfactory as it was in all essential points. The conference, however, proceeded, on the request of the chairman, who said, "Let us see what we can do with the document first, and then we will find out what our future action is to be."

For the evil of jurisdictional strikes, the most disastrous and perverse of all, the unions were as eager to find a remedy as the employers. The only objection offered to this feature of the employers' plan was the probability that a local arbitrament would decide contrary to the national policy of the two unions concerned, and it was argued that the matter should therefore be left to the local unions and referred by them to the national organizations, without any trouble to the employers themselves. But it was readily answered that the unions, neither local nor national, had been able to settle their own disputes, and that therefore the employers of conflicting unions were as much interested as the unions themselves in widening their jurisdiction. This clause was therefore left undisturbed.

It would seem that the most radical amendment made to the employers' plan was that requiring the exclusive employment of union men. Yet the employers explained that all of the existing agreements were already exclusive and were to continue in force, and that the proposed plan was not a substitute for those agreements, but an addition to them, intended only to remedy the two evils of sympathetic and jurisdictional strikes. The chairman brought out strongly this position of the employers in answering a question whether a union would have a right to strike if a member of the employers' association should sublet a part of his work to a nonunion contractor. He replied:

> If any nonunion men are on a building in connection with union men, and our employees come to any member of the employers' association and notify them, at once we will notify that contractor, owner, or whoever he is, that, unless he removes those men from that building at once, we will order our trades withdrawn. Is that plain enough, gentlemen? The only point is this, gentlemen, that we expect to work together hereafter for each other's interests. This is distinctly an arrangement between your association and ours. The only thing is that we shall not be willing to interrupt work and have every one do as he likes. We will have a regular arrangement for handling those cases, and you will get your redress perhaps quite as quickly and with less loss to yourself.

Since the unions, however, wished the new agreement to be explicit on this point, the matter was taken up and discussed at great length. It developed that, while existing agreements were exclusive, yet a few of them contained a provision that in busy seasons, when the union could not furnish men, the employers might take on nonunion men on probation cards or otherwise, who were to be discharged as soon as union men appeared, unless the union chose to take them in. To care for these exceptional cases a union spokesman proposed that the employment of nonunion men in emergencies should be referred to the General Arbitration Board. This proposal was adopted at the second conference.

It will be seen from the above-quoted reply of the chairman and from the arbitration plan that the employers had in mind from the beginning not only the employment exclusively of union men, but a more effective and less expensive enforcement of that rule than any that the walking delegate with the sympathetic strike could contrive. This alone has taken from the delegate the bulk of his duties, since under the rules of procedure the secretary of the arbitration board, as soon as a complaint is lodged, notifies the contractor to remove the nonunion man. In order to facilitate this procedure, one of the early acts of the Board of Governors after the arbitration plan went into effect was to notify the unions that they should not decline to work with nonunion men on a job until twenty-four hours after filing notice with the general secretary. The employers reasoned that contractors who employ nonunion men are not members of the association, and that the plan is not designed to protect nonmembers. If the unionist were required to work with the nonunionist, the outside contractors with nonunion labor could underbid the members who employ union labor at higher wages, and soon members would drop out of the association, being protected just as much outside and getting their labor cheaper. Consequently, to let the unions enforce the union clause of the plan within twenty-four hours is to protect themselves in paying union wages. There have been three or four strikes under these conditions, and they were promptly settled. The outside contractors, being thus placed at a disadvantage in dealing with the unions, forthwith apply for membership; and in this way the unions themselves are strengthening the employers' association.

The clause affecting unskilled labor is one where the employers seem to have departed more than elsewhere from their original program. They had included the helpers' unions, such as those of the tile layers and steam fitters, in their arbitration plan, since these were unions of apprentices; but they had not included the laborers. It will be remembered that the skilled mechanics had seceded from the Board of Delegates. They took the position that the majority of the troubles of the board had sprung from the unskilled unions. But when the matter came up in conference, the mechanics argued that the bricklayer, the plasterer, and so on were as much dependent as the employers upon their laborers; that they could not disregard the claims of the laborers for protection in hours and wages; and that, if the mechanics bound themselves not to strike, they should also be in a position to hold their laborers from striking. The employers had taken the ground that wages and hours were not involved in the present dispute, and when a union representative proposed that the wages paid to unskilled trades should not be reduced, nor the hours increased, and that the laborers should have representation through the mechanics, this was agreed to. The first case of arbitration under the perfected plan was that of the plasterers' laborers, and the arbitration board awarded them $3.25 a day.

The position of the walking delegate or business agent under the arbitration plan becomes similar to what it is in unions in other trades, namely, an executive officer and prosecuting witness of the union. His legislative powers are taken away when his power to order a strike on his own judgment is taken away. It becomes his business solely to look for violations of agreements. The procedure under the rules of the arbitration board are undoubtedly slower than the summary procedure of the walking delegate; for instead of calling out his men as soon as he sees a violation, or as soon as he can assemble his fellow-delegates, he must submit the complaint to the secretary of the union, the secretary must submit it in writing, with seal attached, to the secretary of the arbitration board (known as the general secretary), and the latter must address a copy to the employer complained of and a copy to the secretary of the association to which the employer belongs. Then the union and the employers' association become the parties to the complaint, and they must each select two arbitrators from the General Board, not members of their own organizations, who must meet within twenty-four hours after notice is sent by the general secretary. Before this board the business agent appears as a witness. Under this procedure decisions at first seemed painfully delayed, and there was keen dissatisfaction among the unions. But the dissatisfaction was such as is always found where constitutional law and courts supersede military law and trial by battle. They are the defects of deliberation. Their virtue is in the prevention rather than in the cure of wrong. The rules have been liberally interpreted, so that at present the walking delegate makes the complaint directly to the general secretary, thereby avoiding the delay of passing it through the hands of the union secretary. It has also been found, as predicted by the employers, that petty grievances are disappearing. The combined weight of the entire employers' association and all the unions is brought to bear upon an individual employer, so that a notice direct from the general secretary usually brings a correction ; at the same time the employers are careful to avoid violations. Of course, the business agents retain all their prerogatives in dealing with contractors not members of the association, and for this purpose they have organized a new Board of Delegates, known now as the Board of Representatives of the Building Trades of New York and Vicinity. This board is not recognized in the arbitration plan, nor by the employers of the association.

The General Arbitration Board, composed of two representatives of each union and of each employers' association, has had an interesting and peculiar development. As originally conceived by the employers, it was to be not really a board, but a panel from which to select the arbitrators on any particular dispute. It was to elect an executive committee of employers and employees in equal number and a general secretary, and these were to select the special arbitration board whenever the parties to a complaint failed to do so. The powers of the General Board were to end with the election of the executive committee. But gradually the board has become a joint conciliation body for the building industry, endeavoring to settle disputes without resort to arbitration or else arranging the terms of arbitration. At first, when a meeting was called, the union representatives held a caucus on the evening preceding, and in the general meetings the two sides were inclined to line up solid. But as the earlier suspicions wore off, the board inclined to divide more according to individual judgment of the merits of the question and less on class lines.

It was stated above that several of the unions delayed signing the agreement, and that work went on in their stead with other workmen. The fortunes and misfortunes of some of these unions make a vivid chapter in the history of the New York building industry. So prolonged and spectacular was the fight of one of them under a dare-devil leader and so widespread were the sensational accounts of its doings that to the outside world the entire industry seemed to be tied up. These sensations undoubtedly made owners timid and retarded new enterprises, and this timidity of capital was the card, and the only card, that this union had to play. But many of the other unions and many seceders from this union returned quickly to work.

The Brotherhood of Carpenters, after blunderingly starting the revolution and finding itself already starved when the real tumult began, hurried to sign the employers' agreement; and thus by an unconditional surrender to the employers it won a victory over its rival, for the Amalgamated Carpenters by delaying to sign were permanently disbarred.

A different outcome befell the rival unions in the painters' trade. The Amalgamated Painters signed promptly, hoping to bar their rival, the Brotherhood, which delayed a month. But the Brotherhood had an exclusive contract with the Interior Decorators, already referred to, and so was admitted. The Amalgamated then demanded an arbitration on the ground that it was discriminated against by these employers. This was the second case before the board. The special board decided that the exclusive agreement with the Brotherhood was in force when the joint arbitration plan was signed, and under Article 19 was to be respected. But the board went further and ordered the Amalgamated Painters to join the Brotherhood, this being the national organization, adding that when this should be done and the rivalry stopped, wages should be advanced 50 cents a day, to a minimum of $4. This latter remarkable decision was challenged by the Amalgamated, and the General Board referred it to a judge of the Supreme Court, who promptly declared that the board had exceeded its powers in ordering a union, party to the agreement, to extinguish itself. The award of 50 cents of course fell with this decision, and the two unions of nearly equal strength continue their rivalry within the board.

A jurisdictional dispute of ten years' standing between the carpenters and the wood workers was decided by an umpire and is enforced, although the same dispute under charge of the two national organizations is as far from settlement as ever. The same is true of another dispute which for fifteen years has been venerable with the critics of unions and has caused more inconvenience than any jurisdictional matter in the building line. This is the contest between the bricklayers and electrical workers. In their case the two employers' associations joined with their respective unions as parties to the complaint. The question was as to which union should cut the brickwork or fireproofing necessary for the installation of electric conduits. The decision is recognized by competent parties as not merely "splitting the difference," but as a reasonable division according to the nature and circumstances of the work.

The contest that centered about the Structural Iron Workers' Union, or rather a faction of that union, was the one of most dramatic interest. The leader of the union was its delegate, Sam Parks, who also organized the Board of Delegates, and headed its corrupt clique. Parks claimed the credit of having raised the iron workers from an ill-paid, disorganized rabble at $2.50 a day to a powerful union of 4000 men at $4 a day. But this credit belongs also to the conditions of the trade, for wages elsewhere had risen in similar proportion. This fact the union was beginning to recognize; and a faction within the union, dissatisfied with his bullying and dishonest methods, had been able a year before to elect as president Robert Neidig, a man exactly the opposite in every respect to Parks. Neidig's faction at the semiannual election, January, 1903, had been almost able to defeat Parks for walking delegate; indeed, he was barely elected at the foot of the list of four delegates, two of whom were Neidig men. The narrow margin discredited him, and the Neidig faction was confident just prior to the July election that they could defeat him. But the employers unwittingly came to the help of Parks. They furnished testimony to the district attorney on which he was arrested for extortion. He and his faction raised the cry of persecution. He appealed to his union to vindicate him by an election, boasting that the employers would then drop the prosecution and promising at once to resign. His appeal was all the more taking because the particular charge on which he was arrested was a case where he had collected $2000 "waiting time" for his men; the men had actually received the money, or a part of it, and had voted him a diamond ring in admiration of his services. As a matter of fact, this case was dropped by the district attorney, and Parks when he was convicted three months later was sentenced on another charge of taking $250 at a different time and place. He secured his vindication and was reëlected, but Neidig and his faction carried all the other offices but one. Parks did not resign, but made the most desperate fight of which his bullying methods were capable. He drove Neidig from the chair and Neidig's faction from the hall, and essayed even to capture the national convention and displace the national president, who had meanwhile expelled his union. He succeeded in having his union reinstated and failed by only three votes to put his man in the presidency. His union depleted its treasury in his defense before the court; but he was convicted, as were two confederates in other unions. About this time the Fuller company joined the employers' association and paid a heavy fine. The success of the plan of arbitration was evident. Thereupon a "neutral" element in the Iron Workers' Union gained control. It appointed a new strike committee, with power to make a settlement with the Iron League, the trade association of employers. But the employers meanwhile had organized the Independent Housesmiths' Union of New York, with a state charter, and had entered into an exclusive agreement with it. The foremen, with Neidig, had held aloof from Parks and his faction, though retaining membership in the union; and they undertook to teach the new men gathered in the new union. This was possible because the structural iron worker is not strictly a skilled mechanic. He is simply a riveter, working in a gang on a sky-scraper or a bridge. The iron framework is constructed in the shop, where the pieces are shaped and the holes are drilled ready for the rivets. The requirements for the trade are not so much mechanical skill as recklessness and daring. The men say they do not die, but are jerked over the river. The strength of the union is the danger of the trade and the rivet that drops on the head of the nonunion man. This accounts in part for the success of a man like Parks, and makes all the more surprising the success of a churchgoer like Neidig. For three months after Parks' removal negotiations continued. National officers of the union, the executive committee of the American Federation of Labor, and committees of central bodies took a hand, but without result. Work proceeded with the new union. The employers did not wish to run the risk of another Parks, and the new union stood on its agreement. But a settlement to be permanent must be in harmony with the national organization, of which the Parks union still held the local charter. Finally, Neidig was induced to take hold. He brought about the dissolution of both unions, a reorganization into four locals chartered by the national organization, to be governed by a representative district council, a committee on membership with himself at the head to exclude the "vicious and criminal element," acceptance of the employers' plan, and an agreement with the Iron League. This closed the last breach, and in January, 1904, was rounded out the new form of joint government in the New York building trades.

J. R. COMMONS.

[The arbitration plan as described above was revised in March, 1905. The principal change was in creating a General Arbitration Board in place of a mere panel of jurors, so that the enforcement of agreements and awards is to be accomplished through the joint action of unions and employers' associations instead of through the separate action of the latter. The plan does not apply where nonunion men are employed. — J. R. C.]

V

THE CHICAGO BUILDING TRADES DISPUTE[1]

During the past year (1900) there has been fought out in Chicago a contest between capital and labor which will receive a prominent place in the history of trade unionism. It was one of the longest labor conflicts of any magnitude in the building trades that the country has ever known. But it is not so much its duration or magnitude or costliness that has given it such importance as it is the principles involved. The struggle was not between individual employers and the various unions, but between the federated bodies of the building contractors, on the one side, and of the building trades, on the other.

The point at issue was pretty clearly defined from the beginning of the controversy. The contractors were contending for freedom from the tyranny of ignorant and irresponsible labor leadership and for the abolition of various trade restrictions. To secure this end they sought to destroy the federation of the unions and to deal with each trade separately, while the unions insisted on the maintenance and recognition of their central body. Other issues were made at the start, but they were gradually reduced to one, — the maintenance of the central organization of the unions, the Building Trades Council. The question of hours and wages entered only incidentally and never for a moment stood in the way of a settlement. A study of the labor organizations in Chicago is, therefore, necessary to a thorough understanding of the building trades dispute.

I. The Building Trades Council

In Chicago the labor organizations are centralized in three councils, — the Chicago Federation of Labor, the Building

[1] From the *Political Science Quarterly*, Vol. XVI, 1901, pp. 114–141, 222–247.

Material Trades Council, and the Building Trades Council. All unions are eligible to membership in the Federation of Labor, while in the other two councils only such trades as are connected with building and building material can be admitted. In the Federation of Labor there are ninety-six different trades affiliated. Many of the same trades which compose the Federation are also members of the other two councils. The Building Material Trades Council, as the name indicates, is composed of trades engaged in the manufacture of building material, such as brickmakers and wood workers. There are in all forty-three unions in this council, representing fifteen trades, and the membership is about 33,000. The Building Trades Council is a compact organization or delegate body, composed of representatives of all the unions in the building trades. About thirty-two trades were affiliated with it, and at the beginning of the dispute it had a membership of from 25,000 to 30,000.

Such "allied trades councils," as they are called, are found at present only in the building and printing trades.[1] The Chicago Building Trades Council was organized on November 22, 1890, and incorporated under the general incorporation law of Illinois, on March 14, 1892. The purpose of the organization may be best seen from the preamble of the constitution.

> The object of this council is to construct a central organization which shall subserve the interests of all the labor organizations engaged in the erection or alteration of buildings; for the purpose of assisting each other when necessary; thereby removing all unjust or injurious competition, and to secure unity of action for their mutual protection and support.

The objects were further set forth, in the application for a charter, as follows:

> To promote the interests and welfare of all trade and labor organizations connected therewith and to extend a helping hand to such other organizations as the said council may direct.

[1] Cf. Wm. M. Burke, "History and Functions of Central Labor Unions," *Columbia University Studies in History, Economics, and Public Law*, Vol. XII, No. 1, 1899, p. 116.

The representation of the several affiliated unions in the council is based on their numerical strength, no trade organization having less than five or more than twenty delegates.[1] The thirty-two unions in the council elect about 200 delegates to the central body, which meets once a week. The usual corporate officers are elected, but their duties are largely routine, the real power being vested in the standing committees and in a somewhat anomalous body called the Board of Business Agents, more commonly known as the walking delegates. The standing committees, consisting of five members each, are a credential committee, an organization committee, a grievance committee, and a legislative committee.[2] The duty of the organization committee is

> to seek out every branch of unorganized industry in the building trades, use every effort to organize them into unions; to instruct and enlighten them on all questions relating to their advancement as working men; and render all assistance necessary to increase the membership of all the different organizations affiliated.

The legislative committee is

> to determine what legislation will be best for the interest of the laboring man, draft bills for such legislation, present them to the proper legislators, and report from time to time the best methods of securing the passage of the same.[3]

The *imperium in imperio* is the board of walking delegates, or business agents, which is composed of all the properly elected business agents of the various unions represented in the council. The object of the board is "to unite and associate together all business agents for the purpose of mutual assistance and to better accomplish the work in all parts of Chicago and Cook County." [4] It meets three times a week, for the purpose of rendering all assistance necessary for the enforcement of the various trade and working-card rules of the council.[5] Every sympathetic strike called must be first brought before the board and sanctioned, although the business agent of any

[1] Constitution, Article III. [2] *Ibid.*, Article VII. [3] *Ibid.*, Article VIII.
[4] By-Laws, Article II. [5] Constitution, Article IX.

trade can call a strike of men in his own trade without consulting the board. The Board of Business Agents has a set of by-laws governing its work, independent of the council, and could exist, through an understanding among the trades, even if the Building Trades Council were disrupted. Although it is not necessary to be a delegate to the council to entitle one to a seat in the Board of Business Agents, most of the latter are delegates to that body; and when a measure comes up in the central organization, if the business agent of a certain trade speaks either for or against it, he usually carries the entire delegation from his trade with him. Much of the present trouble is laid by the contractors at the door of the Board of Business Agents. While the Building Trades Council is the superior body and is supposed to have jurisdiction over the Board of Business Agents, the conditions are practically reversed; for the smaller body has controlled the council.[1]

The working cards mentioned above are issued quarterly to the members of the affiliated unions at a price fixed from time to time by the council. They must be carried by all union men, and may be demanded at any time by the business agents or by fellow-workmen.[2] It should be noted that this simple device for revenue — namely, the sale of the working card — is really a system of licensing outside of the law; for it is implied that no man shall work at a building trade unless he is in possession of such a card.[3]

The most important sections of the constitution are those relating to strikes and arbitration. Article XII provides that action on agreements or demands for an advance in wages or an abridgment in the hours of labor, if concurred in by two thirds of all trades present in the council, shall be binding on all. But any trade may act on its own responsibility. Article XIII is sufficiently important to be quoted in full.

[1] On August 17 this was partially remedied by giving the executive committee of the Building Trades Council full power to act in all matters pertaining to the calling of strikes and the general conduct of business.

[2] Constitution, Articles XI and XVI.

[3] S. H. Wright, "A Local Phase of Labor Combination" (a paper read before the Chicago Literary Club, November 27, 1899, and privately printed), p. 12.

When trouble occurs on any building or job affecting any trade represented in this council, it shall be the duty of the business agent to immediately endeavor to settle same with contractor or owner in accordance with the trade rules and to the satisfaction of the trade involved. Failing in this and a strike being necessary, the business agent shall have power to call a general strike, but before doing so he shall lay the matter before the council or board of business agents at their next meeting and be governed by their action or decision, which shall be equally binding on all trades in this Council engaged on the job or building. When a trade has no business agent the chairman of the board shall have power to call members of said trade off when strike is ordered. It shall require a majority of the trades voting to order a strike. Unit rule to prevail.

It will be seen from this that it is practically in the power of a majority of the business agents of the trades interested to order a general strike. There is no provision made for a referendum vote on such a question by the total membership, nor is such a vote taken in practice.

It would be interesting to know what proportion of those engaged in the building trades of Chicago are members of the affiliated unions, but figures on that point are confessedly only guesses.[1] Some of the smaller and better organized unions practically include all the workers in the respective trades: such are the hoisting engineers, the architectural iron workers, the stonecutters, the mosaic tile layers, the plumbers, and the gas fitters. On the other hand, some of the larger trades — as the carpenters, the hod carriers, and the painters — are not so

[1] The following unions, with their approximate memberships, are members of the Building Trades Council: Architectural Iron Workers (300), Bridge and Structural Iron Workers (700), Bricklayers and Stone Masons (3500), Carpenters (5230), Boiler Makers (500), Electrical Mechanics (500), Elevator Constructors (350), Gas-fitters (400), Gas-Fixture Hangers (125), Gravel Roofers (250), Hod Carriers and Building Laborers (5200), Hoisting Engineers (160), Lathers (600), Marble Cutters (100), Marble Cutters' Helpers (100), Italian Mosaic Workers (200), Mosaic and Encaustic Tile Layers (100), Mosaic Helpers (100), Mosaic Glass Workers (100), Painters (3500), Plasterers (1200), Plumbers (1400), Paper Hangers (400), Sheet-Metal Workers (400), Steam Fitters (300), Junior Steam Fitters (300), Slate and Tile Roofers (150), Stonecutters (800), Stone Derrickmen (200), Stone Sawyers and Rubbers (275), Stone Carvers (100), Tunnel Miners (300); total, thirty-two unions, with a membership of about 30,000.

well unionized. Within the city of Chicago the greater part of the workers belong to the unions,[1] but in the suburbs and outside of the city they are not so well organized.

II. The Contractors Council

Corresponding to the Building Trades Council there exists in Chicago a parallel organization of employers, known as the Building Contractors Council.[2] This is a close federation of some fourteen associations of employers, representing about 2500 individuals or firms.[3] A temporary organization had been effected as early as 1894 in the form of a building conference committee, composed of eight or nine trade associations; but the present body dates from April, 1899, when it was organized for the express purpose of opposing the Building Trades Council. It was perfected in September of the same year and is in all essential respects similar to its prototype, being a delegate body with representatives from the various affiliated masters' associations. Organized distinctly as a "war measure," as one of the contractors expressed it, the Contractors Council would probably not have become permanent, as it now threatens to be, had not the struggle with the Building Trades Council provided it with a *raison d'être*.

The purposes and methods of the Contractors Council are plainly avowed in its working rules, among which are found the following:

Rule I. This organization shall be known as "The Building Contractors Council," and its object shall be to foster, protect and

[1] Wright, *loc. cit.*, p. 19, estimates 80 per cent. One of the best informed of the labor leaders estimated 85 per cent of the carpenters and practically all of the others.

[2] The following associations are members of the Contractors Council: Chicago Masons and Builders, Master Carpenters and Builders, Master Carpenters, Cut Stone Contractors, Master Plumbers, Master Steam Fitters, Master Painters, Master Plasterers, House Draining, Sheet-Metal Contractors, Mantel and Tile, Mosaic Tile, Marble Manufacturers, and the Iron League.

[3] The discrepancy in numbers of trades represented in the masters' and journeymen's councils is accounted for by the fact that in some cases two or three of the trades are represented by a single masters' association. Four groups of the contractors are not organized at all. These are the electricians, elevator constructors, stone carvers, and tunnel miners.

promote the welfare and interests of its members, engaged in the construction of buildings in Cook County, Illinois.

RULE VII, Section 1. The Council shall have full power to take any action which may be for the best interests of any Association allied with the Council; and, should the condition demand, a lockout may be ordered by the Council to protect its interest.

Section 2. No Association allied with this Council shall hereafter enter into an agreement with their journeymen which shall prohibit a sympathetic lockout.

RULE X. Should any differences arise between employer and employee, whereby the interests of any Association shall be impaired, such Association may make a full statement of the facts, through the secretary, to the Council; and he shall call a meeting of the Council to take active measures to secure and protect the interests and rights of the Association so aggrieved.

In addition to the Contractors Council, there are a number of other organizations of employers, corresponding to the various organizations of the men. Among these are the Association of Material Manufacturers, who furnish all the building supplies to the contractors; the Chicago Architects' Business Association; and the organization of the real estate men. While not all of these were direct employers of labor, they sided with the Contractors Council in their contest with the Building Trades Council.

The building trades dispute was a struggle between these two federated bodies, and in tracing the causes that led up to the final outbreak in February, 1900, we shall have to consider in some detail the relations between the opposing organizations. Friction had existed between the employers and the Building Trades Council for some years, and the occurrences which immediately preceded the lockout and strike were not the ultimate causes. In outlining the latter the blame may be about equally divided between the employers and employees. On one side, the unions claimed that the foundation of the trouble was the refusal on their part to make exclusive agreements with the contractors; while the contractors asserted, on the other hand, that the arrogance and corruption of the Building Trades Council had become unbearable. As there was an element of truth in both charges, we cannot do better than to examine them carefully and in that way ascertain the causes of discontent.

III. Exclusive Agreements

In the general tendency toward combination no movement is more significant than the union effected between capital and labor in the Chicago Building Trades by means of the so-called "exclusive agreements." The contractors in a given trade who were members of the employers' association made an agreement with the members of the union in that trade, according to which the contractors were to employ only members of the union, while the latter pledged themselves not to work for any outside firms. In this way it was proposed to secure a practical monopoly in the building trades, as all the contractors and workmen would speedily be compelled to join the respective organizations. Thus it was hoped to secure an advance in wages and an increase in profits. Such agreements were made with the carpenters, bricklayers, steam fitters, plumbers, painters, hod carriers, and some other unions.

The experience of the carpenters will serve to illustrate the purpose of these agreements. Their union had made exclusive agreements with the builders' association in 1896 and 1897, but in 1898 a difficulty arose over a clause in which the union reserved the right to work, if necessary, for firms not members of the association. The builders wished an absolute agreement, according to which the union carpenters should work only for members of their body. When the union remonstrated that not more than one third of the builders of Chicago were members of the employers' association and that these could not give employment to all the men, they were told that, if they would refuse to work for outside firms, work would soon be found for them. It was thus very evident that it was the purpose of the employers to use this means to force contractors into their association. The carpenters accordingly struck, and by the end of a week forced the contractors to sign individual agreements without the exclusive clause. No further negotiations were had between the union and the association until the close of the lockout of 1900.

The bricklayers had profited probably more than any other union by its exclusive agreements, of which the one understood to have been made with the Sewer Builders' Association will serve as a type.[1] The Contracting Sewer Builders' Association, composed of about thirty firms, was originally organized as a surety company for its members, but soon gained control of sewer construction in Chicago and began to advance prices. When a piece of work was advertised the associated contractors assigned the work to one of their number and then put in seemingly independent bids; and as the lowest bid was placed much higher than necessary, the surplus profits thus realized were divided among the members of the combination.[2] It was also reported that the contractors had an agreement with the material men, from whom they secured material at lower prices than the independent contractor; while additional strength was given them by the sewer inspectors, who were alleged to have harassed contractors not members of the association by condemning bricks, cement, and other material. Competition was most effectually stifled, however, by an agreement made by the Sewer Builders' Association with the Bricklayers and Stone Masons' Union on April 1, 1899, and renewed April 1, 1900. The agreement was absolute, the bricklayers binding themselves to work for none but members of the Sewer Builders' Association, an infraction of this rule being punishable by a fine of from $5 to $25 and suspension from the union. In return, an eight-hour day and a wage scale of $1 an hour were provided for, only union men were to be employed by the contractors, and all inspectors were to be members of the Bricklayers' Union. While this agreement served to build up in the sewer construction business a strong combination among the contractors, it also secured to the workmen's union a monopoly of the labor market within the combination.[3]

[1] Chicago *Tribune*, November 18 and 19, 1900.

[2] Compare the methods of the plumbers' "trust," *infra*.

[3] Another striking example of the successful exclusive agreement was that between the Bricklayers and Stone Masons' Union and the Chicago Masons and Builders Association. It continued some four or five years, during which time the membership of the builders' association increased from 90 to 500. — *The Bricklayer and Mason* (New York), April, 1900, p. 4.

Other unions had given up the exclusive agreements with the employers, because, as one of the men said, "they got the worst of it." The one exception to this rule was the Hod Carriers and Building Laborers' Union. This was composed of the most unskilled labor in any branch of the building trades, and the members were exposed more than any other union to the pressure of outside competition. Accordingly, an exclusive agreement with their employers was a decided advantage to them, and they were unwilling to give up the arrangement. Finally, however, the Building Trades Council passed a resolution that individual unions should not be allowed to make exclusive agreements with employers' associations, and the laborers were forced to break this arrangement. Up to this time the council had permitted each trade to make its own agreements. Now, however, it was felt that the laborers must conform to the position of the other unions and that no more exclusive agreements should be entered into. It was this action on the part of the Building Trades Council, the union men claimed, that embittered the contractors against it and made them determined to destroy it, for they thought that they might then be able to force the individual unions to help them build up a monopoly in the building trades.[1]

[1] The following statements of prominent labor leaders will show what their belief in the matter was:

They are not making this fight on account of grievances against the unions, but for aggressively selfish purposes. They aim to crush the Building Trades Council and to establish absolute agreements with the unions under which union workmen will take employment only from them. — E. A. Davis, secretary Building Trades Council.

The main object of the contractors is to secure absolute agreements by which union workmen will work only for members of the contracting organizations. They refuse to deal with the unions except through their own council. — John A. Long, president Board of Business Agents and of the Gas Fitters' Union.

The contractors had absolutely no complaint against the architectural iron workers. They shut us out simply because we belonged to the Building Trades Council. We refuse to work solely for members of their organization and will work for any employer who abides by our rules. This is the condition which the contractors want to change for their own advantage and for the disadvantage of laborers and citizens generally. — Thomas Lynch, president Architectural Iron Workers' Union.

The contractors are responsible for this fight. They are trying to force us to join them in crushing out contractors not members of their council and in gouging the public. — John Clinch, president Plumbers' Union.

IV. Causes of the Dispute

That the purpose of the Building Trades Council was to control and so far as possible to monopolize the labor market in the building trades industry is obvious. In this it did not differ from the component unions. But it is evident that the employers had encouraged them in this as long as they shared in the results. The Building Trades Council, however, considered itself strong enough to assert its power without the coöperation of the employers' associations. There is no doubt that for the year preceding the lockout and strike of February, 1900, the utmost friction had existed between the two parties, largely owing to the overbearing attitude of the labor leaders. They were "glutted with success," as one of the laboring men put it, and would make no concessions to the contractors. By petty and often arbitrary demands they interfered constantly in the construction of buildings, until the employers were goaded to the point of rebellion. "The time had come," said one of the contractors, "when one might as well go out of the business as submit to the demands of the Building Trades Council." This feeling culminated in the lockout and consequent strikes of February 5.

There were, however, other causes which led the contractors to seize this particular time for the struggle with the council, among the chief of which may be mentioned the demoralized state of the building industry in Chicago and the high prices that obtained for all building materials. At the time of the World's Fair in 1893 building had been enormously stimulated in Chicago, and the overproduction of that period had continued for the succeeding six years. Both contractors and real estate men insisted that under existing conditions there was no money in buildings. The upward movement in prices, too, had particularly affected iron and steel products, the prices of which had become practically prohibitive. In addition to this there was the uncertainty and demoralization of a presidential year, which always affects the building trades disastrously. As a last straw there should be taken into account a concerted demand about the beginning of the year for higher wages,[1] on the part of most of the unions in the building trades.

V. Relations between the Councils

Such were the causes of the dispute. To make the narrative of the controversy a connected one, however, we must go back and review the relations between the Building Contractors Council and the Building Trades Council from the previous summer. On August 30, 1899, the Building Contractors Council appointed a committee of five and requested a conference with a similar committee from the Building Trades Council "to correct existing abuses and to arrange a plan whereby future strife may be avoided."[2] The committees held a meeting at which the contractors stated the conditions under which they proposed to work in the future. No action was taken by the Building Trades Council; and, accordingly, on November 17 the Building Contractors Council passed a series of resolutions stating that, while there was no disposition to question present wages or hours or the principle of legitimate unionism, it would not, after January, 1900, recognize (1) any limitation as to the amount of work a man shall perform during his working day; (2) any restriction of the use of machinery; (3) any restriction of the use of any manufactured article, except prison-made articles; (4) the right of any person to interfere with the work-

[1] At the end of December, 1899, the carpenters' unions had demanded a new wage scale of 50 cents an hour, an increase of 7½ cents over the existing rate, to begin on April 1. Early in January the marble workers struck for uniform payment of $3.50 a day to all cutters and setters, whether working in factories or outside, an increase of about 10 cents an hour; they also demanded that nonunion-cut blocks should not be used in the construction of buildings. The teamsters were granted an advance of 25 cents a day; the electricians, of 3⅞ cents an hour; the stonecutters, of 16⅔ cents an hour. The Hod Carriers and Building Laborers' Union demanded an increase of 5 cents an hour, to become effective on March 1; and the list might be extended.

[2] Letter of executive committee of Building Contractors Council to Mayor Harrison, February 24, 1900.

men during working hours; (5) the right of the unions to prohibit the employment of apprentices; (6) the sympathetic strike.

These six points, which were later expanded into eight, were maintained as their "cardinal principles" by the contractors in all their subsequent manifestoes. No notice was taken of these resolutions by the Building Trades Council. Before the time came, however, when these rules were to be enforced another attempt at a conference was made, under the leadership of Martin B. Madden. A committee of seven was appointed by each of the councils, and after a number of amicable meetings an agreement was reached on December 29. This was known as the "Madden agreement" and covered the six points raised by the contractors in their resolutions of November 17.[1]

[1] The following is the Madden agreement of December 30, 1899, "for the purpose of regulating and adjusting differences that may arise in the future between the Building Contractors Council and the Building Trades Council":

ARTICLES OF AGREEMENT

Section 1. Each council shall elect a board of arbitration of five members, who shall jointly constitute a final board of arbiters.

Section 2. The right of a steward on the job to protect the journeymen's interest is recognized. All complaints, disputes, or violations of joint agreements by employer or employee to be adjusted by the contractor or his agent and the steward or business agent of the Building Trades Council or affiliated unions, who shall be allowed to visit all jobs during working hours to interview the steward or workmen, but will not in any way interfere with their work. In case of failure to adjust any complaint, dispute, or violation of agreements, the subject-matter shall at once be referred to the standing arbitration committee of five from the employers and five from the employees representing the trade interested, who shall immediately decide the matter at issue. [In] Any case at issue that cannot be adjusted by the trade directly interested, appeal shall immediately be taken to the final board of arbitration, as provided in section 1, to adjust all matters referred to it by any of the associations affiliated or may become affiliated [*sic*] with party to this agreement, and their decision shall be final.

No strike or lockout shall be called or authorized by either party to this agreement or by any member or association affiliated or by their business agents by reason of any dispute arising between the unions represented in either association. Work shall continue uninterrupted while any case is pending before the final board of arbitration.

Section 3. No limitation as to the amount of work a man shall perform during his working day.

Section 4. Question of machinery referred to the different organizations of employers and employees. In the event of failure to agree either party shall have the right of appeal to the final board of arbitration.

Section 5. Each established employer in each respective trade shall be allowed to have at least one apprentice, whose time of apprenticeship expires before the age of twenty-two years.

It was signed by all the members of the committee from the Contractors Council and was ratified by the council the following day. Of the committee from the Trades Council only four members signed it, and when it was referred by them to the council no further action was taken on it. On January 17 the Building Contractors Council notified the secretary of the Building Trades Council that they expected a definite answer as to the intentions of the Trades Council not later than January 27. When nothing was heard by that time, the contractors prepared a new set of rules to govern all work and fixed a scale of wages to go into effect February 5. The attempt to enforce these rules was the immediate cause of the dispute and resulted soon in tying up the whole building industry of Chicago.

There is no doubt that the Building Trades Council made a great mistake in ignoring the Madden agreement as they did, especially after it had been drawn up and adopted by their own committee. E. A. Davis, secretary of the council, later[1] attempted to explain their failure to ratify the agreement by saying that the matter had been referred to the different unions for a referendum vote and that before such a vote could be taken the contractors issued their ultimatum in the form of a new set of rules. As a matter of fact, the matter had not been

Section 6. No restriction on the use of building material other than cut and sawed stone, granite, exterior marble work, common brick, wood mill work (except mantels and movable furniture), and prison-made material.

Section 7. It remains optional with contractor as to number of men he shall employ.

Section 8. No rules other than those of this agreement to be made by either side, unless authorized by the final board of arbitration.

Section 9. Rules to be drawn up by both sides at once.

Section 10. Members of the Building Contractors Council to receive as favorable treatment from the Building Trades Council as other contractors.

Section 11. It is agreed that as long as this contract is faithfully kept by the Building Trades Council and its affiliated unions the members of the associations affiliated with the Building Contractors Council in the erection of buildings will employ at the buildings in Cook County none but the workmen carrying Building Trades Council working cards in good standing in their respective callings, except where it may be otherwise agreed by the joint arbitration committee of the trade involved.

The text of this agreement is printed in *Carpentry and Building* (New York), February, 1900, p. 56. The above was copied from the original document, *verbatim et literatim*.

[1] In an interview in the Chicago *Times-Herald*, March 9.

so referred; and the writer has been assured by several prominent labor men that there was no intention on the part of the unions of ratifying the agreement. This treatment undoubtedly angered the contractors and rendered them both firm and united in their subsequent action.

The notice of January 29, issued by the Contractors Council, which was to go into effect on February 5, read as follows:

> The unions affiliated with the Building Trades Council having absolutely ignored the joint arbitration agreement and failed to ratify the same, we hereby make the following rules . . . and you will govern yourselves accordingly: no limitation as to the amount of work a man shall perform in a day; no restriction as to the use of machinery; no restriction as to union or nonunion-made material; the foreman shall be the agent of the contractor; the right to employ and discharge whomever he may choose is reserved to the employer; eight hours shall constitute a day's work; the prevailing rate of wages in all trades; time and one half will be allowed for all overtime; double time for Sundays and holidays.[1]

The position taken by the Contractors Council was indorsed the day following by the general contractors of Chicago, including many who were not members of the council. To give effect to their action the contractors notified members of the Plumbers', the Hod Carriers and Building Laborers', and the Hoisting Engineers' unions that the rules of the Building Contractors Council would be enforced after February 5, and that the unions' rules which were objected to would be disregarded. The master plumbers led the movement and notified their employees that they must sign individual contracts. The men, with a few exceptions, refusing to do this, they were locked out.

The attitude of the Building Trades Council was at first very pacific. President Edward Carroll stated on February 4 that "the council has not ordered a strike and does not

[1] It will be seen that the position of the contractors, as stated here, was not as liberal as that of the Madden agreement. After the refusal of the unions to ratify that agreement they would at no time consent to as great concessions.

intend to do so. The affiliated unions know their duty as union men and are expected to act accordingly." From the very beginning of the dispute the unions composing the Building Trades Council insisted that the contractors were wholly to blame for the trouble, since by instituting new rules they had violated agreements which would not have expired for a month or so.[1] On February 6, however, the Hod Carriers and Building Laborers' Union, the first organization to take official action, instructed its representatives to call strikes on every building in the city where men were working under the new rules. The movement did not take on large proportions until Saturday, February 10, when the carpenters were involved in the struggle. For several years they had been working only half of Saturday, but under the new rules of the Building Contractors Council, which were indorsed by the carpenter contractors, they would be compelled to work all of Saturday. Instructions were therefore given by the district council of the carpenters' union that no member of the organization would be permitted to violate the old rule. Accordingly, at noon on Saturday, February 10, building operations in the city were practically suspended, when the carpenters refused to work after the noon hour. The number of men rendered idle was variously estimated at that time from 3000, according to the labor men, to 7000, according to the contractors. This number continued to grow steadily during the next few weeks, as the workmen were called out on sympathetic strikes by the affiliated unions or were locked out by the contractors, until about 50,000 men were affected.

Throughout the entire time of the dispute there seemed to be doubt as to whether it should be called a "strike" or a "lockout." The choice of a name was usually decided by the desire to favor one side or the other, the contractors claiming that the men had struck, while the unions asserted that there was no strike, but that they had been locked out. The responsibility

[1] Agreements were in force between the employers and the individual unions, some expiring March 1, others May 1, and others not till 1901.

is not, however, to be fixed by the choice of a name.[1] In some cases the contractors took the initiative, and in others the unions. Yet it is but fair to insist that the posting of the new rules by the contractors was in most cases tantamount to a lockout, as they knew that the men would be compelled to cease work by the rules of their unions; and even in a case where the contractors' rules did not conflict with the rules or agreements of the union, the men could not remain at work if nonunion men were put on the building or if, as was generally done, a sympathetic strike was ordered in accordance with the constitution of the Building Trades Council.

VI. Position of the Material Men

The mills and factories furnishing building materials were soon involved in the building trades dispute, and in this case the initiative seems to have been taken by the unions in calling sympathetic strikes among the wood workers and others as early as February 19.[2] The manufacturers and mill owners were really in a difficult position. On the one hand, they had made agreements with the building contractors, according to which the contractors were to buy their materials only of firms in the combination, and in return were to receive lower prices. Thus the brick manufacturers in the "brick combine" and the Masons and Builders Association are reported to have had an agreement, which was to continue to April 1, by which members of the latter were able to buy bricks at one dollar a thousand less than was charged to outsiders, lime fifteen cents a barrel cheaper, and vent linings, copings, and so forth, at a proportionate rate. In addition to this the association was to be

[1] It is almost impossible at times to distinguish in practice between a lockout and a strike, and the distinction was given up in the English labor reports as long ago as 1894, the generic name "dispute" being used for all forced cessations of work. In the American reports the attempt is still made to distinguish the two kinds of dispute.

[2] On February 26 the Material Trades Council called a strike in two brickyards which furnished material to buildings where nonunion labor was employed. — Chicago *Record*, February 27.

paid a bonus of one dollar a thousand for all bricks sold to builders who were not members of the association.[1] A part of this sum was currently reported to have been paid into the treasury of the contractors' council. On the other hand, the material men had entered into agreements with the labor unions not to furnish material for jobs where nonunion labor was employed. This worked very well until the February lockout and strike, when the contractors began to employ nonunion labor. The material men were then placed in a predicament. If they refused to furnish the contractors material, the former could go outside the city to make their purchases; if they furnished the material, they would violate their agreements with the unions and a strike would probably result.[2]

On March 1 the mill owners and building supply men held a meeting and took a definite position, throwing in their lot with the Building Contractors Council. They decided not to furnish supplies to contractors who were not members of this body. If this plan were carried out, no contractor could break the tie-up in the building industry by hiring members of the Building Trades Council under the old rules, until the united contractors permitted it. The contractors could then gradually resume building with nonunion labor and have material supplied only to jobs designated by them. This plan seems to have been agreed to by the mill owners and a majority of the material men, namely, those dealing in rubblestone, crushed stone, lime, cement, copings, and pressed brick. The brick manufacturers, however, refused thus to restrict their sales and declared in favor of an open market, in which they might sell to any one who wished to buy. A few days later the other manufacturers of building material took a new stand and decided that after filling existing contracts they would not undertake

[1] Mr. Falkenau, chairman of the press committee of the contractors' council, while denying that there was any discrimination, admitted a difference in prices. This he explained by saying that it was due to the discount the large firms received for wholesale orders and for cash payment. — Chicago *Times-Herald*, May 14.

[2] As early as February 9 the Brickmakers' Union threatened to call strikes in all brickyards unless the agreements with them were maintained by which brick could be sold only to employers of union labor. — Chicago *Record*, February 10.

any new contracts until the difficulties in the building trades were settled, believing that the dispute could be settled most quickly if material should be refused to every one.

This position was consistently maintained by most of the material men, and their plants were either closed entirely or kept running to supply only the immediate demands of the trade.[1] The union men claimed, however, that there was a secret agreement between the contractors and the material men, according to which supplies were refused only to employers of union labor, and that the announced policy was only a cover for discriminations against contractors outside of the council. Charges against the Masons and Builders Association and some ten or twelve firms, mostly plumbers, were taken before the May grand jury, where the material men were accused of boycotting and conspiracy. The charges could not be substantiated, however, and were dismissed for lack of evidence. That some such agreement was actually made seems not open to doubt. One of the leading contractors, a member of the Contractors Council, admitted to the writer that such a combination existed among the plumbers, and the evidence seemed to show that similar arrangements had been made by other material men.

As the plumbers' "trust" has come in for a large share of public attention, it will be instructive to examine its methods. The following is probably a fairly accurate account.[2] The association of master plumbers, who control from 65 to 70 per cent of the plumbing work of Chicago, employed a system that raised the price of all the work they secured. If eight or ten of them were invited to bid on a piece of work, they would do so; but instead of submitting their bids at once to the contractor, they would meet and in the presence of one another would open their bids. Then the contract would be awarded to the lowest bidder, who would add to his bid two per cent of its

[1] Between 10,000 and 20,000 men were thrown out of employment in the building material trades during the dispute.

[2] Testimony of J. S. Kelly, president of the United Association of Journeymen Plumbers and Gas Fitters, before the Industrial Commission, October 11, 1900.

amount for each of the other bidders. Each of the unsuccessful bidders would then increase his bid an equal amount, and the amended bids would be submitted to the contractor. It is said that several firms were dismissed from the Master Plumbers Association because of their refusal to pay over the two per cent to the unsuccessful bidders, and that in each case the Journeymen Plumbers' Union, which had an agreement with the master plumbers, was called on to forbid its men from working for the dismissed member of the masters' association.

VII. Contentions of the Two Councils

To ascertain exactly what the truth is in a complicated quarrel where every issue is controverted and every statement is a matter of dispute is not easy. But we can probably not do better than to examine at this point the claims of the two contending parties as set forth in their published statements. Both the contractors and the labor unions evidently thought it necessary to justify their position before the public, and circulars were early drawn up by both sides explaining the situation. The Building Trades Council was first in the field with a statement [1] of its position. The most important section of the paper was the following:

> We are willing to furnish our services to whomsoever needs them in the erection and construction of buildings, irrespective of whether they are members of contractors' associations or not, the only stipulation we ask being that *union conditions* shall prevail on the building.

There followed an indictment of the Building Contractors Council on the ground that though it claimed to be working for the elimination of the Building Trades Council, it fined any of its members for making individual agreements with a trades union. Finally, as regards arbitration, the labor men insisted that they had never refused to arbitrate, that most of the agreements they had made with the contractors provided for arbitration, and that they intended to live up to these agreements.

[1] See Chicago papers of February 8.

In conclusion [said the Trades Council] we mean to carry out the agreements entered into by our unions in good faith; and, if work is stopped and the building industry paralyzed, it will be no fault of ours. The blame rests entirely on the contractors.

An answer to this statement was soon prepared by the Building Contractors Council and given to the public.[1] The contractors seized upon the paragraph in which "union conditions" were demanded and proceeded to enumerate and criticise seven or eight demands which were insisted on by some of the unions and which they were unwilling to grant. It will be profitable to consider these in detail, for the contractors based their case largely on the charges which they made in this connection, and in these conditions is to be found, if at all, the justification for the contractors' position.

1. The first "union condition" to which the contractors objected was "the limitation of the work a man is permitted to perform in a day." Such a restriction existed in the rules of the lathers, gas fitters, steam fitters, plasterers, and plumbers. The lathers limited a day's work to twenty-five bundles of lath, for which they received $3; they had formerly done thirty-five bundles for a daily wage of $1.75.[2] Plasterers were limited to thirty square yards a day; the steam fitters were permitted to lay only ninety feet of steam pipe per day; but the plumbers had the most objectionable rules and restricted materially the amount of work that could be done in a day.[3] These and similar

[1] See Chicago papers of February 11.

[2] One of the labor men stated to the writer that they often finished by four o'clock and then "rushed the can" for an hour.

[3] The rules of the plumbers limiting the amount of work were as follows:

RULE I. When working on lead work, eight wiped joints shall be considered a day's work.

RULE II. When working on iron pipe, the measuring, cutting, threading and placing in position of fifteen threads of one inch or under shall be considered a day's work.

RULE IV. When finishing on flats or apartments, hotel or office buildings, one fixture shall be considered an average day's work, except laundry tubs, when each apartment shall constitute a fixture.

RULE XI. Any member violating any of these rules shall be fined one day's pay for the first offence, two days' pay for the second offence, and if he persist in the violation the association shall deal with him as it sees fit.

rules[1] of the unions were defended by them on the ground that they were necessary to secure careful work and to prevent the "rusher" from setting the pace for a fair day's work. There seems to be no doubt, however, that all legitimate limitations had been exceeded, and that in all cases the so-called day's work could have been performed by the average workman in a few hours. In justice to the unions, it may be said that most of them admitted the unfairness of these restrictions. Thus, John Clinch, president of the Plumbers' Union, conceded in an interview that "the rules were made hastily, and they may be defective." It is worthy of note, too, that the Journeyman Plumbers' Union a little later[2] adopted a new form of agreement, leaving out the clause that fixed the maximum amount of work and providing for a permanent board of arbitration.

2. "Another 'union condition' is the delay caused by the quarrels between the unions as to which shall perform a specific piece of work." Instances were cited where work had been delayed for weeks, while the unions decided which should perform certain tasks. Such disputes occurred between the freestone cutters and the granite cutters, between the ornamental iron workers and the structural iron workers, between the steam fitters and the plumbers, and in other cases, in some of which the work was done twice and twice paid for, and in all of which it was delayed. On this count there is no doubt that the contractors had a just grievance. In many instances the Building Trades Council had not paid sufficient respect to their interests in deciding these disputes.

3. "The union shall dictate to the contractor how many men he shall employ on a specified building, and that he shall not discharge a man to whom they wish to give work, even if he is a lazy and incompetent workman."[3] There are evidently two counts under this charge. As to the second, the right of

[1] One of the rules of the Carpenters' Union provides that "any member guilty of excessive work or rushing on any job shall be reported and shall be subject to a fine of $5."

[2] May 2.

[3] These charges are cleverly, if ungrammatically, worded, and while generally true are not all the truth. They must, therefore, be carefully read.

the contractor to hire and discharge his own laborers was never interfered with by the Building Trades Council, except where the contractor failed to live up to his written agreement with the union or where he had employed nonunion men or was not paying union wages. Certainly the contractors could not fairly complain on this score if after having made exclusive agreements with the unions to employ only union men the latter should attempt to enforce this principle without such agreements. But as to the first count, that the union dictated how many men in a given trade should be on a building, the contractor had just grounds for complaint. Such a rule was made, for instance, by the lathers, according to which six lathers must be employed on every job. On a small building there was caused by this an unnecessary cost for scaffolding, carting, and so forth, if all the men were to be kept busy; and it was often the case that in interior work, as on stairs, it was physically impossible for six men to work at the same time. Such rules had the same purpose as those limiting the day's work, but are even less defensible.

4. "A fourth of these 'union conditions' is that the union shall dictate to the investor where he shall buy his building materials and by whom they shall be finished." In answer to this charge the officers of the unions insisted that they had always been willing to work with union-made material and had objected only to the introduction of prison-made materials or those produced under nonunion conditions. This, however, was not the whole truth, for they had objected to using material made by nonunion men, even if under union conditions in other respects, and had often insisted that work should not be done outside of Chicago. Thus, marble or granite to be used on buildings must be cut and dressed, as far as possible, in the city by members of the local union. Whether these demands were right or wrong, the contractors fairly exposed themselves to the charge of inconsistency in complaining of the action of the unions on this score. As a student of the matter has said:

While vigorously, and in part very justly, protesting against the interference of organized labor with the liberty of its contractors to purchase material from whom they pleased, they countenanced and abetted, if they did not organize, a boycott of building material producers against the employers of union labor allied with the Building Trades Council.[1]

The unions had been educated up to this position both by the combination between contractors and material men and by the system of exclusive agreements into which they had entered with the contractors and the manufacturers.[2] The union men might justly have replied to this charge, *Tu quoque*. There is no doubt, however, that the attempts to enforce such rules and thereby to give assistance to their comrades in the material trades were the cause of a great many strikes and of a great deal of annoyance and loss. Probably one half of all the strikes that occurred in the building industry in Chicago during the year 1899 were caused by the use of nonunion-made material.[3]

5. "It is a 'union condition' that industry is to be blocked by the prohibition of machinery, as in the case of the stonecutters, who have shut down all the planers in Chicago; and the carpenters, who will not allow a patent miter box to be used."[4] While not defending this position in general, the union men retorted that the contractors themselves had been the first to advocate the prohibition of machinery, and pointed also to the case of the stone cutters. Of the eighty stone cutting firms in Chicago only twenty had machinery; accordingly, when the other firms made their agreements with the union they insisted on an antimachinery clause. Now, however, claimed the union men, they wished to mislead the public by

[1] Professor Graham Taylor, "Between the Lines in Chicago's Industrial Civil War," in *The Commons*, April 30, 1900.

[2] A striking instance of the willingness of the contractors to do on occasion what they condemned in the unions occurred in connection with the Federal Post Office Building. The specifications of this building called for granite, but the Chicago contractors wished to have this changed to native stone. They therefore sent a delegation of labor men to Washington to lobby for this purpose. With the labor men they used the argument that such a change in the material would provide them with additional work. Secretary Gage did not permit the change to be made.

[3] Statement made to the writer by one of the labor leaders.

[4] The trade rule of the Carpenters' Union on this point is as follows: "Any member who furnishes a patent miter box shall be fined $5."

charging this against the union, whereas they were themselves originally responsible for such rules. But even in these cases the labor men in general opposed such restrictions and stated their willingness to submit them to arbitration.

6. "It is a 'union condition' that in many cases the growing youth is not permitted to learn a trade." The limitation of apprentices is a position which the skilled trades unionists have long held, but which is gradually being given up as indefensible.[1] It is defended, however, on the ground that the unrestricted employment of apprentices amounts in many cases to the employment of underpaid child labor. Most of the agreements existing in the skilled trades recognize the principle by limiting in some way the number of apprentices, and in general it may be said that the contractors were not vitally concerned in the abrogation of this rule where it existed.[2] On the other hand, there is no doubt that the unions had frequently abused this condition in their endeavors to secure as complete a monopoly of the labor market as possible.[3]

7. "The unparalleled power of the walking delegate, armed with the sympathetic strike, constitutes another 'union condition.'" In answer to this charge of the contractors, E. A. Davis, secretary of the Building Trades Council, said:[4]

They have no right to attack the walking delegate, as he is merely the servant of his organization. Each such labor representative has been elected by a majority vote of his union. To oppose him is to oppose the opinions and desires of a majority of the members of the union. He does work which the members cannot possibly do for themselves, and in nearly every case he has the full support of his union in his actions, though of course now and then he makes mistakes.

[1] See article by Miss Jane Addams: "Trades Unions and Public Duty," in *American Journal of Sociology*, July, 1899, pp. 448 ff.

[2] In their statement of principles of April 30 and June 12 they explained their demand on this point as follows: "This means that in each trade a fair agreement as to the number of apprentices shall be entered into." See also Section 5 of the Madden agreement.

[3] See article by George C. Sikes: "The Apprentice System in the Building Trades," in *Journal of Political Economy*, June, 1894.

[4] In an interview in the Chicago *Times-Herald*, March 9.

For a considerable period previous to the lockout and strike of February 5 the attitude of the unions toward the contractors had been extremely dictatorial and exasperating, as has already been pointed out. The walking delegates had used their power mercilessly to bring the employers to terms, and had resorted to the strike, actual or threatened, on the slightest provocation. Yet the real fight of the contractors was not so much against the walking delegate *per se* as against the sympathetic strike with which the Building Trades Council enforced its demands. Although there has been a steady decline in the number of sympathetic strikes in the country at large within the last decade, the resort to this measure had been frequent in the building trades in Chicago. The unions having delegated the power to call such strikes to the Building Trades Council, there was no certainty that an agreement made with an individual union, though for a specific period, would not be broken at any time.[1] In order to eliminate the sympathetic strike, the contractors therefore demanded the abolition of the Building Trades Council.

As the smoke of charges and countercharges cleared away, it became more and more evident that the real point at issue was not any disagreement as to wages or hours, but the existence of the Building Trades Council itself. With the utmost frankness the contractors, through the published statements of their press committee[2] or the statements of the chairman of that committee, Victor Falkenau, repeatedly admitted that this was their object. At the very beginning of the dispute they defined their position as follows:

> Let it not be understood that the Contractors Council in the present struggle with the men who dominate the Building Trades Council have any war with union labor, now or at any later time. Above all things, they wish to make very clear their position on that point. The men in the Contractors Council believe in labor unions.

[1] Thus the agreement of the Carpenters' Executive Council of Chicago, Article 10, provide: "A sympathetic strike when ordered to protect the union principles herein laid down shall not be a violation of this agreement."

[2] This press committee was finally dispensed with, July 27, on the ground that it was too talkative.

Both for the benefit of the mechanic and for the employer as well, such organizations, unabused, are of positive and lasting benefit. But they have come to the place in the present instance where no man is assured of life, liberty or the pursuit of happiness unless the domination of the Building Trades Council shall cease. . . . Between the Chicago Building Trades Council and the Contractors Council there can be no compromise.[1]

A week later this was followed by another statement, in which it was said, "There is not the slightest desire on the part of any one to discourage membership in the unions. But there is a definite and unconquerable purpose of fighting the Building Trades Council to the death.[2]

This challenge was accepted by the unions, and the question at issue resolved itself into the dissolution of the Building Trades Council. The unions refused to give up their central organization, and the contractors refused to treat with them until they did. Other issues were raised and discussed from time to time, but this remained the keynote of the struggle until the end.

Both sides now settled down to what promised to be a long-drawn-out fight. Each party adopted measures and tactics to win over public opinion and to force a surrender from the other. In addition to publishing statements of their position and displaying cards in the street cars and elevated trains showing the rates of wages which they had paid and were willing to pay, the contractors attempted to continue work on the most important buildings under construction with the help of non-union men. On February 13 the press committee of the Building Contractors Council reported that about 1000 men were at work on ninety-five jobs throughout the city,[3] most of them being "independent union" men or sailors and farm hands who had come to the city in response to advertisements. All the work done was "emergency" work, which had to be

[1] Statement of the Building Contractors Council. See Chicago papers of February 10.

[2] See Chicago papers of February 17.

[3] On March 14 they reported 2000 nonunion men at work and on June 21, 3500. The labor men would not admit more than 1000.

finished as soon as possible. Their energies were concentrated on a few buildings, on which not only nonunion men and members of the Colored Federation of Labor went to work, but even some of the contractors themselves. As the non-union men were exposed to attack by union pickets and sympathizers when they left the buildings, the contractors next resorted to the plan of housing and feeding their employees in the buildings on which they were working. Between 150 and 200 men were so cared for in the Merchants' Loan and Trust Building and the Western Electric Building.[1]

The labor men, on their part, did not long remain passive, but early took more active and aggressive measures to insure success in the struggle. The first attempt of the unions was to extend the strike to other cities and to secure sympathetic strikes on all buildings which Chicago contractors were erecting outside of Chicago. A resolution[2] to this effect, in which the Bricklayers and Stone Masons' Union called upon the International Union to take such action, was speedily followed by a similar move on the part of the Building Trades Council. They induced the National Building Trades Council to send out from its headquarters in St. Louis a circular letter to all the local bodies, asking all union men to refuse to work on buildings erected by Chicago contractors or architects. This seems not to have been successful, owing to ignorance on the part of the union men as to where such contracts were held; for towards the end of May[3] the Building Trades Council repeated the request. This time, however, they were backed up by the Material Trades Council and the Wood Workers Council, which secured the pledges of their national organizations to refuse to handle material or to work for Chicago contractors in other cities.[4]

[1] One of the picturesque tactics of this industrial warfare was the placarding of this building with excerpts from the state constitution, statutes, ordinances, etc., all designed to show that the strikers were in the wrong.

[2] Of February 13.

[3] May 27. Still another notice was sent out on June 18 by the National Building Trades Council, warning all union men to keep away from Chicago.

[4] The writer has been able to learn of only one case where a building constructed by a Chicago contractor in another city was held up. This was in Denver.

In addition to thus boycotting Chicago contractors outside the city, the unions adopted the plan of attempting to boycott all business men who owned or rented buildings erected with nonunion labor in Chicago. Later this system of boycotting was extended to all merchants and others who expressed sympathy with the contractors. Action was also taken to prevent by persuasion, intimidation, and force the employment of nonunion men by the contractors.

VIII. Effects and Conduct of the Dispute

The bad effects of the long continuance of the dispute were felt not only by the contending parties but by the general public as well. While it is impossible to say just how many men were thrown out of employment, since the estimates varied widely, the number probably did not exceed 50,000. *Bradstreet's* for March 10 reported the number of idle men at 50,000, and the following week put it at 54,000. On March 27 James O'Connell, vice president of the American Federation of Labor, estimated the number at 40,000. The close of the twelfth week of the dispute showed 30,800 men idle, according to estimates of the unions;[1] by the end of June this number had been reduced to 15,000 or 20,000.[2] The number of unemployed diminished, as some of those originally on strike returned to work or found other occupations, while many obtained employment at their trades in other cities. The fact that so many men were without employment for so long a time necessarily caused considerable want and even suffering among the strikers, though the unions claimed to have sufficient funds to care for all their members. Some of the stronger unions, like the carpenters and plumbers, paid weekly strike benefits of about $5 per member. In the majority of cases the Building Trades Council itself furnished orders for food and paid the rent of those in actual need. Contributions were made by the national organizations

[1] Chicago *Record*, May 4.
[2] Estimate of the labor men to the writer.

of several of the trades,[1] as well as by trades unions in other lines, both in Chicago and elsewhere. Thus, the "convention of all trade unions of Chicago," held on May 13, voted to assess all its members fifty cents a week to assist the Building Trades Council during the rest of the dispute.

That these and even larger contributions would be needed became evident, as the dispute dragged along without indication of speedy settlement and distress showed itself more plainly among the idle men. Striking proof of the bad effect of the long idleness was found in the growth of the pawnbroking business,[2] the extension of the credit system among the stores catering to the working classes, the falling off in the business of the department stores, theaters, and street railways,[3] and the migration of many workers in the building trades from Chicago. Real estate dealers stated that hundreds of laborers had been forced to cease payments on houses which they were buying on the installment plan and were in danger of losing their homes.[4] But the building trades dispute threatened to have more serious consequences than the temporary suffering of those engaged. By the beginning of the fourth month of the dispute it was estimated that between 3000 and 5000 workmen had left the city and found permanent employment elsewhere, while almost every union in the Chicago Building Trades Council had applications on its books for men to go to other points. Builders stated at the beginning of June[5] that there were 500 unfinished buildings in Chicago, and architects claimed that they had an equal number of plans of

[1] For example, the bricklayers and stone masons, the carpenters, the National Building Trades Council, the steam fitters, the plumbers, and the gas fitters.

[2] Within the month of May eleven new "loan banks" were licensed in Chicago.

[3] Street railway men claimed that they were losing $1000 a day during the dispute, while one of the largest department stores, where the working people dealt largely, reported that sales fell off $50,000 a week.

[4] Other proofs of the hardship caused by the building trades dispute, though less apparent, were the increase in the number of women and girls from the strikers' families who went to work during this time and the increased patronage of the "free-lunch" counters in saloons. These facts were attested by workers from Hull House and the Chicago Commons.

[5] Chicago *Record*, June 9.

new buildings which were being held until industrial peace should be restored.[1] Freight managers and material men united with the retail merchants and others in lamenting the depression in business and urging a speedy settlement. But more important, if true, was a statement [2] to the effect that twenty manufacturers were getting ready to move from Chicago as a result of the labor troubles, while eight or nine more had already selected sites.[3] It became evident that Chicago's commercial and manufacturing supremacy was threatened by the continuance of the trouble.

The progress of the building trades dispute was marked by the usual amount of lawlessness. Most of the outbreaks consisted in assaults upon nonunion men by union pickets and sympathizers. During the first five months of the strike the papers reported about two hundred and fifty specific cases of assault upon nonunion men, of which about thirty resulted in serious injuries, from the effects of which there were three deaths. Two union men were killed and a dozen were assaulted, as were also contractors, special policemen, and others. Less than twenty arrests were reported during this time. During the summer there was a lull, but in November the union pickets instituted a series of attacks on the nonunion laborers employed on the Mandel Building, in which a foreman was shot to death and a number of men injured.

One of the chief causes for the great number of assaults that took place was undoubtedly the nonenforcement of the law against the strikers. At the very beginning of the dispute the contractors had demanded police protection for their property and for nonunion men whom they employed, while the Chicago

[1] See an open letter of Hibbard, Spencer, Bartlett & Co. of November 28, which stated that unless more stable conditions prevailed among the unions, a store and warehouse which they were planning would either "be erected without the employment of a union man, or it will not be erected at all."

[2] By M. B. Madden, president of the Western Cut Stone Company, April 13.

[3] The International Power Company, of Providence, R. I., had selected Chicago as the location of a large automobile factory and secured options on property there, but after investigating the condition of the labor market they decided to go elsewhere. — Chicago *Tribune*, December 1, 1900.

Federation of Labor protested against the use of police for such purposes. Failing to secure adequate protection from the city police, the contractors swore in about five hundred detectives and special policemen to guard their buildings;[1] the Building Trades Council protested to the mayor against the employment of these men.[2] At first the attitude of the police had been merely to prevent rioting and to permit picketing so long as the pickets did not openly molest the nonunion workers. An opinion of the corporation counsel showed, however, that where intimidation enters, whether by reason of threats or of large numbers, picketing is illegal. As a result of this opinion and of a vigorously expressed public demand, the chief of police finally issued an order to his men "to arrest the ringleaders in all assaults." Mayor Harrison further directed that only two pickets should be allowed to remain at each building. When the second outbreak occurred in November a large force of policemen was detailed to guard the buildings and protect nonunion workmen, and the disturbances were soon quelled. Such repeated lawlessness on the part of the walking delegates and union pickets seemed to indicate that they had learned nothing from the long-continued controversy, and served only to alienate public sympathy.

The contractors claimed throughout the dispute, and apparently not without good cause, that "politics was mixed up in it." On this point an indictment of the unions by one of their best friends may be cited.

Public opinion claims the right to criticise frankly and fearlessly the policy of the Building Trades Council. It criticises the policy that tolerates the acceptance of appointive political offices as the most disastrous policy that has ever paralyzed the power or menaced the future of organized labor in Chicago. These offices are offered as

[1] They were employed for ten weeks, and the cost to the contractors was estimated at $75,000. — Chicago *Record*, May 5.

[2] The attitude of the latter organization is indicated by a statement made by John A. Long, president of the Board of Business Agents, before the Industrial Commission, to the effect that he did not approve of police protection, "because the men who are at fault and who are causing the trouble are not entitled to protection."

subsidies. Their incumbents are really held as hostages for the delivery of the labor vote.[1]

While it is impossible to ascertain exactly how many of the labor leaders held appointive offices under the city administration there is no doubt that the number was disgracefully large.[2] The most conspicuous case was the appointment of Edward Carroll, president of the Building Trades Council, to the presidency of the Chicago Civil Service Board.[3] That there was a deliberate pact between the labor leaders and the politicians in power seems sufficiently indicated by a change that was made in the constitution of the Building Trades Council two or three years ago, by which Section 3 was stricken out. This section read as follows:

> No person shall be eligible as a delegate to this council who holds a political office, either elective or appointive . . . (a political office shall be defined as being employed in any capacity by the nation, state, county or city).

There is no doubt that many of the leaders of the Building Trades Council had subordinated the best interests of that body to their own personal advantage and that the best elements were not in control. This was felt by the unions themselves, and a complete reorganization of the council would undoubtedly have been effected through the efforts of the rank and file, had not the opposition of the employers given the leaders a rallying cry. The officers and business agents appealed to the members to show their devotion to the cause of union labor by upholding the organization. The men responded loyally to this appeal; but after the contest had dragged along for almost

[1] Speech of Professor Graham Taylor before the labor mass meeting of May 13.

[2] The result of an investigation in the fall of 1899 was said to show that two thirds of the officials of the Chicago Federation of Labor and of the Building Trades Council held such offices. A list of thirteen names was published by the New York *Sun*, May 27, but there were undoubtedly others. W. J. Chalmers, in his testimony before the Industrial Commission, March 20, stated that twenty-two leading men of labor organizations held positions in the city hall.

[3] Mr. Carroll resigned, under pressure, on April 29.

six months, with no prospect of a settlement, dissatisfaction began to manifest itself. At the end of July occurred the election of officers of the Building Trades Council, and as this gave the members the first opportunity of passing judgment on the administration since the beginning of the dispute, it was regarded as very important by both contractors and labor men. But the election by the council on July 27 of all its old officers seemed to place the stamp of approval on the acts of its executive and at the same time destroyed all hope of a compromise settlement. A week later the Board of Business Agents reëlected all its former officers.

The conservative element was strong enough, however, to insist on certain reforms within the Building Trades Council itself. One of these was the amendment of the constitution so as to forbid the holding of a political office by a delegate, another was a modification of the basis of representation so as to give more power to the larger unions, and a third was the substitution of the vote by individuals for the "trade" or unit vote. The carpenters were particularly anxious for these reforms, and it was understood that their adoption was the price which had to be paid for the support given to the council by the carpenters when the question of withdrawal from the strike came up for vote. The growth of dissatisfaction with the policy of the leaders in the Building Trades Council found more decided expression a little later in the retirement of Edward Carroll from office. First his own union, the plasterers, refused on September 1, by a vote of two to one, to reëlect him to the office of financial secretary, which he had held for ten years. A month later, on October 5, Mr. Carroll resigned, under pressure, from the presidency of the Building Trades Council. In his letter of resignation he gave as his reason the alleged announcement of the contractors that if he resigned they would make agreements with all the unions. William G. Schardt was elected president in his place, but as the same political clique was back of the new president, no noticeable change of policy was inaugurated. It had by this time become pretty clear that no compromise could be hoped for, and the struggle narrowed down to a test of endurance between the Building Trades Council and the Building Contractors Council.

IX. Attempts at Arbitration

The history of this dispute proves that there are some matters in labor troubles which cannot be settled by arbitration between employers and employees. Such questions as those relating to wages or hours of labor may well be settled in that manner, for they turn on a single economic fact and may be determined according to that fact. Broader issues connected with the labor problem are not always capable of being arbitrated, and such an issue was raised here. Briefly stated, it was a contest for control of the conditions under which work should be carried on, and involved the right of interference in the conduct of the business of the contractors by the representatives of the unions. It was a struggle over an economic principle and could not be settled by the dictum of any court of arbitration; nor was it subject to compromise, for it called for the surrender of one side or the other. This was the issue involved in the demand of the contractors for the dissolution of the Building Trades Council.

Arbitration did not fail for lack of attempts on the part of outsiders to bring the parties to the struggle to some sort of agreement. No less than seven attempts were thus made. Only a little more than two weeks after the beginning of the dispute Mayor Harrison wrote[1] both to the Building Contractors Council and the Building Trades Council, asking them to appoint committees for the purpose of conferring together with a view to harmonizing the differences between the two organizations. He suggested that the meetings be held in his office and offered to act as chairman. This invitation was accepted by the labor men, but declined by the Contractors Council. The latter stated that they were unwilling to enter into negotiations, because two attempts which

[1] On February 21.

they had made at arbitration with the Building Trades Council had failed.[1] But

> the reason back of all others in the refusal of the contractors to have further dealings with the Building Trades Council is the knowledge that, as an organization, it has become so tyrannical, corrupt and lawless that its existence will render the prosperity of the building industry an impossibility. The first step toward solving the problem is the dissolution of the Building Trades Council.

For this refusal to arbitrate the contractors were much criticised by the unions and others, and the unwillingness to submit their case to a court was cited as evidence of a bad cause. Such action, however, does not necessarily put the party so refusing in the wrong. From the very beginning the contractors took the position that they would not arbitrate with the Building Trades Council, but expressed themselves as ready at any time to come to terms with the separate unions, provided they would withdraw from that body. Whether right or wrong they were at least consistent in maintaining this attitude throughout the struggle. Though the union men professed themselves ready to submit their case to arbitration at any time, they would do so only through the medium of the Building Trades Council. Such an utterly antagonistic attitude as was assumed by the two parties to the dispute made arbitration impossible from the very beginning — so much so that during the investigation made in Chicago by the Federal Industrial Commission, Mr. Harris, a member of the subcommittee, was led to exclaim,[2] "It looks as though you had placed the whole matter beyond the power of arbitration."

Another offer at mediation, by the Civic Federation of Chicago, met with no encouragement from either side.[3] An attempt made by P. J. McGuire, of the Brotherhood of Carpenters and Joiners, to secure a conference failed on the same ground.[4] The next move was the result of a conference

[1] September and December, 1899.

[2] To Edward Carroll, president of the Building Trades Council. See Chicago *Times-Herald*, March 29.

[3] March 11.

[4] April 3.

between the mayor and the building material dealers.[1] The latter threatened that if either side refused a fair offer to restore harmony, they would aid the other side in the struggle. In spite of this threat, however, the contractors refused to arbitrate with the Building Trades Council and the unions refused to arbitrate except through that body.[2] Undaunted by the failure of the mayor to bring the dispute to an end, the city council now appointed a special committee of six aldermen, who together with five citizens were to investigate the labor troubles and try to secure a settlement of them.[3] The Building Trades Council again announced its willingness to aid the committee, while the Building Contractors Council again refused any offer of mediation. They restated their readiness to arbitrate with any single union, provided it would withdraw from the council, but refused to meet representatives from that body. Moreover, they asserted that the "cardinal principles" for which they stood could not be submitted to arbitration.

The next effort at mediation was made under the leadership of Professor Graham Taylor, as the outcome of a "convention of all trades unions" held on May 13, with 600 delegates representing 190 labor organizations in attendance. It was decided that a committee of seven persons should be created to "investigate the building trades lockout thoroughly and endeavor to reach a settlement," this committee to consist of three members of labor organizations outside of the Building Trades Council, three disinterested men from commercial organizations, and Professor Taylor as chairman. The committee was never fully organized, as members of the Real Estate Board and other business associations declined invitations to serve, and the Building Contractors Council refused to participate in the investigation. On July 1, however, the labor members made a report, which expressed their confidence in the officers of the Building Trades Council and placed the whole responsibility for the dispute upon the contractors. Still

[1] April 19.

[2] In explanation of their position the contractors issued a statement, later referred to as the "circular of April 30." See below, p. 125.

[3] April 25.

another attempt was made by the Real Estate Board on May 22, when its directors were authorized to act as arbitrators whenever requested to do so by both parties to the controversy. No results followed this action, however, as neither the contractors nor the union men requested the intervention.

Finally, the American Federation of Labor took up the matter some two months later, and at a meeting of its executive council at Denver, July 19, appointed a committee of three, with President Gompers at the head, to investigate and to attempt to arbitrate the difficulty. Toward the end of the month conferences were held in Chicago by the committee, with both the Building Trades Council and the Building Contractors Council; but these efforts at arbitration failed for the same reason that had prevented settlement before, namely, the refusal of the contractors to enter into agreements with the Building Trades Council. The contractors, however, expressed their willingness to make agreements with representatives of national or international unions or with the American Federation of Labor. As President Gompers refused to consider this proposal, negotiations ceased. Additional suggestions for the settlement of the dispute were freely made by prominent citizens, newspapers, and others interested in its conclusion, but they all proved equally futile. Throughout the controversy the state board of arbitration was completely ignored by both parties.

At one time the action of the Building Trades Council itself in requesting the Contractors Council to appoint a conference committee seemed likely to lead to a conclusion of the dispute. This invitation was accepted by the Contractors Council on condition that the union conferees should not be their business agents or delegates to their council. As this demand was acceded to, a conference was held[1] between representatives of the unions and of the employers' associations for the purpose of effecting a settlement. As the basis of the conference the contractors presented their declaration of principles of April 30 together with the interpretation they put upon them. This

[1] On June 12 and following days.

was practically only a reiteration of their former principles. They announced their willingness to enter into agreements with the individual unions, provided the following conditions were observed:

1. (*a*) That there shall be no limitation as to the amount of work a man shall perform during his working day.

(*b*) That there shall be no restriction of the use of machinery or tools.

(*c*) That there shall be no restriction of the use of manufactured material, except prison-made.

(*d*) That no person shall have the right to interfere with the workmen during working hours.

(*e*) That the use of apprentices shall not be prohibited.

(*f*) That the foreman shall be the agent of the employer.

(*g*) That all workmen are at liberty to work for whomever they see fit.

(*h*) That employers shall be at liberty to employ and discharge whomever they see fit.

2. That the following conditions are made a part of the agreement:

(*a*) That eight hours shall constitute a day's work.

(*b*) That the rate of wages shall be [that prevailing in each trade the previous year].

(*c*) That time and one half shall be paid for overtime, and double time for Sundays and holidays.

(*d*) That the agreement shall cover a period of not less than three years.

(*e*) That an arbitration clause to provide for the adjustment of possible difficulties in the future be made a part of the agreement.

(*f*) That no by-law or rule conflicting with this agreement shall be enforced or passed by the association or union during the life of the agreement.

(*g*) That this agreement shall become operative only when the union withdraws permanently from the Building Trades Council and agrees not to be affiliated with any organization of a like character during the life of the agreement.

The unions were unwilling to give up their central organization, but in return proposed a plan for the establishment of standing arbitration committees which should settle all matters in dispute, work to continue pending their decision, thus doing away with the sympathetic strike. As the objection of the contractors to the Building Trades Council was based largely on the latter's use of the sympathetic strike to enforce its demands, it was thought that they would permit its continuance if robbed of this weapon. Upon the flat refusal of the contractors to accept anything less than the dissolution of the Building Trades Council itself, the negotiations were broken off at this point. A few days later, however, the labor men requested another conference with the contractors and this time submitted a statement of their position on the various points raised by the contractors' circular. They conceded five demands without a change, namely, the first, third, fifth, and seventh of the first set and the fifth demand of the second set. The questions of machinery and the rate of wages were to be left to arbitration, and a standing arbitration committee was to be established, to which should be referred all disputes. On the other points there was a slight difference: the unions insisted that their agent should visit all work when necessary; that the foreman, while an agent of the employer, should be a union man; and that they should reserve the right to refuse to work with nonunion men. No mention was made of the dissolution of the Building Trades Council, but the right to order strikes was taken from it and it was thought that this concession would meet the wishes of the contractors on this point. The labor men had gone considerably more than halfway to meet the requirements of the employers, and when the latter rejected absolutely these propositions of the unions, it was felt that they had determined upon the rule-or-ruin policy. As no compromise was possible, negotiations were broken off for the second time.

X. Defections from the Building Trades Council

The contractors were undoubtedly influenced in assuming this uncompromising attitude by the belief that the unions could not hold out much longer and would soon be compelled to surrender unconditionally. At first it seemed as though their calculations were correct, for on June 26 the Bricklayers and Stone Masons' Union, one of the most powerful organizations in the Building Trades Council, decided to withdraw from that body and sign a separate agreement with the Chicago Masons and Builders Association. This agreement was to run for three years and contained most of the principles for which the contractors had stood out; it provided also for a joint arbitration board.[1] Although this defection was heralded by the contractors as the beginning of the end, it was claimed by the labor leaders that the withdrawal of the bricklayers removed the one inharmonious element in the Building Trades Council and left that organization a unit to carry on the fight.[2]

For the next month there was a decided calm in building trades circles. The contractors evidently expected other unions to follow the lead of the bricklayers, while the efforts of the labor leaders were directed toward keeping them in line. The apparent success of the Building Trades Council, by the election at the end of July of all its old officers, seemed also to show that it was determined to pursue its former policy; and from that time began the slow disintegration of the central body. For the next few months the history of the dispute is

[1] The bricklayers' agreement served as a model for a uniform agreement which was submitted early in September to all the unions. This began by reciting that it was for the purpose of preventing strikes and lockouts and of facilitating a peaceful adjustment of all grievances and disputes which might arise from time to time. As a basis for joint-working rules and to govern the action of the arbitration board there was laid down a code of principles which consisted of the eight cardinal demands of the contractors. The following points were also contained in it: eight hours as a day's work; the Saturday half holiday during the months of June, July, and August; time and a half for overtime and double time for Sundays and holidays; no work on Labor Day; all disputes to be submitted to a joint board of arbitration with the fullest power to enforce its edicts. By the last provision the sympathetic strike was abolished. The agreement was to become operative only when the union should withdraw permanently from the Building Trades Council and should agree not to become affiliated with any organization of a like character during the life of the agreement.

All the agreements made subsequently with the various unions followed the lines of this one, though modifications were often made in particular points.

[2] The Bricklayers and Stone Masons' union had not joined the Building Trades Council until April, 1899, and had never been in complete harmony with that organization. — *The Bricklayer and Mason* (New York), April, 1900, p. 4.

a record of the action of the several unions. A split in the union of the hoisting engineers was the first act to follow the withdrawal of the bricklayers, and on July 28 the seceding faction, composed of about fifty members, afterwards organized under the name of the United Brotherhood of Hoisting Engineers, signed a working agreement with the Building Elevator Contractors' Association. As E. A. Davis, the reëlected secretary of the Building Trades Council, was a member of this union, this was regarded as an especially significant move. The next break came in the suspension of the Brotherhood of Electrical Mechanics from the council. The latter body had ordered the Brotherhood to turn over certain work to the gas fitters, and on their refusal had fined them $300 and suspended them from the organization. Suspension carried with it the loss of union working cards in Chicago, but the electricians later obtained these from the National Building Trades Council. While there was thus no formal withdrawal from the local council, the action of the electricians was considered tantamount to this.

An attempt on the part of some of the members of the Cut Stone Contractors' Association to secure the withdrawal of that organization from the Building Contractors Council met with signal defeat about this time, showing that the contractors were determined to hold together.

Next to the Bricklayers' Union that of the carpenters[1] was the most important and powerful in the Building Trades Council, and its rather vacillating course during the next few months was watched with anxiety and interest. After a failure to reach an agreement with the contractors, owing largely to disagreement over the Saturday half holiday, and the rejection by a small majority of a proposal to withdraw from the Building Trades Council, some of the dissatisfied members formed an independent organization and in September signed a three-year

[1] There are two organizations of carpenters in Chicago — the United Brotherhood of Carpenters and Joiners, which is composed of nineteen unions and about 4700 members, and the Amalgamated Society of Carpenters and Joiners, which has five unions and some 300 members.

agreement with the employers' associations. Further negotiations with the contractors were had during October and November by the regular unions, but without result. Finally, however, on February 7, 1901, just a year from the beginning of the dispute, an agreement was reached by which the men secured the Saturday half holiday and agreed to leave the council. In all essentials the agreement resembled that adopted by the bricklayers, although one clause provided that the union might join "a new central body, composed solely of mechanic trades employed on buildings, . . . and that said body shall not be called the 'Building Trades Council.'" The very name was evidently under the ban of the contractors! Several of the strongest unions, therefore, applied for admission to the Chicago Federation of Labor.

The Plumbers' Union had proposed to the contractors in July that if they would withdraw from the Building Contractors Council, the plumbers would withdraw from the Building Trades Council, and they could then frame an agreement together without difficulty. The Master Plumbers Association refused, however, to act upon this suggestion. Two or three further attempts to secure agreements with the contractors failing, and efforts to secure the withdrawal of the union from the Building Trades Council being unsuccessful, some of the dissatisfied members of the union withdrew individually and went to work for all contractors who paid the union scale of wages and employed only union men, without reference to any agreement. The seceders organized themselves later into an independent union under the name of the Journeymen Plumbers Association and on December 18 secured a charter. By January the old union also was ready to withdraw from the council and a unification of the two organizations was effected, after which an agreement similar to the others was made with the employers.

The second organization to withdraw from the Building Trades Council in its corporate capacity was the Plasterers' Union. On July 9 they had refused to ratify an agreement with the contractors similar to that made by the bricklayers, but a month later another agreement along the same lines was brought before the union. Withdrawal from the Building Trades Council was of course provided for, and in other respects it differed but slightly from the bricklayers' agreement. Ratification of this agreement seemed probable, but was defeated by the arbitrary methods of Edward Carroll and other members at the meeting of the union, — an action which undoubtedly hurt the Building Trades Council more than anything else. At the end of September Carroll was forced from the presidency of the council, and a day later the Plasterers' Union appointed a committee to confer with the Employing Plasterers' Association for the purpose of arranging an agreement with that organization. After some rather dramatic maneuvers by both factions, this was finally ratified by a majority of the members on October 5, a move which carried with it the withdrawal of the union from the Building Trades Council.

The Bridge and Structural Iron Workers formally withdrew from the Building Trades Council on October 25 and at the same time entered into an agreement with the Iron League, the association of the contractors. This was the third organization to sever its connection with the council, and while not as strong numerically as the other two, it was made up of the *élite* of the skilled workers in the building trades and had considerable influence. Their agreement followed the general lines of the uniform agreement, such as was entered into with the bricklayers and plasterers, the main difference being a clause giving the contractors the right to hire nonunion men in other lines on the same job. One significant clause provided that the union might belong to a new central organization not the Building Trades Council.

If it was to win in the struggle with the contractors and save itself, it was apparent that the Building Trades Council must stop the disintegration that threatened to end its own existence. It was, accordingly, now decided to adopt the plan of fighting the contractors one at a time until each was forced in turn to capitulate. The first job singled out for attack was the new Mandel Building, and on November 20 all the men at work on that building were called out on strike. Although this was the first aggressive move that the Building Trades Council had made in several months, they seemed not to have learned wisdom in that time, for the progress of this strike was marked by a new outburst of lawlessness. The strike was of short duration, for the places of the strikers were soon filled, while the immoderate action of the labor leaders served to alienate public sympathy. Many of the nonunion men who had taken the place of the striking union men during this trouble and previously were Negroes, who, with the exception of the bricklayers and hod carriers, were practically unorganized in Chicago. An attempt was now made to align them on the side of the Building Trades Council. The Chicago Federation of Labor issued an appeal on December 2, inviting them to join the unions. While it does not appear that this invitation was acted upon by the Negroes, it certainly evidenced a more pacific policy on the part of organized labor.

These measures were insufficient, however, to restrain the seceding unions, and in the middle of December the steam fitters withdrew from the Building Trades Council. After the failure to reach a settlement with the unions early in August several of the master steam fitters had withdrawn from the Contractors Council and signed three-year agreements similar to the old ones. The principal demand of the contractors — that the unions should withdraw from the Building Trades Council — was not insisted on, but the agreement provided that there should be no limitation as to the amount of work that might be done in a day, and that no strike should be called until the grievance had been submitted to a permanent board of arbitration. The threatened break from the Contractors Council did not become general, however, and things remained quiet in this trade until December. Negotiations were then begun between representatives of the Master Steam Fitters' Association and those of the Journeymen Steam Fitters' and the Junior Steam Fitters' unions, which resulted in the signing of a three-year agreement between the organizations of employers and men. The conditions were substantially the same as those of the uniform agreement signed by the other unions.[1] Withdrawal from the Building Trades Council and the establishment of a joint arbitration board were the most important features. The eight cardinal points of the contractors were conceded and they were given greater liberty in the employment of helpers. The men got the Saturday half holiday, double time for all overtime, and some other demands. The wage scale remained unchanged. Permission was given to the unions to join another central trade body, provided only it was composed of mechanics whose trades were closely allied. In accordance with the terms of this agreement the Journeymen's and Junior Steam Fitters' unions withdrew on December 14 from the Building Trades Council.

A few days later, on December 18, a three-year agreement was concluded between the Master Plumbers Association and the Gas Fitters' Union, embodying the general features of the agreement signed by the steam fitters. It was reached only after considerable friction over the clause concerning the employment of nonunion men. The question was settled through a sort of compromise, by which it was provided that while the bosses should have the right to hire whom they pleased and the men to work for whom they pleased the latter were also given the right to cease work when they chose, the latter contingency doubtless having reference to the employment of nonunion men. Another significant clause in the agreement was to the effect that the Master Plumbers' Association should notify the union when any member of the association lapsed from membership. It seemed to point clearly to a tacit understanding that the members of the union were not to work for any master plumber who was not a member of the association. No mention was made of a new central body such as was referred to in the agreements of the carpenters, iron workers, and steam fitters. In other respects it followed the lines of the uniform agreement.

[1] The details of the agreement may be found in "The Chicago Steam Fitters' Settlement," in *The Metal Worker* (New York and Chicago), December 22, 1900, p. 36.

The new year saw no interruption in the disintegration of the Building Trades Council. Early in January the plumbers withdrew, and shortly thereafter the Hod Carriers and Building Laborers' union entered into an agreement with the Chicago Masons and Builders Association, by the terms of which they also withdrew from the central body. As this was next to the carpenters the largest union in the council, its action was a severe blow. The carpenters only waited for the semiannual election of officers in the council on January 27; when the result showed that no change of policy was contemplated they also severed their connection. This was the beginning of the end, and the movement of secession was kept up by the withdrawal of dissatisfied members in the unions of the stonecutters, the slate and tile roofers, and the mosaic tile layers and helpers. Every symptom points clearly to the final disintegration of the Building Trades Council, though the president of that organization has denied emphatically that it will dissolve. The constitution provides that it shall exist as long as five trades desire to retain the organization. While the council may thus never be formally dissolved, there is no doubt that its usefulness is past and that it is practically moribund. As one of the union men himself expressed it, "The council is about as useful as a dead horse." Twelve months after the beginning of the dispute the membership of the council had been reduced from perhaps 30,000 to about one third of that number. It was said that about 5000 workmen had left the city in search of employment elsewhere since the beginning of the dispute. Indeed, the end might have come sooner, had not both contractors and unions tacitly agreed during the summer not to push the matter to a conclusion at that time.

The statistics of building operations in Chicago show that they had been only temporarily checked by the labor troubles and by July, 1900, had resumed their normal activity, soon exceeding in volume those of the previous year. The contractors pointed to this fact as evidence that the strike had failed and that the men had deserted the Building Trades Council, but the real explanation was somewhat different.

Both contractors and union men were anxious to resume work, but it had to be done under conditions that would not indicate a surrender on either side. In order to quiet disaffection and permit the men to provide for the winter, the unions allowed their members to work for members of the Contractors Council in violation of their rules. The contractors, on the other hand, were willing to accept workmen without inquiring too closely as to whether they belonged to the Building Trades Council or not, though such an act violated their mutual agreement. Fearing lest such a policy should disrupt their association, the contractors next adopted the plan of requiring all workmen to join the Industrial Union,[1] which was in favor with the Contractors Council, or to sign an agreement certifying that they had resigned from their union. To meet this move the men received permission from their unions to sign without detriment to their union standing. Accordingly, a number of the union men, notably the carpenters, joined the Industrials, or signed resignations from their own unions and secured work on these terms. In some cases the contractors were reported to have paid the initiation fee for the men who joined the Industrial Union. There was a tacit agreement on both sides to resume work without insisting on a formal surrender from either. In the middle of the summer it was calculated by one of the best-informed labor leaders that over half of all the men employed were union men, that fully one third of the members of the unions affiliated with the Building Trades Council were employed, and that at least three fourths of these were getting union wages from the contractors.

Owing to the number of nonunion men employed and the decrease in the amount of building, there was a distinct surplus of laborers as soon as the union men began to return to work. In recognition of this fact, several of the unions abandoned their demands for an increase in wages and others adopted temporarily a lower wage scale. There seemed to be imminent danger that the unions would lose all the gains of years in this struggle of the Building Trades Council.

[1] An organization composed of nonunion men.

XI. Conclusion

This recital of the progress of the building trades dispute has made clear the fact that the sense of responsibility in their position as trustees has not controlled the leaders of the Building Trades Council. Organized ostensibly to promote the interests of labor, it had subordinated these to the cause of a political machine in whose service it had attempted to use the organization. In its dealings with contractors the Building Trades Council had become arrogant and arbitrary. Assuming that it had unlimited power, it had pushed its demands to such a point that the employers were goaded to resistance in self-defense. If any single lesson is to be drawn from this dispute, it is the necessity for wise and unselfish leadership of organized labor.

But while condemning the one side we cannot hold the other free from blame. There were hot-headed men in the lead on both sides. After the dispute had continued for some time success became a personal matter. Many of the contractors had expressed themselves so decidedly that they were unwilling to concede a single point; they had staked their personal reputation, as it were, on the outcome and would accept nothing less than the complete submission of the Building Trades Council. In justice to the Contractors Council, it should be said that there were many members in their association, as there were in the unions, who would have been glad of an honorable compromise at any period of the dispute. The attitude of the Contractors Council in demanding the dissolution of the Building Trades Council while refusing to disband themselves must be recognized as inconsistent, to say the least. They later receded from this extreme position, when in the agreements signed with some of the unions provision was made for the organization of a new central body. It now seems clear that the dispute might have been settled by mutual agreement, had the leaders on both sides been less uncompromising.

* * * * * * * *

On April 26 the Building Trades Council voted to disband, the motion being opposed by only the paper hangers and the boiler makers. A few days later a new organization, under the name of the Chicago Building Trades League, was formed by fifteen of the eighteen strong trades in the building industry, representing 15,000 workmen. The membership is restricted to trades engaged in the actual construction of buildings, and thus fifteen of the trades that were affiliated with the former organization are made ineligible. There are to be no sympathetic strikes; differences are to be settled by arbitration; no person holding political office is eligible as a delegate; and unity of the trades is to be fostered. This new central body was perfected entirely through the efforts of local labor men who opposed the policies of the old council and desired to live up to the agreements recently made with the contractors. The outcome of the year-long dispute must be regarded, therefore, not merely as a victory for the contractors but also as a victory for the better element in the trades unions, signifying the substitution of conciliatory methods of settling disputes for those of bluster and threat.

ERNEST L. BOGART.

VI

THE INCORPORATION OF TRADE UNIONS[1]

[The legal character and responsibility of a labor union are discussed from different points of view in the following selections from a symposium of replies to an inquiry submitted by the secretary of the National Civic Federation. The question asked was whether unions should seek to become incorporated. — Ed.]

Don C. Seitz, Member of the American Newspaper Publishers' Association and Business Manager of the New York *World:*

When an employer recognizes a labor union he ceases to recognize the individual. The latter has no place in the economy of his establishment. He must deal with the concrete idea represented by unionism and forsake the theory that he can handle the individual as such. This we have done, and the results, I think, are satisfactory, so far as anything that interferes with liberty of action and freedom of purpose can be satisfactory. When, however, we do get ourselves into this attitude we certainly increase the responsibility of the union and expect this responsibility to be met.

Coercive as most unions are, they naturally cannot learn to respect the rights of employers or men who will not affiliate with them. I think there is now less tyranny in the printing trade than formerly, and we have the insurance of our admirable arbitration agreement. Certainly, too, there is more intelligence and a greater appreciation of what is right among most of our employees than in any other grade of labor, and the proposition I am about to present is not specific to our own interests. I believe that we shall have constant and more menacing troubles unless the newspapers, whose duty it is to arouse public sentiment and bring issues home to the minds of the people, shall insist that labor unions be made legally responsible bodies by incorporation. This done, a vast deal of trouble would disappear. It would, no doubt, be difficult to organize unions, because of the responsibilities involved by such legislation,

[1] From the *National Civic Federation Monthly Review*, April, 1903.

— as men would stop and do some thinking before assuming a legal liability, — but in the end the unions that were brave enough and honest enough to comply with the conditions would benefit largely by the result. In short, legislation should be had to provide for the incorporation of the trade unions just as we have it for forming other corporations or trusts, and self-constituted bodies founded to coerce employers would have no status under the law and would become conspiracies where they failed to comply with the requirement to incorporate.

You cannot properly establish the Merry Toughs' Social Club without incorporating it. You cannot join with a few friends to promote the simplest business enterprise without incorporating it. You cannot even establish a church without going through a legal process. But it is perfectly possible to get together a body of workingmen who without regard to your contracts or their obligations take you by the throat with intimidation and boycott without any serious fear of interference by law or any collection of damages from the courts.

Large sums of money are raised by the unions from individual assessments, but not one cent of this is reachable to recompense the industry that bears the brunt of the conflict. When the suggestion is made to the average labor leader that such incorporation ought to be enforced, we at once meet with the answer that it would be fatal to their methods, which is an open confession that their methods are illegal and wrong. Business men incur millions of responsibility in obedience to the law, while labor, much more closely knit, is immune.

It is only recently that in overburdened England the court of last resort ordered the Amalgamated Society of Railroad Servants to pay the Taff Vale Railroad £28,000 damages for a strike and boycott. The appellate court held that, incorporated or not, an organized body could not keep itself outside the law, and that it must be held pecuniarily responsible for its acts. This decision of vast importance to all concerned swept away the pleasant fiction that lawlessness and boycott are always to be condoned where the "workingman" is trying to "elevate" himself. In short, in England the worm has turned and hereafter the unions will be forced to meet the responsibility they incur, just as the railroad does when it wrecks a train and kills or injures its passengers. The playful incendiaries, the murderous boycotters, and the delightful dynamiters may escape as individuals, but the union which precipitated the conflict which brought this all about must settle. This is what we must come to here, if there is to be any human right or human liberty left in the land.

The argument in favor of incorporating is a simple one. A certain number of carpenters desire to get together for the betterment of their condition. They must raise a fund, elect officers. They must have a concrete existence, if they would incorporate as a business body. This would be the situation: When an employer called upon the guild, as it would best be named, the condition of employment could be made plain: the responsibility of taking the work would be incurred and the duty of performing it would be enforced. Can there be any honest objection to this practice? We have now in this city the most chaotic conditions. Men drop out every day at will in the building trades and great losses are incurred by the contractor and owner; the situation is fast becoming intolerable.

Judge Parker, in a recent decision, holds that the laborer has the right to do as he pleases about working or not working. This is incontestably true, yet I should say that when the laborer had agreed to perform a certain task for a certain price there should be some method of making him keep his agreement. The employer is responsible for wages, and if he has agreed to hire a man for a year and uses him only one day, the law makes him pay for the whole period. But the plasterer can throw down his trowel and quit in the middle of his employment because he dislikes the expression on his foreman's face. If, however, we had an incorporated union of plasterers instead of a guerrilla one, the union would have to come forward and complete the task.

J. W. Sullivan, Typographical Union, New York:

A union has ways of its own in conducting the affairs that relate mainly to itself and its membership. It is a big self-governing family. In periods of strike the prescribed order of written constitution or by-law sometimes proves less desirable than the short cut obvious as a war measure. The members then become aware that in drawing up their laws they were unable to foresee the situation confronting them, and they may, for example, unconstitutionally confide absolute power temporarily in an officer or a committee. In times of peace a union often reaches conclusions and interpretations dictated by the common sense of a meeting rather than by the statutes as written, leaving the majority either satisfied or in a mood to accept the judgment for better or worse. Such proceedings may relate to trials of members, to executive session work, to appropriation of funds, to informalities or irregularities in elections or referendum votes, to the opening or closing of books for inspection, to the reading or silencing of reports, to appointing or dismissing committees, to maintaining discipline, to accepting or rejecting candidates for membership, to suspending or expelling or reinstating members, to passing judgment on aggressions of employers tending to end in strike, to investigating the conduct of members prejudicial to the organization, and to settling questions in which rule or precedent or necessity of the local union conflicts with international union law. In all such proceedings two principles usually govern, — self-preservation of the union and good fellowship. A popular employer, in general fair, who in a fit of temper has willfully violated a clause in a contract or the union scale, will be adjudged innocent. A sound and active union man who has misappropriated a small sum will be found not guilty and given time to refund. In these matters an unincorporated union is in the main a law unto itself. It is free. It may make many changes in its internal methods and in administration without lessening its responsibility as a contracting party.

But an incorporated union would in all these steps be subject to much revision and correction through the agencies of the law. Work here for judges, lawyers, and enemies. The incorporated body, as a creature of the state, must be kept in health by the state. Disturbers, instigated by influences inimical to a union, might kindly aid the state. In incorporating, a union would have admitted non-kinsfolk as masters at the family table — the judge, of another blood, come to set things right; the sheriff, with keys to a jail and a money sack for fines; the policeman, with a club and handcuffs.

These officials now occasionally regulate family affairs in the unions, but the courts, only acting when called upon, refuse to interfere if the union's proceedings are in accordance with its own rules, which are subject to change at the will of the majority. But if these rules depended for regularity upon the terms of incorporation, and if informers were sent into the unions to report infractions, the sins of unions would be multiplied and the lawsuits ensuing would work pleasure to scabs. The knowing are fully conscious of what they are saying when they express a desire for an increase of the authority of the law over trade unions. They would wreck them from within.

John Frankenheimer, Counselor at Law, New York:

The question, Should trade unions be incorporated? will be found, in its final analysis, to be predicated upon the question, Do you believe in trade unions? For those who believe in trade unions will answer your question quite differently from those who oppose this established form of labor organization. As a believer in trade unionism, I shall answer your question from the trade-union standpoint. There is no blinking the fact that the struggle between capital and labor has many of the features of an internecine warfare. The forces on each side are becoming daily more disciplined and consolidated,—the trust on one side, the federated trade unions on the other. In a struggle of this kind discipline will count. Whatever will weaken the disciplinary control of a trade union over its members will necessarily weaken the trade union in its contest with organized capital. It is because incorporation of a trade union will deprive it of much of the power it now possesses over its members and the management of its internal affairs that the chief legal objection to incorporation seems to lie from the trade-union standpoint. It is well settled that a voluntary unincorporated association, such as a trade union, club, or stock exchange, has a much greater power not only over the admission but also over the expulsion of its members than an incorporated association. Membership in an incorporation is a statutory right in the nature of a franchise, which can neither be withheld nor taken away by the act of the corporation unless the power to do so be given by the charter. On the other hand, membership in a voluntary association is derived exclusively from the body that bestows it and may be conferred or withheld at its pleasure. A person acquires by his admission to membership in a voluntary association only such rights as the constitution and by-laws of the association give him. He may be suspended or expelled according to the rules of the association, and if the proceedings are regular and the investigation a fair one the decision of the association cannot be reviewed on its merits by the courts. As was said recently in a stock exchange suit, voluntary associations are themselves the exclusive judges of their mode and manner of proceeding in the suspension or expulsion of a member.

It has repeatedly been said by the courts that their power over voluntary associations was not as great as it is over corporations; that the constitution of voluntary associations is the contract between the parties, and that if its provisions are not illegal, immoral, or contrary to public policy, it must be upheld, whether reasonable or not; and that this is one of the main distinctions between a voluntary association and a corporation.

It is undoubtedly because of this greater disciplinary power of a voluntary association over its members that the most successful trade union in this country, the New York Stock Exchange, has refused to be incorporated. Members of this association will admit that the maintenance of the standard rate of commissions and of the established rules of the trade are due to the untrammeled power of suspension and expulsion vested in the governing committee of the exchange. Members have been suspended or expelled for "splitting" commissions, "bucketing" orders, "fraudulent" sales, and other acts deemed detrimental to the best trade interests of the association, and although frequent appeals have been made to the courts in such cases, the invariable answer has been that the court cannot interfere if the proceedings are regular. It stands to reason that a powerful and wealthy trade organization, such as the Stock Exchange, which commands the best legal talent, would not persist in remaining an unincorporated association unless it derived great advantage therefrom.

The fundamental advantages of an unincorporated association over a corporation are the greater power the former possesses over its members and over the management of its internal affairs and its greater freedom from interference by the courts in these matters.

I take it that from the trade-union standpoint the object desired is untrammeled disciplinary power over its members and freedom from interference in its internal affairs by the courts. This can undoubtedly be attained more completely in the form of a voluntary association than in that of a corporation, and for this reason, if for no other, trade unions should oppose incorporation.

Were a trade union to be incorporated, every member who may have been disciplined, suspended, or expelled would appeal to the courts for redress, and the organization would be constantly embroiled in litigation of this kind. Moreover, sinister influences might be brought to bear upon a sufficiently strong minority to justify interference by the courts in the internal affairs of the association, if incorporated, which would not be justified, however strong the minority, if the association were a voluntary one.

As to the legal liability of a trade union for the authorized acts of its members or officers, there is no difference in this respect, under the laws of the state of New York, between a voluntary association and a corporation. The former can sue and be sued as well as the latter.

In my opinion, considering the whole question from the standpoint of the labor unions, — and this is the only practical point of view to take of the question, — incorporation of trade unions is inexpedient. It will weaken the power of the association over its members and over its management of its internal affairs and will increase greatly the power of the courts over the association in all its affairs. Let the trade unions follow the example of the New York Stock Exchange — which is essentially a trade union and a very successful one — and persist in maintaining their present voluntary and unincorporated organization.

Levy Mayer, General Counsel Illinois Manufacturers' Association:

A corporation exists as such only by virtue of a grant from the state and the acceptance of such grant by the persons composing the corporation. No one can be compelled to accept such a grant, nor to become a member of the corporation against his will. To compel labor unions to incorporate is to compel individuals composing the union to become members of a corporation and to assume the burdens and responsibilities of that relation without their consent, or to prohibit such members from voluntarily associating themselves together for a lawful purpose. It is not within the province of the legislature to say to a person: "You cannot join a union unless that union is incorporated." That would be equivalent to saying that a person desiring to become a member of a labor union has to become a member of the corporation or cease to be a "union" laborer. Such persons would thus be prevented from pursuing a lawful purpose and would be deprived of a right to assemble for a purpose not in violation of law. The proposed law would interfere with the liberty of the citizen, the right of lawful assembly, and the freedom of contract. This view is supported by authorities. Chancellor Kent, in his Commentaries (Vol. II, p. 277), says:

"It requires the acceptance of a charter to create a corporate body, for the government cannot compel persons to become an incorporated body without their consent or the consent of at least a major part of them."

In *Mason* v. *Finch*, 28 Mich. 282, the Supreme Court of Michigan laid down the law as follows:

"It would not be competent for the legislature . . . to compel any person or society to become incorporated without its consent."

In *Hampshire* v. *Franklin*, 16 Mass. 76, 87, the Supreme Court of Massachusetts said:

"No man can be compelled by the legislature to become a member of a corporation without his consent."

See also Angell & Ames on Corporations (eleventh edition), Sections 31, 81, 86.

Again, the proposed law, if applicable only to labor unions and not to all other unincorporated associations similarly situated, would probably violate the constitutional inhibition against "class legislation." There is nothing in the nature of a labor union which requires special regulation which does not equally apply to other unincorporated associations. The members of a labor union are joined together in furtherance of a common enterprise, in which the public at large is not directly interested or concerned. If the public is affected, it is only indirectly. Such union, therefore, is not a public association in the same sense that it is subject to public regulation and control.

I have heretofore, on April 12, 1902, given an opinion to the association that the members of a labor union are legally responsible for damages caused by an illegal boycott. The compulsory incorporation of a labor union would not make the members of the association any more responsible than they are at present, except in so far as the corporation might possess property. The creation of a corporation not for pecuniary profit does not and would not ordinarily create any more financial responsibility than now exists on the part of individuals who would constitute the corporation.

For the reasons above stated I am of the opinion that the proposed law, if enacted, would be unconstitutional. Even if the law were constitutional, I do not believe it would accomplish the purpose for which it would be designed. If a law could be devised to compel the formation of such corporations, it would soon be discovered that such corporations could readily avoid accumulating or possessing any property.

Frederick H. Cooke, Author of "Trade and Labor Combinations," Attorney at Law, New York:

The importance of the decision of the House of Lords in *Taff Vale Railway Company* v. *Amalgamated Society of Railway Servants*,

L. R. App. Cas. 426 (1901), resulting in a recovery for a large amount of damages against the defendant trade union, has, in my opinion, been much exaggerated. That an association of this character should be mulcted in so large an amount is, to say the least, unusual and may be a sociological fact of interest and importance. But from a strictly legal standpoint the decision is comparatively insignificant. The doctrines applied are trite, and it was simply a narrow question of statutory construction that was really involved.

The effect of the decision was that the defendant trade union was liable in an action for damages, that is, in tort, for unlawful acts of its agents in the course of the management of a strike.

Before considering the precise ground of such decision, let us consider the general principles applicable in determining the liability of a trade union or its officers, members, or agents for such acts.

In the absence of statutory provision a trade union is nothing but a number of persons associated for a particular purpose. As in the case of such associations generally (frequently termed voluntary associations), the law ignores the circumstance of association in determining liability for unlawful acts of members of the association. That is to say, if the members of a trade union, whether acting singly or in combination, assault a person or trespass upon his property, or otherwise injure him, it is merely as individuals that they can be held liable. For instances of members being thus held liable, injunctions being allowed, see *Hopkins* v. *Oxley Stave Company*, 83 Fed. 912, 49 U. S. App. 709 (8th Cir., 1897); *Cumberland Glass Manufacturing Company* v. *Glass Bottle Blowers' Association*, 59 N. J. Eq. 49, 46 Atl. 208 (1899); *Reinecke Coal Mining Company* v. *Wood*, 112 Fed. 477 (Cir. Ct. Ky., 1901); *Sherry* v. *Perkins*, 147 Mass. 212, 17 N. E. 307 (1888); *Murdock* v. *Walker*, 152 Pa. St. 595, 25 Atl. 492 (1893); *Wick China Company* v. *Brown*, 164 Pa. St. 449, 30 Atl. 261 (1894). So in actions for damages: *Temperton* v. *Russell*, 1 L. R. Q. B. 715 (1893); *Quinn* v. *Leathem*, L. R. App. Cas. 495 (1901). See also *Thomas* v. *Cincinnati, N. O. & T. P. Ry. Company*, 62 Fed. 803 (Cir. Ct. Ohio, 1894); *Brace* v. *Evans*, 3 Ry. & Corp. L. J. 561 (1888); *Carew* v. *Rutherford*, 106 Mass. 1 (1870). That, however, the trade union itself is not liable in such a case, see *American Steel & Wire Company* v. *Wire Drawers' Union*, 90 Fed. 598 (Cir. Ct. Ohio, 1898); *Plant* v. *Woods*, 176 Mass. 492, 57 N. E. 1011 (1900); 22 Encyclopædia of Pleading and Practice, p. 242.

In some instances, indeed, an unincorporated trade union seems to have been assumed to be liable in the absence of statutory provision, but this assumption doubtless resulted from inadvertence. See, for instance, *Consolidated Steel & Wire Company* v. *Murray*, 80 Fed. 811 (Cir. Ct. Ohio, 1897). And the following are instances of trade unions being held liable, in some of which, at least, such unions were, so far as appears, unincorporated: Thus, in allowing injunctions, *Coeur d'Alene Consolidated & Mining Company* v. *Miners' Union*, 51 Fed. 260 (Cir. Ct. Idaho, 1892); *American Steel & Wire Company* v. *Wire Drawers' Union*, 90 Fed. 608 (Cir. Ct. Ohio, 1898); *Otis Steel Company* v. *Local Union No. 218*, 110 Fed. 698 (Cir. Ct. Ohio, 1901); *Southern Railway Company* v. *Machinists' Local Union*, 111 Fed. 49 (Cir. Ct. Tenn., 1901); *Allis Chalmers Company* v. *Reliable Lodge*, 111 Fed. 264 (Cir. Ct. Ill., 1901); *Vegelahn* v. *Guntner*, 167 Mass. 92, 44 N. E. 1077 (1896). So in an action for damages, *Old Dominion Steamship Company* v. *McKenna*, 30 Fed. 48 (Cir. Ct. N. Y., 1887).

But the liability of the union in such a case is sometimes created by statute. Thus, in the state of New York, by provisions substantially in force since 1851, "an unincorporated association, consisting of seven or more persons," may be sued in the name of its president or treasurer, and a judgment against it binds its property. Code Civ. Pro., Sections 1919 and 1921. The action, though in form against such officer, is in substance and reality against the association. *Mason* v. *Holmes*, 30 Misc. 719, 64 N. Y. Suppl. 596 (1900). These provisions unquestionably apply to a trade union. Indeed, by virtue thereof, in *Curran* v. *Galen*, 152 N. Y. 33, affirming 2 Misc. 553, 22 N. Y. Suppl. 826 (1892), an action for damages was held to lie against an unincorporated trade union for acts resulting in taking away the plaintiff's means of earning a livelihood and preventing him from obtaining employment. Why, then, attach so much importance to the decision in the Taff Vale Railway Company case, when we have a decision at home that covers the ground thereof? For other instances of unincorporated trade unions held liable by virtue of such provisions, see *Connell* v. *Stalker*, 20 Misc. 423, 45 N. Y. Suppl. 1048, 21 Misc. 609, 48 N. Y. Suppl. 77 (1897); *Coons* v. *Chrystie*, 24 Misc. 296, 53 N. Y. Suppl. 668 (1898); *Matthews* v. *Shankland*, 25 Misc. 604, 56 N. Y. Suppl. 123 (1898); *Beattie* v. *Callanan*, 67 N. Y. App. D. 14, 73 N. Y. Suppl. 518 (1901). See also *Van Aernam* v. *Bleistein*, 102 N. Y. 355 (1886); *Rourke* v. *Elk Drug Company*, 75 N. Y. App. D. 145, 77 N. Y. Suppl. 373 (1902); *Hanke* v. *Cigarmakers' International Union*, 27 Misc. 529, 58 N. Y. Suppl. 412 (1899).

Similar statutory provisions exist in other states; thus, Connecticut (General Statutes, Sec. 588), Michigan (3 Compiled Laws, Sec. 10,025), New Jersey (2 General Statutes, 2588). See *Beck* v. *Railway Teamsters' Protective Union*, 118 Mich. 497, 77 N. W. 13 (1898); *Mayer* v. *Stonecutters' Association*, 47 N. J. Eq. 519, 20 Atl. 492 (1890); *Barr* v. *Essex Trades Council* 53 N. J. Eq. 101, 30 Atl. 881 (1894).

I have already said that in the Taff Vale Railway Company case it was simply a narrow question of statutory construction that was involved. That is to say, an unincorporated trade union was held liable in an action for damages, notwithstanding the absence of any statutory provision expressly making it thus liable, such liability being, however, regarded as inferentially created by other provisions, particularly those enabling it to hold property and act by agents. The liability there regarded as inferentially created is, as we have just seen, expressly created by statutes in New York and other states. I repeat, then, that from a strictly legal standpoint the decision is comparatively insignificant.

By act of Congress, 1886, chapter 567, as well as by statutes in a number of states, provision is made for the incorporation of trade unions. The following provisions applicable to a trade union created by act of Congress are typical of provisions applicable to corporations generally. It has the right "to sue and be sued, to implead and be impleaded, to grant and receive in its corporate or technical name property, real, personal, and mixed, and to use said property, and the proceeds and income thereof, for the objects of said corporation." It may be added that its liability to be sued involves subjection of its property to a judgment obtained against it. Such a union would also be subject to various statutory provisions, differing in detail according to the locality. By way of illustration merely, the following provision of the act of Congress, 1898, chapter 370, applicable to unions incorporated under the act of 1886, is here stated: "A member shall cease to be such by participating in or by instigating force or violence against persons or property during strikes, lockouts, or boycotts, or by seeking to prevent others from working, through violence, threats, or intimidations. Members of such incorporations shall not be personally liable for the acts, debts, or obligations of the corporations, nor shall such corporations be liable for the acts of members or others in violation of law." Under such a provision it would hardly be held, as in the Taff Vale Railway Company case, that a trade union is liable for the unlawful acts of its agents. But for instances of incorporated trade unions held liable for the unlawful acts of their agents, see *Moores* v. *Bricklayers' Union*, 7 Ry. and Corp. L. J. 108 (1889); *Casey* v. *Cincinnati Typographical Union*, 45 Fed. 135 (Cir. Ct. Ohio, 1891); *Lucke* v. *Clothing Cutters', etc., Assembly*, 77 Md. 396, 26 Atl. 505 (1893).

In view of what we have seen, incorporation of a trade union, ordinarily at least, creates a responsibility not existing independently of statute, though the extent of such responsibility may widely vary according to local statutory provisions. But it is clear that wherever there exist provisions of the character already considered, making even an unincorporated trade union liable to be sued, incorporation is not necessary for the purpose of creating such responsibility.

I do not dwell here upon the economic or sociological effects of such creation of responsibility, though here is involved a broad and interesting field of inquiry, including such questions as whether the existence of such responsibility will tend to discourage the creation of such unions or their active intervention in strikes or boycotts instituted in the interest of their members.

I. A. Hourwich, former Counsel to the United Brotherhood of Cloakmakers, New York City:[1]

I shall take up the law of the state of New York, first, because I am more familiar with it as far as it bears on this subject; and, second, because it is probably more liberal than the laws of other industrial states.

First of all, let us consider the status of the labor union. It may be either an unincorporated association of workmen or a corporation.

It must be admitted that under the existing laws a trade union has a more unhampered course if it does not incorporate at all. It is then free to choose any legitimate line of activity open to an individual, without coming in conflict with the provisions of a corporation law not adapted to the special needs of labor unions. There is a Federal law for the incorporation of labor unions, but it requires the headquarters to be located in Washington. This provision makes it inapplicable to any but the great national bodies. An organization such as the United Brotherhood of Cloakmakers,

[1] Testimony before the U. S. Industrial Commission. Reports, Vol. XIV, pp. 152–155.

which has branches in New York and New Jersey, with a membership of about 15,000, cannot incorporate under the Federal law.

The New York state law of corporations divides them into stock corporations and nonstock corporations, the latter being again divided into membership corporations and religious corporations. Prior to the latest revision of the corporation laws, there existed a law for the organization of coöperative companies, that is, associations where the stockholders contribute not only their money but also and chiefly their labor. The name was retained by the revisers, but the law itself was repealed and no other law enacted to take its place. How is a labor organization to incorporate under these laws? If it incorporate as an ordinary membership corporation, it is no more than a mere social club. Its chief purpose, "coöperation for the purpose of obtaining an advance in the rate of wages," cannot be accomplished, for it would be beyond the powers of a social club and would fall within the definition of the objects of a business corporation. To incorporate as a business corporation is impracticable. It would impose upon the labor union the necessity of having a capital stock and of increasing it from time to time; no assessments could be levied for current expenses; no "stockholder" would forfeit his membership by nonpayment of dues; no member could be disciplined; stock could be sold by individual members to outsiders who do not belong to the trade, but may be interested in having a controlling voice in the councils of the organization. In other words, a labor union is in its very nature different from a business corporation.

In 1897, being elected counsel to the United Brotherhood of Cloakmakers, I was confronted with this problem of incorporation. In the absence of law on the subject we had to make law, and we accordingly incorporated as a "coöperative corporation," leaving it to future litigation to construe the powers of such a corporation. We had one case in the New York Supreme Court, where the defense of *ultra vires* was raised against us and we were sustained by the court. Yet the decision in this case can hardly be said to have established a precedent, since the opinion did not go into a full discussion of the aspects of a "coöperative corporation," nor was it passed upon by a higher court.

Next comes the question as to the methods of enforcing the labor contracts. It is a sad commentary on our law that a labor union has practically no other remedy than a strike against a violation of the labor contract by the employer.

A contract with an employer may be made by the union as contracting party, or by the individual workmen. The latter method has been practiced in the tailoring trades in New York City. Aside, however, from its unwieldiness, none but an utterly unintelligent employer, such as the average sweat-shop "boss," would enter into such a contract, for it would bind him to keep every workman who happened to be with him at the time the contract was made. Nor does it serve the ends of the union, since it leaves the employer free to hire additional help not belonging to the union. On the other hand, it places the individual member of the union in a position where he may override the decisions of the majority of the organized body, since under the technical form of the contract he is the party to the same and may modify its terms by agreement with the employer.

The only method that suggests itself is therefore a contract made by the union, as such, with the employer. But when the contract is taken into court the union can prove none but nominal damages. Suppose the employer has declared a reduction of, say, 10 per cent on the agreed rates before the expiration of the contractual term and has locked out the members of the union, who insisted upon union rates. The individual members who lost their positions have suffered damage, but the union is a corporation, and as such is distinct from its members. Being a coöperative corporation, it can make no profit on its contracts for itself, and consequently can sustain no damages through a violation of the contracts.

Of course legal ingenuity will suggest some device to so frame the labor contract as to bring it within the established rules of damages. But it means that the attainment of a perfectly legitimate end must be sought under disguise.

And, lastly, there is always open the defense of duress. Very often the agreement is reached in the course of, or in the apprehension of, a strike. Whenever the agreement is sued upon by the union it is met with the defense that the agreement had been obtained by threats to injure the defendant's business in case he would not agree to the terms of the union. That such threats, expressed or implied, are actually resorted to may be freely conceded. The question is, however, Is a threat to injure the defendant's business unlawful?

It goes without saying that a threat to commit violence against the person or property of an employer or any one else is within the purview of the penal statutes prohibiting threats, etc. But there are cases where one may inflict an injury upon another without becoming liable therefor, either civilly or criminally. If I build on my vacant lot adjoining my neighbor's house it will shut out the light from the same and its rental income will go down, — a fact familiar to every landlord in the upper part of Manhattan Island; yet I would not be liable in damages to my neighbor. And if I offer to sell to my neighbor that lot at my own figure, threatening that I shall otherwise erect a building on it and thus cause him a loss on the value of his property, I am not liable. Similarly, if a walking delegate threatens a manufacturer of ladies' garments that unless he accedes to the terms of the union a strike will be kept on in his factory until the end of the season, and he will lose his orders, which will go to his competitors, it is not against the law. Yet, at least in one case, I have had the experience that a defense alleging, in the vaguest possible terms, threats "to injure the defendant's business," without specifying any unlawful act, was sustained by Judge Truax, of the New York Supreme Court, as a sufficient defense (on a demurrer). The case is probably not an exception.

In general, it cannot be said that the right of workmen to refuse by concerted action to work for an employer, if the terms do not suit them, has received unqualified recognition. The common law regards every strike as a conspiracy. The New York statute exempts from this inhibition a strike for the purpose of obtaining an advance in wages or for opposing a reduction of wages. But as this statute creates an exception from the common law, it will under the familiar rule be construed strictly; anything not expressly contained in it is still governed by common-law principles. Now, a strike is not always the result of differences as to the rate of wages, and contracts are often made by peaceable agreement, without resort to a strike, for other purposes as important to the union as an advance in the rate of wages.

One of the fundamental demands persisted in by every union and strenuously opposed by employers is what is called the "recognition of the union." The demand is usually regarded by the employers as an encroachment upon what is technically known as "the freedom of labor." As a matter of fact, however, it is identical with similar restrictions inserted in every contract, whereby one party agrees to deliver goods or render services to another. If a railway company bids for transportation of troops at so much per soldier, it is quite natural for it to stipulate that it shall have the exclusive privilege of transportation between the particular points contemplated in the contract. If a labor organization makes a contract of employment, it must insist upon a similar provision, lest its contract should become inoperative. Indeed, the demand of an employer for help is elastic, subject to expansion and contraction. He has the privilege of laying off as many hands as may at any time be superfluous to him. If he should reserve the further privilege of subsequently replacing them by outsiders who are not bound by the terms of the union contract, it would enable him practically to rescind the contract with the union without openly saying so.

No less important is the injury to the discipline of the organized body, which must inevitably result from suffering a number of outsiders, not subject to the jurisdiction of that body, to work side by side with the members of the union. A union of workmen will avail itself primarily of the same remedies to enforce the terms of its hiring as will a single hired man. In case of a breach of contract on the part of the employer, the individual employee may quit; if he is reasonably certain that he is wanted by his employer, he may thus succeed in obtaining redress. But under similar circumstances, when one half of the force of a factory do not belong to the union, what will it avail the other half to quit, if the outsiders remain at work? Whoever has had any experience on the labor side of this matter is forced to the conclusion that a union can sooner concede a reduction in the rate of wages than waive this fundamental demand. Now, what is the attitude of the law on this subject?

The appellate division of the New York Supreme Court has lately made a new departure (in the case of *Davis* v. *United Portable Hoisting Engineers*, decided in 1898) by adopting the view of the British House of Lords, which has unqualifiedly recognized the right of a labor union to refuse to work with nonunion men and to demand the discharge of nonunion men where union members are employed. This view is at variance with New York precedents — for example, the case of *Curran* v. *Galen* — decided by the Court of Appeals as late as 1891, where a similar demand by a labor union was held to be an unlawful interference with the right of every citizen to work at whatever terms he chooses.[1]

From all this it may be seen that the law has not kept pace with the industrial growth of this country. The old common-law hostility to "combinations in restraint of trade" has blocked the way of combinations of capital as well as of combinations of labor. Both have developed, however, although denied the opportunity to invoke

[1] See cases cited by Cooke above, p. 146. Also, in the following chapter, p. 183.

the assistance of the law. It cannot be gainsaid that this is an anomalous condition. These legal relics of a past age handicap labor more than capital.

My brief acquaintance with both employers and employees in the New York tailoring trade convinces me that this condition exercises a demoralizing influence upon both employers and employees. Manufacturers make contracts with labor unions as a mere matter of form. I could name many a cloak manufacturer who told me, while affixing his signature to the contract, that he did not think it was worth the paper it was written on and that it could not be enforced. I know of many prominent cloak manufacturers who violated their agreements no sooner than they were made; some of them confessed it to me confidentially. On the other hand, the union, knowing that its agreements must yet be tested in court before their validity may be established, is sometimes impelled to make unreasonable demands upon the employers, such, for example, as the deposit of cash or promissory notes as security for the faithful performance of the agreement; and what is still more important, having little expectation of obtaining redress in court, the union quite naturally resorts to the strike, whenever practicable, as the only efficient method of settling its differences with the employer.

What is imperatively needed is that the law frankly recognize combinations of labor for the object of fixing the terms of the joint contract of employment. The law ought to recognize the peculiar nature of the trade union as distinct from an ordinary business corporation. There ought to be a law permitting the incorporation of associations of workmen in such a manner as to give efficiency to their contracts with employers of labor. The law should expressly recognize the identity of interest between the association and its members; it should be so framed that a breach of a joint contract of employment would give the union a right of action for the damages sustained by its members through resulting loss of wages or employment. The scope of this enabling act must be sufficiently broad to include all legitimate objects for which agreements are to-day made between labor unions and employers.

This would virtually introduce arbitration by the courts in labor disputes, thus to some extent superseding the strike by ordinary methods of settling disputes in organized society.

It is one of the first steps to be taken if it is desired to create a *modus vivendi* between capital and labor instead of the present state of warfare.

A. F. Weber, Chief Statistician, Department of Labor, Albany, New York:

The compulsory incorporation of trade unions does not seem advisable to me at the present time. The principal argument in favor of that policy is the impossibility of holding unincorporated unions to their contracts. No one familiar with industrial operations is disposed to deny that local unions have been wont to keep or break agreements at their own convenience. But the remedy for this lack of control may be found in the organization of employers, without resorting to experimental legislation which might introduce greater evils than the existing ones. The contracts so frequently broken by unions are almost always contracts with individual employers. Just as rapidly as the employers have come together for concerted action and replaced these individual agreements with one general agreement between the association of employers and the union of workingmen, they have been able to hold the unions strictly to the terms of their agreement. It is in this way that the mason builders in New York and Boston have for some fifteen years preserved industrial peace with the journeyman bricklayers and masons. In those cities the single annual agreement entered into by representatives of the two bodies of employers and employees has been kept inviolate, while in cities where agreements have been signed by individual employers there have been frequent strikes, lockouts, and violations of contract.

The experience in the coal-mining industry has been the same. In the anthracite district agreements, so far as they have been entered into at all, have been signed by individual operators and have not proved satisfactory to either side. But in Illinois and other central states the agreement is between an employers' association and the International Union of miners. All the testimony available goes to show that during the five years' duration of this arrangement industrial relations have been more stable and satisfactory in every way than they ever were before 1898, or than they are at the present time in regions where such an arrangement is wanting. Considering the fact that a large proportion of the workmen in the mining industry are unskilled and uneducated, this experience seems to afford a complete answer to the affirmation that responsibility can be secured among such workingmen only through the incorporation of their unions. Other tests of loyalty to the joint agreement are familiar, — such as that of the longshoremen's union, when the international president sent nonunion men to work in the place of members who had gone on strike contrary to the agreement, — while the history of railroad transportation in this country shows that contracts would not be treated with greater respect by incorporated unions of engineers or conductors than they are now by the unincorporated organizations.

On the other hand, compulsory incorporation might discourage the movement toward organization, which we all recognize as the basis of the economic independence of wage workers. Such would be the effect if that policy promoted litigation, which it would probably do; for it would be difficult to frame a law that would make the union responsible for the acts of its officers or committees and not hold it responsible for unauthorized acts of its individual members. In the affairs of the ordinary business corporation the unauthorized acts of an individual stockholder cannot embarrass the corporation because all power is lodged in the hands of the directors. But authority in a trade union cannot be so readily concentrated in a board of directors, since an agreement with employers necessarily calls for the coöperation of every individual member; and if the courts should entertain suits against the union for unauthorized acts of individual members, the field for intrigues between designing employers and avaricious members would be very large. The unions might find it impossible to maintain any funds whatsoever, and that would of course spell the death of unionism and collective bargaining.

Any such movement to injure or destroy trade unionism would be disastrous to the best interests of the people, because collective bargaining through the organization of labor is an indisputable necessity in modern industry. If a frank, open policy of organization is prevented or seriously embarrassed by legal restrictions, there will probably come into existence secret and unlawful combinations such as agitated England before the repeal of the combination laws. And if the trade unions' educational work among the emigrants — an educational work that ranks second only to the work of the public schools in American life — should be stopped or seriously hampered, we should soon witness a revolution in our politics only dimly foreshadowed in the socialism engendered by the recent coal strike. The effect of the Taff Vale decision in England has been a markedly increased participation in politics by the organized workers as a class.

VII

DECISIONS OF COURTS IN LABOR DISPUTES

I. Injunctions and Trial by Jury[1]

The following extracts from decisions of courts illustrate the use of the injunction under various circumstances in labor disputes, and certain conflicting decisions in different jurisdictions. It is not intended to give leading cases on the technical points so much as to illustrate the industrial facts involved. While the decisions generally sustain the increased use of writs of injunction, it is well to call attention to their significance by way of protests which legal writers have felt called upon to make. F. J. Stimson, in writing of "The Modern Use of Injunctions," says:[2]

We have seen, in private law suits between individuals or corporations, courts of equity — civil, not criminal courts — invoked to restrain, not alone parties to the suits, but anybody, the whole world, with or without actual notice of a court order or injunction, not merely from interfering with property which is the subject of the suits, but also from committing, or conspiring to commit, or aiding or advising others to commit, acts which are criminal; and

[1] See also C. C. Allen, "Injunction and Organized Labor," Reports American Bar Association, Vol. XVII, p. 299 (1894); same, *American Law Review*, Vol. XXVIII, p. 828; Charles Noble Gregory, "Government by Injunction," *Harvard Law Review*, Vol. XI, p. 487 (1898); Wm. Draper Lewis, "A Protest against administering Criminal Law by Injunction," *American Law Register*, Vol. XXXIII, p. 879 (1894); Ben. S. Dean, "Government by Injunction," *Green Bag*, Vol. IX, p. 540; P. L. Edwards, "Labor Strikes and Injunctions," *Central Law Journal*, Vol. LIX, p. 23 (1904); Hearings, Judiciary Committee, House of Representatives, on Anti-Injunction Bill, January 13 to March 22, 1904, Government Printing Office; Stimson, "Handbook to the Labor Law of the United States," 1896; Report of the Massachusetts Commission on Employer and Employed, 1904; Groat, "Trade Unions and the Law in New York," Columbia University, 1905.

[2] *Political Science Quarterly*, Vol. X, p. 189 (1895).

sometimes only on the ground that they are criminal acts, criminal at common law or made so by the recent statutes known as the Anti-Trust Law and the Interstate Commerce Law. We have seen more: we have seen persons committing, or about to commit, or said to be about to commit, such acts, arrested by these civil courts, deprived of their liberty, and punished by imprisonment; and this, as in the Debs case and others, *after* the emergency which furnished the excuse for invoking the protective jurisdiction of the equity court had long gone by. And we have seen persons punished without the usual safeguards of liberty afforded by the criminal law — without indictment, without right to counsel, without being confronted with witnesses, without trial by jury — and sentenced without uniform statute, at the discretion of the judge.

Similarly Richard C. McMurtie[1] spoke of the

value of the rule that removes criminal jurisprudence from even the apparent caprice of the judiciary and compels the intervention of a public trial, with the witnesses and the accused brought face to face, a jury to determine the facts, the public discussion of the admissibility and effect of evidence, and a fixed standard of punishment, with a right to a review and to an appeal to the pardoning power. . . . The whole system of administering the criminal laws is changed in the one particular that we and our ancestors have thought essential to political freedom, and which the experience of the world proves there is no other sure support for that which is beyond all price — that is, assuring to the accused of any crime for which there can be fine and imprisonment imposed, a trial by jury, according to the course of the common law, that is, with the witnesses produced and examined in the presence of the accused and before the world. If these things are not deemed important, there is nothing more to be said.

Judge Caldwell, of the Federal Court, in a dissenting opinion in a case where the union was charged with boycotting,[2] said:

Courts of equity have no jurisdiction to enforce the criminal laws. . . . It is said by those who defend the assumption of this jurisdiction by the federal courts that it is a swifter and speedier mode of dealing with those who violate or threaten to violate the

[1] "Equity Jurisdiction applied to Crimes and Misdemeanors," *American Law Register*, Vol. XXXI (N.S.), pp. 2, 14 (1892).

[2] *Hopkins* v. *Oxley Stave Company*, 83 Fed. at p. 924 (1897).

laws than by the prescribed and customary method of proceeding in courts of law: that it is a "short cut" to the accomplishment of the desired object; that it avoids the uncertainty and delay incident to a jury trial, occasions less expense, and insures a speedier punishment. All this may be conceded to be true. But the logical difficulty with this reasoning is that it confers jurisdiction on the mob equally with the chancellor. . . . It can make little difference to the victims of short-cut and unconstitutional methods whether it is the mob or the chancellor that deprives them of their constitutional rights. It is vain to disguise the fact that this desire for a short cut originates in the feeling of hostility to trial by jury, — a mode of trial that has never been popular with the aristocracy of wealth or the corporations and trusts. . . . No reasoning and no precedents can avail to deprive the citizen accused of crime of his right to a jury trial guaranteed to him by the provisions of the constitution "except in cases arising in the land and naval forces, or in the militia when in actual service in time of war or of public danger." . . . With the interpolations essential to support government by injunction, the constitution would contain the following further exceptions to the right of trial by jury: "And except when many persons are associated together for a common purpose, and except in the case of members of trade unions and other labor organizations, and except in all cases of persons 'of small means.'"

Stimson also holds that the courts by the use of this writ may encroach on the executive branch of government:[1]

It makes the courts no longer judicial, but a part (and it bids fair to be a most important part) of the executive branch of government. More briefly and picturesquely: the federal courts may thus grow into mere star-chambers and run the country.

Wm. H. Dunbar makes an analogous charge of encroachment on the legislative branch of government, saying:[2]

Courts of equity, like courts of law, are established for the determination of controversies between individuals. The power to issue preliminary injunctions is incidental to the power of determining such controversies. The right to lay down general rules for the

[1] *Loc. cit.*, p. 193.

[2] "Government by Injunction," *Law Quarterly Review*, Vol. XIII, p. 362; reprinted in *Economic Studies*, Vol. III, pp. 1–43.

government of the community, to declare *ex cathedra* in advance of any contentious proceedings in which the question arises what may and what may not lawfully be done, to impose on the whole community a duty to refrain from doing a certain act, is in its nature a legislative right. . . .

The power of courts to punish by summary proceedings for contempt all persons who obstruct the administration of justice or disobey the lawful orders of the court has often been described as the most unrestrained power exercised in our system of government. Such matters are tried by the court itself and without any right of appeal for error of fact or law. This power is absolutely essential to the efficient administration of justice. It behooves the judiciary, therefore, not only to exercise it with discretion, but to avoid extensions of jurisdiction which may lead to the necessity of exercising this power in matters properly cognizable by the courts of criminal law and by a jury. A community in which the jury system is still preserved and guarded as a bulwark of liberty will not tolerate encroachments on the part of the courts of equity by which, in those very cases in which a large part of the community is most disposed to rely upon the jury as a check upon the supposed partiality of the courts, the process of punishment by contempt is made to take the place of trial by jury. The machinery essential to the ordinary work of the courts is in danger of being ruined by its use in such extraordinary emergencies. It is strangely inconsistent with established principles that courts of equity should take jurisdiction in order to prevent the ultimate issues being tried by jury; that they should grant injunctions which appear at least to be designed primarily as a means of drawing to the court power to punish by proceedings for contempt acts which should have been prevented by the executive authorities and should be punished by the criminal law. A preliminary injunction granted not as an incident to a controversy between individuals, not seeking to restrain a defendant until the rights between him and the plaintiff can be ascertained, not acting upon known persons to prevent them from doing certain acts, but seeking to throw the *aegis* of the court over certain property so as to protect it from all persons whatsoever is of itself an anomaly in juristic procedure. When such an injunction is granted under circumstances which preclude its enforcement, except by assuming the duty lodged with the executive of preserving public order, and apparently largely for the purpose of assuming that duty, it presents a serious menace to the very framework of government.

A similar warning is uttered by Joel H. Benton, Jr., in the annual address before the Grafton and Coös Bar Association, in 1898. He said:[1]

It means that the courts have, in the judgment of many of the most intelligent and thoughtful citizens and of Congress, exceeded their just powers; that they have by the so-called exercise of equity powers practically assumed to create and to punish offenses upon trial by themselves without a jury and with penalties imposed at their discretion. And this means that, if the courts continue in this course, their power to enforce their orders by proceedings for contempt will be limited by legislation. The people will not, and they ought not, to submit to decisions like those in the Northern Pacific and Ann Arbor cases. The result will be to deprive the courts of the power to enforce orders where they ought to have power to enforce, and the mischief that will come can hardly be estimated. The remedy is not by legislation. The subject is not one for partisan debate, and should not enter into politics in any degree whatever. Thoughtful, intelligent, conservative discussion by the profession will remedy the evil, and to that discussion all members of the bar who have the good of the republic at heart ought to bring their best effort.

The question of trial by jury, raised by members of the bar, has been decided by the Supreme Court of the United States in the case of Debs.[2] The opinion says:

. . . It is objected that it is outside of the jurisdiction of a court of equity to enjoin the commission of crimes. This, as a general proposition, is unquestionable. A chancellor has no criminal jurisdiction. Something more than the threatened commission of an offense against the laws of the land is necessary to call into exercise the injunctive powers of the court. There must be some interferences, actual or threatened, with property or rights of a pecuniary nature; but when such interferences appear, the jurisdiction of a court of equity arises, and is not destroyed by the fact that they are accompanied by or are themselves violations of the criminal law. . . . The law is full of instances in which the same act may give rise to a civil action and a criminal prosecution. An assault

[1] "What is Government by Injunction? Does it exist in the United States?" Concord, N.H., 1898.

[2] *In re Debs*, 158 U. S., at p. 593 (1895).

with intent to kill may be punished criminally, under an indictment therefor, or will support a civil action for damages; and the same is true of all other offenses which cause injury to person or property. In such cases the jurisdiction of the civil court is invoked not to enforce the criminal law and punish the wrongdoer, but to compensate the injured party for the damages which he or his property has suffered; and it is no defense to the civil action that the same act by the defendant exposes him also to indictment and punishment in a court of criminal jurisdiction. So here the acts of the defendants may or may not have been violations of the criminal law. If they were, that matter is for inquiry in other proceedings. The complaint made against them in this is of disobedience to an order of a civil court, made for the protection of property and the security of rights. If any criminal prosecution be brought against them for the criminal offenses alleged in the bill of complaint, — of derailing and wrecking engines and trains, assaulting and disabling employees of the railroad companies, it will be no defense to such prosecution that they disobeyed the orders of injunction served upon them and have been punished for disobedience.

Nor is there in this any invasion of the constitutional right of trial by jury. We fully agree with counsel that "it matters not what form the attempt to deny constitutional right may take; it is vain and ineffectual, and must be so declared by the courts." And we reaffirm the declaration made for the court by Justice Bradley in *Boyd* v. *U. S.*, 116 U. S. 616, 635, that "it is the duty of courts to be watchful for the constitutional rights of the citizen, and against any stealthy encroachments thereon. Their motto should be *obsta principiis.*" But the power of a court to make an order carries with it the equal power to punish for a disobedience of that order, and the inquiry as to the question of disobedience has been from time immemorial the special function of the court. And this is no technical rule. In order that a court may compel obedience to its orders, it must have the right to inquire whether there has been any disobedience thereof. To submit the question of disobedience to another tribunal, be it a jury or another court, could operate to deprive the proceeding of half its efficiency. In the case of *Yates*, 4 Johns. 314, 369, Chancellor Kent, then chief justice of the Supreme Court of the state of New York, said: "In the case of *Earl of Shaftsbury*, 2 St. Trials, 615, S. C. 1 Mod. 144, who was imprisoned by the House of Lords for 'high contempts committed against it,' and brought into the King's Bench, the court held that they had no authority to judge of the contempt, and remanded the prisoner. The court in that case seem to have laid down a principle from which they never have departed, and which is essential to the due administration of justice. This principle that every court, at least of the superior kind, in which great confidence is placed must be the sole judge in the last resort of contempts arising therein, is more explicitly defined and more emphatically enforced in the two subsequent cases of *The Queen* v. *Paty* and of *The King* v. *Crosby*." And again, on page 371, "Justice Blackstone pursued the same train of observation, and declared that all courts, by which he meant to include the two houses of Parliament and the courts of Westminster Hall, could have no control in matters of contempt; that the sole adjudication of contempts and the punishments thereof belonged exclusively, and without interfering, to each respective court." In *Watson* v. *Williams*, 36 Miss. 331, 341, it was said: "The power to fine and imprison for contempt, from the earliest history of jurisprudence, has been regarded as a necessary incident and attribute of a court, without which it could no more exist than without a judge. It is a power inherent in all courts of record, and coexisting with them by the wise provisions of the common law. A court without the power effectually to protect itself against the assaults of the lawless, or to enforce its orders, judgments, or decrees against the recusant parties before it, would be a disgrace to the legislation, and a stigma upon the age which invented it."

The so-called "blanket" or "omnibus" injunction to which reference has been made has also been upheld by the Supreme Court in the following words:[1]

The facts that the petitioner was not a party to such suit, nor served with process of subpoena, nor had notice of the application made by the complainant for the mandatory injunction, nor was served by the officers of the court with such injunction, are immaterial, so long as it was made to appear that he had notice of the issuing of an injunction by the court. To render a person amenable to an injunction it is neither necessary that he should have been a party to the suit in which the injunction was issued, nor to have been actually served with a copy of it, so long as he appears to have had actual notice.

[1] *In re Lennon*, 166 U. S. 554.

The following cases further illustrate the circumstances and furnish the grounds on which the courts base their use of the writ of injunction.[1]

II. Picketing

In the case of the *Union Pacific Railway Company* v. *Ruef*, 120 Fed. 102 (1903), Judge McPherson, of the United States Circuit Court said:

. . . I believe, and that without a doubt, that in so far as propositions are involved in this case, the law is as follows:

1. The defendants acted within their right when they went out on strike. Whether with good cause or without any cause or reason, they had the right to quit work for the Union Pacific Railroad Company, and their reasons for quitting were reasons which they need not give to any one. And that they all went out in a body, by agreement or preconcerted arrangement, does not militate against them or affect this case in any way.

2. Such rights are reciprocal, and the company had the right to discharge any or all of the defendants, with or without cause, and it cannot be inquired into as to what the cause was.

3. It is immaterial whether the defendants are not now in the service of the company because of a strike or a lockout.

4. The defendants have the right to combine and work together in whatsoever way they believe will increase their earnings, shorten their hours, lessen their labor, or better their condition, and it is for them, and them only, to say whether they will work by the day or by piece work. All such is part of their liberty. And they can so conclude as individuals, or as organizations, or as unions.

5. And the right is also reciprocal. The railroad company has the right to have its work done by the premium or piece system, without molestation or interference by defendants or others. This is liberty for the company, and the company alone has the right to determine as to that matter.

6. When the defendants went on a strike, or when put out on a lockout, their relations with the company were at an end; they were no longer employees of the company; and the places they once occupied in the shops were no longer their places, and never can be again, excepting by mutual agreement between the defendants and the company.

[1] See also Bulletins of the U. S. Bureau of Labor, containing Decisions of Courts.

7. No one of the defendants can be compelled by any law, or by any order of any court, to again work for the company on any terms or under any conditions.

8. The company cannot be compelled to employ again any of the defendants, or any other person, by any law, or by any order of any court, on any terms, or under any conditions.

9. Each, all, and every of the foregoing matters between the company and the defendants are precisely the same, whether applied to the company or to the defendants.

10. The company has the right to employ others to take the places once filled by defendants; and in employing others the defendants are not to be consulted, and it is of no lawful concern to them, and they can make no lawful complaint by reason thereof. And it makes no difference whether such new employees are citizens of Omaha or of some other city or state. A citizen of Chicago, or from any state in the Union, has the same rights as to work in Omaha as has a citizen of Omaha.

11. Defendants have the right to argue or discuss with the new employees the question whether the new employees should work for the company. They have the right to persuade them if they can. But in presenting the matter they have no right to use force or violence. They have no right to terrorize or intimidate the new employees. The new employees have the right to come and go as they please, without fear or molestation, and without being compelled to discuss this or any other question, and without being guarded or picketed; and persistent and continued and objectionable persuasion by numbers is of itself intimidating, and not allowable.

12. Picketing in proximity to the shops or elsewhere on the streets of the city, if in fact it annoys or intimidates the new employees, is not allowable. The streets are for public use, and the new employee has the same right, neither more nor less, to go back and forth, freely and without molestation, and without being harassed by so-called arguments, and without being picketed, as has a defendant or other person. In short, the rights of all parties are one and the same.

It remains to examine the evidence, and ascertain whether any of the foregoing matters and things and rights have been trampled upon by the defendants, and, if so, by whom, and who are responsible.

The complainant, with its thousands of miles of railroad, has shops at various places, and a large one at Omaha, where much work is done on its cars, engines, and other appliances. Most of the defendants were employees in the Omaha shops. About May 12, 1902, certain shopmen, through committees, presented to the company what they claimed were grievances. Conferences were held, but without result. . . . Notices were given and posted by the company that the outgoing employees must return at once to their work. They did not return, but from that time on they all continued on the strike, and the strike is still on. The company employed many new men for the shops, some of them citizens of Omaha and some from other states, to take the places once occupied by the strikers. The strikers have almost daily had meetings in a hall. A system of pickets from their own number was organized. These pickets were officered by captains and lieutenants to place the pickets and command them. These pickets were sometimes placed singly, but generally in squads. They were placed in close proximity to the shops, and more particularly at the gates leading to the shops. Sometimes they would be on the streets some blocks away from the gates, but at points where it was known the present employees must, or probably would, pass.

The officers of the pickets gave orders that the pickets must reason and argue with the new men and those refusing to go on the strike, and try to persuade them that they were fighting labor, and in working for the company they were in hostility to the interests of the laboring men, and that they ought to quit. The defendants' position is, as they admit in evidence, that, if they could take from the company all men from the shops, the engines would not be repaired and that the motive power would be destroyed. Such is their avowed purpose. Then the company would either be compelled to cease carrying passengers, freights, and mail, or, if it continued in business, would be compelled to reëmploy the strikers on the terms named by the strikers.

The question of fact in this case is this: Have the methods to destroy the motive power of the company been by argument and persuasion and by peaceable methods? If so, the writ of injunction, under the law as evidenced by the authorities cited, should be denied. Or have the methods to destroy the motive power of the company been attended with assaults and violence and intimidations and terrorizing? It is undisputed that, so far as known at least, the orders of the lodges and by the officers were to use none but peaceful methods, by argument and persuasion. Directions were given that all pickets must not drink liquor, and to wholly refrain from all improper conduct, under penalties of discipline, including fines.

The evidence shows that many of the defendants are peaceable and orderly men, and that many of them in person have committed no assaults, nor have they been guilty of any acts of violence or intimidation. And many of the defendants named in the bill, in my judgment, should not be named in the permanent injunction to be issued herein, for the reason there is no evidence to warrant such holding against them. It is contended that the writ should issue, even though the evidence is meager or wholly lacking. And statements to that effect can be found in some of the cases of the Federal trial courts: "that the writ of injunction can do no harm to a law-abiding man, even though not warranted by the evidence." I do not so believe. I would resist such an application for two reasons: (1) I should not be mulcted in the costs. (2) I should not be humiliated by having an injunction run against me, when there is no evidence that I have done, or, so far as evidence shows, am not likely to do, any of the things complained of, and am not acquiescing, by silence or otherwise, in what my colaborers, or men in a class to which I belong, are doing. There must either be evidence against such parties, or the evidence must show that such parties belong to the class or to the organization of those to be enjoined.

Certain parties, to be mentioned in the decree, will be dismissed from the case. But they will be held to have knowledge of this opinion and of the decree herein. And those in any way related in a business way to the other defendants — those who are servants, agents, or employees of the defendants who are enjoined, and those who are fellows or companions of defendants who are strikers — are and will be bound by the writ of injunction issued herein, to the same extent and as fully as if named in the writ. (*In re Reese*, 47 C. C. A. 87, 107 Fed. 942; *Ex parte Lennon*, 166 U. S. 548, 17 Sup. Ct. 658, 41 L. Ed. 1110.) And any action by those dismissed from the case, as well as all others, in any way in conflict or in violation of the writ of injunction will subject themselves to the same penalties as though they were named in the writ of injunction. So that the order of injunction herein will not include by name those against whom there is no evidence, yet the writ will include, in effect, all those who quit the company's service and are engaged in the strike with the purpose of compelling the company to reëmploy them by attempting to impair the motive power of the company or otherwise cripple its service. In other words, the class of men will be controlled by the injunction, and the class of men above alluded to will not violate the writ, excepting at their peril.

Some of the defendants, as the evidence shows, have been guilty of most inexcusable offenses, and some of conduct the most outrageous and brutal, in carrying on the general design of destroying the motive power of the road by preventing its repair or replacement. In some instances those guilty of misconduct and intimidation and terrorizing and brutalities were not identified, and it cannot be said that all were done by the strikers, because part of it was done by sympathizers.

Details of a number of acts of violence, including the killing of an employee, were recited, and Judge McPherson then said:

No man who has read the 1186 pages of evidence which I have read can have the slightest doubt but that these assaults and these acts of violence and these threats and these blasphemous denunciations would not have occurred but for this picketing. Many of the defendants took no part in them, being honorable men. No doubt whatever is there in my mind but that a great many of the defendants deprecate it. But deprecation ought to be accompanied by words of denunciation. But both deprecation and denunciation ought to be accompanied by some affirmative acts to stop it or, at least, to cut loose from such men.

Picketing, as evidenced by the facts in this case, is wrong and cannot be countenanced by law-abiding men, and such picketing cannot but be condemned by any court. As said before, the rights and duties and obligations of employer and employee are reciprocal and the same in requiring fair treatment. And, if one unfairly treats the other, such other cannot retaliate by some other unlawful act. Suppose the company would arm all of its employees in the shops, and with the guards would go to assaulting and threatening and vilifying and intimidating the pickets; would any self-respecting man indorse it? Would we not then surely have a reign of terror in Omaha? Suppose the company would place pickets in front of the residences of the strikers and on the streets they pass, to and from their homes; would any one indorse it?

The defendants claim to have the belief that physical violence alone is to be condemned. But all persons know that intimidation by words, by menaces, by numbers, by position, and by many things is just as effective as by using clubs or brass knuckles or knives. Aggressive or daring employees would be deterred by none of the unlawful acts. But there are two classes of employees who are deterred. One class is the frail and the timid. And they are entitled to protection. Another class, comprising the greater part of men of this country — the law-abiding, peaceable men, those who do not engage in brawls and who never fight excepting when driven to the wall. They are entitled to the protection of the law, and the complainant has the right to have them protected.

This "picketing" has been condemned by every court having the matter under consideration. It is a pretense for "persuasion," but is intended for intimidation. Gentlemen never seek to compel and force another to listen to the art of persuasion. To stop another on the street, get in his road, follow him from one side of the street to another, pursue him wherever he goes, stand in front of his residence, is not persuasion. Intimidation cannot be defined. Neither can fraud be defined. But every person knows whether his acts are fraudulent, and he knows whether his acts are intimidating. And the courts, when the facts are presented, adjudge accordingly.

Are all the foregoing facts, supplemented with the brutal murder, evidence of intimidation and terrorizing? If not, what can be? In some instances the employees were drunk and quarrelsome. But very few of the assaults were provoked or brought on by the employees. It is the system of picketing that did it, and it is unlawful, and must be enjoined.

The restraining order prohibits the strikers from "following" the employees to their homes or on the streets. It is contended that one man has the right to walk on the streets in the same direction another man is going. But that is not "following," as every one understands what "following" means. No striker can fail to understand what it means. But, to avoid criticism, the injunction will be so worded as to be understood by all. And the writ of permanent injunction will issue, and the unlawful picketing and the wrongful interference with the rights of others brought to an end.

A decree for complainant was entered as follows:

It is ordered, adjudged, and decreed that each and all of the respondents not dismissed as aforesaid, and any and all other persons associated with them in committing the acts and grievances complained of in said bill be, and they are hereby, ordered and commanded to desist and refrain from in any manner interfering with the free use and occupation by complainant of any and all of its property or premises of every kind and character; and from entering upon the grounds or premises of complainant for the purpose of interfering with, hindering, or obstructing its business; and from compelling or inducing, or attempting to compel or induce, by threats, intimidation, force, or violence, any of the employees of complainant to refuse or fail to perform their duties as such employees; and from compelling or inducing, or attempting to compel or induce, by threats, intimidation, force, or violence, any of the employees of complainant to leave the service of complainant; and from preventing, or attempting to prevent, any person or persons, by threats, intimidation, force, or violence, from entering the service of complainant; or from preventing, by violence or in any manner of intimidation, any person or persons from going to or upon the premises of complainant for any lawful purpose whatever, or from aiding, assisting, or abetting any person or persons to commit any or either of the acts aforesaid; and the said respondents, each and all of them, are forbidden and restrained from congregating at or near the premises of complainant for the purpose of intimidating its employees or coercing said employees, or preventing them from rendering their service to said complainant; and from inducing, by intimidation, coercion, or threats, any employee to leave the employment of said complainant, or from attacking, assaulting, threatening, or by use of abusive language, or in any manner of intimidation, at any place within the city of Omaha, attempting to prevent any of the employees of complainant from continuing in its service, or any person or persons from engaging in the service of complainant; and each and all of them are enjoined and restrained from going, either singly or collectively, to the homes of complainant's employees, or any of them, for the purpose of intimidating or coercing any or all of them to leave the employment of complainant, or from entering complainant's employ, and as well from intimidating or threatening in any manner the wives and families of said employees for the purpose of preventing any employee from remaining in the service of complainant.

It is impossible, as well as impracticable, for the court in advance to specify all the acts and things which shall or may constitute intimidation or coercion. This must be left to the wisdom and intelligence of respondents. Any violation of the order will, however, be done at the party's peril.

III. Boycott — Irreparable Damage[1]

This case arose on the complaint of Mr. Barr, proprietor of the Newark *Times*, against eighteen labor unions affiliated in the Essex Trades Council. The Typographical Union, which was a member of the council, had withdrawn its members from the office of the Newark *Times* on account of the use of imported "plate matter" by the proprietor in contravention of a rule of the union requiring type to be set in the office. The Essex Trades Council took up the dispute and issued a circular, entitled "The Union Buyer; Official Bulletin of United Fair Custom of Newark and Vicinity." It contained the following announcement:

Our Mission. To support the supporters and boycott the boycotters of organized fair labor; to promote its public welfare by the diffusion of common sense, urging all to carry these in trade only to those who will return them to the people in the shape of living wages.

The grievance against the *Times* was stated as follows: "Workingmen and advertisers, remember that plate matter means 45 cents a day, and understand why the Newark *Times* is an unfair office." The court said:

It thus clearly appears that an injury to the complainant's business in circulation and advertising, resulting from the acts of the defendants, comprising a large number of persons and associations acting in concert, has not only been inflicted but threatens to be continued. Is this illegal on the part of the defendants? Not in the sense of being criminal and punishable as such; for, in my judgment, the case does not, as seems to be assumed by some in similar cases, require an expression of opinion on that point for two reasons: First. The jurisdiction of the criminal and civil remedies for acts the result of a conspiracy spring from different sources; for while the statute in the former now requires an overt act, at common law the act of conspiring constituted the crime. On the other hand, the injury done intentionally, and without legal excuse,

[1] New Jersey, Court of Chancery, *Barr et al.* v. *Essex Trades Council et al.*, 53 N. J. Eq. Reports, 101 (1894).

or maliciously, is the gist of the civil remedy. Second. And, as a consequence, while it is a short, proper, and effective way to dispose of a claim of defendants that their act was in the exercise of a legal right, to show that it was criminal, the jurisdiction of this court to interfere by injunction cannot be based on any such conclusion, but must arise from conditions which involve well-established grounds of equity jurisdiction. When, therefore, the question is here asked if causing injury to the complainant's business is illegal, it is meant, Is it an actionable wrong? That is, Has the complainant a remedy by civil action against the defendants therefor, or are the defendants privileged to do the acts charged in the manner and under the circumstances complained of, even though the natural result thereof be an injury to complainant's business? On the solution of this question depends the claim of the defendants that they have acted within their legal rights. . . . Are the defendants, then, privileged knowingly to inflict this injury on the complainants? A man's business is property. By the first section of the bill of rights of the constitution of New Jersey, the right of acquiring, possessing, and protecting property is classed as a natural and inalienable right which all men have, with those of enjoying and defending life and liberty, and of pursuing and obtaining safety and happiness.

. . . This freedom of business action lies at the foundation of all commercial and industrial enterprise. Men are willing to embark capital, time, and experience therein, because they can confidently assume that they will be able to control their affairs according to their own ideas, when the same are not in conflict with law. If this privilege is denied them, if the courts cannot protect them from interference by those who are not interested with them, if the management of business is to be taken from the owner and assumed by (it may be) irresponsible strangers, then we will have to come to the time when capital will seek other than industrial channels for investments, when enterprise and development will be crippled, when interstate railroads, canals, and means of transportation will become dependent on the paternalism of the national government, and the factory and the workshop subject to the uncertain chances of coöperative systems.

The bare declaration by the Typographical Union that it no longer recognized the Newark *Times* was, according to Mr. Beckmeyer's affidavit, sufficient under this perfect organization to render it incumbent upon every member of these different unions to withhold his patronage from it. Not only this, but by the passage of the resolutions mentioned by the different unions and the distribution thereof among advertisers, a moral intimidation was brought to bear upon the latter to further cripple the paper, either by wholly withdrawing their advertisements or by leaving spaces, a most effective method of calling attention to the fact that the paper was under the ban of organized labor. Why this action? It must have had a purpose. None of the different labor organizations, or the members thereof, except the Typographical Union No. 103, had or has any grievance against the complainant. Their action, in the language of the times, was purely sympathetic. As to the Typographical Union, its members had no complaint against Mr. Barr, except that he used certain appliances which were not acceptable to the union. He paid the wages fixed by, and employed only members of, the union. The withdrawal of certain of the members from his employment was solely because he chose to use plate matter interdicted by the union, and it is plain if the complainant would forego his own judgment in the management of his business in this regard and comply with the wishes and determination of the Typographical Union with reference thereto, all matters being as they were, the whole difficulty would be at an end. To effect this purpose, therefore, the Typographical Union, through the Trades Council, enlisted the coöperation of the other organizations in an attempt to so impair the success of the newspaper that the complainant would be forced to accept the alternative proposed rather than sustain the loss.

We return to the question whether defendants' acts are actionable. Malicious injury to the business of another has long been held to give a right of action to the injured party.

. . . The right of action depends, then, not so much upon the nature of the act as upon the intent with which it is done, always assuming that injury has attended the doing of it. . . .

This renders necessary an inquiry as to the intent of the defendants, to ascertain if the case falls within the class in which it is held that a malicious motive in the defendant may make an act which would not be wrongful without the malice a wrongful act when done with malice (*Steamship Company* v. *McGregor*, 23 Q. B. Div. 598–608). From the authorities, the test is, Has the injury been inflicted intentionally and without legal excuse? When we speak, in this connection, of an act done with a malicious motive, it does not necessarily imply that the defendants were actuated in their proceedings by spite or malice against the complainant, Mr. Barr, in the sense that their motive was to injure him personally, but that they desired to injure him in his business, in order to force him not to do what he had a perfect right to do. In this case the defendants have, I doubt not, no personal spite against Mr. Barr individually and no desire to do him a personal injury. Nor do I suppose they wish to permanently injure his enterprise, for they undoubtedly want reëmployment for those who left him. They only wish, by crippling his business, to compel him to accede to their views as to materials he shall use in the make-up of his paper. They in fact claim that they had no intention to injure the business of the complainant, and that their only desire was for the protection of themselves. If the injury which has been sustained or which is threatened is not only the natural but the inevitable consequence of the defendants' acts, it is without effect for them to disclaim the intention to injure. What other result than injury could ensue to the business of the Newark *Times*, published and circulated in Newark and its vicinity, if organizations of individuals representing there a purchasing power of $400,000 a week, each and every one not only determined not only not to patronize the paper or to buy it, but by resolutions passed in their various organizations call upon the trading community to cease advertising in it, with implied threats that the appearance of an advertisement by a tradesman in the paper would be a warning to the members of the organization to avoid trading with such persons? Loss of business is the only natural result to be expected from such a condition of affairs, and, if continued, the failure of the enterprise would seem to be inevitable. . . .

The next inquiry is, Have the defendants a legal excuse for doing the acts which have occasioned and threaten further damage to the complainant's business? It is claimed that the term "boycott," as used in the circular and publications, has not the offensive signification sought to be placed upon it by the complainant's bill; "that it does not in any way mean, indicate, or imply any threats, violence, intimidation, or coercive action on the part of the said defendants, or any or either of them, or the members of any such organization; that such word has a technical meaning in the said labor organizations, and simply expresses and implies that the members of the said organizations should simply refrain from trading or dealing with those persons who oppose such organizations by their own actions and doings; that the use of the word is not intended, and does not, in fact, encourage, advise, or urge in any manner, whether violent or otherwise, attacks upon or against the said newspaper, or any person or business, but merely advises and encourages those who have earned their money by giving their services and labor to spend such money among those who are friendly to fair trade and fair dealings and are in sympathy with the efforts of organized labor to advance its own interests and welfare by peaceable, proper, and lawful means, and not otherwise"; and further, "that of his own knowledge, obtained from long intercourse and association with the various labor organizations, there is nothing in the use of the word 'boycott' calculated or intended to intimidate or incite violence, or induce to coercive measures, or indicate any threat, and that its meaning is universally understood in the said organizations to have no other or greater effect than above stated," — from which it is to be gathered that the use of the word "boycott" in the publications, as applied to the *Times*, would be regarded by the members of the various unions to mean only that they should refrain from trading or dealing with the complainant and with those who oppose the organizations in their actions and doings with reference to the complainant. I do not see that this changes the character of the injury, but even if it does so far as the members of the organizations are concerned, the difficulty is that these communications were addressed to the public and indiscriminately circulated. They were intended not only for members of the order by whom a technical signification would be given to the word "boycott," but for the general public, who would read them and give the word its accepted meaning. . . . All the organizations represented in the trades council, and the individual members thereof, in strict conformity with the purpose and object for which the said council was organized, withheld this patronage from the said newspaper on the mere announcement by the Typographical Union to the trades council that that union had withdrawn its indorsement from the *Times*. Why? It is said that it was only the exercise by each member of his right to spend his money as his own will dictated. The fallacy of this is apparent. It loses sight of the combination, the whole strength of which lies in the fact that each individual has surrendered his own discretion and will to the direction of the accredited representatives of all the organizations. He no longer uses his own judgment, but by entering into the combination agrees to be bound by its decree. . . . It is common knowledge, if, indeed, it does not amply so appear by the papers in this case, that a member of a labor organization who does not submit to the edict of his union asserts his independence of judgment and action at the risk, if not the absolute sacrifice, of all association with his fellow-members. They will not eat, drink, live, or work in his company. Branded by the peculiarly offensive epithets adopted, he must exist ostracized, socially and industrially, so far as his former associates are concerned. Freedom of will under such circumstances cannot be expected.

Next, as to the advertising public. Tradesmen advertise in newspapers for the sole purpose of drawing customers to their stores. An authoritative announcement, not from one but from many sources, that the body of organized labor in the city or county, representing a purchasing power of $400,000 a week, would cease to deal with those whose advertisements appeared in the newspaper would have a much more deterrent effect than any threat of violence. To say that this is only advice or an intimation to the advertiser for his guidance, if he sees fit to accept it, is trifling with the language. Advice behind which lurks the threat of the withdrawal of such a volume of business could have no other effect than to intimidate and coerce, as it did in fact make several change their judgment, which had previously led them to advertise in the paper. The claim that this boycott was attempted to be enforced without intimidation or coercion will not bear the light of examination.

A legal excuse for the action of the defendants is next sought in the claim that the Essex Trades Council is a business institution, and that what it has done has been in prosecution of such business; seeking, I suppose, to bring the case within the rule of *Steamship Company* v. *McGregor*. That case proceeded on the doctrine of a lawful competition in business, both parties being engaged in carrying on the same character of business, and the acts complained of having been adopted for the advancement of the defendant's own trade, viz., carrying goods on a steamship line, although thereby damage to the other party necessarily ensued. I see no similarity in the business of these parties. That of the complainant is the publisher of a newspaper. Members of the Typographical Union and Stereotypers' and Pressmen's Union are skilled workmen, whose services might be employed in such business, but they are not carrying on any enterprise in competition with that of the complainant. So far as the other unions are concerned, the most, if not all of them, have no connection with such trade. Neither does the claim of the Essex Trades Council that it is a business institution stand on any firmer ground. The only element of business which it is engaged in would appear from the facts to be the furnishing to tradesmen of printed cards, certifying that they are proper persons for the members of trades unions to deal with, suitable to be displayed in conspicuous places in such tradesmen's places of business. This was supplemented by the issue under date of March 31, 1894, of the small pocket pamphlet, entitled "The Fair List of Newark, N.J.," containing the names and addresses of tradesmen and persons in business in Newark, with items of information and advice. Why this is called a "business" does not appear. It is not stated that any compensation is either required or received by the Trades Council from the tradespeople for granting or continuing these indorsements, but whether this is so or not, it is in no sense a competing business with the publication of a daily newspaper, and therefore does not come within the principle of the case referred to.

It appearing that injury to the business of the complainant has been knowingly, without legal excuse, and therefore in law maliciously, inflicted by the defendants, it was an actionable wrong, for which the complainant is entitled to his remedy; and that brings us to the question raised by the answer, and most strongly insisted upon by counsel in the argument, as to whether this court has jurisdiction to grant relief by way of injunction. Even when there is a legal remedy, equity will interfere by injunction to prevent (1) an injury which threatens irreparable damage, or (2) a continuing injury when the legal remedy therefor may involve a multiplicity of suits. This jurisdiction is established and unquestionable. In practice, the criterion of its application is the inadequacy of the legal remedy, depending on whether (1) "the injury done or threatened is of such a nature that, when accomplished, the property cannot be restored to its original condition or cannot be replaced by means of compensation in money"; (2) whether full compensation for the entire wrong can be obtained without resort to a number of suits. (3 Pom. Eq. Jur. §§ 1338, 1346, 1357.) The difficulty of satisfactorily estimating damages to business is frequently recognized in applying those principles to suits relating to good will, trade-marks, patent rights, and copyrights. The complainant's paper is published daily. While no one has a right to be hedged in and protected from competition in business, every one is entitled to a chance for the patronage of the public, uninfluenced by malicious interference to excite prejudice,— "a right to require that the course of trade should be kept free from unreasonable obstruction." Representations calculated to reduce the paper's circulation with the public or to influence by fear of loss of customers the number or extent of advertisements operate not once for all but, as it were, day by day, as the paper goes to and comes from the press, and each loss will be a distinctive cause of action. No more vulnerable object could be presented for the operation of a boycott than the advertising columns of a newspaper. They bear on their face the only information necessary as to the salient points of attack. To successfully appeal to a legal tribunal for redress for such injury as is here shown would involve either waiting until all the damage was done, or the bringing of innumerable suits successively, as the damage was ascertainable. While the combination of the defendants does not constitute complainant's right of action to recover redress for injury inflicted on his business, it has great bearing on the extent of the damage thereto which may be threatened by defendants' conduct. There would be no difficulty for complainant to successfully defend his enterprise from the attacks of one or more individuals. This is the common expectation of every one who embarks in any business. But when opposition through the agency of already established organizations, reaching in their locality every part of the county and in their membership almost every industry in prominent operation, comprising in the territory in which the paper must look for its support operatives of a purchasing power of $400,000 a week, is put on foot; when such an organization, not satisfied with its potential authority over its own members, appeals to the public to boycott the paper, to cease buying or advertising in it, with the significant suggestion that disregard of the appeal will bring upon such person the like opposition of the organizations, — who can estimate or approximate the natural damage short of ruin? The legal remedy in this case thus not only involves multiplicity of suits but the threatened damage seems irreparable. Authority is not wanting that a court of equity will enjoin a boycott. Being itself a proceeding of modern origin, of course no cases are to be found until recent years. [Cases cited.] The said order to show cause must be made absolute, with costs; and an injunction may issue against them, restraining them from distributing or circulating any circulars, printed resolutions, bulletins, or other publications containing appeals or threats against the Newark *Times* or the complainants, its publishers, with the design and tending to interfere with his business in publishing said paper, and from making any threats or using any intimidation to the dealers or advertisers in such newspaper tending to cause them to withdraw their business from such newspaper.

IV. Boycott — Free Speech[1]

The clothing company here named sought by injunction to prevent Watson and his associates from declaring or enforcing a boycott against it by inducing its customers and others who might become such not to deal with it to the injury of its business. A temporary injunction was granted, but on a hearing in the St. Louis Circuit Court this injunction was dissolved and the petition dismissed. The company then appealed to the Supreme Court, which affirmed the action of the court below.

Marx & Haas had had trouble with their clothing cutters for some years, resulting first in a boycott by the Knights of Labor in 1895, and again in 1898 in a boycott undertaken by a joint board of the Knights of Labor and the United Garment Workers of America, affiliated with the American Federation of Labor. In furtherance of this latter effort a circular reciting at some length the various difficulties and grievances was issued, and distributed freely among the patrons and possible patrons of the firm. This circular concluded:

We are positive we have proven to you the justice of our position, and we hope it will not be necessary to inform the labor and reform organizations with which we are affiliated who are in your locality, as we are satisfied we have convinced you that the stand we have taken in this case is a just one and will command the support of all fair-minded men. We therefore request you to write to Messrs. Marx & Haas and inform them that you would request them to settle the dispute with their employees, or otherwise you cannot afford to handle their goods as long as they are antagonizing organized labor, who are your friends and customers. By doing this you will aid us in getting simple justice from this more than unfair firm. Should this firm make a settlement with us, you will be informed of the fact under the seals of the joint organizations. Until such time we trust there will be no report made to our office that Marx & Haas have shipped you any more goods. Kindly inform us what action you take in this matter, and any further

[1] Missouri Supreme Court, *Marx & Haas Jeans Clothing Company* v. *Watson et al.*, 168 Mo. 133 (1901).

information you may desire will be cheerfully furnished by writing to headquarters of joint executive board, No. 911 Pine Street, St. Louis, Missouri.

In addition to the sending of this circular, committees visited various merchants in St. Louis and vicinity to present the matter more fully, and in some instances threats were made by members of these committees that the patronage of the boycotters and their friends would be withheld from certain merchants unless they discontinued their business dealings with the clothing company. In no instance, however, were there threats of resort to violence or unlawful intimidation.

The petition of the clothing company concluded with the request that

the defendants, their associates, confederates, agents, and representatives be enjoined and restrained by a temporary order of injunction, to be made final upon the hearing of this cause, from boycotting, or making effectual, promulgating, or in any wise proclaiming, any boycott upon or against the plaintiff or its goods, and from sending, conveying, or delivering in any way to any person, firm, corporation, or association any boycott notice, verbal or otherwise, referring to the plaintiff or its goods, and from in any way menacing, hindering, or obstructing the plaintiff from the fullest enjoyment of all the patronage, business, and custom which it may possess, enjoy, or acquire independent of the action of the said defendants or any of them.

Judge Sherwood announced the opinion of the court. After stating the above facts and reviewing the evidence given before the court below he disposed of the question of the jurisdiction of the Supreme Court in the case. Proceeding to the points in issue, he said:

Section 14 of our bill of rights declares that "no law shall be passed impairing the freedom of speech; that every person shall be free to say, write, or publish whatever he will on any subject, being responsible for all abuse of that liberty." The evident idea of that section is *penalty* or *punishment*, and *not prevention*. Because, if *prevention* exists, then no *opportunity* can possibly arise for one becoming responsible by saying, writing, or publishing "whatever he will on any subject." The two ideas — the one of absolute freedom "to say, write, or publish whatever he will on any subject," coupled with responsibility therefor, and the other idea of *preventing* any such free speech, free writing, or free publication — *cannot coexist.*

And just here it must be observed that the right of free speech, free writing, or free publication were not *created* by the constitution, which recognizes those rights as now existing and only seeks their protection and perpetuation. . . . Section 14, *supra,* makes no distinction and authorizes no difference to be made by courts or legislatures between a proceeding set on foot to enjoin the publication of a *libel* and one to enjoin the *publication of any other sort or nature, however injurious it may be,* or to prohibit the use of free speech or free writing on any subject whatever; because, wherever the authority of *injunction begins,* there the right of free speech, free writing, or free publication *ends.* No halfway house stands on the highway between *absolute prevention* and *absolute freedom.* The rights established by Section 14 can neither be impaired by the legislature, nor hampered nor denied by the courts.

Nor does it in any way change the complexion of this case by reason of its being alleged in the petition "that the defendants, and each of them, is without means and has no property over and above the exemption allowed by law wherefrom the plaintiff might secure satisfaction for the damages resulting to it from the acts aforesaid." *The constitution is no respecter of persons.* The impecunious man "who hath not where to lay his head" has as good right to free speech, etc., as has the wealthiest man in the community. The right to enjoin in the former's case is precisely the same as in the latter's ; no greater, no less. In short, the exercise of the right of free speech, etc., *is as free from outside interference or restriction as if no civil recovery* could be had or *punishment inflicted because of its unwarranted exercise.*

And in this connection it is to be constantly borne in mind that the principle is firmly rooted in equity jurisprudence that, though there be no remedy at law, this does not necessarily and of itself give a court of equity jurisdiction to afford relief. The authority to enjoin finds no better harbor in the empty pocket of the poor man than in the full pocket of the rich man. And such authority to enjoin can have no existence in circumstances such as the present case presents, if the constitution is to be obeyed.

If these defendants are not permitted to tell the story of their wrongs, or, if you please, their supposed wrongs, by word of mouth or with pen or print, and to endeavor to persuade others to aid them by all peaceable means in securing redress of such wrongs, *what becomes of free speech and what of personal liberty?* The fact that in exercising that freedom they thereby do plaintiff an actionable injury, such fact does not go a hair toward a diminution of their right of free speech, etc., for the exercise of which, if resulting in such injury, the constitution makes them expressly responsible. But such responsibility is utterly incompatible with authority in a court of equity to prevent such responsibility from occurring.

Judge Sherwood then stated that the question of the power of the court to enjoin in cases of intimidation, threats of violence, or of destruction of property was not passed upon, as not being involved in the record, and concluded:

Holding these views, we affirm the decree of dismissal entered in favor of defendants by the court below.

Judge Robinson dissented from the above.

V. Blacklist [1]

This is a bill brought by Boyer and others to procure an injunction against the Western Union Telegraph Company, prohibiting the discharge of employees on account of membership in the Commercial Telegraphers' Union, and also prohibiting the maintenance by said company of a black list. The bill also alleged that the company had conspired to destroy the Telegraphers' Union. The injunction was denied. The points involved were discussed in the following manner by Judge Rogers, who delivered the opinion of the court:

The first cause of complaint is that plaintiffs have been discharged without notice from the service of the defendant from no other cause than that they joined that union. But the answer to that complaint is, that in a free country like ours every employee, in the absence of contractual relations binding him to work for his employer a given length of time, has the legal right to quit the service of his employer without notice and either with or without cause at any time; and in the absence of such contractual relations

[1] United States Circuit Court for the Eastern District of Missouri, *Boyer et al.* v. *Western Union Telegraph Company*, 124 Fed. Rep. 246 (1903).

any employer may legally discharge his employee with or without notice at any time. The second ground for complaint is that defendant, its officers and agents, have unlawfully combined and confederated together to destroy the said union, and intend discharging all the members of said union from the service of the defendant, and by threats, intimidation, and coercion, and otherwise, are interfering with the plaintiffs and with others of their employees for uniting with the union, and are seeking to prevent those discharged from obtaining employment. I need not take time to multiply authorities to show that there is no such thing in law as a conspiracy to do a lawful thing. If the last allegation means anything, it is that the defendant, its officers and agents, have conspired to destroy the union by discharging all its members in its employ and refusing to employ others solely for the reason that they were members of the union. But it is not unlawful, in the absence of contractual relations to the contrary, to discharge them for that or for any other reason, or for no reason at all. Hence there is no such thing in law as a conspiracy to do that, and it matters not whether you call such an agreement a conspiracy, a combination, or a confederation.

True, it is alleged that defendant, its officers and agents, unlawfully combined and confederated to destroy the union. But what is unlawful is a question of law; whether a thing done is unlawful depends on what is done or threatened to be done. But what the defendant company, its officers and agents, combined or confederated to do in order to destroy the union is the precise thing the complaint fails to show. The court must always be able to look at the facts and say that if these facts are true they are illegal; otherwise there is no ground for invoking its protective agency.

But it is said that defendant maintains a black list containing a list of names of such persons as may have incurred its displeasure and have been discharged from its service, and that by methods not known to them it prevents such discharged persons from getting employment as telegraph operators; that they have blacklisted people solely because they belong to the union, and that they intend to blacklist others for the same thing, etc. We have seen it is not unlawful to discharge plaintiffs because they belong to the union. Is it unlawful for defendant to keep a book showing that they were discharged because they belonged to the union? The union presumably, and especially in view of the allegations in the bill, is an honorable, reputable, and useful organization, intended to better the conditions and elevate the character of its members. Is it illegal for defendant to keep a book showing that it had discharged members of such a union solely because they belong to it? That seems to be the real essence of the bill. Is it illegal to notify others that it keeps such a book and that they can inspect it, or to inform others what such a book shows? That seems to be the ground of complaint. There can be no question about it; the positive, direct, and unequivocal allegation is that defendant keeps such a book; that plaintiffs are placed on it solely because they belong to the union and have been discharged solely because they did belong to the union. Can a court of equity grant relief to a man who says for his cause of action that he belongs to a reputable organization and that he has been discharged solely because he did belong to it; that his employer, who discharged him keeps a book on which is placed his name and has set opposite thereto the fact that he discharged him solely because he belonged to such organization; and that he gives that information to other persons, who refuse to employ him on that account? Suppose a man should file a bill alleging that he belonged to the Honorable and Ancient Order of Freemasons, or to the Presbyterian Church, or to the Grand Army of the Republic; that his employer had discharged him solely on that account; that he had discharged others of his employees and intended to discharge all of them for the same reason; that he kept a book which contained all the names of such discharged persons and set opposite the name of each discharged person the fact that he had been discharged solely on the ground that he belonged to such organization; and that he had given such information to others, who refused to employ such persons on that account. Is it possible a court of equity could grant relief? If so, pray, on what ground? And yet that is a perfectly parallel case to this as made by the bill.

VI. Employment of Nonunionists

The present position of the law in American states on the right of a union to refuse to work with nonunion men is set forth in an article by Bruce Wyman, on "The Maintenance of the Open Shop," [1] from which the following summary is taken:

Whatever weight may be given to those two decisions as authority [*National Protective Assn.* v. *Cumming* (New York) and *Clemmett* v.

[1] *Green Bag*, Vol. XVII, 1905, pp. 21–29.

Watson (Indiana)], they represent the view of the minority. The contrary holding undoubtedly has the majority. That the nonunion man is protected against the union is the law of the following jurisdictions at least: Maine, *Perkins* v. *Pendleton*, 90 Me. 166 (1897); Maryland, *Lucke* v. *Clothing Cutters Assembly*, 77 Md. 396 (1893); Massachusetts, *Plant* v. *Woods*, 176 Mass. 492 (1900); Pennsylvania, *Erdman* v. *Mitchell*, 207 Pa. 79 (1903). In the following jurisdictions the issue is in doubt: England, *Allen* v. *Flood* (1898), A. C. 1, and *Perrault* v. *Gauthier*, 28 Can. Sup. 241 (1899), are for the union, but *Quinn* v. *Leatham* (1901), A. C. 495, and *Giblau* v. *National Amalgamated Union* (1903), 2 K. B. 600, are distinctly for the nonunion man; New York, *Curran* v. *Galen*, 152 N. Y. 33 (1897), and *Davis Machine Co.* v. *Robinson*, 41 Misc. 329 (1903), are for the nonunion man, but *National Protective Association* v. *Cumming*, 170 N. Y. 315 (1902), and *Davis* v. *United Hoisting Engineers*, 28 App. Div. 396, held for the union. In two jurisdictions at least the law permits the union to force the nonunion man out: New Jersey, *Meyer* v. *Journeymen Stonecutters' Association*, 47 N. J. Eq. 519 (1890), which, however, is based on the court's interpretation of the local trades union statutes; Indiana, *Clemmett* v. *Watson*, 14 Ind. App. 38 (1895), in which again the court relies upon the repeal of the former conspiracy statutes. It is, therefore, the general American law that legal wrong is done by a union procuring the discharge of a nonunion man. Even if their motive is self-interest, — to get all the work for their own members, — still most courts hold that the union cannot be allowed to use the force of its members to crush the nonunion man. . . . Any discussion which leaves out the fact of conspiracy and defends the union upon the basis of the permission given individuals to compete as they please misses the real point upon which the discussion turns.[1]

Following are two decisions referred to above, taking opposite grounds on this question:

New York Court of Appeals. *National Protective Association of Steam Fitters and Helpers* v. *Cumming et al.*, 170 N. Y. 315 (1902).

This was a case in which the plaintiffs applied for an injunction to restrain the defendants, the Enterprise Association of

[1] See also Wyman, "The Perpetuation of the Open Market," *Green Bag*, Vol. XVII, pp. 210–221; Lindley D. Clark, "The Present Legal Status of Organized Labor in the United States," *Journal of Political Economy*, Vol. XIII, pp. 172–200.

Steam Fitters, from preventing the employment of its members and from coercing or obtaining by threats, strikes, etc., the discharge of its members. The plaintiffs had applied for membership in the defendant labor union, but being denied or having been expelled, they organized a dual union, the National Protective Association of Steam Fitters and Helpers. Being refused employment on account of the threats of a strike by the defendant union, they brought the suit. An injunction was granted in a lower court, but was withdrawn by an appellate court, and the latter decision was sustained by the Court of Appeals. Chief Justice Parker, speaking of the defendant association, said:

> Their restriction of membership to those who have stood a prescribed test must have the effect of securing careful as well as skillful associates in their work, and that is a matter of no small importance in view of the state of the law which absolves the master from liability for injuries sustained by a workman through the carelessness of a co-employee. So long as the law compels the employee to bear the burden of the injury in such cases, it cannot be open to question but that a legitimate and necessary object of societies like the defendant associations would be to assure the lives and limbs of their members against the negligent acts of a reckless co-employee, and hence it is clearly within the right of an organization to provide such a method of examination and such tests as will secure a careful and competent membership, and to insist that protection of life and limb requires that they shall not be compelled to work with men whom they have not seen fit to admit into their organization, as happened in the case of the plaintiff, McQueed. . . .
>
> It is well known that some men, even in the presence of danger, are perfectly reckless of themselves and careless of the rights of others, with the result that accidents are occurring almost constantly which snuff out the lives of workmen as if they were candles, or leave them to struggle through life maimed and helpless. These careless, reckless men are known to their associates, who not only have the right to protect themselves from such men, but, in the present state of the law, it is their *duty* through their organizations to attempt to do it, as to the trades affording special opportunities for mischief arising from recklessness.
>
> I know it is said in another opinion in this case that "workmen cannot dictate to employers how they shall carry on their business,

nor whom they shall or shall not employ," but I dissent absolutely from that proposition, and assert that, so long as workmen must assume all the risk of injury that may come to them through the carelessness of co-employees, they have the moral and legal right to say that they will not work with certain men and their employer must take their dictation or go without their services. . . .

Stated in other words, the propositions quoted [from Judge Vann's opinion] recognize the right of one man to refuse to work for another on any ground that he may regard as sufficient, and the employer has no right to demand a reason for it. But there is, I take it, no legal objection to the employee's giving a reason, if he has one, and the fact that the reason given is that he refuses to work with another who is not a member of his organization, whether stated to his employer or not, does not affect his right to stop work, nor does it give a cause of action to the workman to whom he objects because the employer sees fit to discharge the man objected to rather than lose the services of the objector.

The same rule applies to a body of men who, having organized for purposes deemed beneficial to themselves, refuse to work. Their reasons may seem inadequate to others, but, if it seems to be in their interest as members of an organization to refuse longer to work, it is their legal right to stop. The reason may no more be demanded as a right of the organization than of an individual, but if they elect to state the reason, their right to stop work is not cut off because the reason seems inadequate or selfish to the employer or to organized society. And if the conduct of the members of an organization is legal in itself, it does not become illegal because the organization directs one of its members to state the reason for its conduct.

The principles quoted above recognize the legal right of members of an organization to strike, that is, to cease working in a body by prearrangement until a grievance is redressed, and they enumerate some things that may be treated as the subject of a grievance, namely, the desire to obtain higher wages, shorter hours of labor, or improved relations with their employers, but this enumeration does not, I take it, purport to cover all the grounds which will lawfully justify members of an organization refusing, in a body and by prearrangement, to work. The enumeration is illustrative rather than comprehensive, for the object of such an organization is to benefit all its members, and it is their right to strike, if need be, in order to secure any lawful benefit to the several members of the organization, as, for instance, to secure the reëmployment of a member they regard as having been improperly discharged and to secure from an employer of a number of them employment for other members of their organization who may be out of employment, although the effect will be to cause the discharge of other employees who are not members.

And whenever the courts can see that a refusal of members of an organization to work with nonmembers may be in the interests of the several members, it will not assume in the absence of a finding to the contrary that the object of such refusal was solely to gratify malice and to inflict injury upon such nonmembers. . . .

It seems to me illogical and little short of absurd to say that the everyday acts of the business world, apparently within the domain of competition, may be either lawful or unlawful according to the motive of the actor. If the motive be good, the act is lawful; if it be bad, the act is unlawful. Within all the authorities upholding the principle of competition, if the motive be to destroy another's business in order to secure business for yourself, the motive is good; but, according to a few recent authorities, if you do not need the business or do not wish it, then the motive is bad; and some court may say to a jury, who are generally the triers of fact, that a given act of competition which destroyed A's business was legal if the act was prompted by a desire on the part of the defendant to secure to himself the benefit of it, but illegal if its purpose was to destroy A's business in revenge for an insult given. . . .

Nowhere throughout the finding will be found even a hint that a strike was ordered or a notification given of the intention to order a strike for the purpose of accomplishing any other result than that of securing the discharge of the members of the plaintiff association and the substitution of members of the defendant associations in their place. Such a purpose is not illegal within the rules laid down in the opinion of Judge Vann, nor within the authorities cited therein; on the contrary, such a motive is conceded to be a legal one. It is only where the sole purpose is to do injury to another, or the act is prompted by malice, that it is insisted that the act becomes illegal. No such motive is alleged in that finding. It is not *hinted* at. On the contrary, the motive which always underlies competition is asserted to have been the animating one. It is beyond the right and the power of this court to import into that finding, in contradiction of another finding or otherwise, the further finding that the motive which prompted the conduct of defendants was an unlawful one, prompted by malice and a desire to do injury to plaintiffs without benefiting the members of the defendant associations.

I doubt if it would ever have occurred to any one to claim that there was anything in that finding importing a different motive from that specially alleged in the finding, had not the draughtsman characterized the notice given to the employers by the associations of their intention to strike as "threats."

The defendant associations, as appears from the finding quoted, wanted to put their men in the place of certain men at work who were nonmembers working for smaller pay, and they set about doing it in a perfectly lawful way. They determined that if it were necessary they would bear the burden and expense of a strike to accomplish that result, and in so determining they were clearly within their rights, as all agree. They could have gone upon a strike without offering any explanation until the contractors should have come in distress to the officers of the associations asking the reason for the strike. Then after explanations the nonmembers would have been discharged and the men of defendant associations sent back to work. Instead of taking that course they chose to inform the contractors of their determination and the reason for it.

It is the giving of this information, a simple notification of their determination, which it was right and proper and reasonable to give, that has been characterized as "threats" by the Special Term and which has led to no inconsiderable amount of misunderstanding since. But the sense in which the word was employed by the court is of no consequence, for the defendant associations had the absolute right to threaten to do that which they had the right to do. Having the right to insist that plaintiff's men be discharged and defendants' men put in their place if the services of the other members of the organization were to be retained, they also had the right to threaten that none of their men would stay unless their members could have all the work there was to do.

* * * * * * * *

A man has a right under the law to start a store and to sell at such reduced prices that he is able in a short time to drive the other storekeepers in his vicinity out of business, when, having possession of the trade, he finds himself soon able to recover the loss sustained while ruining the others. Such has been the law for centuries. The reason, of course, is that the doctrine has generally been accepted that free competition is worth more to society than it costs, and that on this ground the infliction of damages is privileged. (*Commonwealth* v. *Hunt*, 4 Metcalf, 111, 134.)

Nor could this storekeeper be prevented from carrying out his scheme because instead of hiding his purpose he openly declared to those storekeepers that he intended to drive them out of business in order that he might later profit thereby. Nor would it avail such storekeepers, in the event of their bringing an action to restrain him from accomplishing their ruin by underselling them, to persuade the trial court to characterize the notification as a "threat," for on review the answer would be: A man may threaten to do that which the law says he may do, provided that within the rules laid down in those cases his motive is to help himself.

A labor organization is endowed with precisely the same legal right as is an individual to threaten to do that which it may lawfully do. . . .

Pennsylvania Supreme Court. *Erdman et al.* v. *Mitchell et al.*, 207 Pa. 79 (1904).

This case came before the supreme court of Pennsylvania on appeal from the court of common pleas of Philadelphia County, the action being brought by William C. Erdman and others, members of the Plumbers' League of the city of Philadelphia, against Robert T. Mitchell and others, officers and members of the Allied Building Trades of Philadelphia. It appeared that Erdman and his associates were employed as journeymen plumbers in the erection of a large building on which were employed also a number of nonunion workmen and a larger number of workmen of various trades who were affiliated with the Allied Building Trades above mentioned. After the work had progressed for some time, a strike was ordered by the executive board of the Allied Trades, and all workmen affiliated therewith were ordered to desist from further labor because of the employment on the building of nonunion men and members of the Plumbers' League, which was not affiliated with the Allied Trades. After this strike had gone into effect, the defendants, Mitchell and others, as representatives of the Allied Trades, called on the manager of the firm that had a general contract for the building and said that if he would remove the objectionable workmen from the building the strike should cease.

An agreement was finally reached, which was reduced to writing, to the effect that plumbers should be employed who had the card of the Allied Trades, and that all other workmen of other trades now or hereafter employed on the building should have in their possession current cards from unions in affiliation with the defendants' organization. In accordance with this agreement, Erdman and his associates were dismissed from further employment on this building and work was resumed. The nonunion workmen who had been employed were allowed to continue their service and were not molested. The plaintiffs, Erdman and others, then undertook to find employment elsewhere, but were not able to secure and retain employment in the city on account of the action of the officers of the Allied Trades, who announced to the president of the Plumbers' League, of which Erdman was a member, that it was the purpose of the Allied Trades to prevent the employment of any plumber in Philadelphia who was not a member of a union affiliated with them, and that they would use the same means that they had used in the case above described wherever they had the opportunity of doing so.

On these facts the court of common pleas had issued an injunction prohibiting the defendants, Mitchell and others, and each and every one of them, their committees, agents, and servants, from interfering with and from combining, conspiring, or attempting to interfere with the employment of the plaintiffs, or any one or more of them, either by threatening loss to any employer who might take them into his service, or by any scheme, combination, or conspiracy among themselves or with others to annoy, hinder, interfere with, or prevent any person or persons or corporation from employing or continuing to employ such plaintiffs, or any one or more of them, by putting them in fear of loss or trouble, or to do anything to hinder, impede, or obstruct the plaintiffs, or any one or more of them, from securing employment or continuing in employment. From this injunction the officers of the Allied Trades took an appeal to the supreme court, with the result that the decree of the court below was affirmed and costs assessed upon the appellees.

Judge Dean, for the supreme court, spoke in part as follows:

We have before us the somewhat unusual case of two warring trades unions invoking the law for the settlement of their respective rights and the determination of their legal conduct in carrying out the purpose of their respective organizations. . . .

The court below was of opinion that in so far as defendants, in furtherance of the purposes of the council of the Allied Building Trades, undertook by intimidation of plaintiffs and their employers to coerce the plaintiffs into joining their organization or any particular organization and by such action caused the workmen to suffer damage, such action was unlawful and ought to be restrained by equity. This conclusion is correct. This is not an indictment for a statutory offense nor for a common-law conspiracy, which last the legislature by Acts of 1872, 1876, and 1891, has practically abolished. It is a suit in equity to restrain an unlawful act. It is argued by appellees' counsel that an act may be clearly unlawful, although not the subject of criminal prosecution; that an agreement by a number of persons that they will by threats of a strike deprive a mechanic of the right to work for others merely because he does not choose to join a particular union is a conspiracy to commit an unlawful act, which conspiracy may be restrained.

We do not question that defendants may under their constitution and rules resolve that they will not work with members of other organizations or with nonunion men, and act accordingly. That is their right, and their organization, when the conduct of its members is limited to refraining from work themselves according to such resolution, is not unlawful. But it is manifest from the findings of fact and the testimony that defendants went far beyond this. The contractors undertook the erection of a large and expensive building. They employed a large number of men skilled in all branches of the building trades, a majority of whom were members of defendants' union. No notice was given by the organization to the contractors that their members would not be permitted to work on the same building with members of plaintiffs' union or with nonunion men. After the building had progressed until it had reached what may be called its critical stage, a strike was ordered of all the workmen affiliated with defendants' union, and two thirds of all at work quit. After the strike negotiations for calling it off were opened between defendants and the manager for the contractors, and the result was the agreement with their union heretofore noticed. Then followed the discharge of plaintiffs from work on that building, and then an interview between the president of plaintiffs' union and the secretary of defendants'. The latter told the president that the Allied Trades intended to pursue the same course as at the Mariner and Merchant Building on every building in the city for the purpose of driving every plumber into a union affiliated with the Allied Trades. This evidence would have established a criminal conspiracy at common law. Concede that it would not under our present legislation now establish it; nevertheless it is still an unlawful act. There was no complaint as to wages by any of the workmen on the building when the strike was declared. All wanted to work and their employers wanted them to work. But these defendants who did not work on the building had a grievance. Plaintiffs refused to and would not join the defendants' union. They must be driven to joining it by threats of loss of work, and their employers must be compelled to aid defendants by threats of loss of money on their contract. This is so plain that it is waste of time to more than state the facts to convince that the conduct of defendants was calculated to intimidate both employees and employers and consequently was unlawful. The frightened employers, to avoid further loss, yielded. The plaintiffs did not yield, and, to prevent further intimidation of those who would otherwise employ them, they seek by this suit to restrain defendants from future acts of intimidation.

The first article of the constitution says: "That the general great and essential principles of liberty and free government may be recognized and unalterably established, we declare that all men are born equally free and independent and have certain inherent and indefeasible rights, among which are those of enjoying and defending life and liberty, of acquiring, possessing, and protecting property and reputation, and of pursuing their own happiness." Then follows the conclusion of this section: "Everything in this article is excepted out of the general powers of government and shall forever remain inviolate." This clause, unlike many others in the constitution, needs no affirmative legislation, civil or criminal, for its enforcement in the civil courts. Wherever a court of common pleas can be reached by the citizen these great and essential principles of free government must be recognized and vindicated by that court, and the indefeasible right of liberty and the right to acquire property must be protected under the common-law judicial power of the court. Nor does it need statutory authority to frame its decrees, or statutory process to enforce them against the violators of constitutional rights.

The right to the free use of his hands is the workman's property, as much as the rich man's right to the undisturbed income from his factory, houses, and lands. By his work he earns present subsistence for himself and family. His savings may result in accumulations which will make him as rich in houses and lands as his employer. This right of acquiring property is an inherent, indefeasible right of the workman. To exercise it he must have the unrestricted privilege of working for such employer as he chooses, at such wages as he chooses to accept. This is one of the rights guaranteed him by our declaration of rights. It is a right of which the legislature cannot deprive him, one which the law of no trades union can take from him, and one which it is the bounden duty of the courts to protect. The one most concerned in jealously maintaining this freedom is the workman himself.

A conspiracy is the combination of two or more persons by some concerted action to accomplish an unlawful purpose. It is unlawful to deprive a mechanic or workman of work by force, threats, or intimidation of any kind. A combination of two or more to do the same thing by the same means is a conspiracy. That by the legislation referred to such conspiracy is no longer criminal does not render it lawful. At common law the courts held that such combination was so prejudicial to the public interests and so opposed to public policy as rendered it punishable criminally; but the legislature, which generally determines what is and what is not public policy, has declared that it is no longer a crime or misdemeanor. But this is as far as it has gone. It is as far as it could go without abolishing the declaration of rights. To do that the whole people of the commonwealth must be directly consulted and they must give assent. For while the plain implication from the declaration is that the power to limit this indefeasible right rests solely with the people, yet when they adopted the constitution of 1874, with an extreme of caution they expressly said, "Everything in this article is excepted out of the general powers of government and shall forever remain inviolate." That is, shall forever remain with the people. They will not trust their own legislature with power to minimize or fritter it away — much less, a trades union. If the legislature to-day abolished indictment for willful and malicious trespass or abolished the writ of estrepement, to-morrow courts of equity would still be bound, under the declaration of rights, to protect the citizen in the peaceable possession and enjoyment of his land, even if to do so they were compelled to imprison the lawless trespasser who refused to obey their writs. So the same courts are still bound to protect the humblest mechanic or laborer in his right to acquire property. . . .

It is argued that defendants, either individually or by organization, have the right now to peaceably persuade plaintiffs and others not to work and their employer not to hire them. So they have. It is further argued that they can quit work when they choose. So they can. But neither of these suggested cases is the one before us. Here a strike on a large building was declared because plaintiffs would not join a particular society. The declared purpose of the strike was to cause loss of employment to plaintiffs because they would not join the Allied Building Trades — chose to remain faithful to their own union, the Plumbers' League. The Allied Trades would not declare the strike off and permit work on the buildings to proceed until the employers entered into contract, practically stipulating that they would discharge plaintiffs and not reëmploy them. It is not important that apt language precisely expressing the threat should have been used. The meaning of their declarations and acts was well understood by all parties. The men lost their work. The employers, after a damaging stoppage, were permitted to proceed because they yielded to the threat; that is, they were intimidated because they feared further loss. How absurd it is to call this peaceable persuasion, and how absurd to argue that, if the law attempts to prevent it, the right of the workmen to organize for their common benefit is frustrated! And then, what about the right of the Plumbers' League to organize for the common benefit of its members, of whom the plaintiffs are a part? The declared purpose of the Allied Trades is by these acts to absorb this union and thereby destroy it. Under no possible view of the conduct of defendants was it lawful. . . .

And so, as already intimated, it comes simply to the question, Shall the law of an irresponsible trades union or shall the organic law of a free commonwealth prevail? We answer, Every court of the commonwealth is bound to maintain the latter in letter and spirit.

VIII

STATE ARBITRATION AND THE MINIMUM WAGE IN AUSTRALASIA[1]

* * * * * * * * *

On all sides there is a desire to discover a method whereby peace may be secured without injury to the just claims and expectations of the workers. The same feeling prevailed in the Australasian colonies when industry had been laid waste by the maritime strike of 1890, the shearers' strikes of 1891 and 1893, and the miners' strike of 1892. Trade unionism had collapsed, but after the victory of the conservative forces came a revival of progressivism, and with it an eager searching after some sane means for dealing with the claims of labor. The result has been a body of legislation which by its results challenges the respect if not the assent of all engaged in industry. New Zealand led the way under the guidance of the Hon. W. Pember Reeves, then Minister for Labor, now Agent General in London for the colony, who introduced his first Industrial Arbitration and Conciliation Bill in 1891. Not till 1894, however, did he succeed in carrying his measure for the compulsory reference of trade disputes to state boards of conciliation and for the establishment of a state court of arbitration whose decisions were backed by the whole force of the law. Victoria, in 1896, after a fierce agitation against sweating, passed a Factory and Workshops Act, setting up wage boards for the determination of wages in the sweated trades. These two measures have been the models for subsequent legislation in other

[1] From the *Political Science Quarterly*, Vol. XVIII, 1903, pp. 112–140. See also article by Victor S. Clark, "Labor Conditions in New Zealand," Bulletin U. S. Bureau of Labor, No. 49 (1903); Reeves, State Experiments in Australia and New Zealand, Vol. I, pp. 59–181.

colonies, and a description of their details and their working will occupy the bulk of this paper. South Australia, after an abortive and badly drawn arbitration act in 1894, adopted the Victorian plan in 1900. In the same year West Australia copied the New Zealand Act, and late in 1901 the New South Wales legislature passed an act based, but with important modifications, on Pember Reeves' model.

The New Zealand Act of 1894 was amended in 1895, 1896, and 1898, and was replaced in 1900 by a consolidating and amending act which was itself amended in the following year. Although the recent amendments are important, yet the working of the system will be best understood if the original act is first summarized, and then the amendments described which were passed to give effect to the teachings of experience.

The "industrial matters" which were brought within the scope of the law were defined to be "all matters or things affecting or relating to work done or to be done, or the privileges, rights, or duties of employers or workmen in any industry, and not involving questions which are or may be the subject of proceedings for an indictable offense." The basis of the act was that it took no notice of irresponsible persons. An individual employer was a person with property which could be attached by law, but the individual worker was not in such a position. The act therefore dealt only with organized bodies of work people, and since the trade unions were chary of risking their privileges by coming to close quarters with the law, it provided for the establishment for the purposes of the act of "industrial unions" of not less than seven workers or seven employers. These unions had to be genuine organizations, with rules, committees of management, and funds, and when registered they became corporate bodies with powers to sue and be sued, but only for the purposes of the act. No member could retire without giving three months' written notice, and all members by registration of the union became subject to the act. Trade unions could register as industrial unions, each branch being considered for this purpose a separate union, and several industrial unions could unite to form an "industrial association."

The object of the author of the act being to foster mutual settlements of disputes, the measure proceeded next to provide that industrial unions or associations of workers might enter into "industrial agreements" with any employer or employers or union or association of employers in relation to any industrial matter. Such agreements were to be filed in the supreme court and enforced in the same manner as awards under the act. In default of such agreements any party to a dispute, being an industrial union or association of workers or employers or any employer, could refer the matter at issue to a board of conciliation, and after such reference no strike or lockout was permitted. The physical conformation of New Zealand leads to the splitting up of trades into local sections and to the accentuation of local feeling. The act consequently provided that the governor might divide the colony into districts, in each of which there should be a board of conciliation and a clerk of awards. Each board was to consist of four or six persons elected in equal proportions by the industrial unions of workers and employers in the district respectively, and of a chairman elected from outside at the first meeting of the board or, in default thereof, appointed by the governor, who could also nominate members in case any section declined or neglected to elect its representatives. The voting unit was an industrial union, each union having as many votes as there were members to be elected by its section. The term of office was three years, and one half of the members plus the chairman formed a quorum, the chairman having a casting vote only. When a dispute was referred to it the board had full powers to call for evidence, including books and documents, and to inspect factories, and, notwithstanding the way in which the dispute was referred to it, it could make any arrangement that was necessary to insure the dispute being brought before it in a complete shape. Special boards could be appointed "to meet any case of emergency or any special case of industrial dispute." Parties could appear before the board either personally or by their agents or, if all parties agreed, by counsel or solicitor; but such consent has very rarely been given. The duty of the board was first of all to strive to induce the parties to come to a "fair and amicable settlement" of the dispute, and if they failed they were to "decide the question according to the merits and substantial justice of the case." But their decision only became operative if all parties agreed, for any party could require the clerk of awards to refer the dispute to the court of arbitration.

The court of arbitration consisted of three persons appointed by the governor: the president, who must be a judge of the supreme court, and two persons recommended by the industrial associations or unions of employers and workers respectively. The term of office was three years, and one member and the president formed a quorum. The court had jurisdiction whenever a matter was referred to it by a board, or by a party dissenting from a board's recommendation, or by any party in a district where no board had been constituted. The proceedings before the court were similar to those conducted before a board; frivolous cases could be dismissed and costs awarded. The court was to decide cases by a majority of its members present "in such manner as they find to stand with equity and good conscience." It could admit evidence which was not strictly legal, and its proceedings could neither be impeached for want of form, nor removed to any other court or reviewed "on any account whatsoever." Its award had to be made within one month after the beginning of the case and was to specify "each industrial union, trade union, association, person, or persons" bound by it and the period not exceeding two years during which it was to be in force. From this enumeration it will be seen that though unorganized workmen could not appeal to the act they could nevertheless be bound by decisions under it. On the application of any party the award was to be filed in the office of the supreme court and became then enforceable like any other judgment or order up to the sum of £500 against any "industrial union, trade union, association, or person," and to £10 against any person in virtue of his membership in a union or association. The maximum penalty for each breach of an industrial agreement was fixed at £500.

The act came into force on January 1, 1895, but most of that year was occupied with making the necessary arrangements, and the first case was dealt with early in 1896. Seven districts were constituted each with a board, and a return to the legislative council of the colony shows that during the four years, April, 1896, to March, 1900, twenty-nine cases were settled by the boards, fifty-seven by the court, and one was settled by the parties. The cost of administration was £5404. Under the Act of 1900 the applications to the boards have greatly increased. There have been only seven strikes and all of these occurred among unorganized workmen or government employees who did not come under the act. In two cases the men afterwards organized and took advantage of the law; in all cases the disputes were trivial and involved only a few men and a short stoppage of work, — at the outside three hundred altogether were concerned. Although the description of New Zealand as a "land without strikes" is not strictly accurate, the few cases of cessation of work among unorganized work people only bring out in bolder relief the general success of compulsory arbitration. The most remarkable feature about the results is the small number of cases settled by the boards, contrary to Mr. Reeves' expectations. This is largely due to the ill-will with which employers at the beginning regarded the act. While the workers were confident enough to register their trade unions as industrial unions instead of forming separate organizations, the employers held aloof and would not elect representatives to the boards. In such cases Mr. Reeves contemplated that the disputes would be taken straight to the court, and that the boards would operate only where both sides by taking part in their formation were disposed towards conciliation. The government, however, completed the boards by appointing representatives of the employers, and although no whisper has been raised against the integrity of these gentlemen, they naturally did not command the full confidence of their class. Besides, we must reckon with the fighting instinct which leads the Anglo-Saxon not to surrender a "right" until the last court has decided against him.

The rush of applicants and the frequency of appeals naturally led to much delay in the settlement of cases, and the chief amendments in the Act of 1900 were directed toward the strengthening of the boards. Unless any party dissatisfied with the decision of a board appeals to the court within a month the decision becomes an industrial agreement. The Act of 1901 goes farther and permits any party to a dispute to take the case straight to the court without its passing through a board. The Act of 1900 made some other interesting amendments. Two employers can now form an industrial union; the court may decline to register an industrial union if there is one in the same locality which the applicants might conveniently join; and the boards are reduced to three or five members. The court of arbitration restricted the application of the act to persons engaged in work "of an industrial character"; but the term "worker" is now defined (by the Act of 1901) to include any person "employed to do any skilled or unskilled manual or clerical work for hire or reward." The term of agreements and awards is extended (by the Act of 1900) to three years, and notwithstanding their expiration they are to continue in force until superseded by fresh agreements or new awards. The boards can no longer demand the production of employers' books, that power being confined to the court. A board or the court may require at any time the appointment of two experts, one nominated by each side, to assist as assessors but not to act as judges. When industries are related either by being "branches of the same trade," or by being "so connected that industrial matters affecting the one may affect the other," then a board or the court may consider and deal with such related industries in making its recommendation or award. An industrial union of workers may refer a dispute to a board even although no one of its members is directly concerned. An award applies to nonunionist workmen and to new employers coming into the locality within which the award is in force during the currency of the award. Finally, the court may now make an award covering the whole area of the colony, "where the award relates to a trade or manufacture the products of which enter into competition in any market with those manufactured in another industrial district." The Act of 1901 placed trade unions in the same position as industrial unions for the purposes of the Industrial Conciliation and Arbitration Acts.

In March, 1900, there were 26,067 members of industrial unions out of 48,938 industrial workers. The passing of the Act of 1901 gave a great impetus to organization; 85 unions were registered in eight months, and in December, 1901, there were 241 industrial unions of workers and 12 industrial associations. At the same date there were 71 industrial unions of employers and 1 industrial association, but there are still a very large number of employers unorganized.

The briefest summary of the work of the boards of conciliation and the court of arbitration is to say that in the course of the last six years they have had to deal with every kind of industrial question, — time wages, piecework, overtime, hours of labor, traveling allowances, position of union officials, trade unionism, introduction of machinery, control of the factory, — in fact, every thorny problem which has disturbed industry in other lands. The awards are prepared with the most painstaking care. For example, the wages schedule in the case of the Auckland compositors decided in 1900 covers nine pages of the *Journal of the Department of Labor*, and in the Auckland boot trade award of 1899 there are 796 rates of pay specified. In all cases a minimum wage is fixed, and then usually follows this remarkable provision which removes a fertile source of dispute:

Any workman who considers himself not capable of earning the minimum wage may be paid such less wage as may from time to time be agreed upon in writing between any employer and the secretary or president of the union; and in default of such agreement within twenty-four hours after such journeyman shall have applied in writing to the secretary of the union stating his desire that such wage shall be agreed upon as shall be fixed in writing by the chairman of the conciliation board for the industrial district upon the application of such journeyman after twenty-four hours' notice in writing to the secretary of the union, who shall, if desired by him, be heard by such chairman on such application. Any journeyman whose wage shall have been so fixed may work and be employed for such less wage for the period of six calendar months thereafter, and, after the expiration of the said period of six calendar months, until fourteen days' notice in writing shall have been given to him by the secretary of the union requiring his wage to be again fixed in manner prescribed by this clause.[1]

[1] Canterbury lithographers' award, August 19, 1901.

An example of the famous clause relating to preference to union men must also be given in full:

So long as the rules of the union permit any person of good character and sober habits, and a competent tradesman, to become a member on payment of an entrance fee not exceeding 5 *s.*, upon his written application, without ballot or other election, and so to continue upon contributing subscriptions not exceeding 6 *d.* per week, the employers shall employ members of the union in preference to nonmembers, provided that there are members of the union equally qualified with nonmembers to perform the particular work; but this shall not compel an employer to refuse employment to any person now employed by him. When union and nonunion men are employed together they shall work in harmony and shall receive equal pay. The union shall keep in some convenient place within one mile from the chief post office in the city of Dunedin, and also at some convenient place at Invercargill and at Alexandra, a book to be called "the employment book," wherein shall be entered the names and exact addresses of all the members of the union for the time being out of employment, with a description of the branch of the trade in which each such journeyman claims to be proficient, and the names, addresses, and occupations of every employer by whom each such journeyman shall have been employed during the preceding two years. Immediately upon any such journeyman obtaining employment a note thereof shall be entered in such book. The executive of the union shall use their best endeavors to verify all the entries in such book, and the union shall be answerable as for a breach of this award in case any entry therein shall in any particular be willfully false to the knowledge of the executive of the union or in case the executive of the union shall not have used reasonable endeavors to verify the same. Such book shall be open to every employer without fee or charge at all hours between eight A.M. and five P.M. on every working day except Saturday, and on that day between the hours of eight A.M. and noon. If the union fails to keep the employment book in manner provided by this clause, then, and in such case, and so long as such failure shall continue, any employer may, if he so thinks fit, employ any person or persons, whether a member of the union or not, to perform the work required to be performed, notwithstanding the foregoing provisions.[1]

It will be noted that by these provisions the odious nonunion quarrel is avoided, open unions are provided and encouraged,

[1] Otago boilermakers and iron-ship builders' award, August 26, 1901.

the right of the employer to select his work people is preserved, unionists are guarded against victimization, and the union is utilized as a highly skilled labor bureau.

Some other interesting decisions may be quoted. On the introduction of machinery we have the following:

In the working of all machinery used in conjunction with the curriers' trade, preference shall be given to curriers, provided that such curriers shall have had a previous experience with such machines and are equally competent with the other workmen who are not curriers. Apprentices to the curriers' trade shall be taught to use the machines.[1]

It is the manufacturer's right to introduce whatever machinery his business may require and to divide or subdivide labor in any way he may deem necessary, subject to the payment of wages as set forth in the rules hereinafter set forth.[2]

In the event of linotype or typesetting machines being introduced into any office, the members already employed in such office shall have the first opportunity of being employed as probationers, and finally as regular operators, after having attained the required standard of efficiency, in preference to imported operators.[3]

On the vital question as to the control of factories a decision was given in these words:

The employers shall have the fullest right of control (subject to the special provisions of this award) of the factories and may make such rules for the necessary and proper management thereof as they may deem expedient.[4]

A colonial award was given under the Act of 1900 which deserves some attention. The parties were the New Zealand Federated Boot Trade Industrial Association of Workmen, the New Zealand Boot Manufacturers' Industrial Union of Employers, and ten nonassociated employers in Christchurch. Employers were to give preference of employment to unionists, who in their turn were to give preference of service to the associated employers; at any time within twelve weeks the union was to have the right to supply capable men to take the places of nonunionist

[1] Canterbury curriers' award, August 15, 1901.

[2] Christchurch bootmakers' award, May 4, 1901.

[3] Auckland compositors' award, June 6, 1900.

[4] Canterbury slaughtermen's award, August 14, 1901.

workmen then employed who declined to join the union; a working week of forty-eight hours and a minimum weekly wage of £2 2 *s.* were fixed; incompetent workmen and apprentices were also regulated; the award was to continue for two years and extend over the districts of Christchurch, Auckland, Dunedin, and Wellington; any union in the federation could take proceedings for the enforcement of the award within its own district; no industrial agreement was to be entered into between the manufacturers' association and nonunionists, or between the union and nonassociated masters without notice to the present parties.[1]

The ordinary objection that compulsory arbitration is useless since awards could not be enforced is refuted by the simple fact that no breach of an award has been committed in New Zealand by any body of workmen, though in some cases the decisions have been displeasing to them. Nor has there been any concerted attempt by employers to frustrate the working of the act, such breaches as have been proved being few and quickly punished by fines, in one case amounting to £25. The great care taken by the court to meet cases of special difficulty has helped the ready acceptance of its decisions. Current contracts are very often exempted, and in the Consolidated Gold Company's case, 1896, the court decided that the men should submit to a reduction for a limited period on account of the company's heavy expenditure in development work.

As to the effects of the act on capital and industry we fortunately have the independent evidence[2] of Judge Backhouse, who was commissioned in 1901 by the government of New South Wales to inquire into the working of compulsory conciliation and arbitration laws in New Zealand, Victoria, and other colonies. After exhaustive local inquiries he reported on this head:

> Generally, I should say that my investigations showed that with possibly one exception industries have not been hampered by the provisions of the act. To attempt to decide whether capital under other conditions would have been invested in particular industries is

[1] Christchurch bootmakers' award, May 4, 1901.

[2] Report of Royal Commission of Inquiry into the Working of Compulsory Conciliation and Arbitration Laws (New South Wales, 95 A, 1901).

to undertake a task which has merely to be mentioned to show its impossibility. No doubt general statements were made that this abstention had been practiced, but I found it more than difficult to get specific instances. Any cases which were mentioned, on investigation hardly bore out the view put forward.

The one exception referred to is the boot trade, but that industry was in a depressed state in 1893 and has continued in the same condition, as it has also in other Australasian colonies. The real cause of the depression is American competition, as is shown by the rise in the importation of boots from £115,205 in 1895 to £186,088 in 1900. Since the passing of the act New Zealand has grown steadily more prosperous. In 1894 its export and import trade was £16,000,000, in 1901 it was £23,000,000; in 1895, 29,879 hands were engaged in factories and workshops, in 1901, 53,460. As the fiction that the New Zealand labor laws have injured the prosperity of the colony is constantly being repeated, it may be as well to quote an Australian correspondent of the *Times* (April 4, 1902), a hostile but plainly a well-informed witness:

> New Zealand, having recklessly borrowed English capital and alienated its best land, was in a very bad state till the Ballance government came into power. That government and the Seddon government which followed it proceeded by heavy taxation and by compulsory resumption to force the good land back into the market. They passed factory acts and compulsory arbitration acts and compelled government contractors to pay high wages to their employees; they are opening a state coal mine and have in force a system of state life insurance. And yet, in spite of all this, — or because of all this, — New Zealand is at present one of the most prosperous places on earth.

While this prosperity has made the working of the act smoother in some respects, it has led to increased demands on the part of labor, which fortunately have taken the form of increased recourse to the courts instead of to strikes. It has also inevitably brought about a rise in prices which Judge Backhouse mistakenly attributes to the working of the act.

The rush of applicants caused some temporary impatience with the workmen and no doubt contributed to increase the appeals from the boards to the court. The apparent inefficacy of the boards has led to suggestions for their reform or abolition. It is somewhat doubtful whether the payment of members has worked well, and, though the great majority of the members are highly respected, yet in Judge Backhouse's opinion some, by "taking an active part outside in the furtherance of the claims of one of the parties," render their boards "boards of irritation rather than conciliation." Yet both Mr. Reeves and Mr. Justice Cooper, the president of the court of arbitration, believe, and rightly, that the boards are necessary. The double threshing out of a case leads to the more careful avoidance of injustice or of injury to trade. Such delay as there is is well paid for by this great gain.

A final quotation from Judge Backhouse will fitly close this part of our investigation:

The act has prevented strikes of any magnitude and has, on the whole, brought about a better relation between employers and employees than would exist if there were no act. It has enabled the increase of wages and the other conditions favorable to the workmen, to which, under the circumstances of the colony, they are entitled, to be settled without that friction and bitterness of feeling which otherwise might have existed; it has enabled employers, for a time at least, to know with certainty the conditions of production and therefore to make contracts with the knowledge that they would be able to fulfil them; and indirectly it has tended to a more harmonious feeling among the people generally which must have worked for the weal of the colony. A very large majority of the employers of labor whom I interviewed are in favor of the principle of the act. . . . The awards generally have been in favor of the workers, and it is therefore easy to understand that the unionists to a man believe in the act, and, as I have already mentioned, the nonunionists, as far as my observation goes, find no fault with it. . . . But while the effects of the act so far are good, the time has not yet come when it can be said with any certainty that it is a measure which will provide for the solution of all labor troubles. Since it came into operation in New Zealand everything has been in favor of an increase in the emoluments and of an amelioration of the conditions of labor, and there cannot be the slightest doubt that wages would have risen if there had been no act. . . . When lean years come, as come they must, . . . when wages will be cut down instead of being raised by the awards, — then, and not till then, can any one speak with authority as to whether the principle involved is workable or not.[1]

The legislation of Victoria in regard to Minimum Wage Boards is contained in the Factories and Shops Act, 1896, No. 1445, amending Acts of 1896, 1897, and 1898, and in the consolidating and extending Factories and Shops Act, 1900, No. 1654. The original act dealt only with the sweated trades — clothing, furniture, and bread making — and was to remain in force for five years; the amending acts remedied various defects which came to light; and the Act of 1900 extended the legal regulation of wages to all trades and was to be operative until the session of Parliament next following May 1, 1902. A commission was appointed under the last-named act to inquire into the working of the acts and their effect on trade, manufacture, labor, and commerce; but up to the summer of 1901 it had taken evidence principally as to early closing.

In summarizing the law it will be most convenient to take the Act of 1900. Section 15 (1) runs:

In order to determine the lowest prices or rates which may be paid to any person or persons or classes of persons for wholly or partly preparing or manufacturing, either inside or outside a factory or workroom, any particular articles of clothing or wearing apparel or furniture, or for bread making or baking, or to any person or persons or classes of persons employed in any process, trade, or business usually or frequently carried on in a factory or workroom or employed in the process, trade, or business of a butcher or seller of meat or maker or seller of small goods, the governor in council may if he think fit from time to time appoint a Special Board consisting of not less than four or more than ten members elected as may be prescribed, and a chairman, and may at any time remove any member of the Special Board. In fixing such lowest prices or rates the Special Board shall take into consideration the nature, kind, and class of the work and the mode and manner in which the work is to be done and the age and the sex of the workers and any matter which may from

[1] *Loc. cit.*, pp. 25–26.

time to time be prescribed. Provided that no such Special Board shall be so appointed except for the process, trade, or business of a butcher or seller of meat or maker or seller of small goods, and except in the case of any trade or business which at the commencement of this act is included under the provisions of the Factories and Shops Acts as regards Special Boards, unless a resolution has been passed by either House of Parliament declaring that it is expedient to appoint such Special Board.

The board may fix either a time rate or a piecework rate (based on the time rate) of wages or both, except that "for wholly or partly preparing or manufacturing outside a factory or workroom articles of clothing or wearing apparel a piecework price or rate only shall be fixed." The occupier of a factory or workroom may require the board to fix a piecework rate for persons operating machines. Instead of specifying piecework rates the board may determine that such rates based on the time rates fixed by the board may be paid, and any employer who pays piecework rates under this provision must base them "on the earnings of an average worker working under like conditions to those for which the piecework prices or rates are fixed and who is paid by time at the wages rates fixed by such Special Board"; the Inspector of Factories may require a list of such piecework rates to be sent to him, and if he is dissatisfied with them he may get the proper board to fix a suitable rate, the employer being bound to pay to his employees twice the amount by which his wages are deficient for the period elapsing after the inspector has given him notice of his dissatisfaction. When a time rate only has been fixed by a board it is illegal to pay piecework rates. The board shall also fix the number and determine the wages of apprentices or improvers or both; determine the maximum number of hours to be worked per week at the minimum wage; and fix rates of overtime. A minimum wage of half a crown a week must be paid to any person employed in a factory or workroom except "any member of the employer's family related in the first or second degree by blood or marriage to the employer." "If it is proved to the satisfaction of the Chief Inspector that any person by reason of age or infirmity is unable to obtain employment at the minimum wage fixed by any Special Board," a renewable license to work at a specified less wage for twelve months may be issued.

A first breach of the act is punishable by finé up to £10 ; a second by fine from £5 to £25 ; and a third by fine from £50 to £100 and cancellation of the registration of the factory or workroom. A determination of a special board can be challenged for illegality before the supreme court only, and the governor may suspend a determination for six months to give the board an opportunity of reinvestigating the case and deciding whether to alter or adhere to its decision. A determination once fixed continues in force until altered. The members of the boards are elected one half by the employers, one half by the workmen, lists of those qualified to vote being prepared from information supplied by the employers. In the case of the special board for men's and boys' clothing the representatives of the employers must consist of three representatives of makers of ready-made clothing and two of makers of order clothing, elected by separate rolls of voters. Owing to difficulties arising from the number of Chinese engaged in the furniture trade the special board in that industry is appointed by the governor in council. The chairman of a board is appointed by the governor on the nomination of the other members. The term of office of a board is two years, and the chairman is paid £1 and the members 10*s*. for a whole-day sitting and half those fees for a half-day sitting.

Under the Act of 1896 six special boards were appointed: Bakers, Boot Makers, Clothing Manufacturers, Furniture Manufacturers, Shirt Manufacturers, and Underclothing Manufacturers. Under the Act of 1900 twenty-one more boards were appointed up to the end of 1900: Butchers, Brick Makers, Carriage Makers, Cigar Makers, Confectioners, Coopers, Engravers, Fellmongers, Jam Manufacturers, Jewelers, Millet-Broom Makers, Pastry Cooks, Plate-Glass Workers, Printers, Pottery Makers, Saddlers, Stonecutters, Tanners, Tinsmiths, Wood Workers, and Woolen Workers. In 1901 and 1902 eleven additional boards have been appointed, making a total of thirty-eight boards settling the conditions of labor in trades employing 35,000 men out of a total of 57,000 engaged in factories and workshops. The Act of 1900 came to an end in the summer of 1902, when an unexpected general election prevented its renewal; but both sides pledged themselves to reënact it as soon as the new Parliament met. During the brief period of its abeyance there was an ugly relapse of some of the employers into the old sweating practices, which taught both public and politicians the sharp and needed lesson that the baser sort of master is not easily reformed. As soon as the new session opened the act was renewed for a further period.

The most significant fact about the later boards is that many of them were asked for by many of the employers in the trades concerned. This eloquent testimony to the utility of the boards of 1896 will lead us to look with leniency on the defects which were discovered in their working. The general results as to wages will be seen from the following table:

	Average Weekly Wage		Minimum Wage
	1896	1901	
Baking, Males	£1 12*s.* 5*d.*	£2 2*s.* 6*d.*	1*s.* ½*d.* per hour
Clothing, Males	1 15 3	2 0 5	7*s.* 6*d.* per 8-hour day
Clothing, Females	15 5	18 3	3*s.* 4*d.* per 8-hour day
Boots, Males	1 6 10	1 14 5	7*s.* per 8-hour day
Boots, Females	13 4	15 3	3*s.* 4*d.* per 8-hour day
Shirts, Females	14 5	14 8	4*d.* per hour
Underclothing, Females	11 3	12 7	4*d.* per hour
	(1898)		
Furniture, Males	1 9 7	2 0 7	1*s.* per hour
Furniture, Females	14 1	1 0 4	3*s.* 4*d.* per 8-hour day

The average wages of men and women are of course much higher when allowance is made for the children and young persons employed, and in the case of time workers they are always well above the legal minimum. The number of apprentices fixed in different cases is as below:

Clothing, one male apprentice or improver to every three male adults; one female apprentice or improver to every two female adults.

Boots, three female apprentices or improvers to every two female adults.
Shirts, one female apprentice or improver to every three female adults.
Underclothing, two female apprentices or improvers to every female adult.
Furniture, one male apprentice or improver to every four male adults.
Butchers, one male apprentice or improver to every three male adults.

In the shirt trade employers are allowed to fix piecework rates inside factories, provided they enable an average worker to earn not less than 4*d.*, 4½*d.*, and 5*d.* per hour according to the class of work done. In the underclothing trade, owing to the hundreds of lines manufactured, the employers are also allowed to fix their own piecework rates based on the time-wage minimum of 4*d.* per hour. "The utmost that can be said in favor of this system of fixing piecework rates," according to the Chief Inspector in his report for 1899, "is that it is better than nothing and enables the department to interfere when competition cuts the prices so low that even a skilled worker cannot earn the 4*d.* per hour fixed by the determination."

The object of the act was to prevent sweating, and on this point Judge Backhouse says: "That the act has to a large extent put a stop to 'sweating' there can be little doubt, but it is very questionable whether, as far at least as some of the workers are concerned, a state of things has not been brought about which is quite as unsatisfactory." Before the Commission on Unemployment in 1899 it was maintained by the employers that it was more profitable to employ young and quick men at the minimum wage, and therefore the old and slow workers were displaced in greater numbers; that girls were dismissed as soon as they had finished their apprenticeship; that workers had to work harder and more consistently; and that for all these reasons the Factory Acts tended to create unemployment. Particular complaint was made about the boot trade, where the determination of the board came into force on December 29, 1897, and it was shown that the number of persons employed fell from 4590 in 1897 (after having risen steadily from 3795 in 1894) to 4235 in 1898. Mr. Harkness, one of the chief manufacturers, declared:

I freely admit that the average earnings of the operatives actually in work have been substantially increased by the minimum weekly wage, the established piecework rates, and by the restriction of boy labor. Those in employment, of course, form the large majority of the workers, but it is no consolation to operatives debarred from working by the conditions now prevailing to know that those conditions have operated to the advantage of those more favorably circumstanced than themselves.

Mr. Peacock, the Chief Secretary, suggested that the decrease fell on apprentices and improvers. He said:

In one factory there were formerly 15 males, 20 apprentices, and 3 improvers, now there are 24 males, 6 apprentices, and 7 improvers; in another there had been 10 males, 7 apprentices, and 1 improver, now there are 12 males, 3 apprentices, and 3 improvers; in another there had been 15 males and 17 apprentices and improvers, now there are 56 males, 13 apprentices, and 8 improvers. It had been predicted that the minimum would become the maximum, but this was not so. There were 1749 males last week in 111 factories. Of these, 439 or 25 per cent were paid 45*s.* or more, 115 40*s.* to 45*s.*, and 221 were on piecework, leaving 974 who were getting from 36*s.* to 40*s.*, and a good many of these were getting less than 36*s.* before the determination. In these 111 factories there were only 4 where the wages had been reduced to 36*s.* These figures were obtained by special inquiry.[1]

At that time 36*s.* was the minimum wage. The workmen also pointed out that the employers had worked their factories day and night to accumulate stock in anticipation of the act, and that stagnation had naturally followed. By 1900 the trade had to a great extent recovered, the persons employed in that year being 4304, and exports having risen to £61,463 compared with £48,213 in 1897. It must also be borne in mind that trade during the last few years has suffered from American competition and from a forty-five per cent rise in the price of raw materials.

The incapacity of the old and slow to earn the minimum wage had not been foreseen by the framers of the Act of 1896, and the factory department had to prevent injustice by issuing permits to such persons to work at reduced rates, fifty-eight

[1] *Melbourne Age*, February 24, 1898.

being granted in 1899. This plan was legalized in 1900, but it is clumsy compared with the New Zealand method of meeting the same difficulty. Judge Backhouse estimates that "at least 250 hands" are employed below the minimum wage, the factory inspectors being deceived by false entries in the books. The same charge of evasion is made with regard to the other trades, but what the chief factory inspector said in his report for 1899 about the baking trade applies generally: "I have never been able to get evidence which would justify such a charge; . . . if the men have not the courage to see that they get their legal rights, I do not see what further can be done." In the baking trade evasion was practiced by working men part of their time as pastry cooks, but that section of the trade has now a special board.

One notable result has been the reduction of out-work in the clothing trade, where the piecework rates were fixed a little higher than the time rates to compensate the workers for rent and loss of time in conveying goods. The employers have replied by introducing machinery and getting the work done in their factories, — exactly the result which all students of the "sweating" problem wish to see achieved.

The improved organization of labor which always follows the enactment of factory acts is again exemplified in the baking industry, where the men are paid as much now for forty-eight hours' work as they were formerly for sixty, but do as much in the shorter time as they did in the longer. The protection which the acts have been to the workers is seen in the case of dungaree trousers, where the price paid by the wholesale houses to the manufacturer fell from 13*s.* per dozen before 1897 to *7s. 6d.* in 1899. Under free competition this loss would have fallen entirely on the workers; under the acts the manufacturers recoup themselves by better organization and improved methods, and where they raise the price to the warehouses the latter still retain an ample margin of profit without raising prices to the consumer. In the underclothing trade, that special home of sweating, it is worth noting that the lady factory inspector reports that the home workers as well as the factory workers have "greatly benefited" by the act. The results in the furniture trade are the least satisfactory of all, owing to the impossibility of overcoming deception by the numerous Chinese in the industry. Here, too, the "old and slow" workmen are a source of trouble, since they set up for themselves in unlicensed home workshops.

Up to 1895 trade had been depressed; since that time it has gradually recovered. To that extent the rise in wages may be attributed to general trade conditions, but no other trades show such remarkable increases as those granted by the special boards. The average wage in the printing trade, an industry which is a barometer of prosperity, was in 1897 27 *s.* 3 *d.* and in 1899 27 *s.* 4 *d.* The average wage in the dressmaking trade was 11 *s.* 1 *d.* in 1897 and 10 *s.* 11 *d.* in 1899; in biscuit making 18 *s.* 3 *d.* in 1897 and 16 *s.* 3 *d.* in 1899, — results which may with advantage be compared with the wages in cognate trades under special boards. Although the employment figures of the regulated trades show a steady rise industry has not been in the flourishing condition which has prevailed in New Zealand, but while improving has been on the whole dull. We are, therefore, by the experience gained in Victoria, able to discount the criticism leveled at the New Zealand success that it is due entirely to the prosperity of the colony. In good times and dull times we learn that regulation of wages is possible.

As much complaint, if not more, has been made about the regulation of the number of apprentices as about the determination of wages, the employers contending, as they also contended in New Zealand, "that in time to come there will not be a sufficient number of skilled hands to meet the requirements of some of the industries." Complaints were particularly abundant in the clothing trade, where the scarcity of competent female labor caused employers to assert that the proportion of female apprentices permitted, one to three adults, was too small. The fault, however, lay largely with employers, especially in the order trade; for while in the ready-made clothing trade the full legal numbers were always employed, one of the lady inspectors reported in 1899 about the order trade:

There are a very considerable number of employers in this branch of the trade who do not take apprentices at all and who will not take them, preferring that other people should have the bother of teaching them, and then expressing astonishment at the fact that so few skilled hands are obtainable. . . . The pieceworkers, who are supposed to gain by having an apprentice, do not care to take them, as they say they lose more in teaching the girl than they gain by her extra work. The employees on weekly wages could not possibly have any objection to taking apprentices, but the employer is often averse to it, as he considers that too much of the time of the employee is wasted in teaching girls who may leave at any moment.

The difficulty is but one particular instance of the universal breakdown of apprenticeship which we find in all industrial countries, and it will be interesting to observe whether the legislatures of Victoria and New Zealand will be successful in retaining a system for which, despite its faults, we have so far been unable to find a completely satisfactory substitute in any scheme of manual training. Meanwhile the trouble in the Victorian clothing trade has not been appeased by raising the proportion of female apprentices to one to every two adults, and since the employers will not organize the industry, the government must by technical schools or otherwise see that the trade does not leave the colony.

The clothing trade well exemplifies the difficulty of regulating a thoroughly disorganized trade. While the Special Board was toiling through nine months in preparing an exhaustive "determination" of thirty-five closely printed foolscap pages, the employers were frantically laying up stock, and in the slack time which necessarily followed they took advantage of the necessities of their work people to try evasions of the law. When prosecuted for illegally employing an apprentice they succeeded in getting the conviction upset by maintaining, in the absence of indentures, that she was an improver. The minimum wage for apprentices was evaded by requiring back as a premium on Monday morning the half crown which had been paid as wages the previous Saturday, and by other variations of the premium system. By the Act of 1900 all such evasions are prohibited. In the boot trade more apprentices are now at work than were employed in 1896 when there was no limitation, and the factory inspectors answer the cry that there is a difficulty in getting skilled tradeswomen by pointing out that the employers do not train their apprentices properly. A dearth of workers is also reported in the underclothing trade, but a factory inspector suggests that "owing to the very low prices paid in the past there has not been sufficient inducement for girls to stay at the trade."

The Butchers' Board introduces us to a special difficulty arising out of the social habits of Australia and probably not existing elsewhere. The average wage fixed since January 1, 1901, is 45*s*. per week of fifty-two hours. Judge Backhouse says:

> The general complaint of the master butchers is that they have a difficulty in arranging that the men should work the prescribed hours only. The most of the business is done in the early part of the day, and work must commence at the latest at six o'clock in the morning to enable breakfast meat to be delivered, while the shop cannot shut before five unless the public is to be inconvenienced. To get over the difficulty some employers give two half holidays to their men, arranging the times so that they always have some one in the shop; others allow long dinner hours. The price of meat has risen for the best joints 1½*d*. per pound, most of which I think is due to the higher price of stock, but some undoubtedly to the rate of wages and hours fixed.[1]

In all the trades under the newer boards the same story is told of increased wages, of the decrease of sweating, of the general prevalence of average wages considerably above the fixed minimum, and of the resulting better organization of industry. The general opinion of employers after experience of the new conditions is that they would not return to the old. Of course there has been some friction. The employers' representatives on the Woolen Trade Board objected to one of the men's representatives since he was not practically acquainted with the trade, but after some months' negotiations the difficulty was settled, and a "determination" embodying fifty rates of wages is now in force.

[1] Report of Royal Commission, *loc. cit.*, p. 34.

The master fellmongers retired from their board in the spring of 1901 because the majority carried a resolution fixing a 48-hour week. No other representatives of the employers would take their places, so the governor in council appointed five persons to fill the vacancies and a determination was framed. The employers then unsuccessfully appealed to the supreme court to quash the determination on the ground that the governor's nominees could not be representatives of the employers under the act. Still bent on resistance, most of them closed their premises for a time, and the 309 men at work in 1900 were reduced to 127 in 1901. But the workmen stood firm by the board, and in the spring of 1902 only the two largest yards were still closed. Trouble is pending also in the jam and confectionery trades, where wages have been fixed not according to the skill but according to the age of the workers. This naturally works to the detriment of the women over twenty-one years of age and is unequivocally condemned by the factory inspectors.

On the whole, while we must admit that there has been a considerable amount of friction in the working of the Victorian wage boards, there has not been more than might reasonably have been expected. Administrators tackled the hardest part of the industrial problem first and gained their experience by dealing with the chaotic sweated trades instead of with those which had reached a fair stage of organization and where employers and employed were trained to negotiation. Comparing the Victorian with the New Zealand system, the former has the advantage that no dispute is necessary to set the law in motion, and that the legal determination of wages is posited as part of the established order of things. On the other hand, the New Zealand requirement that the initiative must be taken by an organized body throws a grave responsibility on the plaintiffs, and the careful preparation of their case which is required necessarily exerts a sobering influence. In New Zealand the administration of the law is kept out of reach of the politicians, while in Victoria the consent of Parliament is needed for the formation of new boards, and "determinations" can be suspended on appeal to the governor, provisions which render possible at least the suspicion of political influence. The difference in the powers of the two sets of authorities is obvious, but the institution of trade boards in Victoria will commend itself to the workers in older settled lands rather than the local boards of New Zealand. New Zealand has another advantage in the greater elasticity of its law. Other defects of the Victorian law are the cumbrous system of electoral rolls and the clumsy method of dealing with the old and slow. The term of office of the boards, two years, is also too short. Finally, it is a serious omission that nothing is done to foster organization among the workers.

The legislation of the other colonies can be dismissed more briefly. The South Australian Conciliation Act of 1894, very similar in principle to the New Zealand Act of the same year, was nullified in the first case raised under it by the employer adopting the simple device of discharging his workmen on hearing that there would be a reference, and maintaining that having no employees he had no dispute. In December, 1900, that measure was supplemented by a Factories Amendment Act providing for the establishment of minimum wage boards on exactly the same plan as in Victoria; the lowest minimum wage for any employee was fixed at 4*s*. per week, and the boards were enabled to give special rates to the old and infirm. It is as yet too soon to ascertain how the act has worked. In West Australia, also, in December, 1900, the Industrial Arbitration and Conciliation Act became law. Judge Backhouse, writing some six months later, says: "It is modeled on the New Zealand acts. Although I understand there have been industrial disputes, neither side has, as far as I could learn, taken advantage of its provisions."[1]

After a failure in the preceding year the Industrial Arbitration Act of New South Wales was assented to on December 10, 1901, a measure presenting many remarkable features. Based, as every section shows, on the New Zealand acts, it differs from them fundamentally in omitting the boards of conciliation. The reason for this omission was, doubtless, partly the greater concentration of industry obliterating local patriotism, partly objection to the

[1] *Loc. cit.*, p. 34.

delays under the New Zealand law; but it is doubtful whether too high a price has not been paid for rapidity of decision. As already indicated, there are many merits in the dual authorities established in the southern colony. The industrial unions of workers are defined to be trade unions, or branches thereof, registered under the act and thereby incorporated solely for the purposes of the act, a bold recognition of the utility of trade unions not possible seven years earlier. Industrial unions of employers are any person or company or association of persons or companies employing at least fifty work people. Industrial agreements may be made and enforced at law. The court of arbitration consists of a judge of the supreme court and two members nominated by the governor on the recommendation of the industrial unions of employers and workers respectively, the members of the court holding office for three years; the salaries are £750 per annum each. The fullest freedom is conceded to the court to exercise its functions in the manner which may appear to it most suitable, and its decisions are final. Disputes may be referred to the court by any of the parties thereto, if industrial unions, and by the registrar or chief executive officer of the court when any one of the parties is not an industrial union. This latter provision is intended to make the act operative even in unorganized industries and contemplates a state of things worse than has been found in New Zealand, where even the sweated trades have organized to take advantage of the law. A strike or lockout before a reasonable time has elapsed for a reference to the court or while proceedings are pending is punishable by fine up to £1000 or imprisonment up to two months. This drastic method of abolishing the right to lock out aggrieved employees is probably the most forcible limitation of the liberty of employers which has yet been legalized in any free country. Whether the punishment be ever inflicted or not, the mere fact that it was instituted by the legislature is eloquent of the state of public feeling in the colony. The act goes on:

If an employer dismisses from his employment any employee by reason merely of the fact that the employee is a member of an industrial union or is entitled to the benefit of an award, order, or agreement, such employer shall be liable to a penalty not exceeding £20 for each employee so dismissed. In every case it shall lie on the employer to satisfy the court that such employee was dismissed by reason of some facts other than those above mentioned in this section. Provided that no proceedings shall be begun under this section except by leave of the court.

The most notable clause is the "common rule" clause, for which Mr. Wise, the author of the act, said he was indebted to the study of Mr. and Mrs. Sidney Webb's Industrial Democracy; and he maintained that it was "the most logical, complete, and effective method of enforcing the awards." It provides that in any proceeding the court may

(1) declare that any practice, regulation, rule, custom, term of agreement, condition of employment, or dealing whatsoever in relation to an industrial matter, shall be a common rule of the industry affected by the proceeding; (2) direct within what limits of area and subject to what conditions and exceptions such common rule shall be binding upon persons engaged in the said industry, whether as employer or as employee, and whether members of an industrial union or not; (3) fix penalties for any breach or nonobservance of such common rule as declared as aforesaid.

In New Zealand the same purpose of bringing the rate-cutting employer and his nonunionist accomplice under the same rules as their honorable fellows has been achieved by the slower method of piling award on award until the whole colony has been brought under regulation; but even in New Zealand the need for a swifter jurisdiction to meet the case of competing industrial districts has been acknowledged by the provision for colonial awards under the Act of 1900. The maximum penalties for any breach or nonobservance of any award, order, or direction are a fine not exceeding £500 in the case of an industrial union or any person bound by the award who is not a member of an industrial union, and a fine not exceeding £5 in the case of any individual member of an industrial union. The awards are not limited in time. Lastly, it may be noted that contrary to the excellent New Zealand precedent parties may appear before the court by counsel.

This summary of Australasian legislation conclusively proves that the legal regulation of the conditions of labor, whether by compulsory arbitration or some other form, is possible. It would be too much to say that it is possible under all circumstances, but it has been shown that under certain widely varying circumstances it has been successful. It can no longer be disposed of by *a priori* arguments based on book theories of economics or politics, and that alone is a great gain. It is now incumbent on the older countries with more complex industries to take up the experiment and ascertain the value of the principles by applying them to their own problems. For this purpose it will probably be best to follow Victoria and establish trade boards, since artisans, in Great Britain at least, are apt to show great distrust and jealousy of the interference of outsiders with their trade. The new method should be tried first in one or two selected trades and gradually extended to others as experience advised. In Great Britain suitable trades would be the railway workers, who are already in favor of the principle, and the miners, who have had a long experience of the working of conciliation. A court of arbitration, appointed as in New Zealand, should be established for each trade, and boards of conciliation should be set up in the various centers of the industry. Generally speaking, the procedure of New Zealand should be followed, care being taken to keep all the provisions of the law as elastic as possible. The courts and boards should create their own methods of working from their own experience and should strive to foster conciliation and the regulation of industry by voluntary agreements. Employers would gain by the stability of industry, workers by their rise in status. A grave problem is before us; it is worth while, it is imperative, to attempt a solution.

HENRY W. MACROSTY.

LONDON SCHOOL OF ECONOMICS.

IX

LABOR CONDITIONS IN SLAUGHTERING AND MEAT PACKING[1]

On September 9 the Executive Board of the Amalgamated Meat Cutters and Butcher Workmen of North America "called off" the strike of their 50,000 members against the five packing companies. In the Chicago stock yards, where 22,000 came out, followed by 8000 allied trades, this was the third general strike. For fifteen years after the Knights of Labor strike in 1886 every man or woman who ventured to start an organization was discharged; and after 1890, when the "combine" of packers became effective, many of them were blacklisted. The strike of 1894 was sympathetic and unorganized. The strike of 1904 was a mistake on the part of the union; for the employers had offered arbitration sixteen hours before the men went out, and arbitration was what the leaders had asked for. They were out eight days and went back on an agreement to arbitrate, but after an hour's work were again called out on the ground of discrimination. This was in violation of the agreement just made, which bound them and their employers to submit discriminations and all other grievances to arbitration. The mistake was natural. It followed a history of grievances on both sides and a conviction on the part of the workmen that the packers were determined to destroy their union.

The national union dates from July, 1897, and is designed to include all wage-earners in slaughtering and packing establishments and all meat cutters employed in stores. The country was fairly organized before Chicago was attacked in 1900. For a year or more the organizations were secret,[2] but eventually

[1] From the *Quarterly Journal of Economics*, Vol. XIX, 1904, pp. 1–32.

[2] Conditions described in this article are mainly those of Chicago, the center of the industry.

they felt strong enough to throw off their cloak; and in August, 1901, they united in the Packing Trades Council. This eventually comprised twenty-two locals under the jurisdiction of one national organization. Each local is organized on the line of a department. The cattle butchers form one local. Others are the sheep butchers, pork butchers, beef carriers, beef-casing workers, sausage makers, wool workers, hide-cellar men, canning-room employees, oleo and butterine workers, and twelve more. At first only the skilled men in each department were organized; but these gradually extended their numbers to take in the unskilled, and finally departments altogether unskilled were organized. Each local made its own demands and agreements at different times under the approval of the national organization; but in May, 1904, a combined scale for all departments and classes of labor was submitted to the employers. It was this scale that precipitated the strike; and the point of division was the demand for a minimum wage of 20 cents an hour, afterwards reduced to 18½ cents, for all unskilled labor. Demands of this kind had been made and granted in departments where skilled workmen such as cattle butchers and sheep butchers prevailed, but had been rejected in other departments.

In analyzing the labor situation in the industry, we may begin with the leading group of workmen, the cattle butchers.

The cattle butchers' local unions number 5500 of the 50,000 members, and of these about 2000 are the most highly skilled of all the workmen in the slaughtering and packing industry. Their importance has brought to them the title of "butcher aristocracy." Their strategic position is explained by the character and expensiveness of the material they work upon. The cattle butcher can do more damage than any other workman; for a cut in the hide depreciates its value 70 cents, and a spotted or rough carcass will be the last to sell, with the risk of the rapid depreciation of a perishable product. The sheep butcher merely "pulls off" three quarters of the hide, but the cattle butcher can pull off only 2 per cent. The entire hide must be neatly cut off, leaving the "fell," or mucous covering, intact on the carcass to give it a good appearance. The "splitter," too, must make a neat and smooth cut straight down the middle of the ivorylike "fins" of the backbone, or the wholesaler cannot quickly dispose of the piece. Yet, notwithstanding the high skill required, the proportion of skilled workmen in the butchers' gang is very small, owing to a minute division of labor. It would be difficult to find another industry where division of labor has been so ingeniously and microscopically worked out. The animal has been surveyed and laid off like a map; and the men have been classified in over thirty specialties and twenty rates of pay from 16 cents to 50 cents an hour. The 50-cent man is restricted to using the knife on the most delicate parts of the hide (floorman) or to using the ax in splitting the backbone (splitter); and wherever a less skilled man can be slipped in at 18 cents, 18½ cents, 20 cents, 21 cents, 22½ cents, 24 cents, 25 cents, and so on, a place is made for him and an occupation mapped out. In working on the hide alone there are nine positions at eight different rates of pay. A 20-cent man pulls off the tail, a 22½-cent man pounds off another part where the hide separates readily, and the knife of the 40-cent man cuts a different texture and has a different "feel" from that of the 50-cent man. Skill has become specialized to fit the anatomy.

In this way, in a gang of 230 men killing 105 cattle an hour there are but 11 men paid 50 cents an hour, 3 men paid 45 cents, while the number getting 20 cents and over is 86, and the number getting under 20 cents is 144, as follows:

TYPICAL CREW OF CATTLE BUTCHERS AND HELPERS

Rate of Pay per Hour	Number of Men at Rate	Rate of Pay per Hour	Number of Men at Rate
50 cents	11	25 cents	6
45 "	3	24 "	1
40 "	5	22½ "	16
32½ "	6	21 "	4
31½ "	2	20 "	20
30 "	2	18½ "	5
27½ "	4	15 to 18 cents	139
26½ "	6	Average 21 cents	Total 230 men

The table on the following page shows the list of occupations as provided for in the agreement of 1903–1904, with the number of men in each occupation for a gang of 230, their rates of pay, and their schedule of output. The agreement went only as far as knife men, who received 20 cents an hour. Those receiving less than that rate were the shifting population of laborers who had never been included in the scale and who would have been raised to a minimum of 18½ cents, had the demands of 1904 been granted.

The division of labor grew with the industry, following the introduction of the refrigerator car and the marketing of dressed beef in the decade of the seventies. Before the market was widened by these revolutionizing inventions the killing gangs were small, since only the local demands were supplied. But when the number of cattle to be killed each day increased to a thousand or more an increasing gang or crew of men was put together; and the best men were kept at the most exacting work. At what point the greatest economy is reached was discovered by experiment and by comparison of one house with another. Each firm has accurate knowledge of the labor force and the output of every other house, and in this way each improvement becomes general and each superintendent is keyed up. Taking a crew of 230 butchers, helpers, and laborers handling 1050 cattle a day under the union regulations of output, the time required for each bullock from the pen to the cooler, the hide cellar, and all the other departments to which the animal is distributed is equivalent to 131 minutes for one man. But this is made up of 6.4 minutes for the 50-cent man, 1¼ minutes for the 45-cent man, and so on; and the average wage per hour for the gang would not exceed 21 cents, making the entire labor cost about 46 cents per bullock.

Three objects were gained by this division of labor. *First,* cheaper men — unskilled and immigrant labor — could be utilized in large numbers. *Second,* skilled men became more highly expert in the quality of their work. While, on the one hand, this greatly increased the proportion of low-wage men, it also pushed up the wages of the very few skilled men on the delicate

CATTLE BUTCHERS, GANG OF 230 MEN

No. of Men	Position	Scale of Wages per Hour	Scale of Work (Number of Cattle per Hour), 1903-1904
3	Penner	$0.18½	Left to House Committee
1	Knocker, when raising gates and dumping out	.24	60
	Knocking only	.24	80
2	Shackler	.18½	Left to House Committee
2	Hoister	.20	" " " "
4	Sticking	.32½	" " " "
	Heading and sticking	.32½	25
	Heading only	.32½	30
1	Dropper	.20	Left to House Committee
2	Pritcher up	.20	" " " "
1	Gullet raiser	.20	" " " "
3	Foot skinner	.22½	35
3	Leg breaker	.25	25 sets
1½	Ripper open	.25	80
7	Floorman	.50	15
1½	Breast sawyer	.25	75
1½	Caul puller	.26½	50
	Pulling cauls and opening eich	.20	40
1	Eich opener	.20	75
1	Tail ripper	.20	20
3	Fell cutter	.27½	25
	Cord cutter	—	Left to House Committee
2½	Rumper	.40	40
3	Fell beater	.22½	
	Fell puller	—	60
2	Gutter	.26½	40
2½	Backer	.45	40
3	Tail sawyer	.26½	30
4	Splitter	.50	25
2	Hanging off	.22½	60
2½	Clearing out	.30	40
2½	Hide dropper	.32½	40
	Clear out and drop together	.32½	20
1½	Neck splitter	.31½	60
2½	Skirt trimmer	.21	60
3	Ladder men	.22½	Left to House Committee
4	Bruise trimmer	.22½	" " " "
1	Scribe sawyer	.20	" " " "
1	Cutting out tongues	—	100
6	Boning heads	$1.05 per 100	32½
	All other knife men	.20	
	Laborers not covered by agreement	.16½ to .19½	

and particular parts of the work. An all-round butcher might expect to earn 35 cents an hour, but the highly specialized floorman or splitter earns 50 cents an hour. Some of these expert floormen work a week at a time without cutting a single hide, so deft and delicate becomes their handling of the knife. If the company makes a few of these particular jobs desirable to the men and attaches them to its service, it can become independent of the hundreds who work at the jobs where they can do but little damage; and their low wage brings down the average to 21 cents where, if all were all-round butchers, the average would be 35 cents. Consequently, in the course of time the companies put a few of the strongest men and those with a particular knack for their work on "steady time," paying them a salary of $24 to $27 a week, regardless of the time actually worked; but the other nine tenths of the gang were hired by the hour and paid only for the time at work. These steady-time men not only stood by the company, but acted as pace setters; and in this way a *third* object of division of labor was brought about, namely, speed. Take the occupation of splitting, for example. In the year 1884 five splitters in a certain gang would get 800 cattle in 10 hours, or 16 per hour for each man, the wages being 45 cents. In 1894 the speed had been increased so that 4 splitters got out 1200 in 10 hours, or 30 per hour for each man, — an increase of nearly 100 per cent in 10 years. The wages, except for the steady-time men, were reduced to 40 cents per hour. Other occupations had been speeded up and other rates of pay had been reduced in similar proportions. This was undoubtedly the grievance above all others which led to the organization of 1901; for the first act of the union was not directed toward wages or hours, but towards a reduction of the output. This the union did by adopting a "scale of work" and putting it into force without consulting the foremen, superintendents, or proprietors. In the case of the splitters the output was reduced from an average as high as 30 cattle an hour in some establishments to a uniform 25 an hour, and thereafter, in order that the gang might get out 120 an hour, the number of splitters had to be increased to 5. Similar changes were made in other occupations, the floormen being reduced from an average of 20 to a limit of 15, and so on. An exception is the "head boners" or trimmers, who are the only class of workmen in the cattle gang paid by the piece. In this occupation the rate was formerly 7 cents per head, but it had been reduced to 9 mills per head; and the union, without placing a limit on the amount of work, secured two advances in the rate, bringing it to $1\frac{1}{4}$ cents per head. At this rate the leader of the boners can make 40 cents an hour.

The packers admit that some of them had gone too far in rushing the men, but they hold that the union has gone too far in restraining them. The union contends that their scale of work is the same as that which already existed in the Hammond plant and in one of the Swift houses. At any rate, the inelastic restriction of output is set forth by the packers as the most objectionable and arbitrary of all features of the union. They cite the fact that it applies equally and without distinction to "canners" that weigh 800 or 900 pounds and to corn-fed steers that weigh 1800 pounds. The justice of this criticism is acknowledged by some of the men, though they hold that the quantity of work does not vary in proportion to the weight of the animal and that, if the limit is low for canners, it is high for steers, so that the average is fair. The packers cite cases where a floorman is compelled to "kill time" sharpening his knife or strolling along in order to hold himself down to the union limit of work. There are undoubtedly exceptional men, and nothing is more surprising to the outsider than these wide differences. One man, whose knife slips down the hide as though he were playing, is turning out twice as much as his comrade, who seems to be a hard worker. Individual splitters have been known to reach as high as 60 cattle an hour, working on canners, at the time when the average was 30; and, of course, when the union sets the limit for each man at 25 an hour these swift men find spare time on their hands. Taking them as a standard, some of the packers say that the union reduced the output 50 per cent, whereas the reduction below the average might have been 16 to 25 per cent, according to the plant.

After the limit was set the companies discontinued the "steady-time" men and placed them all on the hour basis, since their services as pace makers were no longer useful. This reduction in expense must be considered as a compensation partly offsetting the reduction in work. The steady-time men have opposed the action of the union because their earnings were reduced; but the majority of the skilled men consider the restriction as the main blessing which the union has brought them; for they say that formerly they were speeded up until they were "in a sweat" all day, exhausted at night, and useless after forty years of age, "but now it is a pleasure to work."

In the first written agreement, dated September, 1903, it was agreed that "in the absence of any skilled man, those doing the same kind of work will attempt to make up the loss in the amount of work caused by such absentee." This was a valuable concession; for otherwise the absence of a floorman would reduce the output of the gang 150 cattle a day, or the absence of a splitter 250 a day, and so on. An offer on the part of one of the companies to pay the time of the absentee to those who made up the loss was declined by resolution of the union, because they feared it would increase absenteeism, and that the greed of the men would thus urge them on permanently to the former speed.

The artificial limit on output works against the employer in another way, for it prevents economical adjustment of the gang. Two floormen handle 30 cattle, but one splitter handles 25. Hence the foreman must hire two splitters and set them at other work which could be done by cheaper men — with a loss of time, moreover, in changing work. In the earlier days of the industry the number of men to be assigned to one position was determined by speeding up a man, if possible, to the gait of the gang; but, if he could not keep up, another full man was set to help him. Later the idea was adopted of putting a "half man" or a "quarter man" to help him; and the rate of pay for the half time or quarter time was the rate for that occupation. The significance of this device appears in the contention between the union and employers over "laying off" men in dull seasons. The custom has always prevailed in all departments of laying off a part of the force for three or four months when work is slack in order to give nearly full time to the others. In a killing gang the foreman would lay off the lowest ranks of unskilled labor and set higher paid men to doing a part of the work in the lower paid jobs. This dropping down would be carried through to the highest grades of labor, and in this way half men, one third men, and one quarter men were invented. This led to a crisis at one time, when the union insisted that a 50-cent man, who was put quarter time on a 40-cent job, should receive the higher rate of pay for all his time. The union finally receded; but at a later time, by threat of a strike, they stopped the practice itself of laying off men and succeeded in keeping the gang at full number through the year. This episode illustrates the diametrically opposite points of view of the employers and the men. The men preferred to have all of their number employed short time during the dull part of the year and thus to share equally the disadvantages of slack work. The employer considered it better to attach two thirds of the men to his work by giving them full time through the year; and he pointed out that it was exactly the complaint of short time that gave force to their demands for higher wages. For it was admitted on all sides that the hourly rates of pay, if they could be earned for sixty hours a week, would place the butcher workmen in a better position than that of similar grades of labor in other industries. But in order to do this they must lay off a large part of the force; and consequently when the packer speaks of steady work he does not take into account those laid off, — the work is steady only for those retained. The union, however, includes all the workmen; and from their standpoint steady time cannot be secured except by a different distribution of the work through the year, — a thing apparently impossible in a seasonal industry like slaughtering. After the strike the packers resumed the practice of laying off men in the slack season.

Notwithstanding this policy of laying off men, the companies have never been able to furnish full time, even for those who are not laid off. In the killing gangs, for instance, the man who makes full time in December makes only two fifths to three fifths time from February to July. Taking it altogether, such a man, regularly employed through the year, has averaged in years past 35 to 46 hours of work per week. This is shown by the following table of hours and wages of the highest paid labor in the cattle-killing gangs, showing the earnings of a splitter or floorman who "made killing time," that is, worked practically all the time when a certain gang was working. All the time lost by sickness, accident, or other ground of absence has been added, so that the table shows the full time of the gang, not the full time of any one man in the gang. The table represents the 25 or 30 men, in an establishment of 5000, who could have earned the highest possible wages for men paid by the hour.

WAGES OF SPLITTER OR FLOORMAN (1888–1904)

Year	Rate of Wages per Hour	Average Number of Hours per Week	Average Earnings per Week	Per cent of Possible Time and Earnings
1888	$0.40	41	$16.24	68.0
1889	.40	39	15.86	65.0
1890	.40	46	18.46	76.6
1891	.45	39	17.69	65.0
1892	.45	43	19.48	71.6
1893	.45 (7 mo.) .40 (5 mo.)	40	16.66	66.6
1894	.40	37	14.72	61.6
1895	.40	37	14.99	61.6
1896	.40	35	14.20	58.3
1897	.40	35	14.11	58.3
1898	.40	36	14.33	60.0
1899	.40 (9 mo.) .45 (3 mo.)	42	16.60	70.0
1900	.45	38	16.15	63.3
1901	.45	46	21.00	76.6
1902	.45 (8 mo.) .47½ (4 mo.)	46	21.70	76.6
1903	.47½ (9 mo.) .50 (3 mo.)	42	20.02	70.0
1904 [1]	.50	34	17.16	56.6

[1] Six months, slack season.

The table shows that the rate of wages per hour, beginning at 40 cents, was raised to 45 cents during the years 1891, 1892, 1893, then reduced to 40 cents until 1899, then again raised to 45 cents, and that two further advances, to 47½ cents in 1902 and 50 cents in 1903, were secured by the union. Similar changes were made in the rates for other skilled positions.

It will be seen that the average weekly earnings of this highest skilled workman who had a "steady job," though not "steady time" (since he was paid by the hour), have varied from $14.11 in 1897 to $21.70 in 1902, and that the average number of hours per week varied from 35 to 46, so that the time actually worked and the wages actually earned varied from 58.3 per cent to 76.6 per cent of possible time and earnings on the basis of 60 hours per week for 52 weeks.

Taking this position as a standard, it will be seen that the average weekly earnings of the men in the same gang getting 20 cents an hour have ranged from $5.64 in 1897 to $8.68 in 1902, while the men getting 16½ cents an hour have ranged from $4.65 to $7.16. These earnings are for men who have been kept on the force throughout the year and not laid off by slack work, sickness, or other cause. Evidently the average earnings of the men who were laid off for three or four months have been still lower, unless they have found work in other industries.

After the strike of 1886 the packers introduced what was known as "the contract system," that is, a contract to work, signed by each workman, authorizing the company to keep back ten days' pay and requiring the workman to give two weeks' notice of withdrawal. This practice continued until 1901, when the cattle butchers, irritated by the hardships of a man who was refused his deposit when his child was sick, made a demand; thereupon the system was abolished throughout the industry and all of the deposits were returned.

Perhaps the most remarkable gain secured by the cattle butchers' union, and one that was shared by all the others, was the adoption of regular hours of work. Cattle reach the stock yards during the night and are purchased by the packers early in the morning. Seldom, however, can they be driven over the chutes and delivered on the killing floors before nine o'clock, and often not until ten or eleven o'clock. Furthermore, it was always held that they could not be kept over night, but must all be killed on the day of arrival, since the charges of the stock-yard company for holding over night are 50 cents a head. Consequently, the men would report in the morning between seven and nine o'clock, as notified the night before. If the cattle were on hand, they began work. If the cattle were not yet ready, after waiting awhile a notice would be posted to begin work at ten, eleven, or twelve o'clock, as the case might be. The men received no pay for the time spent in waiting; and then they would be required to work often until late at night in order to dispose of the day's arrivals. It was nearly two years after the union was organized before it felt strong enough to take up this matter. A strike was threatened, but finally a conference was secured with a leading packer. The union spokesman told him of these hardships, comparing their position with his own, in that they never knew beforehand when their work would begin or be done, while he could finish up his day's work and go home. The packer only replied that he had never known that such conditions existed. From the date of that interview, although no promises were made, overtime has been abolished for the cattle butchers in all the establishments. The men begin regularly at seven o'clock, work until the day's killing is done, and go home not later than half past five P.M. If after ten hours' work there are cattle left over, they are held until the next morning. That a union had to be organized and threaten a strike in order that the owner of the business might learn of conditions of which his own conscience promptly disapproved is a fact full of meaning for all who are disturbed by the modern unrest of labor.

The union also secured four of the legal holidays which they had never enjoyed before, and these were shared by the other departments.

The cattle butchers devoted much time to perfecting a line of promotion, which they say shall be "according to superiority and oldest men to receive promotions." By "superiority" is evidently meant "seniority." This is designed to prevent favoritism on the part of the foremen, to prevent the introduction in the lower positions of outsiders, who may then be "jumped over the heads" of the older men, to diminish jealousy, and to maintain the feeling of equity and comradeship necessary among the members of a union. These rules of promotion do not find favor with the superintendents, who contend that forced promotion often takes a man away from work that he does well and gives him a position which he may not be able to hold. Neatness and superior quality of workmanship are natural to some men and never acquired by others; and, if the foreman is required by reason of seniority to promote an awkward man to a position where he may damage the hide 70 cents or retard the sale of the carcass, then the gang as a whole suffers. The antagonism at this point shows clearly the nature of the conflict between capital and labor, — a conflict irrepressible, as proved by the strike.

In a gang of sheep butchers the pace is set by the "pelter," who loosens the hide so that it can be pulled off without tearing the "fell," or mucous covering, and by the "setter," who starts the carcass on the trolley. One pelter and one setter in a gang were formerly steady-time men, and the pelter's speed had been pushed up to 60 and even 75 sheep an hour. The union, which was organized a year after that of the cattle butchers, set the limit at 40 per hour and later by an agreement with the firms raised it to 46½; and the companies placed all the steady-time men on the hourly basis. The speed of other positions was reduced proportionately; that is, there was a reduction of 30 or 50 per cent, according as it is measured by the average speed or by the speed of the swiftest men.

Irregular time was a grievance even more serious with the sheep butchers than with the cattle butchers. There are some twelve styles of dressing mutton, according to the locality of the market, — "Alleghenys," "Bostons," "New Yorks," and so on. The packer must wait each morning for orders from different parts of the country before he can decide the styles and quantities of work for the day. This compelled the men to wait sometimes until two o'clock in the afternoon, and to go home late at night. They finally refused to work after half past five P.M. under any conditions, the reason being that they could have got out the work by that time if they had begun at seven o'clock A.M. When the union was first organized one of the packers discharged several of the members, but after a threat to strike by the international union they were reinstated.

In the hog-killing and pork-cutting departments the local union was organized at the same time as that of the sheep butchers; but in these departments a limit has not been placed on the amount of work. A larger number of mechanical contrivances are used than is the case on the other killing floors, such as a huge wheel for hoisting the shackled hog, a scraping machine to take off the hair, and a trolley on which the carcass is hooked and passed from one worker to the next. The pace setters are the sticker, the scalder, the hooker on, the splitter, and the chopper, the latter being in the pork-cutting room; and, since the union has not set a limit on the amount of work, these positions have continued on "steady time." The proposed scale, as submitted in 1904, for the first time set a limit in this department; and, had this scale been adopted, the scalder, for example, would have been restricted to 500 hogs an hour, and his wages placed at 40 cents an hour instead of "steady time."

In this department the seasonal character of the work is more marked than in sheep and cattle killing; but there is, of course, a great improvement over the period preceding refrigeration, when hogs were killed and packed only in the winter months. On account of the very irregular supply of animals the union has not attempted to keep the gang at full force, but it has tried to establish the rule that "the last man hired is the first laid off; and when the gang is increased the oldest man with the house shall be hired first."

The sausage department has the credit of furnishing steadier work than other departments. The union of sausage makers, composed mainly of Germans, had a checkered and disastrous career. They imitated the cattle and sheep butchers in demanding a minimum pay for their gang; but they went further and applied the minimum of 18½ cents to all common labor. This demand they supported in 1903 in violation of their agreement by a strike. Their union had reached a membership of 1300; but they found that the unskilled laborers receiving less than 18½ cents an hour could not appreciate the advantages of the union and would not pay their dues. Since the strike was "illegal," the Amalgamated refused to support them, and the packers filled their places. When the agreements expired in 1904 it was this demand of the sausage makers, applied to all departments, that the Amalgamated took up and lost in the strike.

In the sausage department piecework prevails more than elsewhere, except in the canning department. The rates are based on the thousand pounds of sausage. The piecework system was introduced in 1891 in stuffing sausages by machinery, and up to the time of the union organization in 1902 the rates and practices were such that the best man in the best year could earn a yearly average of $12 a week, ranging from $8 to $16 in different parts of the year. In other years he earned less. In some cases piece rates had been reduced; and in 1899, without an organization, a strike forced an increase of 10 per cent in certain bologna prices that had been reduced 20 per cent. After the union was organized in 1902 other rates were increased.

A peculiar feature of the piecework system in pork sausages, as distinguished from bologna sausages, is the limitation of earnings per hour through the substitution of inferior casings when the men's earnings exceed a certain amount. In first-class casings without "leaks" twenty feet can be filled at one expulsion of the steam stuffer; but on second-class and third-class casings the workman must tie the casings wherever a leak appears, and this reduces the number of pounds of sausage to his credit. Since the superintendent is charged with the cost of material and labor and is credited with the value of the product, sometimes getting a bonus on the margin, it is to his interest to get not only a low labor cost but also a low cost of the expensive casings, a considerable part of which is purchased in the open market. He therefore watches his opportunity to substitute second-class and third-class casings for first-class. At what point it is safe to do this depends on the point of hourly earnings below which the workmen will resist, which was found to be about the rate of 27 cents an hour. He refrained from cutting the piece rates, as he had done in the case of bolognas; and, since the rates are the same for all classes of cases, he contented himself with putting slower work on the men by substituting inferior casings. This might require the men to work overtime in busy seasons to get out the product. Consequently, when in 1902 the union enforced its demand for a one and a half piece rate on all work done after a ten-hour day, the superintendent in the next busy season furnished first-class casings, and permitted the men to earn 35 to 36 cents an hour.

Women and girls have been taking the place of men in this department during the past five or six years, a peculiar instance being that of trimming meat from the bones and tying casings, where formerly older men, who were in a way kept as pensioners, have given way to girls, who work much faster. The strike of 1903 opened an opportunity for Slav women to take the place of German men.

The beef "luggers" are one of the most interesting specialties of this most highly specialized industry. They are the powerful men who load the sides of beef into the cars. There are but 60 of them in the yards; but they have taken into their organization the cooler hands and truckers who work with them. Prior to 1891 the luggers were paid 28 cents an hour, and earned $8 to $10 a week. Their hours of work are irregular, beginning at two or four o'clock in the morning, and they work only when the cars are switched in place. In 1891, on account of irregular hours, they asked for weekly wages and in place of 28 cents an hour secured $12.50 a week without an organization. In 1892 they again asked an advance and received $15 for a week of 54 hours. In 1902, after they had formed the Beef Carriers' and Helpers' Local, they got $17, and their demands for 1904 were for $18.50. At $17 on "steady time" their yearly earnings were nearly as high as those of the splitter or floorman, who is paid 50 cents an hour "killing time." The luggers also reduced the amount of their work, so that where 5 or 6 men loaded 60 to 70 cars a day, which, in their own words, "certainly was slavery, as any one who understands the work will admit," it thereafter required 8 men to load 60 cars. However, in the fall of 1903, after four men in a house had been making up work for a fifth member of the gang who was sick a month, the firm reduced the number permanently to 4. The luggers went out on a strike; but not being supported by the Amalgamated organization, they lost.

The number of women employed in the industry in 1890 was 990, or 2.2 per cent of the total number of employees. This was increased by 1900 to 2954, or 4.3 per cent. In Illinois the number is put at 1473, or 5.3 per cent. This proportion has undoubtedly been increased since the last census year; and it is generally stated that the number of women employees in Chicago alone is 2000, or about 9 per cent of all employees. This increase has come about partly through the introduction of foreign-born women into the sausage department and meat-trimming rooms at times when the men went on strike. Prior to that time women were not employed in the large establishments at work where the knife is used, their work being principally painting and labeling cans, soldering and stuffing cans, sewing up ends of bags, packing chipped beef, packing and wrapping butterine.

The majority of the women and girls are paid by the piece; and the Illinois Bureau of Statistics in 1892 showed that piece workers earned from $3.58 to $11.57 per week of 60 hours, the average being $6.78. At that time girls paid by the week of 60 hours earned $4 to $8.25, the bulk of employment per year ranging from 35 to 40 weeks. Weekly rates were gradually equalized, until in 1902 the prevailing rates of pay were $4.50 to $5.50. Much the larger number of women work at piece rates, and these were gradually reduced as the girls acquired greater speed, until in 1900, prior to the organization of the men and without any organization on their own part, the girls in one of the largest canning establishments went on strike against a further cut in rates. At that time the swiftest girl, who one year later died of consumption and overwork, was said to be able to earn $20. This girl, whose high earnings had tempted the company to cut the rates, joined with others of Irish-American stock and led the strike; and when they were defeated by the introduction of foreign-born women they found themselves blacklisted by the other large companies. Nine of them brought suit against the four leading companies for $50,000 damages; but the suits were decided in May and June, 1901, on demurrer in favor of the packers. The court declared[1] that "the defendants agreed not to reëmploy those who went out upon a strike. This they had a right to do. According to the allegations of the girls' declarations the purpose for making this agreement was bad, because by such agreement the plaintiff cannot get employment at her trade and is thus injured. This gives her no right of action, for a bad motive does not make a lawful deed actionable." The court also intimated that a union was judged by the same standard. "The right of union laborers to quit work or to refuse to work where nonunion men are employed is established beyond controversy, and that without reference to how pitiful the consequences may be to him who is thus deprived of an opportunity to earn bread for himself and family."

This decision had undoubtedly an effect upon the men and women in the stock yards in determining them during the next two years quietly and thoroughly to organize the whole industry. The men began to organize in June, 1900, four months after the girls' strike, and several departments were organized by the men before, in March, 1902, a women's local was chartered with fourteen members. The initiative was taken by the head worker of the University of Chicago Settlement, who had noted the exclusion of the women from the men's locals. It was decided to organize the women of all departments in one local, although the men were organized by departments. In this way the women secure representation in the Packing

[1] Chicago papers, June 11, 1901. The court was not a court of record.

Trades Council and in the conventions, whereas they would be outvoted were they to be distributed among the department organizations. Since the scales of wages and work are agreed upon by these superior bodies before they can be submitted to the packers, the girls have a voice through their own delegates in formulating them, which they would not have were they organized by departments.

An interesting illustration of this influence is seen in the compromise agreed upon at the Cincinnati Convention in 1904, respecting the employment and wages of women in the sausage departments. It was in this department that Slav women had been employed in place of Germans out on strike, as described above; and the men afterwards insisted that in the new agreement the women should be discharged. But the girl delegates opposed this demand, even though the women were not members of the union; and finally it was agreed that the union should demand that women be paid the same wages as men. This concession to the girl delegates was not faithfully carried out; and the scale, as actually submitted in May, provided for "abolition of women labor in the sausage departments." But the original compromise is significant as showing the standards which the union women were willing to have applied to women's work. These standards were also adopted for all other girls working in those occupations which had been recognized as "women's work," where they were not paid by the piece; and the demands there were the same as for the men, namely, a minimum of 20 cents an hour. This would have amounted to an increase of 100 per cent, since girls paid by the week receive 9 cents and 10 cents an hour, whereas the increase for the lowest paid men, bringing them up to the same minimum, would have been only 10 to 15 per cent. Even the compromise offer of 18½ cents an hour would have raised the girls 85 per cent. These standards were agreed to by the girls in full view of the fact that, at the same rates of pay (except in piecework), the women would probably be displaced by men.

Immediately following the organization of the women's local all the charter members, to the number of 14, were discharged;

but in the course of the year, with the assistance of the men's locals, they reached a membership of 1200. It has never been possible for them to bring into their union the non-English-speaking women, many of whom are married. But they secured practically all the Irish-American, German-American, and Polish-American girls; and this gave them entire control of some departments where only such happened to be employed. They elected their own business agent, secured reinstatement of several members who had been discharged for union activity (though not their president and secretary), gained advances in some of the piece rates, and advances of 50 cents to $2 in weekly rates. The normal rate paid now to these American girls is $5 for beginners, rising to $6 with experience. In one department, for example, employing 62 American-born girls, there are only 8 who get as high as $6 a week. Here the girls begin at $5 at sixteen or seventeen years of age. Very few work more than three years, the majority leaving within that period, usually for marriage. Numbers of Slav women return to work after marriage, but this is not the case with the American-born. Bohemian women and girls are increasing in number more rapidly than other nationalities, with the Poles and Lithuanians next; and they are doing heavy and disagreeable work, such as stuffing cans and trimming meat, where in many cases they have displaced men.

A significant fact in the history of the women's local is that, though they are the only class of labor generally employed at piecework, and though such a method of payment had led them to serious overexertion, they have yet made no efforts to limit the amount of work, some of which, especially in the can-making departments, depends on the speed of the machine. It seems that for the few years during which most of the girls expect to work in the industry they choose to overlook the strain of excessive speed, which to the men, as they grow older, becomes the greatest of all their grievances. The girls feel like working to their utmost for a period, in order to save up a sum of money and quit the work for a home of their own.

The number of children under sixteen years of age employed in the industry was 700 in 1890. This had been increased in 1900 to 1651, or 2½ per cent of all employees. The number in Illinois was 596, or 2.28 per cent. The intermittent work of the packing houses fosters in the children unsteady habits, and even the most industrious workmen trained in this school dislike more than four days' work in the week. The probation officer of the juvenile court strongly urges the boys and girls under suspended sentence not to work in the stock yards, and endeavors to find other jobs for them. The parochial schools of the neighborhood have been defective after the third or fourth grades; and in the Slovak school none of the teachers speak English, while the Polish school has but recently introduced English. The capacity of the public schools has been inadequate, though lately it has been increased. Since the census year (1900) the compulsory school law has been strengthened by amendments to the child-labor law, largely through the efforts of the butcher workmen's organizations, which sent a delegation to Springfield in behalf of the proposed law. Many of the men and women now working in the yards began at eleven or twelve years of age; but by the new law the work of children under fourteen years is prohibited and the work of those under sixteen is limited to eight hours per day. An age and school certificate, showing ability to read and write, is required from the health and school authorities for those under sixteen; and each establishment is required to keep posted in a conspicuous place a list of all children employed and the hours of beginning and quitting work. The enforcement of this law is intrusted to the state factory inspector and his deputies; and, after sixty convictions had been secured against some of the packers, certain firms went so far as to issue orders to their foremen not to employ children under sixteen, though permitted to do so by law. The short-time clause makes the services of children undesirable, except in the offices as messenger boys, where the entire force works but eight hours. The companies usually require as a measure of protection an affidavit from children above sixteen, although an affidavit is not required by law. The union does not admit persons under sixteen years of age. Viewed as a piece of legislation to exclude children under fourteen years of age, the law is effective.

The foregoing are departments of peculiar interest in the industry. The others are composed mainly of unskilled labor, as will be seen from the large percentage of those whose wages are less than 20 cents an hour, such as the oleo workers and glue workers, 95 per cent, the wool workers, 70 per cent, and so on. Taking the industry as a whole, it is maintained by the union statisticians that two thirds of the employees eligible to membership received less than 18½ cents per hour. The packers assert that the proportion was only 6 per cent. The United States census showed that in the year 1900 67.2 per cent of the employees received less than 18 cents an hour, and the United States Bureau of Labor showed that in 1903 the laborers, who constituted 84.8 per cent of the total number of the employees, received an average rate of 17.46 cents per hour. These reports covered only selected establishments, but they were typical for the industry.[1]

The motives on the part of the strikers were partly sentimental, partly for self-preservation. The sentimental side appealed to the public and was strongly emphasized. But there was also a profound self-interest involved in that through the minute division of labor promotion from the lower ranks can be made without much training. The packers contended that in the case of the unskilled the law of supply and demand, with its market rate of wages, could not be overruled; and they pointed to the 3000 to 5000 transient laborers who gathered every morning at seven o'clock at the several time-keeping stations asking for work, when not one tenth of their number could be employed. It was not a question of ability to pay the minimum asked; for the five packing companies controlled the bulk of the business, and through favorable freight rates, their own car lines, utilization of by-products, and minute division of

[1] Special Report, Twelfth Census, "Employees and Wages," p. 581; Bulletin No. 53, U. S. Bureau of Labor, p. 890.

labor, their position was more favorable than that of the "independents," who did not have these advantages and yet were paying the wages asked for. The packers proposed to reduce the minimum pay of men in the killing, cutting, casing, and beef-loading departments to 17½ cents an hour, a reduction of 1 cent. All other classes of unskilled labor were to be left "open" without a wage scale, by which transient labor might be paid as low as 16½ cents. A minimum wage of 18½ cents was more than such inexperienced labor was worth. It was necessary to have this floating supply only in order to fill the places of absentees, so that the gangs might not suffer. But the union contended that when once employed at 16½ cents an hour those who were getting 18½ cents would be discharged; and there were known enough cases of men at 18½ cents being discharged and rehired at 16½ cents to convince them that such would happen all along the line. After the strike the packers reduced large classes of their regular unskilled labor 1 and 2 cents an hour.

The demand for a minimum wage above the market rate was also necessary to the permanency of the union, since it had been found that those who received only market wages refused to pay dues. It is true that nearly all of them came out on strike with the others; but it was the union theory that, if a minimum of 18½ cents could be established, the companies could not then afford to employ transient labor which was worth only 16½ cents, and therefore better men would seek these positions, and union men would be preferred by the employers to nonunion men. This was in lieu of a demand for the "closed shop," for which none of the unions had asked, but which the skilled men had secured in practice, as is shown by the agreement of the cattle butchers that in the absence of any skilled man those doing the same kind of work would attempt to make up the loss. A minimum wage would have lessened the number of transient laborers employed and would have made the position of union laborers steadier through the year. The importance of this factor is seen by consulting the census[1]

[1] Vol. IX, p. 398.

of 1900, which shows that in the industry as a whole the greatest number employed at any one time during the year was 81,416 and the least number employed at any one time 57,119. In other words, 30 per cent of the employees are unemployed in the slack season. This proportion agrees with that of one of the largest houses in Chicago, whose employees number about 4000 in the slack season and 6000 in the busy season. If practically one third of the employees are laid off, then, of course, there is a wide opening for new men, unless blocked by the "closed shop" or obstructed by the minimum wage. The employers, as compensation for reduction in hourly rates of pay, have promised to make work steadier, so that the yearly earnings will be larger. They began during the strike by enlisting the aid of the commission men and by sending thousands of circulars to cattle raisers and shippers, urging a better distribution of their shipments through the week. The custom has long existed of shipping live stock on Saturday and Sunday, so that the arrivals of cattle during a typical week would be 30,000 on Monday, 8000 on Tuesday, 30,000 on Wednesday, dwindling to 200 on Saturday. If the shippers were organized, this appeal might be effective; but there is at present no certainty of its results. And, even if shipments were equalized through the week, this would not remedy the more serious inequality in distribution through the year, since live stock is a seasonal product following grass and corn.

Perhaps the fact of greatest social significance is that the strike of 1904 was not merely a strike of skilled labor for the unskilled, but was a strike of Americanized Irish, Germans, and Bohemians in behalf of Slovaks, Poles, Lithuanians, and negroes. The strike was defeated by bringing in men from the companies' own branch houses for the skilled occupations and negroes and Greeks for the unskilled occupations.

This substitution of races has been a continuing process for twenty years. At the time of the strike of 1886 the men were American, Irish, and German; and the strike was defeated by splitting their forces rather than by introducing new nationalities.

After that date the Bohemians entered in large numbers, although a few of them had begun work as early as 1882. Bohemians have worked their way forward, until of the 24 men getting 50 cents an hour in two of the cattle-killing gangs 12 are Bohemians, and the others are German, Irish, and American. The Bohemian is considered to be the coming man in the business. The Americans as wage-earners have practically been driven out of the stock yards and are being followed by the Irish and Germans. Those who have accumulated money leave for something more certain. The Germans are held mainly by the large number of homes they have purchased in the neighborhood; and this has seemed to be the future of the Bohemians and Poles, who have been purchasing homes for several years, and of the Slovaks and Lithuanians, who have begun during the past two years. The feeling of security since the union was established three years ago has stimulated the tendency to home ownership among all these nationalities, although as yet there are many Slovaks and Lithuanians who return with their savings to their native land. The Irish show wide diversities of character, noticeable in contrast with the uniformity of other races. In general there is a rising class and a degenerating class. Neither class shows any inclination towards home ownership. But the Irish of the rising class have a much stronger desire than the Germans or Bohemians to educate their children rather than to put them to work. This class of Irish have been leaving the industry, except as held back by a foremanship or skilled trade, or by a salaried position in the union, of which they have been the aggressive organizers and leaders. With the defeat of the union doubtless many more of them will leave. The other class, the degenerating Irish, displaced by the Slav, have become casual laborers, without definite place in any industry.

The older nationalities have already disappeared from the unskilled occupations, most of which now are entirely manned by Slovaks, Poles, and Lithuanians. The Poles began to appear at about the same time as the Bohemians, though not in as large numbers; and they have not advanced in the same proportion. The Slovaks and Lithuanians were first seen in 1899. One Slovak who has been in the yards ten years has worked himself up to a 50-cent job; but he is exceptional, and these two races have as yet only shared with the negroes the unskilled positions. The negroes first came during the strike of 1894, when many were imported from the South and large cities. An intense race hatred sprang up among the Americans and Europeans, who thought the negroes were favored by the employers; and this seemed to be leading to a race war. The conflict was averted by the union, which admitted the negroes on equal terms with the whites. This hatred has been renewed during the recent strike, when several thousand negroes were again imported. Notwithstanding the alleged favoritism towards the negroes, they have not advanced to the skilled positions, mainly because they dislike the long apprenticeship and steady work at low pay which lead to such positions. As strike breakers they were attracted by the easy work, free board and lodging, and wages of $2.25 a day instead of the $1.85 asked by the union; but in times of peace they are not steady workers at the low wages of the Slav.

Italians have never found a place in the trade; and the experience of the Greeks, who first appeared in 1904, has been curious. Several hundred Greeks in Chicago have established themselves as fruit dealers. When three hundred of their countrymen, recently landed from Macedonia, entered the yards these storekeepers were boycotted and several of them bankrupted. Through the Greek consul and the Greek priest the merchants endeavored to persuade the Greeks to withdraw from the yards; but they did not leave until the strike was settled, and then they went in a body to another part of the country.

It will be seen that the mingling of races in the stock yards is similar to that in other large American industries, and the problem is a trying one both for the civic neighborhood and for the union organizers. Unlike the union in 1886 under the Knights of Labor, the present organization sprang from the butcher workmen themselves; the former had been officered from without. In the union meetings the speeches are translated often into three or four languages, and much trouble has been occasioned by dishonest or prejudiced interpreters, though with experience these are weeded out. The races are brought together; and, where four years ago scarcely a Polish, Slovak, or Lithuanian family had a member who could speak or understand English, now nearly all have each at least one such member. Race conflicts were infrequent because the races were kept apart by language, distrust, and the influence of the priests; but there were frequent factional fights between religious societies of the same race, especially among the Poles, each society having its own patron saint. There were also many arrests for drunkenness, wife-beating, and neighborhood quarrels. Curiously enough these disorderly acts dropped off entirely from the date when the strike took effect, and the arrests fell off 90 per cent. The strike continued eight weeks, and the police inspector in charge of the district is reported as saying: "The leaders are to be congratulated for conducting the most peaceful strike Chicago has ever had. Compared with other big strikes, such as the railroad strike of 1894, the teamsters' strike of 1902, or the stock-yards strike of 1886, there was no violence."

The substitution of races has evidently run along the line of lower standards of living. The latest arrivals, the Lithuanians and Slovaks, are probably the most oppressed of the peasants of Europe; and 18 cents for a day of 12 or 14 hours in the Carpathian foothills becomes 18 cents an hour in the stock yards. Even with only four days' work a week, the Slovak's position is greatly improved; for in Uhrosko he had no work in winter. Yet his improved position shows itself, not in more expensive living, but in fabulous savings gained by packing sometimes as many as twelve persons in three rooms, taking in boarders, and sending his children to work. The new arrivals of this class of labor swell the ranks of the thousands waiting at the packing-house gates every morning, and to them there is little difference between 18 cents and 16 cents an hour. Yet it is most remarkable that those already on the ground came out with the union and did not go back until the strike was declared off.

It is not surprising that, with wage conditions, racial elements, and former grievances such as they were, the union, when it acquired power, should have carried a high hand. Besides the restrictions themselves the manner in which they were enforced was irritating. Every department or division had its "house committee" of three stewards, who often acted as if they had more authority than the foreman or superintendent; and frequently, when a union rule was violated, they stopped the work "in the middle of the game." When it is stated that the superintendent of one of the largest firms had to deal with one hundred and twenty of these committees, it need create no surprise to learn that he felt relieved when the strike came. The principal grievance was the violation of their own constitution and agreements, which forbade locals or house committees to stop work and required all matters to be referred to higher offices for settlement with the company. The rank and file and the lower offices were insubordinate. Yet the superintendents observed that the unions, as they gained experience, were electing more conservative leaders and that petty troubles were being more easily handled. This encouraging prospect for the union was blighted by the blunder and disaster of the strike. When they returned for work the union leaders and spokesmen were either not reëmployed or were laid off afterwards when business slackened.

J. R. Commons.

X

THE INTRODUCTION OF THE LINOTYPE[1]

In 1887 typesetting was essentially the same art as in the sixteenth century. While other branches of the printing trade had been revolutionized, the compositor had not advanced in his process beyond the point he had reached four hundred years before. Probably no other handicraft employing such a large number of persons underwent as little change during this period, so full of industrial reconstruction. Since 1890 machine composition has been rapidly supplanting typesetting by hand. The machine is still constantly encroaching on the field of the hand compositor, but the period of introduction may properly be considered as concluded by the year 1900. By that time the craft had adjusted itself to the new conditions and the future trend of events could be foreseen with some clearness.

It is the purpose of the present study to estimate the displacement of labor due to the linotype,[2] to describe the policy pursued by the union printers with reference to the machine and the economic effects of the machine on the workmen engaged in the trade, and finally to examine how far the policy of the International Typographical Union may be successfully adopted by other trade unions during periods of machine introduction.

[1] From the *Yale Review*, Vol. XIII, 1904, pp. 251–273. See Nicholson, The Effects of Machinery on Wages, London, 1892.

[2] There are several kinds of typesetting and typecasting machines, but the Mergenthaler linotype has exercised such a predominant influence that attention may be confined to it without danger of serious error. According to the returns made by local unions to the secretary of the International Typographical Union, the total number of typesetting and typecasting machines of all makes in operation on January 1, 1904, in union and nonunion offices within the jurisdiction of six hundred and twenty-five local unions was 7129, and of these 6375 were linotypes. The proportion of linotypes was probably not quite so great outside the territory covered by the Typographical Union, but the correction required would not be very great.

The displacement of hand compositors by the introduction of the linotype may be estimated with some accuracy and will afford an index to the industrial disturbance involved. The following table gives the number of linotypes manufactured in the United States and Canada for each year from 1887 to 1903:

Year	Number	Year	Number
1887	55	1896	757
1888	66	1897	510
1889	57	1898	636
1890	57	1899	566
1891	69	1900	714
1892	288	1901	661
1893	568	1902	757
1894	890	1903	891
1895	1076	Total	8618

Of the 8618 machines manufactured somewhat less than 500 have been shipped out of the United States and Canada and an approximately equal number have been destroyed by fire or otherwise put out of use. About 7500 linotypes were in operation in the United States and Canada on January 1, 1904.[1]

The average rate of composition on the linotype at the present time is estimated by competent authorities at between 4000 and 5000 ems per hour. The rate of hand composition does not on the average exceed 1000 ems per hour. A linotype operator is, therefore, able to set as much in one hour as a hand compositor does in four. Assuming that the 7500 machines are in operation the same number of hours each day as hand compositors formerly worked, the possible displacement of hand compositors to January 1, 1904, may be reckoned at 30,000. Two modifications must, however, be made in this calculation. In the first place, many linotypes are worked by two or three shifts of operators.[2] The number of machine operators in the United States, operating 7129 machines of all makes, within the jurisdiction of the International Typographical Union on January 1, 1904, was 10,604, or approximately 150 per cent of the number of machines.[3] If allowance is made for this fact,

[1] The officials of the Mergenthaler Linotype Company have kindly supplied data on which the above estimate has been based.

[2] See *The Typographical Journal*, February, 1904, p. 212. [3] *Ibid.*

the estimate of possible displacement is increased to 45,000 hand compositors. Some deduction must be made from this total on account of the reduction in working hours. The hand compositor worked on the average about ten hours per day, while linotype operators do not average more than eight hours.[1] Deducting 20 per cent for this cause, we may finally estimate the possible displacement of hand compositors at 36,000.

The actual displacement has been far less than the possible displacement. A large part of the 7500 linotypes would never have come into use if the economies incident to their operation had not been so large as to lead to an increase in the amount of printing done. There is no practicable method of separating the displacement occurring at the outset from that later apparent displacement due to expansion of the market. An examination of the table on page 251 leads, however, to the conclusion that the years 1894, 1895, and 1896 were marked by a large amount of actual displacement of hand compositors.[2] The rapid introduction of machines in these years resulted chiefly from the desire of newspaper publishers to reduce the cost of composition. A considerable part of the more moderate increase of machines since 1896 has been due to an increasing demand for the product of the machine.

Number of offices included in investigation	15
Number of linotypes in use	293
Average number of ems set on a linotype in an hour	3445
Number of printers employed before the introduction of machines	1512
Number of substitutes employed before the introduction of machines	396
Number of printers employed after the introduction of machines	968
Percentage of decrease	36

Even, however, during the earlier period there is evidence that the displacement was not nearly so great as the estimate of possible displacement would indicate. The above statistics, compiled from a report made in 1895 by Mr. William Ferguson, secretary of the New York Typographical Union,

[1] See p. 264 for the data on which this calculation is made.

[2] Additional evidence to this effect is found in the many complaints of displacement contained during these years in *The Typographical Journal*, the official journal of the union printers. These decrease greatly after 1896.

to the New York Labor Commissioner, throw considerable light on this point.[1]

The figures given include the whole working force of printers, many of whom, on account of the character of their work, were entirely unaffected by the machine. It appears that 293 linotypes displaced 544 printers. The actual displacement in these offices in the initial stage was, therefore, at the rate of less than two printers for each machine.

This difference between the possible displacement of hand compositors and the actual displacement of printers in the early period was due to several causes. First and most important was the practice of putting men already at work as hand compositors in charge of machines. The 229 machines were manned by from 300 to 400 journeymen printers. The displacement of hand compositors was therefore much greater than the displacement of printers. Moreover, the speed of the machine operators was less than it is at present. The average number of ems set per hour, it will be noted, was found to be 3445. The present rate of 4000 to 5000 ems was attained only after a considerable part of the operators had been some years at the machine. New operators in most cases reach the present average rate only after some years of practice.

Although the great increase in the demand for the machine product naturally came after the machine had been somewhat generally introduced, even in the introductory period the cheapness of machine composition led to an increase in the amount of composition done. For some years prior to the introduction of the linotype the practice of using "plate matter" had been growing among newspaper publishers, the high cost of hand composition having forced the publishers to the use of an undesirable substitute. The extension of this practice had been for many years a frequent occasion of friction between the publishers and the local unions of the International Typographical Union. The low cost of linotype composition caused in most machine offices an entire abandonment of the use of "plate

[1] Annual Report of the Commissioner of Labor of the State of New York, Vol. I, 1895, pp. 370–372.

matter," resulting in an immediate increase of printers' work. Furthermore, the producing power of the composing room was increased in order to secure a greater effectiveness during the last few hours before going to press.[1] Editors canceled machine-set matter with much less reluctance. To a casual observer the composition of a newspaper would appear an unpromising field for the operation of the law of elasticity of demand, but the common experience of printers and publishers indicates that in numerous ways the cheapening of the cost of composition acted as an immediate stimulus to the demand.

In the second period, roughly designated as beginning with the year 1897, consumers shared more largely in the economy of production resulting from the use of the linotype. The larger profits of newspaper publishers led to strong competition, which partly took the form of an increase in the size of the newspapers. The linotypes installed for this purpose did not displace hand compositors, but on the contrary enlarged the field of employment for those printers who could learn the operation of the machine.[2] In the book and job trade the cheapening of the product through competition caused an enormous increase in the amount of composition done. As early as 1896 the *American Bookmaker*, a trade journal, naïvely complained that "employing printers foolishly give to the public advantages which should accrue to them. . . . It is probably safe to suggest that not one in ten of those who have adopted type-setting machines are making any more net profit than they did when all of their type was set by hand."[3] The result has been that since 1897 an expanding demand has more than offset the displacing power of the machine.

A large percentage of the hand compositors affected by the introduction of the linotype were members of the International

[1] See below, p. 264.

[2] The general opinion among printers and publishers appears to be that in those newspaper offices which introduced linotypes about 1895, the number of printers employed by the year 1900 was as great as it was before the introduction of linotypes. See on this point Report of Industrial Commission, Vol. VII, p. 279 (testimony of Mr. Donnelly, president of the International Typographical Union).

[3] Quoted in *The Typographical Journal*, Vol. VIII, p. 204.

Typographical Union. While this union enjoys the distinction of being the oldest national organization of trade unionists in the United States, the subordinate unions were until recently almost independent of the national body. About 1888 the national body began to absorb power from the subordinate unions, and this movement has gone on slowly to the present time. To a considerable extent, therefore, the policy of the printers with reference to the machine was determined by the local unions. So large, however, were the interests evidently at stake that local unions followed certain general lines of policy laid down by the national conventions and advised by the national executive board.[1]

At the thirty-sixth annual session of the International Typographical Union, held in Kansas City in June, 1888, a resolution was adopted that "the International Typographical Union favors the recognition of such [typesetting] machines," and "recommends that subordinate unions . . . take speedy action looking to their recognition and regulation, endeavoring everywhere to secure their operation by union men upon a scale of wages which shall secure compensation equal to that paid hand compositors."[2] At this time less than 100 machines were in operation in the United States and Canada and the greater part of these were being run experimentally.

By the time the session of 1889 was held the growing importance of the question led to the formulation of the union's policy in a general law, controlling the action of all subordinate unions. With unimportant changes in phraseology, this law has remained in force. In its original form it read as follows: "The International Typographical Union directs that in all offices within its jurisdiction where typesetting machines are used practical printers shall be employed to run them and also that subordinate unions shall regulate the scale of wages on

[1] The evident necessity for the adoption of a common machine policy has been a powerful influence in hastening the movement toward centralization in the Typographical Union.

[2] Report of Proceedings of the Thirty-Sixth Annual Session of the International Typographical Union, 1888, p. 181.

such machines." [1] Curiously enough, the printers were at first reluctant to operate the machines, and at the thirty-eighth session resolutions were adopted urging "that members of subordinate unions should learn to operate . . . machines wherever in use." [2]

By June of the next year, 1891, when the thirty-ninth annual session of the Typographical Union was held, the delegates were convinced of the grave importance of the machine question. In February the subordinate union at Indianapolis had sent two of its members to New York to investigate at first hand the working of machines. The committee found that operators on the improved linotype were able to produce an average of 3000 ems per hour and believed a speed of 4000 ems possible. They recommended that wages for operators should be on a time scale and that the hours of labor should be shorter than those prevailing for hand composition.[3] The report of this committee, published both as a pamphlet and in *The Typographical Journal*, exercised a large influence on the convention held in the following June. At that session a special committee on typesetting devices recommended "that a weekly or time scale be adopted for the operation of machines," and "that the hours of labor upon them be reduced to the lowest possible number, eight hours being the maximum." [4] It was urged that a time scale was more equitable than the piece system on account of the newness of the work and the consequent difficulty of estimating the average output to be expected. The demand for a reduction in hours was based on the ground that "the work upon machines was of a more exhaustive character mentally and physically than hand composition."

[1] Report of Proceedings of the Thirty-Seventh Annual Session of the International Typographical Union, 1889, p. 91.

[2] Report of Proceedings of the Thirty-Eighth Annual Session of the International Typographical Union, 1890, p. 153.

[3] Typesetting Machines. Report of an Inquiry into their Merits and the General Situation surrounding them, made by Typographical Union No. 1, Indianapolis, Indiana.

[4] Report of Proceedings of the Thirty-Ninth Annual Session of the International Typographical Union, 1891, p. 196.

The recommendations of the committee were adopted and became binding on the subordinate unions. The strong feeling in the craft for local autonomy secured the repeal of these two laws at the session of the International Union in 1893,[1] but they became the basis for practically all wage scales formed, and the great majority of linotype operators work at the present time on a time scale and have an eight-hour day.

The machine policy of the union was evidently based on the requirement that the machines should be operated only by journeymen printers. This rule had two distinct parts. In the first place, it asserted the claim that the operation of the machine was printers' work. Important as this part of the rule was in minimizing displacement, it involved no break in the former practice of the union and in effect was simply an extension of jurisdiction over machine operators. A different phase of the law was the prohibition against the operation of the machine by apprentices. The uniform custom of the International Typographical Union hitherto had been to consider any of the work in a printing office proper for an apprentice.

There has been a slow movement towards the incorporation of machine work in the regular training of the apprentice. In 1893 it was provided that "apprentices may work on machines in the last year of apprenticeship, who shall be paid two thirds of the wages of regular operators until their time of apprenticeship shall have expired."[2] This rule was anomalous in two particulars: it restricted the time of learning the machine to a part of the apprenticeship period, and it formulated a wage scale for a class of apprentices. In both respects the regulation was entirely opposed to the former practice of the union. The increasing use of machines and the rapid displacement of hand compositors led at the next session of the International Union to a reaction and to the withdrawal of this slight concession. The new enactment provided that "indentured apprentices may work on machines during the last six weeks of apprenticeship, providing they receive the scale of the

[1] Report of Proceedings of the Forty-First Annual Session of the International Typographical Union, 1893, p. 201.

[2] *Ibid.*, p. 200.

subordinate union."[1] As very few apprentices in the printing trade have been indentured during recent years, this modification of the prohibition was not important.

By a law passed at the national session of 1899, "regularly employed apprentices in machine offices" were "privileged to practice on machines during all of the last three months of their apprenticeship."[2] Since the product of apprentices who "practiced" on machines could not be used by the employer, while any other part of their output had a market value, not many employers were likely to put apprentices during working hours at "practicing" on machines. An apprentice by virtue of the law might, however, acquire a small amount of knowledge out of working hours. It was not until 1903 that the union printers were willing to permit the machine product of apprentices to be used. The session of 1903 enacted that "regularly employed apprentices shall be privileged to work on machines during all of the last three months of their apprenticeship and the learners' scale shall apply to such apprentices."[3] This small relaxation was proposed and strongly urged by the executive committee of the International Union.

The Typographical Union has been actuated by two motives in the enactment of legislation prohibiting the operation of machines by apprentices. The members felt strongly that as far as possible the opportunity to learn the new devices ought to be restricted to the displaced hand compositors. The apprentices had far greater adaptability than the displaced men, who, in a great majority of cases, must learn the machine or quit the trade. The slight modification in the restriction of machine work to journeymen is due to the passing of the early stage in the introduction of the machine. The printer who was displaced by the machine has either found his place in the trade or has abandoned it for some other occupation. The

[1] Report of Proceedings of the Forty-Second Session of the International Typographical Union, 1894, p. 31.

[2] Report of Proceedings of the Forty-Fifth Session of the International Typographical Union, 1899, p. 50.

[3] Report of Proceedings of the Forty-Ninth Session of the International Typographical Union, 1903, p. 110.

maintenance of the rule in its present form is due to the strong fear that machine work may fall into the hands of men who are not printers. If the Typographical Union were fully convinced that the operation of machines was neither practicable nor profitable except by journeymen printers trained in the trade as a whole, there would be no reason for the continuance of the restriction on the operation of machines by apprentices.

In order to facilitate the policy of manning the machines with printers the subordinate unions found it necessary to provide for journeymen an opportunity of learning the new device. Since a linotype operator produces for the first few weeks only a small amount of matter, employers required some concessions in wages during this period. The unions, usually after conferences with employers, formulated what are known as "learners' scales." The wages paid under these scales was lower than the regular wage for operators and the period of apprenticeship was limited. The International Union left the decision as to the terms of "learners' scales" entirely to the subordinate unions, except that from 1896 to 1898 the period of apprenticeship was fixed at two months. The local unions showed themselves for the most part keenly alive to the importance of securing for their members a knowledge of the machine. The formulation of a "learners' scale" obviated the necessity of bringing expert operators from other cities, and in so far as this was accomplished avoided the friction which would have resulted from the transfer of operators from one city to another.

So important did the avoidance of local displacement appear to the union printers that they attempted in 1894 to strengthen the hands of local unions by a general law, which required that "members of a subordinate union employed in an office at the time of the introduction of machines shall have preference as operators, one expert operator being allowed."[1] This law only remained in force a short time. An appeal against its enforcement was taken to the international president by an expert operator, who maintained that his rights as a member of the

[1] Report of Proceedings of the Forty-Second Annual Session of the International Typographical Union, 1894, p. 38.

union were thereby infringed. President Prescott, in the case of *Wandress* v. *San Francisco Typographical Union, No. 21*, sustained this contention on the ground that the law was a violation of the constitution of the International Union, under which a member with a traveling card is entitled to the "friendship and good offices" of any union to which the card may be presented.[1] Mr. Prescott was careful to point out that the rights of a traveling member would not be abridged where an employer "of his own volition or at the instigation of any person or persons decided to receive no application for situations until those who were working in his office had been given an opportunity to show their ability or inability to manipulate machines."[2] The burden of avoiding local displacement was thus placed entirely on the subordinate unions, and in the great majority of cases agreements were concluded with employers by which their old employees were retained as machine operators.[3]

Several of the larger local unions went further in their anxiety to meet the demand for skilled operators. Machines were bought or rented and members were permitted to practice on them.[4] The introduction of machines was undoubtedly much facilitated by the constant efforts of the unions to supply the needed operators. The unions were actuated by a keen desire to control the machine and the fear that, if the printers did not furnish the operators, they would be secured from some other source.

The subordinate unions frequently had to deal with propositions to decrease the scale for hand composition in order to enable employers to meet the competition of the machine. This matter was entirely within the jurisdiction of the subordinate unions, but the officials of the International Union strongly advised against any attempt to keep the machine out by cutting down the price for hand work. In his address to the forty-second annual session Mr. Prescott said: "Those familiar with

[1] *The Typographical Journal*, Vol. VIII, p. 301. [2] *Ibid.*

[3] Some unions pursued a less far-sighted policy by refusing to grant reasonable "learners' scales." See *The Typographical Journal*, Vol. VI, p. 3. The officials of the International Union constantly impressed upon the locals the necessity of securing for their members an opportunity to learn the machine.

[4] *The Typographical Journal*, Vol. VI, p. 7.

the productiveness of machines are agreed that hand work cannot begin to compete with them, and it is therefore futile to attempt to stay the tide of their introduction by a reduction in the scale unless we are prepared to suffer level decreases amounting to 40 to 50 per cent, and at that figure a better living could be secured at almost any unskilled avocation. A serious reduction in the rate of hand composition is sure to affect the machine scale also."[1] Notwithstanding this eminently sane advice, some of the hand compositors, as they saw themselves displaced, turned to their only weapon of defense, competition with the machine.[2] One method was for a group of compositors to form a partnership and furnish matter ready set to publishers at a price as low as that formerly paid for composition in the publishers' offices. The compositors paid their own rent, their fuel and light bills, as well as the cost of type. The scale of the union was thus underbid by its own members. Another practice much in vogue in small cities was for a number of displaced compositors to print on a coöperative plan a small newspaper. Assisted by the sympathy of the community, they were able in some cases to make a living wage.[3] The unions in common decency could hardly deal harshly with such covert methods of competition, but the union scales for hand composition were rarely lowered for the purpose of competing with the machine.

There was practically no direct opposition to the introduction of the machine. Occasionally a small union refused for a time to make a scale for machines, but the International Union steadily discountenanced such a policy, and, since the subordinate unions could not legally declare a strike without the sanction of the executive board of the International Union, they were soon persuaded to adopt a different line of conduct. The Kansas printers were able to keep the machine out of the state printing office for a time by political influence.[4] But in

[1] Report of Proceedings of the Forty-Second Annual Session of the International Typographical Union, 1894, p. 3.

[2] *The Typographical Journal*, Vol. VI, p. 1; *ibid.*, Vol. X, p. 251 and p. 342; *ibid.*, Vol. XI, p. 304.

[3] *Ibid.*, Vol. VI, p. 7 and p. 3.

[4] *Ibid.*, Vol. X, p. 453.

general the printers acquiesced in the new order of things without a struggle.

During the years 1894 to 1896 many printers were unable to secure work. The depression of business intensified the distress occasioned by the introduction of the machine. No safe estimate can be made of the extent of unemployment among printers at this time, but some indication is furnished by the fact that the Germania Typographia, the national union of the German printers, with a membership of about 1300, paid $17,262.50[1] in out-of-work benefits during the fiscal year 1893–1894. Twenty per cent of its members were unemployed in October, 1893.[2] The proportion of unemployed among the members of the Typographical Union was not nearly so large, but it was undoubtedly very great.

The International Typographical Union has never paid an out-of-work benefit, but has relied for the relief of unemployed members on the sharing of work. In former periods of industrial depression members without regular employment had been given a part of the work controlled by their more fortunate fellow-unionists. The desire to facilitate the sharing of work had led to the building up of an elaborate set of rules constituting what is known among union printers as the "substitute system." In the first year of the introduction of the machine this system gave temporary relief to the unemployed, and as machines were installed the displaced compositors flocked into the remaining hand offices as substitutes. The continual decrease in the number of hand offices added to the number of substitutes and diminished their opportunities for securing employment. The unemployed were chiefly workmen of advanced age who were unable to operate machines at sufficient speed. They could not secure employment in other branches of the trade because they had become highly specialized in the setting of straight matter. Some of them went to the smaller towns to which the machine had not come; others abandoned the printing industry.

[1] Fünfundzwanzigjährige Geschichte der Deutsch-Amerikanischen Typographia, von Hugo Miller, p. 58. [2] *Ibid.*, p. 45.

Even if the International Union had had an adequate system of out-of-work benefits, it is doubtful if this class of compositors would have been materially helped. Their retention in the printing trade was an impossibility, and the inevitable readjustment could be made better at an earlier time than after a period of precarious livelihood made possible by benefits. Other printers were only temporarily displaced and, with the revival of business and the enlargement of demand, they found places in the trade. The large local unions exerted themselves to tide their unfortunate members over the period of depression. In several cities the number of days which any member might work in a week was limited to five, in order that the substitute system might afford relief for larger numbers.

The most pronounced economic advantage accruing to the printers from the introduction of the machine has been the material reduction secured in the length of the working day. Certain peculiar trade conditions favored the Typographical Union in its demand for a short working day on machines. The machine was first introduced in newspaper offices, and even at the present time the number of machines in newspaper offices far exceeds the number in book and job offices. The following table gives the number of machines in use in each class of offices for the years 1901, 1902, and 1904:[1]

	1901	1902	1904
Book and job offices	837	981	1638
Newspaper offices	4138	4834	5491

The requirements of the newspaper office have consequently been an important factor in setting the length of the working day on machines. Prior to the introduction of the machine wages for hand compositors in newspaper offices had been almost uniformly on a piece basis, the union scale regulating the price per thousand ems set. The unions required the

[1] Compiled from returns made to the secretary of the International Typographical Union. See *The Typographical Journal*, Vol. XVIII (supplement); *ibid.*, Vol. XXIV, p. 212.

publishers to give employment for a fixed minimum number of hours each working day. The maximum working day had never been a matter of concern to the unions so far as newspaper offices were concerned. The stress had always been the other way, since the publishers were desirous of keeping in their employ as large a number of printers as possible in order that any sudden strain might be met. The printers, with many local variations, had adopted the rule that six or seven hours' work must be furnished each day. Allowing for time spent in distribution of type and in pasting up "dupes," the usual working day on newspapers was rarely less than ten hours.

Newspaper publishers always need the largest composing force during the last few hours before the paper goes to press. In a peculiar sense it is true in newspaper work that the usefulness of a workman is not reduced proportionately with a decrease in the length of the working day. The cheapness of machine composition made it possible for publishers to increase the capacity of their force in order to secure a much desired increase in effectiveness during the last hours. The proposition of the union for an eight-hour day on machine composition seems for this reason to have met with small opposition from the employers.

The following table shows the length of the working week for machine operators in offices controlled by the Typographical Union, according to scales in force January 1, 1904:[1]

Number of Hours constituting a Week's Work	Morning Newspaper Offices	Evening Newspaper Offices	Weekly Newspaper Offices	Book and Job Offices	Total
Unions reporting less than 48 hours	48	38	11	18	115
Unions reporting 48 hours	266	296	199	193	934
Unions reporting more than 48 and less than 54 hours	15	37	38	23	113
Unions reporting 54 hours	53	139	93	86	371
Unions reporting more than 54 hours	1	0	0	2	3

[1] Compiled from returns made to the secretary of the International Typographical Union. See *The Typographical Journal*, Vol. XXIV, p. 211.

Of 1536 scales for operators in the various kinds of machine offices 68 per cent fix forty-eight hours or less as the maximum working week. The proportion of operators having a forty-eight-hour week is still greater, since the larger unions usually have shorter working days than the smaller ones. The relatively large number of scales for evening newspaper offices fixing more than forty-eight hours as the maximum working week is due to the fact that many small towns have evening newspapers and no morning newspapers. It is probable that between 80 and 90 per cent of the union machine operators in the country have at present a maximum working week of forty-eight hours or less. In the larger cities the length of the working day is usually the same on morning and evening newspapers, while it is somewhat longer on weekly newspapers and in book and job offices. The other printers employed in the composing rooms of the newspaper have profited by the reduction in the hours of machine compositors. "Admen," "floormen," proof readers, and hand compositors employed in machine offices usually enjoy the short working day of their colaborers, the operators, who have set the hours of labor for the entire composing room.

The effect of the machine on wages is difficult to estimate on account of the change in the method of payment from the piece to the time system. The table on the following page gives for each of the largest ten cities in the United States the union scale for hand composition in 1891 and the union scale for machine operators in 1904.[1]

Assuming that a hand compositor was able on the average to set 1000 ems per hour, the wages per hour of machine operators at present is about 20 per cent higher than that of hand compositors was in 1891. Since, however, the hand compositor worked ten hours as against the operator's eight, the day wages for the two kinds of work do not differ materially. A simple comparison of the union scales for the two classes of

[1] This table is compiled from reports made to the secretary of the International Union. See Proceedings, 1892, p. 204 *et seq.*, and *The Typographical Journal*, Vol. XXIV, p. 213 *et seq.*

	Union Scales for Hand Composition per 1000 Ems, 1891		Union Scales for Machine Operators per Week, 1904		Number of Hours constituting a Week's Work for Machine Operators	Wages of Machine Operators per Hour	
	Day Work	Night Work	Day Work	Night Work		Day Work	Night Work
New York	40c.	50c.	$24	$27	48	50c.	56 1/4c.
Chicago	41	46	24	26.40	48	50	55
Philadelphia	40	40	20	25	48	41 2/3	52 1/12
St. Louis	38	43	23.25	26.10	46	50 25/46	56 17/23
Boston	38	45	22.36	24.36	42	53	58
Baltimore	40	45	21	22.50	42	50	53 1/2
Cleveland	40	43	21	24	48	43 2/3	50
Buffalo	33	35	19.50	22.50	42	46 3/7	53 4/7
San Francisco	45	50	27	30	45	60	66 2/3
Cincinnati	41	45	22	25	48	45 5/6	52 1/12
Average	39.6	44.2				51	57

workmen neglects, however, an important consideration. Under the piece system few employers paid any of their workmen more than the minimum rate, while a considerable part of the machine operators in all the cities included in the table get more than the scale.[1] The speedy and accurate operator receives a differential wage over the slower workman.[2] Machine operators in these cities, therefore, receive somewhat more on the average for eight hours' work than hand compositors did at the introduction of the linotype for ten hours' work. The difference in favor of the operator is even greater in the smaller cities.

Regularity of employment has been up to the present far greater among the machine operators than it was formerly among the hand compositors as a class. The constant expansion in the demand for operators has kept the competent workmen fully employed. The "learners' scales" have been so

[1] In the arbitration proceedings held in June, 1903, to determine the wage scale for machine operators in New York City, the New York union laid stress on the fact that one half of the newspaper operators in that city received more than the existing scale.— Arbitration Proceedings, *Typographical Union, No. 6* v. *New York Newspaper Publishers* (MS.).

[2] In Chicago a bonus is paid all operators on matter set beyond a fixed amount. In the other cities the differential is not fixed so exactly, but works itself out by individual bargaining.

arranged that employers train new operators only when they are needed. The machine, moreover, has increased indirectly but materially the regularity of employment for all printers through its effect on the number of apprentices. As long as straight matter was set by hand there was a profit to the employer in having apprentices, since within a comparatively short time they became proficient enough in this branch of the trade to more than repay the employer for the low wages paid them. The result was that the number of apprentices was out of proportion to the growth of the industry. Largely as a result of the overcrowding in the trade a class of printers came into existence who were known as "tramp" printers. Drifting here and there in search of work, many of them acquired dissolute habits. Printers holding regular situations were expected to share work with these fellow-unionists, and in many cities it became the custom for unmarried newspaper compositors to work only two or three days each week during periods of depression.

The first convention of the Journeymen Printers of the United States, held in 1850, was strongly of the opinion that "too many printers had been manufactured of late years."[1] The local printers' unions always put forward as one of their chief aims the restriction of the number of apprentices, but achieved only a very partial success. The introduction of the machine has appreciably diminished the importance of the apprenticeship question to the printers. Since straight composition is the branch of the work to which the machine is best suited, the profit from apprentices has sensibly decreased, and as the machine extends its field the future needs of the business become the controlling factor in the regulation of the number of apprentices. The "tramp" printer, a sign of an unhealthy trade condition, has almost disappeared and confines his operations to the smaller towns in which hand composition still maintains its hold.

Besides the length of the working day, the rate of pay, and regularity of employment, one other factor in the conditions

[1] Proceedings of the National Convention of Journeymen Printers of the United States, New York, December 2, 1850 (Philadelphia, 1851).

of work is worthy of attention in every trade, — the intensity of labor required. Linotype operators are universally agreed that the high speed attained on the machines makes the work far more exhausting than hand composition. The International Typographical Union has at times gone close to limitation of output in its desire to keep the speed required within what the union considers reasonable limits. At the forty-first annual session it was enacted that "no member . . . shall be allowed to accept work . . . where a task, stint, or dead line is imposed by the employer on operators of typesetting devices."[1] The same session prohibited operators from accepting a "bonus per thousand above the regular scale."[2] The fear that the employers would raise the required amount so high as to make the work a very heavy strain or that through the incentive of a bonus the standard would be put up by especially skillful operators to a point difficult of attainment led to the enactment of these laws.

The prohibition on the payment of bonus was repealed in 1894,[3] but the sentiment against this form of wages remained very strong, and in 1902 it was enacted that no bonus should be accepted by machine operators where "such bonus is voluntary on the part of the employer and is not provided for in the scale of prices."[4] The session of 1902 went much farther than any of its predecessors and recommended "that subordinate unions establish a stated amount of machine composition which is considered a fair day's work."[5] The laws of the Typographical Union, if they had been literally enforced as they stood in 1902, denied the employer the right to place any definite stint, but gave the union the right to do the very thing prohibited to employers. Despite the prohibition against employers fixing the accomplishment of a certain amount of work as a condition of employment, this was done in nearly all newspaper offices, and in 1903 the Typographical Union repealed

[1] Proceedings of the Forty-First Annual Session of the International Typographical Union, p. 200. [2] *Ibid.*, p. 201. [3] *Ibid.*, p. 38.

[4] Proceedings of the Forty-Eighth Session of the International Typographical Union, p. 141. [5] *Ibid.*, p. 142.

its prohibition.[1] The same session struck out the section recommending the "establishment by the local unions of a fair day's work."[2] The rule against the acceptance of bonus except when paid according to the union scale is the only remaining law of this kind, except a provision that "members shall not engage in speed contests."[3] The purpose of this unique prohibition is to prevent exaggerated ideas arising of the amount proper for an operator to perform.

Such rules as those described have seemingly been entirely ineffective in checking the increase in the speed of operators. Occasionally a local union has sheltered an unreasonable demand behind such rules, but in the main the speed of the operator has been determined only by his ability. The large number of operators receiving more than the minimum wage scale indicates that as a class their output is not arbitrarily limited. A large part of the supporters of the legislation described desire to secure by this means employment for operators who are not able to reach the standard set. The constant increase in the speed of the operator has made the old provisions for learning the machine inadequate. The proper remedy is for the unions and employers to revise the "learners' scales" to conform to existing conditions.

The success of the International Typographical Union in enforcing the rule that printers shall be employed as linotype operators has been frequently attributed solely to the strength of that organization. In his testimony before the Industrial Commission Mr. Gompers, president of the American Federation of Labor, said: "The printers have had a remarkable history, particularly within the last five years. The machine . . . was introduced and it is one of the cases where a new machine revolutionizing a whole trade was introduced without involving a wholesale disaster even for a time, and it is due to the fact that the International Typographical Union has grown to be an organized factor, recognized by those employing

[1] Proceedings of the Forty-Eighth Session of the International Typographical Union, p. 123. [2] *Ibid.*, p. 136.

[3] International Typographical Book of Laws, 1903, General Laws, section 69.

printers as a factor to be considered."[1] A more explicit statement of the same view was made before the commission by Mr. D. F. Kennedy, an organizer of the Federation of Labor for Indiana. He said, "These [typecasting] machines would now be run by typewriters, not typesetters, had it not been for the union taking possession of the situation to that extent that they compelled them to use typesetters to run the machine."[2]

If a union can force in every period of machine introduction the preferential employment of its members on the new devices, one solution of the much discussed problem of the displaced workman is offered. The introduction of machinery frequently leads to the employment of less highly trained and less skillful workmen; in many cases to the replacing of skilled artisans with poorly paid women and children operatives. The printers require an apprenticeship of four years before the workman is permitted to operate the linotype. How far is it true that the Typographical Union by sheer force of combination has been able to force the employment of highly paid workmen to perform work which might be done by a much cheaper class of laborers? On the answer to this question depends the decision as to the possibility of similar combinations of workmen in other trades utilizing the experience of the printers on these occasions when fundamental reconstructions of their trade are in progress. A policy which requires the employment of skilled workmen for work easily within the power of less skillful employees would be clearly uneconomic, and its continued enforcement would be against great economic pressure.

The International Typographical Union undoubtedly occupied an advantageous strategic position in the introduction of the machine. Its chief strength for many years had consisted in the control of the greater part of the larger newspaper offices. It is entirely probable that the union did secure the control of the machine in some of these offices because the publishers feared the boycott, which is peculiarly effective against newspapers. A second advantage possessed by the

[1] Report of the U. S. Industrial Commission, Vol. VII, p. 615.
[2] *Ibid.*, Vol. VII, p. 748.

union lay in the fact that, as the machine was introduced in the smaller newspaper and job offices, the supply of expert workmen trained in the offices of the large union newspapers furnished a ready labor market for the employers installing linotypes.

Several facts point, however, to the conclusion that the policy of the printers has succeeded not simply through the power of combination. In the early years of the introduction of the linotype much was said about the possibility of operating machines with unskilled labor.[1] The experiment was tried in several cities, but with such small success that employers have abandoned the attempt to recruit their linotype operators from this class of labor. Nonunion offices with substantial uniformity employ printers as machine operators. The union rules do not bind these employers and their policy is dictated by economic interest. The same practice prevails in all other countries where the linotype is in use.[2] No tendency to replace male with female labor has ever appeared. The proportion of female to male operators is smaller than the proportion of female to male hand compositors. In January, 1904, the number of women operating typesetting and typecasting machines in the United States and Canada was 520, about 5 per cent of the total number of linotype operators.[3] The number of women engaged in the United States in 1900 as printers and compositors was 15,875,[4] about 15 per cent of the total number of printers and compositors.

A trade-union rule without economic justification would probably have won its chief success at the outset. The returns made to the officers of the Typographical Union show that so far from the union losing control of the machine the proportion of union to nonunion operators is increasing. The following

[1] The printers were profoundly affected by the fear that they would be supplanted by a cheaper class of labor. The continuance of the restriction on apprentices working the machine is due to the persistence of this fear. See above, p. 258 and p. 267.

[2] See Webb, Industrial Democracy, p. 407; Radiguer, Maîtres Imprimeurs et Ouvriers Typographes, p. 482.

[3] *The Typographical Journal*, Vol. XXIV, p. 212.

[4] Twelfth Census of the United States, Population, Part II, p. 507.

table shows by years the percentage of union operators and machine tenders.[1] At the present time 92¾ per cent of all machine employees according to these returns are members of the union.[2] In no other branch of the trade does the union control so large a proportion of the workmen.

	Percentage of Total Number		
	1901	1902	1904
Male machine operators	92	92	94¼
Female machine operators	63	56	62½
Machine tenders	86	89	95
Operator machinists	100	90	93

A consideration of the technical character of the linotype confirms the conclusion that it differs from many machines in requiring for its most profitable operation the skill of the superseded handicraftsman. The amount produced on a linotype is directly proportional to the skill of the operator, while the great mass of labor-saving inventions reduce the work of the laborer to that of tending the machine. Every part of the hand compositor's knowledge is useful to the machine operator, except an acquaintance with the location of the case boxes, and instead the operator must learn the keyboard of the machine. In addition the operator must think far more quickly. He must not only know the same things, but he must be able to use knowledge more rapidly.[3]

The real merit of the policy of the Typographical Union was that it secured for its members an opportunity to show to the

[1] Compiled from *The Typographical Journal*, Vol. XVIII, No. 11 (supplement); *ibid.*, Vol. XXIV, No. 2, p. 212.

[2] The census made by the union officials omits more nonunionists than unionists, but the conclusion as to the tendency is not weakened by such omissions.

[3] The present linotype operators were trained at hand composition. As this method of production falls more and more into disuse, it is a grave question whether apprenticeship in a printing office will form a sufficient training for the operators. The knowledge of spelling, punctuation, and capitalization which the apprentice gets from hand composition will probably have to be obtained in trade schools, or the apprentices intended for linotype operators will be recruited from a better educated class of boys. For some time, however, this will not be an urgent question.

employer that the union printer was more profitable than the unskilled workman as a machine operator. This policy required the frank recognition of the machine, its honest working, and fair concessions to employers during the period of machine apprenticeship.

GEORGE E. BARNETT.

JOHNS HOPKINS UNIVERSITY.

[Following is the statistical table compiled by the secretary of the union for the year beginning January, 1904, and referred to on pages 271 and 272 preceding. It will be noted that the number of female machine operators (omitting machine tenders and operator machinists) in nonunion offices (195) is about 28 per cent of the total number of nonunion operators (714), but the number of female operators in union offices (325) is less than 4 per cent of the total number of union operators (8851). — ED.]

Class of Employees	Union	Nonunion	Total	Per Cent Union
Male machine operators	8526	519	9045	94¼
Female machine operators	325	195	520	62½
Machine tenders	596	31	627	95
Operator machinists	970	69	1039	93
Total	10,417	814	11,231	92¾

XI.

THE PREMIUM PLAN OF PAYING FOR LABOR[1]

Broadly speaking there are two methods of paying for labor in common use. Under the first method payment is made in proportion to the amount of time consumed in doing the work, while under the second payment is made in proportion to the amount of work done. In the vernacular of the shop these are called respectively the *day's-work* and the *piecework* plans.

A third plan deserves attention, not because of its connection with the subject but because of its intrinsic importance. It is in a sense a combination of those named and, measured by the extent of its use, it is next to them in importance. I refer to the New England Contract Plan under which certain leading men, who are called sometimes foremen and sometimes contractors, are given contracts for doing certain work. The shop and its facilities are the property of the employer, but the contractors proceed much as though the shop was their own. They engage the help and arrange their rates of pay, this pay being by the day, the men as a whole having no interest in the contracts. The contractors are not capitalists and do not furnish the capital or pay their men, who are paid by the employer precisely as though there were no contract plan in the shop, but the wages as paid are charged against the various contracts, and as the work is turned in the contractors are paid the difference between the contract price and the wages paid out.

There is no question that this plan has had a large influence on the development of the metal-working industries of New England. It has, moreover, extended far beyond the confines

[1] From the *Sibley Journal of Mechanical Engineering*, Vol. XVI, March, 1902. On this and related subjects see also Schloss, Industrial Remuneration, 3d edition, 1898.

of New England. Some very large works — among them the Baldwin Locomotive Works — operate on this plan.

Inquiry regarding this plan will frequently be baffled by its contradictory aspects to the different parties. To the employer it is piecework, as he ultimately pays for the work by the piece, and he will frequently call it by that name. To the workman, on the other hand, it is simple day's work, with the addition of an unusually energetic and lynx-eyed foreman. Except as he learns it accidentally, he need not even know that the shop is at bottom a piecework shop, as his own rate of pay, as well as that of his associates, is exclusively by the day.

The day's-work and piecework plans are in their leading faults antithetical. From the nature of the day's-work plan the workman has no direct share in any increased production which he may bring about by more intelligent or increased exertion, the benefits of such increase going wholly to the employer. The only inducement the workman has toward increased effort is the hope that through it he may eventually obtain a slight increase in his daily wages.

From the nature of the piecework plan, on the contrary, the employer has no direct share in any increased production which the workman may bring about by more intelligent or increased exertion. He has the indirect benefit due to the increased production from a given plant, but the wages cost remains the same regardless of the production.

I have spoken of these features of the two plans as their chief faults, and they are such because through them and in consequence of them community of interest between employer and employee in the reduction of costs is impossible. Neither offers any basis for such a community of interest, and it is this which it is the prime object of the premium plan to supply. The piecework plan has upon its face the appearance of equity and fair dealing. "It pays for the work done and in proportion to what is done. The industrious are rewarded in accordance with their industry," etc., etc. The universal opposition of labor unions to it is looked upon as another evidence of their total depravity. Of course, in so far as the objections of the unions are a reflection of the opposition which some of them have to their members doing a large amount of work it cannot be defended and is not worth discussion, but for other reasons and on other grounds their position of opposition is impregnable. Near acquaintance with the system shows that it is not what it appears to be. It is in fact a remarkable illustration of how completely a thing may differ in appearance from what it is in reality. It is in appearance a system of rewards, but it is in fact a system of punishments, and worse still a system of *punishments for doing well.*

As this is a severe arraignment it requires an examination of the actual workings of the system. A piece of work has been done by day's work and it is proposed to change it to piecework. The piece cost[1] under day's work is first determined and a somewhat smaller piece price is then set and given to the workman. If he has had no experience with piecework, he feels that he cannot "make wages" and objects. He is then told that if he will not take it some one else will; in other words, he is compelled to take it, and this is the first objection to the plan, — it involves compulsion. If this were all that could be said against the system, it would not have much weight, but it is nevertheless worth noting. Leading is always better than driving, and compulsion is a good thing to avoid if possible.

No man knows what he can do under an incentive until he has tried it. The workman in saying that he cannot "make wages" at the piece prices offered when piecework is first introduced is entirely sincere, but he is nevertheless mistaken. All experience shows that when the test comes the increase of output under the incentive of piece rates is far beyond what any one — manager or workman — would have believed possible. The output mounts up and the wages with it, and the employer soon finds that he is paying an extravagant rate of daily wages, an extravagant rate being understood as a rate materially in excess of what it would be necessary to pay another workman for doing the same work, he having the first man's experience

[1] The actual wages paid for doing the work, or the "wages cost" only, is considered here.

before him. The employer submits to this for a time, but the wages continue to increase and ultimately he is driven to his only recourse,—he cuts the piece price. This is an immediate announcement to the workman that the promises of piecework are false. He was told that he would be paid a certain rate per piece, but he finds that to be true up to a certain limit only. The workman, again under compulsion, accepts the new price, but unless he is very dull he has learned a lesson. If he is very dull, it may require a second cut to enforce this lesson, and this second cut, either on the price of his own work or on that of some fellow-workman, is soon forthcoming. The lesson is that if he pushes his production to a point which raises his earnings beyond a certain more or less clearly defined limit the direct result will be a cut in the piece price. Perhaps new men come in or the old ones are given new work to do, — the result is the same. If any one is so unwise or so unfortunate as to do a large amount, he is at once punished for it by having his rate cut. Such cuts from the workman's standpoint have but one result, — he is compelled to work harder than before, but he earns no more. This is the result of his own efforts to increase his output, and hence it is that I call the piecework system a system of punishment for doing well.

The net result of the system is a somewhat greater output and somewhat higher wages than would be obtained with the day's-work system, but there is no spirit of progress. The workmen push their earnings as near to the limit as they dare and then stop making further effort to increase their output. If one man has several pieces of work, on some of which the prices are high while on others they are low, he makes out false time tickets, charging time to one job which belongs to another, so as to equalize matters and give a fair average and thus take advantage of the high rates on some pieces to equalize the low rates on others. The whole tendency is to cultivate deceit and antagonism. The piecework plan is, in short, simply a mischief-maker and a discord breeder.

The workman of course looks upon these cuts as an exhibition of pure hoggishness on the part of the employer. While the employer may take undue advantage in this way, the fact remains that if he does not make the cuts from choice he will eventually do it from necessity, for it can be shown that these cuts are an integral part of the piecework plan, which can no more be operated without them than a windmill can be operated without wind, for the reason that as the years go by the whole tendency of prices is downward. . . .

The day's-work and piecework plans are, as has been shown, antithetical in their faults, and the premium plan is an effort to obviate these faults by splitting the difference between them, so to speak. By this is meant that whereas with the day's-work plan the immediate gains due to increased effort by a workman go to the employer, while with the piecework plan they go to the workman, with the premium plan they are divided between the workman and his employer, and this is the essence and substance of it.

To understand this suppose that a piece of work has been done upon the day's-work plan and that it is proposed to change it to the premium plan. The time which it has required is determined, and the workman, who is still paid the old day rate, is told that if he will reduce that time he will, in addition to his daily wages, be paid a premium for each hour or part of an hour by which he reduces the time, *this premium per hour being less than his hourly rate of wages*. Please note this, as it is by this device that the division of the gains is made. If he objects, he is simply told, "Very well, try or not as you think best; there is the work and the offer, and the premium is ready whenever you have earned it." In other words, the proposition is simply an offer of a reward for an increase in output without a trace of anything in the nature of compulsion. It is of course expected and usually found that with this reward before him the workman will sooner or later endeavor to increase and succeed in increasing his output. . . .

To gather the exact workings of the plan assume a concrete case. A workman is paid say $3 per day and produces one piece of a kind per day, that is, in ten hours. He is told that he will continue to be paid his $3 a day as before, but that if he will reduce the time on the piece he will be paid in addition to his wages a premium of 10 cents for each hour saved. If he reduces the time by an hour, that hour represents in money value a gross saving of 30 cents. Ten cents of this amount is paid to him as a premium, leaving the remaining 20 cents in the employer's possession, this sum making itself manifest in the reduced cost of the work. If the workman goes on reducing the time in which the piece is made, the same process is repeated, each hour saved resulting in an increase in the workman's wages of 10 cents and in a reduced cost of the piece of 20 cents. In other words, the wages go up and the costs go down simultaneously, this apparently paradoxical result coming about from the fact that the gross time saved is divided between employer and employee, part of it going to increase the wages of the latter and the remainder going to reduce the cost to the former. This is shown in the accompanying table, which, for purposes of illustration, is extended until the workman has doubled his output, in which case the wages cost of the work has gone down from $3 to $2, while the workman's earnings per day have advanced from $3 to $4.

THE WORKINGS OF THE PREMIUM PLAN

1	2	3	4	5
Time consumed	Wages per Piece	Premium	Total Cost of Work = Column 2 + Column 3	Workman's Earnings per Hour = Column 4 ÷ Column 1
10 hours	$3.00	$0.00	$3.00	$0.30
9 "	2.70	.10	2.80	.311
8 "	2.40	.20	2.60	.325
7 "	2.10	.30	2.40	.343
6 "	1.80	.40	2.20	.366
5 "	1.50	.50	2.00	.40

There is of course a considerable gain to the employer due to the increased production from a given plant, since the secondary costs of production — the expense items which make up the burden and which must be added to the cost of labor and material in order to obtain the ultimate or true cost — are increased but little in consequence of the intensified production. It is, however, easy and customary to exaggerate the employer's gains from the system, a subject that will be discussed more fully further on.

It will be seen that superficially the plan has some resemblance to the profit-sharing plan. The chief difference is that whereas the profit-sharing plan treats the business as a whole and the workmen in a body, the premium plan treats each individual and his work separately. Under the profit-sharing plan the gross profits at the end of the year are determined and a certain percentage of these is divided among the workmen regardless of individual merit, whereas under the premium plan each workman's earnings depend solely upon his own efforts. . . .

As outlined above the premium plan is a very simple thing, an almost absurdly simple thing, and it would seem to be so obviously correct in principle as to be accepted without question. It has, however, required much time and effort to get it tried. It is now being tried, however, on a scale which will determine its merits and insure its permanency, if it is really what it appears to be. No very exact idea of the extent of this trial can be given, as interested parties who at first came to me for information and suggestions now go to their friends. It is known to be in use in the United States, Canada, England, Scotland, Germany, Italy, and Belgium. Interest has been shown in Sweden and Austria, but it is not known to me whether the plan is in use there. It has apparently attracted more intelligent and serious attention in Great Britain than here or elsewhere, — a fact which may perhaps be due to the considerable feeling there that British industrial methods need improvement. . . .

The first question to be decided after the adoption of the plan has been determined upon is the rate of the premium, that is, what proportion of the value of the time saved is to be given to the workman who saved it.

For this there is a perfectly clear principle to guide us and that principle is precisely the one which we use in buying anything whatever with money, namely, to pay what is necessary to get what is wanted but to pay no more. If we have a fence to paint or a roof to shingle, the only principle we ever think of following in order to get the work done is to pay enough to induce some one to do it. If we offer less than that, the work will go undone, while if we pay more the surplus is a simple gratuity. So here. A workman has been working at the usual pace and has been paid the usual daily wages. If we wish to induce him to do more, we should offer enough, but no more, as a premium to induce him to make the extra exertion. If we offer too little, he will reject the offer, the offered returns being too small to recompense him for the effort, and the desired increase will not be obtained. On the other hand, if we offer too much, the surplus, as in the case of painting the fence or shingling the roof, is a simple gratuity.

Looked at from this standpoint it is clear that there can be no single rate of payment which will apply to all classes of work. In the machine shop, for example, increased output is largely a matter of intelligence. The workman uses coarser feeds, higher speeds, and deeper cuts. He has several tools at hand and grinds one while another is at work so that as soon as one is dull another may be slipped into its place without loss of time. In other words, he crowds the machine rather than himself. In the blacksmith shop or foundry, however, increased output can be secured only by actual increased muscular effort by the workman. It is clear that in the first instance a smaller premium will suffice than in the others.

I have always considered this feature of the plan, whereby the incentive can be graded according as the work is laborious or not, to be one of its best features, though it has attracted less attention than it deserves.

Looking at the premiums when settled in accordance with this simple principle of paying what is necessary but no more, we learn several things, of which the first is that they are in no sense bonuses or gratuities, but that, on the contrary, they are, in the fullest sense of the word, earnings. . . . We learn, secondly, that they do not need to be cut from time to time, but that so long as the methods of production do not change the rates may be permanent. The plan contemplates increasing the workman's earnings as a reward for increased effort by himself. Should the proprietor introduce a new labor-saving machine, it would be economically wrong to continue the old rates, since the increased output of the new machine is not the result of the workman's efforts. Under such circumstances a new base time must be determined and the premiums be based on that.

If the rates have been settled in accordance with this principle, there need, however, be no change in them so long as the methods of production remain the same, and indeed there must not be. Such cuts would introduce the objections of piecework and destroy the workman's confidence in the system and with it his incentive to further effort. To cut the rates is to kill the goose that lays the golden egg. It is essential that the limit to the workman's earnings shall be set by his own capacity to produce and not, as with piecework, by an arbitrary ruling of the office.

It has often been objected that the proprietor may cut the rates if he chooses, and that after all the plan still has the same fundamental objection as piecework. True, the plan does not make rate cutting impossible, but it does make it unnecessary and unprofitable. Smaller initial rates than those determined by this principle would have been less profitable to the employer, and to cut them when once set would not only lead to less profitable rates, but it would stop further progress by destroying the workman's confidence. Under this plan it is to the employer's interest not to cut, while, as has been shown, under piecework such cuts are sooner or later forced upon him.

With the rates set in this manner we see, thirdly, that with a single limitation we have secured an ideal economic condition, a condition under which and under given methods of production we will obtain the highest possible production and the lowest possible cost, while the workman will receive the highest wages to which he is economically entitled. In other words, we will secure the maximum possible efficiency of plant. . . .

Considering the premiums as set in this way and considering also the rates which experience shows to be sufficient, we learn, fourthly, the fundamental defect of piecework, — *its initial incentive is too high;* that is, it offers a reward for increasing the output which is larger than is necessary to produce that increase and larger than it is economically possible for the employer to continue to pay. It is from this defect that all the difficulties with piecework spring. Cutting the rates is a clumsy and disastrous method of correcting this defect.

When it comes to the actual setting of the premium rates it must be owned that our guiding principle gives us but little help, but that is equally true of it as applied elsewhere. The real difficulty we have to face is that whereas if we have a fence to paint or a roof to shingle we have a large body of experience to draw upon, in the matter of premiums the body of available experience is small. In the one case the custom of the locality settles for us what rate we must pay, whereas in the other custom has not yet been established. In this matter I am satisfied that the tendency is to set the rates too high, that is, to set them so high that in the future the employer will be apt to find as with piecework that another workman would be glad to take the work at a lower rate, if that rate were guaranteed. The premium rates actually paid range between one third and one half the wages rates. The former figure for machine-shop work I regard as about right, but the latter, except in shops which were under a high state of efficiency before the adoption of the plan, I regard as dangerous. In my own use of the system in Canada the highest rate paid to men was one third the wages rate, and it ranged from this down to one quarter, and this rate seemed there to be ample, although the lowest of which I have any knowledge. At the same time everything in the way of wages, salaries, and incomes is on a smaller scale in Canada than here, and the rate would probably be too low here. . . .

The question of the extent of the gains made is of course a legitimate one. Several tables giving comparisons of the three items affected before and after the adoption of the system have been published and the gains are uniformly greater than would be believed possible. In one case a certain corporation had made thirty-five large, heavy machines, and at a later date they entered upon a second contract for twenty duplicates which were made under the premium system, the base time being taken from the cost records of the first machines. At a certain stage of progress with the second lot I was given a table of the records of the two contracts, the figures given including all records, good and bad alike, that had been made on the second lot. The extent of the exhibit is shown by the fact that the time reported in it for the first contract aggregated about 20,000 hours. Taking the time, wages cost of the work, and wages earned per day on the first contract as unity, the second contract showed a reduction in time of 43 per cent, a reduction in the wages cost of 25 per cent, and an average increase in wages per day of 29 per cent.

It is scarcely possible to collect from the results of everyday work data of any kind which are in all respects satisfactory. It is especially difficult to preserve that fundamental condition of all intelligent experimenting that but one condition shall be varied at a time, and candor requires it to be said that this criticism applies to this exhibit. In the nature of things one of these lots of machines came first chronologically. A piece of work done the second time is usually done with a reduction in the time expended, and, other things being equal, the second lot of machines, without any premium at all, should have shown some saving in time and cost. Other things were not equal, however, the second lot being for twenty machines while the first was for thirty-five, and in these matters the advantage goes with the larger lot, which should, other things being equal, be made proportionately more quickly than a smaller lot. To correct the figures for these influences is impossible, but it is perfectly certain that without the premium system no record approaching that given above could have been made.

The same corporation gave me a second exhibit, which was not open to these objections, though unfortunately it was much smaller. This exhibit showed the results on certain parts which had been reduced to a strictly manufacturing basis. They had been made over and over again and the advantage of sequence was thus eliminated, while the lots were of the same size in both columns of the exhibit. The numbers in the lots of different pieces varied between one hundred and three hundred. Both workmen and foreman were positive that the time on these parts was down to the minimum and that it was useless to apply the premium plan to them. Nevertheless the pieces for which the figures were given showed an average reduction in time of 41 per cent.

Another exhibit of considerable magnitude was supplied by an electrical manufacturing company, the average results shown being a reduction in time of 39 per cent, a reduction in wages cost of 28 per cent, and an increase in wages per day of 23 per cent.

These gains are so large as to excite incredulity. Most men of experience will not seriously consider a system which deliberately proposes to increase output by 70 per cent while reducing wages costs and increasing daily wages by 25 per cent, and I am satisfied that if the plan did about half as well as it really does its growth would be much more rapid than it is. Apart from exact figures, which are difficult to get, is testimony from many men in many lines of work, which is substantially unanimous in saying that the system works in the manner described, and this testimony is not a matter of geography or nationality. . . .

F. S. HALSEY.

THE PREMIUM PLAN AT THE WORKS OF DAVID ROWAN & CO., GLASGOW, SCOTLAND [1]

Work as recorded on a job ticket is given to a workman on a time allowance, and if he reduces this time allowance his rate of wages per hour while he is working at the job is increased by the same percentage as that by which the time allowance has been reduced. It is of course apparent that data must be collected for the purpose of arriving at the time to be

[1] From the *American Machinist*, January 9, 1902. Correspondence of Mr. James Rowan with Mr. Halsey.

allowed to do work. For this purpose a special department (rate-fixing department) is required, and when instituted, data accumulate very quickly. The period occupied in doing work under the usual time-payment conditions may be accepted as the time allowance of the premium system.

When a job is given to a workman a job ticket is issued to him with a description of the work to be done and the time allowed to do it. On completion of the work the job ticket is initialed and the time of day recorded on it by the foreman, and this is the time of commencing the next job. When the work has been examined and passed by the works inspector the job ticket is handed to the rate-fixing department, which passes the same for payment. In the case of a job being rejected by the inspector, any premium which would otherwise have been earned by the workman by reason of his having reduced the time allowance is forfeited. No clerical labor devolves upon the workmen and very little upon the foremen.

The time allowance for a job given to a workman rated at say 8 *d.* per hour is 100 hours, and the actual time occupied on the job amounts to 75 hours. We have then 100 hours at 8 *d.* = 800 pence against 75 hours at 8 *d.* + 25 per cent (2 *d.*) = 750 pence, giving the workman a premium = 150 pence, or 2 *d.* per hour, and the employer a reduced cost = 50 pence. Provided the time allowances are equitable to employer and employed, and based on the average attainments of hourly labor, it will be evident from the foregoing that the higher the premium earned by the workman the greater will be the saving in cost. The output of the machines is also increased, but it is a hard matter to put a value to this.

The table shows your method of premium system, that adopted by Messrs. G. & J. Weir of this city, and our system. Messrs. Weir's is exactly the same as yours in principle, with the exception that the workman receives half the time saved and in your case he receives one third.[1] My system is totally

[1] Mr. Rowan is of course in error in assuming my idea to be thus limited. The amount of the premium rate has received in these columns as much or more discussion than any other feature of the system. — F. S. H.

Comparison of Different Methods of calculating Premiums

Halsey's Method

Wages Rate 30 Cents per Hour			Premium earned on Job	Total Labor Cost	Workman's Rate per Hour
Hours allowed	Hours taken	Time Wages on Job			
100	100	$30.00	$0.00	$30.00	$0.30
100	90	27.00	1.00	28.00	.311
100	80	24.00	2.00	26.00	.325
100	70	21.00	3.00	24.00	.343
100	60	18.00	4.00	22.00	.366
100	50	15.00	5.00	20.00	.40
100	40	12.00	6.00	18.00	.45
100	30	9.00	7.00	16.00	.533
100	20	6.00	8.00	14.00	.70
100	10	3.00	9.00	12.00	1.20
100	1	.30	9.90	10.20	10.20

Weir's Method

Hours allowed	Hours taken	Time Wages on Job	Premium earned on Job	Total Labor Cost	Workman's Rate per Hour
100	100	$30.00	$0.00	$30.00	$0.30
100	90	27.00	1.50	28.50	.316
100	80	24.00	3.00	27.00	.337
100	70	21.00	4.50	25.50	.364
100	60	18.00	6.00	24.00	.40
100	50	15.00	7.50	22.50	.45
100	40	12.00	9.00	21.00	.525
100	30	9.00	10.50	19.50	.65
100	20	6.00	12.00	18.00	.90
100	10	3.00	13.50	16.50	1.65
100	1	.30	14.85	15.15	15.15

Rowan's Method

Hours allowed	Hours taken	Time Wages on Job	Premium earned on Job	Total Labor Cost	Workman's Rate per Hour
100	100	$30.00	$0.00	$30.00	$0.30
100	90	27.00	2.70	29.70	.33
100	80	24.00	4.80	28.80	.36
100	70	21.00	6.30	27.30	.39
100	60	18.00	7.20	25.20	.42
100	50	15.00	7.50	22.50	.45
100	40	12.00	7.20	19.20	.48
100	30	9.00	6.30	15.30	.51
100	20	6.00	4.80	10.80	.54
100	10	3.00	2.70	5.70	.57
100	1	.30	.297	.597	.597

different. You will notice in the last line of the table showing the results of your system that a workman, if he is allowed 100 hours to do a piece of work and does it in one hour, receives about 34 times his hourly rate of wages; with Weir's system he receives 50 times; with our system not quite double. Also compare the next to the last line, showing with your system his wages are increased 4 times, with Weir's 5½ times, with mine 90 per cent, or 10 per cent less than double.

In quoting the last two lines of the table showing the results of your system, Weir's system, and my system, you will no doubt remark that these are extreme cases and seldom to be met with, but these are the cases we are aiming at and hope to arrive at some day, although it may be a long way off. When we do arrive at them we will not require to cut the man's rate, but you will, and so will the Messrs. Weir; so that while yours is a decided improvement upon the ordinary piecework system at the earlier stages, there is no great improvement upon the ordinary piecework system when you come to great reductions in the hours taken, and these are the stages at which you wish to encourage the men as well as at the earlier stages; here I think my system has a great advantage over any other system of which I have yet heard.

XII

THE PRINTING TRADES AND THE CRISIS IN BRITISH INDUSTRY[1]

Jeremiads, apart from any literary value they may have, are not of any conspicuous service to mankind. For one thing, they are apt to come when the need for them is over, as the particular variety of prophet who is responsible for them loves not to talk at sluggish or incredulous ears. Further, they are generally discouraging at a time when perhaps the condition of affairs is beginning to improve. Lastly, they take the common form of recrimination between those who should be fellow-citizens, or fellow-workers, or partners in some joint enterprise. The present discussion on the decadence of British industry, which has been continued for some time, partakes at best of the unphilosophical character hinted at above, while at times it degenerates into an avowed polemic against trade unions. It has been begun by a would-be encyclopedic correspondent of the *Times*,[2] from whose columns the controversy — and why should it be a controversy? — has overflowed into half the magazines and journals of the country. The difficulty now is to lend so vast a subject-matter some unity for the purposes of fair discussion, if we would not allow ourselves to be drawn into a partisanship in what is unnecessarily supposed to be a conflict between the interests of employers and employed. As far as the articles in the *Times* as a whole are concerned, they are chaotic enough to be considered impartial on this disputed question, even if that be not their intention. While the main

[1] From the *Economic Journal*, Vol. XII, 1902, pp. 1–12. The writer is manager of the *Manchester Guardian*.

[2] The *Times* articles are reprinted under the title "Trade Unions and British Industry," London, 1904. — Ed.

argument, printed in aristocratic "bourgeois," seems to be that British workingmen are incompetent enough to be dishonest and dishonest enough to remain incompetent, there are not wanting little jewels of knowledge, printed in unassuming "minion," where an intelligent employer, not afraid to be straightforward, gives some sound raps to his own class and a generous acknowledgment of the merit of the best men under him. . . . What is more obviously wanting in the *Times* articles as a whole is some proper methodical treatment of the confused mass of material collected. A single industry treated with adequate knowledge would give more solid ground for sound generalizations than all the display of undigested technical information ranging over twenty different trades, which makes such an impression on the nonindustrial public. Supposing there to be a need of some vital amendment of our industrial organization, which is within the range of imagination even of an optimist, there is room in such a study of the question for many aspects omitted or scantily treated in the articles which have appeared in the *Times*. I will not quarrel with their correspondent for setting aside, on the whole, the vexed question of tariffs, which would lead us into unnecessary ramifications; but it seems to me that in each industry there should be considered in any comparison of ourselves with competing countries or with a particular competing country the following points: material resources, efficiency of traffic conditions, average scale of transactions, facilities for securing capital, and, especially while we are discussing the efficiency of labor, the efficiency also of the employing class. My inclination is to believe that where we are now falling behind our competitors — and I mean generally in this article to keep America in mind as the chief one of them — is much more in respect to the other items that I have mentioned than in the supposed average inefficiency of British labor or on account of the trade restrictions imposed by labor organizations.

Let me attack without delay my own particular subject, the printing trades. It is clear from Article VIII in this series of the *Times* that their correspondent has taken great pains to inform himself from instructed persons of the conditions of a business not known to him at first hand. His information, so far as it goes, is correct and many of the reflections are just, but in his sketch there is so much missing that any deductions from his inadequate material are too narrow to be of general value. Of the three common processes of printing, by which I mean the composition of types, the stereotyping of printing surfaces, and printing proper in the press, he has inverted the natural order, and speaks first of machine minding or the tending of printing presses. In this class of work he treats of only one variety of press, the two-revolution flat-bed press, now in a state of transition. This is a kind of press still covering a very wide range of work, but less than it used to do a few years ago. For the steady improvement of rotary presses proper — that is, where the paper passes continuously between two revolving cylinders instead of in sheets between a revolving cylinder and a flat reciprocating bed — is gradually robbing a larger and larger portion of magazine and good-class illustrated work from the older and slower machine. I know that at present two of the leading printing-press manufacturers in America, where we still look for our new ideas and processes, have got their minds fixed on improvements adapted for this special purpose as being the next probable step in the gradual advance of efficiency. Now in Article VIII there is no word of mention of these fast rotary presses, whether single, triple, quadruple, or sextuple, whether made by Hoe, Goss, Foster, or the Victory Company, and the slow-working presses at the other end of the scale, such as the platen press or the power die press, are passed over in similar silence. However, taking the narrow class of work to which the contributor of the *Times* does refer, he has raised one interesting point, which shows how dangerous it is to argue from the particular to the general without a full command of the facts. He writes:

A curious illustration of these restrictive methods of working is afforded by the fact that some of the fast American presses introduced into this country have actually been thrown out of order because of the unwillingness of the men to work them at the rate for which they are designed. There can, however, hardly be any patriotic prejudice against these "American" machines as such, because, though designed in the United States, they are now built in England from English materials by English workmen, and these English-made machines are declared to be better made and capable of quicker running than those constructed in America. *Obviously the real motive of the printers is to "leave work for some one else."*

Although it is not quite clear, I take it that by the words "thrown out of order" no accusation of rattening is brought against British workmen. Still, as it stands, we have here an instance of what is labeled in the *Times* articles as "ca' canny," in other words, the deliberate manufacture of work in order to increase employment. But the instance brought forward, which happens to be within my knowledge, is a rather absurd exaggeration of an experience common to every employer. Here we have a Miehle machine, a comparatively new kind of machine, introduced by the Machinery Trust, evidently for the first time, in an office where acquaintance with this grade of press was inadequate. The Miehle was designed for a run of 2000 an hour; but it is not easy for a machine minder accustomed to feed a Wharfedale at 1200 or 1500 an hour to jump at once into the habit of the increased speed, and in this case the workman, perhaps from stupidity, more probably from timidity, geared the machine, or had it geared, to work at a lower speed. In nine cases out of ten this would have had no result except that sooner or later the employer or his foreman — supposing the office to be in capable hands — would have found that the machine was not running up to contract speed and would have wished to know the reason why. Then either the employer would have insisted on the proper output from the machine minder, or else complaint would have been made to the manufacturers. In this particular case — and I have never heard of a similar one — the machine was so delicately constructed that it was injured and thrown out of order by running under its proper speed. But apart from the fact that the accident may have arisen quite as much from overcaution as from carelessness, if an employer is to interpret every case of laziness or incompetence as conspiracy, the columns of the *Times* for a year would not hold the evidence that could be brought forth. . . .

With regard to the primary process of printing, the composition of types, whether by machine or by hand, only the former is dealt with in the article which we are considering. Great stress is laid on the performances attained in certain competitions on the linotype machine held in London, Glasgow, and Manchester, performances to which employers of experience will attach no very great value. There can be no harm in these competitions, and I greatly regret that the Typographical Association in a narrow-minded spirit should have discouraged, and the London Society have forbidden, any participation by their members in these tests of skill under artificial conditions. But it must not be assumed that competitions of this kind set up any standard of output available for practical purposes. We have not, as I myself believe, at all reached a possible or even creditable output in England in machine composition, but the adoption of deceptive records such as those obtained in competitions seems to do more harm than good. Of more interest in the said article are passages quoted from the remarks of an employer evidently well versed in the condition of the London trade and also in the details of the recent dispute between the masters and the London Society of Compositors. There is much truth in his statement that masters in the printing trade—and it is as true of the provinces as in London—are not sufficiently acquainted with the extremely difficult technicalities of composition, and in all dealings with their men they put themselves at a further disadvantage by the universal employment in union houses of union men as their overseers. This is not to say that among this able and faithful class of men there is a general disloyalty to the firms which employ them, but simply as a matter of human nature it is impossible for a man to serve two masters; it is enough to expect of a newly appointed overseer, who has been a good union man for say fifteen or twenty years and who is still on the sick and superannuation funds of the society and dependent for all prospective benefits from these funds on the votes of the men under him, that he should be at most impartial when difficulties arise between his employers and the union. But impartiality is hardly the virtue required by a business man from his own agent; one would not expect it from a solicitor nor even from an expert witness.

To sum up the consideration of this question of machine composition, just objection can be taken to the policy of the Typographical Association and also of the London Society of Compositors in the two following important respects, — their refusal to allow any form of bonus or premium system in union offices and their prohibition of any marking or checking of copy whereby the output of individual operators can be ascertained. It is further true, although less so of the Typographical Association, which is the provincial organization, and more so of the London Society, that the effect of their action — and it is difficult to believe, considering how able a body of men have been their leaders, that their intentions have always been directed the other way — has been to delay and obstruct the introduction of linotype and other typesetting machines and to hamper their use. Circumstances, in the shape of an obsolete table of extra payments for "fat" matter and antiquated traditions and regulations as to what may be assigned to "house" hands and what are the functions of "stone" men and correctors, have also militated against the full development of the new efficiency of machinery. But we can find a useful instance of how much employers themselves are to blame for many of their present troubles in a comparison between the position now occupied by union houses in London and in the provinces. The provincial employers have been organized for some years in the Linotype Users' Association, to which also many London houses nominally belong. Some four or five years ago a useful working agreement was made between them and the Typographical Association, covering the greater part of their area but not London, whereby all questions relating to working on what is called the "stab" or weekly wage system were regulated on a satisfactory basis. The agreement has been loyally observed, and although it does not cover the whole ground and is not to be regarded as final, still under it linotype users, at present mostly newspapers, enjoy the real control of their offices, as well as an option between two working systems. Of the two systems the weekly wage system has been found to be more advantageous and has been generally adopted by union houses in the provinces. The London houses, on the other hand, were slower to adopt the new machinery and slower to resort to combination. At the time of the provincial agreement they neglected to take steps to join the larger and on the whole stronger body of their brethren and to effect either together with them or simultaneously an equally advantageous working arrangement. That is the position they are now in. Neither the morning nor the evening newspapers in London are at liberty to adopt the "stab" or weekly wage system so long as they remain union houses. In all the expensive details of charges for extras they are in the hands of the London Society. Headings, small caps, rules, italics, and "fat" matter of every kind have all to be paid for two or three times over. And it is not so much the additional cost of these impositions which constitutes a burden on the employer as the continual impediment they offer to efficiency. Some idea of how much this amounts to in the long run can be seen in the parallel cases of three London houses now turning out the same class of work. Two of these houses employ only Society hands, and the output per hour is 4000 ens[1] and 5000 ens respectively. The third office is non-Society, and their men are paid an inclusive rate on the piece system, while no extras are recognized. The result in efficiency is astonishing, as the output is 7500 ens an hour. Another instance can be shown in the case of the *St. James Gazette*, which, to escape from the toils of "extras" under the piece system, offered their men a fixed weekly wage as an alternative, but were refused by the union a right possessed by every employer in the provinces. The only resource of the newspaper was to become a non-Society house. In all this the moral to me is that

[1] Equivalent to 2000 ems according to the American standard of measurement. — Ed.

employers should have the foresight to provide for their own interests; and for this barrier to efficiency the London Society is in only a minor degree to blame. The remedy is within the reach of London employers whenever they will take the trouble to combine to protect themselves against a rather elementary form of oppression. . . .

The common-sense view of the condition of the printing trade in Great Britain is that it is now in a very fair condition of prosperity and efficiency. The nature of the work takes it out of the rank of those industries in which foreign competition is possible to any great extent. By far the greater part of printing, for instance all newspapers, magazines, weekly papers, and the smaller kind of jobbing work, must be done by each country on the spot where it is wanted, and even supposing this natural condition of the business were removed there is little doubt that so far from the bulk of our printing going to the continent, we should soon be doing, provided we had the stocks of type and the command of the languages, a good deal more of their work than they would be doing of ours. There is very little demand for cheap printing. If there were, country offices can be found in England where straightforward work would be quite as cheaply done as in Middelburg, Holland. There was a town in the north of England where I heard of rates for machine composition which were about a fourth of the London rates, but the proprietor was not making a fortune. No, if comparisons are to be made between printing in our country and printing elsewhere, some other standard must be taken than mere cost per square foot of paper. There can be no doubt that our efficiency in nearly every matter relating to printing is very much higher than it was ten years ago, and with hardly an exception, unless perhaps in some improvements in the most delicate color printing, our lessons have come from America, whence also we have received nearly all our new processes and our improved machinery. For all this we cannot plume ourselves on having surpassed those who have lately been our instructors. There is still a great deal for us to learn from the American printers, who, although not so far ahead of us as they used to be, are more efficient, both masters and men, than we. Take for instance the composition of types by machine, about which a great deal has been already said. Statistics valuable for comparative purposes here are hard to get, as there is no absolute standard and working conditions vary immensely in different offices. But from inquiries and comparisons made on visits to America in 1899 and 1901 and from much correspondence which I have read both in American and in English papers on the subject, my opinion is that the output on the linotype machines there is on the average not less than 60 per cent greater than here in a given time.

This difference is certainly a great deal more than it should be, and as the linotype machine has become of general use in the country now for five or six years we ought to be past the transition stage. As matters now stand in the provinces, where, as pointed out above, we have come nearer to a permanent settlement than in London, most offices are working on the "stab" system, where the rates are fixed by agreement with the Typographical Association at an increase of 12½ per cent on the local rates for hand setting in vogue before the introduction of typesetting machinery. Under the present terms, however, the rate of production is much lower than it should be, and employers must look around for some needed stimulus. This stimulus is not supplied by the "piece" scale, which, being based on a slight advance on the old "piece" hand rates, does not take into account the enormously increased productivity of the machine. The present piece rates now enforced by the Typographical Association and the London Society of Compositors, although never yet officially sanctioned by the Linotype Users' Association, which is the organization of the employers, besides the fact that they sanction the continuance of obsolete and obstructive regulations as to extras, which are even more oppressive than they are costly, practically bring an easy and luxurious living within the reach of the careless and incompetent. It is possible now for a compositor who has received a year's training on the linotype machine to attain without special skill or unusual exertion an output of five thousand ens[1] per hour, or about half the average rate of an American compositor. As his weekly bill will be augmented at least 10 per cent by extras and fat matter and he will probably have copy for forty-five hours during the week, some of which will be overtime at higher rates, this prince of workingmen will receive in London or Manchester on a morning newspaper some seventy or seventy-five shillings a week. This is a higher income than a graduate of Oxford or Cambridge with first-class honors can often obtain in the scholastic market.

In all this I want to make it clear that I have no quarrel with the high wages but with the fatal obstacle to all improvement. There is many a student who has been of less use to the world than a first-rate linotype operator; but it is not just that a student who works hard should find it more difficult to earn a living than the compositor who plays with his work. Undoubtedly the lack of efficiency in this branch of the printing industry is the serious thing. The facts are clear, and employers should rouse themselves to put an end to it. Naturally it is not the function of the Typographical Association or of the London Society of Compositors to lower the wages of their own members, nor does the primary responsibility for securing increased efficiency and a better output rest with them while their employers remain supine.

In two respects only is the policy of the two great trade unions of the compositors open to objection, both of which have been mentioned above and were referred to in the *Times* article. The first and most important is their refusal to countenance any form of premium or bonus system. Their resistance to this is theoretically indefensible, as a premium system consults equally both the interests of the workman who requires a living or minimum wage and the interests of the employer who wants to be secured a minimum output. There is further a supreme interest which combines both these and is often forgotten by each side, — the common welfare of the trade.

[1] That is, 2500 ems American measure. See Chapter X, "Introduction of the Linotype," p. 253. — ED.

The premium system, after providing for the workman a regular weekly wage, insures also to the employer a definite weekly output. When the rights of both have been fully secured they are partners in further progress, and the employed receives a share of the profit which he is making for his employer. Not only is it the system which prevails in and is responsible for the progress of the most ably conducted engineering industries in America, not only is it adopted in perhaps the best-regulated manufacturing enterprise in the world, the Steel Works of Pittsburg, but its principle has been accepted and it is now in force in many prosperous workshops in our own country. Its adoption by the printing industry would soon enable both master and men to reach a standard equal to that now attained in America.

The second restriction on progress with which we can reproach both the Typographical Association and the London Society of Compositors is not extremely serious and is not so discreditable to the intentions of their officials as to their intellects. They forbid any attempt to get the operator working on a weekly wage to furnish any account of his output. As the employer now has the means of detecting by an automatic arrangement on the machine what work each individual has done, the continuance of this obsolete and useless regulation among the union rules can have no effect but to prejudice them in the eyes of the public. . . .

Before leaving the subject of composition and compositors I should like to add a tribute to men whom I have personally known among the leaders of the Typographical Association of Great Britain and Ireland. I can remember during a period of ten years negotiations with more than three presidents and two secretaries and many, many committeemen. My impression from prolonged conferences and frequent dealings with them as opponents was not only that they had a better command of detail than we employers who had to meet them, but that they were a farsighted, able set of men, whose influence over their followers was in the direction of progress. They honorably observed any engagements made with us, even at times when they had great difficulty in bringing the men whom they represented into line. . . .

The course of the last ten or fifteen years in the printing trade has been one long process of education from America. An employer must reckon it part of his duties nowadays to take a trip across the Atlantic as often as possible to inquire into new processes and look up new machinery. There is nothing to be ashamed of in this course, for during the greater part of the last century the pilgrimage was the other way. And our imitation is not slavish, nor does our capital go altogether to American manufacturers. We have to buy our experimental machinery mostly from the land where it was invented, but our manufacturers are quick to take up the American patents and to borrow their models, so that the industry is not lost to this country. To mention a few specific instances of especial importance, this has been the case with the linotype typesetting machine and the whole class of fast rotary newspaper presses with the triangular former, commonly called the Hoe folder, a type now adopted by all English manufacturers but first introduced from the other side. The same is true of two special classes of flat-bed presses, some systems of applying electrical power to printing machinery, and also the latest product of American invention, the autoplate stereotyping machine. In all the above cases, while the patterns and patents come from the other side of the water, this machinery is now being manufactured in England.

There seems to be a generally prevalent opinion among employers who have made inquiries for themselves — and I am not speaking now especially of my own business but referring to all kinds of manufactures — that although wages are universally higher in America both in money and in real value, still labor is cheaper because it is so much more efficient. This feeling is at the bottom of the curious outcry against trade unions lately prevalent at a time when trade unionism is much less aggressive than it was fifty years ago. It is assumed, and it is quite true, that our material in labor equals that of the best country in the world. The deduction is that the labor organizations are to blame for keeping back the proper output of their members, and a great deal of evidence has been collected, especially in the series of articles published in the *Times*, to prove the existence of a subtle conspiracy labeled "ca' canny" pervading unionism and encouraged by its leaders, whereby a given quantity of work can be distributed to as large a number of hands as possible. Now we all know what "making work" means. Every employer knows what it means; every one who has ever employed a plumber can imagine what it is like. But the accusation that "making work" has been adopted as a system by unionism in general and that trade-union leaders encourage it I maintain is not proven, and moreover it is not true. Knowing personally some of the trade-union leaders I most certainly accept their explicit denials on the subject; they are too intelligent to adopt deliberately a policy which must tend to general degeneration. No, "ca' canny," as it is called, is something much more simple than the *Times* would have it to be; it is just poor human nature, or the vices of laziness and ignorance, from which employers themselves are not exempt. Let us imagine the position of the trade-union leader and its difficulties. He is elected to specific duties which mostly concern the relations between his constituents and their employers. He has often to bargain on their behalf about terms and conditions of labor, and my experience is that he is generally better up in the points of his brief than are his opponents. When the fixing of wages is in question his plain duty is to secure the highest price for their labor. *Caveat emptor.* It is the employer on whom the responsibility rests of testing the quality of the article he buys.

If we have been passed in the race of industrial efficiency by America,—which I take to be a proved fact in more industries than one,—the trade unions are not to blame. For one thing their power is absurdly exaggerated, and more so by the weak employer than by one who is capable. The strongest trade union in Great Britain, the Amalgamated Society of Engineers, went down before the combination of masters who were contending for a point of efficiency. Whenever the newspapers of this country care to combine in earnest to secure the more efficient working of linotype machines, a point on which I have dwelt above at some length, not all the efforts of the Typographical Association nor the London Society of Compositors can stand in the way. Nor would they struggle against it. The difficulty in this matter is to induce employers to see their common interest. In America, where unionism is more powerful and more aggressive than here, the employers as a class have been taught to combine more readily on emergency, they aim more at securing efficiency of labor and less at low money wages, and above all they will make any sacrifice to secure the real control of their own enterprises.

On the contrary, in England the employers are in comparison apt to attach too much importance to low money wages, they are lazy in resisting small encroachments on their liberty which may later on become a dangerous interference, and they are much slower to swallow individual jealousies for a common purpose. But then we have not the same level of ability to draw upon for our employing class here as in the newer country. The capable man rising from below has much greater difficulties in his way, difficulties which are the result of centuries of prejudice and class interests. On the other hand, the best of the brains of our upper classes will go anywhere but into industry, — into a bank or a merchant's office perhaps, but not into horny-handed manufacture. The attractions of dignified and cultured ease, of politics or the learned professions, are too dazzling for that increasing class of people, those with small independent means. Besides, our university and other higher education is not yet adjusted to the new importance with which industrial needs are confronting us. The older universities, given up to the cultivation of the most refined forms of pleasure, are well adapted to the requirements of persons born to high position. But such are few, and without capital or position waiting for him the young Oxford or Cambridge graduate starts in business, if he is not above it, in ignorance of two or three elementary lessons which the office-trained boy has learned at nineteen, such as, for instance, the amount of concern which the world takes in the fate of interesting young men between twenty-three and thirty. We want a university training for the modern employer, but a wasted ten years is too high a price to pay for it. Every year the older universities carry out faithfully their grand system of attracting, selecting, and sorting out the best of the young talent of England, a system not excelled in any other institution or set of institutions in the world. The best are sent forward to ambitious careers. A large number who are not needy receive a compensation for their diminished energy in a greater appreciation of cultivated pleasure. But every year a goodly proportion of young intellectual England sinks back into a disappointed obscurity. And all the while what the industries of this country need are brains — brains and trained brains. But we need to train the brains at the top more than the brains at the bottom.

G. Binney Dibblee.

Manchester, England.

XIII

THE SYSTEM OF APPRENTICESHIP AT THE BALDWIN LOCOMOTIVE WORKS[1]

. . . The Baldwin Locomotive Works have always maintained a system of apprenticeship. . . . In January, 1901, however, a new system was inaugurated in which the apprentices were divided into three classes. The different classes and requirements are shown in Diagram 1; the horizontal lines represent the number of apprentices employed and the vertical lines their age and occupation, from which it will be seen that there are:

1. First-class apprentices, of whom there were 232 in service on January 1, 1904; they are required to have a good common-school education and are not to be over 17 years and 3 months of age. They are indentured for four years, and are required to attend a free night school for at least two evenings in each week during the first three years of the apprenticeship. The first year the apprentice is expected to take up elementary algebra and geometry, and the rudiments of mechanical drawing during the remainder of the two years.

2. Second-class apprentices, of whom there were 99 in service on January 1, 1904. Applications for indenture in this class are considered from boys who have an advanced grammar- or high-school training and who are not over 18 years of age. The term for this class is three years, and the apprentices are required to attend night school which shall teach them the rudiments of mechanical drawing for the first two years of the indenture.

3. Third-class indenture; this is in the form of an agreement with young men of 21 years of age who are graduates of colleges, technical schools, or scientific institutions having courses in the higher mathematics, natural science, and drawing. They are not required

[1] From the *Engineering Magazine*, Vol. XXVII, 1904, pp. 321–333. See also "Trade and Technical Education," Sixteenth Annual Report of the U. S. Commissioner of Labor, 1902.

DIAGRAM I. CLASSES AND REQUIREMENTS OF APPRENTICES, BALDWIN LOCOMOTIVE WORKS

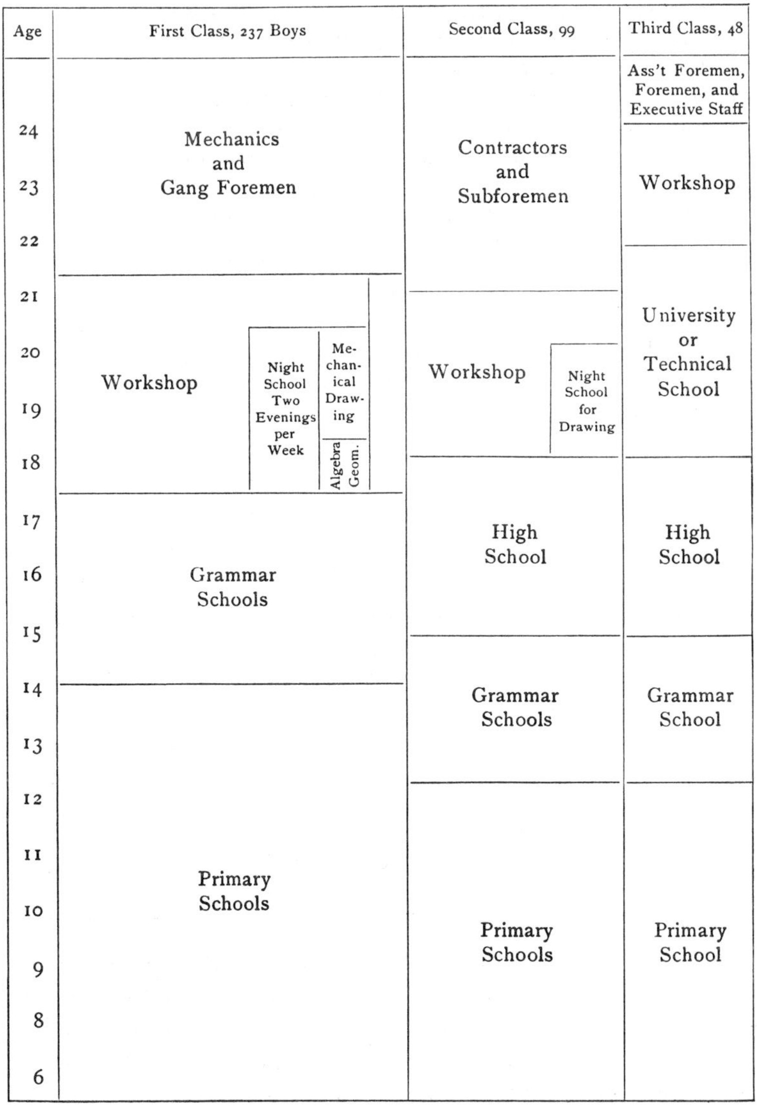

<table>
<tr><th>Age</th><th colspan="3">First Class, 237 Boys</th><th colspan="2">Second Class, 99</th><th>Third Class, 48</th></tr>
<tr><td></td><td colspan="3" rowspan="4">Mechanics and Gang Foremen</td><td colspan="2" rowspan="4">Contractors and Subforemen</td><td>Ass't Foremen, Foremen, and Executive Staff</td></tr>
<tr><td>24</td><td rowspan="3">Workshop</td></tr>
<tr><td>23</td></tr>
<tr><td>22</td></tr>
<tr><td>21</td><td rowspan="4">Workshop</td><td colspan="2"></td><td rowspan="4">Workshop</td><td></td><td rowspan="4">University or Technical School</td></tr>
<tr><td>20</td><td rowspan="3">Night School Two Evenings per Week</td><td rowspan="2">Mechanical Drawing</td><td rowspan="3">Night School for Drawing</td></tr>
<tr><td>19</td></tr>
<tr><td>18</td><td>Algebra Geom.</td></tr>
<tr><td>17</td><td colspan="3" rowspan="3">Grammar Schools</td><td colspan="2" rowspan="3">High School</td><td rowspan="3">High School</td></tr>
<tr><td>16</td></tr>
<tr><td>15</td></tr>
<tr><td>14</td><td colspan="3" rowspan="8">Primary Schools</td><td colspan="2" rowspan="2">Grammar Schools</td><td rowspan="2">Grammar School</td></tr>
<tr><td>13</td></tr>
<tr><td>12</td><td colspan="2" rowspan="6">Primary Schools</td><td rowspan="6">Primary School</td></tr>
<tr><td>11</td></tr>
<tr><td>10</td></tr>
<tr><td>9</td></tr>
<tr><td>8</td></tr>
<tr><td>6</td></tr>
</table>

to attend any night classes, but in lieu of this must read some technical journal and turn in a synopsis of all the articles of some journal. This matter is used for indexing the articles in the publication. The indenture in each case places upon the firm the obligation to teach the apprentice his art thoroughly and to furnish him abundant opportunity to acquire a practical knowledge of the business. The employer is also bound to retain the apprentice in service until he has completed the term provided for in the indenture, with the reservation of the right to dismiss the apprentice for cause.

DIAGRAM 2. RATES OF PAY OF APPRENTICES, BALDWIN LOCOMOTIVE WORKS

First Class		Second Class		Third Class	
1st year, 5¢	Planer Planer Shaper Shaper	1st year, 7¢	Shaper Planer Lathe Bench Work	1st six months 13¢	Lathe Bench Work
2d year, 7¢	Slotter Bench Work Bench Work Lathe	2d year, 9¢	Planer Boring Mill Bench Work Bench Work	2d six months 16¢	Planer Shaper Highway Office
3d year, 9¢	Test Room Planer Shaper Erecting Gang	3d year, 11¢	Boring Cylinders Planing Cylinders Erecting Gang Erecting Gang	3d six months 18¢	Test Department Valve Gang
4th year, 11¢	Erecting Brass Work in Erecting Shop Throttle Gang Valve Gang			4th six months 20¢	Erecting Gang Track Foreman
Bonus $125		$100		———	

The rates of pay are shown in Diagram 2; this diagram also shows how well the works discharge the obligation to the apprentice, for these statements have been compiled from actual cases and show the work upon which the apprentices are engaged for each three months of service. . . . It will be seen that the apprentices are changed every three months, and the first-year apprentice is given experience of such an extended character as to make him a first-class and thorough mechanic. At the end of his service he is given a bonus of $125; he is then at liberty to sever his connection with the works and has the means of traveling halfway across the continent in search of a job satisfactory to him.

It will be seen, as shown in Diagram I, that the course for the first-class apprentices is designed to develop first-class mechanics and men for positions of minor responsibility; the object of the course for the second class is to develop men for the positions of contractors and subforemen; and the assistant foremen, foremen, and executive staff are developed from the third class of apprentices, although no limitation is placed upon the height to which any class of apprentice may aspire or rise, and the first class of apprentices may and do rise to places of higher responsibility than those held by the third class.

It is very essential that men holding positions of responsibility should acquire a habit of making observations and keeping record of them, and in this manner develop habits which will prove very valuable to them when asked to look after the work of several men or the material required for a gang or shop. In order to systematize this work a form is provided for the second and third class of apprentices which each is required to fill in. This form contains all the data necessary to establish piecework prices. The better class of apprentices is thus organized into an elemental rate-fixing department, and information is secured from which can be obtained a very accurate estimate of the cost of labor or of any piece of work. The superintendent of apprentices also secures a very accurate knowledge of the work being done by each apprentice and a means for comparing the work of the different apprentices.

The management carefully guard against any tendency toward paternalism, in an effort to bring out the individual qualities of the apprentices, and with the belief that the apprentices will develop into better and stronger men if they are compelled to rely upon their own resources. There are no special

No............

MACHINE INSPECTION

Shop..................Foreman................Machine................No............Date.. ....

Contractor.........................Class of Work.........................Card......................

Material.................................. ....Engine.............................

Operation	Size of Tool	R.P.M.	Feed	Depth of Cut	Speed	Total Time	Average Time	Minimum Time

Remarks:

Tool steel used Apprentice..

lectures and no clubs or social features; the blue overalls level all social distinction; princes and sons of men of wealth work shoulder to shoulder with those less favored, and it is such an everyday experience as to call for no comment.

Since January 1, 1901, at which time the present system of apprenticeship was inaugurated under the supervision of Mr. N. W. Sample, there have been indentured 545 apprentices,— 352 first-class, 124 second-class, and 69 third-class. Of this number 153, or about 28 per cent, have been discharged for reasons other than expiration of their terms of apprenticeship. The total number of apprentices carried on the shop rolls at the close of the year 1903 was 379, of which number 345 are machinists, 5 blacksmiths, 5 brass finishers, 10 molders, 12 pattern makers, 1 boiler maker, and 1 sheet-iron worker. There are 232 first-class, 99 second-class, and 48 third-class.

In addition to indentured apprentices there are 23 special apprentices, largely from foreign countries, one being a native of Finland, one of Costa Rica, two of San Domingo, five of Cuba, one of Spain, four of Japan, three of Porto Rico, and one of Mexico.

The number of apprentices indentured during the year 1903 was 165; of this number 156 were indentured to the machinists' trade, 5 to the trade of pattern making, 1 to brass finishing, 1 to molding, and 1 to boiler making. There are 97 first-class, 40 second-class, and 28 third-class. There have been 61 apprentices discharged during the year and 13 dropped from the rolls by reason of expiration of apprenticeship.

Two apprentices in the first class completed their terms during the year. Both are exceptionally good hands and at the expiration of their time were employed as machinists. Eleven apprentices in the third class completed their terms during the year; six of this number have been promoted to places of responsibility in the erecting and machine shops and in the maintenance department; five others are employed as machinists in the erecting shop.

During the year 1904 15 first-class, 31 second-class, and 19 third-class apprentices will complete their terms of apprenticeship. The attendance of the apprentices at the second term of the school year, commencing January 5 and ending February 25, 1903, was 63 per cent of all the first-class and second-class boys on the rolls at the opening of the term, and it is expected that the percentage of attendance for the present year will be even greater.

These figures show that the Baldwin Locomotive Works are doing their share to prevent "race suicide" of the trades worked upon in their establishment. It will also be seen that the plan is not altogether a philanthropic one, for the incorporation of the several features mentioned before makes the system self-supporting. The chief advantage, however, is the development of a loyal, brainy set of men with a thorough training in the mechanic arts and especially developed in certain lines. Those of them that remain will lend their energy to assisting and building up the business of their employers, and they are just as proud of the works and their accomplishments and just as jealous of their reputation as the proprietors themselves, for they consider themselves the children of the works. The manufacturing plant that has a loyal, intelligent body of workmen who make their employers' interest their own, has the very best equipment for meeting the strenuous competition of the present day.

S. M. VAUCLAIN.

From *Proceedings of the Engineers' Club of Philadelphia*, Vol. XIX, January, 1902, pp. 60–64. Remarks by Mr. Vauclain, answering inquiries.

. . . In handling several thousand apprentice boys it became apparent to me that no matter how well the apprentice was taught in the workshops, or how much he was encouraged to go to the various night schools in our city, such as the Franklin or Spring Garden Institute, the Young Men's Christian Association, Drexel, or others for the technical part of his education, we found that he desired something to show that he had learned the art or that he had served a specific time at this art. In other words, he was just as anxious to get his diploma as the young man who graduates from the university, or from Sibley or Stevens, or some such institution, and in my opinion was just as much entitled to it. It also became apparent to me that if we were to remain successful in competition with the world we should have to get to work at once and systematically educate our apprentices not only in so far as the handicraft is concerned, but so that they should have a certain amount of technical knowledge to go with it, and that this technical knowledge should go hand in hand with the manual training that they were receiving in the shops. Very naturally the thought occurred to me, "What are we going to do with the great unwashed, — the boys who cannot go to school, the boys who are turned out of the grammar schools perhaps before they have barely entered them?" The parents must put these boys to work, and, fortunately for us, the laws of Pennsylvania relieve us of this mass of humanity — poorly trained and poorly educated, and whose parents have no thought in placing them at work but the greed of gain. The law allows the employment of any boy under sixteen years of age and over thirteen only when his parents go before a magistrate and get a permit; consequently we are able to keep out of our workshops all boys under sixteen, except those who are the sons of widows and who must have employment somewhere. These boys we employ as messengers, and keep them and train them and bring them along until such time as we can put them to a trade. Our idea in establishing three grades of apprentices was to take care of the three grades of boys that come to us. First, the boys of the masses, — the boys of ordinary education, very ordinary education indeed; these boys we compel to remain with us four years. We require that they shall go outside at night to some of the many night schools and take a one year's course in elementary geometry and algebra in order to get a slight knowledge of these subjects. The second and third years they must attend drawing school. They must take a two years' course in drawing outside of the workshops. At the expiration of the four years we give these boys a bonus and we discharge them from our employ. They get a diploma — their indenture is their diploma; their bonus is their reward and the wherewith to go elsewhere and seek employment. Now, the high-school boys are well-educated boys. I defy any young men of eighteen to go before an employer with a better education than these boys who come to us from our Philadelphia High School. They have a good knowledge of geometry and many of the higher branches of mathematics; they know something of mechanical drawing, enough to go on with the work. Therefore we omit with such boys the preliminary course in elementary algebra and geometry and we prescribe that for two years they must attend night school in mechanical drawing in order to perfect themselves, — in order to learn to express their thoughts upon paper as they absorb ideas in the workshop. We also give such young men a bonus, and we require only three years of service from them on account of the superior education they have when they come to us. The superior education enables us more quickly to grasp the needs, — the place to put them, — and they absorb more or less readily the instructions given them from their immediate superiors through the superintendent of the shop. The bonus these young men get is $100 in place of the $125 of their more unskilled companions. This $100 we think is sufficient to enable them to go elsewhere and secure employment, and we are never ashamed to let one of these apprentices go for that. He always shows up well. The third man to take care of is the graduate of our universities, the ordinary mechanical engineer who comes to us not quite so green as grass so far as mechanical handicraft is concerned. He is willing to get down to the hardest work we have in our shop, and he works at it like a steam engine. He has all the technical knowledge that is necessary. He has it, but he does not know how to use it. We encourage him in this manner: We cannot indenture him, being a man, but we make a specific contract with him for two years and pay him enough to keep body and soul together. We give him thirteen cents an hour for the first year, sixteen cents an hour for the second year, and a clean certificate at the end of that time. We have not had a man of that description for that length of time who has not been lifted out of the position he had contracted for and who is not enjoying a very much more remunerative position and one in the line of promotion. It is from these men that we must fill the superior offices in our workshop, and these boys we promote. The man or boy who has determined to get to the top and will burn his candle at night to gain the knowledge that his more favored companion has received in a better institution of learning than he has attended also gains his reward. The third boy we must have to fill the ordinary ranks in the workshops, and the better educated we can have the ordinary rank and file in our workshops the better chance we will have of competing with foreign manufacturers and the better chance we will have of extending the markets of American manufactures throughout the world; it is only in this way that we can do so. You have asked me why we can afford to do this, — why we can afford to turn away from the doors every year several hundred young men. We do not expect to keep them all. We will keep the better ones that we come across from time to time. We promote them so that their ambition will permit them to stay with us. Have you not already seen the point? Every one of these men that go forth from an establishment of this kind will sing its praises forever. They will shout just as lustily for the Baldwin Locomotive Works as they have done for Yale, Harvard, or the university, or any other institution they have left. You will have an advertising medium that cannot be surpassed by anything; and further than that, you will have established in your own workshop a set of men that will be invaluable, that you can never hire in the open market. When I hear a manager say he has had so many men call in his efforts to secure a foreman, he has tried and tried to get certain men to do certain work and failed, I pity that man. That man has not the courage to go down in his pocket and labor for a few years to train men to fill these positions, and if you can put out your coin, if you have the small courage to hand it over to these young men, you will get it back tenfold before you know where you are.

Q. — I should like to ask Mr. Vauclain to what extent the instruction of the apprentice is conducted under the direct supervision of the Baldwin Locomotive Works.

MR. VAUCLAIN. — The Baldwin Locomotive Works do not intend to give night instruction. They do not intend to impart the technical knowledge. We depend upon the various night schools established throughout the city, and we pray for the establishment of more and better night schools to give instruction for that portion of the training of the apprentices. The manufacturer has the commercial side of the question to deal with. He can impart the commercial side of the business in connection with the technical training. He must be a manual student commercially. He must be able to make that work pay. He must be able to get it out for a certain sum of money, and he must be able to get it out well for that money, because the better his product is the more work will come into that workshop; therefore, if the foremen, or the superintendents, or the owners, or the managers of these manufacturing institutions will give their time and attention to the handicraft, the manual training, they certainly should expect to get the technical portion of the training of their students outside. Now, in order to make a scheme of this sort successful, one must make a business of it. You cannot hand these boys over to the tender mercies of a foreman, because it is not one out of fifty who can take a boy and who can say to himself, "That boy is perfect on that work; here, give him another planer; there is no use keeping that boy on that work any longer." No, he will keep him there until the superintendent says, "You must not keep that boy there any longer; you are doing him an injustice." In order to avoid such a condition of affairs I felt that we should have a superintendent of apprentices, a man whose business should be to look after the apprentices not only in the shop but out of the shop, a man who would see that they are taken care of and that the foreman does not take advantage of them, but that as fast as a boy learns he is pushed along. We hire him for what he learns from us for the future, and we must have that boy pushed along so that he can learn, so that he can absorb everything that is capable of being absorbed in that shop. If he is not capable of being pushed along so fast, he is pushed along slowly and more care is taken of him. We do not want to allow that boy to sink down into disappointed youth. We just want him, when he is twenty-one, to be able to work and to go on and keep on working with irresistible energy. Now, this superintendent of apprentices must do that work, and he must further see that the boy carries out his side of the contract, — that he attends these night schools. He must see where he goes; he must examine into the matter; he must see the boy's teacher or professor and he must report upon his progress, so that we can form a determination of the value of this apprentice from a technical standpoint. We find it very difficult to provide for a certain branch of this work, but great effort is being made to carry it on for any number of boys. The public schools are taking an interest; everybody will take an interest in it after a while, when it becomes known. It is the right policy, if we can only interest manufacturers to establish a system of this kind. All those interested will find all they can do to keep up with the other end of the business if the manufacturer will take care of the handicraft; and until that time does come, if we cannot obtain the technical education for these young men outside at night, as we should, the only thing to do is to establish an educational institution of our own and take these boys so many hours from work and say, You must go there and receive it. Insist upon it. It does n't cost much. You can get a good educator for $3000 a year, and what is $3000 when you divide it up among a thousand boys? Three dollars for each boy; and if those boys are worth anything they will not only earn their wages but they will earn a great deal more. They will earn the money you might spend upon their education, and in the years to come they will be grateful for the trouble you have taken to make better men of them.

Q. — I would like to ask Mr. Vauclain if he can say whether or not, taking the last six months of the work of the three grades, the high school or the university men show a decided advantage and adaptability with tools and otherwise over the other class that lack education.

MR. VAUCLAIN. — That goes without question. The better educated a young man is the better his work is all the way through; that is, I am speaking of them as a whole, as an entirety. You occasionally find a young man who has had no chances when he was young, — a boy that we have taken in, perhaps, as an errand boy, whom we have brought along and raised by common education. The foremen give him a book on arithmetic and they let him work problems in his spare time. The clerks in the office teach him how to handle figures, and in that way he gets some education before he is apprenticed; when he gets apprenticed he wants to know more. He goes to the Spring Garden Institute and he learns how to put his thoughts on paper. He will ask you enough questions to set you crazy. That is one of the boys that you cannot keep down, and his work of the fourth year will shine alongside the work of the more educated person. He is not the man the more educated person is, and he realizes it and absorbs all he can from him. He listens and profits by what this man is willing to give him. One of the greatest things in the success of a young man is his ability to handle men, and unless he has that ability he is next to worthless as a manager. In this connection we try to give as many of our young men as show any capacity whatever for handling men an opportunity to improve. As soon as we perceive they can handle two or three men we give them the opportunity, and we increase the number and are glad to increase it, because we have vacant places waiting at the top for men who can fill these positions; until then we have to fill them from the few we hire from the outside.

XIV

THE SWEATING SYSTEM IN THE CLOTHING TRADE[1]

The term "sweating," or "sweating system," originally denoted a system of subcontract, wherein the work is let out to contractors to be done in small shops or homes. "In practice," says the report of the Illinois Bureau of Labor Statistics,[2] "sweating consists of the farming out by competing manufacturers to competing contractors of the material for garments, which in turn is distributed among competing men and women to be made up."

The system to be contrasted with the sweating system is the "factory system," wherein the manufacturer[3] employs his own workmen, under the management of his own foreman or superintendent, in his own building, with steam, electric, or water power. In the sweating system the foreman becomes a

[1] From Report of the U.S. Industrial Commission, Vol. XV, 1901, pp. 319–352.

[2] Report of the Illinois Bureau of Labor Statistics, 1892, p. 358.

[3] The term "manufacturer" in the clothing trade has a peculiar significance. It means the wholesale merchant, or warehouseman. The exact designation would be "merchant manufacturer." Such a manufacturer usually has an "inside shop" and several "outside shops." The inside shop is usually on the manufacturer's own premises, and includes the cutters who cut the cloth for the contractors, the examiners who inspect the garments on their return, and the "bushelmen" who repair and reshape the garments if necessary.

The "outside shops" are the shops of contractors who take the goods out from the manufacturer for stitching and finishing. If the manufacturer does his own work directly under a superintendent or foreman, instead of indirectly through a contractor, this shop also is known as an "inside shop." Workmen employed by a contractor often speak of themselves as employed by the manufacturer who furnishes the work to the contractor. Since the manufacturer sets the contract price, it might almost be said that the contractor is really the manufacturer's foreman, who takes the responsibility of finding help, doing the work, and making such wages of management as he can at the price set by the manufacturer.

contractor, with his own small shop and foot-power machine. In the factory system the workmen are congregated where they can be seen by the factory inspectors and where they can organize or develop a common understanding. In the sweating system they are isolated and unknown.

The sweating system has undergone significant changes during the past fifty years. The early part of the last century, when the term seems to have originated in England, it applied to ready-made new clothing in the form of army clothing given out to contractors. At that time each tailor usually made the entire coat at home. The manufacturer of ready-made clothing and army clothing would give his work to a contractor who was a responsible party, usually not a tailor himself. This contractor would then give the work to some man who kept a tailors' boarding house or a saloon where the tailors were accustomed to come together. This boarding-house keeper or saloon keeper was a subcontractor, though not a tailor. He in turn would give this work out to the individual tailors whom he personally knew, who were responsible for the work. The money received by these subcontractors for their part was called "sweat money," implying that their profit was the difference between the price they received from the manufacturer or contractor and the price paid to the tailor for making the garment, and that they invested no labor in the transaction.

There was an agitation in the United States in the early fifties against this system because of the low condition of the tailors. They worked for very low wages and many of them were unemployed much of the time. The work used to be made between seasons for one third and one fourth of the regular price.

In the sixties the influx of the Russian Jews into the ready-made clothing trade, replacing the native and Irish tailors, began to be felt. Here the incursion of the foreigner seems to have been irresistible. His success was not always due to the lower wages he was willing to take, for he was competing with the outcasts of the English tailoring trade, the unskilled Englishwoman and the wretched and often imported Irishman, whose wages were as low as the contractor was willing to pay. But the success of the immigrant was due to his willingness to change the mode of production by using the sewing machine and division of labor, against which the native tailor showed a decided aversion. Here the influx of the foreign Jew has wrought a complete change in the contract system. The old contractor was a mere middleman and had no need for any knowledge of the tailoring trade; he was generally a lodging-house keeper, who secured the work by giving a cash deposit for the goods he took from the manufacturer and distributed among the wretched tailors in the lodging house and the helpless women in his vicinity, who completed the whole garment. He was replaced by the Jewish contractor, who made his work in a shop. This Jewish contractor was not a mere middleman; he was necessarily a tailor and an organizer of labor, for his work was done by a system of division of labor calling for various grades and forms of skill, namely, the baster, machinist, and presser, with various subdivisions, such as fitter, busheler, finisher, buttonhole maker, feller, basting puller, etc.

The position of the contractor or sweater now in the business in American cities is peculiarly that of an organizer and employer of immigrants. The man best fitted to be a contractor is the man who is well acquainted with his neighbors, who is able to speak the languages of several classes of immigrants, who can easily persuade his neighbors or their wives and children to work for him, and who in this way can obtain the cheapest help. The contractor can increase the number of people employed in the trade at very short notice. During the busy season, when the work doubles, the number of people employed increases in the same proportion. All the contractors are agents and go around among the people. Housewives, who formerly worked at the trade and abandoned it after marriage, are called into service for an increased price of a dollar or two a week. Men who have engaged in other occupations, such as small business and peddling, and are out of the business most of the year, are marshaled into service by the contractor, who knows all of them and can easily look them up and put them in as competitors by offering them a dollar or two a week more than they are getting elsewhere. It is the contractor who has introduced the Italian home finishers into the trade; he has looked them up and taught them the work and is getting it made for less than half the wages that he formerly paid for the same work.

The contractor never has at one time a large amount of work. Through him the industry is scattered over a wide area, among all kinds of people, and he thrives as long as they do not know one another. The contractor is an important factor in the clannishness of the immigrant nationalities. It is in part due to him that we have in large cities the Jewish districts, Polish districts, Swedish districts, etc., with very little assimilation. The contractors establish their shops in the heart of the district where the people live, and since they can practically earn their living at home, they have no opportunity of mingling with others or of learning from the civilization of other peoples.

The following is a typical case: A Polish Jew in Chicago, at a time when very few of the Poles were tailors, opened a shop in a Polish neighborhood. He lost money during the time he was teaching the people the trade, but finally was a gainer. Before he opened the shop he studied the neighborhood; he found the very poorest quarters where most of the immigrant Poles lived. He took no one to work except the newly arrived Polish women and girls. The more helpless and dependent they were the more sure they were of getting work from him. In speaking about his plans he said, "It will take these girls years to learn English and to learn how to go about and find work. In that way I will be able to get their labor very cheap." His theory turned out to be practical. He has since built several tenement houses.

The contractor in the clothing trade is largely responsible for the primitive mode of production, — for the foot-power sewing machine, for the shops in the alleys, in the attics, on top floors, above stables, and in some cases in the homes of the people. These small shops are able on account of low rent and meager wages to compete successfully, although with foot power, against the large shops and factories with steam or electric power. Usually it is not necessary to have more than fifty dollars to start a shop with foot-power machines. As there is no investment in goods, the contractor runs no risk. Little managing ability is required, because the number of employees is small.

The unlimited hours of work, often seven days in the week, is a feature of the contracting system. The contractor himself works unlimited hours. His shop is open most of the time. He deals with people who have no knowledge of regular hours. He keeps them in the dark with regard to the prevailing number of hours that other people work.

The contractor is an irresponsible go-between for the manufacturer, who is the original employer. He has no connection with the business interests of the manufacturer nor is his interest that of his help. His sphere is merely that of a middleman; he is practically useless in a large factory. He holds his own mainly because of his ability to get cheap labor, and is in reality merely the agent of the manufacturer for that purpose. In this he generally succeeds, because he lives among the poorest class of people, knows them personally, and knowing their circumstances can drive the hardest kind of a bargain. A very large number of the people who work in the sewing trade for contractors usually hope to become contractors themselves. When they succeed in this they reduce the prices, since the contractor when he first takes out work takes it for less money than other contractors.

Usually when work comes to the contractor from the manufacturer and is offered to his employees for a smaller price than has previously been paid, the help will remonstrate and ask to be paid the full price. Then the contractor tells them, "I have nothing to do with the price. The price is made for me by the manufacturer. I have very little to say about the price." That is, he cuts himself completely loose from any responsibility to his employees as to how much they are to get for their labor, throwing the responsibility on the manufacturer who originally gave him the work. The help do not know the manufacturer. They cannot register their complaint with the man who made the price for their labor. The contractor, who did not make the price for their labor, claims that it is of no use to complain to him. So that however much the price for labor goes down there is no one responsible for it.

In case the help form an organization and send a committee to the manufacturer, the manufacturer will invaribly say, "I do not employ you and I have nothing to do with you"; and when they go back to the contractor and file their complaint, he will invariably say, "I am not making the price for your labor. I am simply paying you as much as I can out of what I get from the manufacturer." This is also true with regard to any agreements of a labor organization that may be made. If an agreement is made with a contractor, it is usually worthless, because he has no property invested that can be levied upon. If the agreement is made with the manufacturer, it does not hold, because he is not violating it. In this irresponsible state of the business it is extremely difficult to devise any way in which organizations can make agreements and enforce them.

There is always a cut-throat competition among contractors. A contractor feels more dependent than any of his employees. He is always speculating on the idea of making a fortune by getting more work from the manufacturer than his neighbor and by having it made cheaper. Usually when he applies for work in the inside shop he comes in, hat in hand, very much like a beggar. He seems to feel the utter uselessness of his calling in the business. Oftentimes the contractor is forced to send work back because he cannot make it under the conditions on which he took it, yet he does not dare to refuse the offer for fear the manufacturer will not give him more of his work. So he tries to figure it down by every device, and yet, perhaps, in the end is forced to send it back.

The contractor is always speculating on what is coming next in the busy season, and sometimes in the busy season he can, as a matter of fact, save some money; but this is only for a short time. The most of the year, probably for about nine months, he is in this cut-throat competition. This is indeed the worst factor in the trade.

It must not be inferred from what precedes that the contractor is the cause of the sweating system, or that the sweating system is identical with the contract system. Both the contractor and the sweating system are the product of a disorganized and crowded labor market. This distinction is not apprehended even by the tailors' unions, who direct their energies mainly to the abolition of the contractor instead of to the abolition of the conditions which produce the contractor. The factory system itself is not always clearly marked off from the contracting system. A factory foreman may send work out at night to be done by his own employees at their homes. A factory may use partly mechanical power and partly foot power. A manufacturer may employ subcontracting within the factory. On the other hand, the small manufacturer may practice the same oppression and impose the same insanitary conditions upon his employees as would be done by a contractor. In the manufacture of cigars the "sweater" is not a contractor, but is a manufacturer who buys his material on the market and sells his product to jobbers or regular purchasers. In the manufacture of clothing the "sweater" is a contractor who agrees to take out material owned by the merchant and to return it to him as a finished garment. The only difference is that in the cigar business the raw material is owned by the one who directly employs the labor, while in the clothing business the raw material is the property of the merchant. In both cases the labor is equally "sweated."

The futility of directing the energies of reform solely against the contractor may be seen in New York in one branch of the clothing trade, that of ladies' ready-made garments, including cloaks and so-called "tailor-made suits." Already in this line of manufacture fully 75 per cent of the product has passed out of the hands of contractors into those of "manufacturers." Ten years ago probably 90 per cent of women's clothing was made by people who worked for contractors, while now only about 25 per cent of the trade are working for contractors. But so far as the people employed in the business are concerned there has not been any material change for the better, since these small manufacturers retain all the abuses of long hours, small pay, and insanitary shops. The way in which this new class of manufacturers has arisen in the clothing trade and has driven out of business the large manufacturer on Broadway who sent his work out to contractors is one of the remarkable developments of this remarkable trade. These former large manufacturers who have abandoned the ready-made business have gone into the retail or custom trade and have set up model "inside" factories on Broadway, where they cater to the more well-to-do purchasers. Small manufacturers on Division and other streets, who have absorbed the former wholesale trade, have followed a method somewhat as follows.

A contractor who had been able to save five hundred or six hundred dollars makes up in a small shop a number of samples and designs. He then communicates with the buyers of wholesale dry goods or with clothing houses, cloak jobbers, country merchants, "mail-order" houses, or department stores, stating that he has opened a shop and is able to sell new and first-class designs in the several patterns of cloaks and suits at a much lower price than the cloak manufacturers are doing. He does not send out traveling salesmen, but waits for buyers to call and see his samples and leave their orders. Having received an order, he takes it to some convenient bank, which usually extends him credit with a woolen house somewhat approximating the amount of the order, furnishing also a certain amount of cash with which to pay his help. The bank takes the order from him as guaranty, and also collects the bill after the goods are made and delivered. In this way a man with very little money is able to blossom out from a contractor into a manufacturer and to do business to the amount of the orders he is able to get.

The saving by this small man as against the large cloak manufacturer is in the following ways: he does not have to pay a high-priced designer, since he designs his own patterns; he does not have to pay a superintendent, since he manages his own business; nor does he pay high rents, since he is usually located in the poor quarter of the city. He can get labor as cheap as any contractor because he runs his shop in the same method when he becomes a manufacturer as he ran it when he was a contractor; that is, his shop is open day and night, and people can work as many hours as they wish. He is always on the lookout for cheap help and he is careful in regard to saving the goods and pieces, which cannot be saved in the same manner in the large factory. So by selling goods in some instances for thirty and forty per cent less than the wholesale cloak manufacturer can possibly do he can give the buyers of these wholesale and jobbing houses and also the retail and department stores the benefit that was formerly derived by the large wholesale manufacturer. In reality he is little more than he used to be, a contractor, with the difference that he now does his own cutting and his own marketing; and the profits on his labor and on the capital invested in the business are shared with the banker.

The Task System

Accompanying the immigration of Jews from 1876 to 1882 the remarkable "task system" was introduced in the coat shops in New York. This system produces at the present time perhaps one half the coats made in that city. The task system is peculiar to the city of New York, where it originated and continues. It exists neither in other cities of the United States nor in other countries. It is peculiar, also, to the Jewish shops.

The task system was the first real division of labor in coat shops. It has a double characteristic. There is a "team," or "set," of workmen, and the wages are paid by the piece. The number of workmen in the set is three, — the machine operator, the baster, and the underbaster or finisher. The pressing is usually done by a fourth man, who is not a member of the team. With such nicety has this system been adjusted, through the pressure of competition, that at the present time it is found that one presser can press more coats than one team can complete in a day; and, on the other hand, two teams can furnish more work than one presser can complete; consequently the standard shop, in which four fifths of the task work is done, is that of the "three-machine" shop, that is, the shop of three teams of operator, baster, and finisher to two pressers. Sewing on buttons and tacking pockets is done by a girl working by the week. Originally in many cases where the shop was small the contractor himself was one of the team, but at the present time, with three teams, he is the fitter or bushelman. Each team, therefore, is composed of the following : one operator, one baster, one edge baster or finisher. To every three teams, two pressers ; two girls for sewing on buttons, tacking pockets, and so forth ; one or two girls for buttons, felling armholes, and so forth.

When the task system originated with the Jewish immigrants, about the year 1877, it took the place of the journeyman tailor in the ready-made work. The coat for which the tailor received $5 or $6 as custom work, and for which he received $2.50 to $3 in the dull season as ready-made work, was made in these Jewish task shops for $1.50 to $2. At this price the Jews earned as much money as the merchant tailor and even more. The latter made very little use of the sewing machine. Most of the work on the coat was done by hand. When the division of labor was introduced in the Jewish shops each particular division became a trade in itself. The machine operator did not know how to do pressing or basting, the presser could not do the work of the others, and so on. The sewing-machine operator now became an important factor in the trade. He was able to do many parts of the work by machine that were formerly done by hand, and as a result the coat was made much quicker. Then again, the men who were engaged only in basting were able to do their work much quicker and probably better. The same was true of the presser and finishers.

In addition to the division of labor, the characteristic of the task system as distinguished from a piece system consists in the fiction that the workmen are earning a standard amount of wages per week. The scale originally fixed upon, and adhered to at the present time, was $18 for the operator, $16 for the baster, and $7 to $9 for the girl edge baster or finisher, or $11 to $12 for the man edge baster who has latterly taken the girl's place. Starting out upon this basis, it was found twenty years ago that a team could complete per day eight or nine cheviot coats with plain seams and with welts on the outside. At this rate the price per coat for the team was about 80 cents. The present price is only 28 to 35 cents.

The process by which the price of labor was reduced, following the great influx of Hebrews in 1882, was somewhat as follows. The contractor, who was, perhaps, himself a member of the team on a kind of coöperative basis with the others, would go to the manufacturer and ask for work. Finding that there was but little work to be had, he would offer to take the coats cheaper than the price theretofore paid. When he came home he would tell his men that there was not much work and he was obliged to take it cheaper, and, since he did not want to reduce their wages and pay them less per day, all they would have to do would be to make another coat in the task. That is, if they were accustomed to make 9 coats in the task, they would be required to make 10, then 11, and so on. The wages were always reduced on the theory that they were not reduced at all but the amount of labor increased. In this way intense speed was developed. The men who had been accustomed to making 9 coats in a task would make 10, and so on up to 15, 18, and even 20, as is the customary task at the present time. The hours began to be increased, in order to make the task in a day. Within the last three years it is said by the men that it is only in very rare cases that a set can make a task in a day; that it is usual for these sets of three, even when working twelve or thirteen hours per day, to make only 4½ or 5 tasks in a week. In previous years, they claim, men were able to make 7 and 8 tasks or days' work per week.

This increased number of coats per task probably explains why, in the evolution of the trade, women could not hold their own as edge basters and finishers. About 1500 to 2500 girls have been driven out and men have taken their places at wages fifty per cent higher. This is because both the hours and the speed were increased continually so that women were physically unable to perform the task.

The task system, it is said, has two advantages, — the men work substantially by piecework and have a personal inducement to perform their work as quickly as they can; and since they are in a team, each has to keep up with the others, so that a higher speed by any one induces higher speed by the other two. So nicely are the members of these teams adjusted to each other that frequently a baster or an operator is out of work because for the time being he cannot find the other two members whose speed is exactly fitted to his. By this queer coöperative production in the form of team work, combined with the personal interest of piecework, the Hebrew tailors in New York have devised what is perhaps the most ingenious and effective engine of overexertion known to modern industry.

One reason why piecework and high speed have become the framework of the contractors' shops is probably because the Jewish people are peculiarly eager to earn a big day's wages regardless of sacrifice. The Jewish workman is willing to work very hard for this, and does not wish to have it said that there is a limit to his earning capacity. It is the desire of the Jew to have his employment so arranged that he can speculate and bargain upon his earning capacity and can make use of the seasons. Piecework gives him that opportunity. In a rush season he will demand a decrease in the number of coats to the task, making more tasks per week and consequently earning higher wages. If the work is slack and the number of coats in the task is increased, he will speculate upon his ability to work harder and still earn high wages. Usually he is anxious to accumulate money and open up a contractor's shop for himself, or to go into some kind of business. It is not for love of hard work nor because of lack of other enjoyment that the Jew is willing to work so hard, but for the sake of getting rid of work. At the same time it is true regarding green immigrants of all races that the conditions of a strange land stimulate them to the hottest exertion of which they are capable. The Jewish immigrant is peculiar only in that he is not by nature a wage-earner, and he keeps before himself continually the goal of emancipation from hard work.

This characteristic of the Jew shows itself in his irritation under the discipline of the factory. He is willing to work long hours, but does not like to have any one dictate the time when he shall begin work or stop work. He does not like to be driven nor have his attention called to the fact that he has not made much work. He wants to have freedom. This he usually has in the contractor's shop. He is very nearly "his own boss"; he can smoke, talk, run around, stay at work an hour longer, come in an hour earlier, or come later. The conditions of sweat-shop employment which favor this are piecework and an almost complete absence of factory regulations and factory management.

While the task system displaced the journeyman tailor in the manufacture of ready-made coats, it has itself in the past five years met a competitor in the factory, or large shop. In this contest the task system appears to be antiquated and uneconomical. During the twenty-five years of its existence in New York it shows no material change. The division of labor is but slightly different from what it was originally. We now have the operator, baster, and edge baster or finisher, with a helper or two in each branch of work, just as formerly, except that the edge baster or finisher is now a man, while originally this work was done by women. But the task itself, instead of being 8 or 10 coats, was raised to 20 to 24 coats, though reduced to 10 or 12 at times by the union. The workmen make up in overexertion what they lack in shop organization and division of labor. The team system lacks elasticity and the power of expansion. The division of labor can go no further than to pass the coat through the hands of not more than nine or ten persons. If the shop grows in size the growth is not organic, it is segmentary. It cannot add a man here and a girl there, but must add an entire team; in fact it must add three teams in order economically to adjust the work of the two pressers.

There has, indeed, been a cumbersome attempt during the past ten years to introduce a further division of labor in the task system. It consists in a curious reduplication of the team. The operator in the original team becomes the first operator and does the parts requiring more careful work. He takes with him another man, called "two thirds of an operator," who does operator's work requiring less skill and is paid two-third wages, and still a third man, called "one third of an operator," who does the least skillful work and gets one-third pay. The same threefold division is made for the baster and for the edge baster, so that there is also a "whole baster," a "two-thirds baster," and a "one-third baster." A shop of this kind is called not a three-team shop but a "two-team" shop, since it requires a whole man plus a two-thirds man plus a one-third man to make two "whole men." This awkward subdivision is not making headway, but the entire task system is yielding to the more elastic and organic factory system. This is known in the trade as the "Boston system," or "section work," in order to distinguish it from the task system, which is peculiar to New York. It is not really a "Boston system," since it is found also in Philadelphia, Chicago, and elsewhere, but it has been slow to gain a foothold in New York because the task system has met it by its unique capacity for overexertion. Now that it has been introduced on the basis of New York's wages and standards of exertion those contractors who have adopted it are confident of its future. The "factory" employs 50 to 200 persons, where the task system employs 10 to 20. It has a minute division of labor and an elasticity of expansion far beyond that of the task system.

Nationalities and Organizations

The Jew occupies a unique position in the clothing trade. His physical strength does not fit him for manual labor. His instincts lead him to speculation and trade. His individualism unsuits him for the life of a wage-earner, and especially for the discipline of a labor organization. For these reasons when the Jew first lands in this country he enters such light occupations as sewing, cigar making, and shoemaking. Only about eleven per cent of the Jewish immigrants were tailors in Europe. The reason why so many of them take up that occupation in America is because the work is light. They begin as helpers and advance to full-fledged mechanics. After they have worked for some time and have learned the trade they open contractors' shops for themselves. They can begin with a capital of fifty dollars. From that they go into the wholesale manufacture of clothing. A similar development occurs in cigar manufacture. Jews do not enter in large numbers those industries where machinery plays an important part, but if they do enter they strive to set up as small manufacturers or contractors. Probably the only place in the United States where shoes are made outside of factories by the old sweating system is among Jewish contractors in New York.

Jewish women are employed to a much less extent than the women of other nationalities, and their children are kept in school until fifteen or sixteen years of age. It is quite unusual for Jewish tailors to teach their children their own trade. The young generation seek other callings.

The Italian tailor in his own country receives only about one half the wages received by the Russian, Polish, Hungarian, and Roumanian Jews in their own countries, and about one quarter of the wages paid for similar grades of work in western Europe. Consequently in the United States, with his standard of living, he can successfully compete with the newly arrived Russian Jew and much more successfully with the German or Englishman. The Russian Jew who is not a tailor but learned his work in this country and works in the shop as operator or presser is usually from the stock of small business men in the old country who have a fairly good standard of living, and he is regarded among the clothing workers as of the better class. He will insist on better living and higher wages for his particular kind of work than the tailor. This accounts for a curious paradox in the task system in New York, where the operator, who usually comes from the commercial classes in Russia, will command $3 instead of $2.66, which is paid to the skilled tailor for the basting. This also holds true in other branches, such as cloak making and pants and vest making. The operator usually gets more money than the tailor, due to the fact that this line of employment has been taken up by a class of people who did not work in the clothing trade in the old country and whose standard of living was not as low as that of the tailor.

But when we come to the Italian we find that he will work at operating, or pressing, or any branch of the trade which he learns in this country at exceedingly low wages. He has usually been a farmer or farm hand, and the standard of living of the Italian farmer is even below that of the tailor. While as yet the Italians have not come into the trade in very large numbers, since they have sought mainly the common outdoor employments, yet those who have taken up this branch of work usually accept much less wages than skilled tailors. Considering the large immigration of Italians it seems that the future clothing workers in this country are not likely to be the Jews but the Italians.

One point at which the Italians have an advantage is the employment of their wives and sisters. The Italian and his wife will come to the shop together. If he is a pants operator she is usually his helper, or if he is a cloak maker she is his hand sewer and finisher, and so both labor together to cover the expenses of the family. In the case of the Jews, the Jewish woman will not go to work in the shop after she is married. There are numbers of cases where the Italian and his wife together work for the same price which the Jew receives for his labor alone, and in this way the Italian is able to crowd the Jew out of the trade.

The Italian, like the Jew, has a very elastic character. He can easily change habits and modes of work and adapt himself to different conditions. He is energetic and thrifty and will work hard, with little regard to the number of hours. It is quite usual for an Italian cloak maker, like the Jew, after he has worked ten hours in the shop with his wife to take a bundle of work home at night. But, unlike the Jew, he not only does the work at home himself, but he is assisted by the women in his family and often leaves a part of the work for them to do during the day.

By comparing the Italian and the Pole it will be found that it is the Polish women who enter the sewing trade, whereas the former Polish farmer clings to common work requiring hard labor. The Italian is able to control such work as the manufacture of clothing, silk weaving, hat making, and other trades where taste and a fine sense of touch are essential for a successful performance of the work. The Polish farmer can successfully compete in factory work, where hard, automatic labor is necessary; but the Italian dislikes mechanical work and is better adapted to diversified pursuits where manipulation is required.

The mode of production among the Germans and Bohemians is similar; the women and girls are operators, edge basters, and finishers, with men as first basters and trimmers. The Bohemians probably employ their children in the shops more than the Germans. The Bohemians are a fairly well-educated people, and have a number of unions among their working population. When the price for labor is reduced they usually start a movement in resistance.

The Poles work in the same way as the Germans and Bohemians. Owing to the opposition of their priests they have never made any attempt to join a labor organization. During the strike in Chicago in 1896 it was the Polish shops that continued at work and defeated the strike. The Poles are a submissive people while working, and it is in their shops that the hardest driving is done. They have greater endurance and will work for a lower rate of wages than any other nationality. The contractors are mainly Jews. The Polish children begin to work early. In a shop of sixteen persons there will usually be four to six children under sixteen years of age.

Notwithstanding the competing power of Polish women they can probably be outclassed by Italian women. While a great many Polish women have entered the trade they have not yet developed great speed nor been able to work in factories producing the best grades of work, while Italian women are almost perfect imitators. The Italian woman can develop speed and can work with skill. Like the Poles, they also are obedient to orders.

The best people in the clothing trade in Chicago are the Scandinavians, including Swedes, Norwegians, and Danes. They are engaged in the manufacture of pants and vests, under contractors of their own nationality. They do not work more than ten hours a day as a rule, usually in large shops with steam power. They uphold the price for their labor more than the Bohemians or Poles and have developed the best labor organizations in the trade.[1] Their standard of living is high, and many of them are fairly well educated. The Swedes do not put their children to work but send them to school.

The women of the above-mentioned nationalities — Germans, Bohemians, Poles, and Swedes — are generally employed in the shops. In many cases they work even after marriage. The mother or grandmother stays at home keeping house and taking care of the children while the younger women of the family are in the shop. There are in the Swedish shops about five women to one man on pants and vests, and about two women to one man in the Polish and Bohemian coat shops. In the Jewish shops there are about equal numbers of men and women, although the women are mainly of other nationalities.

The standard of living of all nationalities has been gradually raised after their immigration to this country. Probably the Jewish immigrant changes his standard of living soonest. When the Jew wishes to make more money he will leave his former occupation as operator or baster and will become a contractor or storekeeper. So that instead of trying to raise the standard of living in the trade, he will try to leave the trade and throw in his lot with people whose standard of living is somewhat higher. In this way his commercial instinct militates continually against making active efforts to better the condition of his trade.

The Poles and Italians adhere to a lower standard of living for a longer time. During the last few years immigration from their countries has been continual, yet there is not much evidence of a material rise in the standard of living among the clothing workers. While it may be that the clothing workers are earning more money and are living under somewhat better conditions than they did in the old country, yet here in this country their lot in life has not improved. The low standard

[1] These organizations were locked out and defeated in 1904–1905 on the "closed-shop" issue. The teamsters struck in sympathy with them. See footnote, p. 64.

of living on the part of those immigrants who are continually coming into the trade is always a successful check on the efforts of immigrants of longer residence to better their condition. So they have no choice except either to stay in the trade and submit to the conditions of the newly arrived immigrant or to leave the trade and go into business. The Jews have been successful in doing the latter. As regards the condition of the clothing workers, it is about the same as it would be if all these Poles, Jews, and Italians had begun to engage in the trade yesterday. Those who have had a better standard of living, such as the Germans and Irish, have been crowded out of the trade and have been replaced by the Italians, Jews, and Poles.

The movement of wages in the clothing trade is directly affected by the fate of labor organizations. Considering the continual influx of immigrants unaccustomed to unionism, the employment of women and children, and the prevalence of home work, the problem of organization is indeed serious. In New York the Jews have controlled the trade for the past twenty years, so that conflicts of nationalities within the union have not occasioned difficulty. The problem has been the nature of the Jew himself. The Jew's conception of a labor organization is that of a tradesman rather than that of a workman. In the manufacture of clothing, whenever any real abuse arises among the Jewish workmen, they all come together and form a giant union and at once engage in a strike. They bring in ninety-five per cent of the trade. They are energetic and determined. They demand the entire and complete elimination of the abuse. The demand is almost unanimous and is made with enthusiasm and bitterness. They stay out a long time, even under the greatest of suffering. During a strike large numbers of them are to be found with almost nothing to live upon and their families suffering, still insisting, on the streets and in their halls, that their great cause must be won.

But when once the strike is settled, either in favor of or against the cause, they are contented, and that usually ends the union, since they do not see any practical use for a union when there is no cause to fight for. Consequently the membership of a Jewish union is wholly uncertain. The secretary's books will show 60,000 members in one month and not 5000 within three months later. If perchance a local branch has a steady thousand members from year to year, and if they are indeed paying members, it is likely that they are not the same members as during the year before. A German union, on the contrary, will have the same members year after year, well or ill, with little change. The Jew joins the union when it offers a bargain and drops it when he gets, or fails to get, the bargain.

The Jew is also exceedingly abstract and metaphysical and greatly interested in general principles. His union is always, therefore, except in time of a strike, a forum for the discussion of socialism and the philosophy of the labor movement. The socialist element acquires control when the workingmen stay away from the union, and they urge an organization devoted mainly to propaganda on the principles of the solidarity of all labor, without much attention to trade differences. The Jewish labor press, pamphlets, and speakers, nearly all recruited from the socialists, have continually engaged in these discussions, neglecting the formation and strengthening of their unions. These statements are substantiated again and again in the history of the trade in New York. It is a saying on the East Side that there is always a strike going on somewhere.

J. R. COMMONS.

XV

SLAVS IN COAL MINING

ANTHRACITE MINES[1]

Prior to the inauguration of the strike of the anthracite mine workers in 1902 the writer was a witness of an eviction scene in one of the mining "patches." A "patch" in the hard-coal fields of Pennsylvania is a small group of houses situated near a colliery and used as residences by the mine employees. The houses in this instance had been occupied up to the time of the eviction by members of English-speaking races. They were in arrears for rent, and their belongings were being put out upon the public highway by the constable and his deputies.

One particular house had been the home of the families of a Scotchman and his son. These two men, with their wives and the three small children of the younger, occupied the four rooms, two of which were on the first floor and two on the second. Of the seven members of the household the two men were the only wage-earners. All their effects on this eviction day were piled along the highway, — a bureau, "straw ticks," a stove, several chairs, a rag carpet or two, with here and there a lithograph scattered incongruously among boxes, kitchen utensils, and the separated parts of beds. These and other belongings were of such quantity and cumbersomeness as to make necessary the employment of a wagon with horse and driver to remove them. This description would apply as well to the scenes presented at the other miners' houses in this particular "patch" on this eviction day.

A week or so later I was again at this mining "patch." Into the houses unwillingly vacated by the English-speaking mine workers representatives of the Slav races were moving. They

[1] From *Charities*, Vol. XII, December 3, 1904. See also Warne, The Slav Invasion and the Mine Workers, Philadelphia, 1904.

came not along the highway, with their belongings in wagons, but by trail across the mountain from the railway station at Hazleton, with their household effects in blanketed bundles and trunklike boxes slung across their backs. The women, of whom there were but few, carried with seeming ease huge bundles, one on top of the head and one under each arm, and, like the men, represented a beast-of-burden adaptability to the most exacting physical labor under pressure from hard circumstances. Eight men and one woman took up their quarters in the particular house in which the families of the two English-speaking mine employees had lived.

The cooking utensils of the newcomers were of the barest in quantity and quality. They had neither chairs nor bureaus. Their meager supply of clothing was all but limited to the garments they wore. "Straw ticks" and beds were conspicuous by their absence, the new occupants being content with rolling themselves in blankets and sleeping upon the uncarpeted floor.

Thus in the concrete is illustrated the meaning of the Slav invasion of the anthracite coal fields of Pennsylvania, a phenomenon which has been going on, unobserved by most of us, for the past quarter of a century and more.

Previous to the coming of these alien races the English, Welsh, Irish, Scotch, Germans, Canadians, with the native Americans, formed the mining population of the hard-coal fields and dominated the labor supply of the anthracite industry. Beginning about 1875, the Slav and Italian invasions swept into the coal fields, bringing a group of races wholly foreign to those already dominant there, not only ethnically but in habits and customs, language and institutions. The Pole, the Slovak, the Ruthenian, the Bohemian, the Magyar, the Lithuanian, the Italian, and like nationalities crowded into the mining settlements, precipitating new factors into the already complicated industrial situation and making intensely acute the problem of race assimilation. Briefly, down to 1900 the most striking effect of this invasion was the migration in large numbers of members of the English-speaking nationalities not only from the anthracite industry itself but from that section of Pennsylvania.

Immigrants from Poland, Austria, Russia, Hungary, and Italy in the eight hard-coal-producing counties increased from 1925 in 1880 to 45,007 in 1890 and to 89,328 in 1900. The English-speaking foreign-born inhabitants — those from Ireland, Germany, Scotland, England, and Wales — in the anthracite region increased from 102,421 in 1880 to 123,636 in 1890; by 1900 they had decreased to 100,269. At the same time the total foreign-born population increased from 108,827 in 1880 to 170,582 in 1890 and to 193,692 in 1900. In brief, the English-speaking races, who composed nearly 94 per cent of the total foreign-born element in the eight hard-coal-producing counties in 1880, formed less than 73 per cent in 1890 and no more than 52 per cent in 1900. From less than 2 per cent of the total foreign-born population in 1880 the central European races increased to over 25 per cent in 1890 and to over 46 per cent in 1900.

This tendency in the anthracite industry of the Slav races to increase and of the English-speaking nationalities to decrease is even more clearly shown in statistics of employees of the coal-mining companies. The foreign-born Slav and Italian workers in and about the mines of the Philadelphia and Reading Coal and Iron Company, the largest single employer of mine labor in the lower or Schuylkill field, increased from 5839 in 1890 to 9521 in 1901. The foreign-born English-speaking employees decreased from 14,176 to 1152 during the eleven years. For the same period the employees grouped as "born in America" — for the most part descendants of English-speaking immigrants, doing the easiest work in and around the mines — increased from 4719 in 1890 to 15,627 in 1901.

The movement of the Slavs into and of the English-speaking race out of the hard-coal industry is distinctly traceable also according to the coal fields, being first marked in the Schuylkill field, then in the middle or Lehigh field, and lastly in the northern or Wyoming field.

This remarkable and sudden change in the racial composition of the anthracite-mine laborers has been the result of marked differences in the standards of living of the Slav and Italian and English-speaking mine workers, — differences which are very clear to those who have observed closely at first hand this industrial phenomenon. Specific illustrations are on record in nearly every "company" store in the family grocery bills of these newcomers and of the English-speaking mine employees. The differences are also indicated in the fact that the English-speaking mine worker has usually been married and has had children; the incoming Slav, generally speaking, has neither wife nor children. He has thus been free from the family outlay and from the necessity of having a wage income sufficient to meet the expense these goodly possessions entail. Unlike the English-speaking miner, the Slav has not had the parent's cost of sending his children to the public school; he has not had the property owner's tax contribution to meet; he has not had the male citizen's expense of voting, for the individual's cost for such political privileges, where they have been exercised by the Slav, has usually been met by the political faction which hoped to profit by the Slav's use of suffrage. In church contributions, in insurance against injuries and death while at work in the mines, in the dues of beneficial societies, and in the cost of like social and industrial activities, the Slav has not had as great an expense as the English-speaking nationalities in the mines.

All these represent the money cost to the individual of civic responsibilities, the proper exercise of which is of incalculable benefit to a community. For our particular purpose they indicate also some of the sources of cost to the English-speaking mine employee which enter into determining his standard of living and which he can meet only by the sale of his labor. The incoming Slav has been practically free from the necessity of meeting these and other expenses, since his standard of living has been much lower in cost than what the English-speaking mine worker has been compelled to meet. In consequence two distinctly marked groups of labor bearing different prices have competed in practically the same market for the sale of their labor.

It is an economic commonplace that where two commodities are offered for sale, other things being equal, the consumer chooses the one bearing the lower price. In the anthracite industry the consumers of mine labor were the railroad mining companies. With an oversupply of labor almost daily offered for sale, they purchased that of the Slav and Italian because it was the cheaper. It was not only because of their lower standard of living but also because they plied their picks in more dangerous places, worked thinner seams, and put up with conditions of employment which the English-speaking mine workers would not brook. In consequence the older nationalities began to be forced out of the industry and the migration already mentioned resulted. It was inevitable that the English-speaking mine workers who desired to remain in the industry should do one of two things, — either sell their labor for the price this new competition set or compel the Slav and Italian to work for a wage, that is, to sell his labor for a price sufficient to support the higher standard of living. The former, as we have seen, was the tendency down to 1900; but by the strike of that year, and much more so by that of 1902, this competition has been brought under the control of the English-speaking miner. How long this condition is to remain is likely to be definitely settled in 1906, when the award of the Anthracite Coal Strike Commission terminates.

In the struggle of 1900 the United Mine Workers of America had the greatest difficulty in prevailing upon the Slav and Italian to "join the union." Up to this time racial antipathies, social distinctions, language, and so forth, were among the strong barriers which prevented unity of action by the English-speaking and the non-English-speaking groups. These obstacles were finally overcome by the union by securing as industrial leaders of these races men of their own nationality who could speak English.

Through the support of the Slav and Italian the strike of 1900 brought to all mine workers an increase in wages and a mitigation of some of the hard conditions of employment. The Slav's industrial self-interest being thus brought home to him, he made the "best" striker in the strike of 1902. In this way and so far the United Mine Workers have controlled competition to the advantage of all mine labor in the hard-coal fields.

For the twenty-five years down to 1900 the racial forces in opposition to assimilation between the Slav and English-speaking nationalities in the anthracite industry were dominant. But the industrial disturbances of 1900 and 1902 have put into operation new and different forces, or rather they have directed the social forces into a different channel. On the broad ground of industrial self-interest racial ties are being broken down, largely through the instrumentality of the United Mine Workers of America. The English-speaking races have established what is practically a minimum wage in most of the occupations about the collieries, and by so doing are the sooner bringing the Slav up to a higher standard of living. In consequence assimilation between the English-speaking and the Slav races will not be such a remote possibility as formerly. With a higher wage and better conditions of employment, there are indications that the Slav races and their descendants are responding with alacrity to the influences tending toward conformity to American industrial conditions. They are, in general, frugal, industrious, peaceable, and for the most part possess qualities of character which will in time and under proper conditions make them a valuable addition to American citizenship. The present problem in the coal fields is how to bring favorable influences to bear upon them. This small geographical area in northeastern Pennsylvania, containing twenty-six different nationalities, with their different languages, customs, traditions, and habits of thought and action, — a heterogeneous mass of races in the course of assimilation, — presents one of the most remarkable social phenomena of our time. From its progress much of value should be learned to aid in the greater problem yet to be faced.

Not only, as has been shown, was this immigration of cheaper labor from European countries one of the principal causes which operated to give rise to the coal miners' strikes in 1900 and 1902, but it had much to do with bringing about the strike of the steel workers in 1901, that of the textile workers in 1903, and that of the meat handlers at Chicago in 1904. All these strikes centered about the unskilled occupations in the different industries, the very occupations toward which the competition of Slav and Italian was directed by virtue of their being unskilled workmen. They were indications of a widespread conflict waged by immigrants to secure a foothold in American industries. The movement is one which continues to furnish a serious menace to our industrial stability.

Slav immigration would not be the serious problem that it is to-day if its distribution had been intelligently effected. It has become an acute problem in many sections primarily because the distribution of its elements has been neglected. Salvation now must be in a reliance upon American institutions to assimilate this great influx of aliens. That this task is to test those institutions very near to their breaking point is clear to all observers of industrial and social conditions.

Experience thus far should teach the necessity for immediate and well-organized action looking toward the directing of at least a portion of this immigration stream into those sections of the country — into the South, for example — where it is most needed, instead of permitting it to follow the haphazard channel of its own making into the large industrial centers where its elements congregate in "foreign quarters" and give rise to municipal and other problems whose tendencies are working serious injury to our communities. Already some of the southern railroads have undertaken this task, but it must be planned on a much larger scale and be supported much more comprehensively than there is now any evidence of, if we are to hope for a solution of some of the more important problems arising out of immigration.

FRANK JULIAN WARNE.

BITUMINOUS MINES[1]

The special significance of a paper on the Slavs in the bituminous mines of Illinois is found in the effect on them of the mine workers' union. Practically all the Slavs in Illinois, outside of Cook County, are at work in or about the mines, as very few of them are employed on railway and other kinds of construction which attract the Italians. Of the 37,000 mine workers in Illinois about 60 per cent are foreign-born, and of this 60 per cent about one fourth are Slavs and Lithuanians. The four or five

[1] From *Charities*, Vol. XII, December 3, 1904.

divisions of the Slavs exceed in number any other nationality of the foreign-born, the Italians coming next, to the number of 3000. Among these the Slavs predominate in the order Poles, Slovaks, and Bohemians, while the Lithuanians number less than 1000. The great majority of them have entered this field since 1894, their introduction at that time being brought about through the general strike of the American and west European miners. The strike ended in a complete defeat of the improvised union of the time, and as a result the Slavs and the Italians have become in certain districts the predominating elements.

The circumstances of their immigration cannot be understood without a word on the characteristics of the mining industry in the state of Illinois. The northern field was the first in development, but it had the disadvantage of exceedingly thin veins of coal, a seam of forty inches being a prevailing depth. The southern field, on the other hand, is characterized by veins of six to ten feet in thickness. Owing to the greater facility of mining in the southern field, the introduction of machinery, and the thickness of the seam, the competition of coal in the markets had become so serious that many mines in the northern field were reduced to two or three months' work in the year, and even at prices per ton for mining double the prices in the southern field the miners were unable to earn similar wages. On this account the northern field has been the source of labor agitation, and the prominent leaders of the mine workers' union both in state and national fields have had their training in that section. It was, consequently, into this field that the majority of the Slav and Italian immigrants were brought by the operators, as is plainly shown by the statistics compiled by the Illinois Bureau of Labor Statistics, showing that in the first, second, and fourth mining districts of the state the percentages of foreign-born miners are respectively 89 per cent, 72 per cent, and 62 per cent; whereas in the other parts of the state the highest proportion is 51 per cent, and in the seventh, the most southerly district, only 20 per cent are foreign-born.

This distribution of the Slavs, who with the Italians constitute the bulk of these large percentages of foreign-born inhabitants, applies not only to districts throughout the state but also to working places within the mines. For it is the Slav and the Italian who are willing to take the places where the difficulties of mining are greatest and where consequently the output and earnings of the miner are least. The American and west European stock tend to distribute themselves in the better districts of the state and to keep the better-paying positions within each mine.

After the strike of 1894, notwithstanding a remarkable decrease in wages, there was practically no improvement in the mining business for three years. The conditions not only of the English-speaking miners but even of the Slavs and Italians became so oppressive that in 1897, when the strike was called by the remnant of the former union, practically every miner and mine worker in the state, including Slav and Italian, laid down his tools. The union entered the strike with no treasury and only a few hundred members, but at the end of four months won a complete victory and a general increase in wages, together with the eight-hour working day. The organization in Illinois is much stronger than in other parts of the bituminous field, mainly because the mine workers in this state held out at least a month longer than those in the other states of the competitive field and thereby secured terms in the final settlement with the operators more to their advantage than the terms secured in the other states. Since the success of the strike in 1897 the mine workers' union has made annual agreements with the operators, the terms regarding both wages and conditions of work being most minutely described.

The English-speaking miners universally show an inclination to keep Slavs and Italians from coming into the mines, and their immigration has been very slight since 1897. Practically the only way in which the Slav coming from the old country can now get employment as a miner is through the intervention of a relative or friend who agrees to be responsible for him. The state law requires two men to work together in a "room," and the miners' union requires them to share their earnings equally. Consequently a new miner who wants work must find an old miner who will teach him and share with him. This naturally is not easy to do. Furthermore, he must serve a year's apprenticeship above ground as a laborer before going below. This applies to miners proper who are paid by the ton. A different restriction, to be mentioned below, exists for "mine workers," who are paid by the day.

The union at first established an initiation fee of fifty dollars, which practically excluded all newcomers. Owing to the strenuous opposition of the operators in their annual conferences, this initiation fee was reduced to ten dollars, at which figure it now stands. At the same time the agreements distinctly provide for the open shop, the employer being given the right to hire new men not members of the organization provided he does not discriminate against union men. However, on account of the high minimum wage for day labor which the union secured and has been able most effectually to enforce, it is not to the interest of the operator to employ fresh and inexperienced men, provided older employees are on the ground. The significance of the minimum wage will be seen in the fact that whereas for common labor the rate of pay for ten hours' work prior to the strike of 1897 had been reduced as low as $1.40, the union gradually increased the minimum rate for all day labor employed above ground to $2.02½ in 1903, although a reduction was accepted in 1904, bringing it to $1.91 for eight hours' work. For underground work the minimum was increased until it stood at $2.56 in 1903, but was reduced in 1904 to $2.23 for eight hours' work. With such a high minimum, notwithstanding the open-shop privilege, the employer has little inducement to take on new men.

The high minimum has also an important effect on the employment of boys and on the attitude of the Italian and Slav toward the public-school system. At such rates of pay the employer is not inclined to take boys into the mines; in fact they secure their employment after they reach the age of sixteen mainly through the responsibility which their fathers and brothers assume on their part. Owing to the complete exclusion of boys from the mines in any capacity whatever, there has been a remarkable increase in school attendance of foreigners' children, who otherwise would be found at work in order to help out the family income. The Slavs are beginning to take an interest in the public-school system, several instances being known where representatives of this race. as well as of the Italian, have been elected to the school boards. This fact, however, should not be made too much of, since their participation is mainly owing to the effort of Americans — business men and mine superintendents — to invite and urge Slavs and Italians to accept such representation on these boards. The object of course is to interest foreigners in the school system, but the interest must be cultivated from without and does not spring voluntarily from the Slavs themselves. In many cases it is a difficult matter to secure a Slav or an Italian who will accept such a position.

The Italian shows more intelligence and appreciation of his position in the union than does the Slav. The policy of the mine workers' union is to distribute the offices among the different nationalities in order to have interpreters at their meetings and agents to keep the several nationalities in line. Undoubtedly the greatest difficulty encountered in the mining region at the present time under the system of agreements with the operators is the presence in such large numbers of non-English-speaking miners and mine workers. The enforcement of the interstate and state agreements is a matter of difficulty, sometimes on account of the dishonesty of the interpreter, and often on account of his inefficiency, and this is especially serious in the northern fields where the unions are controlled by the Slavs and the Italians. There have been several local strikes and violations of the agreement on account of this barrier of language, and there is no one object which appeals more to the operators of the state than that of instruction in English. This object of course did not appeal to them prior to the organization of the mine workers and the establishment of the agreement system, but now that they have for eight years been running their mines in coöperation with the union, they find it necessary to assist the latter in bringing forward its more conservative and intelligent members and in raising the general level of intelligence of the mass. This accounts for the interest which they show in the public-school system, and there is no subject of which the operators speak with greater pride than of the high grade of schools in the mining districts. Frequently a superintendent or other officer of a company will be found on the school board in company with a Slav, an Italian, and representatives of other nationalities. The parochial schools, which are attended by a majority of the Slav children, are of an unusually high order, and not only is the English language taught in all of them, but English may be said to be the language of the parochial schools.

The fact which interests the observer most of all is the marvelous thrift of the Slavs. Notwithstanding the prevalence of the use of intoxicants among them and other nationalities, large numbers have good bank accounts, and the movement toward purchasing homes has become perhaps the most noticeable feature of mining communities. In many cases company houses have been sold to employees, and often it happens that a Slav miner is able to pay in cash six hundred to a thousand dollars for his house. These houses are of course not elaborate, but there are none so inferior as those which one sees in the southern anthracite fields. It is agreed on all sides that the stability of employment which has prevailed since 1897 has been the main incentive of this movement toward home proprietorship.

Compared with the situation of the Slavs in the cities, that of those living in the mining districts of Illinois is idyllic. Their houses though small are not overcrowded, as they are in Chicago, each has its garden plot, and the hills and woods are near. Notwithstanding their work is underground, ventilation is always good, temperature is even the year round, hours are short, and in addition the union has a way of taking holidays for all nationalities whenever a particular nationality has a saint's day.

Of course the isolation of the mining camp brings its special problems, a peculiar one being the absence of the wider and higher educational opportunities. The situation is ripe for a large movement of an educational kind, based on instruction in English, with the addition thereto of manual training and household economics for the young people and centers of amusement and civic education for all. The friendliness of the mining companies and their superintendents toward a movement of this kind would be insured from the start, while the strong organization of the mine workers, reaching every individual, would coöperate if the enterprise were properly launched.

As might be expected, the English-speaking miners do not look upon their own position with that degree of satisfaction shown by the Slavs and Italians. Although they are not leaving the mines, yet they are the ones who make complaints and who lead in agitations for improved wages and conditions. Judging themselves by the American standards with which they are familiar, their inability to maintain these standards on the earnings of the Slav is a constant source of irritation. While they come to the front in the Mine Workers' Union, yet the union has been too much occupied with economic questions to permit time and thought for educational and social improvements. This line of progress must be inaugurated by the operators, and there could hardly be found in any industry a field more receptive for that kind of interest in their work people which has come to be known as "welfare work."

J. R. Commons.

XVI

THE NEGRO ARTISAN[1]

. . . Here we have perhaps the best key to the situation in the South before the war; there was little demand for skilled labor in the rather rude economy of the average slave plantation, and the Negro did the most of this. The slave artisan, however, was rather a jack-of-all-trades than a mechanic in the modern sense of the term, — he could build a barn, make a barrel, mend an umbrella, or shoe a horse. Exceptional slaves did the work exceptionally well, but the average workman was poor, careless, and ill trained, and could not have earned living wages under modern competitive conditions. While then it is perfectly true to say that the slave was the artisan of the South before the war, it is probably also true that the average of workmanship was low and suited only to rough plantation life. This does not of course gainsay for a moment the fact that on some of the better plantations and in cities like Richmond, Savannah, Charleston, and New Orleans there were really first-class Negro workmen who did good work.

Even before the war a movement of slaves to the cities took place, first of house servants with the masters' families and then of slave artisans; if the slave was a good artisan he was worth more hired out in the city than on the country plantation. Moreover, the Negro greatly preferred to be in town, since he had there more liberty, more associates, and more excitement. Probably in time there would have been evolved in the South a class of city serf artisans and servants considerably removed

[1] Extracts from The Negro Artisan: Report of a Social Study made under the Direction of Atlanta University. Edited by W. E. Burghardt Du Bois. Atlanta University Press, 1902. See also Hoffman, "Race Traits and Tendencies of the American Negro," *Publications of the American Economic Association*, Vol. XI, pp. 250–309.

from the mass of field hands. It is significant that the Georgia law prohibiting slaves from hiring their time specifically excepted certain of the larger towns.

After emancipation came suddenly, in the midst of war and social upheaval, the first real economic question was the self-protection of freed workingmen. There were three chief classes of them, — the agricultural laborers, chiefly in the country districts; the house servants in town and country; and the artisans, who were rapidly migrating to town. The Freedmen's Bureau undertook the temporary guardianship of the first class, the second class easily passed from half-free service to half-servile freedom. The third class, the artisans, however, met peculiar conditions. They had always been used to working under the guardianship of a master, and even though that guardianship in some cases was but nominal, yet it was of the greatest value for protection. This soon became clear as the Negro freed artisan set up in business for himself. If there was a creditor to be sued, he could no longer bring suit in the name of an influential white master; if there was a contract to be had, there was no responsible white patron to answer for the good performance of the work. Nevertheless these differences were not strongly felt at first, since the friendly patronage of the former master was often voluntarily given the freedman, and for some years following the war the Negro mechanic still held undisputed sway. Three occurrences, however, soon disturbed the situation. These were the competition of white mechanics, the efforts of the Negro for self-protection, and the new industrial development of the South.

These changes were spread over a series of years and are not yet complete, but they are the real explanation of certain facts which have hitherto been explained in false and inadequate ways. It has for instance been said repeatedly that the Negro mechanic carelessly threw away his monopoly of the southern labor market and allowed the white mechanic to supplant him. This is only partially true. To be sure, the ex-slave was not alert, quick, and ready to meet competition. His business hitherto had been to *do* work but not to *get* work, save in exceptional cases. The whole slave system of labor saved him from certain sorts of competition, and when he was suddenly called to face the competition of white mechanics he was at a loss. His especial weakness was the lack of a hiring contractor. His master or a white contractor had usually taken jobs and hired him. The white contractor still hired him, but there was no one now to see that the contractor gave him fair wages. Indeed, as the white mechanics pressed forward, the only refuge of the Negro mechanic was lower wages. There were a few Negro contractors here and there, but they again could only hope to maintain themselves by markedly underbidding all competitors and attaining a certain standing in the community.

What the Negro mechanic needed then was social protection, — the protection of law and order, perfectly fair judicial processes, and that personal power which is in the hands of all modern laboring classes in civilized lands, namely, the right of suffrage. It has often been said that the freedman, throwing away his industrial opportunities after the war, gave his energies to politics and succeeded in alienating his friends and exasperating his enemies by proving his inability to rule. It is doubtless true that the freedman laid too much stress on the efficacy of political power in making a straight road to real freedom. And undoubtedly, too, a bad class of politicians, white and black, took advantage of this and made the reconstruction Negro voter a hissing in the ears of the South. Notwithstanding this the Negro was fundamentally right. If the whole class of mechanics here, as in the Middle Ages, had been without the suffrage and half free, the Negro would have had an equal chance with the white mechanic and could have afforded to wait. But he saw himself coming more and more into competition with men who had the right to vote, the prestige of race and blood, the advantage of intimate relations with those acquainted with the market and the demand. The Negro saw clearly that his industrial rise depended to an important degree upon his political power, and he therefore sought that power. In this seeking he failed, primarily because of his own poor training, the uncompromising enmity and apprehensions of his white neighbors, and the selfishness and half-hearted measures of his emancipators. The result was that the black artisan entered the race heavily handicapped, the member of a proscribed class, with restricted rights and privileges, without political and social power. The result was, of course, that he was enabled to maintain himself only by accepting low wages and keeping at all hazards the good will of the community.

Even here, however, he could not wholly succeed. The industrial conditions in the country were rapidly changing. Slowly but surely the new industrial South began to arise and with it came new demands on the mechanic. Now in the very nature of the case the Negro mechanic could not meet these demands. He knew how to do a few things by rule of thumb, such as building one of the rambling old-fashioned southern mansions or a slave shanty; he could construct a rough sugar hogshead and resole a shoe; in exceptional cases he could do even careful and ingenious work in certain lines; but, as a rule, he knew little of the niceties of modern carpentry or iron working, he knew practically nothing of mills and machinery and very little about railroads, — in fact he was especially ignorant in those very lines of mechanical and industrial development in which the South has taken the longest strides in the last thirty years. And if he was ignorant, who was to teach him? Certainly not his white fellow-workmen, for they were his bitterest opponents because of strong race prejudice and because of the fact that the Negro works for low wages. Apprenticeship to the older Negro mechanics was but partially successful, for they could not teach what they had never learned. In fact it was only through the lever of low wages that the Negro secured any share in the new industries. By that means he was enabled to replace white laborers in many branches, but he thereby increased the enmity of trade unions and labor leaders. Such in brief was the complicated effect of emancipation on the Negro artisan, and one could not well imagine a situation more difficult to remedy.

LOCAL CONDITIONS: TEXAS[1]

We have always had among us some men who have been more or less skillful in the use of tools. During the days of slavery these men built the houses, made the plows, carriages, and wagons, and performed nearly all that class of labor. The constant doing brought to them experience, and experience ripened into a degree of skill. Slavery was their trade school and experience their instructor. After the Civil War these workmen followed the trades, and at first they had the field to themselves.

In the course of time labor-saving machines were introduced and new methods of doing things were adopted; the old workman entered a new era; he found himself face to face with new conditions; his school did not give instruction in the use of machines and he was unable to keep step with the onward march. Some of them who did keep up have finished their work and gone to their reward. No one has taken the vacant places, and to-day the ranks of Negro artisans need — sadly need — recruiting.

Texas offers great opportunities to skilled workmen in various trades. Her natural resources surpass those of any state in the Union. It is her proud boast that within her broad domain is to be found everything from a salt mine to an oil geyser. These resources are but partially developed, some not at all. The Negro artisan has had a share in this development, and will have a larger share in the future provided he will fit himself for this larger share. I have had opportunity to observe conditions among artisans only in the cities, towns, and country districts of southern Texas.

Ours being an agricultural state, blacksmiths are in greater demand than perhaps any other tradesman. You will find a Negro blacksmith in nearly every town and at every country crossroad. They are found managing shops on many of the large cotton and sugar plantations. One of the largest sugar

[1] By E. H. Holmes, of the Prairie View Normal School. [The Report contains similar contributions from other states. — ED.]

farms in the Southwest, located at Sugarland, Texas, employs a Negro foreman of its blacksmith shop at a salary of $1080 per year. In the towns the majority of them are doing business for themselves; a few own their shops and are making a living and accumulating property. There are still others who work by the day in shops owned by whites. These receive wages according to their skill. White men having the same degree of skill would receive no more. There is such a shop at Brenham, Texas. Some weeks ago the owner of this shop stated that he worked a few colored men, that he would employ more if they could do superior work, and that there was no discrimination practiced in his shop; he also expressed the hope that our school would send out more students who could make drawings and work from drawings. It is difficult to tell the percentage of Negro artisans in the towns, since they do not register their occupations. Whatever is known must be learned by inquiry or from personal contact. Let us consider conditions at Houston, Texas. This is a city having a population of 60,000, one third of whom are Negroes. It is in every respect a liberal and representative city. There are seven blacksmiths who own and run their shops, and two of these shops employ from three to five workmen. The proprietors make a good living, and nearly all of them own their homes. The largest carriage and iron repair shop, owned by a white man, employs five Negro blacksmiths on its working force. Two of these manage their own fires. They are paid according to skill, although sometimes discrimination is made on account of color. Two boiler and foundry shops employ Negro workmen. They receive the regular molders' wages, $4 per day, and a few of them have been in the service of the firms for years. The Southern Pacific Railway System employs them in two of its shops. In these shops are some who manage their fires, one who operates a steam hammer, some who build and repair cars, and a large number of helpers who rank several grades above common laborers. A few of these men have been steadily employed for twenty-five years, some longer. The wages range from 15 to 25 cents per hour, according to skill. It might be of interest to remark just here that one of the helpers long years ago was foreman of the shop. Time and improved machinery forced him down. So far as employment goes there is practically no discrimination against blacksmiths, and I do not know of any blacksmiths' union in the whole state.

Carpenters are fewer in number than blacksmiths. In the small towns they are journeyman workers. As a class they do inferior work. Their wages range from $1.25 to $2 per day. White journeymen do the same poor quality of work but receive higher wages. Their pay ranges from $1.50 to $2.50 per day. The best carpenters drift to the cities, because the people there appreciate and demand good work and live in better houses. Competition is sharp and the labor unions are strong. In the city of Houston we have four men who contract for themselves. They do good work and find ready employment. They get contracts not exceeding $2500. In the same city are several old contractors who have been forced to retire on account of close competition. Two white contractors work a force of Negro and a force of white carpenters, separately of course. They pay according to skill, white and black alike. More discrimination is shown against carpenters than against any other class of tradesmen. Negro carpenters have been urged to form unions which would affiliate with white unions, but have not thought best to do so. They know that they would be called upon to strike in concert with the other unions, and they feel that in the end they would get the worst of it. As long as they find employment they prefer to work independently of the unions.

Brickmasons are fewer than carpenters. This class of workers are in demand, wages are high, and discrimination is reduced to a minimum. There are no brick contractors in Houston, and only one or two in the state. Bricklayers in the towns are journeymen and most of them do a good grade of work; wages are from $3 to $4 per day. In the cities wages are a little better. I know of no plasterers. Sometimes men are called from New Orleans to do that sort of work. The finest plastering in our state capitol was done by Negroes brought from Chicago. Nearly all the employees in the cotton-seed-oil mills and cotton compresses are Negroes. They are not all common laborers. It requires skill to operate some of the machines and to get the products ready for market. Wages are from $1.50 to $3 per day. In some of the trades we do not find the Negro at all, or if found they are so few that they do not count in trade competition. Houston has no shoemakers, no plumbers and harness makers, and I know of but one tinner in the state. These are the conditions as they now exist among Texas artisans. I have observed that any man who knows how to do something and knows how to do that something well and is willing to do something will find ready employment. Opportunities are not wanting, but many times when these opportunities present themselves we are not able to grasp them because of lack of training. The world wants trained workmen, men whose trained minds will direct skilled hands, men who are masters of their craft. Not more than three per cent of our young men in Texas are entering the trades, and at the present death rate among the old workmen it will not be long before we shall be conspicuous for our absence from all the trades. On the other hand, a very large percentage of young white men enter the trades. We have a great influx of emigrants from Europe. They come and work the farms. They are better farmers than any one else, — they make a crop, rain or no rain. The American needs rain to make his crop, and in a few years he finds that he cannot compete with the foreigner because his land is too poor. He abandons the farm and seeks refuge in the trades, or he moves to another county to begin farming anew.

There are some reasons why our young men avoid the trades. There is a class of young men who after finishing some school course do not believe in manual labor, skilled or unskilled. When the slaves were emancipated their first thought was to send their children to school like the white folk, to dress them like white children, and to keep them from work like the white children. To do any sort of manual labor was to their minds a badge of humility and a relic of slavery. The old master was a gentleman and he did not work; their sons must be like him and like his sons. This idea was taught the children and it has grown up in them and still remains in them. If a record could be made of all that these dear old parents suffered and endured, of how they toiled and what sacrifices they made, that their children should be ladies and gentlemen who did not have to work, it would make a tale far more pitiable than Uncle Tom's Cabin. They passed from the slavery of the white man to the slavery of their own children.

Another hindrance is that society looks down upon a man who works with his hands, however much skill he may possess or however much remuneration that skill commands. This class distinction does not exist among us alone. It is hard to see how a man can be intelligent and at the same time be a mechanic. We cannot associate the two ideas. Fear of nonemployment keeps another class from entering the trades. Those who oppose industrial education never fail to present this argument, and they have made an impression on some which nothing but time and changed conditions will ever efface. Another class would enter the world of workingmen but for the fact that they are ambitious to excel in whatever line of work they may choose, but to become an intelligent artisan requires years, long years of hard work and patient study on short pay. They cannot wait; results are too long coming. Many of our young men who do follow the trades are not living up to the full measure of their opportunities. In the first place, the employer cannot always depend upon them. They are just as likely not to come to work at the appointed time as they are to come. It matters not how busy the employer may be or how anxious he is to finish the job, our young workman feels that he is under no obligation to see him through. He feels free to take a day off and go fishing, or to enjoy himself in some other way. That's his idea of liberty. When the next Negro workman comes along and asks for a job the contractor says, "No, we don't want any more Negroes." Then we say that that man is prejudiced. I used to think so, too, but I do not think so now. I have hired some of them myself, and I know that unreliability has kept Negroes out of more good jobs than incompetency ever did. Unsteadiness is another barrier to success. In the lumber district of eastern Texas there are numerous sawmills which run the year round. The owners employ Negro workmen for places requiring skill whenever they can be found. I have in mind one man who has been with a certain firm for eighteen years. In fact he has been with the company so long and has given such faithful service, the managers have forgotten that he is a Negro. He is now a competent sawyer and receives $6 per day. The sawyer's place at these mills is perhaps the best-paying place of all, outside the management. The wages run from $4.50 to $6 according to skill. The places are open to Negroes and occasionally they take them, but after working for ten or twelve months they conclude that they have made enough and retire. The job is too steady. I do not mean these general statements to apply to all our workmen, but I do say that they apply to the majority. Our artisan must be more competent, more faithful, and more reliable. It 's the only way to hold what we have. We must be progressive. We have clung to the old ways — the methods of half a century ago — too long. If we do not make the best use of these trade advantages which are now ours, we not only shut ourselves out but we close the door of opportunity in the faces of our boys who expect to enter.

The Employment of Skilled Negroes in the South

In 1889 and 1891 the Chattanooga *Tradesman* made inquiries into the status of Negro labor in the South. The employers questioned in 1889 employed 7000 Negroes, of whom possibly 2000 were skilled or semiskilled. "The general tenor of the replies indicated perfect satisfaction with Negro labor." In 1891 replies were received from the employers of 7395 Negroes, of whom 978 were skilled and many semiskilled, and the editor concluded that "the Negro as a free laborer, as a medium-skilled and common worker, is by no means a 'failure,' — that he is really a remarkable success."

In 1901 a third joint investigation into Negro skilled labor was made by the *Tradesman* and the Sociological Department of Atlanta University. It was not an exhaustive inquiry and there is no way of knowing what proportion of the employers of skilled Negro laborers were reached. In 1891 12 per cent of the Negroes employed by those written to were skilled or semiskilled; in 1901, 20 per cent; 344 firms answered in 1901, employing 35,481 men, of whom 16,145 were Negroes, and 2652 of these were skilled or semiskilled workmen. The following tabulation is made in answer to the question "How do Negroes compare in efficiency with white workmen?"

Answers	Establishments answering	Negroes employed	
		Skilled	Semiskilled
"Far inferior"	17	96	38
"Not as good"	28	135	55
"Poor average, some as good"	23	260	57
"Better" for "this work" or "at same wages" or "than available whites"	42	382	89
"As good"	43	456	145
"Better"	19	665	80
No answer	4	79	—
"Cannot say"	3	34	—
"Cannot compare, employ no whites"	9	49	7

Some comments were: "No good, but the white help is mighty poor, too." "Not reliable—lack judgment." "Have n't as good hands for skilled work." "Would give perfect satisfaction if they were steady." "Prompt, willing, and steady, but lack judgment." "Not as quick to learn, but stick closer to work." "More easily controlled." "As good or better." "Perfect satisfaction."

The employers were also asked the question "What effect has this education had?"

Answers	Establishments answering	Negroes employed	
		Skilled	Semiskilled
"Bad effect"	16	73	66
"No effect"	9	134	22
"A little learning is a dangerous thing"	4	30	57
"Little effect"	4	7	13
"Cannot say"	5	41	—
"Helps some, hinders others"	5	31	—
"Would help, if industrial"	1	40	—
"Good effect"	28	257	89

Some comments follow:

Think they feel more responsibility than the ignorant ones,—want more and are more willing to work to get what they want.

Somewhat improved by it.

The education has had a good effect on them and I had rather employ these Negroes with education than if they had no education.

Educating a Negro makes him worthless as a laborer. He gets saucy and thinks he is as good as a white man. Uneducated Negroes give no trouble. Educating a Negro makes him mean and indolent. You find more criminals in educated Negroes than in uneducated.

Makes them better citizens by giving them means to employ their minds. The bad Negro, as a rule, is the most ignorant.

There is some more indolence and disposition to loaf among Negroes who have a smattering of education, although there are exceptions. We would much prefer to have a man who can at least read, write, and figure a little than one entirely ignorant, provided he is a steady worker.

Enables them to undertake more. It is questionable whether education tends to modify or decrease their humility toward white men; probably it does. They are still, on the whole, inferior to the white man.

Can't say, except in our opinion it follows as a matter of course that the more a man learns the more he is worth.

Has done but little good, owing to lack of sense to start with.

We believe educating the Negro is having the effect of taking them from the farms, going to the towns and cities hunting public works at better pay. This is but natural, and we believe in the end will prove beneficial.

We can't but feel that education improves them. Our experience, though, has been that those who have some knowledge of books are profligate. This may be due to bad selection on our part.

What kind? We guess you mean training. A Negro cannot be educated. We only want a Negro with educated hands and bodies. Some darkies can learn to read and write a little—and just then they are ready and ripe for the penitentiary or for Hades.

From our observation the result is not good from an industrial standpoint, our opinion being that the trouble is that the little education they have received has been literary instead of industrial.

It has detracted from his usefulness in positions where he is the most useful, such as hard manual labor, without fitting him to take a better position in the ranks of skilled labor.

We have but few positions where education of itself would be of much value. Coupled with other good qualities it would have value. Our colored people are generally self-respecting and we believe better because of their steady employment, but they seem to lack in thrift, frugality, and in saving their wages.

We believe that education would have a good effect if with it there was some systemized effort to make them property owners and to build up a healthy interest in their particular community. This does not seem to be the trend of affairs, and until present conditions change, as they will perhaps sooner than any of us think now, we do not look for much radical improvement.

We have heard a good deal about education spoiling the colored man as a laborer. Our experience here, however, convinces us that the better he is educated the better he is able to compete with the white man in giving close attention to the business that employers require of him, thereby giving better satisfaction and better work. It is true in many cases that an education seems to spoil the colored man, but we think he would be spoiled anyway, just the same as among white men many times the highly educated seem to feel themselves above doing manual labor.

Some general comments on Negro workmen follow:

Yes, they understand my way of having work done and are willing workers when treated right. I never allow them imposed upon by any one and have no strikes. They are the best judges of human nature on earth.

The most satisfactory sawyer, shopman (blacksmithing and woodworking), green-yard fireman, train-track fireman, logging-engine fireman, log trippers, cant-hook man, night watchman, edger man, trimmer man, or teamsters, and men grading lumber in sawmill, are all Negroes.

Best laborers we can get. We believe the Negro the best laborer in the South.

Are more tractable, steadier, and can be depended upon in their particular places. In an emergency whites have better judgment. On the whole we prefer Negroes where it is possible to use them.

The work they do is well done and for furnace work equally as efficient as that of white men and indeed I prefer them.

Some are just as good as any or most white men, while a greater number are just as poor as the white trash.

After living in the South for twenty years and employing from one to twenty Negroes all the time will say from any standard there are no skilled workmen with black skins, and I have employed the best to be found in Montgomery as carpenters, bricklayers, engineers, firemen, and machine operators.

We find that many of our most thrifty and intelligent Negroes are drifting north and securing employment in the large industries about Pittsburg, and many of them making good records for efficiency.

We have just this day begun the employment of Negro molders for our stove foundry. We have been employing white molders for the past fifteen years, but as nearly all the foundries in this city are employing Negro molders and seem well satisfied with the result, we decided to do so also. We believe we will make a success of the venture, but will not be able to answer your questions until we have had them at work for a while.

We consider them a necessity in our business, because white labor is not obtainable. Considering the condition of their ancestry and the conditions in which they themselves live, I think they are doing very well indeed. Future generations will doubtless see the race in a better condition and more intelligent, making better citizens.

In this line they are much superior to white labor. White men would not stand the heat and grease. We don't want white labor. They are too prone to strike. Give them the earth and they would strike for the moon. White men *could* be more efficient than Negroes, but they *won't*.

Do the same work and obey better; more profit, less trouble.

Some of them display excellent judgment, while others are stupid. They don't expect as much as white men and do, if anything, more faithful work than the white labor.

The younger class are more given to loafing and light work. When given places as foremen, or semiresponsible, they are usually very exacting.

A Negro is a Negro with us, and is made to keep his place.

The white workmen do not like to work side by side with the Negro workmen. However, they treat them politely, and there is the kindliest feeling between whites and blacks here.

THE ATTITUDE OF ORGANIZED LABOR

The attitude of the American Federation of Labor may be summed up as having passed through the following stages:

1. *The working people must unite and organize irrespective of creed, color, sex, nationality, or politics.*

This was an early declaration but was not embodied in the constitution. It was reaffirmed in 1897 after opposition. Bodies confining membership to whites were barred from affiliation.

2. *Separate charters may be issued to central labor unions, local unions, or federal labor unions composed exclusively of colored members.*

This was adopted by the convention of 1902 and recognizes the legality of excluding Negroes from local unions, city central labor bodies, and so forth.

3. *A national union which excludes Negroes expressly by constitutional provision may affiliate with the American Federation of Labor.*

No official announcement of this change of policy has been made, but the fact is well known in the case of the railway trackmen, telegraphers, and others.

4. *A national union already affiliated with the American Federation of Labor may amend its laws so as to exclude Negroes.*

This was done by the stationary engineers at their Boston convention in 1902, and an attempt in the same line was made by the molders at their convention the same year. The Federation has taken no public action in these cases.

This is a record of struggle to maintain high and just ideals and of retrogression; the broader-minded labor leaders, like Samuel Gompers, have had to contend with narrow prejudice and selfish greed; it is a struggle parallel with that of the Negro for political and civil rights, and just as black Americans in the struggle upward have met temporary defeat in their aspirations for civil and political rights, so too they have met a rebuff in their search for economic freedom. At the same time there are to-day probably a larger number of effective Negro members in the trade unions than ever before; there is evidence of renewed inspiration toward mechanical trades and a better comprehension of the labor movement. On the other hand, the industrial upbuilding of the South has brought to the front a number of white mechanics who from birth have regarded Negroes as inferiors and can with the greatest difficulty be brought to regard them as brothers in this battle for better conditions of labor. Such are the forces now arrayed in silent conflict.

With reference to the attitude of national and international organizations of the several trades we may make the following list in the order of increasing hostility toward the Negro:

Miners — Welcome Negroes in nearly all cases.
Longshoremen — Welcome Negroes in nearly all cases.
Cigar Makers — Admit practically all applicants.
Barbers — Admit many, but restrain Negroes when possible.
Seamen — Admit many, but prefer whites.
Firemen — Admit many, but prefer whites.
Tobacco Workers — Admit many, but prefer whites.
Carriage and Wagon Workers — Admit some, but do not seek Negroes.
Brickmakers — Admit some, but do not seek Negroes.
Coopers — Admit some, but do not seek Negroes.
Broom Makers — Admit some, but do not seek Negroes.
Plasterers — Admit freely in the South and a few in the North.
Carpenters — Admit many in the South, almost none in the North.
Masons — Admit many in the South, almost none in the North.
Painters — Admit a few in the South, almost none in the North.

The evidence on which the above is based cannot all be given here; it is, however, pretty conclusive. There are, for instance, numbers of competent Negro painters, carpenters, and masons; yet who has seen one at work in a northern city? There are numbers of brickmakers, wheelwrights, and coopers, but few have been brought into the unions and in the North few can get in. The seamen, firemen, and tobacco workers have many Negroes, but Negroes fear to join them lest by demanding union wages their white fellow-workmen will hasten to supplant them. This has virtually been admitted by labor leaders and others. A South Carolina employer says that among bricklayers of equal skill Negroes receive $1.75 and whites $2.50 a day, and "the object of the white men in organizing the Negroes is to get them to demand the same wages that the whites demand." Messrs. Garrett and Houston, president and secretary of the Georgia Federation, confirm this, as do many others, and the secretary of the Southern Industrial Convention adds: "There is discrimination even in the union. The white members try to get employment for each other and to crowd out the colored members." The same thing occurs in the North; now and then a Negro is admitted to a union, but even then he stands less chance of getting work than a white man.

Local Option in the Choice of Members. The general attitude of the Federation of Labor, and even of the national unions, has little more than a moral effect in the admission of Negroes to trade unions. The present constitution of the Knights of Labor admits members "at the option of each local assembly." The real power of admission in nearly all cases rests with the local assemblies, by whose vote any person may be refused, and in a large number of cases a small minority of any local may absolutely bar a person to whom they object. The object of this is to keep out persons of bad character, or sometimes incompetent workmen. In practice, however, it gives the local or a few of its members a monopoly of the labor market and a chance to exercise, consciously or unconsciously, their prejudices against foreigners or Negroes.

The following unions require a majority vote for admission to the locals:

Boot and Shoe Workers
Amalgamated Carpenters
Bottle Blowers
Glass Workers
Wood Workers
Coopers
Stogy Makers
Amalgamated Engineers
Metal Polishers
Stove Mounters
Bakers
Barbers
Steam Engineers
Coal-Hoisting Engineers

The wood workers, coal-hoisting engineers, and coopers require an examining committee in addition.

The following require a two-thirds vote for admission to the locals:

Brotherhood of Carpenters	Sheet-Metal Workers
Painters	Pattern Makers
Tile Layers	Tin-Plate Workers
Flint-Glass Workers	Broom Makers
Iron and Steel Workers	

Nearly all these require also the favorable report of an examining committee. Among the iron and steel workers two black balls can make a second election necessary.

The following unions require more than a two-thirds vote for admission:

Electrical Workers, two-thirds vote, plus one, and examination.
Molders, two-thirds vote, plus one.
Core Makers, two-thirds vote, plus one.
Boiler Makers, three black balls reject.
Blacksmiths, three black balls reject, two require second election.
Street Railway Employees, three-fourths vote.
Leather Workers (horse goods), three black balls reject.

The Typographical Union and printing pressmen and many others leave all questions of admission to the local unions absolutely, except that an appeal lies to the national union. In nearly all cases save that of the cigar makers the adverse vote of a local practically bars the applicant. It is here and not usually in the constitutions of the national bodies that the color line is drawn ruthlessly in the North.

In like manner the methods regulating apprenticeship militate against Negroes in nearly all the trades. Many unions, like the hatters, trunk makers, printers, stonecutters, glass workers, and others, limit the number of apprentices according to the journeymen at work. Very often, as in the case of the hatters, the union prescribes the terms of apprenticeship and oversees the details. In the case of the coal-hoisting engineers, elastic-goring weavers, and some others, the consent of the local must be obtained before any particular apprentice is admitted. In other cases there are age limits, and there is very general demand among the unions for still more rigid regulation and the use of articles of indenture. Strong unions go so far as to refuse to recognize a workman who has not served his apprenticeship in a union shop, or begun it between the ages of seventeen and eighteen. The tin-plate union especially enjoins its members from teaching their trade to any unskilled workingmen about the mills. The black boy who gets a chance to learn a trade under such circumstances would indeed be a curiosity.

Summary of the Attitude of Organized Labor. Putting the strength of organized labor in the United States at the conservative estimate of 1,200,000, we may summarize the situation as follows:

Unions with 500,000 members include 40,000 Negroes.
Unions with 200,000 members include 1000 Negroes.
Unions with 500,000 members include no Negroes.

The rule of admission of Negroes to unions throughout the country is the sheer necessity of guarding work and wages. In those trades where large numbers of Negroes are skilled they find easy admittance in the parts of the country where their competition is felt. In all other trades they are barred from the unions, save in exceptional cases, either by open or silent color discrimination. There are exceptions to this rule. There are cases where the whites have shown a real feeling of brotherhood; there are cases where the blacks through incompetence and carelessness have forfeited their right to the advantages of organization. But on the whole a careful, unprejudiced survey of the facts leads one to believe that the above statement is approximately true all over the land.

The president of the American Federation of Labor writes:

It has been and is now our endeavor to organize the colored workers whenever and wherever possible. We recognize the necessity of this if it is hoped to secure the best possible conditions for the workers of every class in our country. I should say that your statement is neither fair nor accurate. After careful perusal of the summing up of the attitude of the A. F. of L. toward colored workmen I should say that you are inclined not only to be pessimistic upon the subject but you are even unwilling to give credit where credit is due.

The Employer, the Artisan, and the Right of Suffrage

A few quotations throw an interesting side light on the suffrage question in the South and its relation to the Negro. The last Southern Industrial Convention at Chattanooga said:

We recommend that every possible means shall be used to educate the public sentiment of the South to regard the Negro as a factor in the upbuilding of the South, and that as such we should use all possible means to make him as efficient as possible, and pledge him the fullest guaranty of earning a living in every honest field of honest endeavor, and protection in his God-given right of self-support.

A prominent southerner said before the Industrial Commission:

I believe that in the Negro labor of the South lies the panacea for the wrongs frequently committed by organized labor and a reserve force from which can be supplied any needed number of workers when the time shall come when they shall be needed.

Most workingmen in the South laugh at such threats because they are certain the Negro cannot become a formidable competitor in skilled labor. A writer in the *Molders' Journal* makes considerable fun of the exaggerated predictions as to the Negro molder and writes him down as a "dismal failure." Another writer, however, takes the previous one to task and asserts that he

will woo us into a sense of fancied security and induce us to look upon the Negro problem in our trade as one that will solve itself by the Negro's demonstrating his incapacity and being ignominiously dismissed from the foundry.

That is very flattering to our vanity, but it is contrary to facts. I believe I am well within the mark when I say that in the last twenty years Negro molders have increased five hundred per cent, and that excluding the Negro pipe molders, whom I do not class as skillful mechanics, I know of two foundries at least where the molding is done entirely by Negroes, — three if we include the Ross-Mehan annex in Chattanooga. There is the one at the foot of Lookout Mountain and another in Rome, Georgia. A few years ago a mere handful of Negroes worked at molding in Chattanooga; to-day there are over two hundred; and I am convinced that the question of what shall be done with the Negro molder is one which in the very near future will demand more of our attention, if we would maintain for ourselves fair wages and conditions in the South.[1]

On the other hand, a white speaker in the Tenth Barbers' Convention said:

> Is the disfranchisement of the Negro the first step toward making history repeat itself? I for one will not believe it, as I have too much confidence in American manhood to think that they will allow it. Those of you who live in the South may feel, you may even say, it is right, and then I will say to you, If it is right to deny the right of franchise to any American citizen, though his color or nationality be what it may, then it may be your turn to-morrow, because those who seek to disfranchise the Negro to-day will seek to extend their power by disfranchising you to-morrow. Our protection for to-morrow calls on us to protest in favor of the disfranchised Negro of to-day.

Here, then, are the four great forces: the northern laborer, the southern laborer, the Negro, and the employer. The southern laborer and the employer have united to disfranchise the Negro and make color a caste; the northern laborer is striving to make the whites unite with the Negroes and maintain wages; the employer threatens that if they do raise labor troubles he will employ Negroes. The Northern laborer sees here the danger of a disfranchised, degraded, and yet skilled competitor, and raises the note of warning. Is not this a drama worth the watching?

Summary

We have studied in considerable detail the history of the Negro artisan, the condition of Negro mechanics throughout the country, the attitude of organized labor toward the Negro, and the opinions of employers. On the whole the survey has been encouraging, although there is much to deplore and criticise. Our conclusions may be summed up as follows:

1. Slavery trained artisans, but they were for the most part careless and inefficient. Only in exceptional cases were they first-class mechanics.

[1] See Chattanooga *Tradesman*, November 1, 1901.

2. Industrial schools are needed. They are costly and as yet not well organized or very efficient, but they have given the Negro an ideal of manual toil and helped to a better understanding between whites and Negroes in the South. Eventually they may be expected to send out effective artisans, as they have already begun to do.

3. There are a large number of Negro mechanics all over the land but especially in the South. Some of these are progressive, efficient workmen. More are careless, slovenly, and ill trained. There are signs of lethargy among these artisans and work is slipping from them in some places; in others they are awakening and seizing the opportunities of the new industrial South.

4. The labor unions, with 1,200,000 members, have less than 40,000 Negroes, mostly confined to a few unions and largely semiskilled laborers such as miners. Some labor leaders have striven against color prejudice, but it exists and keeps the mass of Negroes out of many trades. This leads to complicated problems, both industrial, political, and social.

5. Employers on the whole are satisfied with Negro skilled labor and many of them favor education as tending to increase the efficiency of Negroes. Others think it will spoil the docility and tractableness of Negro labor. The employment of Negro skilled labor is slowly increasing.

6. The Negro evinces considerable mechanical ingenuity.

On the whole this study of a phase of the vast economic development of the Negro race in America but emphasizes the primal and emphatic need of intelligence. The situation is critical and developing swiftly. If the Negro is deftly guided with the larger wisdom of men and deeper benevolence of great hearts, an outcome of good to all cannot be doubted. If he is muddled by half-trained men and guided by selfish and sordid interests, all the evils of industrial history may easily be repeated in the South. "*Wisdom* [*then*] *is the principal thing; therefore get wisdom: and with all thy getting get understanding.*"

XVII

WOMEN IN THE CLOTHING TRADE[1]

I. The Factory System in the Overalls Trade

. . . The manufacture of overalls and workingmen's garments is the branch of the clothing industry into which the factory system was first introduced and in which it is now most largely employed. As early as 1871 there was in Wappinger's Falls, New York, the nucleus of the establishment that claims to have been the first overalls factory in the United States. . . . There are at least three reasons for the early use of machines run by mechanical power in this line of work. First, it is harder to drive a needle through the closely woven cotton fabrics of which these suits are made than through woolen goods. Second, the work is less complicated than that on regularly tailored suits, and it is consequently of advantage to be able to keep up a constant high rate of speed. Third, it is work that can well be done by women, but the use of foot-power machines would have made it, in some cases at least, more difficult to increase rapidly the number of operatives of the class desired.

During the year 1900 there were 2901 people in New York state engaged in making overalls and workingmen's suits.[2] These were found in thirty-four establishments. The average number of employees in a factory was therefore eighty. This is in marked contrast to the situation that we have found in other branches of the ready-made clothing trade. If our official statistics on this subject are of any value they establish two facts :

[1] From Chapters VII and IX of "The Employment of Women in the Clothing Trade," *Columbia University Studies in History, Economics, and Public Law*, Vol. XVI, pp. 298–312, 329–360.

[2] Compiled from the Fifteenth Annual Report of the Factory Inspector of the State of New York, 1900.

first, that the overalls industry is carried on chiefly under the factory system; second, that it flourishes in small cities. Among overalls manufacturers, however, there is an impression that large quantities of the cheaper grades of overalls are made in New York City in shops in which the operatives are chiefly Jewish or Polish men. Neither the reports of the factory inspectors nor the opinions of labor leaders familiar with the situation in the clothing trade in the city justify this opinion. It is difficult to find half a dozen such shops, and while a small number certainly exist, I find no reason to think that they manufacture any appreciable percentage of the total output.

Because of the relatively unimportant position held by New York City in this branch of the clothing trade I have extended my investigations to include Newburg, New York, a city frequently referred to as the center of the overalls trade. . . . There three establishments, and in fact overalls factories in general, are under the direct control of the manufacturer. The contractor does not appear, and no work is given out to be done in the homes. The factory serves all purposes. Here the garments are cut, and are made up on machines driven by steam, gas, or electricity; buttonholes are made and buttons sewed on by machinery; and the completed goods are packed and shipped directly to the retail dealer. The output of these factories is large, and the variety of goods manufactured in them is noteworthy. There are overalls of all kinds, unlined duck coats, pants made of various kinds of cotton goods, and sometimes even woolen suits, which are of a substantial character but lack the cut and finish that a tailor would give. Many factories, however, probably a majority of them, confine themselves to the manufacture of the various styles of cotton suits needed by men working at trades.

In such factories the division of labor between the sexes is almost everywhere the same. The cutting, whether done by machinery or by hand, is under the charge of men, and they alone are found also in the shipping department. With rare exceptions all the work of making garments is done by women. They form 83 per cent of the total number of employees in the factories in New York state engaged in making overalls and workingmen's clothing. The 17 per cent comprising the men are found in the two departments before mentioned.

Except in the establishments where woolen suits as well as cotton are made up, nearly all the women, certainly more than 90 per cent of them, are employed in stitching up the garments. The remainder put on buttons, bars, or tags, or make buttonholes by machine, or serve as examiners of the work. The woolen suits require some hand finishing. This work does not differ much from the finishing work previously considered. The method in which a pair of overalls, a duck coat, or a pair of cotton pants is stitched up by machinery differs somewhat in different factories. It is common to find that the entire garment is sewed up by a single girl. In the case of overalls she may do all the stitching except on one seam, which is sewed on a double-needle machine. Sometimes, however, we find section work, but even this involves a very slight division of labor. For example, the work may be divided among three girls, each of whom has only a particular part to do. Usually a girl has to understand not only how to put together an entire garment of a certain kind but even how to make up several kinds of garments. It is customary to divide the operators in a factory into coat operators, pants operators, and overalls operators. This means, however, that each of the girls has her special kind of garment to make only when there is plenty of work of all kinds. . . .

It is contrary to the practice of these three factories to admit girls under 16 years of age. Of the 900 women employed only 3 were below that limit. On the other hand, the work demands quickness of movement, and the superintendents state frankly that they have no use for a woman over 45. Probably none even of that age would be taken on, but individual instances may be found where women as old as 62 are still retained in the factory. A large majority of the employees are strong, healthy-looking women of between 20 and 30 years of age. The girls entering the factory have in almost all cases graduated from the grammar schools, and some of them both speak and write with considerable force and ability. . . .

The somewhat varied nature of the work required, especially the necessity of passing from one kind of work to another, demands some intelligence on the part of the worker. Quickness of movement is perhaps the primary requisite of a good machine operator in this line of work. But it is noticeable that the brightest girls, provided they take an interest in their work, not only learn it in the least time but also become usually the most rapid workers. Ability to concentrate attention is absolutely essential. For this reason there is a class of girls that have been especially successful, the deaf-mutes. In spite of the constant whir and buzz of machinery in the large rooms and the movement of passing people, nothing distracts their attention. . . .

Few of the women are married, and none of those who marry do so with the expectation of remaining at their work. Misfortune, however, may send them back to it. There are several cases on record where former operators have returned to the factory after the death of their husbands, and have been able to bring up their children on their earnings. Opposite one of the large Newburg factories is a day nursery, where children are cared for while their mothers are at work. The attendant in charge says that she has never had more than three children whose mothers were working in the overalls factory, in spite of the fact that it employs between five hundred and six hundred women. Of this number about five per cent, according to the superintendent, leave every year to marry.

The popular idea of a clothing factory has been formed largely from the distressing, and unfortunately true, descriptions that have from time to time appeared of the small, ill-ventilated, and dirty clothing shops in the Jewish quarter of New York City. Yet the workingman who buys a pair of overalls for seventy-five cents, especially if it bears a union label, may be reasonably sure that it was made up under sanitary conditions that could not easily be improved. The New York factory under consideration is not a large one, but it is well lighted, and the employees are provided with all conveniences. No employee has a word of private criticism to make in this respect. The Newburg establishments are large and are especially adapted to the work to be performed. In one the light comes entirely from overhead, in order that it may be less trying to the eyes. In both factories there is an evident and an intelligent effort made to provide everything that may be conducive to better work or to greater comfort on the part of the employees. The supply of operators is here scarcely equal to the demand for them, and this fact forms an additional incentive to consideration for their welfare.

In the Newburg factories the regular ten-hour working day is observed. It extends from 7 A.M. to 6 P.M., with one hour intermission for dinner. The doors are closed at 7.05 A.M. and 1.05 P.M., and any employee not within the building at that time loses his half-day's work. These hours of work are the ones generally observed in the overalls factories. The shortest regular working day of which I know is that of a large and prominent western factory. Here a nine-hour day is observed, with a Saturday half holiday throughout the year, and no work overtime is permitted. . . .

Employment is regular throughout the year in all these three factories, except during the ten days or two weeks when account of stock is taken. The legal holidays are of course observed. Occasionally there is not sufficient work to keep all classes of employees busy, but this is unusual. The operators have work practically all the time. It seems a surprising thing to find clothing establishments in which the women, instead of complaining of lack of work during part of the year, actually absent themselves from work at times because they wish to do other things. There are two reasons why employment is more regular in the manufacture of overalls and workingmen's garments than in other branches of the clothing trade. The primary reason is found in the facts that styles are less frequently changed and that the demand, especially for certain classes of garments, is less rigidly determined by the season. Of course there are certain months when orders come in more frequently, as the spring months in the overalls trade, but it is possible to forecast the future demand to quite an extent, and working for stock commonly supplements the order work during the dull season. The second reason for steady employment, but one that would remain inoperative without the first, is found in the amount of capital invested in the plants. The capital must not be permitted to lie idle. The absence of girls from work, especially in the busy season, is regarded as a positive injury to the employer, since their machines stand idle. No definite regulations have been adopted, however, by the manager of any of these three factories to restrict this evil. The relations existing between the management and the employees are in general friendly, and when there is a special pressure of work a request is made that there be as few absences as possible. Such a request is usually heeded. Special admonitions may be resorted to in individual cases, but after all the chief security for regular attendance at work is found in the fact that absence entails loss of wages. With the great mass of the workers these motives are quite sufficient to insure regularity. That no more stringent measures are adopted in the few cases in which these prove unavailing is to be explained, as one of the superintendents asserts, by the fact that the places of the girls could not well be filled. "Otherwise," he added, "we might attempt to regulate the matter, since at times we are certainly inconvenienced."

. . . None of the experienced operators earn less than $1 a day, and there are at least twenty who appear in the records as averaging over $1.50 per day throughout the year. These twenty earn regularly, therefore, from $9 to $10 a week. Probably no woman averages more than that in this line of work, though for a short time some of them may earn more.

How long does a girl need to learn machine operating on overalls? There have been several cases where girls were earning a dollar a day by the end of the second month. Some superintendents claim that any bright girl should be able to do that, but among the women themselves the impression prevails that it is no disgrace to spend three or even four months before attaining that degree of speed. From the beginning the women are paid at piece rates and therefore begin to earn something at once. The work can be learned only in the factories, where a teacher is provided. One firm estimates that the actual cost of teaching each new worker is twenty-five dollars. This amount is apparently obtained by making allowance for the profit that would accrue to the establishment if the machine were run by an experienced hand.

. . . In Newburg the greater part of the women belong to families that have resided in Newburg for a number of years. Many of them were born there. There are, however, two other classes. The first and smaller one consists of girls who have come to Newburg with their parents, or more frequently with the mother alone, in order to enter the factories. The second class is composed of girls who have come to the city alone and who board usually in some private family. Except in connection with the latter class, which comprises not more than one fourth of the girls, one is almost as strongly impressed with the essential economic unity of the family as was the case among the very different classes of women in New York. What is earned by these women is in general simply a part of the family income, and not in any sense a fund for separate maintenance. The character of the home, the amount spent on clothing, and the social activities of the women are determined by the general economic status of the families rather than by the ability of the women themselves. But when we come to consider the extent to which the family status is here affected by the employment of the daughter we meet with quite a different situation. The women are in many cases the chief support of the family. We find here to a certain extent a repetition of the experiences of some of the New England towns. The opportunities for men to work have not increased as rapidly as have those for women. The latter were never better than they are to-day. In the case of the former, however, it is not only true that the industries in Newburg in which men are employed have not expanded, but in some instances works have actually been abandoned, as has happened to certain foundries and shops for the manufacture of steam engines. In some instances men who were old and could not readily find similar work elsewhere have undoubtedly been led to remain in Newburg on account of the excellent factory positions held by their daughters. More frequently, perhaps, it is a widowed mother who remains with her daughters, while her sons find work elsewhere. There are still, of course, many men industrially employed in the city, and in these cases the wages of the daughters or sisters form a less important part of the family income. While in few instances, perhaps, may the employment of the women of the household be regarded as directly a reason for less exertion on the part of the men, indirectly, by interposing an obstacle in the way of free movement elsewhere on the part of the family, it undoubtedly has had that effect.

There are no "factory boarding houses" maintained in the city. The girls who are without families board in private homes. Seldom more than two or three board in one place. One result of this practice is that they blend quite readily with the people of the city and do not form a distinct class by themselves. From three to four dollars a week is the usual charge for board and lodging.

The energy of the young women is by no means exhausted by their industrial activity. Opportunities for social intercourse come in connection with their church work and with their trade unions, as well as in the varied life of a small city. A number of the girls take music lessons and find time and interest to practice with more or less regularity. During the winter of 1900 and 1901 forty of the girls were members of the Young Women's Christian Association, an organization that here does not draw strict denominational lines but admits Catholics as well as Protestants. The general fee for membership is one dollar. There are for the members both free classes and pay classes. The factory girls are quite as ready to join the latter as the former. The gymnasium and the cooking classes have proved especially popular with them, though sometimes dressmaking is taken up.

Practically all of the women carry life insurance. In the case of those with no near relatives this usually amounts to about

$200, which is regarded as enough for burial expenses and miscellaneous items. A larger proportion of them are insured for $500, and while I can present no definite records in support of the statement, on the strength of information from various reliable sources I feel justified in saying that there are probably as many as a hundred women in one factory employing five or six hundred women who are carrying insurance to the amount of $1000, usually for the benefit of the mother.

Few of the women save money. Those who are independent of relatives pay three or four dollars a week for board, maintain their insurance, meet a few incidental expenses, and spend the rest on clothes. A few belong to benefit societies, such as the Ladies' Branch of the Foresters, which insures its members a weekly payment of five dollars in case of sickness. A small number, however, have bank accounts. . . .

Certain broad general contrasts appear between the women working on coats, pants, and vests in New York City [1] and the women employed in the manufacture of overalls and workingmen's suits. The former class is composed chiefly of Italian immigrants, with an admixture of Jewish and German women; the latter is made up almost exclusively of American-born women of Irish, American, or sometimes German parentage. The majority of the former class do not speak English; nearly all of the latter have received a grammar-school education. The former are generally married women, engaged in finishing garments by hand at home; the latter are single women, operating machines in factories. The wages of the former class are small and irregular; those of the latter are relatively high and stable. Although in both cases the wages ordinarily form a part of the family income, the share contributed by the Italians is supplementary, while the overalls workers are in many instances the main support of the family. A considerable number of this class of employees are independent, self-supporting women. These protect themselves by life insurance and occasionally by membership in benefit societies or by deposits in the bank.

[1] See Chapter XIV on the sweating system. — ED.

II. Trade Unions

The United Garment Workers of America is an international union which now includes in its membership almost all the organized men and women in the United States engaged in the manufacture of men's ready-made clothing, together with a number in Canada. . . . In its establishment the women workers bore no part either directly or indirectly, and the first officers chosen were all men. Before the second convention, which was called late in 1891, twenty-four charters had been granted. Of these three were taken out by women's unions. One of these unions never paid any dues and was shortly dropped from the records; another led a precarious and nervous existence for some years and at last went to pieces; the third, formed through the influence of the employer, who desired the label, has continued to the present time.

In April, 1902, the United Garment Workers was composed of 179 local bodies, of which 83 admitted men only, while 96 were made up either exclusively of women or of both men and women. In the unions of the last kind the women were usually in a large majority. The total membership was about 25,000, of which number approximately 8000 were women. It has been the general policy of the United Garment Workers to organize men and women in separate unions. The existence of "mixed" bodies has come about in many cases through the creation of unions among the employees of single factories. In the overalls trade, for example, the mass of the employees are women operators, but a half dozen or more men are usually employed in each factory as cutters. The unions in these factories would naturally include the men, and it is frequently in this way that the mixed unions have arisen. In this respect the garment workers differ from the cigar and cigarette makers, among whom the women are usually admitted to the men's unions. These two industries, cigar making and the manufacture of clothing, are practically the only ones in this country in which women have been organized in large numbers. The United Garment Workers claims both a larger number and a greater proportion of women than is to be found in any other national union.

. . . While the leaders of the union were beginning to question the efficacy of the strike as a universal panacea for the ills of the clothing trade, the increase in the demand for the union label, which prior to 1896 had been in an experimental stage, turned their hopes in another direction. The union has found in the label a powerful lever. It is to-day the most important factor in determining the policy of the United Garment Workers, and as it is largely owing to the label that so many women's unions have been established in this country, we may consider somewhat fully the conditions which limit its use.

The labels of the United Garment Workers are sold to any manufacturer of ready-made clothing who is willing to enter into an agreement to employ in the manufacture of garments only members of the union, to maintain proper sanitary conditions in his shop, to comply with the requirements of the state laws relating to workshops, to regulate hours and wages in accordance with the union standards that are maintained in the locality or that may be agreed upon with the employees, and to refer to the general offices of the United Garment Workers for mediation all difficulties arising between employer and employees which they themselves are unable to settle. In the overalls trade no labels are granted except to manufacturers who have all the work done upon their own premises without the intervention of a contractor. All garments must bear the label. For this branch of the clothing trade a general minimum price list for the whole country has been drawn up, but there are numerous complaints that the rate is not uniformly enforced. There is one other point of importance to be noticed. Within the last year the Garment Workers have issued a declaration of war upon the contract system. It is recognized that it will be extremely difficult to restrict the label to employers who give out no work to be done off the premises, but it is the aim of the union to crush out the contract system so far as possible. As a first step the requirement that all goods shall be made up in the factory or shop of the manufacturer has been made a further condition of granting the label to applicants in New York City. Manufacturers already possessing the right to use the label are given six months' time in which to comply with the new provisions. The gradual extension of this new condition to all other cities is contemplated, and those cities will be considered first in which the worst abuses are found.

It is evident that if the requirements were strictly and fairly enforced by the union the label would guarantee to the purchaser of clothing to which it was attached that the goods were manufactured by fairly paid laborers under sanitary conditions. It is the aim and desire of the union that the label shall stand also for good quality and good workmanship, good relatively to the class of clothing to which the article in question belongs. Although it is doubtless true that in earlier days the presence of the union label bore almost no significance, the numerous precautions and safeguards that the union is now throwing about it should tend to arouse both respect for it and confidence in it, not only among those in sympathy with the union movement but on the part of the general purchasing public as well.

The agreement entered into between the unions and the employers is in some respects a flexible one and varies somewhat in different sections of the country. This policy has had three results. It has given color to the claim that the union label does not stand for a definite reliable minimum of protection to the laborer; it has caused dissatisfaction among employers in some localities, who claim that they would be willing to enter into a uniform agreement to be enforced equally against their rivals, but maintain that under the present system they are discriminated against; and, finally, it has resulted in the maintenance of some union shops in localities in which the rigid enforcement of all the requirements would have made them impossible. Because the label does not always stand for definite conditions, because many of the well-to-do classes object to the requirement that only union labor shall be employed, and because many others have given no thought to the matter, the demand for clothing bearing the label is restricted almost exclusively to the laboring classes. For this reason the label is found chiefly on garments intended for their use. In August, 1901, there were 125 manufacturers of labeled clothing in the United States and Canada, and 12,000 garment workers, of whom more than one half were women, were working under the label agreement. During the preceding year, from August, 1900, to August, 1901, fourteen and a half million labels had been sent out.[1] A paid label secretary is now employed. It is the purpose of the General Executive Board to devote as much time and money as possible to extending the use of the label and the demand for it.

The formal organization of the United Garment Workers is democratic. The initiative and referendum have been preserved, and appeals are frequently made to the whole body of members, but, as is usually the case under such provisions, only a small vote is cast, rarely representing more than twenty-five per cent of the members. The guiding power is exerted by a small group of men who from the beginning have held responsible offices in the union and who represent perhaps the most conservative influence in the body.

Such are the characteristic principles of the United Garment Workers, and I think it but fair to say that in the determination of the general policy of the union the women have had little if any influence. In the conventions they rarely speak on questions of broad interest, or upon the action to be taken in particular cases except those in which they are immediately concerned. They then occupy somewhat the position of expert witnesses. Their testimony is given only upon those points on which they are peculiarly fitted to speak, and when it is given it is directly to the point. Miss —— describes the conditions in the —— factory, and the convention at once dispatches a telegram to the firm threatening to withdraw the label unless the demands of the employees are immediately conceded. The Syracuse women make a united appeal for the aid of the

[1] Report of the General Secretary, Tenth Annual Convention, *The Garment Worker*, Vol. V, No. 12, p. 10.

international body in the establishment of a nine-hour day in the tailoring trade, and the women from the overalls factories all press for the establishment of a minimum price list for the making of overalls. In most cases the women delegates have been sent for the express purpose of presenting some such request. These appeals are usually fully discussed in the committee meetings, where some of the women manifest considerable ability. In general, then, it may be said that while the routine business remains exclusively in the hands of the men, and while the men are responsible also for the determination of the general policy of the union and its action in the greater number of specific cases, the women perform valuable supplementary work. I might add that I am given to understand that the presence of the women has contributed not a little to the orderly character of the conventions and to the rapid dispatch of business.

So far as financial contributions to the International Union and the benefits received from it are concerned men and women stand nominally on precisely the same footing. In practice, however, there is a slight advantage in favor of the latter, since financial assistance in strikes is granted to them somewhat more readily. The chief income of the union is obtained from a per capita tax, which has increased by varying increments from three cents a month in 1891 to the present monthly tax of twelve cents. In addition to this the General Executive Board is permitted to levy a special strike assessment of five cents a week when it is considered necessary, and it has assumed the right to levy special assessments for other purposes. From August, 1900, to August, 1901, but six such special assessments were levied, amounting in all to thirty cents per person.[1] Even this was an unusually heavy burden. Finally, twenty-five cents of each initiation fee also passes to the general body. The total receipts during the year were $35,853.79. The chief expenses aside from the cost of labels, which is usually fully covered by the proceeds of their sale, are

[1] For these figures and those which follow see Report of the General Secretary, Tenth Annual Convention, *The Garment Worker*, Vol. V, No. 12, pp. 7 and 8.

those involved in organizing unions, in paying the salaries of the president, secretary, and clerks, and in advertising the label. Strike benefits paid during the year amounted to only $3251. It is an interesting point that of this sum $2725 went to women overalls workers engaged in a strike in Kansas City. Only when a strike has been indorsed by the General Executive Board do members have the right to call upon the United Garment Workers for aid. Then, if the funds permit, they have the right to a weekly payment of five dollars apiece. In addition to this, or when it is impossible to pay this, the General Executive Board may authorize the striking local union to send appeals for assistance to other local bodies. While the rights of all are equal, it is claimed that there is rather more readiness on the part both of the General Executive Board and of the local unions to extend aid to women than to men. This benefit is paid until the General Executive Board declares the strike at an end or until the funds are exhausted.

Ever since the establishment of the union there has been a constant agitation in favor of the introduction of higher dues and of sickness and death benefit provisions. To the higher dues the women have always been opposed, and such increase as has been made has been in the face of their opposition. The plan for the establishment by the International Union of a sickness and death benefit fund has met with opposition, especially from the cutters. It has at length been entirely abandoned in favor of the maintenance of such provisions by the local unions.

Let us pass now to a study of the local unions composed either wholly or in part of women. [The statistical table shows that from 1891 to 1900 82 women's locals had been organized, of which in 1900 33 had disbanded and 49 were in existence. — ED.]

First. It is shown that the unions in which both men and women are found in this industry are composed so largely of women that it is not necessary to distinguish between them and the unions composed exclusively of women.

Second. Up to April, 1900, women had conducted or participated in the affairs of 82 unions.

Third. This figure is somewhat deceptive, since 12 of the unions practically never existed at all; that is, a charter was taken out by some enthusiastic unionist, in which proceeding the women may possibly have had no share whatever, and the prospective organization failed to come to life, no dues were paid, and no record of members was obtained.

Fourth. Weak unions formed among women usually fall apart in less than two years, some not even living through the year. Of those that had maintained themselves more than two years all but two still survived in 1900.

When we consider the circumstances under which the unions that have fallen apart were formed we are usually able to discover at once the reasons why they were unable to maintain themselves. Such an investigation throws considerable light upon the feasibility of attempting to establish women's unions where the conditions are unfavorable. Each of thirty-three such unions was formed originally in one of three ways. Sometimes an employer engaged in the manufacture of clothing wanted the union label, and since in order to obtain it it was necessary to employ only union hands, he ordered the women to form a union. Such was the case in at least ten of these unions. These included six unions formed in small towns in Maine where the women worked for Boston firms desiring the label. These women were far removed from the mass of organized labor, had little if any communication with the general body except by letter, and were not only indifferent to the formation of the union but were in some cases actually opposed to it, as it was regarded as nothing but an additional drain upon their low wages. Two of these label unions were formed in Columbus, Georgia, each of which consisted of the employees of a single shop. Of the other two cases one was that of a union in Scranton, Pennsylvania, in which the girls took no interest until they got into a disagreement with the General Executive Board; and the other was formed in Chicago in a shop from which the label was withdrawn owing to bad sanitary conditions. In all of these cases the label was withdrawn after a short time, usually either because the employer failed to find it profitable or because he failed to comply with the requisite conditions. Upon the withdrawal of the label the unions immediately went to pieces. In no instance were there surrounding circumstances of such a character as to arouse the interest or enthusiasm of the members. The membership was small, rarely exceeding twenty in a union.

In other cases unions were established through the influence of some man or of a small number of men. This group of unions is much larger than the preceding one and includes eighteen of the thirty-three unions. The men were in some instances tailors who desired the women in the trade to be organized that they might give aid in enforcing concessions from an unwilling employer; sometimes they were zealous unionists from other trades. In this group were several of the unions previously noted as having had practically no existence. Typical of this class was Local Union 137. This was composed of Polish tailoresses who, having been called together and addressed by some man, immediately voted to form a union but never held another meeting. In other cases the unions were not only formed but officered by men, and with two possible exceptions all these unions dragged along without voluntary coöperation on the part of the women. There was no growth from within. Their suspension was speedily brought about through the non-payment of dues. There were two cases, however, to which this general description does not apply. Local Union 33, of Baltimore, Maryland, called the Ladies' Protective Association, and composed largely of Germans, showed marked independence. In the strike of 1896 these women encouraged the men to remain out and did everything in their power to prevent them from yielding. Even when the latter gave up the contest the women refused for some time to go back to work. They were finally forced to make concessions, however, and in the general disaster of that year the union went to pieces. The other independent union was also in Baltimore. Local Union 98 was formed of Lithuanian women, and was dissolved under the same circumstances as No. 33. This union had combined with its industrial functions a certain semireligious, semisocial character, which fact had undoubtedly contributed to its strength. The meetings were held in a church in the presence of the priest, but partook largely of the nature of social gatherings.

Of the unions that have disappeared only one group remains to be noticed, and that the smallest and most interesting class. It consists of the unions formed not through the efforts of the employer or of the men but at least in part by the spontaneous movement of the women themselves. There were but five of these unions. First of them comes the charter union, Local Union 16. It is with the history of this union, and often with this alone, that the student of women's unions is most familiar, if his attention has been confined to New York City; yet it has perhaps the least typical history of any of the eighty-two unions. Local Union 90, of Brooklyn, is the only other union whose experiences have been at all similar. Local Union 16 was composed largely of Jewish girls, a few of whom were bright, attractive speakers, interested in the establishment of their union and eager to extend their influence even beyond their own group. But it has been the experience of trade organizers, not only here but elsewhere, that it is extremely difficult to arouse in young Jewish girls any permanent interest in their work. It is not merely that they leave it upon marrying, — in general the American girls do the same, — but the possibility of marriage seems to interfere with any serious or earnest interest in work, while the American girls so long as they remain at work are interested and ambitious. Possibly owing to a clear understanding of the situation the East Side Jewish tailor refuses to regard the industrial activity of the Jewish girls as worthy of serious attention, and thinks it hopeless to expect the women employees to be unionists. As a result we have from Local Union 16 what is, so far as I am aware, the only complaint issued by women in the garment trade of failure on the part of the men to give all due assistance. . . . With reference to the influences instrumental in the formation of the 49 unions in existence in 1900 we notice a marked contrast between this class and the preceding one. While in the latter class 18 unions owed their establishment to the personal exertions of the union men, in the present class only 4 trace their origin exclusively to that influence, although in many instances the men undoubtedly gave some assistance. As against 10 of the extinct unions organized through the label, 37 of the existing unions were so organized, — a very large percentage of the total number. Under the general heading of unions formed through the label I would suggest three subclasses, the first to include all unions where the employees are entirely indifferent or are opposed to organization; the second to consist of those bodies the members of which are now active unionists; and the third to include the remaining cases, in which the relations between employer and employee are influenced by special and differing conditions. In the class characterized by perfect passivity on the part of the employees we must place at least 11 unions. Any one of these would go to pieces at once if the label were withdrawn; the existence of the organization at present confers no benefits upon its members. Typical cases under this head are unions formed in two of the southern factories among the girls working in cotton mills. In as many as 23 cases, however, we find that unions formed under the influence of the label are active and progressive. In this number are included most of the large women's unions regarded by the entire body of garment workers as successful. Of the 23, 11 are composed of employees in large overalls factories, while 4 of the others are located in Syracuse, a city which has the distinction, from the trade-union point of view, of being better organized than any other city in the country. Of the third class there are 3 unions, one in a coöperative factory in Alabama the stock for which was subscribed by union men, a second in Ontario under a philanthropic employer who is trying to create a model factory, and a third in Dover, New Jersey, where the employer is himself a union man.

In addition to the large group of unions formed under the label and the small group previously referred to as organized by union men, there is among existing unions a group of seven in the establishment of which the women have taken the initiative. Among these the organization at Streator, Illinois, is perhaps the most prominent. It existed for some time as a social club before assuming the form of a trade union.

From the study of these individual cases we are justified in drawing certain general conclusions:

1. That while nine or ten years ago, in the early days of the United Garment Workers, the great part in the organization of women's unions was performed by men and the union, if maintained, was kept up chiefly through the efforts of the men, this is no longer the case.

2. That at the present time the most powerful influence for the formation of unions among women is the union label.

3. That although the union label is unable of itself to guarantee the continued existence of an efficient union, yet the existence of such a union is essential to the protection of the label.

4. That the support and sympathy which come from the presence of a large body of unionists in the community are of great importance.

5. That although women have as yet rarely established permanent local unions, they can and do successfully maintain them under favorable circumstances.

. . . What are the functions actually performed by these women's unions? Have they after all anything more than the mere form of an organization, with a membership created by an artificial stimulus and incapable of performing any real service? Of some of them, as we have already noticed, this is a fair description, but it is not true of all. It proved to be practically impossible to make a detailed study of the economic, educational, and social functions of the ninety-six unions existing in 1902. Therefore, in order to get a more accurate idea of the actual results of the organization of women workers, I concentrated my attention upon eight of the oldest unions, with a total membership of about two thousand women and two hundred men. None of these unions is less than five years old, and one has been in existence twice that length of time. The conditions found to prevail in these organizations should then be fairly typical for the stronger unions.

The members of these organizations are practically all girls born in America, frequently of Irish or German parentage but in perhaps the majority of cases with American parents. There is a slight sprinkling of Jewish and Polish women, constituting probably not more than one per cent of the total number. Nearly all the girls have had a common-school education. In all of the eight unions the women are employed on light cotton coats, pants, or vests, or on overalls. In rare cases some work is performed on workingmen's woolen suits not regularly tailored. In each case all the members of the union work in a single shop or factory for one employer who uses the label on his goods. What are the relations between this employer and his employees? Does the union exist chiefly in his interest, in order to secure to him the right to use the label? Is it entirely subservient to his purposes?

In the first place, these unions are not directly subsidized by the employer. In five of the unions he has never given financial aid to the organization. To one union the firm employing the members offered to give one hundred dollars to help establish a sick-benefit fund. In the case of another union the traveling expenses of a delegate to the national convention were paid by the firm in one instance. In a third case donations have been made once or twice when especially requested. All of these were isolated and special acts of kindness on the part of friendly employers. The financial burdens of the unions were borne by the members.

What are the relations between the employer and the union when questions of wages are in dispute? Practically all the women are paid at piece rates. In each of these factories the rates are fixed by an annual agreement between the employer and a committee appointed by the union representing the different departments of the shop. There is a union standard of piece rates which is supposed to serve as a minimum in all union factories. Two of the factories have schedules corresponding very nearly to the union standard, one pays higher rates on some articles and lower on others, and the remaining five pay apparently somewhat higher prices. Does the existence of the union have any measurable effect upon the scale of prices? In one factory the connection has been clear. The right to use the label was refused until the wages were raised to the standard rates, and they have not since been reduced. In a second factory difficulty in adjusting the rate of wages has occurred on four or five occasions; the general officers of the union have been called in and a compromise has been reached. In the remaining six cases no appeal for the assistance of the general officers has been made, but the comparison of prices and privileges, which connection with the union has made possible, has placed the employees in a position where they were better able to decide what demands they might properly make and insist upon. Local abuses in the matter of fines, local exactions, and local low prices are less easily maintained when employees are thoroughly familiar with the conditions prevailing elsewhere.

In some cases, however, disagreements cannot be amicably settled. Frequent strikes are much to be deplored, but a union which is never ready to strike to enforce its demands has little strength. If these label unions are, as is sometimes claimed, only tools in the hands of their employers, we shall certainly never find them resorting to such measures. Of these eight unions four have at one time or another declared strikes. They have engaged in five strikes, in four of which they were successful. One was against a reduction of wages, and three for an increase. The fifth case was one in which there was a misunderstanding as to the price agreement. The General Executive Board investigated the case, decided that the employer was right in his contention, and ordered the members of the local union to return to work. None of these strikes were prolonged over three weeks, and in only one was any assistance required from either the international body or other local unions. In the history of other unions of women clothing workers, however, there are records of longer and more persistent strikes. One in Peoria, Illinois, which had lasted three months and in which one hundred and twenty-five women, operators on overalls and shirts, had participated, was terminated on May 1, 1902, by the success of the strikers.

These strikes have usually been conducted in a firm and dignified manner. The advantages possessed by the union women on strike consist not so much in the financial support on which they can count, though this is in some cases extremely important, as in their habit of acting together with a common purpose and in their possession of trained leaders in whom they have confidence. The women holding official positions in the unions or sent as delegates to the central federations or the national conventions find in their union work a school in which knowledge of the prevailing conditions of the trade is gained, clearness of judgment is developed, and a sense of responsibility and fair-mindedness is attained. In every large union of women is found a small group of able members whose influence is generally felt throughout the body. Their position is frequently conservative, and their influence is often exerted to prevent hasty and ill-considered action. It would be unfair to leave the impression that the existence of the unions tends to frequent disagreements between employer and employed. It is perhaps as often true that they are responsible for the recognition of the fact that some claims cannot be pushed as that others can. And in many cases difficulties are settled through the mediation of the national officers which in unorganized factories would undoubtedly result in strikes and temporary abandonment of work. While in several instances the formation of a union has been opposed by employers, as in the Peoria case previously mentioned, other employers prefer to deal with an organization, feeling that it works in favor of the fair employer against the unfair.

It is upon the ability of labor unions to improve the economic condition of their members that their chief claim to consideration is usually based. Various methods which have as yet found no place in the women's organizations have been adopted to accomplish this object. Competition among the women working on the class of goods that we have been considering is not keen, and the demand for their work is increasing. Consequently there has been no attempt to limit the supply of labor by apprenticeship regulations and no attempt to increase the demand by limiting the output. The desire has been to make the hours, wages, and general conditions found in the best factories prevail throughout the trade and steadily to raise rather than to lower the standard. While in some cases the formation of the union has made little difference in the economic standing of its members, in others, in the various ways and for the various reasons already noted, it has been efficacious.

To the educational benefits which some of the women derive from the union reference has already been made. Naturally there are comparatively few who participate in these. The majority of the women are not deeply interested in union matters or much affected by them. But the sanity of judgment and the business ability developed in some of the women are noteworthy, and are to a great extent responsible for the economic benefits obtained by the body as a whole.

Aside from external influences, such as the employer's desire to retain the union label and consequent encouragement to the union, the most important factor in keeping these women's unions together is probably to be found in their social functions. These are especially prominent in the small towns and cities, and do much to retain the interest of the members when no immediate economic incentive to membership exists. The great problem is not to induce a group of women to form a union when they wish to rebel against some injustice, realizing that they can do so effectively only in combination. The real difficulty is to persuade them to remain together, to hold regular meetings, to pay regular dues, when all is peaceful and they see no immediate return for such expenditure of time and money. For various reasons sickness, death, and out-of-work benefits appeal less strongly to the women than to the men. Among the latter these constitute probably the most powerful inducement to retain membership during seasons of peace and plenty. In the women's unions the development of social attractions performs much the same service. Unless through practical compulsion from without, I doubt whether any women's union has maintained itself with a large membership for a considerable number of years without the aid of dances, card parties, and social gatherings of other kinds. The greater ease with which social bonds are developed in the small towns and cities accounts largely for the greater activity of the unions located in small places.

To the general statements already made on the subject of the establishment of women's unions we may add, from our study of eight well-established organizations, the following conclusions:

1. Successful unions have usually been found among fairly well-educated American girls of American, Irish, or German parentage.

2. Such women are chiefly engaged in the more highly skilled and highly paid work on clothing, that is, in operating on light-weight goods rather than in finishing clothing.

3. They are found chiefly in factories working for employers using the union label.

4. While the desire of the employer to retain the label is a powerful support to the union, such a union acts frequently for the independent good of its members and not as the mere tool of the employer.

5. There are numerous instances in which the economic benefits derived by members from the existence of the union are clearly shown.

6. One of the most important results flowing from the existence of women's unions is to be found in the development of trained, intelligent, and conservative workingwomen.

7. The unions frequently serve to check hasty and inconsiderate action and to substitute arbitration and mutual concessions for more violent measures.

8. Social gatherings of various kinds are extremely helpful, if not absolutely essential, to the retention of the interest of the majority of women members during the prolonged periods when they are working for no direct and immediate economic advantage.

MABEL HURD WILLETT.

XVIII

WOMEN'S WAGES IN MANUAL WORK[1]

In an article which first appeared in the *Economic Journal* for December, 1891, and which has recently been reprinted in Problems of Modern Industry, Sidney Webb presents the results of an investigation made by him concerning the causes of the "alleged differences in the wages paid to men and women for similar work." The facts which the writer had to present were so few in number that no sweeping generalization could be made from them. But though no definite conclusion could be arrived at, the facts seemed to suggest that, so far as manual work is concerned,

> the frequent inferiority of woman's earnings is due, in the main, to a general but not invariable inferiority of productive power, usually in quantity, sometimes in quality, and nearly always in net advantageousness to the employer.[2]

This explanation of the lower wages paid to women would, the writer thinks, be even more true in the United States than in England.

> Custom is presumably less powerful in regulating wages in the United States than in England, and in the United States the proportion which the average earnings of women in manufacturing industries bear to those of the men is, as we have seen, considerably higher than in this country. Where competition rates of wages prevail, and especially where the women are protected by strong trade unions, they often earn wages equal to those of men for equal work.[3]

The suggestion that the lower wages paid to women have at least a partial justification in the inferiority of women's work

[1] From the *Political Science Quarterly*, Vol. XV, 1900, pp. 508–535.
[2] Problems of Modern Industry, p. 63. [3] *Ibid.*, p. 64.

has received the approval of several eminent economists in both England and America. Professor William Smart,[1] John A. Hobson,[2] and Hon. Carroll D. Wright[3] have all agreed that the inferiority of women's work is a leading cause of the lower wages paid to them. This inferiority, it is said, may show itself in several ways and may itself be due to other causes than natural inability; but whatever be the explanation, where men and women do the same work the women "seldom reach man's level in quantity and quality."[4] Until recently this theory of women's wages has lacked adequate confirmation. Mr. Webb acknowledged that the facts cited by him were too few in number to enable definite conclusions to be drawn from them, and none of the later exponents of the theory have furnished us with many additional illustrations.

The importance of the theory is almost self-evident. No one of its supporters has pretended that it is the only explanation of the difference which usually exists between men's and women's wages; and Mr. Webb implies at least that in other than manual work this is probably not the chief cause of dissimilarity. Popular opinion has, however, been directly opposed to the views expressed by the above writers; and the general feeling that employers discriminate against women in the payment of wages has found expression in writings on the labor problem, in the reports of labor bureaus and commissions, and even in legislation, to such an extent that it seems worth while to investigate the matter still further, in order to see how far the theory in question can be sustained by statistical evidence.

I

The Eleventh Annual Report of the Commissioner of Labor (1897), entitled "Work and Wages of Men, Women, and Children," gives us an opportunity of testing by a large number of

1 "Women's Wages," in Studies in Economics, pp. 116 ff.

2 Evolution of Modern Capitalism, pp. 299–304.

3 "Why Women are paid less than Men," *Forum*, Vol. XIII, p. 633.

4 Evolution of Modern Capitalism, p. 302.

facts the theory advanced by Mr. Webb, and of observing how far his prediction that the theory would be found more true for the United States than for England is realized. The report itself was prepared with a view of making possible a comparison of the wages paid to men, women, and children. It furnishes us with a statement of the wages paid to employees in the various establishments;[1] gives the estimates of employers or foremen as to the relative efficiency of the men, women, and children employed;[2] furnishes a comparison of the earnings of women and children with those of men in cases where the efficiency is the same;[3] gives the reasons of employers for hiring women and girls rather than men, and states whether their employment is increasing;[4] and also gives the number of hours of the working week in each establishment.[5]

Like all statistical material, these tables need to be used with great caution, and all conclusions drawn therefrom must be accepted with reservation. The statements of employers and foremen as to the relative efficiency of their employees and the reasons given for employing females must be received with some allowance for imperfect knowledge or unintentional errors. The report itself gives the warning[6] that there is reason to believe that differences in the character of the work performed by the men and the women existed in some instances where no distinction was specified by the employer; and we shall later have occasion to note that this difference may pertain to the amount as well as to the character of the work performed. It is quite improbable that the real grounds of the preference for female labor are always correctly stated. Many of the reasons given explain nothing. Thus it is obviously a contradiction to state that men and women are equally efficient in the performance of a certain kind of work and then to say that the women are "better adapted" for its performance. To state that women are "cheaper" than men is doubtless a sufficient reason for preferring them, if their efficiency is the same; but it does

[1] Table I, pp. 35–513.
[2] Table II, pp. 514–547.
[3] Table III, pp. 548–582.
[4] Table IV, pp. 583–610.
[5] Table VI, pp. 639–645.
[6] P. 26.

not go far toward explaining why their wages are less. Yet although the reasons given cannot be regarded as entirely reliable, they may at times save us from attributing an inferiority to women's work when it does not exist.

Information as to the relative efficiency of the men and the women could be obtained from only 436 establishments out of a total of 931 from which other facts given in the report were obtained. But these 436 establishments are pretty well distributed throughout the chief manufacturing states and represent all the leading industries in which women are employed. The investigation may therefore be considered as on the whole tolerably complete and satisfactory.

The grades of efficiency of the operatives in these 436 establishments are indicated by an alphabetical classification — A, B, C, D, etc. — in which A indicates the highest degree of efficiency, B the next highest, and so on. Accordingly, if we find men and women performing the same work in the same establishment and both designated by A, we know that they are supposed to be equally efficient and to possess this efficiency in the highest degree. If, however, we find men and women performing the same kind of work but with the men designated by A while the women are in grade B, we know that the women are less efficient workers than the men. This seems to dispose of the question of efficiency, but unfortunately it does not do so in all cases. When we come to discuss the question of piecework we shall see that the above classification is open to criticism. With these remarks explanatory of the report, we may now turn to a consideration of the facts furnished by the investigation.

II

The class of occupations known as "domestic and personal service" is represented in the report by forty-four establishments. Eighteen of these report as to the efficiency of the employees, and of these eighteen only six (four laundries and two bakeries) furnish instances of men and women of the same degree of proficiency performing the same kind of work. In the laundries the operatives in question are either ironers, washers, or clerks. The average earnings of the fourteen men are 23 per cent higher than those of the twelve female employees;[1] in the restaurants male cooks receive average earnings 24.6 per cent in excess of those paid to females. There is apparently no reason for doubting that the efficiency of the women employees was equal to that of the men in these occupations, except that among the ironers piece wages seem to prevail, although in some instances the men work by piece and the women by time. This makes it probable that in this suboccupation the women are not equal to the performance of the same amount of work that the men accomplish. It is also to be noted that in one instance where men and women are engaged as pastry cooks the hours of work are longer for the men than for the women. The managers of the laundries claim that the women are "better adapted" to perform the work than are the men, although one manager also explains that they are "cheaper." In the restaurants the women are said to be "cheaper," although in one case they are also said to be "better adapted."

In the manufacture of bakery and confectionery goods only nine establishments out of forty-eight report as to the efficiency of their employees, and only four of these establishments record instances of men and women of equal efficiency performing precisely the same work. There are five instances in these establishments where the average wages of forty women are lower by 10 per cent than are the wages of thirty-one men performing the same work, and one instance where the same average wages are paid to four women shippers as are paid to one man for the same work. It is to be noted, however, that in this case the man's efficiency is of the third grade, represented by C, while the other male shippers are in grade A or B. All the women shippers are in class C, and time wages prevail for all employees. One of these factories reports as its reason for preferring women that they are "cheaper"; another, that

[1] Throughout this paper all of the figures given pertain to adults, — male and female workers eighteen or more years of age.

they are "better adapted"; a third, that they are "better adapted, cheaper, and work more steadily"; while the fourth does not state the grounds of its preference.

In the manufacture of paper boxes it would seem that the efficiency and skill of the female operatives should be fully equal to that of the men, and that here if anywhere the theory of equality of wages for equality of work should show itself. But the facts serve neither to prove nor to disprove the theory. Out of a total of thirty factories represented in the report only three report as to the efficiency of their employees, and only two of these furnish examples of men and women of equal efficiency performing the same work. In a Minnesota factory we find four male workers receiving average wages of $7.75 per week, while fifteen females possessing "equal efficiency" receive on an average only $5.30½, or 46.1 per cent less than the men. The men work on time wages, the women on piece wages. In the other factory, a New York establishment, we find thirteen male workers receiving average wages of $6.68½, while the twenty-three females receive $8.49½, or 27.1 per cent higher than the average paid to men. Both piece and time wages prevail for both sexes, and in both cases the women receive the higher pay. The highest wages paid to the men are $10.87; the lowest, $3.50. The highest wages paid to the women are $13.03; the lowest, $5. The Minnesota firm claims that the women are "better adapted and more industrious," while the New York firm merely says that they are "better adapted."

In the manufacture of brooms and brushes there are four instances in two establishments where sixty-nine men receive wages higher by 55.6 per cent than do the seventy women workers of like efficiency. The difference in wages is inconsiderable in the case of the New York factory, where time wages prevail, but is very great in the Maryland establishment, where both sexes are employed at piece rates.

The boot and shoe industry is one of the largest occupations in which women find employment, and in New England women have been employed in large numbers in this industry since early in the century.[1] The present report gives evidence concerning twenty-eight establishments, in which 2442 adult males and 1183 females are employed. Only seven of these establishments, however, report as to the efficiency of their employees, and of these only six furnish us data for a comparison of men's and women's wages for the same work performed with supposedly equal efficiency. In the six establishments given there are fifteen instances of this kind. In four instances sixteen women receive average wages higher by 6.4 per cent than do the nine men performing the same kind of work. In the other eleven instances the men receive higher wages, the difference in their favor being 28.1 per cent. There are forty-nine men and fifty-nine women covered by these eleven instances. The branches of the occupation in which the men receive the higher wages are stitching, finishing, heel making, skiving, sole cutting, and vamping. The women receive more than the men as stitchers, buttonhole makers, and vampers. Both time and piece wages are paid, but the piece rates are more noticeable in those branches in which women are most largely employed, especially stitching and vamping. The reasons usually given for the employment of women are that they are "better adapted" or "cheaper," though one establishment, which pays less to the women than to the men, says the women are "neater and more rapid."

In the manufacture of "canned and preserved fruits, vegetables, and meats" there are two instances in which seventeen women obtain wages higher by 15.7 per cent than do four men who do the same work with equal efficiency. But there are only three establishments out of nineteen reporting which furnish instances of men and women engaged in the same occupations. The instances just given are cases where men are competing with women in what are essentially the women's branches of the industry.

Fifty-six establishments engaged in the manufacture of cigars, tobacco, and snuff are considered in the report. Only

[1] As early as 1829, $60,000 were paid out annually to women engaged in the boot and shoe manufacture at Lynn, Massachusetts. — Wright, Wages and Prices, 1752–1880, p. 19.

twenty-eight of these report as to the relative efficiency of their employees, and of these only thirteen give instances of men and women of the same degree of efficiency performing the same work. In the thirteen establishments there are twenty-six such instances. In six cases thirty-five female workers receive average wages higher by 14.3 per cent than do twenty-three male workers engaged at the same tasks. In the other twenty instances the average wages of the 321 men employed are 20.4 per cent higher than the average wages of the 469 women who are their competitors. The same general superiority of men's wages has been observed by Mr. Webb in the English cigar establishments. He explains it as due to the better quality of cigars made by the men, although he confesses that the superiority of men's work is not so clear here.[1] In the absence of direct proof to the contrary it would seem that the greater neatness and deftness of the women should give them an advantage in this industry. But it is worthy of note that the majority of cases where the women receive the higher wages are among the lower grades of efficiency, B or C. The statement that men generally receive the higher wages is supported by illustrations from every branch of the tobacco manufacture, while the instances where women receive the higher wages are confined to cigar makers, carton makers, and strippers. Seven of the thirteen establishments say as a reason for employing women in preference to men that the women are more easily controlled ; three say that they are less liable to strike ; two, that they are more reliable ; two, that they are neater ; three, that they are better adapted ; two, that they are cheaper ; two, that they are more rapid ; and single instances are given where the women are more industrious, more easily procured, more careful, or learn more rapidly than do the male operatives.[2] Of the twenty instances where the men earn more than the women seventeen are cases where both men and women are employed at piecework ; two, where both are paid by time ; and one, where the mode of payment is not

[1] *Economic Journal*, Vol. I, p. 639 ; Problems of Modern Industry, pp. 51, 52.

[2] In some instances more than one reason is given.

given. Of the six instances where the women receive the higher wages two are cases of piecework; one, of time wages; two, of the combination of the two modes of remuneration for both sexes; and one, of failure to name the method of remuneration.

The fact that the higher wages are usually paid to men is well illustrated in the manufacture of clothing. In one Missouri establishment engaged in making cloaks thirteen tailors in grades A, B, and C receive average wages much in excess of the sixteen tailoresses who are reported as performing the same work with equal efficiency, while seven tailoresses in grade D receive slightly higher wages than do three men in the same class. The owner of this establishment reports that the women are "better adapted" for the work and are "more easily controlled" than the men. There is another instance in the clothing industry where women receive the higher pay. Three forewomen and designers for dresses and cloaks receive average weekly wages of $41.66½, while the one man similarly employed receives but $30. The women are said to be "better adapted"; and one might readily doubt whether in this instance at least the work is the same for both sexes. A North Carolina establishment has four men and four women engaged in selling clothing and dry goods. The women are said to be as efficient as the men and to be better adapted to the business; but they receive on the average only $4 per week, while the men receive $11. Taking the clothing industry as a whole, so far as represented in this report, we find five instances where the men are paid wages 45.6 per cent higher than those received by women and two instances where the women receive wages 20.3 per cent in excess of those paid to male workers of the same degree of efficiency.

In the printing and publishing business there are five instances in which women earn more than men, the difference in their favor being on an average 16.4 per cent. There are, furthermore, four instances where their wages are equal to those paid to men; but, on the other hand, there are twenty instances where the wages of the men exceed those of the women by 26.6 per cent.

In the manufacture of rubber and elastic goods the wages of men and women approach somewhat nearer to equality. In five instances the women receive higher wages, the difference in their favor being, however, only 3.8 per cent; and in one instance the same wages are paid to men and women. In only four instances do the men receive higher wages for the same work, the excess amounting to 11.3 per cent. But since only two industries in this branch of manufactures report as to the efficiency of their employees, no conclusion of wide application is possible.

It is rather startling to find that in the manufacture of tinware and sheet-metal goods the women receive the higher wages in the only cases where men and women of equal efficiency are found as competitors. But the instances of such competition are only two in number, and these are found in only two establishments out of five investigated. The difference in favor of the women is reported as 7.7 per cent; but an inspection of the figures from which the percentage is drawn shows the difference to be accidental and to be due to that source of so many statistical fallacies, the simple average. Thus in one of the instances given seventy-eight men engaged as solderers earn wages ranging from $3 to $7 per week, the average being $5.09; while thirty women similarly employed have the same upper and lower limits to their wages, but the average in this case is found to be $5.23½. In the other instance one male painter receives $5 per week, while four women who receive from $4.50 to $6 for the same work earn on an average $5.62½ per week. It is also to be noted that in both these instances the men and women are placed as regards efficiency in the second class, that indicated by B. Only men are found in the A class.

In mercantile pursuits the fact that men generally receive higher wages than women even when they perform the same work with apparently the same efficiency is quite easily demonstrated. In the book and stationery trade there is one instance where one man and three women receive equal wages for equal work, and one instance where the men receive the higher wages. In selling general merchandise, insurance, and sewing machines, and in miscellaneous trades, the men receive in all cases of equal efficiency the higher wages; but only eight instances of such efficiency, scattered throughout the same number of establishments, are given.

In the dry-goods trade there are two instances in two establishments where four men and three women receive the same pay for equal work; seven instances in six establishments where eighty-six women receive wages 12.5 per cent higher than those paid to eighty-five men; and one hundred and eleven instances in seventy-four establishments where the men's wages are 61 per cent higher than the wages of the women, who are said to be equally efficient. Here again we find that it is invariably in the lower grades of efficiency, B, C, or D, that the women receive wages equal to or higher than those paid to men. Practically all the instances where men and women are engaged in performing the same work are among salesmen and saleswomen, where the only method of payment is that of time wages.

III

It is the textile industries, however, which afford the best opportunity for testing the theory under discussion by means of the application of statistics. It is in these industries that women have been longest employed and are still found in the greatest numbers.

In the New England states, the chief center of the textile manufacture, we are confronted with the phenomena of long-established industries; traditional methods of work and to some extent traditional modes of living; a highly developed system of factory legislation, devised in the interests of the working classes; strong trade unions among the male workers and in some places organized female labor as well. On the other hand, we have in the cotton manufacture of the southern states an opportunity to study comparative wages where there is an absence of all those restrictions on competition which characterize the industries of New England. Fortunately the report with which we are dealing gives us much fuller information concerning the textile industries, especially the cotton manufacture, than for any other industry or group of industries. The number of factories which have reported as to the relative efficiency of their male and female employees, the number of instances of "equal efficiency" given, and the large number of employees of both sexes show that the results of the investigation are not merely accidental. In the cotton industry, for example, the investigation covers eighty-six factories. Sixty-three of these establishments report as to the efficiency of their employees, and fifty-five of them furnish instances of men and women performing the same work with what is said to be equal efficiency. The eight factories which do not furnish such instances are for the most part small establishments. The total number of adult males in these eight factories is only sixty and of adult females fifty-two. In the fifty-five mills which furnish examples of men and women of like degrees of efficiency performing the same work there are fifty-six instances where the women receive higher wages than do the men. The average wages of these women are 8.6 per cent higher than the corresponding average for men. In one hundred and ninety-five instances the men receive average wages 17.6 per cent higher than the wages paid to the women who perform similar work, while in thirty-six instances men and women receive equal wages for equal work. Owing to the importance of this industry and the number of instances of equal efficiency cited, we shall examine these figures somewhat in detail.

In speaking of women's wages in the cotton industry of England Mr. Webb says:

> Perhaps the clearest case of similar work is that of the Lancashire cotton weavers, where men and women often perform exactly the same work side by side in the same shed under practically the same Factory Act restrictions. Here the piecework rates are the same for women as for men, and clever women often get through more work and thus earn higher weekly wages than some of the men. A similar equality of task wages appears to prevail in cotton weaving in France.[1]

[1] Problems of Modern Industry, pp. 54, 55.

Whatever may be the truth concerning the wages of cotton weavers in England and France, the investigation of the Department of Labor does not show that any such equality in the remuneration of men and women exists among American cotton weavers. There are nineteen instances in ten mills where 201 female operatives receive the same average wages as do 169 men performing the same work with the same degrees of efficiency. There are, furthermore, twenty-nine instances in twenty-one mills where 753 women employed at weaving receive higher wages than do the 585 men who perform the same work with equal efficiency. On the other hand, there are ninety-nine instances in forty-three factories where 3015 men receive higher average wages than those paid to 5560 women who do the same work and are said to be equally efficient.

No other branch of the cotton manufacture furnishes so many instances of men and women performing the same work as does the business of weaving. Nearly all the principal sub-occupations — spinning, carding, speeding, warping — furnish examples of equality of wages in a few instances, but in the great majority of cases the inferiority of women's wages is clearly demonstrated. The table on the opposite page shows the terms of competition between men and women for the cotton manufacture as a whole and for all the leading branches of the industry as well.

It is interesting to notice the geographical distribution of the various cases within the industry where the women receive wages equal to or higher than those paid to men for the same work performed with equal efficiency. As already noted, the cotton factories are generally situated either in the New England or the South Atlantic states, especially in the Carolinas and Georgia. Now, of the thirty-six instances in this industry where men and women receive equal wages for equal work thirty-one are in the South and only five are in New England. Of the fifty-six instances in which the women receive higher wages than are paid to men twenty-four are in New England, twenty-four in the South, and eight in the middle and western states. Of the one hundred and ninety-five instances in

Comparison of Wages of Men and Women in the Cotton Manufacture

Occupation	Men and Women receive Equal Wages				Men receive Higher Wages				Women receive Higher Wages			
	Factories	Instances	Men	Women	Factories	Instances	Men	Women	Factories	Instances	Men	Women
All branches . .	20	36	235	238	47	195	3951	7036	29	56	888	1113
Weaving . . .	10	19	169	201	43	99	3015	5560	21	29	585	753
Spinning . . .	1	1	5	8	7	20	82	563	3	3	12	17
Carding. . . .	1	2	19	3	7	12	47	52	—	—	—	—
Speeding . . .	2	2	5	4	7	10	67	116	4	4	15	32
Warping . . .	2	2	4	2	3	3	8	26	1	1	13	38
Dressing . . .	—	—	—	—	3	7	78	74	—	—	—	—
Doffing	1	1	1	2	2	4	43	52	—	—	—	—
Finishing . . .	—	—	—	—	3	3	40	19	—	—	—	—
Twisting . . .	—	—	—	—	1	1	1	1	2	3	37	15
Beaming . . .	—	—	—	—	—	—	—	—	1	2	54	101
Slubbing . . .	1	1	4	1	4	4	34	55	1	1	3	1
All other . . .	7	8	28	17	6	32	536	518	4	13	169	156

which the men receive the higher wages forty-nine are in the South, one hundred and thirty-five in New England, and eleven in the middle and western states. These facts seem to give some support to Mr. Webb's statement that "where competition rates of wages prevail and where the women are protected by strong trade unions, they often earn wages equal to those of men for equal work."[1] The cotton industry in the South is of recent development, and the high demand for labor has enabled women, as well as men, to secure high wages.[2] Custom is doubtless largely responsible for the lower rate of wages paid to women in New England, where the industry has been long established. In the South both male and female labor is unorganized, while in New England the men have the assistance of strong trade unions. In many places the women do not belong to the

[1] *Economic Journal*, Vol. I, p. 649; Problems of Modern Industry, p. 64.

[2] Nominal wages are of course lower for both sexes than in the New England states. But the labor cost per spindle is somewhat higher in the South than in Massachusetts. — See Labor Bulletin of Massachusetts, No. 5 (January, 1898), p. 5.

same unions as the men, and in many others they are entirely unorganized, so that they are less able to enforce a demand for higher wages. It is also to be noticed that in those instances where men's wages are higher than women's the difference is much greater in New England than in the South, where it is often insignificant.

The results of the investigation which have thus far been presented do not seem to bear out the conclusion of Messrs. Webb, Smart, Hobson, and Wright that where men and women perform the same work and do it equally well their wages are usually the same. Among the cotton weavers, where Mr. Webb thinks the conditions of employment are practically the same for both sexes, we find that out of a total of one hundred and forty-seven instances, representing 6514 women and 3769 men, in only nineteen instances, or 12.92 per cent of the total number, do men and women receive equal wages. The 201 women represented by these nineteen instances form only 3.08 per cent of the entire number of women weavers. In twenty-nine instances, or 19.73 per cent of the total number, the women earn more than the men; but there are only 753 women included in this class, and these constitute only 11.56 per cent of the total number of women engaged in weaving. In the other ninety-nine instances, comprising 67.34 per cent of the total number, the men earn the higher wages. The women here comprise 85.36 per cent of the total number of women weavers. The other branches of the cotton industry make an even less favorable showing for the women employees, as can readily be seen in the above table.

There is still another way of testing Mr. Webb's theory that women usually do inferior work and that where their wages are inferior to men's it is because their work is inferior. If this were true in the cotton industry, we might expect that the instances where the women earn wages as high as or higher than those paid to men would generally occur in the lower grades of efficiency. On the contrary, of the thirty-six instances of equal remuneration for men and women twenty-three are in grade A; while of the fifty-six instances where the women receive the higher pay twenty-six are in class A and seventeen in class B. No final conclusions can be drawn from these facts, but they do not seem to bear out the idea that women's wages in the cotton industry are lower because their work is inferior.

Of the eighty-six industries engaged in the manufacture of cotton goods included in the investigation, all but eight report the employment of women in the mills to be increasing. The reasons given by superintendents and managers for employing women are in sixty-six instances that they are more easily controlled; in seventeen, that they are more reliable; in thirteen, that they are cheaper; in eleven, that they are more industrious; in nine, that they are more rapid; in five, that they are neater; in two, that they are more careful; and in one each, that they are less liable to strike and are cleaner.[1]

The other textile industries present fewer instances of men and women engaged in doing similar work and possessing equal efficiency as workers, but so far as the facts are given they reveal the same results as the cotton industry. In the manufacture of cotton and woolen goods there are in eight factories fifteen instances where men earn wages 20.9 per cent higher than do women for the same work, four instances (one among finishers and three among weavers) where the women earn 9.8 per cent higher wages than do the men, and one instance, among the weavers, of equality in wages. In the manufacture of hosiery, knit goods, and underwear there are represented eighteen factories in which equal efficiency is recorded. In seven instances the women receive the higher wages, the difference in their favor being 7.7 per cent; but in eighteen instances the wages of the men exceed those of the women by 23.1 per cent. In the manufacture of jute goods there are two instances where men earn more than the women and two instances where their wages are equal. In the silk industry, represented by seven establishments, there are seventeen instances of equal efficiency. One of these is among spinners, one among winders, and the other fifteen among weavers. In eleven instances the men receive the higher

[1] In some instances more than one of the above reasons are given.

wages, in five instances the higher wages go to the women, and in one instance the wages are equal. Where men's wages are higher the difference is 20.8 per cent; where women's wages are higher the difference is only 9.4 per cent. In the manufacture of woolen and worsted goods there are ninety-nine instances where the men earn wages higher by 34.3 per cent than do the women, who are said to be equally efficient. In only ten instances do the women receive the higher wages, and the difference in their favor is slight, being only 5.5 per cent. Eight of these instances are among weavers, one among spoolers, and one among finishers. Of the thirty instances in the textile industries other than cotton where women's wages equal or exceed the wages paid to men sixteen are in the highest grade of efficiency and seven in the next highest. The others are scattered through the grades C, D, and E.

IV

The statistics thus far presented show for all the leading industries in which manual labor is employed (1) that men's wages are generally superior to those paid to women, even where the work is the same; (2) that in those instances where the women receive higher wages than the men the difference in their favor is much less than the difference in favor of the men in the instances in the same industries where the men's wages are higher; (3) that while women's wages are more nearly equal to men's in the textile industries, especially in weaving, even here men's wages are unquestionably superior; (4) that in the great majority of instances within the textile industries where the women receive wages as high as or higher than the men the competition between the sexes takes place within the higher grades of efficiency, A and B, and therefore does not indicate an inferiority in women's work. We must now turn to a consideration of certain facts which may serve to modify the conclusions to which our work has thus far led us.

Mr. Webb has pointed out that among the Lancashire cotton weavers, where the women earn wages apparently equal to those paid to men, the payment is by piece;[1] and he further states that weaving "appears to be nearly always paid at equal rates, whatever the material or locality."[2] In this country it is not easy to determine conclusively whether in occupations where piece wages prevail the wages of men and women are more nearly equal than they are in occupations where time wages are the rule. Time wages predominate in the majority of American industries and are unquestionably much more commonly employed than in English industries. In certain branches of some industries, however, payment by piece is the rule in the United States as well as in England, and this is especially true of weaving. Some of the New England cotton mills pay for weaving partly by piece and partly by time, and there are a few instances where the men are paid by time and the women by piece. But among all the eighty-six industries engaged in cotton manufacture that are included in the investigation of the Department of Labor, there is but one, I believe, where weaving is paid for entirely by time.

The question now arises whether, in cases where men and women are engaged in the performance of similar work and are said to be equally efficient, and where the mode of payment is by piece, differences in wages are to be explained by a difference in the rate of payment per piece or by a difference in the quantity produced within a given time. To this question the report itself affords no direct answer. It would seem that any comparison of efficiency should certainly be based on quantitative as well as on qualitative measurements. The introduction to the statistical tables says that the data as to relative efficiency of employees "represent the best judgment of the best-informed officials or foremen of each establishment."[3] Doubt is expressed as to whether the report always distinguishes between the grades of work in an occupation where women and children may be doing lighter work than the male employees; but it implies at least that in other respects the statements as to relative efficiency may be relied upon.

[1] Problems of Modern Industry, p. 52.
[2] *Ibid.*, p. 54. [3] *Ibid.*, p. 26.

It now appears that this is not the case, at least so far as piecework is concerned. In answer to an inquiry concerning this point the Commissioner of Labor remarks that

it was impossible to take account of piece rates. . . . In the report "equal efficiency" is a term which applies more to quality of work done than to quantity. The determination of the efficiency of the parties involved in the investigation was, of course, by foremen. I am satisfied that in most cases their idea of efficiency involved quality more than quantity, — that a woman might weave goods just as well and produce just as good a quality in her results as a man, although she might not weave so many yards in a day; hence there would be a variation in the pay, although the piece rates were the same. It has been our experience that wherever men and women work at piece rates they are paid the same for the same quantity of product, but time worked, quantity, and other reasons might work a variation in the amount paid to each in the aggregate.[1]

From this explanation it would appear that in cases where men and women receive different compensation for performing the same work the difference in wages may after all be due to a real difference in the amount of work performed, — that in all probability this is the real explanation for differences in wages in those occupations where piece rates prevail. If this be true, the report gives much greater support to the theories of Messrs. Webb, Hobson, Smart, and Wright than seems to be the case from a mere examination of the tables. Of the 781 instances recorded where men and women perform the same work "with the same degrees of efficiency," 217 are instances of payment by piece rates. There are, furthermore, 167 instances where both time and piece wages are paid, — in some cases the men being paid by time and the women by piece, in other cases both modes of payment being applied to both sexes. In all these instances where differences in earnings exist they might be explained, in part at least, by difference in productivity. The following table shows for the entire group of industries the modes of payment and the relative standing of the men and women as respects their earning capacity.

[1] Personal letter from Hon. Carroll D. Wright, August 23, 1898.

WAGES AND MODE OF PAYMENT — ALL INDUSTRIES

Relative Wages paid to Men and Women	Total Number of Instances of Equal Efficiency	Time Wages	Piece Wages	Time and (or) Piece Wages	Mode of Payment not given
Men earn more than women	595	279	147	133	36
Women earn more than men	129	35	52	31	11
Men and women receive equal wages	57	30	18	3	6
Total	781	344	217	167	53

Dropping out of consideration the fifty-three instances where the mode of payment is not specified, we find that in over half the remaining instances the amount of work performed enters as a cause — perhaps the chief cause — of differences in wages. The number of instances of equal wages is small, almost insignificant, when compared with the number of instances where such equality does not exist. The number of instances where the women earn higher wages than the men is also small when compared with the instances where the men's earnings are higher; but it is interesting to note that the proportion is higher where women are given an opportunity to earn high wages on the piece-rate plan than it is in the case of time wages. This fact is emphasized by the table on the following page, which shows the modes of payment and the relative earnings of men and women in the seven leading industries in which women are employed.

Returning now to the textile industries and examining the instances of equal efficiency in the business of weaving in the light of our recent discovery as to piece rates, we find that nearly all of the two hundred and forty-two instances of so-called equal efficiency must be considered equal only as respects the quality and not as respects the quantity of the work. The table on page 417 indicates a general inferiority of women's work in this branch of the textile manufacture.

WAGES AND MODE OF PAYMENT — SEVEN LEADING INDUSTRIES

Industry	Relative Wages paid to Men and Women	Instances of Equal Efficiency	Time Wages	Piece Wages	Time and (or) Piece Wages	Mode of Paym't not given
Boots and shoes	Men earn more . .	11	1	1	6	3
	Women earn more	4	—	3	1	—
Cigars, tobacco, and snuff	Men earn more . .	20	2	17	—	1
	Women earn more	6	1	2	2	1
Cotton and woolen goods	Men earn more . .	15	1	5	6	3
	Women earn more	4	1	1	1	1
	Wages equal for men and women	1	—	—	—	1
Cotton goods	Men earn more . .	195	49	59	75	12
	Women earn more	56	9	25	15	7
	Wages equal for men and women	36	14	17	1	4
Silk and silk goods	Men earn more . .	11	—	10	1	—
	Women earn more	5	—	4	1	—
	Wages equal for men and women	1	1	—	—	—
Hosiery, knit goods, and underwear	Men earn more . .	18	5	1	8	4
	Women earn more	7	—	2	3	2
Woolen and worsted goods	Men earn more . .	99	42	26	23	8
	Women earn more	10	3	7	—	—

Although over one third of the total number of instances of equal wages paid to men and women which are given in the report are found in this one branch of the textile manufacture, these instances constitute only about 8½ per cent of the total number of instances of "equal efficiency" found in weaving; and if to these we add the further instances where the women earn the higher wages, we still have only 27.27 per cent of the total number. In other words, in an occupation in which the women employed outnumber the men and one which is universally regarded as suited to the employment of women, in those cases where the same rates per piece are paid to women as to men the superiority of men's work is shown by the fact

WAGES AND MODE OF PAYMENT FOR WEAVING

Industry	Relative Wages paid to Men and Women	Instances of Equal Efficiency	Time Wages	Piece Wages	Time and (or) Piece Wages	Mode of Paym't not given
All textile industries	Men earn more . .	177	1	98	66	12
	Women earn more	46	2	30	9	5
	Wages equal for men and women	20	—	19	—	1
Bags and bagging	Men earn more . .	3	—	3	—	—
	Women earn more	—	—	—	—	—
Carpets	Men earn more . .	2	—	2	—	—
	Women earn more	2	—	2	—	—
Cotton and woolen goods	Men earn more . .	13	—	6	5	2
	Women earn more	3	—	1	1	1
	Wages equal for men and women	1	—	—	—	1
Cotton goods	Men earn more . .	99	—	52	39	8
	Women earn more	29	—	19	7	3
	Wages equal for men and women	19	—	19	—	—
Silk and silk goods	Men earn more . .	11	1	7	3	—
	Women earn more	4	—	3	1	—
Woolen and worsted goods	Men earn more . .	49	—	28	19	2
	Women earn more	8	2	5	—	1

that in nearly three fourths of the instances cited their wages are higher than those paid to their female competitors. This, like the other facts as to piece wages cited above, certainly gives strong support to the opinion that the lower wages of women in manual occupations are the direct result of their lower productivity.

The same conclusions cannot be applied with the same degree of certainty to occupations where time wages prevail, but there are reasons for doubting even here whether the term "equal efficiency" can be made to exclude all differences in the producing power of men and women. When we turn to Table VI of the report, where the number of working hours per week is given, we find that twenty-two instances out of the two hundred and seventy-nine where men earn higher wages than do women and where both sexes are employed at time wages can be explained by a difference in the number of hours worked, the women putting in from one and a half to twelve hours less time per week than the men. It is highly probable, if not certain, that this means lower productivity on the part of the women. We have, as a further indication, if not proof, of the inferiority of women's work, the fact that outside of the industries where women are most largely employed and where piece rates prevail the tendency toward equality of wages or even higher wages for women is quite generally found to exist in the lower grades of efficiency. Reference has already been made to this fact in the case of the manufacture of bakery and confectionery goods, in cigar and cigarette manufacturing, in the clothing industry, in the manufacture of tinware and sheet-metal goods, and in the dry-goods trade. But the same thing is true in the manufacture of bags and bagging, of dress trimmings, of gloves and mittens, of rubber and elastic goods, of watch and clock machinery, and of kindling wood. It is also true of library work and of the book and stationery trade.

In all these industries, although in a few instances women earn wages as high as or even higher than the men in the same occupations, the competition takes place in the lower grades of efficiency, while in the upper grades men alone are employed; or if men are employed along with women, their earnings are higher.

V

The American investigation furnishes considerable support to the opinions of the English investigators, that men and women seldom come into direct competition even when employed in the same establishments. This is naturally the first point to be determined in framing an answer to the question, Why do women receive lower wages than men? If the work performed by men and women is not the same, the inequality of wages may be due wholly or in part to the inequalities of employment. The question then becomes, as Professor Smart puts it, "Why are men and women employed in different groups of employment?"[1]

The supporters of the marginal-productivity theory of wages naturally look to women's wages for confirmation of their views. Professor Smart in his treatment of women's wages clearly has this theory in mind. Since the time of Jevons, says he,

> we have looked for the measure of value in marginal utility; for the value of "production goods" in their marginal utility as instruments of production; and with these for the value of labor in the value of its marginal product and not in any predetermined fund divided out among a variable number of workers.[2]

Accordingly he looks to the price of an article as the first thing to be considered in determining the value of the labor which helped to produce it. Although he rejects the notion that wages are low because goods are cheap, and points out that the initiative in reducing prices comes from producers, he is inclined to think that the explanation for the low wages of women rests in the fact that

> women are in almost exclusive possession of certain branches of trade, and that in these branches the commodities made are recognized by public opinion as being "cheap." Common observation must confirm Mr. Webb's conclusion that there are certain trades where men do not compete with women; indeed, that there is a well-marked relegation of women workers toward certain ill-paid trades; while at the same time there is as well-marked a movement of men toward the better-paid trades.[3]

As the investigation made by the Department of Labor took place in industries where both men and women were engaged in turning out a given product or series of products, we cannot very well find in it either confirmation or disproof of the statement that women are paid less than men because they produce "cheap" commodities. If women stitchers and men lasters are employed in the making of the same shoes, we cannot well claim that the women are paid less than the men

[1] Studies in Economics, p. 122. [2] *Ibid.*, p. 111. [3] *Ibid.*, p. 122.

because their products are less valuable. However, if we can show that women are generally employed as stitchers and men as lasters, we may find a reason, if not a justification, for the lower wages paid to them. It is this view of the situation which the results of the American investigation apparently confirm. A search through Table I of the report, which gives the number of men, women, and children employed in each subdivision of the industries investigated, reveals the fact that outside of the textile manufactures in the majority of the important industries men and women are seldom employed in the same suboccupations. The women's work, therefore, does not come into direct competition with that of men.

The manufacture of cigars, cigarettes, smoking tobacco, and snuff presents an exception to the general rule. There are fifty establishments employing 3327 men and 2989 women represented in the report, and in all of the important branches of the manufacture both sexes seem to be employed. Here we find no direct proof to confirm the opinion cautiously expressed by Mr. Webb[1] that the women do inferior work in this industry, although the facts as to piece rates and the prevalence of women in the lower grades of efficiency give indirect support to the notion that their work is less valuable to their employers.

In the textile industries there are more examples than elsewhere of men and women at work in the same branches of the industry; but even here by far the largest number of the women are employed as drawers-in, spinners, speeders, warpers, and weavers, while the men absorb the majority of the other branches. In the cotton industry, for example, in the eighty-six establishments included in the report there are fifty-five occupations in which women are reported as employees, but in the majority of these occupations there are only a few women. Women are employed in sixty-five mills as weavers, in sixty as spinners, in fifty-nine as spoolers, in twenty-two as drawers-in, in twenty as speeders, in eleven as slubbing-frame tenders, in ten as doffers, in nine as drawing-frame tenders, in

[1] Problems of Modern Industry, pp. 51, 52.

nine as twisters, in nine as winders, in eight as reelers, and in five as carders. All other occupations are represented by less than five instances. In the largest establishment represented in this industry, a New Hampshire mill, there are one hundred and twenty-nine suboccupations given, in but thirty-one of which women are employed. From this array of evidence one feels almost justified in acknowledging the truth of the strong statement with which Mrs. Webb enforces the more cautious conclusion of her husband.

> We are so accustomed in the middle class to see men and women engaged in identical work, as teachers, journalists, authors, painters, sculptors, comedians, singers, musicians, medical practitioners, clerks, or what not, that we almost inevitably assume the same state of things to exist in manual labor and manufacturing industry. But this is very far from being the case. To begin with, in over nine tenths of the industrial field there is no such thing as competition between men and women: the men do one thing and the women do another. . . . And even in those industries which employ both men and women we find them sharply divided in different departments, working at different processes, and performing different operations.[1]

VI

It is somewhat difficult to summarize the conclusions to be derived from such a variety of considerations and such a multiplicity of facts, but perhaps it may be done in some such manner as the following.

1. In the majority of trades and industrial callings men and women do not compete for the same work to any considerable extent. Exceptions to this rule are found in the textile industries, in the manufacture of tobacco and of boots and shoes, and in the dry-goods trade. In all of these industries men and women are usually found performing the same work, though their competition is often limited to a few branches of the industry. Where they do not perform the same work it is impossible to say how far differences in remuneration are due to sex and how far to inequality of work.

[1] Problems of Modern Industry, p. 94.

2. In the leading occupations in which women do compete with men for the same work payment by piece rates seems to be the rule. In such cases the earnings of women are more often equal to those of men than where time wages are paid. Usually, however, women are inferior to men in the quantity produced.

3. In occupations where time wages prevail and men and women perform the same work the lower wages of women can in many instances be explained by a shorter working day for the women than for the men and by the fact that the competition takes place in the lower grades of efficiency. The women workers naturally tend toward these grades, while the higher grades are filled mainly by men. In such cases the women often earn wages as high as or even higher than the men do in these lower grades, but they seldom earn as much as men where the competition takes place in the higher grades.

4. Women's natural disadvantage, due to their lower productivity, is increased by the force of custom. Where competitive rates of wages prevail, as in the textile industries of the South, women's wages are often equal to those of men.

5. In spite of the lower productivity of women there seems to be a tendency to increase their employment in occupations in which they have been at work, as well as to employ them in new fields of industry. This is partly due to woman's greater tractability. It may also happen that the wages of women are lower, when compared with those of men, than is their productivity. Women's lower standard of living, their partial dependence on other means of support, and their lack of combination prevent them from obtaining their true economic wages.

Finally, it must be repeated that these conclusions apply only to manual work. Doubtless they are in a degree applicable also to the higher callings; but here woman's inferiority is usually less, and the influence of custom, of the standard of living, and of the irregular and temporary character of her employment is much greater.

M. B. Hammond.

XIX

EMPLOYMENT OF GIRLS IN THE TEXTILE INDUSTRIES OF PENNSYLVANIA[1]

Pennsylvania, if classified according to the amount of power used in manufacturing, ranks first among the states of the Union. In the decade 1890 to 1900 the increase in the value of its products was greater than that of any other state. There is an aggregate wealth in its banks of over $150,000,000, which is over $500 per capita of the depositors, while in its building and loan associations there is an aggregate assessment of over $112,000,000. The capital invested in instruments of production and real estate devoted to productive industry amounts to over a billion and a half dollars, and the net value of products of its mills and factories in 1900 was over a billion dollars, or nearly $175 per capita of population. In the half century from 1850 to 1900 the gross per capita value of the products increased from $67.07 to $291.19. All this proves, if proof is needed, that the state of Pennsylvania is rich, and is under no necessity of enlisting in its industrial army thousands of young girls whose physical vigor and intellectual power are impaired by continuous and arduous labor.

The labor needed in our factories and workshops to produce articles of social utility, whose net value is over one billion dollars, amounts to over 800,000 hands, of whom 188,578 are females; and of the female employees, 17,286 are girls under sixteen years of age. Many of these children are employed in stores as "cash girls," but the vast majority of them are employees in mills and factories, where tiny fingers labor for ten hours each day for three hundred days in the year. The industries in which most

[1] From the *Annals, American Academy of Political Science*, Vol. XXIII, 1904, pp. 434–444. Consult the same for other articles on child labor; also bulletins of the National Child Labor Committee, New York, and Florence Kelley, "A Boy Destroying Trade," *Charities*, Vol. XIII, 1903, pp. 15–19.

of them are employed are silk throwing, hosiery and underwear, cigars and sweet stuffs, umbrellas and parasols, paper bags and boxes, and so forth. These industries, in which female child labor forms so important a part of the employees, are not equally distributed over the state. They are found for the greater part in the eastern portion. Pennsylvania has sixty-seven counties, but in eighteen of them, all of which are east of Harrisburg, which contain 52.87 per cent of the female population of the state, we find 87.07 per cent of all girls employed under sixteen years of age. The six counties in which female child labor most prevails are Berks, Lackawanna, Lancaster, Lehigh, Luzerne, and Philadelphia. Most of the children employed in these counties are found in factories and mills located in large cities such as Reading, Scranton, Lancaster, Allentown, Wilkesbarre, and Philadelphia. Of all the girls under sixteen years of age employed in the state 69.81 per cent are in the above six counties, which contain only 34.98 per cent of the female population of the state.

There are in Pennsylvania eighteen cities with over 25,000 population. By a comparison of the returns from the factory inspectors and the returns from the superintendent of public instruction of the state we are able to determine approximately the percentages of female children of the age group 13–16 years employed in these cities. The table on the opposite page gives the percentages.

York and Easton, together with the cities mentioned in the preceding paragraph, stand forth conspicuously in this list as centers where young girls are largely employed. The second column in the table gives the percentages of the native-born children of foreign-born parents, and the third column gives the percentages of the foreign-born element of the population of these cities. The table shows that cities such as MacKeesport, Johnstown, Erie, Pittsburg, and Allegheny, which have the highest percentages in the second and third columns, have the lowest percentages of girls under sixteen years employed; while the cities in which the highest percentages of this class of employees are found — with the exception of Scranton and Wilkesbarre — have the

	Percentage of Girls of Age Group 13–16 Years Employed	Percentage of Population having Foreign Parents	Percentage of Population Foreign born
In the state	9.16	22.7	15.6
Allegheny	7.82	37.4	23.2
Allentown	41.63	14.1	8.4
Altoona	10.17	17.9	8.4
Chester	19.28	25.4	14.9
Easton	24.46	17.9	8.4
Erie	3.80	40.9	22.6
Harrisburg	16.09	10.1	4.9
Johnstown	1.00	26.7	20.3
Lancaster	49.40	18.9	8.4
MacKeesport	0.59	32.9	27.3
Newcastle	2.86	22.7	18.8
Philadelphia	19.51	32.0	22.8
Pittsburg	4.12	37.3	26.3
Reading	36.02	12.6	7.5
Scranton	32.95	44.3	28.4
Wilkesbarre	26.03	40.0	23.3
Williamsport	6.16	19.4	7.7
York	31.44	9.2	3.8

lowest percentages of foreign-born inhabitants or descendants of foreign-born parents. This suggests that *entrepreneurs* in mills and factories do not wholly draw their supply of child labor from among the children of the foreign-born element. Whatever degeneracy is associated with the labor of girls of tender years in factories, it prevails among the children of the native-born as well as among those of the foreign-born parents in the state.

Let us now consider three industries of the state, namely, silk throwing, hosiery, and worsted mills. The following table gives us the percentages of female hands employed in them.

	Percentage of Female Employees	Percentage of All Employees under 16 Years	Percentage of All Employees under 21 Years	Percentage of Female Employees under 16 Years	Percentage of Females among All Employees under 21 Years
Silk	70.65	20.20	50.97	22.15	77.49
Hosiery	79.50	18.92	52.19	19.77	83.10
Worsted Mills	57.40	17.83	31.90	23.04	73.75

This table shows that the vast majority of employees in these industries is female, and that of this majority an average of over 22 per cent is under sixteen years of age. Of both male and female employees nearly 20 per cent are under sixteen years, while an average of nearly 50 per cent of the hands is composed of minors. These percentages, which show how prevalent female labor is in these industries, are still further corroborated by studying them in distinct localities. Take the three industries of silk throwing, hosiery, and underwear mills in special localities, and the following table gives the percentages of female labor in them.

	Percentage of Female Employees	Percentage of All Employees under 16 Years	Percentage of All Employees under 21 Years	Percentage of All Females under 16 Years	Percentage of Girls among All Employees under 16 Years
Silk					
In Philadelphia . . .	77.07	6.10	25.08	5.28	66.66
Outside Philadelphia . .	77.68	23.90	52.84	25.00	77.69
Hosiery					
In Philadelphia . . .	77.09	26.00	56.41	26.82	79.53
Outside Philadelphia . .	76.98	24.42	48.73	27.37	86.25
Underwear					
In Philadelphia . . .	87.19	7.68	27.72	7.65	62.50
Outside Philadelphia . .	84.60	9.15	36.60	7.53	69.65

This table shows that among the silk workers in Philadelphia we do not find nearly so many minors and young girls under sixteen years employed as in this industry outside that city. In the hosiery mills the employment of these classes is as great as in territories outside Philadelphia, while in the underwear factories the employment of minors and young girls is not so prevalent as in the other two industries.

A study of the factories and mills in five of the cities where female labor most prevails gives us the table on the following page as to the percentages of minors employed and the percentages of girls under sixteen years employed.

	Percentage of Employees under 21 Years	Percentage of Girls under 16 Years Employed
Lancaster	48.24	18.78
Reading	42.26	20.39
Allentown	51.39	23.16
Wilkesbarre	64.59	22.48
Scranton	55.05	30.87

Let us now consider the wages of these classes of our employees. In the census returns of 1900 we have data given of three industries — silk, hosiery, and worsted goods — whereby we may compute the average annual wage of females. It is as follows:

	Average per Annum	Average per Working Day
Women 16 years and over (silk)	$204.33	68 cents
Girls under 16 years (silk)	128.95	43 "
Women 16 years and over (hosiery)	265.58	85 "
Girls under 16 years (hosiery)	141.61	47 "
Women 16 years and over (worsted goods)	290.61	97 "
Girls under 16 years (worsted goods)	174.54	58 "

In "Industrial Statistics" of our state the daily wage for all employees in silk throwing, hosiery, and worsted yarns is 84 cents, 95 cents, and $1, respectively, which differ from the figures given by the census of 1900, which are 74 cents, 90 cents, and $1.09, respectively. The average daily wages of children under sixteen years employed in silk, hosiery, and underwear in the state is 43 cents, 46 cents, and 47 cents, respectively. Averages, however, do not give us the true wages paid in factories which are located in cities and towns where an abundant supply of cheap labor is near at hand. In factories located in towns and cities in the anthracite regions young girls work for ten hours each day, or sixty hours a week, for from $1.50 to $2 a week. A girl who earns $3 a week is considered fortunate, while forewomen who have charge of from fifty to one hundred girls get only $5 a week. In factories located in small towns the average daily wage of females over sixteen years, as well as that of girls under sixteen years, is fully 25 per cent lower than that of the general averages based on the census returns. Of all industries employing young girls that of silk throwing pays the lowest wages, notwithstanding the fact that "of the several branches of the industry the manufacture of silk stood first in the value of products in 1900." Pennsylvania, according to the last census, ranks second in the industry among the states of the Union.

In the annual report of the factory inspectors for 1902 the chief of inspectors says concerning child labor: "The first year's report of the Department in 1890 showed that over 10 per cent of the employees were children between the ages of twelve and sixteen years. This year's report shows that less than 5 per cent were employed between the ages of thirteen and sixteen years." In the census of 1890 only 3.87 per cent of all employees in the state were children under sixteen years, while in 1900 the percentage was 4.51. During the decade, 1890 to 1900, the increase in the employment of children under sixteen years was 47.80 per cent, while the percentage increase of school children in the decade was 15.3. During the same decade the number of female employees increased 44.87 per cent, while the female population of the state increased 19.5 per cent. The returns of the census for 1870, 1880, 1890, and 1900 showed that the percentages of children employed under sixteen years, as compared with all employees engaged in mechanical and manufacturing pursuits in Pennsylvania, were 6.02, 7.66, 3.87, and 4.51, respectively. The percentage in 1902 as given in the factory inspector's report was 4.51. With these figures before us it is hard to see how the chief of the factory inspectors could make the above statement. In the last generation the percentage increase of female employees in the state was about three times the percentage increase of our population. Since 1870 many legislatures have attempted to regulate child labor in the state, but the number employed has kept pace with the percentage increase of our population. In 1890 the average wage of children under sixteen years was 50.6 cents a day; in 1900 it was 53 cents, an increase of 5.5 per cent. The average wage of females over sixteen years in 1890 was 89 cents a day; in 1900 it was 87 cents, a reduction of 2.28 per cent. The small percentage of children under sixteen years employed in Pennsylvania is no guarantee that child labor is less prevalent here than in southern states, to which public attention has been recently called. Our state has many industries in which few children are employed, such as iron and steel, locomotive and car building, foundries and electric apparatus. Hence, to give the percentage of children under sixteen years employed in all industries of the commonwealth may appear favorable to Pennsylvania (4.51 per cent) as compared with North Carolina (14.70 per cent), but the method of comparison is misleading as to the prevalence of child labor in both states. North Carolina has no large industries in which few children are employed. If a just comparison between north and south is made, the nature of the industries in the respective states should be taken into consideration. Rev. E. G. Gardner wrote in the fall of 1902 that of 45,044 operatives in textile industries in North Carolina, 7996 (17.7 per cent) were under fourteen years of age and their daily average wage was 29 cents. In the textile industries specified in the table on page 426 there is an average of nearly 22 per cent of the employees under sixteen years of age whose average net wage, outside Philadelphia, is not 40 cents a day. In North Carolina 37.8 per cent of the population are employed in gainful occupations and in Pennsylvania 38.8 per cent; but in the former state 64.1 per cent of these are engaged in agricultural pursuits and 12.7 per cent only in manufacturing and mechanical work, while in Pennsylvania only 14 per cent of all employees are in the former class of work, but there are 40.1 per cent in the latter. A just comparison of female and child labor in both states can be made only when we find what percentages of females of the age group 13–23 years and of children of the age group 13–16 years are employed in each. By this method of comparison we find that 16.3 per cent of females of the age group 13–23 years are employed in Pennsylvania and 6.6 per cent in North Carolina, but the percentage of children under sixteen years of age employed in both states is about the same, — in Pennsylvania 20.2 and in North Carolina 20.4. While we censure the states of the South for their exploitation of child labor, we should not lose sight of this evil in Pennsylvania because of the specious argument that only 4.51 per cent of the total employees are children under sixteen years of age.

A study of the laws of Pennsylvania relative to child labor reveals a mass of complicated, contradictory, and confusing statutes. Legislators, in their anxiety to do something, have disregarded the labors of their predecessors. They pass laws wholly oblivious of the importance of historical continuity, and the result is a series of incongruous and disconnected statutes regulating the labor of the wards of the state. But however bungling the work of the legislators is, the student is hardly prepared to find Pennsylvania more indifferent than Russia to the interests of its children employed in factories. England, since the passage of the Ashley Act in 1833, has prohibited the employment at night of persons under eighteen years. Every other European country of any industrial importance has followed England's example. Even Austria and Russia, whence come the Slavs, whose manner of life and customs we so frequently condemn, forbid the labor of young persons at night. But these people coming to Pennsylvania find young girls under sixteen years of age employed at night in our mills. Many deem it cruel to employ these young persons by day for ten hours in stifling mills, but every humane person considers it barbarous to employ them at night. This is a reproach to a state as rich as ours, and, although the wrong was amply exposed before the Coal Strike Commission, there were no legislators found in the last legislature chivalrous enough to champion enthusiastically the cause of the coming mothers of our state.

The Journal of the American Medical Association, in commenting on child labor in the South, said: "When these immature individuals are kept at constant work for long hours the outlook for their future can be imagined. It is bad policy for a state to encourage the increase of degeneracy in this way, to say nothing of the questions of humanity involved. Whatever may be thought of some of the other demands of the labor agitation of the day, that of the abolition of child labor, as it exists in some of the southern factories, can be indorsed by our profession, and should be by the public generally." Suppose the medical profession of Pennsylvania, numbering over 10,000 persons, were to direct its attention to the 17,286 girls under sixteen years of age employed in our state, would not their professional knowledge of the development of the female organism from the ages of thirteen to sixteen years urge them to coöperate in the attempt to abolish this evil? From the days of Quetelet down to the present accurate measurements have been taken of the bodily growth of young girls from thirteen to sixteen years, and the consensus of opinion is that at no period of their life do they grow so rapidly as then. The female, during these years, develops more rapidly than the male, so that the average girl of sixteen years has reached a stage in physical development which boys do not attain until two or three years later. All parents who duly watch over their children know that the factory and the mill are not proper places for girls from thirteen to sixteen years of age.

From the standpoint of economics this employment of young girls cannot be justified. The more wealth produced, the more we have for distribution. The larger the number of persons engaged in gainful occupations the better. But alongside these self-evident truths we must place another, namely, that if the health of our industrial life is to be preserved, the various industries of the state must be self-supporting. Those which flourish by the labor of women and children are not self-supporting, for they consume an amount of energy which they do not replace. They draw upon the capital stock of the nation's vital force and care little or nothing about the degeneracy they effect. When the silk throwers of England were fighting for a living wage, it was asked, "What is a fair day's wage?" and the reply was, "The due reward for our labor may be summed up in these words: shelter, food, and raiment both for ourselves, our wives, and our children." Suppose we apply that rule to the textile industries of Pennsylvania. Is 40 cents a day sufficient to give proper food, raiment, and shelter to a child of from thirteen to sixteen years of age? Can a young lady keep herself in food, clothes, and room on 85 cents a day? The state spent on its youths in the Huntingdon Reformatory in the year 1901 an average of $248.90 per capita, or $4.79 per week, a sum twice as large as that which our young girls earn in our mills and factories. The state has erected a comfortable home for its convicts and spends annually $199.95 per capita on food, clothing, etc.; this is $3.84 a week, or $1.16 less than the average weekly wage of young women over sixteen years employed in the mills, a difference that is barely sufficient to cover the item of rent. The textile industries are not self-supporting. We are safe in saying that 50 per cent of the employees in these industries expend an amount of energy which their wages do not replace. The majority of the women and girls who labor in them cannot provide for their wants with the wages they earn; they must either go short or else the deficiency must be supplied from wages earned in other industries.

But that is not all. The textile industries drain the energy of successive generations of youths and care nothing whence they come or whither they go. Over 50 per cent of the employees are minors. When these come to their majority they pass out of the industry and their place is supplied by successive relays of youths under sixteen years. Every boy or girl at the age of thirteen has cost somebody from $500 to $600; however, the textile industries have not paid the bill. Young men are constantly forced out of these industries when they demand wages that will enable them to establish a home and raise a family, and young women soon reach the maximum wage, and however long they remain in the factory, they have no hope of better wages. Young men who leave the industry face the world at a great disadvantage, and when their industrial capacity diminishes and ailments come upon them which finally end in death, the industries in which they spent their youth bear no part of the burdens which fall upon the community. If these industries existed in a state where the institution of slavery prevailed, they would be obliged to raise boys and girls for the mills, and they would also be compelled to provide for them when ailments, old age, and death came upon them. But here in Pennsylvania the textile industries flourish by absorbing a supply of energy that has cost them nothing.

The children and youths are drained of their strength for a decade and then pushed out into the world. These industries hold the same advantageous position as compared with the self-supporting industries that they would if they received a bounty or subsidy from the government. They flourish by freely drawing upon the capital stock of the nation, and, being under no social pressure to maintain a rate of wages that will keep their employees day by day in unimpaired health and vigor, they wholly lose sight of the larger obligation to maintain each generation unimpaired in quantity and quality.

Society may ask for cheap products from the textile industries, but goods that have in them the flesh and blood of the future mothers of the toiling masses are not cheap. The price paid is degeneracy. Insufficient wages mean insufficient food, liability to diseases, industrial inefficiency, scanty clothing, cramped dwellings, and a vitiated atmosphere. These women and young girls, who under financial pressure yield the strength so much needed in the building up of their frames, pay the penalty in headaches, toothaches, dyspepsia, and sores, dragging pains and chronic anæmia. Do the medical profession find among these young mill hands that state of health which is normal among the young daughters of the professional classes? Communities where textile industries flourish are the scenes of degeneracy, and upon each generation rests a curse. The individuals who are exploited depart farther and farther from the higher type of womanhood which American civilization has held before the world.

The social interest of our state demands that the textile industries be made self-supporting. It cannot be done by collective bargain, for the youths, under existing conditions, cannot be organized so efficiently as to effect this. The better way is to check the excessive use of child labor by raising the age at which boys and girls can be employed. The International Socialist and Trade Union Congress in 1896 demanded that the age of boys and girls beginning to work should be raised to sixteen years. This certainly should be done in the case of our girls, and the medical profession, because of its greater knowledge of the physical organism, should advocate such legislation. Pennsylvania, whose productive wealth annually amounts to over two billions of dollars, should rise to the degree of intelligence which regards the boys and girls not as independent wealth producers who earn their wages from day to day, but as the future citizens and parents of our commonwealth, for whom, up to their majority, proper conditions of growth and education should be secured. The well-being of society demands that all conditions of employment inconsistent with the maintenance of the employees in a state of efficiency as producers should be eliminated. Nothing imperils this imperative of modern civilization so much as permitting young girls to be employed for bare subsistence at an age when nature taxes their system to the limit of profitable endurance. Such a custom works deterioration both in the physical and intellectual spheres, and hinders the continuous existence, generation after generation, of healthy and efficient descendants.

PETER ROBERTS.

MAHANOY CITY, PENNSYLVANIA.

XX

THE PRINTER'S HEALTH[1]

The number of deaths in its membership during the five years and eleven months from June 30, 1897, to May 31, 1903, inclusive, on which benefits were paid by the International Typographical Union of North America, was 2994. Of this total 1323, or about 45 per cent, were from respiratory diseases, that is, pulmonary phthisis, asthma, bronchitis, pneumonia, diphtheria, pleurisy, and pulmonary congestion. Though the official mortuary reports for the period named show that some of the evils of our occupation hasten death through heart and nerve ailments especially, it is the startling figures under this heading of respiratory diseases that must first challenge investigation when we set out to reduce our death rate.

The most striking facts seen are the number of deaths of young men and the number of deaths from consumption. Of the 1323 deaths from respiratory ailments 490, or nearly 38 per cent, were of men between the ages of twenty-one and thirty-two, inclusive. How many of the 1323 were of consumption? Deaths from this disease were not separately recorded until the year ending May 31, 1903. For that year for the first time the causes of death were fully itemized by the union secretary, the method of classification theretofore being under a few general headings. Of the 476 deaths for the year 191 were from respiratory diseases. Of these 191, 128 were from "consumption" (in the words of the report, consumption 72, pulmonary phthisis 11, tuberculosis 44, pulmonary hemorrhage 1). The deaths from pneumonia were 51. Thus the lung ailments grouped in common speech as "consumption" certainly carried away more than

[1] From the *Typographical Journal*, Vol. XXIII, 1903, No. 5, p. 425; No. 6, p. 527, condensed. See also Doehring, "Factory Sanitation and Labor Protection," Bulletin No. 44, U. S. Bureau of Labor; Oliver, Dangerous Trades, the standard authority.

27 per cent of our members dying in that year, and how many of the men dying of pneumonia were at the same time consumptive statistics cannot reveal.

For the year ending May 31, 1904, the deaths in the International Union from respiratory diseases numbered 216 in a total of 578, the number from "consumption" being 95 (consumption 58, pulmonary phthisis 22, tuberculosis 13, hemorrhage of the lungs 2). Pneumonia carried away 72, bronchitis 6, congestion of the lungs 5. The death rate for the year was 12.5 per 1000.

Some further light comes from a random selection of three monthly death reports in the *Journal* and a noting of the causes of death therein given. Of the 93 deaths from various diseases as reported at the International Typographical Union offices for November, 1901, November, 1902, and May, 1903, 28 were given by the local union physicians as from tuberculosis, phthisis, consumption, and hemorrhage of the lungs, and 10 of these 28 were of men under thirty-two years of age. Seven of the 93 deaths were of pneumonia. These figures serve to confirm the fact that the causes of death in our trade are quite uniform year by year in present circumstances, and that the proportion of deaths from consumption may therefore be foretold to a certainty so long as circumstances remain as they are.

The ascertainable statistics hence indicate these conclusions:

First. In America, of the total annual deaths among union printers the proportion dying of consumption is fully 30 per cent.

Second. Of this 30 per cent at least one third die within the early period of life, when the direct effects of occupational evils may be looked for.

Statistics regarding English printers tell a story even more alarming. Of 799 deaths reported by the London Society of Compositors for the ten years 1880–1889, inclusive, 296, or 37 per cent, were due to phthisis alone. Besides, bronchitis and asthma were the causes of 85 deaths, and pneumonia and pleurisy of 65; that is, 446 of 799 deaths occurring from causes falling under one general classification were largely traceable to occupational conditions.

Of 852 deaths occurring in the Typographical Association of England (the union printers outside London) in the six years

1894–1899, inclusive, tuberculosis carried off 287. While from 1881 to 1890 the mean annual death rate from tuberculosis for all males between twenty and sixty-five years of age in England and Wales was but 1.8 per 1000, the rate for members of the Typographical Association in the six years noted was 3.4, and for the London Society 3.9, in either case about double the normal. Says Dr. Thomas Oliver in Dangerous Trades, "It may be taken as a fact that printers are more liable to tubercular consumption than men engaged in most other trades."

In England the phthisis mortality figure for printers is 326, while for agriculturists it is only 102. For occupied males in general the mortality figure for all diseases is 953; for agriculturists it is 602; for printers 1096. Printers die off much faster than miners, for whom the mortality figure, including accidents, is only 935. In plain words, the printer follows an occupation far more dangerous to life than does the miner.

Middle-aged American printers are heard commonly to assert from their own observation that if an apprentice has a sensitive throat or a delicate chest, "something about the office or the business" seems to search out the weak spot in the young man's constitution, to plant disease thereat, and enfeeble him or bring him to an early death. If he can weather through to well past thirty, he may live to the general average term of life. But for any indifference to the ordinary laws of health he speedily meets with cruel punishment. That 40 per cent of the whole number of printers dying of respiratory diseases should officially be reported to be those of men under thirty-three is confirmatory of this common nonstatistical observation. Printers die fast and die young.

What, it may be asked, is this "something about the office or the business" that contributes so greatly to make the printer physically what he is? The conditions need not be guessed at; they are determinable.

Dr. Stühler of Berlin, taking his statistics from the reports of sick-benefit societies, states that of 3000 printers in Berlin 313, or about 10.4 per cent, were annually sick from lead colic. But it is possible that lead colic was a convenient ailment to assign to Berlin printers, perhaps with their own collusion, especially as Berlin seems to be the only city entering such disturbing statistics in the reference books. Chemical analyses are more reliable. Stumpf found that the dust of printing offices often contained as much as 14.43 per cent of lead. Faber collected lead from printing-office dust as follows: from the floor 11.51 per cent; from a shelf 6.59 per cent; from behind the frames of an alley 4.7 per cent. Keygi found 10 to 15 per cent of lead in the floor dust.

Printers breathe air not only heavily laden with lead dust at all times, but strong with noxious fumes from drying type during and following distribution, and while at this work, as well as on rising in the morning, some compositors detect a metallic taste in their saliva. Compositors also absorb lead through the pores of their skin, the hand typesetter from the separate types which are constantly in his fingers while at work, the linotype operator from the slugs, which, hot from the mold and lead-greasy to the touch, turn the hands to a lamp black hue. The careless apprentice who eats his office lunch with type marked fingers takes lead into his stomach. . . . Compositors rarely have acute attacks such as painter's colic, in which convulsions may occur. The form from which they suffer, often unconsciously, is chronic plumbism. . . . But while a risk of plumbism is unavoidable, medical men say it seems never to affect many individuals in the trade, their constitutional powers of resistance enabling them to escape the poison or to throw off its effects easily.

A fact next to be noted is both a consequence and a cause. Printers have a somewhat uniform physical development. The youthful typesetter may take on length, but he commonly lacks breadth; he fails to develop the blacksmith's arms or the sailor's shoulders. Rarely is his appearance that of the athlete. To acquire rounded biceps, hard leg muscles, or even a sun-browned face he must take much open-air exercise. But this he seldom does systematically. Not one youth in many attains his full natural growth in a printing office, and not one journeyman in many retains his full physical powers to a ripe old age without a break. For this, of course, there are causes in addition to lead poisoning.

Typesetting is exhausting work. Standing hour by hour brings on backache, and in some men varicose veins and swollen feet. Sitting on the high printing-office stool doubles up the hand typesetter, constraining his arm motions and interfering with his digestion. The linotype operator has trials more severe. His stool being low, his legs are thrown into cramped positions. From the pot of molten type metal under his machine come a trying heat and offensive gases. He must watch the delicate mechanism of his iron rival lest it go wrong. The electric light thrown on his copy often sharply conflicts with the daylight. His keyboard work with wrist and fingers and his handling of hot slugs result at times in a numbness that threatens scrivener's palsy. Either as typesetter or linotype operator the compositor's brain is active every moment during the workday. Composition can never be mechanical. Attention must be given to deciphering the copy, to spelling, capitalizing, punctuating, office style, and correcting the lines as composed. Each of these distinct mental acts helps to drain the bodily forces. The work as a whole is tedious and monotonous. As the brain becomes fatigued its cells shrink. With every type a man sets there is a touch of wear on the cerebral tissue itself, only to be repaired by the restorative operations of nature, — food, rest, and sleep.

The average printer, consequently, is not robustly developed; he is wan from plumbism and mentally and physically worn through the nature of his occupation as it is to-day pursued. It is this overtaxed state of mind and body, the effect of circumstances in the business which call for a reduced draft upon his powers, that may in turn cause the printer's general health quickly to succumb under other office conditions quite common but wholly avoidable.

The printer frequently works in a place by no means designed to meet the requirements of his health and comfort. Narrow, low-ceiled warehouse lofts, basements, attics, inner rooms of office buildings, inadequately lighted and badly ventilated, — such makeshifts for composing rooms frequently see a large force of compositors and readers patiently pursuing their labors. The annoying racket of presses and line-casting machines, added to the rank odors of inks and benzine, may further set the workman's nerves on edge, while by turns he is made to shiver in cold draughts from open doors and to swelter through hot waves from steam pipes. Before his day's work is done he is in a state of lassitude and extreme fatigue.

In New York by far the larger number of printers die in the winter months. For this fact two reasons are commonly assigned. First, in winter the air of the composing rooms, with doors and windows closed, is more foul than at other seasons, and when the risk of an open window is run pneumonia may follow. Second, the unemployed, underfed, and perhaps consumptive use up their stock of health and strength by midwinter because of the confinement indoors. In effect the two reasons become one; it is a case of pure air against bad air. When doors and windows are open in summer the hands find some relief from print-shop insanitation.

The following table shows the deaths of printers in New York by years and by quarter years and half years, for the period from 1900 to 1903, inclusive.

Year ending June 1	Whole Number of Deaths	Three Months, January to March	Other Nine Months	Six Months, November to April	Other Six Months
1900 . .	69	23	46	35	34
1901 . .	77	23	54	44	33
1902 . .	90	27	63	50	40
1903 . .	100	39	61	61	39
Totals	336	112	224	190	146

The three bad-air months, January, February, and March, in these four years took 33.3 per cent of the deaths instead of the 25 per cent due in each quarter of the year. The 100 deaths of 1903 brought the death rate of Typographical Union No. 6 (New York) up to the extraordinary figure of 17 per 1000, the membership being slightly more than 6000. For the international union, with a membership of 42,436, the death rate in 1903 was 11 per 1000, the average for the last twelve years being 13 per 1000. Comparison with the general average death rate of society brings poor encouragement for printers. The death rate for men, women, and children in some American cities is less than 19 per 1000; in certain large districts in England, even including infant mortality, it is less than 15 per 1000 per annum. For Greater New York, with a population of 3,570,000, the death rate for the week ending October 29, 1904, was 14.46.

For the year ending May 31, 1904, No. 6 lost 112 members by death. The year had brought into its ranks about five hundred new members; hence the usual local death rate was outstripped. The death rate for printers in New York is almost double what it ought to be, as indicated by the general rate in healthy communities. For the International Typographical Union membership the death rate is 30 to 40 per cent higher than the normal.

That there may be no doubt as to the membership of No. 6 and its death rate the number paying per capita tax to the International in the years mentioned is herewith given: July 1, 1898, to June 30, 1899, 5140; July 1, 1899, to June 30, 1900, 4898; July 1, 1900, to May 31, 1901, 4620; 1902, 5258; 1903, 5850. The actual membership each year was several hundred in excess of these figures, as about 5 per cent are usually in arrears.

Some members of No. 6 have the impression that "all the broken down printers of the country flock to New York." This is not confirmed by wide observation. The brother who is bankrupt in health and purse is a figure familiar in every large typographical center. Even in country towns the seldom employed extra hand, in habits identical with his city compeer, is ever to be found. The opinion of our international secretary on this point, founded on his many visits to all the larger cities during his long term, and on his constant tabulation of statistical returns is: "It is impossible for me to say whether or not your relief fund attracts invalids and superannuated members to New York. All of our unions have old members whom they assist in different ways. From what I know of the membership of your union, I do not believe you have more than your share in proportion to the membership."

A comparison between No. 6's own total of deaths from year to year and the total for all the other unions in the I. T. U., with the two consequent but divergent averages, leads one to ask whether the apparent excess of the death rate given for No. 6 is accurate. For example, in the last three years No. 6 itself paid death benefits in thirteen cases not granted by the International. A similar ratio of difference between the actual totals of the other local unions and the International's total would raise the latter's true death rate considerably. And this difference may for other reasons be even greater than it seems. While No. 6's members and their families strain a point to obtain its $150 insurance, in cities which have no extra local death fund members may fall away from the union during the period of old age or a time of prolonged straitened circumstances before death. If this be true, the headquarters rate of 13 deaths per 1000 per year for twelve years is less than the actual figure.

. . . Released from the depressing atmosphere of the composing room after long hours of nerve tension, many an exhausted printer's one absorbing inclination is "to take a bracer." Unless he is a man of self-control, systematically conducting his struggle for life and health, he takes his bracer in some form of alcohol. From every point of view this habit is fraught with danger. If he takes his beer or spirits at home, the sought-for stimulus may be attained after a time only by increasing the quantity of the drink. If he imbibes in a barroom, conviviality may lead him to deprive himself of his needed rest abed and also to consume beyond his appetite. However or wherever a man drinks, the drop he desires as a tonic may become the quantity acting as a poison. The printer's danger is doubled with his allowance of drink. While the depression consequent on plumbism and vitiated air gives him a craving for alcohol, by a counteraction alcohol taken in excess predisposes him to plumbism. Here, indeed, is a vicious circle.

A broken-down alcoholic printer is commonly the compound resultant of:

First. Incomplete physical development as a youth.

Second. Daily exhaustion as either a hand or machine typesetter.

Third. Unsanitary conditions in the printing office.

Fourth. Ignorance and consequently carelessness regarding personal hygiene.

Fifth. Plumbism.

Sixth. Alcohol, with later the interaction of plumbism and alcohol.

Seventh. Vagrant living.

Printers who are victims of alcohol have the same unmistakable stamp. On seeing a knot of them congregated at a corner a literary man exclaimed, "What saturnine faces they have!" Curiously, Dr. Oliver, speaking of the pale and expressionless faces of persons suffering from lead poison, says that acute cases are termed saturnine cachexy. But alcohol drives blood to the eyes and nose. A case of alcoholic plumbism, therefore, presents a bloated face, with heavy and dull outlines, grayish white as to the broader surfaces, mottled red as to middle features, the expression of the whole sullen and sodden.

The high death rate of men in this class is an accepted fact in the trade. Just what proportion of printers falls to the level of the chronic alcohol patient it is difficult to estimate. The impressions of the casual observer may be grossly inaccurate. The veteran proprietor of a daily newspaper once expressed his belief that few of the one hundred compositors he employed were steady men. Never going up to the composing room himself, he took his impressions largely from a group of disreputables always standing about the side-door entrance. Though really less than one tenth of the force, these loungers, with floating "subs," bore false testimony against the other nine tenths who passed in or out of the building without halt. . . .

A rule-of-thumb method of estimating the proportion of alcoholic printers would be to ascertain the probable number among those drawing out-of-work relief at the union rooms. Since 1893 No. 6 has appropriated $25,000 to $47,000 a year for its unemployed, paying the money for stated periods in weekly allowances. Several successive relief clerks and several committeemen have concluded that not more than one man in three drawing relief is incapacitated through drink. Since the largest number of members ever receiving a week's allowance is about

300, this would indicate that of the 6000 members less than 2 per cent are alcoholics at any one time. But it is among this 2 per cent that death is ever busiest. One of the union officials says, "As one set dies off others come to take their places." Not the perfect sobriety of all the remaining 98 per cent keeps the proportion of alcoholics down to 2 per cent, but the havoc of death among the stricken.

Besides chronic alcoholics there are occasionals. A printer, exhausted, depressed and not aware, perhaps, how much he is physically the victim of circumstances, finding relief in a glass and lively company, quits work for a day or a week, with drink his recreation. His vitality having been lowered at his trade and his nerves now deadened by alcohol, he catches cold readily and in a short time develops pneumonia. If he recovers, his chances for sound health are diminished. He may be a sober man the rest of his days, but alcohol has done for him what plumbism and foul printing-office air might never have done. It has probably killed his chances for longevity. His death sooner or later adds one more in the respiratory column of the I. T. U. statistics.

Up to this point we have seen in the main the facts elicited by the query, "Why is the death rate among printers so high?" Let us now ask, "Cannot that death rate be lowered?" It is with this object in view that this study of the printer has been written.

The typographer, as we have seen, is largely "made up" by his trade, — by physical conditions as they exist in that trade. Individuals, many of them, may vary widely from the typical printer. But when we perceive that there is a trade type of man, and that not a high physical type, we naturally desire to have the average printer brought up to normal standards or higher.

The first truth to be recognized is that the remedy lies largely in our own hands, individually and collectively. Individually, because every man has a will and intellect of his own, whereby his acts are effective. Collectively, because every printer suffers more or less from the lack of prevision and care on the part of all the craft.

We must grant a certain influence on all persons who toil within its doors due to conditions in the printing office. The very trend of the printer's mind and spirits uniformly depends in large degree on the state of his body. Printers present to the observer curiously coincident mental attitudes on surface matters. Deeper down, of course, they differ. If compositors are an irritable lot, as evidenced in their explosive denunciations of the proof reader, it signifies in part the evil effects of lead on nerve tissue, which men can no more fully control than they can change a printing-office complexion. If printers are sadly skeptical and prone to censure, it must be due to foul air in the lungs rather than to perverted impulses of the heart. If they know the names rather than the contents of books, it is because their constant perusal of copy during long hours of work satiates their appetite for general reading. The indifference or apathy prevalent in the craft to office hygiene, or even to the first step necessary to hygienic reform, — a study of health conditions, — may be traced to occupational overexhaustion and physical underdevelopment.

And next one must grant the difficulty in changing printing offices for the better. The lunch rooms show little improvement from one year to another. Chapel chairmen in vain declare that foremen or managers ought to prohibit the sale of alcoholic beverages anywhere in the building, creating as it does the very evils that result in many a man's discharge. To enforce fresh-air laws compositors are sometimes obliged to call in the Board of Health. But the crowning difficulty lies in the problem of a workday that unfits the compositor for any duty except his daily shop task.

Yet, if once he is determined to grapple with the remediable evils of the occupation, every individual can fall back on certain resources of his own, while he may also look for the action of the union in a very considerable sphere.

The important point is to know that health is mainly the result of management. When we read that as a class literary men are the longest-lived, we must see plainly on reflection that it is because they are observers and thinkers. Ascertaining as closely as possible the truth as to certain influences relating to health, they proceed to act on this knowledge. As men in general might do if better educated, they observe at least the more obvious laws of health. They know how far the physical state of an individual is the result of accident and how far of taking proper care of himself.

I am inclined to think that with advancing years many printers study their health. Our International Union statistics show that the printer who safely passes forty-five may live long afterward. Of 329 members who died in 1901 and 1902 between the ages of forty-five and seventy-four, inclusive, 197 were between forty-five and fifty-nine, while 132 were between sixty and seventy-four. Thus only sixty-five more died during the first age period of fifteen years after forty-four than during the second; and hence a printer at forty-five would have but three chances of dying before fifty-nine to two thereafter before seventy-four. But these data are slight, of course, and all printers do not die members of the union, a somewhat numerous class being the men who leave the trade while yet young. Printers often meet a man who will tell them: "I once worked at typesetting, but had to quit the business on account of poor health." On the other hand, very few men, it may be safely said, take up our occupation to improve their health.

On passing into the forties, however, many printers take on flesh. The vigorous survivors who have arrived at middle life, if not wholly immune to the effects of lead, resist it successfully, and those who drink regulate their habits with a deepening wisdom. The vitality of the strong then asserts itself in a spread of girth. Proof readers almost invariably grow stouter at their sedentary labors. In 1898 the seventeen readers in the *World* proof room, nearly all men past forty, and all but one or two graduates of the composing room, weighed on the average 174 pounds, about 40 pounds more than the average male American.

How much can be done through obeying the laws of health in rebuilding even the physically ruined man is marvelous. In 1899 No. 6's printers' farm, maintaining on an average forty-six superannuated and invalided men for twenty-seven weeks, rehabilitated their health in nearly all cases and literally fattened many of them like beeves. In six months several gained twenty-five pounds, others fifteen, twelve, or ten. In nine months one gained forty pounds. Some so weak on going to the farm that they could barely walk were soon at work gardening with the sensation of play.

Encouraged by such considerations, the printer, or more accurately the compositor, will ask, "What regimen can I adopt to counteract the conditions in which I work? How can I otherwise strive for health?"

He who has reached the anxious stage must inevitably begin with settling in his mind the question whether or not he really will take proper care of his health. He must decide whether he is to act and live as a man who is impressed with a sense of his duties to himself, his home, and society, or whether he is merely to float along as a worthless piece of human driftwood. If he is to be a man, he will do a man's part. He will make and not mar himself.

Next, on mentally revolving the question in its various phases, he will perceive that even the printer shut up in an office may within certain limits be what manner of man he will. Just as apprentices may or may not employ or neglect their passing opportunities to learn the trade, so may all the members of the craft employ or neglect what means are open to them to preserve their health. One thing is certain, — a man's health rarely takes care of itself.

What should be the principal health rules of a printer?

Few will dispute that the day a young compositor decides to let drink alone he takes the first step in turning his face toward health. With the basis of fair health, his prospects for thrift, uprightness, and mental improvement — and, moreover, respectability and independence — are increased tenfold. He not only fortifies himself against lead poison, but he turns his back on the source of ruin to thousands now among the dead.

To buoyant youth the ills of life are far away. The deadly consequences of drink, seeming so remote, the lively young printer regards lightly. The possibility of his falling to the drunkard's level he can hardly entertain seriously. Yet decade by decade the statistics of drink continue to repeat themselves or to reveal results worse than ever before. Dr. Oliver says the mortality of English printers from alcoholism in 1891 had fully trebled as compared with what it was in 1881. "I can drink or let it alone," vanity whispers to the young compositor as he works on the mortuary tables of his community and observes their frightful testimony against alcohol. In his absorbing self-confidence he detects in himself no weakness for stimulants, yet in a few years more his own name may be set up in the same tabular forms by another compositor, this one, too, perhaps, equally unwise and self-deluded. The whisper of hope that self may go scot-free forever while others die is akin to lunacy. And that men should resort to barrooms, of all places, for health suggestions, or should consult saloon keepers as to remedies for their ills, tells an amazing story of ignorance and credulity. For these professors of hygiene, the publicans, themselves steadily die off like victims of a perennial plague.

If the drink habit is on the increase among printers in England, it may with some certainty be affirmed that it is on the decrease in America. The typecasting machine, no less than all other costly and intricate machinery, requires its operators to be sober and otherwise at their best in body and mind. The machine has also greatly diminished the ranks of the "tourists," that element in the craft most conspicuous in maintaining traditions of a reckless and convivial manner of life. Transit by electricity has enabled many a night hand to get what in horse-car days was impossible, — a dwelling place in the suburbs, where both journeyman and apprentice find social pleasures dissociated from drinking resorts. To-day among American printers more men than ever before are avoiding the drink habit and are quietly influencing others to do likewise. In voicing a sentiment against strong drink one can feel that he is moving with the tide and attacking a diminishing evil. Yet it is still an evil, and invites every blow that can be dealt to it.

On the road to sobriety taken by the young printer personal cleanliness becomes the care first in importance. Next comes eating. The young printer in fair health, working during the day, can practice the plain dietetic rules generally laid down by medical men. . . . The morning newspaper printer whose stomach is about normal may take food four times a day to advantage, as it will lessen his inclination for stimulating drink. Unavoidably, he must go to work after his dinner, the evening meal and the heaviest of the four. The other three meals may be light: breakfast on rising, a full meal; a fruit luncheon at eleven o'clock or midnight; and on reaching home, about four in the morning, something easily digestible, such as hot apple sauce with a piece of bread. Under this regimen the stomach will never become so empty as to bring on weak spells. It is when he is hot, tired, and languid that even the sober compositor feels that a drink might do him good.

The linotype operator, the proof reader, or the compositor not on his feet constantly during the working hours ought to walk home in all kinds of weather if he lives within two or even three miles of the office. A good walk after work will make him breathe deeply, put his blood in active circulation, and benefit the whole inner man. It will "help digestion," "purify the blood," "strengthen the muscles," and "throw off waste products," as the writers of medical advertisements say of their nostrums. Moreover, walking just before going to bed is a prime promoter of sleep.

Sound sleep is necessary to health. He who shuns overwork, eats regularly, takes no strong drink, and avoids harmful food is well on the way to find sleep, if this is possible amid his home surroundings. The morning newspaper printer is at the mercy of day noises, for which there is no prevention. Still, he should sleep with his bedroom windows open. Some night hands have their shades up daytime and yet sleep in comfort blindfold. Regular rest brings regular sleep, if this can be brought at all. But "snub sleep, and she turns away."

Beware of the man who offers you drugs. "Take a little rye whisky," advises the bartender, or it may be beer or brandy. "Take a bottle of this," advises the druggist, handing out the product of a liberal advertiser and profit payer. "Take this prescription for your catarrh," advises the physician, substituting medicine for hygiene. Ninety per cent of the printers swallowing the doses proffered them would be the better for throwing the stuff away, for they would avoid the "after effects" of alcohol, opium, and mistaken local treatment.

But after all the real trouble is that one cannot ordinarily interest most men even in their own health until it is gone. That health should be a subject of daily consideration, especially in connection with food, clothing, workshop, dwelling place, and length of workday, most men have no more conception than children. Many are middle-aged before they know how to take a drink of water; they are not aware that what they call "thirst" in summer or in an overheated room is often no more than a hot throat and mouth, and may be relieved by rinsing and gargling with cold water, perhaps without swallowing a drop.

Usually he who passes unscathed amid conditions killing to others moves blithely along, his mind occupied with affairs of his own. Not until he himself is stricken does the individual who is careless bestir himself. Circumstances detrimental only to the weaker call forth no protest from the stronger. "We're not bothered by any draughts," say the majority to the feeble men who are chilled and want the windows closed. And the shielded care little for the exposed. "There's no lead poisoning in printing offices nowadays," oracularly said a daily newspaper managing editor in my presence; "linotype matter is nearly all antimony and has only a trace of lead," — impressions he might have corrected by consulting the office reference books or inquiry at the type foundry. Moreover, he but substituted one poison for another, for working up antimony is classed by the faculty as a dangerous occupation.

To pass now from the sphere of individual effort to that of collective activity, What can the union do for the health of its members? Briefly, it may:

First. Bring printing offices up to the standards of the Board of Health.

Second. Take sides against alcohol.

Third. Enlist employers in improving printing office conditions.

Fourth. Assume a guardian's protection over helpless members.

Fifth. Stop speeding and overtime at health limits.

Sixth. Continue to shorten the workday.

Justification of the last two measures is plain. There is a limit to the compositor's power of turning out a "string." Every hour added to his day's work after he is thoroughly fatigued is an injury to his health. Where conditions are so unwholesome as in the printing trade it is the right and duty of men to avoid excesses of toil as they would serious excesses of any other sort. The day when printers have natural and reasonable hours will be shown when apprentices enjoy a vigorous growth, when consumption is not a frequent occupational effect, when the proportion of the men predisposed to drink is reduced to the general mean, and when, no less than in healthful pursuits, the average term of life will rise from forty-two years, as it is at present, to half again that age.

In considering the various steps the union may adopt to promote the health of its members, it becomes plain that the first and most promising is to establish the eight-hour workday. Whatever else may be desirable, that object is feasible.

In the large cities the printer must generally rise early and travel far to reach the printing office district from the modest neighborhood to which high rents have driven his family; in New York perhaps thousands in our trade spend two hours a day moving to and fro between office and home. It is the time so consumed that stands in the way of the printer's self-care in many respects. He neglects a cold because he has no time to visit a doctor unless he takes a day off; he lays aside books or papers that he knows are of importance to him and which he never finds time to read; he puts off family matters that need his attention and suffers afterward from their neglect; he fails to take hold of the question of office sanitation because of his hurry to get away and be home at the expected hour. At work he is nowadays expected to be capable of rushing. In some offices rush is the rule. There the man's nerves are racked in nine hours. Machine operating will run him down in less time. With his mind bent on his task while in the office and both body and mind in a state of fatigue in his off hours, he feels that he has hardly opportunity to think. It is certain he cannot make the best of his mental or physical powers. The recreation of his Sundays and holidays can come only after he has performed necessary tasks at home. He may entertain many plans for self-advancement, all to be postponed until he can find time to begin. He may feel he is standing still, only to rejoice, however, that he is not going backward.

. . . The introduction of the machines in the trade was mastered by the union, else we might in many towns see them now operated by girls working ten hours a day. Science and labor organized have herein released the daily newspaper compositors from trade customs little better than slavish. When I was nineteen years of age, in 1867, at a union meeting in Leavenworth, Kansas, the president called upon me, as "the youngest statesman ever seen on the floor," to make a speech. I had within that year been introduced to the morning newspaper system of work then prevailing west of the Mississippi. Composition began at two o'clock in the afternoon and continued three hours; with a second start at seven it kept up, with waiting breaks, until three or later next morning. Distribution began at noon or before and was resorted to during the waits. The working day thus dragged along through fourteen hours or more. In response to the president's invitation I managed to say above a whisper that I should like to see our workday on the newspapers brought down to ten hours, like the rest of the world about us. My words were followed with the outbreak of laughter that is evoked on hearing mention of the impossible. But to-day morning newspaper compositors usually work only eight hours. Some work seven.

The coming four decades may see changes in the trade almost equally striking. Up to the present time unionism in its formative period has perforce paid most attention to preventing a fall in wages and to shortening the workday, the latter largely on economic grounds. In the future, while pursuing these essential purposes, I believe the collective printers will also systematically set about defending their health.

In time the reformed printery will surely come. The building will be designed for a printing office, and not be a structure condemned for all other purposes. Neither will it be a boastful new edifice with every modern improvement except where the printers work. The composing room ceilings will be fourteen to twenty feet high. The walls will be of a cheerful neutral tint. The floors will be swept daily during the absence of the force. The semicivilized hands who still spit will use spittoons ; there will be no sputum on the floor. Mechanical fans will blow out the floating dust; ventilating tubes will run from both floor and ceiling. Type cases will pass under the bellows often. Every man, possessed of his own locker, will wear while at work a suit of clothes designed for the office. The wash rooms, tile laid, will have the appointments of a good hotel. Cases and linotype machines will be ranged out of draughts and so as to give left-hand window lights, and where artificial illumination is used it will be electricity, with the lamp shades tinted, the outer side green and the inner white. Press and stereotype rooms will be separate from the composing room. To the proof readers will be assigned, not stuffy dens or cubby-holes, but spacious private offices. Work in such printing offices will proceed with the joyful drive natural to well-fed, happy, healthy, full-grown men. On the street the apprentices will look like college athletes, the journeymen like prosperous business men. Why not? Many printers so appear now. The office cat will wax fat. The entire force will work but six hours. Wages, let us hope, will be one dollar an hour.

J. W. SULLIVAN.

TYPOGRAPHICAL UNION No. 6, NEW YORK.

XXI

HOURS OF LABOR[1]

Effects of Reductions in Hours

A large amount of testimony has been taken by the Industrial Commission regarding the movement for fewer hours of labor, and the effects of reductions in hours upon production and upon the wages and conditions of workmen and their families. It is brought out that in nearly all occupations an increasing strain and intensity of labor is required by modern methods of production. Trade unions have generally been compelled to abandon their restrictions upon the quantity of work that a man shall turn out. The introduction of machinery and the division of labor have made it possible to increase greatly the speed of the individual workman. This intensity varies in different occupations. In glass blowing payment by the piece and unlimited output have resulted in peculiarly exhausting efforts. The glass-bottle blower, working eight and a half hours, says the secretary of the union, makes double the number of bottles, but his period of usefulness is ten years shorter than it was twenty years ago. In Europe, as formerly in this country, a man can blow glass up to sixty years of age; now in America he cannot work after he is fifty or fifty-five. Machinery operates in some cases to increase the intensity of labor, as in the boot and shoe factories, where the operator is required to handle thousands of pieces in a day and to guide them through the machines. The testimony of a representative of the Cotton Weavers' Association shows this increasing strain of work. He says:

Anybody who works in the mills now knows it is not like what it was twenty-five or thirty years ago, because the speed of the machinery

[1] From Final Report of the U. S. Industrial Commission, Vol. XIX, 1901, pp. 763–793.

has been increased to such an extent, and they have to keep up with it. In some mills in this city, and probably in other cities in this state, the operative is compelled to turn off so much production per week, and if the production does not come up to the point, he or she is discharged. There was a time when that was not the case. They took their sewing and their knitting along, and there was no anxiety about how much work they could get off, but it is not so now. Now they work from the time they go in until they come out. You can see them going to-morrow morning at ten minutes past six, and they will not come out until six to-morrow night.

The intensity of exertion operates to a less degree in work on other classes of machinery, where the feeding is nearly automatic. Even where machinery has not been introduced, as in the case of bricklayers and carpenters, there has come about in the larger cities a more minute division of labor, so that one workman is occupied continuously on one kind of work, in which he acquires great speed.

It is certain that any programme for reducing this intensity of exertion must fail. The entire tendency of industry is in the direction of an increased exertion. Any restrictions on output must work to the disadvantage of American industry, and the employers are often right in their demand, usually successful, that such restrictions be abandoned. This being true, there is but one alternative if the working population is to be protected in its health and trade longevity, namely, a reduction of the hours of labor.

This increased intensity of exertion is not found to so great an extent in farm labor. Nevertheless, testimony before the commission shows that there has been a reduction in the Northern states in the hours of labor on farms, except in the seasons of harvesting. In the case of farm labor there is usually a longer period of rest in the middle of the day, which in the South often runs as high as two hours. This, of course, is a relief to the severity of the work, although it subtracts from the hours of leisure at the beginning and the end of the day.

A reduction in hours in both manufactures and agriculture has accompanied a remarkable increase in the use of machinery and the division of labor, and on this account it is often impossible to measure the effect of a reduction of hours on the quantity of output. It might be presumed that when paid by the day the workman would not increase his output per hour with the shorter day as much as when paid by the piece. But this is not borne out by the testimony. The representative of a silk factory, indeed, holds that when employees are paid by the day the output in nine hours might equal that in ten in some departments, as the weaving department, though not in the spinning department; this might also be true where piece wages are paid instead of time wages. He says:

Where machinery comes in as a heavy element a spindle is a spindle, and the more minutes it runs in a day the more work it will turn off. It cannot go any more in one minute than another, but it runs straight ahead, whereas in weaving the element of personality comes in. One has the knack of keeping his threads in straight, and another is careless and has to stop and mend them and lose ten or fifteen minutes' time. A really good weaver will get off a great many more yards than a poor one on the same machine, whereas a spindle is a fixed quantity and the more hours it runs the more work it does.

[Weavers] are paid by the yard, whereas the spinners are paid by the day. They get day wages and they have no particular incentive to hustle; so long as they keep their ends up and keep the spinning machine going they are doing their duty. . . . There is little if any objection on the part of the hands to working overtime; you cannot keep it up long; they get tired of it after a while, but for two or three months they rather welcome the change.

This witness had not actually tested the nine-hour day, but spoke from his judgment of the probabilities. Another witness, a representative of a large drop-forge establishment, after three months' experience with the nine-hour day, testified that there is a slightly larger average daily output than there was for the ten-hour day in both day work and piecework, though in every other respect work was done under similar conditions. This has not been due to the fact that methods were lax previously, for there was rigid supervision under the ten-hour system. A part of the gain has been made by reason of the fact that under the nine-hour system the men go promptly to work on the minute and work up to the very close of the day; also because a man can work normally without pushing himself at a higher rate of speed for nine hours than he can for ten. The fundamental reason, according to this witness, for the keeping up of the amount of production is to be found in the spirit of the men themselves. If the machines were operated at the highest rate of speed, were in perfect condition, and were continuously fed, a workman could not maintain his output at the same amount, if the hours of labor were shortened; but these perfect conditions are rarely if ever found. It cannot be demonstrated mathematically just how it happens that a man can produce as much in nine hours as he formerly could in ten, but as a matter of fact it has been the experience of almost every manufacturer, says this witness, that "a man can and will and does do more the moment he is justly and fairly and liberally treated."

It is true also that the higher the wages and the fewer the hours the greater is the pressure upon the employer to substitute labor-saving devices and to be more careful in his selection of high-grade workmen. No doubt it is true that a given automatic machine will not often run faster per hour in eight hours than in ten, but industry has by no means reached the limit of invention. Invention will cease only when the employer ceases to adopt new labor-saving machinery, and every reduction in hours and rise in wages keeps the employer further and further away from that sluggish policy. While a particular machine will not go faster in eight hours than in ten, the substitute for that machine which the eight-hour day presses upon the employer to adopt will go faster. Fewer hours have in this way an indirect as well as a direct compensating effect. Not only do they make it possible for the workman to keep up his intensity of personal exertion during each hour of the day and to work more days at a high rate of speed, but they cause the employer to economize his labor at every point and to improve its quality by better selection. One advantage to the employer in fewer hours is the smaller number of breakages and injuries to machinery, owing to more alert attention on the part of the workmen. For the same reason it is often true that the quality of the work is better.

This pressure upon the employees accounts in part for the greatly increased use of machinery and the division of labor in the more highly skilled occupations. A representative of the building trades who testified before the Commission maintained that the lessening of the number of hours made the erection of buildings somewhat more expensive; a contractor stated that it had enabled employers to get better men and better work than under the long workday, and that they do more proportionately in eight hours than they did formerly in nine; also that through invention and the introduction of machinery buildings are now put up as cheaply as they were in 1872 and 1873, when the hours were ten a day. A representative of the Chicago Bridge and Structural Iron Workers' Union holds that the eight-hour day has so increased the efficiency of the laborer that there is actually more work done in eight hours than was formerly done in ten.

A boiler manufacturer who has adopted the eight-hour day testifies that he does not think his men do as much in eight hours as they did in nine, taking one day as the basis of comparison; but that at the end of the year he believes he would find that they had done just as much as they did when they were working an hour longer. One condition necessary to bring about this result is that he is careful to select in his employment the best grade of men and to treat them fairly. A manufacturer of mining machinery holds that it is to the interest of the manufacturer to employ his men only eight hours, since he gets better services out of the men. Formerly, when the hours of machinists were reduced from twelve to ten, and again when they were reduced from ten to nine, the same alarming predictions were made as now when it is proposed to reduce them from nine to eight; yet the inventions in machinery have made it possible for manufacturers to reduce their hours and still make as much money as they did formerly in the longer workday. This witness holds that the eight hours in this industry are needed not so much to relieve the men of severe exertion as because a better-educated man is required to do the work.

Representatives of the machinists' organization do not maintain that a reduction in hours will not immediately reduce the output; in fact, their leading argument for fewer hours is not the severe physical exertion of machinists, but the larger opportunities for work for the unemployed, whose number is now increased by the overproduction consequent on increased efficiency of labor and labor-saving machinery. They declare, however, that the improvements in machinery in this country and the energy of the workmen enable them to produce twice as much as the corresponding English workmen, and a still larger amount as compared with the German. In this way, gradually, the manufacturer overcomes the increased cost of reduced hours.

The eight-hour day in the sheet-steel mills was brought about without difficulty, owing to the economy of adopting three shifts of eight hours each. Prior to 1884 there were two shifts working ten hours, and between turns the furnaces lay idle with coal in them and had to be kept hot until the next set came on. The experiment was tried of increasing the speed and reducing the hours, introducing three shifts; and to-day three shifts are working in all these mills, each making nine instead of seven heats, as was formerly done in the ten-hour day.

Reduction of Hours in Mining [1]

The most important instance in recent years of the adoption of the eight-hour working day has occurred in the bituminous coal mining industry. The strike of 1897 secured in the bituminous mines of the four leading eastern coal states — Illinois, Indiana, Ohio, and Pennsylvania — the eight-hour day, and a similar reduction has been obtained in western states. In Utah the eight-hour day was secured in 1896 by action of the legislature by a law applying to all mines and smelters. The difference in the methods by which this reduction was secured in the two cases adds interest to a comparison of the results which followed.

[1] See testimony on this subject in Reports of the Industrial Commission, Vol. XII.

In Utah the operators and employers did not oppose the legislation at the time of its enactment, largely because they thought it might be the means of keeping down unions and strikes and disturbances among the employees. This object has apparently been obtained, since there are no active unions in the state. A similar law was enacted in Colorado in 1899, but was declared unconstitutional by the state court. At the same time a number of operators continued upon the eight-hour basis even after the law was declared unconstitutional.

It should be noted that the reduction of hours in the bituminous coal mines has not been strictly a reduction from ten hours to eight, since under the eight-hour rule a miner is required to be at his working place when the eight hours begin and when the eight hours end, and lunch time is taken from the miner's time rather than from the employer's time ; whereas formerly the ten hours included the time spent in going from the mouth of the pit to and from the face of the coal. In the Pennsylvania district the period is nine hours instead of eight, but includes the time spent in going to and from the mouth of the pit. Strictly speaking, the reduction is more nearly from ten hours a day to nine than from ten hours to eight. In Utah, however, in the case of the smelting works the reduction is much more extreme, the hours, formerly twelve per day, being reduced to eight. This is a reduction of $33\frac{1}{3}$ per cent in the time, and would make necessary an increase in the working force of 50 per cent, provided there were no increase in efficiency.

There is a general agreement that the fewer hours in the coal mines have increased the energy of the workmen, and that there has been little or no decrease in the amount of work turned out during the day. The men are stimulated "to do a good honest eight hours' work"; the foremen do not find them asleep, as they used to, or lounging around or smoking.

The effect upon the efficiency of the workmen varies, however, with different occupations. While it is generally agreed that the miner does as much work in eight hours as he formerly did in ten, it is held by a few witnesses that this is not true of the furnace men in the smelters, to which the laws of Utah and Colorado applied. The furnace can take only so much material an hour, and the furnace men can do no more work on that account. Another witness, however, asserted that the reduction of $33\frac{1}{3}$ per cent in the hours of labor of smelter employees, which would be expected to require an employment of 50 per cent more men, absorbed only 30 per cent more men and, combined with the reduction in wages of about 23 per cent on the basis of a day's work, resulted in a net increase in the cost of labor of about 10 per cent. The table of wages and hours submitted by this witness is here given in full, to which are added computations showing the wages per hour, the per cent of increase per hour, and the per cent of decrease per day in those wages following the enforcement of the eight-hour law of June 1, 1896. It shows reductions in the pay per day of 11 to $33\frac{1}{3}$ per cent, with increases in the pay per hour of 11 to $33\frac{1}{3}$ per cent.

RATES OF WAGES, HANAUER SMELTING WORKS, UTAH

Occupation	After 10 per cent Reduction, Jan. 1, 1894	Under 8-hour Law, June 1, 1896	After 10 per cent Reduction, 1894	Under 8-hour Law	Per cent Increase per Hour	Per cent Decrease per Day
			Cents per hour	*Cents per hour*		
Crushermen	$2.70 per 12 hours	$2.40 per 8 hours	22.5	30.0	$33\frac{1}{3}$	$11\frac{1}{9}$
Roast firemen	$2.25 per 12 hours	$1.66 per 8 hours	18.7	21.7	$10\frac{2}{3}$	$26\frac{2}{9}$
Roast helpers	$2.25 per 12 hours	$1.50 per 8 hours	18.7	18.7	None	$33\frac{1}{3}$
Blast furnace feeders	$2.70 per 12 hours	$2.00 per 8 hours	22.5	17.5	$20\frac{6}{7}$	25
Furnacemen	$2.70 per 12 hours	$2.00 per 8 hours	22.5	17.5	$20\frac{6}{7}$	25
Furnace helpers	$2.25 per 12 hours	$1.50 per 8 hours	18.7	18.7	None	$33\frac{1}{3}$
Laborers	$1.575 per 10 hours	$1.40 per 8 hours	15.7	17.5	11+	11+
Suppliers	$2.025 per 12 hours	$1.50 per 8 hours	16.8	18.7	11+	26
Teamsters	$2.25 per 10 hours	$2.25 per 10 hours	22.5	22.5	None	None
Night foreman	$4.05 per 12 hours	$3.25 per 8 hours	36.2	40.6	12	20
Day foreman	$144 per month	$144 per month				
Blacksmith	$4.00 per 10 hours	$4.00 per 10 hours	40.0	40.0	None	None
Blacksmith helpers	$2.25 per 10 hours	$1.75 per 10 hours	22.5	17.5	$20\frac{6}{7}$	25
Dump foreman	$2.25 per 10 hours	$2.25 per 10 hours	22.5	22.5	None	None

One witness states that with common labor under the Utah law there is very little difference in the amount of work accomplished; but others maintain that the greater energy applies throughout all employments of a manual character.

In some of the metal mines of Utah and Colorado three shifts have been introduced instead of two shifts of ten hours each. The mine that works eight hours can produce more than one which works ten hours, not only because the men do as much in eight as in ten hours, but also because under the ten-hour system the mine is idle four hours out of the twenty-four; whereas under the eight-hour system one shift takes up the tools at the moment when the preceding shift lays them down, and no time is lost. It is contended by one witness that the system of shifts is impracticable in the bituminous coal mines. The loss occurs in operating the tipple at which the coal is loaded on the outside. It is held that where two hundred or three hundred men are employed the day shift and night shift cannot be successfully introduced, because the tipple cannot be operated at night. On this account this witness claims that the operator endures a loss through the eight-hour day, since he loses two hours in the use of his machinery.

On the other hand, an operator in the Massillon district of Ohio states that where a mine is prepared to take care of the coal a miner can produce as much in the eight hours as he could before in the eight and a half or nine hours, because formerly during a large part of this time he was waiting for cars, and because where the equipment of the mines has been improved and the coal is handled promptly outside there is not much difference in the output.

While the introduction of machinery in bituminous coal mining has for some time been advancing, the greatest advances have occurred in the past four years, following the time when the eight-hour day was introduced. The number of tons mined by machines in the entire United States in 1891 was 6,211,732; this had increased under the ten-hour system to 22,649,220 in 1897, an increase of 16,000,000 tons in six years. On the other hand, from 1897 to 1900, a period of three years under the eight-hour system, the number of tons mined by machines rose to 52,790,523, an increase of 30,000,000 tons. The proportion of the output mined by machines increased from 6.66 per cent in 1891 to 16.19 per cent in 1897, and then to 25.15 per cent in 1900. It is doubtless true that the use of machines would have increased whether or not the eight-hour day had been introduced, and it cannot be shown statistically that the fewer hours have stimulated the introduction of machinery; but individual witnesses who have appeared before the Commission have asserted this to be the fact, and the large increase in machine mining seems to substantiate the claim. The two factors — increased energy on the part of the employees and increased economy on the part of the employer — have certainly in the coal mining industry maintained a daily output equal to that which existed before the eight-hour day was introduced. This is shown in the reports of the United States Geological Survey and of the Illinois Commissioner of Labor on the production of coal for the six years from 1895 to 1900. During the two years 1895 and 1896, under the ten-hour system, the average output per workingman per day was 2.9 and 2.72 tons; while in 1897, during the latter three months of which the eight-hour day prevailed, the average output per man was 3.03 tons per day; and for 1898, 1899, and 1900, three years of the eight-hour day in the majority of the coal mines, the average output ranged from 2.98 to 3.09 tons. Each year of the eight-hour day shows for the country as a whole a larger output per day for each workman than the highest output of the ten-hour day.

Individual states such as Ohio and Pennsylvania, where there has been a great increase in machinery and where since 1897 the eight-hour day is universal, show an increased output per day per man. But there is one state, Illinois, where the proportion of coal mined by machines has remained fairly constant, standing at 19.57 per cent in 1896, increasing to 24.9 per cent in 1899, and falling to 19.73 per cent in 1900. In this state the highest output per day for each workman was in 1897, when it reached 3.36 tons. This was a year when the mines were operated part of the time ten hours a day and part of the time eight. The ten-hour years (1894–1896) show an average output per day for each employee of 2.53 to 3 tons, while the eight-hour years (1898–1900) show an average of 3.11 to 3.21 tons. This increase must be ascribed solely to the increased energy and promptness of the workmen, since, as already stated, the proportion of coal mined by machinery in that state has remained constant.

In the case of Utah, where the law went into effect in June, 1896, there is for the four complete years of the eight-hour day (1897–1900), an output per day of 3.54 to 3.99 tons and for the three ten-hour years (1894, 1895, and 1896), an output of 3.05 to 3.47 tons.

These reports bring statistical evidence to support the testimony of witnesses before the Industrial Commission that in the industry of coal mining the shorter working day has increased the efficiency of both the workman and the management. This being so, it follows that the shorter working day has not increased the amount of employment of miners, and that the increase which has actually occurred in the number of days worked is to be ascribed solely to the improved industrial conditions of the country and not to the reduction of hours. It is true, as stated by one witness, that the shorter working day makes it possible for the individual workman, under such arduous conditions as those of smelting works, to work a larger number of days each month. In the smelting works of Utah, already referred to, the men were able to work under the twelve-hour system an average of only twenty-four days a month, but with the shorter hours they were able to increase their average number of days to nearly thirty. Plainly a change of this kind, to the extent that the workman is able to put in more time, does not widen the opportunities for the absorption of the unemployed. On the other hand, the fact that the operation of the smelting furnaces cannot be greatly speeded does increase the number of employees required for a given output, though not proportionately to the decrease in hours. . . .

Foreign Competition and Reduction in Hours

Lack of uniformity in the hours of labor is burdensome only to those employers who are in the same competitive field. This may be a very limited field, as in the building trades, or it may cover the entire area of the United States, as in most manufacturing industries, or it may reach to foreign lands. Competition with foreign manufacturers, where the hours are longer, is often advanced as an argument against reduction of hours in American industries. A manufacturer of machinery [1] contends that foreign competition, especially competition with Germany and Belgium, where men work low wages and turn out good material during a long workday, makes it impossible to reduce the hours from ten to nine in this country. His objection is based upon the large amount of capital invested in machinery which he cannot afford to keep idle a tenth of the normal time. At the present time the industries of the United States stand well toward the front in the movement for fewer hours, being only less advanced than Great Britain and the colonies of Australasia. While it is impossible to state concisely for different countries the average hours of labor, it is possible to compare countries as regards what might be designated as the prevailing hours in the industries engaged in international competition. From the standpoint of competition, the eight-hour day in Australia has little significance, since the industries of those colonies which affect the world's market are mainly agriculture and stock raising. Great Britain, however, is our severest industrial competitor, with the exception in some industries of France and Germany. At the present time in Great Britain the hours of work per week in factories are quite generally 53; that is, 9½ hours a day, with a Saturday half holiday. The miners have for some years enjoyed a workday not exceeding 8 hours. Compared with Great Britain, therefore, the United States, with the prevailing average of about 9½ hours a day, or 57 a week,[2] has not yet reached the point where foreign competition can be said to be an important consideration as regards further reduction of hours. The recent reduction in the machinery industries to 9 hours per day brings this country more nearly to the level which Great Britain has held in that industry for thirty years; but in other large industries, like

[1] Reports of the Industrial Commission, Vol. VIII, p. 7.
[2] Reports of the Industrial Commission, Vol. VII, p. 622.

that of textiles, there still remains a difference of 5 hours in Massachusetts to 15 hours in the South in excess of the working week of the British workman. On the continent of Europe the workday is longer than in either Great Britain or the United States, ranging from 10 to 12 hours a day in Germany, from 8 to 13½ in Hungary, from 10 to 12 in Spain, from 14 to 16 in Russia (except in iron and steel works, where in some occupations the 8-hour day prevails); in Austria the workday is 11 hours. Yet these countries, with their long workdays, are less able to compete with the United States than is Great Britain. A reduction to 9 hours per day in this country would be necessary in order to reach the British level. A further reduction below 9 hours would be necessary in order to subject American industries to a disadvantage in competition with British manufacturers, who at present are our strongest foreign competitors.

While foreign competition is a matter of moment in considering the reduction of hours in American industries, it is questionable whether it has really as great weight as the competition of different states in the American Union among themselves. There is one advantage which the American workmen have in the matter of foreign competition which does not hold in respect to the more backward states of the American Union, namely, the protective tariff. Whereas a single state with advanced labor legislation cannot protect itself against the cheap labor and long workday of another state, the entire Union is able through the protective tariff to restrict the competition of the longer workdays and lower wages of European and Asiatic labor, and thus to make it possible to raise the level of wages and to reduce the limit of hours to the furthest extent that domestic competition will permit. It is possible, indeed, that an extreme reduction of hours, while not a menace to American industry from the side of the importation of cheap products, might nevertheless restrict the sales of American products abroad in competition with foreign products. While the extension of our foreign trade is a matter to be cultivated and promoted, it does not follow that this should be encouraged if it requires low wages and a long workday for American workmen. . . .

SHORTER WORKDAYS THROUGH LABOR ORGANIZATION

In the absence of legislation the only effective means of securing a reduction of hours is through labor organization. This is, of course, the method by which in recent years the most significant and important reductions in the United States have been secured. The concentration of effort on this point for the past fifteen years by the American Federation of Labor has already accomplished notable results. The general effort, beginning in 1886, is believed to have reduced the day's labor of the working people of the United States by fully one hour. Where the hours had been twelve, they were reduced to eleven; where they had been eleven, they were reduced to ten.[1]

. . . The reports of the New York Bureau of Labor Statistics since 1891 have contained complete investigations of the hours of labor of organized workmen in that state. The following summary, prepared by the commissioner,[2] shows the changes in the hours which have taken place.

The number of employees fluctuated between 186,003 in 1891 and 407,235 in 1899, a growth partly natural and partly due to an increasing number of establishments reporting. The results may be summarized as follows:

PROPORTION OF EMPLOYEES WORKING THE SPECIFIED HOURS PER DAY (1891–1899)

	1891	1892	1893	1894	1895	1896	1897	1898	1899
8 hours or less	9.3%	9.0%	10.7%	14.4%	11.9%	9.4%	9.7%	8.2%	8.1%
9 hours . . .	16.6	16.5	18.1	17.8	17.9	20.3	20.9	22.2	22.1
10 hours . .	72.2	72.5	69.2	65.1	67.9	66.6	65.5	65.8	66.1
Over 10 hours	1.9	2.0	2.0	2.7	2.3	3.7	3.9	3.8	3.7
Total . . .	100.0%	100.0%	100.0%	100.0%	100.0%	100.0%	100.0%	100.0%	100.0%

While the proportion of employees working 8 hours or less has slightly decreased and that of employees working more than 10 hours

[1] Reports of the Industrial Commission, Vol. VII, p. 623.

[2] The data on which this summary is based are found in the report of the New York Bureau of Labor Statistics for 1900.

has slightly increased, the important change has been the growth of the 9-hour group at the expense of the 10-hour group; while in 1891 72.2 per cent of the employees were working 10 hours a day, in 1899 the proportion was only 66.1, and in the same period the percentage of 9-hour workers increased from 16.6 to 22.1 per cent. It is worthy of note that the proportion working short hours (not more than 8) increased temporarily in the years of depression (1893–1897).

Very considerable differences appear between New York City and the remaining portion of the state, as shown by the following table:

	New York City				Remainder of the State			
	1896	1897	1898	1899	1896	1897	1898	1899
8 hours or less	12.6%	13.7%	12.3%	13.1%	6.8%	6.5%	4.9%	4.1%
9 hours	31.8	31.9	34.0	36.3	11.3	12.0	12.6	10.3
10 hours	53.1	51.3	50.6	48.0	77.2	77.0	78.0	81.0
Over 10 hours	2.5	3.1	3.1	2.6	4.7	4.5	4.5	4.6
Total	100.0%	100.0%	100.0%	100.0%	100.0%	100.0%	100.0%	100.0%

Not only do the proportions in the two parts of the state differ in each year, but the tendencies throughout the period are different. While in the metropolis the relative strength of the 10-hour group has diminished in favor of 9-hour work, in the interior towns the 10-hour day has been gaining upon the 9-hour and 8-hour days. In 1899 almost exactly one half of the employees of metropolitan establishments worked 9 hours a day or less, while the corresponding percentage for the remainder of the state was 14.4. The differences, moreover, exist in nearly every industry.

The contrasts in each group are decidedly noticeable and furnish a conspicuous illustration of the power of organized labor. Although some industries are not strongly organized in New York City, — as textiles, for example, — the very fact that 8 or 9 hours is accepted as the limit of their day's toil by the leading workingmen of that city has a natural effect in establishing that as a part of the body of customs, traditions, and habits that go to make up the local standard of life. The figures for Group XII, the building industry, are especially significant; they show that 90 per cent of the New York City work people in those trades work less than 58 hours a week, or 9½ hours a day, as compared with 50 per cent in the other towns of the state.

Returning now to the figures for the entire state for the earliest and latest years of the period 1891 and 1899, we may note that some industries have not shared in the progressive shortening of hours confirmed in the first table.

PERCENTAGE OF EMPLOYEES OF MANUFACTURING ESTABLISHMENTS IN NEW YORK STATE WORKING THE SPECIFIED NUMBER OF HOURS DAILY IN JUNE, 1891 AND 1899

	Group I Stone, Pottery, Glass		Group II Metals, Machinery, etc.		Group III Wood		Group IV Leather, Rubber, etc.	
	1891	1899	1891	1899	1891	1899	1891	1899
8 hours or less	10.6%	16.4%	4.2%	4.8%	0.8%	4.4%	6.6%	1.8%
9 hours	17.1	18.7	10.0	15.7	18.7	16.5	23.8	16.1
10 hours	65.3	58.7	84.8	76.9	79.5	76.9	69.5	82.0
Over 10 hours	7.0	6.2	1.0	2.6	1.0	2.2	0.1	0.1
Total	100.0%	100.0%	100.0%	100.0%	100.0%	100.0%	100.0%	100.0%

	Group V Chemicals, Oils, etc.		Group VI Pulp and Paper		Group VII Printing and Publishing		Group VIII Textiles	
	1891	1899	1891	1899	1891	1899	1891	1899
8 hours or less	8.9%	6.5%	1.7%	0.1%	7.7%	12.8%	4.7%	3.1%
9 hours	25.0	15.3	4.1	0.1	22.2	53.9	8.9	10.5
10 hours	59.2	72.5	65.5	66.3	70.0	32.9	86.3	85.5
Over 10 hours	6.9	5.7	28.7	33.5	0.1	0.4	0.1	0.9
Total	100.0%	100.0%	100.0%	100.0%	100.0%	100.0%	100.0%	100.0%

	Group IX Clothing, Millinery, etc.		Group X Food, Tobacco, Liquors		Group XI Public Utilities		Group XII Building	
	1891	1899	1891	1899	1891	1899	1891	1899
8 hours or less	10.8%	8.4%	36.3%	13.5%	3.1%	12.4%	33.9%	54.4
9 hours	35.3	41.3	17.3	16.8	2.6	1.4	32.6	23.1
10 hours	53.8	50.2	42.0	61.7	75.5	44.2	33.4	21.6
Over 10 hours	0.1	0.1	4.4	8.0	18.8	42.0	0.1	0.9
Total	100.0%	100.0%	100.0%	100.0%	100.0%	100.0%	100.0%	100.0%

There has been an increase in the average working time in the boot and shoe industry (Group IV), in the manufacture of chemicals and the refining of petroleum (Group V), in the paper-making industry. A similar increase in Group X is partly due to the fact that bakeries and breweries, with comparatively long hours, were more strongly represented in 1899 than in 1891, while the reports of cigar factories, with their shorter hours, showed a relatively small increase in the number of employees. One of the noteworthy changes in the way of reduction of hours appears in the printing and publishing industry; whereas 70.1 per cent of the printers worked 10 hours or more in 1891, only 33.3 per cent had those hours in 1899 — and that was before the general nine-hour day was established by agreement between national associations of employers and employees.

It will be noticed that 9667 employees (2.4 per cent of the aggregate number) were reported in 1899 as working regularly more than 70 hours a week. Of these 2153 were workmen in paper mills, a large proportion of which have for several years past been operated 24 hours a day or 72 a week for each if two shifts. A large proportion of the employees of gas companies also work in two shifts of 12 hours each, and the same may be said of stationary engineers and firemen, who are found in nearly all industries, but are especially numerous in breweries. Finally, a considerable number of employees of railway car shops work seven days in the week, thus aggregating 70, 77, or even 84 hours a week.

Legislation governing Hours of Labor

While the efforts of labor organizations in behalf of reasonable reduction of hours are in general to be commended, it is plain that they cannot be expected to reach all classes of labor, nor indeed those most in need of protection in this regard. It has been estimated that labor unions include only 10 or 15 per cent of the wage-earning population. They do not include to any great extent women and children, who in 1890 constituted 20 per cent of the employees in manufactures, and who, on account of physical weakness or immature years, stand in greatest need of reasonable hours. . . .

Legislative regulation of the hours of labor must be considered as supplementary to regulation by private contract and labor organization, to be resorted to where these methods fail and where there is evident reason for the reduction. In England and in America it has generally been held that legislation reducing the number of working hours should apply only to women and minors, and not to men. The latter have been held to be better able to care for themselves and to secure, through organization or otherwise, the improved conditions which they demand. But women and children have been considered weaker in bargaining and more in need of legislative protection. There is a tendency in both countries, however, to depart from this view and to legislate for men as well as for women in the regulation of hours. While such legislation has not as yet been actually enacted in England, it has been adopted in Utah and Wyoming in the case of miners and smelters. With these two exceptions, the legislation of American states, reducing the hours of labor, applies only to women and minors. Where men work in the same factories they generally get the advantage of the shorter workday of the women and children, although this is not always so.

The problem of legislative regulation turns upon three questions: practicability, constitutionality, uniformity.

Practicability. Legislation respecting hours of labor stands upon an entirely different footing from legislation respecting wages. It is practically impossible to devise any legislation which will effectively maintain a minimum rate of wages for any occupation, or for the country at large, even should legislative interference of this kind seem advisable. Secret evasion would quickly nullify such a law. But legislation setting a maximum to the number of hours of employment can be so framed and administered as to prevent evasion. It must be observed, however, that reliance cannot be placed upon prosecution of the employer by the employee. The latter is in a dependent position, and the implied threat of discharge is too heavy a penalty to pay for a doubtful victory in a legal prosecution. Such a prosecution is possible only where the employee is backed by a strong labor organization; and a labor organization strong enough to prosecute an employer under state laws is strong enough to secure its demands without the state law. Legislation is needed only where organization fails. This being so, legislation concerning hours requires the creation of a strong force of factory inspectors. The factory inspector is the public prosecutor of violations of factory laws. The simple provision existing in the laws of Massachusetts, New York, and other states, requiring that the employer shall post in his factory the hours for beginning and quitting work and the interval for the noonday meal, and providing penalties where this notice is not posted, makes it possible for the inspector to discover by his own inspection whether the shop is working overtime or not. With this simple provision, a factory working outside the posted hours is *prima facie* violating the law, and it is not necessary that the factory inspector should call in the employees as witnesses and subject them to the danger of discharge. The inspector, like a police officer, becomes his own witness, with the most conclusive of testimony. Where the legislation respecting hours is evaded, as it undoubtedly is in some cases in New York and other states, it will be found that the defect lies chiefly in the failure to enforce the provision requiring the posting of hours and in the necessity of summoning the employees as witnesses. Sometimes this failure is excused on the ground that the requirement is a mere technicality, and that it would be a petty persecution on the part of the inspector to prosecute for every trifling detail; but in the enforcement of a law of this kind this particular technicality is all important; and if it is intended to enforce the law at all, the posting of the hours is an essential condition of success.

In some occupations, like the manufacture of clothing and notions, it is often possible to evade the short-hour legislation by requiring employees to take work home at night, and where they are not organized they are afraid to refuse. To meet this evasion the provisions in the law of Massachusetts and other states requiring all home workers to have a license, and requiring also that the employer furnish to the factory inspector a list of all his home workers, is the most effective device yet enacted into law. The inspector refuses to grant licenses for home work to those who work in the daytime in the factory, on the ground that they are already working the legal limit and that to take work home at night would be an evasion of the law. Consequently, the inspector, in case of violation, prosecutes the employer, not directly for sending work home at night, but for furnishing work to unlicensed home workers. A prosecution on the former account would require testimony of the home worker, and would result inevitably in connivance and evasion. A prosecution on the latter account requires only careful inspection on the part of the officer.

The foregoing technical details are noticed to show the practicability of legislation regarding hours of labor for factories and mines. It does not follow that such legislation will be practicable for farm labor or for home workers. Its success depends upon the existence of establishments separate from the home. Indeed, legislation of this character is justified mainly by the existence of the factory system, the increased intensity of exertion, the injury to the health of the worker, and the greater profitableness of labor which that system has introduced.

Constitutionality.[1] . . .

Uniformity. The serious defect in legislation regulating the hours of labor in factories is found in the lack of uniformity in the different states. Massachusetts has established the 58-hour week for women and children in factories. The adjoining state of New York places the limit at 60 hours; New Jersey at 55 hours; Pennsylvania at 60 hours; Wisconsin at 48 hours, though permitting contracts for overtime; South Carolina and Georgia at 66 hours; others at 60 hours a week. There are twenty-two states that have no restrictions for adult women, eighteen that have no restrictions for women under twenty-one, and seventeen that have no restrictions on male minors. Utah and Wyoming are the only states that limit the hours of men, and this applies only to workers in smelters and underground mines.

While it is doubtless true that within limits the fewer hours of one state do not place that state at a disadvantage, owing to the greater energy which fewer hours make possible, yet a further reduction by law from the 58 hours of Massachusetts or the 55 hours of New Jersey to, say, 48 hours, as is the

[1] See Chapter XXIII for decisions of courts on this question. — ED.

case in Australia, seems exceedingly difficult to bring about as long as other states retain a maximum as high as 60 or 66 hours and still other states have no restrictions whatever. A greater degree of uniformity of legislation on this point is an urgent requirement. After an experience of seventy years in England and nearly thirty years in Massachusetts, together with the more recent experience of twenty other American states, legislation reducing the hours of women and minors in factories has justified itself as a proper action for any civilized state. It is true that local differences exist in the climate and other conditions, but these should not be considered decisive. Those states which are just now advancing to the position of manufacturing communities might well learn from these examples the lesson that permanent industrial progress cannot be built upon the physical exhaustion of women and children. Factory life brings incidentally new and depressing effects which those whose experience has been wholly agricultural do not appreciate. But the experience of states which have pushed their way from agricultural to manufacturing industries, and have found that their delay in protecting their factory employees has weakened the physical and moral strength of the new generation of working people, would seem to be an experience which the citizens of new manufacturing states should hope to avoid. A reduction in hours has never lessened the working people's ability to compete in the markets of the world. States with shorter workdays actually manufacture their products at a lower cost than states with longer workdays. Several witnesses before the Industrial Commission, both manufacturers and employees, have urged a national law reducing the hours of women and children in factories to a uniform standard. There is evidence that the demand for such a law is growing in strength. But Federal legislation, with the attendant force of Federal factory inspectors, is objectionable. Other countries, even Germany, with its federal form of government, have uniform factory laws covering all parts of the land ; but it has been the pride of the American Commonwealth that except in great emergency no state should be coerced to do that which is either for its own interest or for the interest of other states. This principle is sound, but it cannot be overlooked that those states which profit by their strategic position to hold their sister states below the level of humane self-protection demanded by modern factory conditions are storing up against themselves feelings of resentment and retaliation. It is certainly practicable for any state to bring its hours of labor for women and children in factories down to the standard of 55, set by New Jersey. This standard is near that of our principal competitor, Great Britain. This, at least for the present, should be the standard adopted on its own initiative by every state that enters the ranks of factory production.

Federal Legislation

While in manufactures and mining the regulation of hours belongs to the several states, yet in transportation the interstate character of the industry brings the subject under the powers of Congress. The policy of Congressional action depends upon the need of protecting the traveling public and freight traffic, and the inability of certain classes of employees to organize for their own protection. On account of the nature of train service the hours of railroad employees are necessarily irregular. A certain distance must be covered before the train crew can be released, and the time required may be short, or, under exceptional circumstances, may be exceedingly long. There is, however, a very general tendency of railroad managements to bring the hours of trainmen within reasonable limits, and the ten-hour day is the ideal standard established by agreement for such service. The principal motive actuating the management is the necessity that the trainmen should be wide-awake, and this acts as a protection against unreasonable demands; at the same time, prior to the organization of the railroad unions the workday was much longer than at present. Even now, in the case of the unorganized switchmen, telegraphers, trackmen, and station men, the hours are frequently twelve a day, and in some cases from sunrise to sunset. During the summer, when days are long, trackmen work 14 hours on many roads. In emergencies all these employees are also required to remain on duty much longer than 12 hours.

While it is true that the trainmen are especially responsible for the safety of the traveling public, it is also true, as stated by the president of a leading railroad,[1] that "of the 20,000 names on our pay roll you could pick out very few who do not carry the lives of the passengers in their hands." Telegraph operators occupy a peculiarly responsible position in traffic operations, and it is no uncommon thing for a coroner's jury to ascribe the cause of a railroad wreck to the negligence of a telegraph operator who had been on duty for an excessive number of hours. Railway trackmen are the poorest paid and hardest worked of all employees. They handle heavy material, such as cross-ties and steel rails, and even heavy cars. Both on their own account and on account of the safety of the traveling public, the hours of labor of these unorganized classes of railway employees should be reduced to eight.

The legislation of the several states affecting the hours of employees limits such hours to 10 or 12, and in five states contracts for a longer time are invalid, and a company so contracting is liable to a penalty.[2] The constitutionality of such statutes can now probably be sustained under the decision of the United States Supreme Court on the Utah mining law. Railroad labor, however, is undoubtedly covered by the interstate powers of Congress, and a Federal law regulating the hours of labor would be constitutional. The limitation of continuous runs by engineers or continuous service by telegraph operators or switchmen without a period of sufficient rest, as well as other regulations affecting the surroundings and dangers of the employment, are within the province of Congress. The Industrial Commission has recommended that Congress enact a code covering all the conditions of employment of railroad labor throughout the United States. Such a code would have the advantage of simplifying the conditions throughout the

[1] Reports of the Industrial Commission, Vol. IV, p. 288.

[2] *Ibid.*, Vol. V, pp. 27, 28.

country, and by the force of example would lead the states, it is hoped, to adopt voluntarily the code in cases where Congress cannot properly interfere. This the Commission believes to be one of the most important efforts in the labor interest to which the attention of Congress can possibly be invited.

Sailors and Seamen

On the Great Lakes the hours of seamen are excessive, the men working 12 hours on the schooners, and occasionally as high as 30 hours at a stretch on the steamboats. This includes 24 hours of all kinds of labor, followed by 6 hours steering; they then get 6 hours' rest, and again 6 hours at the wheel. These excessive hours are ascribed to the undermanning of the vessels, which condition, besides requiring many hours, is also unsafe for passengers and property. It is stated that in other countries men are required to stand at the wheel only 2 hours, with 4 hours off, while on the Great Lakes they are required to stand 6 hours, with 6 hours off, and this occurs very often, as stated above, after continuous work for 24 hours.[1] Water transportation comes under the interstate commerce powers of Congress, and the regulation of hours and the requirement of adequate numbers in the crew are matters which Congress is fully competent to deal with.

Hours of Labor on Public Works and Public Contracts[2]

There is one phase of legislation affecting the hours of labor wherein the interests of private employment are not directly affected, namely, the hours of workmen employed directly by the Federal, state, and local governments. These different governments combined are undoubtedly the largest employers

[1] Reports of the Industrial Commission, Vol. IX, pp. 403–408.

[2] See also Hearings of the Committee on Labor, House of Representatives, on Eight-Hour Bill, February 15 to March 29, 1900; February 25 to March 29, 1902.

of labor in the United States, and whatever labor legislation is enacted affecting them has relatively important weight upon the condition of the working people in general. The Federal Government has been the pioneer in reducing the hours of labor of its employees. In 1840, at a time when in private employment 11 or 12 hours was the rule, an order of the President provided for 10 hours in all public employment; and again in 1868, after private employment had reached the standard of 10 hours, Congress reduced the hours for public employees to 8. Even this reduction does not place the manual laborer and artisan in the employment of the Government on the same basis as the clerical and official force, for whom the hours are but 6½ to 7½ a day.

State governments and city authorities have followed the Federal Government in the adoption of the eight-hour day. The first city to introduce this reduction was New York, in 1870. At the present time there are eight or nine states which prescribe the eight-hour day for all labor on public works, whether in the employment of the state or of the local divisions.

There are special reasons in government employment whereby it is possible to advance more rapidly in the reduction of hours than is the case in private employment. The government in the work which it conducts is not subject to foreign or domestic competition; its services are paid from taxes, and it is not compelled to dispose of its products at a market price. For this reason it is free to take broader views of its obligations to its employees than those taken by the private employer. Its action is determined more by the ethical and political standards of the public than by the competitive conditions of industry. In this way the government is able to stand before the industries of the country as a model employer. Undoubtedly the example of the ten-hour day in public employment had some influence in bringing private employment up to that standard, and, again, the lead taken by Congress and by the state and local governments in establishing the eight-hour day has assisted the labor element in securing whatever of that reduction in private employment they have been able to bring about.

Besides the direct employment which the government in its several branches provides, there is a still larger amount of indirect employment on public works, and in the manufacture of goods and material, which is conducted through contractors.. It was not until 1892 that Congress enacted a law which extended the eight-hour day to contractors and subcontractors upon the public works of the United States or the District of Columbia. Later state legislatures have taken this position, the laws on that subject having been enacted mainly in 1899, although the law of Kansas dates from 1891 and that of Colorado from 1894.[1] The efficiency of those laws is not always secured, because there is no provision for their enforcement through a state official. The law in Kansas was a dead letter until in 1898 the legislature placed its enforcement in the hands of the Commissioner of Labor.

It is evident that without the extension of the eight-hour law to public contractors the government is at a disadvantage in a comparison of the costs of production in those enterprises which are operated by its own employees. The extension of the eight-hour law to contractors on public works equalizes the conditions of public and private employment in those branches where work is done partly by the government or municipality and partly by contractors. This discrepancy has, indeed, led to a larger proportionate use of the contract system than was the case before the enactment of the eight-hour law. Even the Federal law of 1892 does not bring contractors up to the level of government employment, since it is defective in the particular that an exception is made in cases of "extraordinary emergency." The character of the emergency is not described, as is usually done in such legislation ; and consequently contractors are accustomed to employ laborers and mechanics for a longer period than eight hours and to certify the extra hours as due to "extraordinary emergency." Undoubtedly, the emergencies contemplated in the act are those only of fire, flood, or military operations, when life and property are endangered. An amendment specifying these classes of emergencies is

[1] Reports of the Industrial Commission, Vol. V, p. 25.

necessary in order that the law of 1892 may bring about the objects intended, and may place contractors on public works on a level with the departments which conduct their work through their own staff of employees. The law, also, is not interpreted in such a way as to regulate the hours of employees at a distance from the actual construction, and on this account, while the eight-hour day may prevail in the erection of a customhouse or post office, the stone may be cut in another state on the nine-hour or ten-hour system.

It is to be noted that the law of 1892 applies only to public works, and not to goods or material furnished to the government. It applies only to such constructions as fortifications, breakwaters, public buildings, and so on. The government is also a purchaser through contract of a large quantity of army and navy equipment, vessels of war, clothing, boots and shoes, and so forth. It is perhaps true that the reasons for applying the eight-hour day to contractors on public works are stronger than those which would apply the same to contractors on goods or material manufactured for the government. It is objected that a law of this kind would require public authorities to trace the material purchased by contractors back to the original manufacturers, and from the original manufacturers back to the raw material extracted from the soil or brought up from the mines. This objection is certainly fatal to a measure which does not make exception of all material purchased upon the open market. It has been decided by the Attorney-General that the act of 1892, providing for eight hours on public works, does not apply to material purchased by contractors, but applies solely to the employees under the immediate direction of such contractors or subcontractors. The same distinction should unquestionably be made in any legislation providing for the eight-hour day upon goods or material manufactured under contract for government use.

More weighty, however, than this objection is that which holds that if manufacturers are compelled to work only eight hours on government work they will be compelled to reduce the hours on private contracts to the same number. Contracts for goods and material are made by establishments manufacturing for the general market, and it would be impossible to separate their government contracts from their private contracts. Doubtless the effect of such legislation would be extensive. It would apply to all vessels of war, all clothing and boots and shoes manufactured for the army, and all army and navy equipment. The probable number of employees affected in these industries cannot be predicted; but it is probable that such legislation would bring about at first a specialization of factories for public work. This might involve somewhat higher prices paid by the government than those paid by private purchasers; but as a practical means for promoting the adoption of eight hours throughout the industries of the country such a measure would unquestionably have wider and more beneficial effect than any other that could be adopted by Congress. Such a bill, reducing the hours of labor on all government contracts to eight hours per day, was introduced in the Fifty-Sixth Congress and passed the House, but failed in the Senate.

XXII

MASSACHUSETTS LABOR LEGISLATION[1]

Economic Effects

Tax on Production. Given this series of laws[2] acting upon manufacturing interests, the first question before the economist is: Have they been a tax upon the productive power of Massachusetts? The laws deal with (1) Child Labor, (2) Hours of Labor for Women and Minors, (3) Sanitation and Safety, (4) The Employment Contract and the Employer's Liability for Injury to Employees, and (5) Wage Payments. Of these we may disregard the expenses imposed by safety and sanitary requirements; for employers themselves recognize such as incumbent upon them, law or no law; while for many years now no complaints of injustice or caprice in the orders of inspectors have been made. It would also be idle calculation from the practical point of view to attempt to place a money value upon the results of restrictions upon child labor, which nevertheless tend to narrow the supply of cheap workers. But the statutes concerning the employer's liability for injury sustained by an employee, the requirement of weekly wage payment, and above all the shortened hours of labor have been loudly denounced as burdensome taxation and deserve careful consideration.

The first two regulations are of minor importance. Under the statute which extends and defines somewhat more broadly

[1] From *Supplement to the Annals, American Academy of Political Science*, January, 1901, pp. 35–78. See also S. N. D. North, "Factory Legislation in the United States," etc., *Bulletin of the National Association of Wool Manufacturers*, Vol. XXV, 1895, pp. 208–271; Webb, The Case for the Factory Acts, 1901 (Great Britain); Hutchins and Harrison, A History of Factory Legislation, 1903.

[2] A review of the laws referred to is found on pages 1 to 35 of the *Supplement*, as cited in preceding footnote.

the common-law principle of employer's liability, it has become very generally the custom to take out a new form of special accident insurance to cover the risk which these more definite obligations impose. This has, therefore, raised the manufacturers' fixed charges by an inconsiderable percentage. The law leaves decisions of fact largely to the jury, and while employers acknowledge the enactment to be commendable, they have had some reason for complaint on account of verdicts rendered more upon grounds of mercy toward the unfortunate than of justice toward the responsible.

As regards the regulation of the method of paying wages, weekly payments have so increased the office work in many establishments that additional clerks have been required to perform it, and the old method of receipt taking has been abandoned as too time consuming. There is advanced also the claim that business concerns are themselves obliged to give long credits on orders received, which make such weekly cash payments on their part decidedly inconvenient, if not actually burdensome.

These expenses appear, however, of but slight consideration when compared with the ever-resisted mandate of shortened hours of labors. The whole battle of the labor movement centers in this issue. On one side stands the claim that the increased efficiency both in labor and management, the higher speed of machinery, and so forth, which are forced upon producers fully compensate — and more than compensate — for the loss of time. To this is opposed the charge that such legislation has already, without corresponding compensation, so taxed Massachusetts' manufacturers that they cannot compete with like industries in other places. Curtailment of hours tends to make fixed charges assume undue proportion; it effectually reduces the volume of machine output.

The facts adducible in support of these conflicting views may be briefly reviewed. The short-hour movement had been long gathering strength before it received legislative recognition in the ten-hour law of 1874. So determined had been the efforts of Fall River unions to secure the concession that many of the mills there, rather than risk warfare at a profitable season, did institute a ten-hour system in 1867, which lived for some twenty-one months. These experiments furnished a few statistics bearing on the issue, which may be summarized as follows:

American Linen Company

1868, 6 wks. 10 hrs. average product, 32.23 yds. a loom *per diem*.
1869, " " 11 " " " 37.14 " " "
Loss due to shorter day 10+ per cent.

Granite Mills

1867, 10 hrs. product, 3861 pieces a week.
1869, 11 " " 4350 " "
1870, 11 " " 4356 " "
Loss due to shorter day 10+ per cent.

Union Mills

1867 (304¾ days) 10 hrs. product, average 36,210 yds. *per diem*.
1869 (208½ ") 11 " " " 39,984 " "
Loss due to shorter day 10+ per cent.

Merchants' Manufacturing Company

5 wks. 10 hrs., 593 hands produced 1,125,000 yds., earned $20,294.
5 " 11 " 486 " " 1,495,351 " " 21,441.90.
11 hrs. running at reduced prices.
Loss due to shorter day 10+ per cent.

Atlantic Mills, Lawrence

First Account.
10-hour system since 1867. Increased speed 5 per cent.
Strict time regulations enforced.
New machinery from time to time.
First two years, product diminished 5 per cent.
1871, stock at a low figure.
Dividend small.[1]

Second Account.
10-hour system since 1867. Increased speed "a little."
"At first" lost 5 per cent.
After 1½ years product "equal to what it had been under 11-hour system."
1871, product as great as under 12-hour system.
Same help, machinery, and class of goods.

[1] M. F. J. Dickinson, "Argument against Ten-Hour Bill," 1871. Hearing before Legislative Labor Committee, p. 17 (pamphlet).

Mr. Dickinson shows no mill conducted on the eleven-hour system in the same class of goods doing any better than the Atlantic Mills.[1]

In the matter of figures employers have the bookkeeper's advantage. The cases here cited do not at all exhaust the list which employers bring forward, whereas I have been able to find only one or two such examples given upon the other side. Nor have I seen these figures anywhere seriously questioned. It is noticeable, however, that the eleven-hour years chosen for comparison were not those which preceded the ten-hour experiment, but in each case those which followed upon it. Such selection might suggest advantages in the later years of such improved machinery or methods as experience had shown to be useful. The margin of difference between the amounts allows some scope for reductions on this score without very materially altering their bearing upon the point at issue. The action of the mill owners was consistent with the figures when, after this experiment had been continued for twenty-two months, they returned to the old hours. The evidence given prevailed to stave off legislative action for several years.

After the passage of the ten-hour law in 1874 we have again a period which ought to furnish some interesting comparative statistics. Although inoperative over the state as a whole, inspectors had some opportunities to note the effects in cases of compliance. In his report for 1878 the Chief of Police inserts an extract from the letter of a Massachusetts mill owner as an example of the results which his department had observed.

> From the means of comparison we have (mills in Massachusetts and Connecticut with equal quality of machinery and the same grade of goods) we find the production of mills per set to be as the hours of labor; that is, a set of machinery running ten hours per day will not turn out more than ten elevenths as many yards of the same grade of goods as one running eleven hours, but rather a small fraction less. . . . There is in Connecticut a saving over Massachusetts

[1] Charles Cowley, "Argument for Petitioners in Ten-Hour Bill," 1871. Hearing before Legislative Labor Committee, p. 5 (pamphlet).

of $2157 per annum, or more than 9 per cent on expenses common to both mills. . . . In mills where longer hours reign there will be a small margin of profit when those of Massachusetts have none or are losing money.

The report goes on to say that a tour in Rhode Island and Connecticut showed manufacturers in these states to be using the most improved machinery and methods eleven hours daily with no apparent injury to the health of the operatives, being happy in their advantage over some Massachusetts competitors. The Chief in his report declares himself fearful of the consequences of the law if thoroughly enforced.

Examining a report a few years later, when efforts to enforce this measure were meeting with decidedly better success, we read: "Results have shown the wisdom of such legislation."[1] And again: "A mass of *facts* had been collected in this and other countries tending to show that no ultimate decrease of production or of profits thereon would follow if the number of hours were lessened; lapse of time has only strengthened these convictions."[2] A case is here also given of an unnamed manufacturer who reduced his time from sixty-six to sixty hours per week and "at the end of six months found his product increased nearly 10 per cent, and the quality of the work done more perfect."

In 1883 the Bureau of Statistics of Labor made a careful study of profits and earnings in Massachusetts, and drew a comparison between the years 1875 and 1880 on these lines.[3] The study concludes:

Examination of the tables shows falling off in the percentage of gross profits in 1880 as compared with 1875. In the state this fall is 7.17 per cent; in Boston, 14.89 per cent; in the state, excluding Boston, 4.91 per cent. In the state in 1880 percentage of stock used had advanced 11.52 per cent; wages had been cut down 4.35 per cent; expenses had increased .02 per cent; and net profits had

[1] Massachusetts Police Report, Inspection, 1882, p. 15.

[2] *Ibid.*, 1887, p. 18.

[3] Although passed in 1874, the ten-hour law was not well in operation until after 1879.

fallen off 7.19 per cent. In other words stock used cost 11.52 per cent more in 1880 than in 1875. To counterbalance this wages were cut down 4.35 per cent and manufacturers lost 7.19 per cent, or 11.54 per cent. If we deduct increase in expenses, .02 per cent, we secure 11.52 per cent as net loss to employers and employees.

Boston stock cost 18.29 per cent more in 1880 than in 1875; of this the employees bore 3.40 per cent, the employers 14.53 per cent, while 36 per cent was gained on expenses.[1]

We must not, of course, make the error of attributing this to short-hour legislation as a chief cause; nor in any event must too great weight be placed upon the testimony of such averages; nevertheless the figures are of interest, as they corroborate other authority.

Continuing the search after evidence, we may add here a few later statements of comparative costs. These are taken after the reduction of hours in 1892 (c. 357) to fifty-eight weekly.

A Rhode Island mill of two thousand looms can produce twenty thousand yards per week more of printed cloth than one in Massachusetts, as the difference between fifty-eight and sixty hours per week.[2]

The Everett Mills have plants both in Massachusetts and Maine. Alike in equipment and grade of product and under identical management, the returns made were as follows:

In Maine, working eleven and a half hours per day, the mills earned a dividend at a time when the Massachusetts branch, working ten hours, was compelled to reorganize. Repeated comparisons all show that longer hours result in proportionally larger earnings.[3]

The Tremont and Suffolk Mills are in very close competition with the Nashua Mills of New Hampshire, and it was affirmed that the increased product of sixty hours per week (over fifty-eight) would mean to the former $50,000 per annum.[4]

[1] Report of Massachusetts Bureau of Labor Statistics. Profits and Earnings, 1883, p. 372.

[2] Quoted from the Boston *Commercial Bulletin*, in *Bulletin of Wool Manufacturers*, September, 1895, p. 264, note.

[3] *Ibid.*, p. 266.

[4] A. S. Covel before Legislative Labor Committee, 1898.

Dividends of the Lowell Manufacturing Company for fifteen years, from 1881 to 1895, have averaged a trifle under 4 per cent. Money could not have been hired at that rate during the period.[1]

Southern mills opened by Northern capital, in several cases as "dependencies" of Massachusetts corporations, earned dividends upon their capital stock during 1897, while the Northern ones failed to do so.[2]

The cotton mills are the chief but not the only complainers. The fifty-eight-hour requirement bears heavily upon smaller, spasmodic trades, such as confectionery, straw plaiting, and millinery. Dealers claim that at holiday seasons and at other times of temporarily increased demand they lose good business orders through inability to fill them in the short hours allowed by law or to get new help for night work. The clause which restricts the making up of time lost to loss within "the same week" (not within seven days) brings pressure and annoyance upon such businesses as laundries, where orders tend to crowd during the first of the week.

I have been unable to find any figures in Massachusetts which oppose these contrary results. The two cases generally cited are the Atlantic Mills already referred to and the Harris Mills, a voluntary experiment in the ten-hour system, at Woonsocket, Rhode Island. The Harris Mills manufactured a high grade of cloth goods which met almost no competition.

The argument in rebuttal, without means of statistical proof, throws doubt on the statements given above. Reference is made to the cases of voluntary reduction to eleven hours in 1853 at Lowell, Lawrence, and Fall River. There, during the eight years which elapsed before the régime became general, no attendant abstraction of capital appeared, but there was a constant growth.[3]

Statement is also made that during the twenty-one months of experiment at Fall River "that city outstripped all competitors."

[1] A. T. Lyman before Legislative Labor Committee, 1898.

[2] See testimony of Mr. Lovering and of A. T. Lyman before Legislative Labor Committee, 1898.

[3] G. E. McNeill, before Labor Committee on repeal of Ten-Hour Bill, 1879, p. 4 (pamphlet).

Again, when an attempt was made in 1879 to repeal the ten-hour law enacted the previous year, action did not proceed from Fall River, "nor Lowell, nor Lawrence, nor Holyoke, nor Chicopee, nor New Bedford, but from West Boylston, Sutton, Suncook, and Edward Atkinson," — not from the great centers of industry, but from comparatively unimportant quarters and was instigated by "an agitator." [1]

The chief criticism upon these claims is that they apply to the cotton industry at a time when it easily held a monopoly, and when a tax no more considerable than that imposed by this shortening of hours would hardly be sufficient to injure its growth. Yet even the reduction to eleven hours had been considered by employers more as a concession to labor agitation than as an economic measure. Concerning the Fall River experiment, statements to be balanced against this claim have been given above. . . .

How far do other effects of these laws tend to offset this burden? Two results are generally admitted.

1. Restrictive labor laws stimulate to greater speed and to other improvements in machinery and management.

2. They increase the efficiency of labor.

Every reduction of hours thus far has been followed immediately by the speeding of machinery; by imposing stricter time regulations; by introducing special discipline in "gang work," so that time may not be lost to a whole shift through the fault of a single member, and so forth; eventually by the replacement of old machines by new ones of greater capacity requiring usually fewer operatives to tend them; and also by such further changes in management or methods as can be devised to accomplish saving. This is the unanimous testimony of employers, laborers, and inspectors.

By these means the old volume of production has been regained. Statistics of manufacture show production to be advancing in Massachusetts, as elsewhere, in spite of the odds against it. The disturbing thought to Massachusetts is that

[1] G. E. McNeill, before Labor Committee on repeal of Ten-Hour Bill, 1879, p. 16 (pamphlet).

although her manufacturers are forced into the lead in making improvements, and leadership often involves costly as well as successful experimentation, her rivals very quickly fall into line. Equipment in neighboring states is equally up to date, and this holds good very generally even of the Southern cotton mills. Where Northern enterprise and capital have lately established themselves in the South it is claimed that the mills are even better equipped, having had no old machinery too costly to be lightly put aside in favor of the new.

Concerning the increase in efficiency through increased leisure, there has been much loose and unprofitable debate.

Where hours were originally excessive reductions were to employees a physical benefit which told in greater vigor of work. Note the traditional effect of reductions from the twelve-hour and fourteen-hour day to the eleven-hour system. It was a policy followed by employers as a concession to labor not in the end disadvantageous to their own interests.

Again, cases are cited in connection with the ten-hour reduction, where the full quota of work was accomplished in the restricted day. These instances are almost invariably found in departments most purely dependent upon manual labor, as in the Holyoke thread mills, in "drawing in" for the cotton web, in cigar shops, and so forth. In machine work speeding the machinery does, of course, set a somewhat higher work requirement upon the tender, in this sense increasing efficiency, but the product depends most intimately upon the speed of the machine as the determining factor.

Of the several labor leaders consulted not one has held that the ordinary factory operative succeeds in accomplishing the same amount of work in a ten-hour day or fifty-eight-hour week as he did before in eleven hours or in the sixty-hour week.

The fact appears to be that the stimulus of "piece wage" has effectually eradicated the lazy employee, while working hours were already short enough to prevent exhaustion in ordinary cases. The exchange of fifty-eight for sixty hours has certainly effected but infinitesimal changes in efficiency.

Compared with the labor of adjoining states, it cannot be said that Massachusetts labor stands appreciably higher in skill. Compared with Southern labor the cotton mills' reports bring astonishing evidence of operatives, new to the occupation, working very long hours and manipulating machinery running at a speed closely approximating that of the mills of Fall River and Lowell.

The Southern labor is of sound mountain American stock, while a large proportion of Northern operatives are short-resident foreigners. This fact is often forgotten in making comparisons between the two sections. The heterogeneous character of Northern mill hands appears from the following extract from the report of the labor committee in 1898 on reduction of wages.

In 1895 the number of persons employed in the cotton mills in Fall River was about 22,398. Of this number 15,823 were foreign born. Places of birth were as follows.

Place	Number	Place	Number
Canada (English)	217	Portugal	587
Canada (French)	6056	Prince Edward Island	25
England	6073	Scotland	344
Germany	64	Sweden	19
Ireland	2130	Other foreign countries	274
New Brunswick	13		
Nova Scotia	21		15,823

We think this is fairly representative of the foreign born at work in the other cotton centers.[1]

Massachusetts labor laws have certainly acted to induce care in methods and to encourage the introduction of improved machinery. Beyond exacting a more constant attention to

[1] The Twelfth Census, Occupations, pp. 303–307, gives the following figures for cotton-mill operatives in Massachusetts. — Ed.

	Males	Females
Native white, native parents	1,925	2,045
Native white, foreign parents	8,849	10,024
Foreign white	28,092	25,843
Aggregate, white	38,866	37,912

work, however, they apparently have not increased the productive efficiency of the normal machine-tending operative. Moreover the figures of manufacturers above presented include all of these factors which are, indeed, quite inextricable from the general problem. Conclusions, therefore, remain the same.

INVESTMENT

Has this tax imposed by labor legislation, then, operated to discourage investment in Massachusetts? It is unequivocally stated that "vast sums of Massachusetts capital have gone to other New England states, driven away chiefly by adverse conditions created by legislation."[1] There has been growth, but in "unmistakably reduced ratio," and this is due to "public knowledge of restrictions and limits greater here than in any other state," constituting "a direct discrimination against capital, against labor, and against the material development of the state."[2] "The result of isolation[3] . . . was visible in the more rapid development of competing industries in neighboring states, notably in Connecticut, Rhode Island, and Maine."[4]

"Upon the passage of the McKinley law both foreign and domestic capital opened new textile industries in the United States; none of any importance chose to locate in Massachusetts. They went to Connecticut, Rhode Island, New Jersey, Pennsylvania, and New York."[5]

These statements are put in a tone of conviction and authority. But there is neither proof nor legitimate protest in the misty realm of "it might have been."

Problem: Given a sum of floating capital in a world full of inviting industrial ventures, determine the point at which it will fall. Did ever an economist solve equations that involved a like proportion of unknown quantities, or seek to trace a curve

[1] *Bulletin of Wool Manufacturers*, September, 1895, pp. 261–262.

[2] *Ibid.*, p. 264.

[3] In 1880 Massachusetts was the only state in which the ten-hour day prevailed. She is still the only state where short-hour laws are well enforced.

[4] *Ibid.*, September, 1895, p. 234.

[5] *Ibid.*, June, 1891, p. 107.

of so many dimensions? The "vast sums" that might have settled in Massachusetts it would be vain for us to seek; nor should we speculate too freely on what might have become of "other New England states" if Massachusetts labor legislation had not "driven" that capital to them. Their commonplace growth, as shown in tables of statistics, should allow Massachusetts to be magnanimous upon this point.

The "unmistakably reduced ratio" of growth in Massachusetts and the "more rapid growth of competing industries in other states" may be verified or disproved by statistics. It is a textile bulletin that makes the statement; it is the textile industry which is most evidently a "competing industry in other states." We may, therefore, very properly take our figures from its history.[1] . . .

These figures certainly do not indicate that the Massachusetts cotton industry was lagging as compared with that of her neighbors; if not the cotton industry, we may be assured that no other was. Massachusetts general industrial returns have not brought consternation to the public. The government annually contemplates them with self-satisfied pride. As a whole, they give no indication of a stunted growth. Outside of textile occupations there is no complaint of injury.

In earlier days Massachusetts, in her great cotton manufacturing centers, long held a practical monopoly of the cotton-goods production of the country. To-day, however, her position is altered; another section competes with increasing strength to force her goods from the market.

The history of the American cotton industry in itself would give plentiful material for economic and sociological study. It begins with the introduction of the factory system in Massachusetts; it has always been a chief subject of tariff regulation

[1] Census statistics show that the number of spindles in cotton manufacture from 1880 to 1890 increased in Massachusetts 3,548,603, or 84 per cent; in New Hampshire 299,502, or 32 per cent; in New Jersey 199,509, or 86 per cent; in New York 158,610, or 28 per cent; in Maine 145,597, or 21 per cent; in Rhode Island 125,053, or 7 per cent; in Connecticut 64,198, or 7 per cent; in Vermont 44,147, or 82 per cent; and decreased in Pennsylvania 118,754, or 28 per cent. See Twelfth Census, Manufactures, Part III, p. 49. — Ed.

and labor-law enactments; it built a large monopoly centered in a single state, later carrying a heavy burden of state taxation and furnishing livelihood to thousands; dependent by its very character upon special natural and social conditions, it has seen a stripling wrestler with nature's bears and lions grow up, now to offer resistance to its Goliath strength.

We will not here attempt needless review of history. The growth of Southern competition is most apparent in very recent years.[1] . . . The following would seem to give an approximation to the actual facts. In advantages the South leads in cost of labor, estimated at from 30 to 40 per cent less than that of Northern labor, or about two cents less per pound of goods. It holds also an indefinite advantage in total freedom in hours. Against the Massachusetts mills, limited to a fifty-eight-hour week, the Southerner may run seventy-two hours at will. The lighter taxation in the South, in many cases amounting even to no taxation at all, is another evident advantage. These claims are very generally conceded. As against the minor advantages of cheap fuel, abundant water power, nearness of raw material, and lower cost of building, counterbalancing considerations favor the North. The North has lower cost for shipping and marketing of goods, at least 10 per cent lower for machinery; a saving in rates of interest on better security, and a larger

[1] Twelfth Census, Manufactures, Part III, p. 28: "In 1880 there were in that part of the country 161 establishments only which made reports to the census; in 1890 there were only 239, an increase of 78, or 48.4 per cent; and in 1900 there were 400 separate establishments, an increase from 1890 of 161, or 67.4 per cent. A scrutiny of the returns by states shows that substantially the whole increase in the South has been in the four states of North Carolina, South Carolina, Georgia, and Alabama. The number of establishments in these four states was 119 in 1880, 191 in 1890, and 355 in 1900. In the other states of the Southern group the number was 42 in 1880, 48 in 1890, and 45 in 1900.

"It would be revealing but a part of the truth to rest the statement of Southern industrial expansion upon the number of establishments; for in the decade from 1880 to 1890 the number of spindles in the four leading Southern states increased almost twofold, from 422,807 to 1,195,256; and the average number of spindles to a mill increased from 3553 to 6258. In the decade from 1890 to 1900 the progress has been at an even greater ration, although the basis of calculation is larger, for the total number of spindles is 3,791,654, the numerical increase 2,596,398, the percentage of increase 217, and the average number of spindles to a mill has become 10,651."

surplus capital which permits the purchase of cotton when the market price is lowest. Other advantages of more intangible nature are also urged, — "economics," "public protection," "experience," "advanced laws," "invigorating atmosphere," "stimulating environment," "intelligent workmen, who have learned to know and protect their rights."[1]

These varied advantages compared in an actual market price have generally favored the South by showing a balance of at least one fourth of a cent in the yard. The difference in actual cost of production is claimed to be two cents per pound, or $33\frac{1}{3}$ per cent less in the South than at Fall River.

It is to be noted that the character of the advantages claimed will show Massachusetts a loser as a result of the leveling influence of time. The claim of higher skill in Northern labor is already losing its force in the face of speed and product shown by Southern machinery. Now ample credit and lower capital must also soon be looked for there. It seems, indeed, to an unbiased onlooker that "Southern competition has come to stay," and that "it is foolish to ignore or belittle it."[2]

The Massachusetts Labor Bureau laid the blame for the distressing conditions of 1897 to 1898 upon the abnormal business depression, "consequent" overproduction, and resulting pressure of competition, and the measure of accuracy of the statement is demonstrated by the return of normal prosperity with the general revival of business activity throughout the country. This must not, however, be permitted to cloak the important bearing upon the present and future situation of the following facts. In spite of an already thoroughly established industry, in a center calculated to attract further investments of capital seeking the occupation, a large competing business has grown up. In order thus to compete against the odds in favor of this well-organized and concentrated industry, it was obliged to produce the same goods at lower prices. This it has done and more. While the Northern mills complained of overproduction, Southern mills were working day and night to fill their orders. The market continued perfectly good at the lower

[1] Labor Bulletin, January, 1898, p. 38 (G. A. Chase). [2] *Ibid.*

selling prices. In the South the mills manufactured at such price and with a profit. Cases are adduced in which the Northern mills relied upon their Southern branches to make good their loss. As an example, the Massachusetts Mills of Lowell have such a branch in Georgia. They went there in order to save their trade with China when they found it impossible to continue the competition from Massachusetts because the Southern mills were underselling them in the New York market. Built in 1895, this mill has been "unable to keep up with orders" and has "made a profit from the start." Mr. Southworth continues: "We are able to sell at a profit goods made in that mill which we could not sell at all if they were produced in Lowell, owing to the difference in cost. Operations in the South have been so successful that we are now considering the increase of our plant there." The Spartanburg Mills tell the same tale. They had languished long at Newburyport, but they have built two new mills out of their Southern profits. The Arkwright Club, reporting upon its investigations concerning this Southern competition, stated its belief in the "hopelessness" of continuing so one-sided a struggle as that in coarse-grade cottons.

As yet Southern mills have not attempted to make the finer grades. There seems no adequate reason why they should not in time, but advantages would at first weigh less strongly on their side. There is, therefore, prospect that the cotton industry of Massachusetts will tend to develop upon these lines. "It will abandon certain kinds of goods which cannot be profitably made; it will extend the output of others and cheapen production by improvements in machinery and processes; the industry in each section will take the form to which it is best adapted."[1] In this conclusion the Bulletin appears to recognize the fact of unproductive conditions in branches of the Massachusetts cotton industry.

Natural conditions weigh against this occupation in Massachusetts; a stronger force than state legislation is determining its future. Years since, Massachusetts lost her iron works;

[1] Labor Bulletin, January, 1898, p. 42.

this was not on account of labor legislation. Nor can we now believe that the repeal even of every labor law would permanently alter the present situation.

Given, however, such weight of adverse conditions; given laws which, as we have seen, impose an appreciable tax, when every least saving counts; we are driven to conclude that this legislation has tended to hasten the departure of the industry of producing the heavier grades of cottons from the state.

Effect on Wages

. . . Approached without prejudice, the problem of ascertaining the rise or fall of wages due to restrictive labor legislation appears at first simple, but so intimately do such variations depend upon other economic forces that almost endless difficulties arise in the process of elimination. Industrial statistics show a constant advance in labor earnings, with little reference to the dates of labor laws; the continual introduction of refinements in machinery has had an overpowering influence upon this progress; concessions to the demands of trade unions have contributed a large but indefinite share, while fluctuations in business prosperity which cause temporary changes in rates further complicate the problem.[1] In cases where special advances have appeared more local reasons are always forthcoming as sufficient causes.

[1] *Changes in Wages, 1880, February to July, 1904.— Textiles.*

February, 1880, advance of 10 per cent.
February, 1884, reduction of 5 to 8 per cent.
February, 1885, further reduction of about 6 per cent.
March, 1886, advance to former list.
April, 1891, advance of 4 per cent to mule spinners only.
July, 1892, advance of 3 per cent to make weekly earnings under fifty-eight-hour law same as before.
September, 1893, reduction of 7 to 10 per cent.
August, 1895, advance of 5 to 7 per cent.
January, 1898, reduction averaging 8 per cent.
April, 1899, restoration to January, 1898, wages.
December, 1899, wages advanced 10 per cent.
March, 1902, advance of 10 per cent in Fall River and New Bedford.
July, 1904, reduction of 12½ per cent in Fall River.

An illustration will perhaps make the situation more intelligible. Here, for example, is a case where the rise in wages was exclusively due to new machinery. A number of old Bigelow carpet looms were replaced by new looms of similar general construction, but running at twice the speed and therefore weaving twice as many yards of goods per day. The output in yards being doubled, the rate of piece wages was cut about 25 per cent, leaving an increase in day wages of about 25 per cent. In this instance the rise in wages was perhaps unusual, owing to the length of time that the old machines had been in use; it serves, however, to indicate the importance of the influence which in hundreds of less evident instances should nevertheless be credited to machinery. Speed is, of course, only one of the many mechanical improvements which have increased the working capacity of labor and accomplished a saving in the cost of production, which redounds to the benefit of both employer and operative as illustrated above. Indeed, practical examples under this head might be multiplied *ad infinitum.*

Again, it hardly needs argument to convince an American public of the strength with which organized labor pushes its interests in the industrial world. So costly are the large strikes to all concerned that no manufacturer will ignore, until the point of outbreak, symptoms of discontent among his operatives, if business conditions warrant a more conciliatory course. Nor are the labor unions slow to recognize and take advantage of seasons of prosperity when their demands are likely to be heeded. All employers appreciate the steady pressure of this force, and it is certainly unfortunate that we have as yet no means which can even approximately measure it. This sensitive wage barometer responds to the slightest changes in business atmosphere; a disturbance of war or rumor of war at hand or in the remote corners of the earth, the surge of a national election, the year's agricultural crop, or increasing markets, — all are registered in some degree in corresponding fluctuations of the wage column.

In such an entanglement of immediate causes, a study of statistics which concern the resultant alone could avail little to enlighten us, and would certainly lead through a wearisome way. Failing figures, the question was religiously put to employers, labor leaders, and government officials, that at least some statement of a general opinion might be entered here. But this also was a vain hope.

Employers said in substance: We have never attempted to figure it out. We have an ample labor market and pay a stated day or, more generally, a piece wage. While there is a steady market this remains the same; but when the demand increases, or gives prospect of increase, or can be tempted even by slightly decreased prices, we put in new machines of greater capacity in proportion to the labor attending; we cut piece wages in less proportion than the machine increases labor capacity, and consequently wages rise. If our operatives grow restless, or threaten to strike for higher wages, if business conditions allow, we advance the day rate or piece rate slightly. We have never knowingly given more wages because of reduced hours or other labor restriction; we have no reason to believe that legislation has had an appreciable effect.

Labor leaders said: We are not scholars or economists to offer a theory, nor can we give you any explanation of the fact; but there the fact stands. Every shortening of the hours of labor has been attended with an advance in wages. That is enough for us to know to keep us working toward more of the same thing.

Inspectors said: We cannot judge at all.

Officers of the Labor Bureau said: Statistics are not yet complete enough to justify deductions. We can only say that in general real wages are rising.

Discussion of this wage question centers in the main about restriction of hours as the effective cause.

In contrast with the attitude of the labor leaders, we have seen the constant voluntary evasion of the ten-hour law by employees.[1] In 1887 the inspectors made note: "Discontent with the ten-hour law is not found among mill owners only, but also among workers who earn less wages."[2]

[1] Massachusetts Police Report, Inspection, 1887, p. 20.

[2] *Ibid.*, pp. 14, 15.

We must conclude, as did the Hon. Amasa Walker, more than thirty years ago, that "there is no sufficient evidence that wages have risen in consequence of, or contemporaneously with, the reduction of hours of labor"[1] or the enactment of other measures of labor legislation.

Employment

For the sake of argument we may allow, then, that shortened hours of labor do not appear to have acted to increase the wage of the individual worker; nevertheless has not this been the result to workers as a class through increase of numbers? Has not this restrictive legislation increased employment? The argument on one side is that under shorter hours, in order to keep up the product, more labor must be employed. (Here it may be noted parenthetically that this statement ignores the previous claim that short hours are already compensated by greater efficiency of the original company of workers; nor does it count the extra wage payments as an increasing cost of production.) The answer rests upon other grounds. The number of employees in a given factory is strictly limited by the amount of machinery there provided for them to tend; such limit upon numbers can therefore be raised only by new investment in like machinery. The contrary tendency is claimed, that restrictions placed upon labor make the manufacturer seek to dispense with it as far as possible, new investment in machinery seeking that of labor-saving value. "The diversion of labor-taxed capital into new investments in other states may there increase employment, but not in Massachusetts."

Cases present themselves in support of both claims. In the building trades, clothing industry, and so forth, such increase of employment has been evident; in cotton mills and generally where machinery is expensive there tends to be a decrease in the proportion of labor. The problem of the unemployed in Massachusetts seems to be as far from solution as elsewhere;

[1] Report of majority of commissioners on Hours of Labor to the Massachusetts Legislature, 1867.

certainly shorter hours have not acted to any appreciable extent to absorb enforced idlers into productive industries.[1]

The claim that legislation has driven employees away from Massachusetts to other states where longer hours prevail is too groundless to deserve discussion. Labor is to a certain extent migratory everywhere, but there has been no perceptible increase of migration from Massachusetts. At a border line a few discontented operatives may have moved to neighboring mills, but their number has been insignificant.

Effect upon Woman and Child Labor

We have seen that nearly the whole of this restrictive legislation bears directly upon the labor of women and children. Has it, then, resulted in decreasing their number in factories?

Inspectors' reports, from 1878 on, note a continued decrease in the number of children employed. In 1882 the reduction in numbers during the previous two years was estimated at 50 per cent.[2] Prosecution for violation became less frequent, and compliant employers found the exactions of school certificates, employment tickets, and so forth, such continual annoyance that they preferred to dispense with child labor so far as possible.[3]

Although allowance must be made here for improvements in machinery which have made automatic many processes before given into the hands of children, and for the public sentiment which frowns upon their employment, we are still warranted in attributing a substantial influence to legislation in the attainment of the above results.

The same does not, however, hold true with respect to women. The proportion of women employed in Massachusetts is not appreciably decreasing. Restrictions upon the labor of women involve far less inconvenience than is imposed by the

[1] Brentano, Hours, Wages, and Production, p. 69.

[2] Massachusetts Police Report, Inspection, 1882, p. 25.

[3] The United States Census chronicles a decrease in Massachusetts from 17,445 in 1880 to 12,556 in 1900, or of 20 per cent in the two decades, of children under sixteen years of age employed in manufacturing industries. — Ed.

details of child-labor laws. The limitation to short hours is the only really serious drawback to their employment. The cheapness of their labor, added in some of the more delicate operations of manufacture to their superior dexterity, is sufficient largely to counterbalance this disadvantage.

Conclusions Summarized

We may summarize our conclusions as to the economic effects of Massachusetts labor legislation as follows :

1. A real and appreciable tax has been put upon the industry of Massachusetts.

2. This has been a goad, increasing the ordinary incentive of competition to urge the use of better machinery and more careful management, and has forced her manufacturers to take the lead in the introduction of improvements. Neighboring states have, however, quickly imitated her successful methods.

3. Improvement in machinery, speed, and so forth, involves somewhat higher work requirements, and to that extent increased efficiency. The reduction of hours below eleven has been accompanied by an offsetting increase of efficiency only in a few cases of arduous and predominatingly manual labor. Piecework had already fulfilled its function here.

4. Whereas statistics of manufacture show Massachusetts to be growing at a normal rate, and with no evidence of injury from her labor laws, one industry of importance is in an unmistakably critical situation. There is reason to believe that the heavy-grade cotton mill is leaving the state. In this case natural conditions weighed already against Massachusetts, and legislative restrictions have been a tax tending to hasten the departure of the industry to the more favored South.

5. The effect upon wages has been slight and is very difficult to estimate. The influences of improved machinery, of the demands of labor unions, and of market conditions have been so great as to overshadow that of legislation. Comparison with other states compels the conclusion that there is no sufficient evidence of a tendency in restrictive legislation to raise wages.

6. We found increased employment in building trades, and so forth, fully offset by tendencies to save labor by machine work. Unemployment remains an unsolved problem in Massachusetts.

7. Protective legislation has unquestionably reduced child labor, both directly by the restriction of such labor, and again indirectly by the stimulus given to mechanical improvements which have raised the requirements of attention, and so forth, and made work before given to children automatic.

8. The number of women employed has maintained a constant ratio. The restrictions, chiefly in hours, have been offset by the cheapness and dexterity of female labor.

9. Among manufacturers the disquieting influence of the constant threat of further protective measures on behalf of labor is noticeable as an obstacle to business confidence. Bills are each year brought before the legislature, backed by a political party of constantly growing strength.

10. Another economic effect of this legislation is the unestimated expense which years of struggle for and against the passage of these laws has imposed upon both laborer and capitalist. This must aggregate no inconsiderable sum of money.

Health

Of prime importance is the standard of health in the community. What has Massachusetts labor legislation done for the health of her workers?

At the time when the ten-hour bill was eliciting warmest discussion (1865–1874), a chief argument presented in its favor was that "the health of female operatives demands it!" So important was this point made that the government called upon the Board of Health for a special investigation in 1871. The report then given upon the "Health of Minors in Manufactories" contained the following statement: "A comparison of the death rate of operatives with that of the whole population at the same ages, for the years 1860 to 1865, allowance being made for war deaths, showed the figures to be 'remarkably close.'" Estimates of absence from work on account of sickness asked for from employers varied approximately from zero to 5 per cent, while many replied that absence from the mills had been too trifling to record.[1] The result of the investigation convinced the board that there was very little evidence of special disease or unhealthiness due to laboring in factories, even in those days of long hours.

The validity of these deductions has been adversely criticised.[2] But Dr. Derby's conclusions do not stand entirely alone in their testimony to the general good health of operatives. The commissions of 1865 and 1866 held the same view; while the opinion of practitioners among factory hands bore out the testimony. More general studies made both in the United States and England further corroborate this opinion on the basis of a wider experience.

That long hours and lack of open-air exercise often led to great fatigue it is not attempted to deny, and the community must recognize that industrial prosperity depends largely upon keeping its labor energy strong and fresh. If, day after day, the worker quits the factory in an exhausted condition this cumulative pressure tends to sap away her vitality, and instead of developing into a more skilled operative she is likely to become less efficient at her task. The passage of the ten-hour law in 1874, however, appears to have put an effectual check to this danger in Massachusetts. Since then the argument of extreme fatigue has been abandoned by labor leaders, who seek to base their claims upon some other ground.

It is noticeable that from the first the health remedy proposed was shortened hours instead of better ventilation and sanitation for the workroom, which would have seemed the prior need. Possibly this was due to the fact, already noticed, that the working class itself instituted the movement and was hardly in a position to appreciate the importance of the latter reform, or it may have been only the easy confusion of argument with object.

[1] G. Derby (M. D.), "Health of Minors in Manufactories," Senate Document, No. 50, 1871.

[2] Charles Cowley, "Argument for Petitioners in Ten-Hour Bill," before Joint Special Committee, p. 102 (pamphlet).

Certainly the construction of old factory buildings displayed little forethought or provision for the health or comfort of employees. Visit to-day the workrooms of an average modern factory, and then that of an old one, be it ever so carefully remodeled to the legal requirements. The light, airy room and cheerfulness of surroundings in the new stand out against the cramped and gloomy quarters of the old in a contrast that must convince even the most skeptical of the blessing of this advance. The worker is confined to the room practically throughout the day. Under conditions of insufficient ventilation the air of a factory could not long be expected to retain its freshness, and to breathe for hours every day such a vitiated atmosphere must have added greatly to the wearisomeness of the day's work. Many processes of production tend in themselves to produce injurious conditions, but until regulated by law this fact was generally unheeded both by employer and workman, either because of indifference to the principles of hygiene or ignorance of them. To-day, however, stringent and, we may fairly say, well-enforced laws control such cases.

The system of ventilation to be used must now be submitted, with the plans of every new factory, for approval by the chief of police or the inspector, and those buildings in which it was originally lacking must be remodeled to the satisfaction of the inspectors. To-day, also, there is a special legal remedy in cases where a process which engenders unhealthy conditions is not properly protected, and the inspector is empowered to order the use of such form of ventilating mechanism, or contrivance "not excessively expensive," as shall answer the necessity of the case. In conditions of ventilation, as the Hon. Carroll D. Wright suggests, the modern factory compares quite favorably with the modern schoolroom or lecture hall.

Ventilation, cleanliness, and sanitary conditions have certainly done as much to check the slow wearing out of life as have safety provisions to guard against the more sudden disasters of accident. We cannot but believe that these more healthful and sunny surroundings have done more than the shortened day to increase the bodily vigor of the factory girl.

Among regulations which have contributed to protection of health the laws concerning child labor must take a prominent place. . . . But let us not enter into discussion where the facts are so palpable and so universally admitted. . . .

Standards of Living

What testimony is there that the legislation reviewed has contributed to raise the standard of living of workers? The same answer is given to this question by employer, inspector, labor leader, and charitable worker. At his work the operative has become accustomed to cleanliness, air, light, and good order, and has begun to miss them in the home, if they are lacking there. Thus the general verdict is that the legal requirements in regard to sanitation and so forth in factories, which have so altered the surroundings of workroom life, have at the same time served perceptibly to encourage like cleanliness and care taking in the home.

The menace of coming illiterate generations which was not at all to be scoffed at in 1870 is no longer feared. Thirty years ago children as young as eight years of age were often to be found at work in mills and workshops, but to-day a legal age limit which banishes children under fourteen years from employment meets with general compliance. The "factory children" of former times have become the "school children" of to-day. If there are still illiterate minors, they must lay chief blame to themselves. There is not to-day any lack of opportunity; lack of appreciation of opportunity is the cause of such illiteracy as prevails, and is confined almost entirely to the newer foreign element. The best-devised law and strongest police force would be obliged to content itself with incomplete achievement here.

Opposition was at first made to the weekly payment of wages. It could be no advantage to the thrifty, who easily secure credit and with monthly pay have the advantage of buying in bulk; it would be an injury to the weak and dissolute, substituting four monthly temptations for one. This statement of opinion on the part of some employers has not yet received the support of figures.[1] Intoxication has not increased; for superintendents make short work of dismissing such unreliable service, with most healthfully sobering effect.

Workers themselves claim an advantage in cash payments, which allow them to trade where they find the best bargains and not only where they can obtain credit. In Lawrence it was remarked that rent, food, and so forth, fell in some cases nearly 20 per cent, and that shops where operatives used to trade exclusively were forced to cut prices and encounter close competition.[2] Under the system of monthly payments operatives had also frequently found themselves obliged to ask for wage advances, a favor generally heavily discounted at the office, often at the rate of 10 per cent.[3] Weekly payments appear, indeed, to have conduced to home economy on the part of the workers.

Citizenship

Lastly, has this legislation had any effect upon the development of citizenship? The shorter hours conceded by law to labor have been little "misused" and have caused no "increase of laziness." The solicitude indicated by this objection appears almost hypocritical in face of the silence which never questions the propriety of erratic shut-downs at the convenience of manufacturers.

The argument for shorter hours appears to be strongly supported here. From the beginning advance towards civilization, and in civilization towards higher attainment, has been conditioned upon leisure time beyond that necessary to the gaining of a livelihood. It is a wide law and it applies throughout. Leisure is equally a requirement for the advance of our laboring classes to better conditions of living.

Short hours in Massachusetts have contributed their increase of opportunity which has not been neglected. Not only do we

[1] See Inspectors' Reports. This testimony was corroborated in interviews by several employers who had made previous voluntary experiment.

[2] Massachusetts Police Report, Inspection, 1887, p. 59.

[3] E. Porritt, Factory Legislation in the United States, p. 192.

find libraries and lecture courses offered, but to-day, as never before, labor flocks to use these and asks always for more of them. On a half holiday we find many in the public museum or gallery. Compare these Massachusetts operatives with those of other states. They stand the acknowledged leaders of their class in this country, organized, intelligent, progressive.

Perhaps their voice has grown stentorian, but they are ready and able to argue their point. It is the testimony of the Board of Arbitration that operatives have shown a knowledge and appreciation of the methods and aims of arbitration, and an intelligent recourse to them, quite equal to that of their employers. The trade union with its problem of organization and its school of free discussion has been the chief instrument in this education, but its efficiency has depended upon hours of leisure away from the factory. Experience of social intercourse, of the necessity of discipline in trade-union organizations, and of the weight of logic in argument have given workingmen a new appreciation of their own relation to order, government, and the community.

Summary

The legal sanitary requirements of cleanliness, light, ventilation, and so forth, in the factory act improve the health and spirits of workers, and tend to induce the same conditions in their homes.

Restrictions upon child labor have expelled at least 75 per cent of the original number of working children from employment, substituted the schoolroom for the factory, and regulated work for minors in general.

Weekly wage payments appear to have encouraged household economy rather than to have fostered dissolute living.

Restrictions upon labor have brought increased social and educational opportunities within reach of operatives; have advanced the interests of good citizenship among them; have tended to raise their standards of living, with important economic consequences in broadening the home market.

SARAH SCOVILL WHITTELSEY.

XXIII

STATE REGULATION OF EMPLOYMENT — DECISIONS OF COURTS

I. Employment of Men — Fourteenth Amendment[1]

The supreme court of Utah had sustained a statute limiting the employment of workingmen in underground mines and in smelters to eight hours per day. Holden, having been found guilty and fined in employing a miner more than eight hours, alleged before the Supreme Court of the United States that the Utah statute was repugnant to the Constitution of the United States in these respects:

It deprives the defendant and all employers and employees of the right to make contracts in a lawful way and for lawful purposes.

It is class legislation, and not equal or uniform in its provisions.

It deprives the defendant and employers and employees of the equal protection of the laws, abridges the privileges and immunities of the defendant as a citizen of the United States, and deprives him of his property and liberty without due process of law.

Justice Brown, after stating the facts, said:

The validity of the statute in question is, however, challenged upon the ground of an alleged violation of the fourteenth amendment to the Constitution of the United States, in that it abridges the privileges or immunities of citizens of the United States, deprives both the employer and the laborer of his property without due process of law, and denies to them the equal protection of the laws. As the three questions of abridging their immunities, depriving them of their property, and denying them the protection of the laws are so connected that the authorities upon each are to a greater or less extent pertinent to the others, they may properly be considered together.

[1] United States Supreme Court. *Holden* v. *Hardy*, 169 U. S. 366 (1898).

Prior to the adoption of the fourteenth amendment there was a similar provision against deprivation of life, liberty, or property without due process of law incorporated in the fifth amendment; but as the first eight amendments to the Constitution were obligatory only upon Congress, the decisions of this court under this amendment have but a partial application to the fourteenth amendment, which operates only upon the action of the several states. The fourteenth amendment, which was finally adopted July 28, 1868, largely expanded the power of the Federal courts and Congress, and for the first time authorized the former to declare invalid all laws and judicial decisions of the states abridging the rights of citizens or denying them the benefit of due process of law.

This amendment was first called to the attention of this court in 1872, in an attack upon the constitutionality of a law of the state of Louisiana, passed in 1869, vesting in a slaughterhouse company therein named the sole and exclusive privilege of conducting and carrying on a live-stock landing and slaughterhouse business within certain limits specified in the act, and requiring all animals intended for sale and slaughter to be landed at their wharves or landing places. (Slaughterhouse cases, 16 Wall. 36.) While the court in that case recognized the fact that the primary object of this amendment was to secure to the colored race, then recently emancipated, the full enjoyment of their freedom, the further fact that it was not restricted to that purpose was admitted both in the prevailing and dissenting opinions, and the validity of the act was sustained as a proper police regulation for the health and comfort of the people. A majority of the cases which have since arisen have turned, not upon a denial to the colored race of rights therein secured to them, but upon alleged discriminations in matters entirely outside of the political relations of the parties aggrieved.

These cases may be divided, generally, into two classes: first, where a state legislature or a state court is alleged to have unjustly discriminated in favor of or against a particular individual or class of individuals as distinguished from the rest of the community, or denied them the benefit of due process of law; second, where the legislature has changed its general system of jurisprudence by abolishing what had been previously considered necessary to the proper administration of justice, or the protection of the individual. . . .

An examination of both these classes of cases under the fourteenth amendment will demonstrate that, in passing upon the validity of state legislation under that amendment, this court has not failed to recognize the fact that the law is to a great extent a progressive science; that in some of the states methods of procedure which at the time the Constitution was adopted were deemed essential to the protection and safety of the people, or to the liberty of the citizen, have been found to be no longer necessary; that restrictions which had formerly been laid upon the conduct of individuals, or of classes of individuals, had proved detrimental to their interests, while, upon the other hand, certain other classes of persons (particularly those engaged in dangerous or unhealthful employments) have been found to be in need of additional protection. . . . They are mentioned only for the purpose of calling attention to the probability that other changes of no less importance may be made in the future, and that, while the cardinal principles of justice are immutable, the methods by which justice is administered are subject to constant fluctuation, and that the Constitution of the United States, which is necessarily and to a large extent inflexible and exceedingly difficult of amendment, should not be so construed as to deprive the states of the power so to amend their laws as to make them conform to the wishes of the citizens, as they may deem best for the public welfare, without bringing them into conflict with the supreme law of the land. Of course, it is impossible to forecast the character or extent of these changes; but in view of the fact that, from the day Magna Charta was signed to the present moment, amendments to the structure of the law have been made with increasing frequency, it is impossible to suppose that they will not continue, and the law be forced to adapt itself to new conditions of society, and particularly to the new relations between employers and employees, as they arise. . . . We do not wish, however, to be understood as holding that this power is unlimited. While the people of each state may doubtless adopt such systems of laws as best conform to their own traditions and customs, the people of the entire country have laid down in the Constitution of the United States certain fundamental principles to which each member of the Union is bound to accede as a condition of its admission as a state. Thus the United States are bound to guarantee to each state a republican form of government, and the tenth section of the first article contains certain other specified limitations upon the power of the several states, the object of which was to secure to Congress paramount authority with respect to matters of universal concern. In addition, the fourteenth amendment contains a sweeping provision forbidding the states from abridging the privileges and immunities of citizens of the United States and denying them the benefit of due process or equal protection of the laws. . . . This right of contract, however, is itself subject to certain limitations which the state may lawfully impose in the exercise of its police powers. While this power is inherent in all governments, it has doubtless been greatly expanded in its application during the past century, owing to the enormous increase in the number of occupations which are dangerous or so far detrimental to the health of employees as to demand special precautions for their well-being and protection, or the safety of adjacent property. . . .

While this power is necessarily inherent in every form of government, it was, prior to the adoption of the Constitution, but sparingly used in this country. As we were then almost purely an agricultural people, the occasion for any special protection of a particular class did not exist. Certain profitable employments, such as lotteries and the sale of intoxicating liquors, which were then considered to be legitimate, have since fallen under the ban of public opinion, and are now either altogether prohibited or made subject to stringent police regulations. The power to do this has been repeatedly affirmed by this court.

After mentioning several forms of legislation for the protection of workmen in factories and mines, which have uniformly been held to be constitutional, the court continued:

But if it be within the power of a legislature to adopt such means for the protection of the lives of its citizens, it is difficult to see why precautions may not also be adopted for the protection of their health and morals. It is as much for the interest of the state that the public health should be preserved as that life should be made secure. . . . Upon the principles above stated we think the act in question may be sustained as a valid exercise of the police power of the state. The enactment does not profess to limit the hours of all workmen, but merely those who are employed in underground mines, or in the smelting, reduction, or refining of ores or metals. These employments, when too long pursued, the legislature has judged to be detrimental to the health of the employees; and, so long as there are reasonable grounds for believing that this is so, its decision on this subject cannot be reviewed by the Federal courts.

While the general experience of mankind may justify us in believing that men may engage in ordinary employments more than eight hours per day without injury to their health, it does not follow that labor for the same length of time is innocuous when carried on beneath the surface of the earth, where the operative is deprived of fresh air and sunlight, and is frequently subjected to foul atmosphere and a very high temperature, or to the influence of noxious gases generated by the processes of refining or smelting.

We concur in the following observations of the supreme court of Utah in this connection: "The conditions with respect to health of laborers in underground mines doubtless differ from those under which they labor in smelters and other reduction works on the surface. Unquestionably, the atmosphere and other conditions in mines and reduction works differ. Poisonous gases, dust, and impalpable substances arise and float in the air in stamp mills, smelters, and other works in which ores containing metals, combined with arsenic or other poisonous elements or agencies, are treated, reduced, and refined, and there can be no doubt that prolonged effort, day after day, subject to such conditions and agencies, will produce morbid, noxious, and often deadly effects in the human system. Some organisms and systems will resist and endure such conditions and effects longer than others. It may be said that labor in such conditions must be performed. Granting that, the period of labor each day should be of a reasonable length. Twelve hours per day would be less injurious than fourteen, ten than twelve, and eight than ten. The legislature has named eight. Such a period was deemed reasonable. . . . The law in question is confined to the protection of that class of people engaged in labor in underground mines, and in smelters and other works wherein ores are reduced and refined. This law applies only to the classes subjected by their employment to the peculiar conditions and effects attending underground mining and work in smelters, and other works for the reduction and refining of ores. Therefore it is not necessary to discuss or decide whether the legislature can fix the hours of labor in other employments. Though reasonable doubts may exist as to the power of the legislature to pass a law, or as to whether the law is calculated or adapted to promote the health, safety, or comfort of the people, or to secure good order or promote the general welfare, we must resolve them in favor of the right of that department of government." (46 Pac. 1105.)

The legislature has also recognized the fact, which the experience of legislators in many states has corroborated, that the proprietors of these establishments and their operatives do not stand upon an equality, and that their interests are to a certain extent conflicting. The former naturally desire to obtain as much labor as possible from their employees, while the latter are often induced by the fear of discharge to conform to regulations which their judgment, fairly exercised, would pronounce to be detrimental to their health or strength. In other words, the proprietors lay down the rules, and the laborers are practically constrained to obey them. In such cases self-interest is often an unsafe guide, and the legislature may properly interpose its authority.

It may not be improper to suggest in this connection that although the prosecution in this case was against the employer of labor, who apparently, under the statute, is the only one liable, his defense is not so much that his right to contract has been infringed upon, as that the act works a peculiar hardship to his employees, whose right to labor as long as they please is alleged to be thereby violated. The argument would certainly come with better grace and greater cogency from the latter class. But the fact that both parties are of full age and competent to contract does not necessarily deprive the state of the power to interfere, where the parties do not stand upon an equality, or where the public health demands that one party to the contract shall be protected against himself. The state still retains an interest in his welfare, however reckless he may be. The whole is no greater than the sum of all the parts, and when the individual health, safety, and welfare are sacrificed or neglected the state must suffer.

We have no disposition to criticise the many authorities which hold that state statutes restricting the hours of labor are unconstitutional. Indeed, we are not called upon to express an opinion upon this subject. It is sufficient to say of them that they have no application to cases where the legislature had adjudged that a limitation is necessary for the preservation of the health of employees, and there are reasonable grounds for believing that such determination is supported by the facts. The question in each case is whether the legislature has adopted the statute in exercise of a reasonable discretion, or whether its action be a mere excuse for an unjust discrimination, or the oppression or spoliation of a particular class.

Seven years after the case of *Holden* v. *Hardy* the Supreme Court of the United States handed down a decision on the constitutionality of a New York statute regulating bakeries.[1]

[1] United States Supreme Court. *Lochner* v. *New York*, 25 Sup. Court Rep. 539 (1905).

Mr. Justice Peckham, after making the statement of facts, delivered the opinion of the court:

The indictment, it will be seen, charges that the plaintiff in error violated the 110th section of article 8, chapter 415, of the Laws of 1897, known as the Labor Law of the State of New York, in that he wrongfully and unlawfully required and permitted an employee working for him to work more than sixty hours in one week. . . . It is not an act merely fixing the number of hours which shall constitute a legal day's work, but an absolute prohibition upon the employer's permitting, under any circumstances, more than ten hours' work to be done in his establishment. The employee may desire to earn the extra money which would arise from his working more than the prescribed time, but this statute forbids the employer from permitting the employee to earn it.

The statute necessarily interferes with the right of contract between the employer and employees concerning the number of hours in which the latter may labor in the bakery of the employer. The general right to make a contract in relation to his business is part of the liberty of the individual protected by the fourteenth amendment of the Federal Constitution. . . .

This court has recognized the existence and upheld the exercise of the police powers of the states in many cases which might fairly be considered as border ones, and it has, in the course of its determination of questions regarding the asserted invalidity of such statutes on the ground of their violation of the rights secured by the Federal Constitution, been guided by rules of a very liberal nature, the application of which has resulted, in numerous instances, in upholding the validity of state statutes thus assailed. Among the later cases where the state law has been upheld by this court is that of *Holden* v. *Hardy*, 169 U. S. 366. . . .

It will be observed that even with regard to that class of labor [underground mines and smelters] the Utah statute provided for cases of emergency wherein the provisions of the statute would not apply. The statute now before this court has no emergency clause in it, and, if the statute is valid, there are no circumstances and no emergencies under which the slightest violation of the provisions of the act would be innocent. There is nothing in *Holden* v. *Hardy* which covers the case now before us. In every case that comes before this court, therefore, where legislation of this character is concerned and where the protection of the Federal Constitution is sought, the question necessarily arises, Is this a fair, reasonable, and appropriate exercise of the police power of the state, or is it an unreasonable, unnecessary, and arbitrary interference with the right of the individual to his personal liberty or to enter into those contracts in relation to labor which may seem to him appropriate or necessary for the support of himself and his family? Of course, the liberty of contract relating to labor includes both parties to it. The one has as much right to purchase as the other to sell labor.

This is not a question of substituting the judgment of the court for that of the legislature. If the act be within the power of the state it is valid, although the judgment of the court might be totally opposed to the enactment of such a law. But the question would still remain, Is it within the police power of the state? and that question must be answered by the court.

The question whether this act is valid as a labor law, pure and simple, may be dismissed in a few words. There is no reasonable ground for interfering with the liberty of person or the right of free contract by determining the hours of labor in the occupation of a baker. There is no contention that bakers as a class are not equal in intelligence and capacity to men in other trades or manual occupations, or that they are not able to assert their rights and care for themselves without the protecting arm of the state interfering with their independence of judgment and of action. They are in no sense wards of the state. Viewed in the light of a purely labor law, with no reference whatever to the question of health, we think that a law like the one before us involves neither the safety, the morals, nor the welfare of the public, and that the interest of the public is not in the slightest degree affected by such an act. The law must be upheld, if at all, as a law pertaining to the health of the individual engaged in the occupation of a baker. It does not affect any other portion of the public than those who are engaged in that occupation. Clean and wholesome bread does not depend upon whether the baker works but ten hours per day or only sixty hours a week. The limitation of the hours of labor does not come within the police power on that ground.

It is a question of which of two powers or rights shall prevail, — the power of the state to legislate or the right of the individual to liberty of person and freedom of contract. The mere assertion that the subject relates, though but in a remote degree, to the public health does not necessarily render the enactment valid. The act must have a more direct relation, as a means to an end, and the end itself must be appropriate and legitimate, before an act can be held to be valid which interferes with the general right of an individual to be free in his person and in his power to contract in relation to his own labor.

This case has caused much diversity of opinion in the state courts. In the Supreme Court two of the five judges composing the court dissented from the judgment affirming the validity of the act. In the Court of Appeals three of the seven judges also dissented from the judgment upholding the statute. Although found in what is called a labor law of the state, the Court of Appeals has upheld the act as one relating to the public health, — in other words, as a health law. One of the judges of the Court of Appeals, in upholding the law, stated that in his opinion the regulation in question could not be sustained unless they were able to say from common knowledge that working in a bakery and candy factory was an unhealthful employment. The judge held that while the evidence was not uniform, it still led him to the conclusion that the occupation of a baker or confectioner was unhealthful and tended to result in diseases of the respiratory organs. Three of the judges dissented from that view, and they thought the occupation of a baker was not to such an extent unhealthful as to warrant the interference of the legislature with the liberty of the individual.

We think the limit of the police power has been reached and passed in this case. There is, in our judgment, no reasonable foundation for holding this to be necessary or appropriate as a health law to safeguard the public health or the health of the individuals who are following the trade of a baker. If this statute be valid, and if, therefore, a proper case is made out in which to deny the right of an individual, *sui juris*, as employer or employee to make contracts for the labor of the latter under the protection of the provisions of the Federal Constitution, there would seem to be no limit to which legislation of this nature might not go. . . . In looking through statistics regarding all trades and occupations, it may be true that the trade of a baker does not appear to be as healthful as some other trades, and is also vastly more healthful than still others. To the common understanding, the trade of a baker has never been regarded as an unhealthful one. Very likely physicians would not recommend the exercise of that or of any other trade as a remedy for ill health. Some occupations are more healthful than others, but we think there are none which might not come under the power of the legislature to supervise and control the hours of working therein, if the mere fact that the occupation is not absolutely and perfectly healthful is to confer that right upon the legislative department of the government. It might be safely affirmed that almost all occupations more or less affect the health. There must be more than the mere fact of the possible existence of some small amount of unhealthfulness to warrant legislative interference with liberty. It is unfortunately true that labor, even in any department, may possibly carry with it the seeds of unhealthfulness. But are we all, on that account, at the mercy of legislative majorities? A printer, a tinsmith, a locksmith, a carpenter, a cabinetmaker, a dry-goods clerk, a bank's, a lawyer's, or a physician's clerk, or a clerk in almost any kind of business, would come under the power of the legislature on this assumption. No trade, no occupation, no mode of earning one's living, could escape this all-pervading power, and the acts of the legislature in limiting the hours of labor in all employments would be valid, although such limitation might seriously cripple the ability of the laborer to support himself and his family.

. . . All that it could properly do has been done by it with regard to the conduct of bakeries, as provided for in the other sections of the act above set forth. These several sections provide for the inspection of the premises where the bakery is carried on, with regard to furnishing proper wash rooms and water closets apart from the bake room, also with regard to providing proper drainage, plumbing, and painting; the sections, in addition, provide for the height of the ceiling, the cementing or tiling of floors, where necessary in the opinion of the factory inspector, and for other things of that nature; alterations are also provided for, and are to be made where necessary in the opinion of the inspector in order to comply with the provisions of the statute. These various sections may be wise and valid regulations, and they certainly go to the full extent of providing for the cleanliness and the healthfulness, so far as possible, of the quarters in which bakeries are to be conducted. Adding to all these requirements a prohibition to enter into any contract of labor in a bakery for more than a certain number of hours a week is, in our judgment, so wholly beside the matter of a proper, reasonable, and fair provision as to run counter to that liberty of person and of free contract provided for in the Federal Constitution.

It is manifest to us that the limitation of the hours of labor as provided for in this section of the statute under which the indictment was found and the plaintiff in error convicted has no such direct relation to, and no such substantial effect upon, the health of the employee as to justify us in regarding the section as really a health law. It seems to us that the real object and purpose were simply to regulate the hours of labor between the master and his employees (all being men, *sui juris*) in a private business not dangerous in any degree to morals or in any real and substantial degree to the health of the employees. Under such circumstances the freedom of master and employee to contract with each other in relation to their employment, and in defining the same, cannot be prohibited or interfered with without violating the Federal Constitution.

II. Employment of Men — State Constitution [1]

This case arose under a statute similar to the one in Utah limiting the hours of labor in mines and smelters. The chief justice said:

In the light of these authorities it is clear: first, that the decision of the Supreme Court of Utah in construing the Utah statute is not an authority here, for the reason that the decision there was based entirely upon the mandatory nature of a provision of the Utah constitution which is not present in our organic act; second, in affirming the judgment of the Utah court the decision of the Supreme Court of the United States in the Holden cases is not a precedent for this court in construing our act, for the reason that the sole question before the Federal court was whether or not the Utah act violated the Federal Constitution. If, however, it could be maintained that this affirmance was in effect a determination that the Utah law was in harmony with the Utah constitution, the decision of the Federal court would not be an authority here, because we have no such constitutional provision.

The extent and meaning of the act in question are not difficult of ascertainment, though it is not a model of statutory composition. That it operates as a limitation both upon the employer and the employee seems clear. It forbids a certain kind of employment. There can be no employment without the concurring acts of him who contracts for employment and of him who contracts to be employed. Both are within the inhibitions of the enactment, and if it is valid each is liable to the penalty for making the forbidden contract. The petitioner, therefore, as a laboring man, is prohibited from entering into a contract to work in a smelter more than eight hours in any one day. If in our constitution there was, as

[1] Supreme Court of Colorado. *In re Morgan*, 26 Colo. 415 (1899).

there seems to be in that of Utah, a specific affirmative provision enjoining upon the general assembly the enactment of laws to protect the health of the classes of workmen therein enumerated, it might be that acts reasonably appropriate to that end would not be obnoxious to that provision of our constitution forbidding class legislation. The two provisions should be construed together so as to harmonize, if that be possible under sound canons of construction, and the general clause forbidding class legislation might be regarded as qualified by the special one which authorizes such legislation in respect to the enumerated classes. Article 16 of our constitution is devoted to mining and irrigation, and section 2 directs that "the general assembly shall provide by law for the proper ventilation of mines, the construction of escapement shafts, and such other appliances as may be necessary to protect the health and secure the safety of the workmen therein." These regulations manifestly embrace only such reasonably necessary mechanical appliances as will secure the end in view, and do not include other kinds of health regulations. We have no constitutional provision which authorizes the legislature to single out workingmen in underground mines and smelters and impose upon them restrictions as to the number of hours they shall work at these industries, from which workingmen in all other departments of industry are exempt.

The act is equally obnoxious to the provisions of our bill of rights, set out in the statement, which guarantee to all persons their natural and inalienable right to personal liberty, and the right of acquiring, possessing, and protecting property. Liberty means something more than mere freedom from physical restraint. It includes the privilege of choosing any lawful occupation for the exercise of one's physical and mental faculties which is not injurious to others. The right to acquire and possess property includes the right to contract for one's labor. The latter is essentially a property right. That this act infringes both the right to enjoy liberty and to acquire and possess property seems too clear for argument. While not conceding that this limitation is not permissible, counsel for respondent, as we understand them, recognize the fact (but, if they do not, the same is only too apparent) that these natural rights are violated by the provisions of the act. The limitation is claimed to be warranted on the ground that these and all other constitutional guaranties must yield to the paramount and sovereign right of the state to exercise its police power to protect the public health, and to this, the principal question in this proceeding, we now address ourselves.

Starting then with the premise, which is practically admitted to be true, that this act contravenes the constitutional provisions quoted in the statement, let us see if, notwithstanding this conflict, it can be justified as a valid exercise of the police power. . . . While invoking as a warrant for this act that phase of the police power extending to the public health, its supporters do not claim that its real and primary object is to protect the public health, or the health of that portion of the community in the immediate vicinity or affected by the operation of smelters. Were the object of the act to protect the public health, and its provisions reasonably appropriate to that end, it might be sustained; for in such a case even the constitutional right of contract may be reasonably limited. But the act before us is not of that character. In selecting a subject for the exercise of the police power the legislature must keep within its true scope. The reason for the existence of the power rests upon the theory that one must so use his own as not to injure others, and so as not to interfere with or injure the public health, safety, morals, or general welfare. How can an alleged law that purports to be the result of an exercise of the police power be such in reality when it has for its only object, not the protection of others, or the public health, safety, morals, or general welfare, but the welfare of him whose act is prohibited, when, if committed, it will injure him who commits it, and him only? What we mean to decide is that in a purely private lawful business, in which no special privilege or license has been granted by the state, and the carrying on of which is attended by no injury to the general public, it is beyond the power of the legislature under the guise of the police power to prohibit an adult man who desires to work thereat from working more than eight hours a day on the ground that working longer may, or probably will, injure his own health.

The result of our deliberation is that this act is an unwarrantable interference with, and infringes the right of, both the employer and employee in making contracts relating to a purely private business in which no possible injury to the public can result; that it unjustly and arbitrarily singles out a class of persons, and imposes upon them restrictions from which others similarly situated and substantially in the same condition are exempt; and that it is not, under our constitution, a valid exercise of the police power of this state, either in the subject selected or in the reasonableness of the regulation.[1]

[1] Following this decision the constitution of the state of Colorado was amended so as to authorize a law similar to that of Utah.

III. Employment of Women[1]

By act approved June 17, 1893, the legislature of Illinois undertook "to regulate the manufacture of clothing, wearing apparel, and other articles in this state, and to provide for the appointment of state inspectors to enforce the same, and to make an appropriation therefor."

Upon the complaint of the factory inspector appointed under this law a warrant was issued by a justice of the peace of Cook County against William E. Ritchie for violating section 5 of the statute in question by employing a certain adult female, more than eighteen years of age, at work in a factory longer than eight hours on a certain day in February, 1894. The case was tried in the criminal court of Cook County, on appeal from the judgment of the justice of the peace, and the defendant was convicted and fined, whereupon the case was brought, on writ of error, before the Supreme Court of Illinois, which tribunal, on March 14, 1895, reversed the judgment of the criminal court and decided that section 5 of the act which declares that "no female shall be employed in any factory or workshop more than eight hours in any one day or forty-eight hours in any one week" is unconstitutional. Judge Magruder said in part:

It is contended by counsel for plaintiff in error that that section is unconstitutional as imposing unwarranted restrictions upon the right to contract. On the other hand, it is claimed by counsel for the people that the section is a sanitary provision and justifiable as an exercise of the police power of the state. Does the provision in question restrict the right to contract? The words "no female shall be employed" import action on the part of two persons. There must be a person who does the act of employing and a person who consents to the act of being employed. Webster defines "employment" as not only "the act of employing" but also "the state of being employed." The prohibition of the statute is therefore twofold: first, that no manufacturer or proprietor of a factory or workshop shall employ any female therein more than eight hours in one day; and, second, that no female shall consent to be so employed. It thus prohibits employer and employee from uniting their minds or

[1] Supreme Court of Illinois. *Ritchie* v. *People*, 155 Ill. 98 (1895).

agreeing upon any longer service during one day than eight hours. In other words, they are prohibited, the one from contracting to employ, and the other from contracting to be employed, otherwise than as directed. . . . Section 2 of article 2 of the constitution of Illinois provides that "no person shall be deprived of life, liberty, or property without due process of law." . . . The privilege of contracting is both a liberty and property right. Liberty includes the right to acquire property, and that means the right to make and enforce contracts. . . . The legislature has no right to deprive one class of persons of privileges allowed to other persons under like conditions. The man who is forbidden to acquire and enjoy property in the same manner in which the rest of the community is permitted to acquire and enjoy it is deprived of liberty in particulars of primary importance to his pursuit of happiness. If one man is denied the right to contract as he has hitherto done under the law, and as others are still allowed to do by the law, he is deprived of both liberty and property to the extent to which he is thus deprived of the right. . . . Women employed by manufacturers are forbidden by section 5 to make contracts to labor longer than eight hours in a day, while women employed as saleswomen in stores, or as domestic servants, or as bookkeepers, or stenographers, or typewriters, or in laundries, or other occupations not embraced under the head of manufacturing are at liberty to contract for as many hours of labor in a day as they choose. The manner in which the section thus discriminates against one class of employers and employees and in favor of all others places it in opposition to the constitutional guaranties hereinbefore discussed, and so renders it invalid.

But aside from its partial and discriminating character, this enactment is a purely arbitrary restriction upon the fundamental rights of the citizen to control his or her own time and faculties. It substitutes the judgment of the legislature for the judgment of the employer and employee in a matter about which they are competent to agree with each other. It assumes to dictate to what extent the capacity to labor may be exercised by the employee, and takes away the right of private judgment as to the amount and duration of the labor to be put forth in a specified period. Where the legislature thus undertakes to impose an unreasonable and unnecessary burden upon any one citizen or class of citizens it transcends the authority intrusted to it by the constitution, even though it imposes the same burden upon all other citizens or classes of citizens. General laws may be as tyrannical as partial laws. . . .

But it is claimed on behalf of defendant in error that this section can be sustained as an exercise of the police power of the state. The police power of the state is that power which enables it to promote the health, comfort, safety, and welfare of society. It is very broad and far reaching, but is not without its limitations. Legislative acts passed in pursuance of it must not be in conflict with the constitution, and must have some relation to the ends sought to be accomplished; that is to say, to the comfort, welfare, or safety of society. . . . There is nothing in the title of the act of 1893 to indicate that it is a sanitary measure. The first three sections contain provisions for keeping workshops in a cleanly state, and for inspection to ascertain whether they are so kept. But there is nothing in the nature of the employment contemplated by the act which is in itself unhealthful or unlawful or injurious to the public morals or welfare. . . . It is not the nature of the things done, but the sex of the persons doing them, which is made the basis of the claim that the act is a measure for the promotion of the public health. It is sought to sustain the act as an exercise of the police power upon the alleged ground that it is designed to protect woman on account of her sex and physique. It will not be denied that woman is entitled to the same rights, under the constitution, to make contracts with reference to her labor as are secured thereby to men. . . . Inasmuch as sex is no bar, under the constitution and law, to the endowment of woman with the fundamental and inalienable rights of liberty and property, which include the right to make her own contracts, the mere fact of sex will not justify the legislature in putting forth the police power of the state for the purpose of limiting her exercise of those rights, unless the courts are able to see that there is some fair, just, and reasonable connection between such limitation and the public health, safety, or welfare proposed to be secured by it.

In another case illustrating this topic arising in the state of Nebraska,[1] William Wenham was convicted of a violation of an act of the legislature which restricts the hours of employment of females in certain industries, and provides for the enforcement of its requirements. It was charged that Wenham in operating a laundry had employed one Lizzie Falconer for fourteen hours per day and eighty-four hours per week.

[1] Supreme Court of Nebraska. *Wenham* v. *State*, 65 Neb. 394 (1902).

Section 1 of the law referred to provides "that no female shall be employed in any manufacturing, mechanical, or mercantile establishment, hotel, or restaurant in this state more than sixty hours during any one week, and that ten hours shall constitute a day's labor. . . ." Before the Supreme Court of the state the law was upheld and the conviction affirmed. Judge Barnes said:

In the case of *Com.* v. *Hamilton Mfg. Co.*, 120 Mass. 383, it was held that a statute prohibiting the employment of all persons under the age of eighteen and all women from laboring in any manufacturing establishment more than sixty hours per week violates no contract of the commonwealth implied in the granting of a charter to a manufacturing company nor any right reserved under the constitution to any individual citizen, and may be maintained as a health or police regulation. The act in question was taken from, and is practically an enactment of, the statutes of Massachusetts; and we may fairly presume that our legislature in adopting this act also adopted the law relating to it, as announced by the supreme judicial tribunal of that state. In many of the states laws have been enacted limiting the hours during which women and children shall be employed in factories. While in some of these states the constitutionality of these laws, as applied to women, has been doubted, yet in most of them they have been upheld. . . .

The members of the legislature come from no particular class. They are elected from every portion of the state, and come from every avocation and from all the walks of life. They have observed the conditions with which they are surrounded, and know from experience what laws are necessary to be enacted for the welfare of the communities in which they reside. They determined that the law in question was necessary for the public good, and the protection of the health and well-being of women engaged in labor in the establishments mentioned in the act. That question was one exclusively within their power and jurisdiction, and their action should not be interfered with by the courts unless their power has been improperly or oppressively exercised. Women and children have always, to a certain extent, been wards of the state. Women in recent years have been partly emancipated from their common-law disabilities. They now have a limited right to contract. They may own property, real and personal, in their own right, and may engage in business on their own account. But they have no voice in the enactment of the laws by which they are governed, and can take no part in municipal affairs. They are unable, by reason of their physical limitations, to endure the same hours of exhaustive labor as may be endured by adult males. Certain kinds of work which may be performed by men without injury to their health would wreck the constitutions and destroy the health of women, and render them incapable of bearing their share of the burdens of the family and the home. The state must be accorded the right to guard and protect women as a class against such a condition; and the law in question to that extent conserves the public health and welfare. On the question of the right to contract, we may well declare a law unconstitutional which interferes with or abridges the right of adult males to contract with each other in any of the business affairs or vocations of life. The employer and the laborer are practically on an equal footing, but these observations do not apply to women and children. Of the many vocations in this country comparatively few are open to women. Their field of remunerative labor is restricted. Competition for places therein is necessarily great. The desire for place, and in many instances the necessity of obtaining employment, would subject them to hardships and exactions which they would not otherwise endure. The employer who seeks to obtain the most hours of labor for the least wages has such an advantage over them that the wisdom of the law for their protection cannot well be questioned. No doubt, these considerations were the moving cause for the passage of the law in question. If the act is the result of a fair, reasonable exercise of police power, it should be upheld. By the general police power of the state persons and property are subjected to many restraints and burdens in order to secure the general comfort, health, and prosperity of the state. The perfect right of the legislature to so exercise such power has never been questioned where it was reasonably exercised. We are unable to find a case where the courts have laid down any rigid rule for the exercise of police power. There is little reason, under our system of government, for placing a narrow interpretation on this power, or restricting its scope so as to hamper the legislature in dealing with the varying necessities of society and new circumstances as they arise, calling for legislative intervention in the public interest. The moment the police power is destroyed or curbed by fixed or rigid rules a danger will be introduced into our system which would be far greater than the results arising from an occasional mistake by legislative bodies in exercising such power.

XXIV

THE BENEFIT SYSTEM OF THE CIGAR MAKERS' UNION

The Cigar Makers' International Union is, with respect to the variety and the value of its benefits, the model beneficiary organization of the United States. Though the system of the Cigar Makers is not yet as complete as is maintained by many English unions, it already includes strike, sick, death, disability, traveling, and out-of-work benefits, while a vigorous agitation is in progress for the introduction of the superannuation benefit. This union is deliberately based upon the principle of high dues and an elaborate beneficial system. Each of its 41,536 members contributes $3 initiation fee and 30 cents per week in dues, while from 1879 to 1904, inclusive, the organization has paid out about $6,400,000 in benefits of all kinds. Its growth in membership has been steady and permanent, and has not been characterized either by sudden increases or by sudden decreases. As compared with other American labor organizations the Cigar Makers' International Union is remarkable for its comparatively slow but certain growth and for the few fluctuations in its prosperity.

The first national union of cigar makers was effected in 1864, and in 1867 this organization adopted the name Cigar Makers' International Union of America. It was not, however, until the convention at Buffalo in 1879 that the beneficial system as now existing was begun by the introduction of loans for the support of traveling members. At the same time the strike benefit was reorganized and new and better regulations adopted. The effect upon the membership of the union was immediate. In 1865 there were 984 members, and in 1869,

5800, falling to 3771 in 1873 and to 1016 in 1877. In 1879 the membership was 2729,[1] but by 1880 it had risen to 4440.

At the Chicago convention in 1880 sick and death benefits were added, and in 1881 the membership jumped to 14,604, falling, however, in 1882 to 11,430. A previous attempt had been made, as early as 1873, to introduce a death benefit which was to be supported by an assessment of 10 cents per member to be levied after each death, but the members refused to pay the assessment and the plan was a failure. The death benefit as adopted in 1880 amounted simply to the payment of $40 toward defraying funeral expenses, but in 1887 there was added to this funeral benefit a plan of insurance for all members of five years' standing, the amount paid being from $200 to $550 according to length of membership. In 1887, moreover, a wife's funeral benefit was established, and in 1893 this was extended to the dependent mothers of single members. Another change made in 1887 was a provision to the effect that a member of three years' standing, on drawing a retiring card, could retain his title to sick and death benefits by the payment of 10 cents per week and the special semiannual tax of 50 cents. Meanwhile the membership, which had risen to 13,214 in 1883, falling again to 11,871 in 1884 and attaining 12,000 in 1885, rose to 24,672 in 1886, and never again sank below 17,000.

Very soon after the introduction of the traveling, sick, and death benefits an agitation began in favor of some system of out-of-work or unemployed benefit. This was, of course, the greatest departure yet attempted from the established practice of labor organizations in this country. Sick and death benefits are comparatively common, but the Cigar Makers' International Union was a pioneer among American labor organizations in the field of out-of-work benefits. The arguments advanced in favor of the system were, not only that it would

[1] The figures before 1879 are from the Report of the Industrial Commission, Vol. XVII, p. 280, while those for 1879 and succeeding years are taken from the *Cigar Makers' Official Journal*, May, 1904. From 1879 to 1881, inclusive, these two sets of figures do not correspond.

relieve the distress of unemployed members, but that it would further the main object of the union, the maintenance and improvement of trade conditions. As early as the 1885 convention President Strasser urged that the success of strikes depended upon the attitude of the unemployed, and at the 1887 convention he said, referring to the out-of-work benefit:

> By supporting our members in such emergency, they will have no excuse for working below the regular scale; nor will they have an excuse for accepting conditions of employment which are injurious to the interests of their fellow-workmen. It will instill into them more manhood and independence to resist encroachments of employers in times of depression. It will be the strongest feature to maintain the rate of wages which has been secured during the favorable seasons of trade.

The English unions, too, were cited to show the steady growth of organizations having strong beneficial systems, and the fluctuations of the American labor movement as compared with the English were attributed to the lack of benefits.

On the other hand, the opponents of the out-of-work benefit urged that, while the sick and death payments bore certain approximate proportions to the membership of the union, the number of unemployed members was dependent solely upon trade conditions, and in case of industrial depression might increase so rapidly as to swamp the union. It was also asserted that the 20 cents per week paid in dues at that time was already high enough to keep out of the union seven eighths of the cigar makers of the country, and that the dues ought to be lowered rather than raised the additional 10 cents requisite to maintain this benefit. Apprehension was expressed, moreover, that an out-of-work benefit would be the source of a great deal of abuse and annoyance.

In 1885 the committee on officers' reports failed to agree to the president's recommendation for an out-of-work benefit, and in 1887, in spite of the support of both the president and the committee, the plan was defeated in the convention after a long discussion. In 1889, however, the out-of-work benefit was adopted, and very soon the misgivings in regard to its practical application were dispelled. Several changes have been made in the details of administration, but the principle remains as originally adopted.

The benefits paid in 1905 by the Cigar Makers' International Union of America were as follows: (1) strike benefit, paid also in case of lockout or victimization; (2) sick benefit, payable in case of sickness or disablement; (3) death benefit, including the insurance payment as well as funeral benefit, and also the wife's and mother's funeral benefit; (4) disability benefit; (5) traveling benefit, or loans to traveling members; and (6) out-of-work or unemployed benefit. No member is entitled to receive more than one of the weekly benefits, such as strike, sick, and out-of-work benefits, at the same time. The *Cigar Makers' Official Journal* for April, 1905, publishes a table showing the amounts paid for each of the benefits, and also the cash balance, by years. In 1904 there were paid out: as strike benefit, $32,888.88; as sick benefit, $163,226.18; as death benefit, $151,752.93; as traveling benefit, $58,728.71; and as out-of-work benefit, $29,872.50.

Members who have been in good standing for at least three months are entitled to a strike benefit, provided the strike is approved by the proper authorities of the International Union, of $5 per week for the first sixteen weeks, and $3 per week until the strike or lockout shall have terminated. The assistance in case of a lockout is the same as in case of a strike, and any member who is discharged by his employer on account of having carried out the orders of his union is entitled to the same payments as if he were out on strike. If a striker secures work and is then discharged within fourteen days, he remains entitled to benefit as a striker; but if he retains this employment for over fourteen days and is then discharged, he is entitled to no further strike payments.

Members who have been such continuously for one year or more are entitled to a benefit of $5 per week in case they become sick or disabled in such manner as to render them unable to work. This sickness or inability, however, must have lasted for at least one week, or seven days, "and shall not have been caused by intemperance, debauchery, or other immoral conduct." This latter provision is found in the same or similar language in practically every union which pays a sick benefit. The Cigar Makers also provide that no member leaving the United States or the Dominion of Canada shall be entitled to any benefit during his absence. Moreover, the constitution states that "female members . . . shall not be entitled to any sick benefit three weeks before and five weeks after confinement." Each member is entitled to receive sick benefit for a period of thirteen weeks in each year, commencing from the date of the first report made to an officer of the union. Members of less than one year's standing are not, of course, entitled to sick benefit, but there is a constitutional provision that they shall not be suspended for nonpayment of dues, during sickness or disability, accompanied by the condition that they shall upon resuming work pay 10 per cent of their wages towards making up the arrears until the constitutional limit is reached. This does not, however, excuse such members from paying their percentages on loans, fines, or other indebtedness during the time of sickness. A member taken sick while traveling has only to deposit his card with the union under whose jurisdiction he is at the time in order to receive his benefit from the International Union, provided he has not left the United States or Canada.

There are a number of provisions designed to guard the sick benefit from fraud. In the first place, it is provided that there shall be visiting committees of not less than three officers or members, who shall visit sick persons at least once a week, no two of the committee visiting a member at the same time. Members are obliged to furnish the financial secretary of their local with their correct address and to notify him immediately of all changes. For failure to do this or to perform their duties as visiting committee they are fined 50 cents. Members holding retiring cards but entitled to sick benefits, as well as active members, may be required to serve on these visiting committees. If the visiting committee is refused admittance to the house or is not allowed to see the sick member, the union is not obliged to pay the weekly allowance, but the committee is excused from visiting members having contagious diseases. When the committee has made its report, if there is no doubt of the sickness or inability of the member claiming benefits, the executive board of the union is empowered to draw on the treasurer for the sick benefit, and to report the fact in writing at the next regular meeting of the union. But if there is any doubt, the executive board may take the opinion of a physician appointed by the union. Physicians' certificates, however, are not accepted unless ordered by the union or the visiting committee. Uniform cards for receipts for sick benefits and also for physicians' certificates are issued by the international president. There is a fine of $25 for officers granting sick benefit otherwise than as specified in the rules.

The Cigar Makers' International Union pays, on the decease of a member who has been such for two years, a death benefit of $50. This is designed to assist in the payment of funeral or cremation expenses, and is paid to the nearest of kin or whoever has the burial in charge. It is, of course, simply a funeral benefit. For members of five years' standing, however, the death benefit is $200, for those of ten years' standing $350, and for those of fifteen years' standing $550. Here the idea of provision for the family through insurance is uppermost, and this benefit has been since 1893 payable to the person designated by the member on joining the union. This beneficiary may be changed at any time, and if a member fails to designate any one to receive the money it is to be paid to his heirs at law. If, however, he designates no one, and no claim is made by the heirs within one year after the death of the member, the beneficiary money reverts to the union. Before the benefit is paid, moreover, all international and local indebtedness of the deceased member is deducted. No sick or death benefits are granted if the performance of military duties is the cause of sickness or death. In case there is no one to take charge of the funeral of a deceased member, that duty devolves upon the president of the local union, who is authorized to expend upon the burial the $50 funeral benefit of a member of two years' standing, or, in case the member is entitled to $200 or more death benefit, a sum not to exceed $100. Any member of fifteen years' standing who has become incapable of working at the trade is allowed to retain his claim on the death benefit by the payment of 10 cents per month, payable quarterly.

A married member of two years' standing is entitled, on the death of his wife, to a funeral benefit of $40, provided that the wife was not engaged in the cigar-making industry or not entitled, as a member of the International Union, to the death benefits as previously described. An unmarried member, moreover, is entitled to the same benefit in case of the death of a widowed mother who was dependent solely upon him for support. No member, however, may receive this benefit more than once, and it is not payable to members who have drawn retiring cards by reason of quitting the trade, even though by the payment of 20 cents per week and all assessments they may still be entitled to receive ordinary sick and death benefits.

Obviously, the death benefit, as compared with the other benefits, offers little opportunity for fraud. Nevertheless, there are certain rules designed to prevent irregularities. The secretary of the local union, for instance, must notify the International president of the death of any member entitled to more than $50 benefit, giving the full record of membership of the deceased as shown in the books of the local, and the International president must compare this with the record of the International office before the local is permitted to pay the benefit. "Any local union violating this section shall be held liable for any amount they may have paid over and above the amount the International records show said deceased member to be entitled to." The International president publishes in the *Cigar Makers' Official Journal* the names, ages, and causes of death of the members on whose account the death benefit has been paid.

The disability benefit is a substitute for the death benefit. That is, if a member has "through total blindness or the loss of both hands become permanently incapacitated for performing any kind of labor," the International executive board, at the request of the local union, and after a conclusive and satisfactory investigation, may cause the payment direct to the disabled person of whatever death benefit he is entitled to at the date of application. Within ten days after receiving this disability benefit the member is issued a final withdrawal certificate, and he is thereafter subject to no further benefits by reason of sickness or death.

The system of loans to traveling members is the oldest of the Cigar Makers' benefits, but the payments are on a different basis from the others, owing to the fact that repayment is expected. The union constitutes itself a loan agency for the benefit of its members, carefully guarding itself, however, from the possibility of loss. Any member in good standing for one year, who is unable to obtain employment and wishes to try another location, is entitled to a loan sufficient for transportation, by the cheapest route, to the nearest union in any direction desired, and also to a loan of 50 cents, excluding the fare. The loans, however, shall not exceed in the aggregate $20, and no more than $8 shall be loaned to a member at any one time. No member may receive a second loan until the first one is paid, and the amount paid is credited in the order that the loans were drawn. When a member has traveled the required number of miles, as registered in his loan book, he is entitled to a loan from any other union. But if a member loses or destroys his loan book, he is not entitled to receive any benefits or a duplicate loan book until after two months, during which time the loss is published in the *Official Journal*. The International Union is able to trace members, whether traveling on loans or not, from union to union, and thus to avoid duplication of benefit payments, by means of the provision of the constitution that every traveling member shall carry a traveling card showing his standing, the number of weeks during which he has received sick and out-of-work benefits, and so forth. Any member leaving the jurisdiction of a local union and failing to provide himself with such a card is fined 50 cents, and any member failing to deposit his card with the nearest union after moving is fined 10 cents per day for the first thirty days, and is then expelled from the union.

The officer intrusted with the duty of granting loans is the financial secretary of the local union, and he is governed by strict rules in the performance of this duty. Blanks to be filled out are furnished by the International Union, and financial secretaries are required to report monthly to the International president all loans granted and collected on cards, with the names of the members concerned and their numbers. Careful records are kept at the office of the International Union, and every six months the names of persons delinquent ninety days in the payment of loans are published in a supplement to the *Official Journal*. The following provisions in regard to the issuing of loans appear in the constitution of the International Union:

The financial secretary in issuing duplicate loan cards shall enter in red ink the balance due on the member's old card, and punch out the amount due. No indorsement of loans paid in a member's loan book shall be considered valid by financial secretaries unless stamped with financial secretary's seal. Members who have grievances caused by the foregoing may by application to the International president have their accounts corrected according to International accounts. Secretaries must use financial secretary's seal as a receipt for loans paid, stamped over their signatures in member's loan cards. Failing herein they shall be fined $5, such fines to be remitted to the International Union.

Moreover, any financial secretary granting a loan larger than the amount specified is subject to a fine of not less than the amount which he granted over $20, which is obtained by collecting 25 per cent of his wages. Members, too, who attempt to alter or erase any figure or change any sum in their loan books are fined $25 for the first offense, and are expelled from the union and their names published in the *Official Journal* for the second offense. If such a person should again desire to become a member, he is obliged to pay an initiation fee of at least $25, together with all loans, fines, and assessments previously incurred, and to pay 25 per cent of his weekly earnings until his indebtedness is canceled. A member accepting an illegal loan is fined $5 for each offense.

The repayment of the loans is provided for carefully and in detail. Every shop must have a collector, who is charged with the duty of collecting all fines, assessments, dues, and loans, and paying over the sums received to the secretary of the union. The shop collector may be elected by the members in the shop, but if these fail to do so he is appointed by the president of the local union. If but one union man is employed, he is the collector. In a town where there is more than one shop the members elect also a town collector, who receives the money from the various shop collectors and turns it over within forty-eight hours to the secretary of the union. The loans are repaid at the rate of 10 per cent of the weekly earnings, but if a member goes to work the latter part of the week he is allowed until Saturday of the following week, when he is obliged to pay 10 per cent of his aggregate earnings during the entire time. If a member refuses or neglects to pay to the shop collector his percentage on loans received from the union, he is suspended, forfeits all previous rights and benefits, and can be reinstated only upon the payment of $3, being considered a new member except for the fact that he is still liable for the indebtedness previously incurred. The shop collector reports such refusal or neglect to the financial secretary, and is liable to a fine of $1 if he fails to do so. The financial secretary and the shop collector are both responsible under penalty for the enforcement of every detail of this system of repayment.

The traveling and sick benefits are paid to members of one year's standing, but the out-of-work benefit, like the death benefit, is paid only to members who have paid weekly dues for a period of two years. Members who are not entitled to the benefit, however, are not suspended for nonpayment of dues and assessments, provided they report themselves out of work at least twice a week. They are obliged upon obtaining employment to pay at least 10 per cent of their weekly wages until they have established themselves within the constitutional limit, and, if they remain out of work until entitled to benefit, all dues and assessments are deducted before the benefit is paid. Such members must obtain signed and sealed certificates from the financial secretary to whom they have reported during their nonemployment.

The amount of the out-of-work benefit is $3 per week, and 50 cents for each additional day, but no benefit is paid during the first week of employment. Members drawing benefit for less than six days, moreover, are stricken from the list. After having received benefit for six weeks a member is not entitled to any further benefit for seven weeks thereafter, and no member may receive more than $54 during any one year, commencing July 1. When a member under fifty years of age has received the full benefit of $54 in the year he must have worked for four weeks before he is again entitled to benefit, but this does not apply to members over fifty years of age, who may apparently draw the full $54 every year without working at the trade at all, thus practically receiving a superannuation benefit to that amount.

Any member who obtains employment before receiving six weeks' benefit, and is then discharged before eight weeks have elapsed, is entitled to the balance of his benefit, but a member obtaining employment for two days or longer before his registration has entitled him to benefit, that is, before the first week of unemployment has elapsed, forfeits his previous registration. Members who have received four weeks' strike or sick benefit are not entitled to out-of-work benefit for four weeks thereafter, and sick members incapable of doing a day's work are not considered as out of work. No out-of-work benefit is paid from June 1 till September 23, nor from December 16 to January 15, — dull seasons in the trade, — and members who are unemployed during these times have no privileges except that from June 1 to September 23 they may, by obtaining a certificate and reporting themselves out of work to the financial secretary at least once a week, obtain remission from suspension for nonpayment of dues and assessments. As in the case of members who have not been such long enough to be entitled to out-of-work benefits, however, this privilege must later be paid for by giving the collector of the union 10 per cent of the weekly earnings until within the constitutional limit, or, if the unemployment continues, by the forfeit of a similar portion of the out-of-work benefit when it comes due. Any member engaging in any other occupation during the period of unemployment is not entitled to benefit. Moreover, the large number of women members has led to the provision that "members doing their own domestic work shall not be entitled to any benefit." A member who voluntarily quits a job is not entitled to out-of-work benefit until he shall have again obtained employment for at least one week. Finally, the constitution of the International Union provides that "any member losing his employment through intoxication, or courting his discharge through bad workmanship or otherwise shall not be entitled to any benefit for eight weeks thereafter, and shall be so recorded in his loan book; inability to hold a job shall not deprive a member of his benefit."

The procedure through which members receive the out-of-work benefit is carefully guarded. In the first place, any member who wishes to apply for this benefit must, after being discharged or laid off, obtain from the collector of the shop a certificate stating the cause thereof, and must present this to the financial secretary of the local union. These certificates are kept on file for inspection by the finance committee and International financier. The applicant is then allowed to register. Each local is provided by the International Union with a registry book, and in this the names of the unemployed entitled to out-of-work benefit are written. This must be signed every day, and if the member does not sign he forfeits his benefit for that day, while if he fails for three consecutive days to sign the registry book he forfeits the benefit of previous registration and is not entitled to any benefit until after the preliminary week has again elapsed. Particular hours are specified during which unemployed members must register. Traveling members before receiving benefits must deposit their cards with a union in which they have been registered for six days, and jurisdiction members who are unable to report at least every second day to the financial secretary must report twice every week in writing and must have their reports countersigned by the town and shop collector, producing additional evidence if demanded by the union. "But in no case shall a member be entitled to out-of-work benefit if he remains in a place where no union shop exists." The financial secretary of the local must report at every regular meeting the names of members who have received out-of-work benefit, together with the cause of loss of employment.

It will be observed that the checks upon fraud are numerous, and that the registry system itself is exceedingly strict. It has been found necessary that this should be so. When the out-of-work benefit was originally adopted it was under a careful registry system, but shortly afterwards this was changed to a card system. At the convention in 1896 the International president reported:

> I am fully persuaded that a serious mistake was made when the old registry system for the out-of-work member was abolished. The present or card system opened the door to fraud and petty abuses, which, I regret to say, has in some instances been taken advantage of. I recommend a return to the book-registry system as being absolutely necessary to the successful regulation and maintenance of one of the grandest and most humane features of our benefit system, and the establishment of such other safeguards as may commend themselves to your judgment and wisdom.

This recommendation was adopted by the convention, and the book-registry system was reëstablished. Still another check is provided by the section of the constitution that imposes suspension and a fine of from $5 to $25, as the union may deem proper, upon any member obtaining benefits or endeavoring to obtain benefits under false pretenses.

For the purpose of obtaining work for the unemployed every union must establish a labor bureau, while it is made the duty of the shop collectors to report to the financial secretary of the local union upon the day of receiving notice of the vacancy any jobs that may be open in their factories. Any shop collector failing so to report, or any financial secretary failing immediately to refer to the factory in question an unemployed member, is liable to a fine of not less than $1. Any member, moreover, who knows where a job is open and fails to report it to the financial secretary is fined $1.

Any member refusing to work in a shop where work is offered him, or who neglects to apply for work in a shop if directed by the financial secretary or any officer of the union, or shop collector, shall not be entitled to any benefit until he has secured employment for at least one week. This shall apply to jurisdiction towns within a radius of ten miles. Shop collectors shall immediately report to the financial secretary the name (if known) of any member refusing to work where work is offered him; failing to so report he shall be fined $2 for each offense.

Two other constitutional provisions relating to the benefit system should be mentioned. In the first place, applicants for membership in the union who are affected with chronic diseases or who are over fifty years of age are not entitled to any out-of-work or sick benefit and to no more than $50 death benefit. They pay the regular initiation fee, but only 15 cents weekly dues, while full beneficial members pay 30 cents weekly dues. The executive committee of the local union is the judge of the class to which a new member is assigned. On the other hand, as has been already mentioned, any retiring member who has contributed dues for three years may continue to be entitled to sick and death benefits by the payment of a certain sum in dues. When the provision was adopted this sum was 10 cents, but it has been raised to 20 cents per week. All assessments of the International Union must also be paid. A retiring member failing to avail himself of this privilege forfeits all previous rights and benefits.

This elaborate system of benefits is supported by the payment for each member of $3 initiation fee, 30 cents per week dues, and special assessments and fines. Any member who is in arrears for eight weeks' dues or assessments, except in such cases of unemployment or sickness as have been already mentioned, stands suspended from benefits. "If the member within two weeks from such suspension places himself within the eight-week limit and remains within such limit for ninety days from date of suspension, he shall be restored to his previous rights. Failing to comply with the above he shall stand suspended from the union."

The benefits come out of what is practically the common fund of the Cigar Makers' International Union. They are paid directly by the locals, but the locals themselves in all financial affairs are carefully regulated by the constitution of the International Union. Each local, for instance, must deposit all its money above a certain minimum amount, depending upon the membership, in an appointed bank, or purchase registered bonds of the United States or Canada. Its expenditures, moreover, are carefully regulated, being limited not only to certain specified objects but to a certain percentage of gross receipts. A union which has thirty members or less may expend on its general budget, each item of which is carefully enumerated, 30 per cent of its gross income, one having from thirty to fifty members 25 per cent, and one having fifty members or over 20 per cent. This does not include benefits, which are paid according to the fixed rules already described, any local permitting illegal expenditure on benefits being fined $25. If the funds of a local union become exhausted by legitimate expenditure, the executive board of the International Union, upon receipt of notice to that effect, orders other unions to forward to the first one whatever sums may be considered necessary. Furthermore, there is a regular system of equalizing the funds of local unions according to the annual and monthly reports of the International president, upon the basis of the benefits paid by each. Thus, if one local pays for legal benefits more than its *pro rata* amount, the deficit is made up to it by those other unions which may have expended less than their *pro rata* amounts. The receipts of the International office for its legitimate expenditures are obtained by simply drawing upon any local union from month to month. The orders for money are made by the International president with the consent of the executive board and are published in the *Official Journal* thirty days prior to being sent to the local.

As for the actual cost of the benefit system, the table on the following page shows the per capita expenditure on the various

BENEFIT EXPENDITURES, 1891–1900 [1]

Light-face type shows total expenditure; black-face, per capita expenditure

Year	Strike	Sick	Death	Out-of-work	Total	Membership
1891	$33,531.78	$87,472.97	$38,068.35	$21,223.50	$180,296.60	24,221
	$1.38	**$3.61**	**$1.57**	**$0.88**	**$7.44**	
1892	37,477.60	89,906.30	44,701.97	17,460.75	189,546.62	26,678
	1.40	**3.37**	**1.68**	**.65**	**7.10**	
1893	18,228.15	104,391.83	49,458.33	89,402.75	261,481.06	26,788
	.68	**3.90**	**1.85**	**3.33**	**9.76**	
1894	44,966.76	106,758.37	62,158.77	174,517.25	388,401.15	27,828
	1.62	**3.84**	**2.23**	**6.27**	**13.96**	
1895	44,039.46	112,567.06	66,725.98	166,377.25	389,377.75	27,760
	1.59	**4.06**	**2.40**	**5.99**	**14.04**	
1896	27,446.46	109,208.62	78,768.09	175,767.09	391,190.42	27,318
	1.00	**4.00**	**2.88**	**6.43**	**14.31**	
1897	12,175.09	112,774.63	69,186.67	117,474.40	311,610.79	26,341
	.46	**4.28**	**2.62**	**4.46**	**11.82**	
1898	25,118.59	111,283.60	94,939.83	70,197.70	301,539.72	26,460
	.95	**4.21**	**3.58**	**2.65**	**11.39**	
1899	12,331.63	107,785.07	98,993.83	38,037.00	257,147.53	28,994
	.43	**3.71**	**3.41**	**1.31**	**8.86**	
1900	137,823.23	117,455.84	98,291.00	23,897.00	377,417.07	33,955
	4.06	**3.46**	**2.89**	**.70**	**11.11**	

benefits in each of a series of ten years. As the period under consideration includes both good and bad times in about equal proportion, these figures show the approximate cost of the entire system under average conditions. It will be observed that the expenditures per capita on strike and out-of-work benefits have fluctuated very greatly, but that the expenditures on sick and death benefits show only slight variations. It is also noticeable that, except in the bad years 1894, 1895, and 1896, the strike benefit is small when the out-of-work benefit is large, and vice versa. In 1904 the strike benefit cost 79 cents per

[1] *Cigar Makers' Official Journal*, May, 1904, p. 7.

capita, the sick benefit $3.93, the death benefit $3.65, and the out-of-work benefit 72 cents. During the same year $1.41 per capita was spent upon the traveling benefit, but as this is generally paid back it should not be counted as a part of the cost of the benefit system. With regard to the traveling benefit International President Perkins states: "The loans are repaid, although the books show that we grant from $2000 to $3000 more loans each year than we collect, and according to records there are now outstanding [April, 1905] $88,000 in loans. Probably $30,000 or $40,000 of this amount is lost."

The membership of this organization, thanks to its benefit system, has been comparatively stable. Though the number of members declined somewhat during the years 1895, 1896, and 1897, and even in 1898 was not as great as it had been in 1894, the decline was not nearly as great as in many other unions during the same period. The Operative Plasterers' International Association, for instance, which pays only death benefits, had 90 locals in 1891, 70 in 1892, 80 in 1893, 72 in 1894, 75 in 1895, 63 in 1896, 62 in 1897, and only 38 in 1898, rising, however, to 131 in 1901.[1] Again, the Bricklayers' and Masons' International Union declined in membership from 27,448 in 1892 to 19,674 in 1894. This union has no national benefit system.[2] The International Wood Carvers, with only death benefits, decreased in membership from 1433 in 1893 to 749 in 1897,[3] and the Seamen's Union decreased from 1750 members in 1891 to 350 members in 1895.[4]

Obviously a strong benefit system has a decided influence in keeping the membership of a labor organization intact during dull times. International President Perkins states with reference to the system:

> The effect upon the loyalty of the members is remarkable, inasmuch as it lessens the suspensions and has a tendency to make the organization more permanent. They usually make better fighters during times of strikes, and, as they become imbued with the spirit that loss of membership means a serious financial loss both to themselves

[1] Industrial Commission, Vol. XVII, p. 154.

[2] *Ibid.*, p. 118. [3] *Ibid.*, p. 202. [4] *Ibid.*, p. 256.

and their families, they are more loyal. The so-called insurance feature in our organization, paying from $50 to $550 upon the death of a member, has a strong influence in the maintenance of loyalty throughout the organization.

The union is especially proud, too, of its out-of-work benefit, and the published statements in regard to the amounts expended on this benefit are often used by labor statisticians as a barometer of labor conditions throughout the country. It should be remembered that all this has been accomplished in the face of unfavorable trade conditions which have rendered it impossible to organize more than a small proportion of the cigar makers of the country.

At present a vigorous agitation is in progress, carried on principally through the *Cigar Makers' Official Journal*, in favor of the establishment of a superannuation benefit. Many old and feeble members, it is said, are now paid out-of-work and sick benefits who ought to be receiving superannuation benefits. Moreover, it is urged that this benefit would strengthen the prestige of the organization. As early as 1893 Samuel Gompers, president of the American Federation of Labor, as delegate to the convention of the Cigar Makers' International Union, introduced an amendment to the constitution establishing a superannuation benefit. His plan was to pay to members of ten years' standing a pension of $5 per month, to be increased to $6 after fifteen years' membership, provided that members receiving for five consecutive years full out-of-work or full sick benefits should be placed on the list of members entitled to superannuation benefit, who should receive, however, only $4 per month until after the ten and fifteen years respectively required for the $5 and $6 pensions. This proposition was apparently introduced simply to bring the matter before the membership. In June, 1904, another incomplete working plan was suggested in an editorial in the *Cigar Makers' Official Journal*. This provided for the payment of a pension of $6 monthly to any member contributing dues for twenty-five years, who was sixty years of age or over, and unable to earn $6 weekly; and monthly pensions of $7 and $10 respectively to members seventy years of age and of thirty years' standing and to members eighty years of age and of thirty years' standing.

In this connection it may be observed that the Amalgamated Society of Carpenters and Joiners, an English organization with over 70,000 members, dating from 1860, pays, on an average, something like a third less for its superannuation benefit than for its sick and funeral benefits combined, so that, if the sick and death benefits of the Cigar Makers are worth, as is assumed in the provision for retiring members, about 20 cents per week, the Cigar Makers' International Union, in which insurance is an important factor in the death benefit, could doubtless easily support a superannuation benefit similar to that of the Amalgamated Carpenters, with an increase of 10 cents per week in the dues. The Amalgamated Society of Carpenters and Joiners pays, in this country, from $2.45 to $2.80 per week superannuation benefit. The only other labor organization in the United States which is paying superannuation benefit at the present time is the Amalgamated Society of Engineers, another English organization, though the Pattern Makers' League of North America has a provision in its constitution for the payment of this benefit after 1920. Thus the Cigar Makers have, so far as the United States is concerned, practically a pioneer field to explore in the establishment of a superannuation benefit.

HELEN L. SUMNER.

UNIVERSITY OF WISCONSIN.

XXV

EMPLOYERS' LIABILITY AND ACCIDENT INSURANCE[1]

I

An illustration of the defective foreign-news service of the American press is afforded by the almost complete ignorance that exists here to-day concerning one of the most far-reaching social movements of the nineteenth century. Although the foremost topic of public discussion in the countries of Europe has lately been the problem of accidents to workingmen, the cable dispatches published in our newspapers have scarcely given an inkling of the fact; and while England, France, Denmark, and Italy within the space of eight months (from August 6, 1897, to April 9, 1898) all enacted comprehensive laws, based on entirely new principles, for the protection and indemnification of wage-earners exposed to industrial risks, the only echo of this almost revolutionary movement that reached the readers of American journals was the report that the Swiss people had made use of the referendum to defeat a proposed law for compulsory sickness-and-accident insurance! The explanation of such apparent prejudice or indifference on the part of foreign

[1] From the *Political Science Quarterly*, Vol. XVII, 1902, pp. 256–283. The principal authority followed in this paper is the Seventeenth Annual Report of the New York State Bureau of Labor Statistics (1899), Part II of which is devoted to the subject of "The Compensation of Accidental Injuries to Workmen." As this document is fully indexed, the present writer deems it unnecessary to make specific references. The report also contains bibliographies of the best sources, to which may be added the following recent articles:

"Accidents to Labor," by W. F. Willoughby, in the Bulletin of the United States Department of Labor, January, 1901.

"The British Workmen's Compensation Act," by A. M. Low, *ibid.*

"Present Status of Employers' Liability in the United States," by S. D. Fessenden, *ibid.*, November, 1900.

correspondents may be left to others with a better knowledge of the cause; the present writer is concerned rather with the contrast between European and American principles of legislation in this important field.

To begin with, it may be stated as emphatically as possible that European interest in the problem has not been due to any greater frequency of industrial accidents abroad than in the United States. On the contrary, as might be inferred by any one who stops to think of the incomparable energy, restlessness, and fearlessness of American workingmen, of the relatively high intensity of work in American shops and factories, and of the vastly greater use that our people make of machinery, more workmen, relatively, are injured here than abroad. Statistical demonstration of this might be extended to an indefinite length; but it will be entirely sufficient to cite the fact that the American railways, as compared with the British, have twice the number of employees and every year kill four times as many of them, the annual ratio of accidental deaths to total employees of all classes being 1 to 420 in the United States as compared with 1 to 950 in Great Britain. And if in Germany, with its 50,000,000 people, 8000 wage-earners are killed and more than 400,000 injured every year, we are fairly safe in assuming that in the United States, with its 75,000,000 people, the army of employees annually killed or injured is 50 per cent greater. The problem of industrial accidents, then, exists as surely in the western hemisphere as in the older continent.

Two possible reasons may be advanced for the fact that the problem has attracted little attention here outside of purely academic circles, while in Europe it has agitated popular forums and extorted consideration from statesmen. The contrast probably rests, first, upon differences in the economic situation of workingmen on the two continents, and, secondly, upon differences of legal philosophy. European workmen, with their cramped position, their slender resources, and the burden of militarism, have not been able to obtain an adequate reward for their toil, and hence are likely to be financially crushed by comparatively slight misfortunes and thereby thrown upon the public charities for maintenance. American workingmen, on the other hand, have earned and received high wages and have thus enjoyed what their European *confrères* would call financial independence; their savings or their insurance in fraternal orders have enabled them to withstand the effects of all but the most serious physical injuries without becoming a burden upon the public. Such relative financial independence, however, is becoming far less general in the United States, and it is in recognition of this fact that many of the larger railroad systems have established relief funds or pension departments through which the employer makes some contribution to the alleviation of distress among his injured employees. In the great stock yards, sugar refineries, iron and steel works, and other industrial plants of American cities the foreign-born laborers earn so little money above their minimum requirements that a severe injury is almost sure to make them dependent upon public or private charity. The natural and logical remedy would be a law requiring all employers to act toward their injured workmen as liberal employers already act, — to pay the necessary medical expenses and a moiety of the wage of the victim during the period of disablement from work.

That such a law has nowhere been enacted in America may be in part ascribed to the prevalent individualistic philosophy, which, refusing to look at the social effects, decrees that the wage-earner, in accordance with tradition, must carry the ordinary risks of his occupation. It is assumed that before accepting employment the workman will calculate the relative advantages and disadvantages of his prospective occupation, including the probable danger to life and limb; and that his remuneration is thereupon so adjusted that his wages will include compensation for possible injury.[1] This legal

[1] See the opinion of Chief Justice Shaw of Massachusetts in the leading case of *Farwell* v. *Boston and Worcester*, 4 Met. 49: "The general rule resulting from considerations as well of justice as of policy is that he who engages in the employment of another for the performance of specified duties and services for compensation takes upon himself the natural and ordinary risks and perils incident to the performance of such services, and, in a legal presumption, the compensation is adjusted accordingly."

fiction,[1] however, has no basis in fact; railroad trainmen, for instance, obtain no more than the wages of ordinary laborers, although one out of every eleven of them is seriously injured every year. Sailors, miners, quarrymen, and other workmen in extrahazardous trades are paid no more than laborers in other occupations, excepting where the matter of skill enters into the question. To suppose that these wage-earners ever seriously consider the matter at all is to impute to them a measure of foresight and of economic strength in the wage bargain that is found only in the skilled artisan class, the "aristocracy of labor."

Nevertheless, the two reasons above recited (the relative economic independence of American wage-earners and the prevalent individualistic philosophy) explain why in this country all practical efforts thus far made to deal with the problem of industrial accidents have been limited to proposals for altering the law of negligence so far as it concerns the relation of employer and employee. Premising that the employees assume the ordinary risks of their occupations, the law holds the employer responsible for accidents due to his own negligence precisely as it holds any person liable to pay damages for such neglect of his duties as results in injury to other persons. But in one essential respect the common law of England and America has discriminated against the servant or employee: it has refused to maintain the doctrine of principal and agent in the case of accidents caused by negligence when the person injured is an employee of the person by whom or upon whose behalf the act of negligence was committed.

To illustrate: if a grocer's delivery wagon runs down a pedestrian, who himself is not at fault, the pedestrian has the right of action for damages not merely against the driver but also against the principal, the grocer, who may in fact have given the most precise instructions to his driver about exercising vigilance and respect for the rights of pedestrians. This ancient

[1] It has been so characterized by Judge Earl of the New York Court of Appeals: "To enforce the supposed public policy a fiction has been invented by which the servant is said to assume all the risks of the service in which he engages." — *Crispin* v. *Babbitt*, 81 N. Y. 529.

and firmly established principle of *respondeat superior*, whereby the principal must answer for negligent acts of his agent, rests purely upon the expediency of giving the victim a legal claim upon some party who is pecuniarily responsible, — in other words, some one who can pay damages. It is, apparently, a universal principle of law, and its justification, aside from the motive of expediency just indicated, rests upon the idea that, if a man finds it convenient or profitable to delegate any part of his work to others, he must still be ready to furnish satisfaction for injuries growing out of such work; if he fears to risk his property by thus giving bonds for the conduct of his agents, he has the alternative of doing his own work alone. Now the injustice of the American law of negligence, as applied to employees, lies in the fact that our courts have created an exception to the universal principle expressed in the maxim *respondeat superior* by refusing to hold the principal responsible for the negligence of an agent when the person injured is a fellow-employee. To recur to the illustration: if the supposed pedestrian run down by a careless driver of a grocer's wagon happened to be a clerk in the employ of the same grocer, he could not obtain damages from the principal.

Crudely illustrated, this is the famous "fellow-servant doctrine" which has naturally evoked antagonism on the part of American workingmen. It is a doctrine that is not tolerated in continental courts, and it was largely abolished by statute in England more than twenty years ago. It has also been considerably modified either by legislation or by judicial decisions in most American commonwealths.[1] But workingmen look upon it as a burden even in its modified form, and to it is apparently due most of their present discontent. Will they be satisfied with its entire abolition? Is an employer's liability law, perfected on these lines, really a solution of the problem of accidents to labor? That

[1] In recent years the courts have stretched the doctrine of "vice principal" so as to cover many coemployees of an injured workman. That is to say, if the agent whose negligence brought about the injury to a coemployee was performing any of the duties properly belonging to the employer, he is regarded not as a "fellow-servant" but as a "vice principal," or *alter ego*, of the employer, who thus becomes liable for damages.

question may most properly be answered by reviewing the experience of other countries.

II

In Germany, as in England and the United States, the problem of industrial accidents did not assume prominence until the advent of railways; but in the German states the legislature did not step aside and leave the courts to develop a law of employers' liability. On the contrary, railway construction had scarcely begun in Germany when in 1838 the Prussian legislature enacted a law which provided that every railway company should be liable for personal injuries to employees (as well as to passengers), unless it could prove in court that the accident was occasioned by the negligence of the victim or by an act of Providence; and still further to strengthen the employee's case, the law specifically provided that the risks inherent in the railroad business should not be considered as rendering accidents inevitable, and hence should not exempt the corporation from responsibility. This Prussian law of 1838 thus goes far beyond the demands of American workingmen at the present time, at least so far as respects railways, which are in truth the subject of most of the agitation; for it transfers the burden of proof from the shoulders of the injured employee to those of the corporation. It distinctly directs that the employer, and not the employee, is to assume the ordinary risks of the industry.

Upon the formation of the German Empire in 1871 this Prussian act of 1838 was embodied in a general-liability law for the Empire, which also defined, though in less stringent terms, the liability of proprietors of factories, mines, quarries, and so forth. The enormous industrial expansion of Germany, following its consolidation under a strong government, rapidly transformed the small shops of handicraftsmen into great factories, in which the employer's responsibility for his workingmen was dissipated among numerous superintendents, foremen, and others who assumed certain of his functions of control. The conditions of labor in factories and mines began to approximate those on the railways, and the earlier reform movements sought to extend the provisions of the railway-liability law to the manufacturing industry and other employments. But far-sighted economists—Schäffle, Wagner, Schmoller, and others — deemed such a reform entirely inadequate, holding that, because of the difficulty of locating the negligence, the law of negligence could by no possibility be sufficiently perfected to secure for injured workmen proper compensation. This difficulty was set forth in the preamble of the accident-insurance bill of 1881.

To burden the person injured with the requirement of furnishing proof of negligence on the part of the employer or his agents transforms the beneficence of the law for the workingman into an illusion in the majority of cases. The procurement of such evidence, sufficiently difficult in any event, is not seldom rendered impossible as respects some of the most severe injuries brought about by natural forces, as happens in mines, establishments with steam boilers, and factories for the manufacture of explosives. Herein the condition of the workplace — the implements and appliances, upon which the whole case of the workman really turns — is so altered by the accident itself as to be unrecognizable; while those persons through whose testimony alone negligence in many cases can be proven have been killed or injured by the accident. The injured, even if not, as is generally the case, parties to the suit, are left in such condition by the catastrophe as to be unable to give formal testimony.

Without entering further into the legislative history of the question, it will be sufficient to state that the economists, aided by Emperor William I and Bismarck, finally triumphed in the passage of the act of 1884, which made employers responsible for all accidents to employees in the course of their occupation except such as should be occasioned by the willful misconduct of the victims themselves. This minor exception is virtually all that is left in Germany of the law of negligence so far as it concerns employees.[1]

To comprehend fully the methods of the German law for indemnifying workmen injured at their work, one must consider an analogous law enacted two years earlier (1882), namely, the

[1] Of course, employers may still be sued for negligence; but such actions are brought only when the negligence is so gross as to promise a considerably larger compensation than that afforded by the accident-insurance law.

sickness-insurance law. This act requires the establishment of sick funds in all industries, one third of the contributions to come from employers and two thirds from the working people. Any employee injured while at work is cared for by the sick funds for the first *three months after the accident;* but if at the end of these thirteen weeks he is still incapacitated, he is entitled to an allowance equal to two thirds of his wages, besides the medical expenses, out of a fund maintained by the employers. If he dies at any time as a result of his injuries, his family is entitled to a yearly pension not exceeding 60 per cent of his wages.

In order to guard the employee against the possible loss of his compensation or allowance through the bankruptcy or failure of his employer, the law provides for the collective responsibility of employers; that is, all employers are grouped together into associations by industries (*Berufsgenossenschaften*), and each association pays the claims of workingmen employed by its own members. The members of each association are annually assessed, according to the size of their pay rolls and the hazard of their business, at a rate sufficient to pay the death claims, the benefits to temporarily disabled workmen, and the pensions to entirely incapacitated workmen and the families of employees killed by accident. The assessments must also cover the administrative expenses of the association, which include the salaries of a large number of engineering and mechanical experts employed by the associations to inspect the factories of members and see that the best appliances are bought and used for safeguarding dangerous machinery. Briefly put, the German law requires every employer to join a mutual insurance company, which indemnifies his employees for all personal injuries sustained in the course of their employment, the question of negligence on one side or the other having nothing to do with the amount of such indemnification,[1] which is fixed by the amount of the employee's wages and, in case of his death, the number of surviving dependents. The administrative

[1] With the qualification that no compensation is paid when the injury is due to the victim's willful misconduct — which in practice has proved unimportant — and that the victim may sue for damages when the employer has been grossly negligent.

machinery for determining the compensation is prescribed by the law, but, on account of limitations of space, cannot be described here.[1]

For eighteen years now this compulsory accident-insurance system has been on trial in Germany, and its success can no longer be seriously questioned. It has been successively extended by the lawmaking authorities, and when in 1900 it was thoroughly overhauled and revised the changes were wholly in the direction of enlarging its scope. The broad result is to be seen in the following facts: About 20,000,000 persons, or nearly two fifths of the entire population and ten elevenths of that part engaged in gainful occupations, are protected by the insurance system, and any one of these persons, in case of a disabling accident, may claim a living allowance as a right and not as a charity; each year about 100,000 accidental injuries are indemnified, of which one half are cases of temporary disablement (exceeding, however, a duration of three months) and one half cases of permanent disablement or death; about $20,000,000 are annually expended through this system, of which 80 or 85 per cent is actually paid to the sufferers, about 2 per cent being expended for the prevention of accidents, and the remainder representing the expenses of management. The actual burden of this insurance upon German industry cannot be determined, for the reason that permanently injured employees are not indemnified with a lump sum of money, but are pensioned with an annual or quarterly allowance for life. Nevertheless, the annual expenditures, which are almost identical with the assessed contributions of employers, have lately averaged only $1.22 per $100 of the annual wage roll, and this is a lower rate than any prevailing from 1892 to 1897. Of course, the rate varies enormously from industry to industry according to the relative risks of accident; it is about twenty-four times as great in mining as in the tobacco industry, which is the least hazardous of the manufactures.[2]

[1] See Chapter XXVI, p. 574.

[2] In 1897 the amount actually paid in the indemnification of injuries was $1.78 per $100 of wages in mining, and only 8 cents in the tobacco industry.

III

The other countries of Europe had been as much concerned as Germany with the question of reforming the law of liability, but they postponed action in order to await the result of the German experiment. Only Austria, which is for the most part a German country, accepted at once the new principle of incorporating in the cost of production of manufactured goods, by the side of the allowance for wear and tear of machinery, an item for the wear and tear of human operatives. But the Austrian law of 1887, though it insures compensation for all injuries, regardless of the question of negligence, differs in many respects from the German law. It permits employers, for example, to deduct 10 per cent of their assessments from the wages of employees, and it requires the capitalized value of each pension to be paid at the time of the accident.[1] Again, the collective responsibility of employers is secured, not as in Germany through associations for different industries, only the railroads having a trade association, but through seven provincial or district associations. Furthermore, the government itself does not undertake the business of insurance, although it establishes the rates. Additional variations from the German law can also be found in the scale of compensation, but these need not be entered into at this point.

The other Teutonic nations of northern Europe could not but be influenced by the long discussion of employers' liability and accident insurance in Germany and the final adoption of the latter principle. Within a few months after the enactment of the German law of 1884 parliamentary commissions were at work in Norway, Sweden, Denmark, and Finland, gathering statistics of accidents, of the methods for alleviating distress in the families of the stricken workmen, and so forth. The Norwegian commission completed its labors and presented draft bills in 1890, and

[1] It appears that the actuaries put the rate of the contributions somewhat too low when they calculated that the average assessment would have to be $1.40 per $100 of the annual pay roll; whereas, for the seven years 1890–1896 the net charges amounted to $1.55 per $100 of wages. The premium required in certain dangerous industries also proved too low, and the next revision of the schedule of rates will result in many increases and but few reductions.

in 1894 the legislature fully accepted the principle of compulsory compensation for all accidents and enacted an accident-insurance law. This law more closely resembles the Austrian than the German act. Compensation begins four weeks after the accident and is fixed at 60 per cent of the victim's wages; in the event of his death the pension to his family is not to exceed 50 per cent of his average annual income. In Norway as in Germany the expenses of indemnification of injuries are to be paid by the employers without deduction from wages; but in Norway the state guarantees the indemnities and collects the assessments from employers through a state insurance office, the expenses of which are a state charge.

In 1895 Finland enacted a workmen's compensation law of less comprehensive scope. While it provides a scale of compensation and requires employers to insure their employees against accident through authorized companies or by depositing securities with the government, it does not grant compensation to employees injured through the fault of fellow-workmen or *vis major*. In other words, it does not cover the unavoidable mishaps which constitute the bulk of all industrial accidents.

The Danish parliamentary commission made its report in 1888, but, owing to differences of opinion as to the wisdom of a system of obligatory insurance, the legislature did not agree upon a law until 1897.[1] The action of Great Britain seemed to have a decisive influence in crystallizing sentiment in Denmark, as in the other continental states. On account of the far-reaching influence of English policy, it is advisable to consider somewhat carefully the steps by which the British Parliament at last definitely abandoned employers' liability based upon the law of negligence and accepted the principle of compensation for all accidents.

IV

As we have already seen, the judge-made law of employers' liability, embracing the indefensible doctrine of common employment, had operated in England and the United States to

[1] Sweden, the remaining Scandinavian country, did not enact an accident-insurance law until 1901.

the great injury of the English and American workmen. And the fact that the "fellow-servant doctrine" was upheld so much more rigorously by the English courts, dominated by the capitalistic House of Lords (the final court of appeal), as well as the fact of the greater relative importance of machine production, inspired in England a movement for legislative definition of the law of liability and led to the adoption of the Employers' Liability Act of 1880, which has served as a model for several American statutes. While this act removed some of the more unjust defenses utilized by employers to avoid the penalties of their negligence, it failed to give general satisfaction. Amendments were offered at nearly every session of Parliament and several commissions were appointed to examine into the question. Finally, in 1893, the Gladstone government accepted the views of the workingmen and introduced an employer's liability bill that was calculated to destroy the doctrine of common employment root and branch. This bill passed the House of Commons, but came back from the House of Lords with unacceptable amendments concerning the power of employers to contract themselves out of their liability by special agreements with their employees. The consequent defeat of the bill ended the prospect of legislation under the Liberals.

But the situation so urgently demanded reform that the Conservatives, upon their accession to power in 1895, could not decline to act, especially in view of their obligations to the Liberal-Unionist wing, which through its leader, Joseph Chamberlain, had promulgated a really liberal labor programme, including reform of the liability law.[1] The government bill, introduced at the session of 1896–1897, went far beyond any of the proposals of the Liberal government by offering compensation for all accidental injuries, quite irrespective of the negligence of this person or that.

The debates upon this bill fill several hundred very interesting pages in Hansard. The average member of Parliament, who was likely to be an employer, could not at first understand why

[1] See Mr. Chamberlain's article in the *Nineteenth Century*, November, 1892.

he should pay indemnification for injuries for which he was not to blame. But the history of employers' liability throughout the era of machine production had demonstrated the impossibility of locating the blame, since, as a matter of fact, the great bulk of industrial accidents are virtually unavoidable. Any person can see that the operator of a buzz saw is exposed to greater risks than a cigar maker, and no amount of care on the part of the employer or the operator will serve to equalize the risks. For the vast majority of accidents, therefore, the liability of an employer under the law of negligence affords no remedy to the victim. Striking evidence of this fact was adduced in the testimony taken by the Royal Commission on Labor in 1894, when one of the great accident-insurance companies testified that in 26,087 cases of accidental injury which it had indemnified under collective accident-insurance policies carried by employers, not more than 3026, or 12 per cent, would have been entitled to compensation under the law of negligence.

Now assuming that a liability law based on negligence would compel employers to pay compensation for that 12 per cent of their injuries to their employees, it could be easily demonstrated that the uncertainties, the expense, and above all the bitterness of class feeling incident to such legal conflicts, would frequently outweigh the advantages of the law. Such a law must of necessity be full of uncertainties, because it attempts to define the duties of employer and those of employee, — duties which are constantly shifted with the progress of invention and the adoption of improvements. One week a court may have held that it was not the employer's duty to provide certain safeguards for a machine because such provisions had not become a part of the usual customs and practices of the business; another week the same court might decide that such guards were necessary and reasonable. In one case, where scaffolding has given way and a workman has been seriously injured, it is decided that the foreman, acting for the employer, should have inspected the defective scaffolding; in the next case it may be held that the obligation of inspecting the scaffolding rested upon the employee himself. Numerous cases of fatal accidents also occur in which the evidence of negligence is destroyed and the workingman's family are thus deprived of their rightful indemnification, even though the law itself may be clear; such cases are of frequent occurrence among colliery explosions, where the witnesses perish along with all evidences of possible negligence.

If the uncertainty and expensiveness of legal actions for damages were not sufficient to deter an injured employee from proceeding against his employer, he would be deterred by the apprehension of losing employment. The official memorandum of the British Home Office summed up the defects of the employers' liability law from the viewpoint of the workingman in the following single paragraph.

> The truth is that to the workman litigation under the act has more than its usual terrors. It is not merely that litigation is expensive and that he is a poor man and his employer comparatively a rich one, — it is that when a workman goes to law with his employer he, as it were, declares war against the person on whom his future probably depends; he seeks to compel him by legal force to pay money, and his only mode of doing so is the odious one of proving that his employer or his agents — his own fellow-workmen — have been guilty of negligence. Add to this that the legal proof of such negligence is often extremely difficult. The broad result is that a legal claim for damages only answers where the injury is very great and the workman is prepared to leave his master's service.[1]

If uncertainty and expensiveness made the law unsatisfactory to the workman, they did not make it satisfactory to the employer. Liability to pay damages for negligence did not lead to any correspondence between the penalty and the degree of culpability. The most criminal negligence might result in a trifling injury, compensated at the expense of a week's wages, while some trifling oversight in the selection of materials might lead to loss of life and heavy damage suits. Employers kept

[1] Appendix to the minutes of evidence taken before the Royal Commission of Labor, 1894, C 7063–III A, p. 351.

in their service an army of lawyers whose remuneration would have afforded compensation to hundreds of injured employees. On the other hand, many a fairly disposed employer found himself prosecuted by professional "damage" lawyers, or "shysters," who stepped in to prevent any peaceable arrangement between him and an injured workman. Mr. Chamberlain, for example, related the experience of a friend who told him that "in two cases which he was absolutely bound to fight and both of which he won, the costs amounted to more than any compensation ever given under the Employers' Liability Act."[1] That act — which, be it remembered, is substantially the law in America to-day — was characterized by Mr. Asquith, the Liberal leader, as "an elaborate series of traps and pitfalls for the unwary litigant, and productive of litigation which, in proportion to its difficulty and cost, is absolutely barren of result."[2]

It was probably the cold, hard fact of the expensiveness of futile litigation under the liability law that appealed more than any other argument to the conservative British capitalists and merchants who compose the House of Commons and induced them to adopt the new principle of compensation for all accidents.

Aside from the experience of foreign countries, never decisive to an Englishman, the country already had some evidence of its own as to the probable workings of the new system. After the passage of the liability act of 1880 there had grown up in England great insurance companies which made a business of relieving employers of suits for damages brought on behalf of injured employees, the premiums for such insurance being a certain percentage of the annual pay roll. These companies, moreover, did a real accident-insurance business on a similar basis, issuing to employers for a somewhat higher premium a workman's collective-insurance policy. The statistics furnished by one of the largest of these insurance companies afforded the instructive comparison shown in the following table.

[1] Parliamentary Debates, XLVIII (1897), 1465.
[2] *Ibid.*, XLIX, 753.

	Liability Insurance	Workmen's Collective Insurance
Claims admitted	1,188	26,087
Claims abandoned	952	97
Claims litigated	327 [1]	4
No claims made	7,750	
Total accidents reported	10,217	26,188

It thus appeared that of 10,217 injured employees only 1327, or 13 per cent, could obtain compensation under the employers' liability law, while under the accident-insurance policy all but an infinitesimal number were compensated. The contrast pointed the way to a new system of legislation whereby the compensation of accidents should be a mere business arrangement rather than a matter of law. The British Workmen's Compensation Act of 1897, like the German act of 1884, the Austrian act of 1887, and the Norwegian act of 1894, virtually makes the employer the insurer of his workmen against all accidents. In the words of Mr. Chamberlain, it says to every employer in the industries covered by the act:

> When you enter upon a business you must consider this compensation is as much a trade charge as is now the provision which you are called upon to make for the repair of machinery. You at present have to put aside every year a certain sum for the repair of the inert machinery, which is a factor in your business. Now the human element in the business has to be considered, and in the case of accident what reparation you can make must be made as a charge upon the business.

The scale of compensation fixed by the law assures to a totally disabled workman a weekly benefit equal to one half his average wages; to the family of a workman mortally injured, a lump sum equal to three years' wages (but not less than $730 or more than $1460). The disability allowance begins with the third week of disablement.

In passing it should be noted that the act of 1897, while affording these new compensations to an injured workman,

[1] Of these 136 were won and 191 lost by workmen.

does not abolish his old rights of action against a negligent employer. On the contrary, he may sue his employer for negligence under the common law or under the liability act of 1880, and if defeated may still claim as a matter of right, not to be disputed, the compensation allowed him under the new act. Provided the workman is disabled from earning full wages for a period of at least two weeks, the only defense the employer can offer is that the accident did not "arise out of and in course of the employment," or that it was attributable to the serious and willful misconduct of the workman himself.

This is not the place to enter upon a discussion of the virtues and defects of the English Workmen's Compensation Act of 1897. Certain things about it, however, are clearly established:

1. The principle of compensation for all accidents has been permanently accepted in England; the only amendment made to the act has been one to widen its scope by extending it to agriculture. The occupations not as yet embraced in the law are domestic service, service in small workshops where no mechanical power is used, the building of structures less than thirty feet high, mercantile pursuits, trucking, and navigation. It will be seen that the only industrial classes still outside the law that are exposed to heavy risks are seamen and fishermen.

2. Litigation, even in the beginning when the law required interpretation, has been insignificant. In the first six months of its operation not a single litigated case was recorded in some of the principal mining districts, which, with a population of 1,500,000, had innumerable accidents. Probably the experience of the Bolton and District Operative Cotton Spinners' Provincial Association is indicative of the operation of the law. Its report for 1901 shows that since the act came into operation the claims of 640 injured members had been paid, of which only 12, or less than 2 per cent, were the subject of litigation. Unofficial returns in other industries show similar results and indicate that the proportion of claims settled without litigation is over 98 per cent.

3. The cost of indemnification has been comparatively low in spite of the high premiums demanded by insurance

companies. In South Roxburghshire, where the insurance companies asked from 22½ to 37½ cents per $100 of the annual pay roll, mutual insurance associations were formed by the employers and indemnities paid on the basis of a premium of only 12½ cents per $100 of wages.[1] As yet the burden of the act, if indeed it has been a burden, has not made itself felt in the competition with foreign countries, most of which, indeed, have similar acts.

V

The action of England in accepting the principle of compensation for all accidents seemed to bring to a head the discussion that had been going on in other countries for a decade or more. In the four years that have since elapsed no fewer than nine states have enacted similar laws, including France, Italy, Spain, Holland, and Sweden, as well as two of the Australasian colonies. The Danish act of January 7, 1898, has already been mentioned; like the English act, it makes insurance voluntary on the part of employers, but gives the injured employee a prior claim on insurance due to the employer in case of accident. The accident benefit, which does not begin until the fourteenth week, is fixed at 60 per cent of the victim's wages, and the indemnity in case of his death is equivalent to four years' wages.

Italy followed with the act of March 17, 1898, which made insurance obligatory, indeed, but left employers the option of insuring in authorized companies or in mutual associations or by the deposit of securities with the government. The disability allowance begins on the sixth day after the accident, and is equal to 50 per cent of the victim's usual wages. In case of permanent disablement or death the indemnity is a lump sum equal to five years' wages.

About the same time France was enacting a workman's compensation law. The question had been before the legislature at every session for years, but the Senate and Chamber of Deputies had not previously succeeded in agreeing upon a

[1] See M. Barlow, "The Insurance of Industrial Risks," *Economic Journal*, Vol. XI (September, 1901), p. 348.

bill. Now the influence of the English act, combined with the exigencies of local politics and the approach of elections, resulted in the act of April 9, 1898. Under this law the accident allowance begins on the fifth day after the accident, and for temporary disablement is fixed at one half the victim's average wages, while for permanent incapacity it is two thirds of his wages. In event of his death pensions to surviving members of his family are not to exceed, in the aggregate, 60 per cent of his annual wage.

The treatment of the insurance problem in this act is peculiar to France, and is the result of a compromise between the Senate and the Chamber of Deputies. Instead of compelling employers to carry insurance for the protection of their employees or against the possibility of their own bankruptcy or failure, the French government guarantees the payment of accident benefits and indemnities. For this purpose a special guarantee fund is to be accumulated by means of a small addition to the regular business tax in the case of concerns subject to the law. This novel experiment will be watched with interest in other countries. While it might easily lead to a state insurance office, France has been noted for the strong development of employers' mutual associations, and it is generally hoped that these may continue to gather strength under the new *régime*.

No new compensation acts were recorded in 1899, but on January 30, 1900, Spain joined the other industrial countries with such legislation. The Spanish act is rather limited in scope, as it does not require the compensation of inevitable accidents (those caused by *vis major*), and in that particular more closely resembles employers' liability laws. But it provides a definite scale of compensation, the temporary allowance to an injured employee being one half his usual wages and the indemnity for permanent disability being a lump sum equal to two years' earnings. In the case of fatal accidents the indemnity to the victim's family is likewise two years' earnings, or, at the option of the employer, a pension equal to not more than 40 per cent of the workman's income.

The New Zealand act of October 18, 1900, and the South Australian act of December 5, 1900, are modeled so closely after the English act as to call for no special consideration.

The accident-insurance law enacted by Holland, January 2, 1901, grants to the workmen perhaps the most liberal terms of any of these acts. The allowance, which begins on the day following the injury, is to be 70 per cent of the victim's regular wage, and that is also the ratio in case of permanent (and total) disability. In case of death the pension to his family is to be 60 per cent of his earnings. Insurance in authorized private companies or the government insurance office is obligatory unless the employer prefers to deposit securities with the government for the payment of compensation to his injured employees. One peculiar feature of the Dutch act is the discrimination against drunkenness; the law provides that, if the accident is due to intoxication, the victim shall receive only one half the usual allowance, and his heirs or dependents none.[1]

On February 21, 1901, the Kingdom of Greece adopted a workmen's compensation act for mines, smelting works, and certain quarries, which is peculiar in that one half of the indemnities due to permanent disabilities and fatalities are to be paid by the Miners' Provident Fund, which is administered by the government. But as the fund is maintained by the taxation of mines, and so forth, the burden really falls upon the industry after all. The allowance for disablement is 50 per cent of the usual wage.

The Swedish act of April 24, 1901, is not so liberal as the earlier Norwegian act, and the scale of compensation differs from all others in that it fixes an invariable sum as the disability allowance or benefit instead of a percentage of the wage earned by each victim; nor does it require indemnification of injuries occasioned by the willful misconduct of third persons, providing they do not exercise authority. By opening the door to disputes respecting the negligence of certain persons and the responsibilities of others the act thus embodies the usual defect

[1] The Dutch law is summarized in the *Bulletin of the U. S. Bureau of Labor*, May, 1901, pp. 190–193.

of employers' liability laws, namely, it does not avoid enormous expenses for litigation.

Switzerland is still debating schemes of accident insurance, having accepted the principle more than ten years ago in the form of a constitutional amendment. After long preparation the federal legislature in 1899 passed a compulsory sickness-and-accident insurance law which was to go into force January 1, 1903; but on the referendum vote in 1900 the law was rejected by a majority of two to one. It seems probable that new projects will be less comprehensive in scope. In the meantime the Swiss have a very liberal employers' liability law, enacted some twenty-five years ago, which, like the Prussian law of 1838, places the burden of proof upon the employer and makes him liable for all injuries, unless he can prove in court that the accident was caused by the act of God or the negligence of the victim.

Russia has a similar law applying to railways and steamships, and is therefore in a more advanced position than the United States.

Belgium is the only other industrial nation of Europe that has not accepted the principle of *risque professionnel.* While a very successful organization of mine owners in Belgium has furnished at its own expense accident aid to injured miners since 1840, interest is by no means wanting in a national accident-insurance system. The ministry itself prepared and introduced a bill in 1898, after the adoption of workingmen's compensation acts in England, France, and Italy; but the bill was referred to a commission, and before it was reported the legislature was dissolved and a general election held (1900). Belgium having already enacted an old-age pension law, it can safely be premised that the problem of industrial accidents will not long await a solution.

VI

The preceding review of European experience with the problem of industrial accidents ought to throw some light upon the probable course of legislation in the United States. Even should the agitation by our workingmen for the statutory abrogation of the obnoxious fellow-servant doctrine prove entirely successful, it will bring us only to the first stage in the evolution of negligence law into accident insurance, — the stage reached by England twenty years ago, after the enactment of the Employers' Liability Act of 1880. This act, indeed, constituted an improvement upon preëxisting conditions; but as a final solution of a large problem it was a flat failure, or, as Mr. Asquith termed it, "a scandal and a reproach to the legislature." We have already sketched its breakdown and noted that its fatal defect consisted in requiring an enormous outlay on the impossible task of locating the blame for the accidents of modern industry. The futile litigation which, on account of its expensiveness, finally convinced Parliament of the failure of negligence law as a remedy for the injuries of employees is characteristic of the United States at the present time. And what is the logical result? The courts, in order to discourage suits and thus restrict the volume of litigation, have betrayed a tendency to throw out cases on technical grounds or to treat lightly the responsibility of the employer. The authors of one of the leading American text-books on the law of negligence plainly declare that

> it has become quite common for judges to state as the ground of decisions the necessity of restricting litigation. Reduced to plain English, this means the necessity of compelling the great majority of men and women to submit to injustice, in order to relieve judges from the labor of awarding justice. . . . The law of master and servant in its relation to the law of negligence affords perhaps the most striking example in the last half century of gross injustice done by this disposition to restrict responsibility and suppress litigation.[1]

It is difficult to believe that any person at all familiar with the operations of the British act of 1880 can look for any decided improvement in American conditions through amendments to the law of negligence.[2] When in 1893 the Liberal party in

[1] Shearman and Redfield on Negligence (1898), pp. iii, vi.

[2] It is doubtful if the American statutes modeled upon the British act of 1880 have brought about any perceptible improvement over the common law. This much, at least, is true, — the liability-insurance companies charge employers no

England sought to improve the act of 1880 without abandoning the foundation principle of negligence, the attempt was defeated partly because the bill came to be known, not as an Employers' Liability Bill, but as a "Lawyer's Employment Bill." This satirical appellation is really descriptive of all legislation on the present subject that aims to rest the responsibility of employers on the ground of negligence.

The term may be said to apply also to a more advanced type of liability law, which, though it has not as yet been proposed in the United States, was adopted in some European countries in the first half of the nineteenth century, namely, the legislation under which the burden of proof of negligence was shifted from the workman to the employer. As long ago as 1838 the Prussian law required a railroad company to pay damages to injured employees unless it could go into court and there produce legal evidence that the accident was caused by *vis major* or by the negligence of the injured workmen. This is still the law in Switzerland for all mechanical industries, and in Russia and Hungary for transportation companies. But none of these countries has been satisfied with such a law, and all of them have either abandoned it already or are preparing so to do.

The third stage in the evolution of accident legislation is reached when a community has once grasped the principle of *risque professionnel*, — the principle, namely, that every trade and occupation has its own risks or dangers, and that, as the bulk of the accidents therein are unavoidable, they should be paid for out of the profits of that trade and not saddled upon the families of individual workmen. The demonstration of the truth of this principle waited upon the collection of comprehensive statistics; but since the establishment of accident-insurance systems in several countries such statistics abound. It will be worth our while just to glance at some of the best of them, shown in the following table.

heavier premiums in Massachusetts, which since 1887 has had a "model" liability law, than in the other New England states, which have enacted no such laws. The inference is that disabled Massachusetts workmen get no more compensation than their comrades protected only by the common-law rules.

ACCIDENTS IN AUSTRIA, 1890–1894

		Number	Percentage
Fault of victim	Imprudence and gross negligence	10,937	22.60
	Disobedience of rules or neglect to use safeguards	1,563	3.23
	Willful misconduct	7	.01
Fault of employer	Defective plant	413	.85
	Omission of safeguards	218	.45
	Gross carelessness	53	.11
Fault of third person		762	1.57
Unforeseen contingencies		33,976	70.20
Unknown		471	.97
Total		48,400	99.99

These statistics extend through five years and embrace nearly 50,000 accidents to employees. It appears that fully 70 per cent of the accidents were declared to be unavoidable by the government officials who investigated them, and whose judgment, since the indemnities had to be paid without reference to the cause of the casualty, may be regarded as wholly unbiased.

It must be clear, upon reflection, that the conditions under which modern industry is carried on preclude the possibility of explaining every accident by somebody's negligence. This much was dimly understood when various countries took the first step of shifting the *onus probandi* from employee to employer. If, now, the employees are not to blame for the innumerable injuries to which they are subject, why should they be made to bear the financial burden of those injuries? Why should not that burden be distributed over the community instead of being concentrated upon a certain number of families who, in any event, will have to bear the physical and mental suffering involved in the death, crippling, or maiming of men? The risk of fire is undeniably greater in a gunpowder mill than in a brewery, but the owner of the mill does not bear the burden by contenting himself with lower profits than the brewer's; he simply pays for the greater risk by higher rates of fire insurance and passes the cost on to the consuming public in a higher price for his product. If the additional expense imposed upon a gunpowder manufacturer through the more frequent losses by fire can be thus recouped from consumers, why should not the expense of indemnifying his workmen for accidents be likewise made a part of the cost of production, and thereby be transferred to the community at large? Only one thing will prevent such shifting of the burden, and that is the ability of competitors to put their goods on the market without incurring like charges. Hence the law must require all competitors in a given trade to make the same compensation for the same injuries. This is what Europe has done; by compelling employers to compensate injured employees according to a fixed scale, it has taxed the community, through higher prices of goods, for the support of its injured members.

Many minds bred in the philosophy of individualism will undoubtedly see in such legislation nothing but injustice to the employer. In reality such legislation is in strict conformance with the innermost spirit of English and American common law. It recognizes the existence of undeserved distress among workingmen and undertakes to alleviate their suffering by giving them a claim upon some person who is pecuniarily responsible. And that is precisely the principle embodied in the time-honored common-law rule that the principal is liable for the acts of his agent.

The course of reasoning thus followed to justify the principal-and-agent theory of liability also justifies the workmen's compensation acts adopted by all the leading countries of Europe, which require the employer to assume all the risks of the employment which he calls into being. But while the employer makes the primary payment, just as he pays for the wear and tear of his machinery or the loss of his plant by fire, the consumers ultimately pay the cost. The alternative to such a general distribution of the financial burdens of industrial accidents is the present method, by which the entire burden is put primarily upon the poorest classes, and when it crushes them, to the damage of the community, is at last tardily assumed by the latter through the public charities.

While the principal European nations have reached the third stage of accident legislation, many of them have advanced to a fourth stage. In England, Denmark, and Spain the legislature was content to prescribe the compensation which an employer should pay for the injury of an employee. It did not furnish to the injured employee any security for such payment further than the usual liens upon the employer's property or upon any insurance money due him. The omission might prove a serious one upon occasion; for example, when a great colliery explosion kills scores of workmen the resulting indemnities would almost inevitably bankrupt the employer unless he had taken out an accident-insurance policy upon his mine. In order to guarantee the payment of these indemnities the countries outside of the three mentioned above have resorted to compulsory insurance. Germany, the pioneer in the whole movement, adopted, as we have seen, the simple expedient of the collective responsibility of employers organized by industries. Austria employs the same system, except that the employers' mutual associations are organized by districts or provinces rather than by industries. In Italy and Finland employers may transfer their liabilities to such mutual associations; otherwise they must carry accident insurance in the state insurance office or authorized companies, or deposit securities with the proper state officers. Holland allows only the three latter alternatives, while Norway has gone still farther and made its state insurance institution the sole means of collecting premiums from employers and paying indemnities to workmen. France, finally, is trying the original method of giving injured working people a government guarantee of their pensions through the proceeds of a special tax upon the establishments subject to the law.

Should the United States, or any of our states, enact a workmen's compensation law, one would expect the example of England rather than the Continent to be followed, at least until the impracticability of leaving the matter of insurance to the initiative of the employer has been fully demonstrated. And while the genius of America favors voluntary rather than compulsory insurance, the private institutions to furnish such insurance are already developing. Should Congress enact a law requiring interstate carriers to compensate employees for all injuries in their employment, it would find many of the largest systems already provided with insurance institutions in the form of relief funds, which, under government supervision, would serve their purpose admirably. On the other hand, should the individual commonwealths enact such compensation laws for all mechanical industries, they would find already in existence a large business in liability and accident insurance, which is being transacted by private companies. These companies are now issuing to employers workmen's collective policies that promise the payment of stated sums for certain definite injuries; for example, in the event of death or the loss of two eyes or limbs, a sum equal to one year's wages, not exceeding $1500; for the loss of one limb, a sum equal to one third the above. Such blanket policies would be issued by many companies, if public statutes required the compensation of accidents upon an established scale; and as insurance companies are already subject to public supervision, it would involve the introduction of no new principle to require their accident-insurance policies to conform to certain standards that might be embodied in a workmen's compensation act.

ADNA F. WEBER.

ALBANY, NEW YORK.

The fate of the first American attempt to establish coöperative accident insurance in place of employers' liability illustrates the difficulties that will attend the realization in this country of the principle of trade risk as it has been accepted throughout Europe. In 1902 the Maryland legislature enacted two laws (chapters 139 and 412) which abolished the doctrines of common employment and contributory negligence with respect to workmen engaged in mining and transportation. But the acts permitted the employers to secure exemption from this additional liability by paying over to the state insurance commissioner an annual sum proportioned to the number of employees and the hazards of their trade, thus creating a fund for the indemnification of the families of workmen so unfortunate as to be killed while at their work. Employees might be called upon for one half the contributions made by each employer. The measure was certainly well-intentioned in spite of its crudeness, and under its provisions seven quarrying companies and two street-railway companies deposited with the insurance commissioner sums amounting to $5314, which was substantially all expended in the payment of five death claims at the statutory rate of $1000 for each employee. On July 3, 1903, however, an employee of the United Railways and Electric Company of Baltimore sued the company for damages on account of personal injury sustained through the alleged negligence of the company. The company pleaded that it had obtained exemption from liability for negligence by contributing to the insurance fund under the operation of the new laws, but the court of common pleas of Baltimore city held (April 27, 1904) that the legislature had no authority to exempt an employer from legal liabilities and thus "take away from citizens a legal right which they had theretofore enjoyed and which could be enforced by them in the courts; nor to deny to them the right to have their cases heard before a jury." The act was also unconstitutional in that it vested "in the insurance commissioner powers and functions essentially judicial in their character."

It is not to be doubted, however, that a workmen's compensation act could be framed that would be entirely in harmony with the requirements of American constitutional law, and it is particularly worthy of note that the Massachusetts Committee on Relations between Employer and Employee, on which there were representatives of both employers and employees, unanimously recommended a workmen's compensation law quite similar to the English act, which has operated with so much general satisfaction that in 1901 it was extended to agriculture.

A. F. W.

AUGUST 25, 1905.

XXVI

WORKMEN'S INSURANCE IN GERMANY[1]

Twenty years have now passed since the first law on compulsory workmen's insurance in Germany went into operation. It represented the first step towards the realization of that broad scheme whose outlines were put forth by the emperor William I in his well-known "Message" (*Botschaft*) of November 17, 1881, the "Magna Charta of German Social Policy," as it is called by some, not altogether unreservedly, for of subsequent legislative measures following in its steps none has overstepped the limits which it describes. Such deliberate and direct evolution adds much to the interest connected with the problem itself; it considerably simplifies the investigation of the question as to what has been the success of the scheme in its contact with life's reality, and how far the wish of the lawgiver was realized "that the cure of social evils be sought for not exclusively in the repression of social-democratic excesses, but also in the active furthering of the workmen's well-being."[2]

. . . Those who visited the Palais de l'Économie Sociale at the Universal Paris Exhibition of 1900 were certainly very much impressed by the obelisk representing the mass of gold equivalent to the insurance benefits that were paid out in Germany to workmen between the years 1885 and 1899. Such an obelisk would have weighed 961,000 kilograms, and would have had a nominal value of 2,400,000,000 marks (about $600,000,000), a truly imposing figure, which exceeded all expectations; the labels with the inscriptions "Grand Prix," that were displayed

[1] From the *Yale Review*, Vol. XII, 1904, pp. 716–730. See also Farnam, "Psychology of German Workmen's Insurance," *Yale Review*, Vol. XIII, pp. 98–113.

[2] Dass die Heilung sozialer Schäden nicht ausschliesslich auf dem Wege der Repression sozialdemokratischer Ausschreitungen, sondern gleichmässig auf dem der positiven Forderung des Wohles der Arbeiter zu suchen sein werde.

everywhere on the walls of this particular pavilion, bore witness to the full expert appreciation.

A few figures will give a more comprehensive idea of this gigantic organization. In 1900 there were 23,021 sick-benefit clubs (*Krankenkassen*[1]); the number of insured was 9,520,763, — that is, 423 insured in each club (409.4 in 1899). Accident business was done by 113 professional associations (*Berufsgenossenschaften*) (48 of these rural), 478 governmental, provincial, and communal executive authorities (*Ausführungsbehörden*), and 13 insurance offices of builders' associations (*Versicherungsanstalten der Baugewerksberufsgenossenschaften*). No exact data can be obtained as to the activity of these latter.[2] Accordingly, any correct estimate as to the number of persons insured would be possible only with reference to associations and to executive authorities. By the former 18,073,174 persons were insured in 1901; by the latter, 793,565. However, the first figure is excessive, as persons occupied simultaneously in industry and in agriculture are insured and quoted twice; in 1895 they numbered about 1,600,000.[3] Bringing in these corrections, we should not be wrong in assuming the number of those insured against accident to be 18,000,000.

Invalid and old-age insurance is done by thirty-one insurance institutions (*Versicherungsanstalten*) and by nine special establishments (*besondere Kasseneinrichtungen*). The number of those compulsorily insured was 11,813,259 in 1895, but now, especially after the reforms of 1899, it should be considerably larger; this fact among others is shown by the returns from the sale of invalid insurance stamps, which show an increase from 93,000,000 marks in 1891 to 134,000,000 in 1901. As regards those insured for invalidity and old age not on the compulsory basis, an attempt towards an exact estimation of their number would meet almost insuperable difficulties.

[1] The difficulty of rendering similar expressions into English rests in the different formation of these organizations in Germany, on the one hand, and in America and England, on the other.

[2] See *Amtliche Nachrichten d. R. V. A.*, 1902, p. 114.

[3] See *Amtliche Nachrichten*, 1902, p. 5, and *ibid.*, 1903, p. 5.

From 1885 to 1897, 2,908,200,000 marks have been collected for workmen's insurance. The individual items composing this sum are as follows:

Benefits	Million Marks			Interest and Other Profits
	Employees	Employers	Government	
Sickness	952.5	401.1		61.9
Accident		547.2		66.6
Invalidity and old age	355.6	355.6	98.4	69.3
Total, 1885–1897	1308.1	1303.9		197.8
Percentage of total expenditure	44.98	44.83	3.38	6.8

The years 1898 to 1900 show returns from sick insurance of 584,800,000 marks; from accidents, 277,800,000 marks; from invalidity and old age, about 441,000,000 marks,—which brings the total up to 4,311,900,000 marks; by this time this sum will beyond doubt exceed 5,000,000,000 marks.

These sums cover the claims and go towards forming the funds of the organizations of workmen's insurance. These funds increase with an extraordinary speed. Thus in 1897 sick-benefit clubs were in the possession of 146,500,000 marks; associations, of 157,800,000; and insurance institutions, of 585,200,000 marks,—forming a total of 889,502,609 marks, while towards the end of 1900 the invalidity-insurance institutions and nine special establishments showed an accumulation of 847,195,466.73 marks.[1]

The costs of administration were during the period from 1885 to 1897 altogether 205,200,000 marks, that is, 10.1 per cent of the total expenditure. They show, however, a tendency to decrease; they were individually as follows:

	1885–1897	1898	1900
Sick insurance	6.0%	5.7%	
Accident insurance	19.6	14.3	9.0%
Invalid and old-age insurance	13.4	10.3	6.4

[1] Towards the end of 1901, 929,162,180.19 marks. *Amtliche Nachrichten*, 1903, No. 1, pp. 146 and 167.

The claims paid show a very steady increase; the amounts are stated in the accompanying table.

Of this expenditure of 2,413,-800,000 marks between 1885 and 1889, 48.3 per cent was covered by the rates of workmen, 45.5 per cent by employers, and 6.2 per cent by the government. For 1900 the expenditure of the individual classes was, respectively, 176,500,000 (sickness), 101,100,-000 (accidents), and 85,900,000 (old age and invalidity), — altogether 363,500,000 marks, almost a million marks daily. In 1901 the expenditure increased in the accident class to 115,000,000 and in the invalidity and old-age class to 98,000,000.

Year	Million Marks	Rate of Increment against the Preceding Year
1885	54.1	
1886	61.9	14.4%
1887	68.1	10.0
1888	78.2	14.8
1889	92.6	18.4
1890	112.7	21.7
1891	140.4	24.6
1892	159.6	13.7
1893	178.9	12.1
1894	189.0	5.6
1895	208.6	10.4
1896	229.1	9.8
1897	256.4	11.9
1898	279.7	9.1
1899	304.7	8.9
1885–1899	2413.8	

The sick benefits paid from 1885 to 1900 numbered 42,800,000 cases, with 720,400,000 days of sickness; down to 1901, 1,033,301 accident claims were paid; from January 1, 1891, to the end of 1901, 734,251 pensions were paid for invalidity, 14,309 for sickness, and 389,971 for old age; in all 1,138,531 pensions were paid by the forty invalidity-insurance institutions and establishments mentioned above. Towards January 1, 1902, these were paying 675,095 individual pensions.

The figures quoted show what enormous sums were collected by the organizations of workmen's insurance and what considerable masses of population were and are benefiting by these. To fully appreciate these results we should compare the present situation of the German workman with that previous to the reforms in question. Thus, for instance, in 1876 there were in Germany 5239 sick-benefit clubs having 869,204 members; as late as 1880 some progress is noticeable in Prussia, but even then we find only one and one-third million insured against sickness and a still smaller number against accident, invalidity, and old age.

The satisfactory part of German compulsory workmen's insurance rests not only upon its financial success; the very fact that 44.98 per cent of the total was contributed by the workmen themselves shows what an excellent school of thrift and providence it has proved itself to the persons concerned. Not much less (namely, 44.83 per cent of the total) represents the contribution of the employers, — a sacrifice which to our mind possesses even greater social importance than the contribution of the workmen. It must not be forgotten, first, that this sum contains an increase of workmen's pay; second, that this increase is employed towards saving and supporting the working power of the employed classes; and that it supplants successfully the contributions which the whole community formerly had to pay towards the maintenance of the pauper workman; and which, after all, went to benefit the employer.

Expenditures	Million Marks		
	1885–1897	1899	1900
Medical aid	243.4	31.92	34.33
Medicaments, etc.	199.5	24.56	25.99
Pecuniary benefits to members	538.2	63.55	69.95
Pecuniary benefits to their families	9.0		
Pecuniary benefits in maternity cases	16.6		
Infirmaries and reconvalescence	138.7	25.28	27.58
Funeral benefits	44.9		
Other expenses, as transportation, etc.	76.7		

Apart from this purely economic point there is the question of popular hygiene yet to consider. Formerly the workman in case of sickness or accident would generally seek medical advice and attendance either too late or not at all. Cures undertaken in the far from hygienic surroundings of the workman's dwellings were not always satisfactory, were hardly ever carried through, and, at the best, expensive drugs had to be dispensed with, because the workman's savings and his credit would soon be exhausted. These evils were palliated considerably by the sick-benefit clubs, which provided the sick with medical aid, medicine, and financial support, thus partly at least making good the loss of wages. An enumeration of the individual items (see table on opposite page) of expenditure in the sick-benefit clubs under the new law will still better show the full scope of their activity. This expenditure shows an increase in fairly constant proportions as follows:

Years	1896	1897	1898	1899	1900
Million marks	118.72	130.44	138.68	155.78	172.70

The immediate result of this activity shows itself in a decrease of mortality among the members of sick-benefit clubs. Between 1888 and 1897 the percentages of deaths by years were: 0.96, 0.95, 0.99, 0.98, 0.98, 0.90, 0.89, 0.86, 0.85.

The influence of associations and invalidity-insurance institutions lies also in a similar direction.

The associations and executive authorities spent from 1885 to 1898 on general medical and medicinal assistance, 39,114,523 marks; in 1899, 6,439,420.19; and in 1900, 6,919,962.45 marks. If to this we add 2,562,790 marks that have been spent by the same institutions on assisting early cases of sickness to the thirteenth week, we find a total expenditure on sickness of over 55,000,000 marks between 1885 and 1900. The importance of such early help follows from the fact that during the year 1896 out of 9619 cases 80 per cent (7677) were treated on this basis with complete success.

In the class of accidents we are also able to trace the favorable results obtained through the activity of associations and executive authorities; we find the proportion of serious cases decreasing, though the general number of accidents insured is constantly increasing (see table on following page).

Finally, we wish to mention here the accident wards (*Unfallstationen*) instituted, for example, in Berlin by eight local associations; in other places it is the duty of these associations to see that boxes with bandages and so forth be kept

NUMBER OF PERSONS TO WHOM BENEFITS WERE FIRST AWARDED

Year	Absolute					Per 1000 Insured				
	Total	Accident Caused				Total	Accident Caused			
		Death[1]	Permanent Incapacity		Temporary Incapacity		Death[1]	Permanent Incapacity		Temporary Incapacity
			Entire	Partial				Entire	Partial	
1886	10,540	2,716	1,778	3,961	2,085	2.83	0.73	0.48	1.06	0.56
1887	17,102	3,270	3,166	8,462	2,204	4.15	0.79	0.77	2.05	0.54
1888	21,057	3,645	2,203	11,023	4,186	2.04	0.35	0.21	1.07	0.41
1889	31,019	5,185	2,882	16,337	6,615	2.32	0.39	0.22	1.22	0.49
1890	41,420	5,958	2,681	22,615	10,166	3.04	0.44	0.20	1.66	0.74
1891	50,507	6,346	2,561	27,778	13,812	2.80	0.35	0.14	1.54	0.77
1892	54,827	5,811	2,640	30,569	15,807	3.04	0.32	0.15	1.69	0.88
1893	61,874	6,245	2,487	36,236	16,906	3.41	0.34	0.14	2.00	0.93
1894	68,677	6,250	1,752	38,952	21,723	3.78	0.34	0.10	2.14	1.20
1895	74,467	6,335	1,668	40,527	25,937	4.05	0.35	0.09	2.20	1.41
1896	85,272	6,989	1,524	44,373	32,386	4.84	0.39	0.09	2.52	1.84
1897	91,171	7,287	1,452	46,489	35,943	5.08	0.41	0.08	2.59	2.00
1898	96,774	7,848	1,109	47,764	40,053	5.30	0.43	0.06	2.62	2.19
1899	104,811	7,999	1,297	51,240	44,275	5.63	0.43	0.07	2.75	2.38
1900	106,447	8,449	1,366	51,111	45,521	5.63	0.45	0.07	2.70	2.41
1886–1900	915,965	90,333	30,566	477,447	317,619	4.03	0.40	0.13	2.10	1.40
1902	116,089	8,359	1,416	54,340	51,974	6.15	0.44	0.08	2.88	2.75

in all factories; also that at least one of the working staff be instructed in first aid to the injured.

Year	Marks
1891	372.84
1892	31,884.20
1893	108,338.52
1894	364,576.61
1895	631,788.98
1896	1,175,504.38
1897	1,993,592.22
1898	2,769,330.23
1899	4,056,975.19
1900	6,210,720.33
1901	7,912,219.85

We find also similar provisions in the Invalid Insurance Act of 1899. The insurance institutions have the right to provide medical and medicinal assistance to sick workmen before the term prescribed (twenty-six weeks), if the disease threatens to end in incapacity to work; in this case these institutions receive a compensation from sick-benefit clubs. Moreover, if there is ground to believe that the person receiving an invalid pension

[1] The number of fatal accidents is given in this table for the sake of convenience.

will regain his ability to work, the insurance institutions may procure for him the means of taking the treatment required. Thus from 1891 to 1901 they expended 16,500,000 marks for the purposes mentioned (see table on opposite page).

Special efforts are made to combat consumption, either by coöperating directly with the Central Committee for Building Sanatoria for Consumptives or by providing the necessary capital at low rates.[1] The returns of these institutions make a very favorable showing. Of consumptive cases which were cured, or at least considerably improved, the percentages were: in 1897, 68; in 1898, 74; in 1899, 74; in 1900, 72; and in 1901, 77. Of other patients in these years, respectively, 69, 73, 71, 72, and 74 per cent. General mortality from consumption is steadily on the decrease; in places with a population above 15,000 it was, per 100,000: in 1895, 249.2; in 1896, 234; in 1897, 230; in 1898, 213.6; in 1899, 221.8, and in 1900, 222.6.

Besides their medical activity the organs of workmen's insurance, and especially the professional associations, are supervising the sanitation of factories and similar establishments. They work in conjunction with the special official inspectors, of whom in 1896 there were 280, while the supervisors of the association numbered 201.

After the exposition of its economical and sanitary influence the question of the moral and educational value of compulsory insurance arises. Many points are, of course, patent at the first glance; almost all writers on the subject accentuate the legal and the social rise of the working class through education to a greater independence in mind and action, the pacifying influence upon social relations, and the encouragement towards a more sober and ordered mode of life. The change wrought by it upon the workman's mental attitude has not, however, received that attention which it indubitably deserves.

Of all evils inherent in the "lower classes" that are at present accessible to the active care of the legislator, there is

[1] In 1900, 3,766,761.78 marks and in 1901, 5,038,751.39 marks were expended by these institutions for this purpose alone.

none worse than the entire absence of motives for thrift and providence. No doubt, the contemporary workman may have the same predisposition, even the same leanings towards social "decency" and prudence; but the conditions of his existence are such that frugality based on individual effort often requires considerable sacrifices and yet often has the result that the first adverse fortune will blow the petty savings to the winds.

As a means to overcome the sullen fatalistic indifference born of such knowledge, compulsory insurance has certainly the least heinous aspect. Its further educational value will, of course, depend upon the form which the subsidies derived from it will take. If the consciousness of the workingman will see in them not benevolence but his due, that has been earned by personal effort and work, his self-esteem is sure to be raised.

There is current in German literature an interpretation of these legal relations which is based upon the principle of the financial law; we find it insisted upon that the contributions paid should be looked upon as a certain kind of tax that has no relation whatever, either economic or legal, to the benefits paid. According to this view workmen's insurance should not be looked upon as an insurance proper, but as a kind of "state provision" (*staatliche Fürsorge*), which is something not far removed from ordinary poor relief.

Not wishing to enter upon a thorough discussion of these views, we merely wish to mention that such theories are supported by nothing extant in legislation, and that their realization would bring forth effects directly opposite to those aimed at. Suffice it to point out the dislike with which any taxation is received by the populace. By calling the law one of "workmen's insurance," and the payments collected from the insured "shares," the legislator has admitted no inconsistency, for it was distinctly emphasized that the insurance benefits have nothing whatever to do with poor relief, and that the "insured" has a legal claim on them in case of illness, accident, incapacity, and old age.

Turning from the workman to the employer, we find that the interests of the latter have visibly profited by the improvement of the conditions of labor of the former, which has been followed by an increased productiveness of his work. There has been, and still is, much opposition of employers to compulsory insurance, yet on the whole there is no lack of conciliatory opinions coming from the same camp. One of the chief objections, namely, that the increased expense of labor would impair the competitive power of German industry abroad, has been met by the argument that even before the time of compulsory insurance many employers did insure their employees with private companies without any prejudice to their own interests; also that the expenditure imposed upon the employer is comparatively insignificant.[1]

Without going to the length of some writers, who would fain ascribe the enormous development which German industry has shown of late to compulsory insurance, it cannot be denied that it contributed to it in no small degree, if it were only by strengthening the purchasing power of the home market.

Compulsory insurance has also vastly improved the relations between workman and employer. Accustomed as the German people are to be led by the government, both parties are enabled to meet on its neutral platform, are brought nearer through discussion of common affairs or arbitration in disputes, are familiarized with quiet and businesslike argumentation, and are better acquainted with each other's needs, wants, and modes of thinking. Thus an *esprit de corps* is developing, drawing the attention from narrowly selfish to broader common interests. Evidence of this is seen in a whole series of social measures which are directed towards these ends and which were initiated by the employers.

It seems almost premature as yet to venture a discussion as to how far the whole nation as such has profited by the measures in question. Some parts of the whole problem may, however, be attacked even now.

In the first place, the poor-law unions have found powerful assistance in compulsory insurance, together with all other branches of official and private benevolence. Although there

[1] According to Greisel, it does not exceed $5\frac{1}{2}$ per cent of the wages.

are no official statements extant on this matter, as it is not considered in German statistics at all, it may suffice to point out that those circumstances that make for indigence are the very ones which are most insured against. Thus, of the total of all cases insured, at least 50 per cent were against contingencies that ordinarily lead towards impoverishment.

It would, of course, be a great mistake to assume that the weight thus taken off the shoulders of poor-law unions should be equivalent to the figure stated; for, apart from the difficulty of bringing into the medley of all causes, objective and subjective, any system that would fit them for the application of statistical calculations, any correspondence of effects would be disturbed by the fact that the poor-law unions coöperate with the insurance organizations, doling out subventions sometimes rather late, and fairly often in insufficient proportions.

Neither can there be any correspondence for the further reason that the new acts (of July 11, 1891, for Prussia, and March 12, 1894, for the Empire) on poor relief have caused a considerable increase in the budgets, these budgets in their turn being largely dependent upon purely adventitious chances and local conditions (for example, a large influx of unemployed).

Finally, the means that are at the disposal of the poor-relief authorities are almost always inadequate, and with the easing of the burden in one direction the expenses of other departments will therefore often increase.

These are the reasons why no exact numerical statements were obtained by the inquiries conducted in 1894 by the German Association for Poor Relief and Charity and in 1897 by the Statistical Bureau of the German Empire on the initiative of the Chancellor. Nevertheless, opinions were everywhere expressed that all benevolent institutions did profit by the activity of compulsory insurance, in spite of the fact that in some cases the budget of these institutions grew considerably larger. The Act on Sick Insurance was everywhere the most helpful, the Old-Age and Invalidity Insurance Act less so, and the Act on Accidents least of all. In a few instances, however, we are even able to give numerical statements. In Saxony the items of expenditure for poor relief were the following (per 10,000 of population):

	1885	1890
Sickness	67.9	54.1
Accidents	7.6	3.9
Old age	31.7	32.3
Funeral benefits	0.3	0.3

In Berlin the expenses for poor relief from 1880–1881 to 1895–1896 were by years per capita the following: 4.16 (marks), 4.15, 3.98, 3.90, 3.77, 3.70, 3.71, 3.59, 3.51, 3.51, 3.24, 3.41, 3.64, 3.38, 3.35, 3.35, 3.29. In Cologne these expenses fell between 1879–1880 and 1896–1897 from 7.81 marks to 4.66 marks per capita.

The workmen's insurance organizations need not necessarily invest their funds in government stock; they also have the right to supply capital to institutions of public utility. The following table shows what considerable sums were loaned for such purposes.

The thirty-one invalidity-insurance institutions and nine special establishments had invested towards the end of 1901:

	Marks
1. Towards building workmen's dwellings	87,529,567.00
2. Towards agricultural credits (on mortgages, narrow-gauge railways, keeping of roads, improvement of soil, cattle farming, etc.)	64,588,410.00
3. Towards building infirmaries and convalescent homes of all kinds, refuges and shelters, public baths, homes for the blind, infants' schools, slaughterhouses, waterworks, canals, drainage, coöperative stores, etc.	108,237,387.80
Total	260,355,364.80

Compulsory insurance may yet be destined to play a very important rôle in the future of Germany in the capacity of a savings institution, hoarding, as it were, a large and cheap capital to be used for sudden and urgent public needs.

A less prominent and tangible yet very valuable service has been rendered by compulsory insurance to Germany in the creation of a wholly new class of small annuitants, which fact, besides being itself very gratifying, has yet the further result, that it has made the annuitants leave the more expensive industrial centers for the country, thus forming something of an antidote to the "rural exodus." Some capital is thus conveyed to the villages, compensating them at least to a slight degree for the loss they suffer from this emigration of the younger element.

As to the influence which compulsory insurance has had upon the physical and moral hygiene of those parts of the nation that it did not immediately concern, we might almost repeat what has already been stated as to its value for the working class. There is the improvement of sanitary conditions, which though starting at one point would necessarily spread through all adjoining social layers; there is also the raising of the nation's vital forces by the increase of the number of healthy and able-bodied individuals.

In this connection it seems justifiable to point out the steady decrease of general mortality, in which compulsory insurance was, of course, not the only factor, yet certainly one of the most important. The yearly mortality per thousand was: in 1851–1860, 27.8; in 1861–1870, 28.4; in 1871–1880, 28.8; in 1881–1890, 26.5; in 1891–1900, 23.5. This sudden decrease is even more forcibly shown by a comparison of the figures giving the average mortality in town and village during the interval from 1867 to 1894. Down to the eighties the mortality in villages was quite 2 per cent lower than in towns; from about the middle of that decade this difference begins to diminish rather quickly, and in 1890 it turns in the opposite direction, till the average mortality of towns falls below that of villages. Without overlooking many other influences combining to produce this effect, we are yet fully inclined to see even in this, to a great extent, the action of compulsory insurance.[1]

[1] It may also be noted that the percentage of suicide in Germany is almost constant, while it continues increasing in other countries.

Improving general social and economic conditions has naturally had an influence also upon the decrease of crime. The following table, giving the number of sentences passed in the respective years for theft per 10,000 of population above twelve years of age, will give a fit illustration of what has been said.

Years	Per 10,000
1882	32.6
1883	31.3
1884	30.1
1885	27.9
1886	27.2
1887	26.0
1888	25.4
1889	27.8
1890	27.2
1891	28.1
1892	31.0
1893	26.9
1894	26.6
1895	25.6
1899	19.4
1900	20.2

In view of the many tangible results that have been obtained in Germany by means of compulsory insurance of workmen, there is nothing surprising in the circumstance that writers on the subject, especially if they be Germans, do not stint their praises for the whole legislation *in toto*, lapsing at every attempt at a critical valuation of its measures into rather full-voiced panegyrics. This very pardonable tendency is strongly inherent even in comparative sketches, which take from it a rather strong color.[1] Official publications[2] are great sinners in this respect, though the tendency shows itself generally merely in a partial depression of the critical faculties, which by no means interferes with the exactness of the material supplied. We find but few voices raised in protest against this exuberance of general satisfaction.

They who point out the insufficiencies and inefficiencies we are guilty of, who are not averse to noticing superiority though it be of a foreign pattern, show certainly more public spirit than those who fold their hands with a self-satisfied conviction that now at last Germany is heading the progress of social reform. . . . It has always been the wiser course to take the good where you find it than to rest on laurels.[3]

There could be nothing worse for us than if now we found full satisfaction in self-pleased pride, ruminating in contemplative idleness over our work so excellently well done.[4]

[1] See Zacher, Die Arbeiter-Versicherung im Auslande, 1898–1900. Boediker, Die Arbeiterversicherung in den Europäischen Staaten, 1895.

[2] See the pamphlet written for the Paris Exhibition, 1900.

[3] E. Fr. in *Soziale Praxis*, 1900, p. 34.

[4] Frankenberg in Braun's *Archiv für soziale Gesetzgebung und Statistik*, Vol. XII, p. 72.

Van der Borght, in spite of the exaggerations he has committed himself to in his book, is also led to the remark:

> Of course, we have no right to rest, jubilating at what we have attained. In the very structure of workingmen's insurance there is much yet to be repaired and completed.

There are certainly many gaps and omissions left in legislation. Yet to us this does not seem to be all that can be said in criticising it; there are some points of no mean importance which should be questioned more seriously than has been done, — a task we intend to take up at some other time.

NORBERT PINKUS.

GÖTTINGEN.

XXVII

INSURANCE AGAINST UNEMPLOYMENT[1]

The purpose of workingmen's insurance is to make provision for the assistance of workingmen when through any incapacity they are unable to earn their usual wages. A workingman may be unable to work as the result of any of four contingencies, — accident, sickness, old age or invalidity, or inability to obtain employment; and a complete system of assistance must necessarily cover all four of these cases. It is now very generally admitted that insurance of some kind, mutual or state-aided, voluntary or compulsory, offers the best means of providing for the first three contingencies, that is, for those involving physical disability. Within recent years, however, the desirability of extending the field of insurance to the fourth contingency, where inability to earn wages is the result of involuntary idleness, has been strongly urged. It is the purpose of this paper to consider to what extent a system of insurance can be profitably employed in this last case.

Fortunately, we need not study this problem from the purely theoretical standpoint. The fact that during the widespread industrial depression of recent years many workingmen have been forced to remain in involuntary idleness has led to

[1] From the *Political Science Quarterly*, Vol. XII, 1897, pp. 476–489. See also Report of the Massachusetts Board upon Unemployment, 1895.

The literature of insurance against unemployment is already extensive. For the best account of the Swiss experiments with which this paper chiefly deals, the reader is referred to two *Circulaires* of the Musée Social, Nos. 2 and 5 of Series B; the report of the French Office du Travail, *Documents sur la question du chômage*, 1896; and the paper by Eugène Rostand, "De l'assurance contre le chômage involontaire," contained in the report of the third session of the International Congress in Relation to Accidents to Labor and Social Insurance, Milan, 1894. The *Circulaires* of the Musée Social give the most complete bibliography of the question that has been prepared.

attempts in various countries to make provision against unemployment through some system of insurance. Conspicuous among them are the out-of-work insurance institutions that have been created in several of the cantons of Switzerland, at Cologne, and at Bologna. Of these the Swiss organizations are of much the greatest importance, and for that reason most attention will be devoted to their operation. A consideration of the efforts there made will serve not only to illustrate the principles involved in the organization of this kind of an insurance system but also to show the practical difficulties with which its administration is attended.

The first attempt under government auspices to provide for insurance against unemployment was made by the town of Berne. On January 13, 1893, the town council provided for the creation of a municipal institution for the insurance of workingmen against unemployment. Though under municipal authority, membership in the institution was left entirely voluntary. Practically the only condition of membership was the payment of monthly dues of forty centimes ($0.077). To the fund thus accumulated the town agreed to add a subsidy, the maximum amount of which was limited to five thousand francs ($965) a year. The constitution also provided for the receipt of gifts from employers and other individuals.

The value of the out-of-work benefits was fixed at one franc per day for an unmarried man, and a franc and a half for a married man. This relief was to be granted only during the months of December, January, and February. To be entitled to receive it a member must have paid his dues regularly during at least the six months next preceding, and must have been unable to obtain work during at least fifteen days. Relief, when granted, however, began to run after the first week of unemployment. Various conditions were placed upon those receiving benefits, in order to protect the institution against imposition. Thus members out of work had to present themselves twice a day in a room set aside for that purpose, where they might spend the day if they desired. A workingman who refused work of any kind lost all right to aid of any kind: a member thus had no right to refuse work because it was not in his trade. There were various other cases in which the workingman lost his right to a benefit: for instance, when lack of employment was the result of his own fault, and especially when he had engaged in a strike. The administration of the fund was intrusted to a commission of seven members, of whom three were to be named by the municipal authorities, two by the employers contributing to the fund, and two by the workingmen.

This institution has now been in existence a sufficient length of time to furnish some indication of the character of the results. The number of members during the first year, 1893–1894, was 404. Of these 166 were aided during the year, receiving $1319.16, or an average of $7.95 each. The highest sum paid to any one person was $20.27. The total expenditure of the year was $1508.30. The receipts for the year were: dues of members, $212.30; gifts from employers and others, $382.14; municipal subsidy, $913.86. It will be seen that the members contributed but 14 per cent of the total receipts, and that they received in actual benefits six times the amount paid in by them as dues. One would think that under such exceptionally favorable circumstances membership would increase rapidly. Such, however, has not been the case. During the second year, 1894–1895, there were but 390 members, or 14 less than during the preceding year. Aid was given to 219 persons, or more than half the members, to the extent of $1869.06, or an average of $8.53 each. Only $263.79 out of the total receipts of $2249.86 came from dues of members. The ratio of this sum to the amount paid out in benefits is 14 per cent, the members thus receiving on an average seven times the amount contributed by them.

The institution was first established for but two years as an experiment. In 1895, the two years having elapsed, the town council determined by an almost unanimous vote to continue it in operation. Some modifications were, however, introduced in its organization. Dues were raised from forty to fifty centimes per month, and the maximum amount of the municipal subsidy was raised from $965 to $1351. Daily benefits were increased to one and a half francs for unmarried and two francs for married members. In addition, the administration of the municipal employment bureau, which had until then been an independent institution, was attached to that of the insurance fund. The result of these changes was to increase the operations of the system. On December 31, 1895, there were 605 members enrolled, of whom 169, or 49 more than during the preceding year to the same date, had been aided. The total receipts during the year 1895–1896 were $2213.99, of which $312.70 were derived from dues. The total expenditures were $2121.30, of which $1932.22 were for benefits. In this third year, therefore, slightly over six times the amount received as dues from the members was paid in benefits.

Saint Gall, a town of about 30,000 inhabitants, was the first to follow the example of Berne in providing for the insurance of workingmen against unemployment. Its policy, however, differed radically from that of Berne in that it adopted the principle of compulsory insurance. By the law of May 14, 1894, the canton of Saint Gall authorized any of its communes to create a compulsory-unemployment insurance institution, and provided further that several communes might combine to organize a general insurance system. It was on the basis of this law that the town of Saint Gall, after an abortive attempt to unite with the neighboring communes of Tablatt and Straubenzell, founded its unemployment insurance fund by act of June 23, 1895.

The principal features of this institution may be summarized as follows: Membership was made obligatory upon all workingmen whose daily wages did not exceed five francs, excluding youths and apprentices earning less than two francs a day. Weekly dues were fixed at 15 centimes for members earning three francs or under, 20 centimes for those earning from three to four francs, and 30 centimes for those earning more than four. The amount of the benefit was likewise proportioned to the wages of the recipient, being 1.80, 2.10, and 2.40 francs per day respectively for the three classes. Benefits could not be paid to any person for more than sixty days in any one year. In order to be entitled to benefits a member must have paid dues uninterruptedly for at least six months, and had to show that for at least five days he had not been able to secure work suited to his occupation at the usual wages of the season. Any man who was without work as the result of his own fault, who had participated in a strike, or who refused without a good reason work assigned to him by the employment bureau which was operated in connection with the insurance fund, was debarred from any right to benefits. Workingmen incapacitated for labor through sickness or accident were not entitled to benefits, since they were otherwise insured against these two contingencies. In addition to dues, the revenue of the fund included a subsidy from the town, which, according to the law, could not exceed a maximum of two francs for each person insured and a subsidy from the canton. No account was taken, apparently, of gifts and donations from employers or other persons. The fund was administered by a commission of nine members, two of whom were appointed by the municipal authorities and seven by the workingmen.

This institution commenced operations July 1, 1895. The law being obligatory, the first duty of the commissioners was to see that all persons to whom the law applied became members. As the result of the first notice 1535 persons joined; a new call a month later added 579 names; and, as the result of further efforts, the total number of persons enrolled during the first year was increased to 4220. This total was secured only after securing over 150 convictions of persons who had neglected to answer the summons to enroll. Of the total number secured 2895 were members of the first class, or those earning not more than three francs; 1179 of the second class; and but 146 of the third.

During the year 430, or about 10 per cent of the members, registered themselves as without work. Of these only 363 received benefits, since many had not made the required contributions for six months. To the beneficiaries was paid a total of $4536.30, or an average of $10.55. The highest amount received by one person was $24.32, and the lowest $1.74. The receipts and expenditures during the year were as follows:

Receipts

Contributions of members	$4183.14
Municipal subsidy, cash	772.00
Municipal subsidy, payment of operating expenses	1084.44
Interest	21.81
	$6061.39

Expenditures

Benefits	$4536.30
Operating expenses	1084.44
	$5620.74
Balance on hand	$440.65

It will thus be seen that the year closed with a surplus in the bank, in spite of the fact that the city paid only a portion of the maximum sum that it could be required to pay. It should be remembered, however, that as this was the first year no benefits were paid during the first six months, since no member could before that time have made the required number of payments. Accordingly, the officials estimated that future charges would be much heavier and that it would be necessary either to increase contributions or to reduce the benefits.

This institution, like that at Berne, was created for a provisional period of two years. Before the end of the second year, however, the city council on November 8, 1896, by a decisive vote ordered the suspension of the fund after June 30, 1897. The first experiment in compulsory insurance against unemployment was thus declared a failure. It is worthy of note also that this suppression was accomplished on the motion and through the votes of representatives of the working classes in the council.

A detailed account of the organization and operations of the institution at Saint Gall has been given, even though its suppression has been definitely decided upon, since in matters such as this information can be gained from failures as well as from successes. It is worth while, therefore, to examine some of the objections that were raised against this scheme. The first was that which inevitably arose from the members who were forced to make contributions without receiving any benefits in return. This is a fundamental objection. The liability to lack of employment varies greatly in the different trades; so that to require all workingmen earning less than a certain sum to become contributors to an insurance fund, as was done at Saint Gall, results in positive injustice. Employees having steady employment, such as factory operatives, are made to contribute to the insurance of workingmen such as those in the building trades, who are certain to be unemployed more or less during the year. The experiments at Berne and at Saint Gall have shown that it is the workingmen in the building trades who suffer most from lack of employment. Thus, in the former city, though membership is open to men of all occupations and the benefits are six or seven times the dues, only day laborers, for the most part in the building trades, and other employees in the same trades have availed themselves of the fund. Out of the 226 persons registered the second year as out of work, there were 163 day laborers, 18 plasterers or painters, 13 roofers, 10 masons, 9 carpenters, 4 stonecutters, 3 cabinet-makers, 2 locksmiths, 1 wood sawyer, 1 cement worker, and 1 fireman. It will be observed that factory employees proper were absolutely unrepresented. Turning now to the experience of Saint Gall under compulsory insurance it is found that, though both factory and building-trades employees were required to be insured, practically all the persons aided belonged to the latter class. Of the 430 persons registered as out of work during the first year there were 205 day laborers, 47 masons, 18 porters, 17 house painters, 14 public messengers, 13 dressmakers, 12 plasterers, 11 carpenters, and 10 roofers, while no other occupation was represented by as many as ten persons.

A second objection was the great difficulty experienced in enforcing membership. The administrators of the fund found it almost impossible to compel persons to become members or afterwards to pay their dues, even though they resorted to prosecution in a great many cases. In the December following the commencement of operations they found it necessary to send notices to 1110 persons who were behind in the payment of their dues. On April 1 over 4000 francs were owing by about 1300 persons.

Finally, it was complained that the indemnities were much too high. It was found that the efforts of those out of work to gain employment were sensibly relaxed. Many seemed to use every effort to obtain as much relief as possible, seeking work earnestly only after they had been aided the maximum number of sixty days. In a word, self-help seemed to have been lessened in just the proportion that assistance was granted.

In spite of the check that the movement for the insurance of workingmen has received in Switzerland through the suppression of the institution at Saint Gall, efforts in this direction have not been abandoned. Though it is generally admitted that both the Saint Gall and the Berne systems had defects, it is claimed that they were such as lack of experience rendered inevitable, and that they can be eliminated by a more scientific organization. At Basel a plan is now under consideration that is of especial interest, since it involves an attempt to meet the objections which have been urged against the two older schemes. The proposed system is beyond doubt in every way a more detailed and more carefully worked out plan of insurance than any that has yet been put into operation.

In 1894 the council of state of Basel submitted to the general council a proposition for the municipal insurance of workingmen against unemployment. This measure, after discussion, was first referred to a committee of experts, the leading spirit of which was M. Adler, professor of political economy at the University of Basel. The commission reported in April, 1896, a modified plan. After a full discussion this report was referred to a committee of the general council, which, after further consideration, reported a specific bill, differing in but slight details from the proposition of the committee of experts. In its final form the plan provides for the compulsory insurance through a municipal fund of all masons and excavators and all workingmen subject to the federal factory law who do not earn more than 2000 francs a year, excluding, however, young people and apprentices earning less than 300 francs a year. In adopting the principle of compulsion, however, the important option is given to the workingmen of insuring themselves through voluntary organizations instead of through the municipal system. This permission was granted in order to meet the objection that was urged against the bill as first framed by the committee of experts, that certain classes of workingmen had already voluntarily insured themselves through their labor organizations and that it would be unjust to compel them to become members of the city organization. This was notably true of the members of the Typographia, an organization of the printers of the city.

The receipts of the fund consist of (1) dues from members, (2) contributions from employers, (3) a subsidy from the city, and (4) gifts and legacies. For the payment of dues and the determination of the amount of benefits to be given, members are first divided into three categories, — factory employees, workingmen in the building trades who are the least subject to unemployment, and other workingmen in the building trades. The object of this division is to take account of the differences in the degree of probability of unemployment. Within each of these categories there is a further division of members into three classes, according as their weekly earnings are 15 francs or under, from 15 to 24 francs, or 24 francs or over. The weekly contributions demanded of these classes are 10, 15, and 20 centimes respectively for members of the first category; 20, 30, and 50 centimes for members of the second; and 30, 45, and 60 centimes for members of the third. The contribution of employers is fixed at 10 centimes per week per workingman insured in the first category, and 20 centimes for workingmen of the second and third categories. The city assumes all the expenses of management and agrees to grant an annual subsidy of 25,000 francs.

The benefits granted to members out of work vary from 80 centimes to 2 francs a day. They are graduated in an ingenious manner according to the class to which the recipients belong and according to their needs. Thus the unmarried man, the married woman, and the widower or widow without children under fourteen years of age receive from 0.80 to 1 franc a day; the widow or widower with children under fourteen years of age, and the married man if he has not more than one child under fourteen years of age receive from 1.20 to 1.50 francs per day; and, finally, the married man with several children under fourteen years of age receives from 1.50 to 2 francs. The benefits of the married man are reduced 20 or 33 per cent if his wife is also employed, or if she receives a benefit from the insurance fund. The maximum length of time during which benefits can be paid is ninety days. An important provision is that there may be paid, in place of the above indemnities, traveling expenses for so great a distance as two hundred kilometers, and an indemnity of 1 franc to an unmarried or 2 francs to a married man who desires to leave the city to obtain work elsewhere. This is to prevent a workingman who has an opportunity of finding work from remaining a charge upon the fund. No benefits are payable when the lack of employment is the result of a dispute of employees with their employer concerning the amount of their wages; when the member voluntarily quits his employment; when he has been dismissed for breaking the factory or other regulations; when the lack of employment is the result of sickness or accident against which the workingman is elsewhere insured; or when, without a valid excuse, the person insured refuses work offered to him.

The question of insurance against unemployment has also received attention in other Swiss cities, notably Zurich and Lausanne. As yet, however, the discussions have not resulted in any distinct propositions; and it will, therefore, be unnecessary to consider them. The institutions that have been actually created at Cologne and Bologna offer few points of interest. The one at Cologne was created in 1896 and is under municipal management. Insurance under it is purely voluntary. Any workingman over eighteen years of age and a resident of the city during two years can become a member by paying a weekly contribution of 25 pfennigs. He thus acquires a "right to work" in case he is unemployed during the period from December 15 to March 15. If work cannot be found for him, he is entitled during the first twenty days of unemployment to a benefit of 2 marks if he is married, or 1½ marks if unmarried. A large guarantee fund has been created through gifts and the contributions of honorary members. In addition, the city itself has granted a subsidy of several thousand dollars as an encouragement to workingmen to become members. At Bologna a voluntary unemployment-insurance institution has been created which affects only employees in building trades. Members must pay an annual contribution of 3.30 francs if they are under twenty years of age, or 5 francs if over that age. The out-of-work benefits are 60 centimes a day for members of the first class and 1 franc for members of the second class during a maximum of forty days commencing with the sixth day of unemployment.

The experiments that have been made in Switzerland and elsewhere, while they are not sufficiently extensive to furnish conclusive evidence regarding the practicability of insurance against unemployment, are fully adequate to bring out the chief considerations that must be taken into account in any attempt to organize such a system.

An examination of the nature of the problem of unemployment shows that insurance principles are ill suited for its solution. Insurance presupposes that the risk involved shall possess two characteristics, — it must be well defined, and it must be the consequence of a chance that can be estimated with some degree of certainty. The risk of unemployment conforms to neither of these conditions. It is not well defined, since there is no fixed criterion as to what work the unemployed should be required to accept. It does not depend upon calculable chance, because the personal element involved in seeking and retaining work, to say nothing of the uncertainty of the employers' action, enters so largely. Though lack of employment is often unavoidable on the part of the workingman, the latter's will and energy play such an important part in the matter that any attempt to distinguish unavoidable idleness is futile. Insurance concerns itself with a risk that can be calculated and provided for in advance; but this cannot be done in regard to lack of employment. The study of the various systems that has just been made shows that, in spite of the fact that the term insurance has been employed, the attempt has not really been made to create insurance systems. In no case has the attempt been made to calculate risks and to adjust contributions accordingly, or indeed to make the system self-supporting. Only nominal contributions have been required from members, while the great burden of expense has been borne by the government and by voluntary contributors. In reality, therefore, it is scarcely proper to speak of these institutions as insurance organizations. What has been created is really a more methodical system of granting relief to the unemployed.

Turning now to the actual organization of the Swiss systems, it will be seen that the radical mistake was the failure to recognize the essentially different conditions obtaining in different industries. The problem of lack of employment in the factory trades, for example, is quite different from that in the building trades or among ordinary day laborers. It may be confidently stated that any attempt to introduce even a modified form of insurance against unemployment should follow strictly trade lines. In this respect the Basel proposition shows a marked advance over the other systems.

This, however, brings us to the consideration of the out-of-work benefit features of labor organizations. If unemployment insurance should follow trade lines, every argument would seem to indicate that such efforts should be made through existing organizations of workingmen. The great work done by these organizations in the way of aiding their members is well known. For example, the chief labor correspondent of the British Board of Trade stated, in his report on trade unions for 1895, that one hundred of the principal unions expended during the year $2,121,775 in relief of the unemployed. In the United States a large part of the expenditures of the trade unions likewise go for this purpose, though it is not possible to make any exact statement of the amount.[1] This method of granting relief possesses manifest advantages over the use of a municipal organization. The work of unions is not charity but the highest order of mutual aid. Labor unions, moreover, are in a peculiarly favorable position to assist their members in obtaining work, and are able to guard themselves against imposition. Finally, as we have seen, unemployment is not a condition beyond the control of individuals, and does not happen with a regularity that can be calculated. Insurance proper affords little room for discretion in granting relief, while each case of unemployment should be considered upon its particular merits. Labor organizations can exercise this necessary discretion in a way that is utterly beyond the power of a municipal institution.

The logical conclusion is that in America, at least, provision against lack of employment can best be made for the established trades by the men themselves through their organizations; and that this provision cannot be made according to hard and fast insurance principles, but must allow for a certain elasticity or discretion in the granting of relief, according to the circumstances of each case and the amount of funds available for this purpose.

Though the Swiss systems must be regarded as faulty in lacking the character of true insurance, it is not desired to give the impression that such municipal institutions cannot be made to serve a useful purpose. On the contrary, there are involved in their organization principles which when properly applied can be of great assistance in solving the problem of unemployment. They may not provide scientific insurance, but they constitute a vast improvement over the old methods of indiscriminate and uncertain relief. They require employees to register and to make some personal sacrifice in order to be entitled to relief; they insure that relief shall be granted only to *bona fide* residents of the city; and they bring the unemployed under the supervision of the public authorities. This last feature greatly facilitates finding work for idle men either

[1] See Chapter XXIV, p. 527, The Benefit System of the Cigar Makers' Union.

through a public employment bureau or in the immediate service of the government. To accomplish their work in the best way, however, the municipal institutions should cease to lay emphasis upon the idea of insurance. The principle of registration, accompanied by the requirement of small monthly contributions, is the really valuable feature of their work. They should seek chiefly to reach those classes which do not possess labor organizations. Finally, they should make assistance to the unemployed in finding work the most important part of their duties. Only after they have failed in this effort should they grant pecuniary relief.

WILLIAM FRANKLIN WILLOUGHBY.

XXVIII

PUBLIC EMPLOYMENT OFFICES IN THE UNITED STATES AND GERMANY[1]

I. United States

. . . From the recentness of the movement for the establishment of these offices it is evident that other attempts must have been made to secure the registration of the unemployed and the equilibration of the labor market. The most important of these agencies in the United States are the private intelligence offices; and it is to a consideration of these that we must, therefore, first address ourselves before we can fully understand either the need of or the demand for offices conducted under the control of the state.

Private employment agencies exist in almost every city of the Union, but no systematic canvass has ever been attempted to ascertain their number or the extent of their business. However, from some scattered data in the reports of several of the state bureaus of labor statistics, it has been possible to compile a few figures which are of interest, and may be considered typical of all. These show the number of private agencies in a few cities, the number of applicants, and the estimated receipts; but none of these statistics can be considered accurate, many of the returns being confessedly only estimates. In Boston there were 119 private employment agencies in 1893, and reports from 87 of them showed 600,934 applicants for employment, of whom 128,912, or 21.45 per cent, secured positions. At the minimum charge of 50 cents apiece, this would yield

[1] From the *Quarterly Journal of Economics*, Vol. XIX, 1900, pp. 341–377. See also Kellor, Out of Work, 1904.

the offices over $300,000 a year.[1] Commissioner Hall gives figures for St. Louis and Kansas City which, he thinks, represent about 40 per cent of the business done in these two cities. In St. Louis there were 6032 applications for employment in seven women's agencies, and 5626 positions secured. The admitted receipts, which Mr. Hall thinks about half of what was in fact received, were $3198. Six other agencies found work for 20,800 out of 106,600 applicants. Their receipts are estimated at $100,000. The Kansas City agencies were only a little behind this, as the following figures show:

Number of Agencies	Number of Applications	Positions Filled	Receipts from Fees
8 (for men) . .	64,740	43,672	$64,464
4 (for women) . .	22,711	3,835	6,103

Commissioner Hall estimates that the $70,567 admitted receipts were less than one half the amount actually taken in.[2]

There were 119 licensed agencies in Chicago in 1896, at which it is estimated that not less than 1,000,000 persons applied for employment during the year. At the minimum charge of $1 apiece, this would give an annual income of $1,000,000.[3] In California 69 well-equipped private employment agencies are reported to exist, whose cost of maintenance alone is estimated at $206,700 a year.[4] Twenty-one private agencies are reported from Colorado, most of them being situated in Denver.

Inadequate as these figures are, they yet serve in some degree to show the extent of the business done by the employment agencies of the country, and to give an idea of the vast sums that are paid annually by the unemployed for the purpose of securing

[1] Twenty-Fourth Annual Report of Massachusetts Bureau of Statistics of Labor, 1893, p. 111.

[2] Fourteenth Annual Report of the Bureau of Labor Statistics and Inspection of Missouri, 1892.

[3] Tenth Biennial Report of the Bureau of Labor Statistics of Illinois, 1898, p. 133.

[4] Seventh Biennial Report of the Bureau of Labor Statistics of California, 1895–1896, p. 52.

employment. That these agencies meet a real want seems not open to doubt. But the further question as to how well they fill it and with what advantage to the unemployed is not so certainly to be answered in their favor. In fact, one of the strongest arguments in favor of the establishment of free public employment offices rests on the abuses which exist in the private agencies. This point is made much of by the commissioners of labor in the various states, and their reports contain many instances of the deception and fraud practiced by these agencies on the unemployed. While they are naturally interested in making out as strong a case as possible against the "pay" agencies, and though a large number of these are of the highest possible character, there is still without doubt a large class which merely preys on the unemployed and takes advantage of their need.

The least of the abuses which are perpetrated is the universal practice of accepting a fee, whether there is prospect of finding a position or not, and of refusing to refund it when a position is not secured.[1] No pay agency will ever admit that the labor market is overstocked.[2] Worse than this is the practice of advertising for laborers to undertake work in distant cities and of sending them to fill purely fictitious openings after accepting their fees.[3] In the case of some of the more dishonest agencies there is an agreement between the foreman and an agency, according to which men sent by the agency are employed, but only for a few days, and then discharged to make way for others. The fees are divided between the agent and the foreman.[4] An additional refinement, which is reported from New York, consists in an illicit connection of employment agencies with alleged employers, who refer an applicant to a guarantee agency, which is also in the league, and which exacts another fee for looking up the references.[5] It is a not uncommon

[1] The laws of a number of states require that the fee be refunded if employment is not secured.

[2] "Fraudulent Advertisement of Lucrative Employment," by P. G. Hubert, Jr., *Lippincott's Magazine*, Vol. LIV, p. 657.

[3] Illinois Report, 1898, p. 133.

[4] California Report, 1896, p. 56.

[5] Bulletin of the Bureau of Labor Statistics, December, 1899, p. 155.

plan to have the employment agency located in the rear of a dram shop, which the men, who are purposely kept waiting in the hope of securing a position, will unfailingly patronize.

Many of the abuses here complained of are largely the result of inadequate supervision and control of the agencies in their dealings with an ignorant and needy class of persons, easily victimized and slow to seek redress. To regulate these evils of the private employment offices, a few of the states have, therefore, required them to pay licenses or give bonds, or do both. Colorado, Illinois, Maine, Minnesota, Pennsylvania, and Washington compel all employment offices to pay an annual license fee, ranging from $1 in Maine to $200 in Illinois. In Louisiana and the cities of New York and Brooklyn a license must be obtained in order to do business; but no payment is required.[1] Five of the states — Colorado, Illinois, Louisiana, Minnesota, and Wisconsin — place the managers of all private agencies under heavy bonds; and all of the states named also provide penalties for infringement of the law. Most of them, too, regulate the charges which the agencies can make, providing that no fee shall be charged unless a *bona fide* position is secured for the applicant.

Free employment agencies, as private or quasi public institutions, already exist in large numbers throughout the United States, especially in the large cities. Many of the charity-organization societies maintain employment bureaus incidental to their work of relief, and sometimes, as in Minneapolis, Brooklyn, and Baltimore, independently thereof. In the two last-named cities this work grew to such proportions as to threaten to overshadow the more legitimate work of the society, and was therefore suspended, except for destitute cases.[2] Many churches have employment features, as do also the Young Men's Christian Associations, Young Women's Christian Associations,[3]

[1] A bill of this sort is now before the New York legislature (Assembly Bill, No. 361, January 22, 1900).

[2] Proceedings of the National Conference of Charities and Correction, Toronto, 1897, p. 211.

[3] E.g. the Y.W.C.A. and Women's Exchange of St. Louis. Missouri Report, 1892.

and social settlements.[1] The Salvation Army has paid much attention to this phase of its many-sided work, more so in England than in this country. Most of the trade unions have this feature more or less developed, restricted usually, however, to the trades interested. In Chicago at least two department stores have conducted employment bureaus, free to their customers, for female domestic servants. In Boston there are fourteen free employment bureaus connected with religious, philanthropic, medical, and other institutions.[2] In New York[3] among many are the Bible House, the Working Girls' Alliance, St. Bartholomew's Guild,[4] and the Cooper Union Labor Bureau, conducted since 1895 by the New York Association for Improving the Condition of the Poor. Perhaps the assistance given the unemployed by many newspapers through the free insertion of want advertisements should be mentioned, since this method of seeking work often takes the place of a resort to the employment office.

Numerous as the free private or philanthropic agencies were in the United States, the stigma of charity attached to their work; and the best class of employees were not to be found on their lists. To meet this objection and at the same time secure their advantages, the next step was accordingly the establishment of free *public* employment offices; and to a consideration of these we may now turn.

Ohio[5] was the first and for a long time the only state to maintain free public employment agencies. The act establishing them was passed April 28, 1890, and was amended the

[1] E.g. Hull House at one time did so. Illinois Report, 1898, p. 135.

[2] Massachusetts Report, 1893, pp. 81–114.

[3] Fourteenth Annual Report of the Bureau of Labor Statistics of New York, 1896, p. 923.

[4] *Year Book*, 1899, p. 295.

[5] Reports of the Bureau of Labor Statistics of Ohio, 1890–1899.

The movement in Ohio was due directly to the example of France. Mr. A. W. J. Lewis, later commissioner in charge of the Ohio Bureau of Labor Statistics, was one of a group of labor representatives who attended the Paris Exposition of 1889; and what he there saw of the great public offices led him to advocate their establishment in his state. See the Report of the Minnesota Bureau of Labor Statistics, 1891–1892.

following year, March 24, 1891. It created five free employment offices as adjuncts to the Bureau of Labor Statistics, and placed the appointment of the superintendents and clerks of the offices in the hands of the labor commissioner. The salaries of the officers were to be borne by the cities within which the offices were organized, but the general expenses were to be defrayed by the state. Each superintendent should make a weekly report to the commissioner, and lists of applications in each office should be sent weekly to every other office and there posted. The amendment of 1891 limited the tenure of office for all superintendents and clerks to two years. Since that time no further change in the law has been made.

Offices were opened during the summer of 1890 in the five leading cities of the state, — Toledo, Cleveland, Dayton, Cincinnati, and Columbus. The success of these offices was marked from the start. For the first six months the applications for employment amounted to over 20,000, for nearly half of whom positions were secured. Perhaps the most striking testimonial to their success is to be found in the fact that, while there were at least twelve well-known private employment agencies in these cities at the time of the establishment of the public offices, the commissioner of labor reported in 1892 that they no longer existed in Columbus, Toledo, and Dayton, while only a few "still managed to exist" in Cleveland and Cincinnati. The facilities of the offices seem to have been made very general use of by employers, the applications for help sometimes outnumbering the applications for employment, especially in domestic service. The superintendents of the offices, reporting on this point in 1891, stated that employers generally favored the establishment of the offices, and that the working people were unanimous in their approval. Two of the superintendents, however, reported that manufacturers denied any need of such a bureau, since so many applications for employment were made directly at the factories. While this is true in general of skilled labor, it is, of course, less true of unskilled labor, and not at all the case with domestic and personal help. The activities of the offices are, therefore, particularly marked in the latter field.

The reports of the offices show a fairly steady growth from year to year in spite of the depression of 1893, and give evidence that the bureaus are filling a real want. While the number of applications for employment on the part of men has not changed materially, the applications for male employees and the number of positions filled has steadily decreased. On the other hand, the number of women dealt with, especially domestic servants, has grown continuously, seeming to indicate that the bureaus are becoming more or less "intelligence" offices of the familiar type for the registration of servants. There seems to be no desire in the state to abolish the offices, but the annual reports of the labor commissioner reiterate the demand for certain changes in the law which shall place them on a firmer basis. Objection is made to the provision which places the payment of the salaries of the superintendents and clerks upon the cities within which the bureaus are situated, partly on the ground that they are at the mercy of municipal politicians.[1] . . .

The third state in the Union to create free public employment offices by law was New York[2] by the act of May 25, 1896, which provided for the establishment of such offices in New York City and Buffalo. Owing to the crude provisions of this measure, which required among other things the sending of a weekly list of all applicants for employment or help to each of the 1168 supervisors of townships in the state, it was repealed in the following year, and replaced by the substitute act of May 13, 1897.

[1] Returns of five Ohio offices for selected years:

	1890		1893		1896		1899	
	Male	Female	Male	Female	Male	Female	Male	Female
Applications for employment	14,529	5,607	14,169	12,685	12,668	15,030	15,259	10,886
Applications for help	11,453	6,701	5,826	11,403	3,078	12,632	6,216	17,681
Positions secured	5,575	3,413	4,566	8,635	2,781	10,164	5,058	9,931

[2] Reports of the Bureau of Labor Statistics of New York, 1896–1898; and Bulletin of the Bureau, September and December, 1899.

This act of 1897 provided for the establishment of free public employment bureaus in cities of the first class, namely, New York and Buffalo. . . . An annual appropriation of $5000 was made for the New York office; and the appointment of superintendent and clerks was placed in the hands of the commissioner of labor, under civil-service regulations. All applicants are required to fill out statistical blanks, giving information as to age, nationality, occupation, wages, cause of idleness, references, and so forth. In addition a confidential letter of inquiry is sent to the last employer of every applicant for employment, requesting testimony as to character and ability, the response being filed with the application. These letters are answered very generally and apparently truthfully. Not only are the interests of the employers thus safeguarded, but those of the employees also by requiring, in cases where help is wanted out of town, that the railroad fare shall be paid to the destination, and that the employer shall meet the employee at the end of the journey.

The statistical information gathered on the blanks which are filled out in the office is tabulated and published in the annual reports of the Bureau of Labor.[1] The statistics of the number of applicants show a decrease after the first few months. This was largely due to the exaggerated expectations that were entertained at the time the office was opened as to

[1] The work of the New York office from its establishment on July 20, 1896, to January 1, 1900, is shown in the following table:

	1896			1897		
	Male	Female	Total	Male	Female	Total
Applications for employment	6458	1582	8040	3966	3319	7315
Applications for help	332	616	948	418	1624	2052
Situations secured			444	378	1127	1505

	1898			1899		
	Male	Female	Total	Male	Female	Total
Applications for employment	2487	2613	5100			5280
Applications for help	302	2344	2646			3043
Situations secured			2000			2401

its ability to obtain work for all applicants. Since then the number of applications has decreased, while the number of positions secured has increased. In one occupation the demand has continually outrun the supply, — domestic service, and more particularly general housework. The activities of the bureau are now confined almost exclusively to this department. . . .

The fifth state to establish free public employment agencies by law was Illinois, which provided for their creation in all cities of fifty thousand population or over by an act approved April 11, 1899. Three offices were accordingly opened in Chicago on July 31, — one on the North side, one on the South side, and the third on the West side of the city. The law provides for the appointment for two years of a man superintendent at a salary of $1200 and of a woman assistant at not more than $900 per annum. All expenses of the office are to be defrayed by the state. Weekly lists showing the number and character of all applicants for positions and for help are to be sent by each office to the Bureau of Labor Statistics, and a complete list to be mailed weekly from that bureau to each free employment office, to each state inspector of factories, and to each state inspector of mines. And it is made the duty of these officials to assist in securing employment for such applicants, and to notify the superintendents of the employment offices of all vacancies that come to their notice. Superintendents of the free offices are, furthermore, empowered to spend not more than $400 a year in advertising for positions. The Illinois law further contains a strike clause, which, as it does not appear in the laws of any other state, deserves to be quoted in full.[1]

The provisions for the collection of statistical data and for registration of applicants are more elaborate than in any other office. Every applicant for employment must answer a list

[1] "In no case shall the superintendent of any free employment office created by this act furnish or cause to be furnished workmen or other employees to any applicant for help whose employees are at that time on strike or locked out; nor shall any list of names and addresses of applicants for employment be shown to any employer whose employees are on strike or locked out; nor shall such list be exposed where it can be copied or used by an employer whose employees are on strike or locked out." — Labor Laws of the State of Illinois, 1899, p. 23, § 8.

of some thirty questions as to age, sex, nationality, conjugal condition, religion, length of residence, number of children, literacy, occupation, affiliations, cause of idleness, wages, health, references. Applicants for help are permitted to fill out a less formidable list. As in New York, and in identically the terms used there, a confidential letter is sent in each case to the last employer of every applicant for employment, requesting information as to character, sobriety, and obedience. When a call for help is made at the office a suitable applicant is at once notified of the position by a reply postal and is requested to use the return card to inform the office whether employment is secured. At the same time a note is sent to the prospective employer, notifying him who has been sent and inclosing a postal card to be used in notifying the office on his part whether he has engaged the applicant sent him. In this way the closest possible control is maintained.

In the city of Seattle, Washington,[1] there was established in April, 1894, a municipal free employment bureau, the only one of its kind in the United States. Originally created as an adjunct to the municipal office of labor statistics, it was later made a part of the civil service department of the city on the adoption of a new city charter in the spring of 1895. The secretary of the civil service commission assumed the office of labor commissioner and has devoted a part of his time to the conduct of the employment bureau. The success of the bureau has been marked; the increasing demands made upon it necessitated the appointment in 1897 of an assistant, a woman, who has charge of the women's department, and in the following year the appointment of an additional clerk. The expansion of the work has also necessitated two removals of the office, each time to more commodious quarters.

The conditions of the labor market in Washington seemed to require the establishment of an employment bureau which should cover the whole field more completely than was possible

[1] Annual Reports of the Commissioner of Labor of Seattle, Washington, 1894–1899.

for the private employment agencies. Situated as it is, Seattle is the outlet of streams of transient laborers on the way to Alaska and other points in the Northwest. Many of the industries, too, which are carried on in the state are of a seasonal and variable character, such as hop picking, fishing, logging, and railroad work, calling for constant readjustment and redistribution of the labor force. This fact is very clearly seen in the statistics of the work done by the bureau, in which I have separated the hop pickers and railroad laborers from the other applicants. Of course, this extension of the business of the bureau would not have been possible without the coöperation of the employers of labor; and in this regard Commissioner Grout seems to have been particularly successful, as practically all labor for the railroads and the hop fields in the state is obtained through the agency of the municipal office.

In the administration of the bureau the commissioner has sacrificed the statistical part of the work, with the accompaniments of detailed registration, to the more practical end of securing speedy employment of all applicants. Accordingly, no figures are given of the number of applications for positions or for help, but only of positions filled. The number of persons for whom work has been secured, even after eliminating the most fluctuating elements, shows a very steady growth. Although a municipal office, its usefulness is not limited to the city, applications for labor having been received from almost every town in the state, and from Alaska, British Columbia, Oregon, Montana, and Idaho. An analysis of the positions filled during 1898 showed that about 63 per cent were of "common, unskilled labor," 30 per cent "vocations requiring some knowledge or skill," while only about 7 per cent represented skilled trades.[1] This last figure was doubled the following year, but the work of the bureau has been largely confined to the class of unskilled labor. About nine tenths of these positions are out of the city. Private employment agencies seem to have been largely displaced by the municipal bureau; and the number of these, though fluctuating, was reduced to seven at the

[1] Fifth Annual Report, 1898.

end of 1899. All private agencies are required to secure a license from the city and pay an annual fee of $100.[1] . . .

The account thus far given of free public employment offices in the United States, taken largely from the reports of the offices themselves, has not been a very encouraging one. Not even the most ardent advocate of their extension would contend that they have been attended with striking success. Of the nine states in which their establishment has been attempted, they have been given up in three, — Montana, Iowa, and California, — while in Nebraska the office is struggling along with very unsatisfactory results. In these cases the establishment of the bureaus seems to have been premature and not called for by the needs of the community (except perhaps in California), but to have been advocated or created by the politicians as a sop to the laboring classes.[2] In only five states — namely, Ohio, New York, Missouri, Illinois, and Washington — is there such an increase in the number of applications and positions secured as to indicate a steady growth in usefulness. The municipal office at Seattle appears to have met with success a real want in the community where it is located, and to have enlisted most fully the coöperation of both employers and employees. But one of the main elements in its success is the

[1] The following figures show the work done by the bureau from April 1, 1894, to January 1, 1900:

POSITIONS FURNISHED IN SEATTLE

	1894[1]	1895	1896	1897	1898	1899
Total	2,623	3,729	3,268	5,952	13,871	18,153
Hop pickers	1,144	2,050	135[4]	2,890	2,235	2,682
Railroad laborers	—[2]	1,311[3]	571[3]	2,784	7,077	2,102
Grand total	3,967	5,779	3,403	11,626	24,183	22,837
Total expenses	$909.65	$1120.00	$727.50	$724.80	$1377.13	$1136.66
Cost of each position furnished	$0.2293	$0.1938	$0.2138	$0.0624	$0.0569	$0.05

[1] Nine months.
[2] Not specified. Office did not act as agent for the railroads before 1897.
[3] General laborers included in totals above.
[4] Almost total failure of harvest.

[2] The commissioner of the Montana bureau, in a letter to the writer, ascribes the failure of the office in that state to the dislike of it as a Populist measure.

fact that it has had to deal largely with unskilled labor. So far, at least, the offices have been used very little by members of skilled or well-organized trades; and their representatives seem to think it doubtful if they ever will be. An analysis of the occupations of those applying for employment, particularly in the large cities, shows that the majority of the men are unskilled laborers; and another large portion may properly be classed under the head of domestic or personal service, — coachmen, gardeners, hostlers, waiters, hotel employees, and the like. The women are recruited almost entirely from this latter class. The writer has visited several of the offices, and in every case has been forcibly impressed by this fact. In so far the expectations of the friends of the offices have been disappointed, for they had hoped to see them used less by domestic servants and more largely by skilled artisans and mechanics.

The public employment offices in this country do not seem to have encountered any opposition[1] due to industrial disputes, such as has made their success problematical in Germany. With the exception of the Illinois law, which forbids the offices furnishing employees during a strike, there is nothing in the various acts to regulate their administration under such circumstances. As a matter of fact, the management of the various offices has differed in this respect, even within a single state.[2] While the representatives of organized labor are, on the whole, in favor of the free public employment offices, they are unanimous in insisting that they shall be held entirely neutral during labor disputes. In the event of strikes they should not be permitted to furnish men to fill the place of strikers, and in case of disputes as to wages they should not attempt to provide employees at a lower rate of wage than that for which contention is being made. It was feared that the insistence upon references would militate against the offices among the working people by introducing the hated "character note"; but so far little objection has been met on that score. Yet one of the

[1] Except in Grand Rapids.

[2] Thus in Ohio the Dayton office sends men to fill the places of strikers. The others do not.

first essentials for the success of such offices lies in the selection of the applicants. Without such selection employers will not as a rule use them. And thus, as to the general outlook for the free offices, the following paragraph from the exhaustive report of the English Department of Labor on "Agencies and Methods for dealing with the Unemployed" will apply equally well to the United States:

> With the best of conditions, labor bureaus can hardly be expected to become the sole or principal means of bringing together employers and unemployed. The bulk of the work of hiring labor and seeking employment will in most trades continue to be done directly between workmen and employers, as is the case where, as in France, the system of bureaus has been carried much further than in the United Kingdom. Nor as regards the organized trades can labor bureaus, as a rule, compare in utility, so far as workmen are concerned, with the work of a well-managed trade society. The chief field of usefulness of labor bureaus is likely, therefore, to be found for some time to come in the less highly organized trades.

II. Germany

Before proceeding to consider the comparatively recent movement for establishing free public employment offices in Germany, it will be instructive to glance at various other agencies which have been resorted to there. These may be divided into at least four groups, — private pay agencies, philanthropic employment offices, and agencies conducted by associations of employers or unions of workmen.

In spite of the rapid growth in number of the free offices, within the last decade especially, the private employment agencies are probably still in the majority; and in certain occupations they exercise almost a monopoly. They are made use of particularly for domestic servants, employees in mercantile establishments, hotels, and restaurants, farm laborers, sailors, and actors.[1] Though evils are complained of in connection with these offices, they are apparently not so great as in the United

[1] V. Weigert, Arbeitsnachweis und Schutz der Arbeitswilligen, Berlin, 1899, p. 2.

States, since all employment agencies are placed under police control by imperial law, and are made to pay a license fee. According to a statistical investigation carried out in Prussia in 1895, the number of such agencies in that kingdom alone was 5216. During the year 1894 these 5000 agencies had received 535,020 applications for employment, 481,358 applications for help, and had secured 381,206 positions.[1]

Under philanthropic employment offices we may include those conducted by religious societies, charitable organizations, communal or police officials, the lodging houses (*Herbergen*) of various societies, the relief stations (*Naturalverpflegungsstationen*), and the like. Together these form a perfect network of agencies throughout the empire for the purpose of securing work for the unemployed; but, inasmuch as they deal largely with the shiftless and incapable classes and those who do not wish to secure situations, the statistical results of their work are not very favorable. Since, however, they are free employment offices, no charge being made, and are also in large part public (in that they are either connected with public institutions or aided by public funds), it will be advisable to consider them briefly.

Most of these agencies are connected with the various institutions established for dealing with and suppressing vagrancy.[2] The anti-begging societies (*Vereine gegen Armennot und Bettelei*), which are organized in all towns and cities throughout Germany, discourage the giving of alms and require their members to refer all applicants to the office of the society. With this an employment bureau is connected, and an attempt is immediately made to secure work for the applicant. The society further provides a relief station (*Verpflegungsstation*), where by a few hours' work the destitute wayfarer can earn a ticket which will entitle him to food and lodging at the lodging house (*Herberge*). If no work can be found for him in this locality,

[1] Zeitschrift des Königlichen Preussischen Statistischen Bureaus, Jahrgang 36, 1899, pp. 7–11.

[2] Vagrancy and Public Charities in Foreign Countries, Special Consular Report, Washington, 1893, pp. 293, 305, 320, 329, 340.

he is next day given a card to the next *Herberge*, where he must report that afternoon and there in turn make application for work. If he wanders from the route which he has chosen, he is liable to arrest as a vagrant. The anti-begging societies are supported entirely by private subscriptions; but practically the same work is done by the public authorities in most of the German states by the establishment of public stations giving relief in kind (*Naturalverpflegungsstationen*). Of 1957 such stations maintained in Germany in 1890, 1707 were maintained by public authority, and 250 by societies. Similar work is also done by the German Lodging-House Society (*Deutscher Herbergsverein*), which has established in all the states a number of lodging houses for wayfarers in search of employment, the institutions being maintained largely by provincial or local societies. These various relief stations and lodging houses, together with the labor colonies, have succeeded in legitimatizing the movements of a class which without them would become mere vagrants. They have, therefore, reduced the number of arrests for vagabondage,[1] but do not seem to have contributed in any permanent way towards solving the problem of the unemployed by securing employment for them.

The establishment of employment offices has also been fostered by the various trade organizations, both those conducted by the employers and those managed by the laborers. While at first their creation seems to have been inspired only by the motive of adjusting the labor supply and demand, of later years they have been used extensively by both sides as a *Kampfmittel* in the struggle between labor and capital. As this movement has led to the establishment of offices by a variety of organizations, it will be necessary to consider these separately.

1. Following the example of the early guilds, the modern *Innungen* have also endeavored to secure employment and help within their respective trades by undertaking the duties of employment offices. Though in the main they comprise only a

[1] In Prussia the number decreased from 23,808 in 1882 (no stations) to 8605 in 1890 (951 stations).

small portion of the members of the various trades, still a few of them, as the barber guild, are of national importance. The possibility of an extension of this side of their activity was afforded them by a provision in the industrial code of July 26, 1897,[1] according to which the establishment of employment offices is expressly enumerated among the privileges of the guilds. It is unlikely, however, that they will assume any greater importance in the future, as they are managed largely in the interest of the employers and seem to be losing ground. They have gained a stronger foothold in northern Germany than in the South. In Prussia 734 such employment offices were reported for the year 1894, of which 642 made no charge. Most of the others charged only a nominal fee. These offices further reported for the same year 121,342 applications for employment, 54,614 applications for help, and 47,093 positions secured.

2. Employers' organizations (*Gewerbe-* or *Fabrikantenvereine*). Towards the end of the eighties the employers of labor began to unite with the avowed purpose of opposing the socialistically inclined laborers' organizations. One of the principal means used by the newly formed unions as well as the older ones was the establishment of employment offices, "which should be managed exclusively by employers, and whose members should pledge themselves to obtain labor only through these offices."[2] The alliance of master masons and carpenters and the association of metal workers were the first larger organizations of employers to adopt this rule, as well as the further one "to employ no laborer who belonged to any social-democratic association." This attitude, it is needless to say, does not commend their employment offices to the mass of laborers, nor indicate that they are managed in an impartial manner. Such agencies have been created, in addition to those of the metal workers and masons and carpenters, by the smiths, bookbinders, paper hangers, painters, cabinetmakers, and potters. They exist also in the textile industries and in the building

[1] Gewerbeordnung, §§ 81 a, 88, etc. Quoted by H. Eckert, Die beste Organisation des Arbeitsnachweises, p. 6.

[2] Weigert, *loc. cit.*, p. 6.

trades.[1] Of such organizations some thirty conducted employment offices in Prussia in 1894, of which about half the number charged a fee. These offices reported 34,873 applications for employment, 17,400 applications for help, and 16,910 positions secured. In addition to the organizations of manufacturers, the agrarian unions have in many instances established employment bureaus, of which sixteen were reported in Prussia. During 1894 these received 3759 applications for employment, 2612 applications for help, and filled 1629 positions.

3. Workingmen's organizations (*Fach-* or *Gewerkvereine*). Since the founding of the Hirsch-Duncker trade unions, which made the employment feature an important part of their work, many of the workingmen's organizations have established employment offices. As a rule, however, they have not attained a position of importance, being necessarily conducted at a disadvantage, usually open in the evenings only, and administered by the secretary or other official of the union in connection with other duties. Unfortunately, their management has often exposed them to the same charges of partiality of which the workingmen are ready enough to accuse the employers' offices. Not infrequently, too, the offices have been used as a weapon in the struggle against the employing class, as in the case of the Berlin beer boycott of 1896. This boycott, which had assumed immense and ominous proportions, was finally settled by the establishment of a joint employment office, conducted by a joint committee of employers and employees. Of offices managed by the workingmen alone there existed in Prussia during 1894 about 300, of which only 230 made reports. These 230 offices received 76,046 applications for employment, 32,968 applications for help, and secured positions for 26,760 persons.

4. A small number of employment offices have been established which are managed jointly by representatives of employers' and laborers' organizations. They have been called into being largely by the efforts of some more liberal-minded employers, who have desired to avoid the unfairness of those offices managed exclusively by employers or by employees;

[1] Richard Calwer, Arbeitsmarkt und Arbeitsnachweis, Stuttgart, 1899, p. 44.

and they have been fairly well received by the laboring men. They were opposed, however, by the Employers' Conference at Leipsic in 1898 and have not obtained any great prominence, especially as the growth of public bureaus has rendered them to a large extent unnecessary. They are especially prevalent in mercantile circles. In Prussia sixty such offices were reported, of which number only forty-six made returns. During 1894 these received 58,584 applications for employment, 33,153 applications for help, and furnished 23,129 positions. About half of these offices required the payment of a fee, ranging from $1.25 to $5.

Although many — in fact, most — of the employment agencies which have already been mentioned are free and are in the main open to all applicants, they are not public in the sense of being supported by public funds. The movement for the establishment of free public employment offices, either communal or municipal, has grown rapidly in the last few years; and at present such offices are maintained in most of the principal cities and towns in Germany. The first such agency seems to have been established at Freiburg in May, 1892, by the joint action of the organizations of employers and the labor unions; but it did not come under municipal management and control until 1897. The real impetus to the movement, however, was given in the autumn of 1893 by a report of the Stuttgart Trade Council (*Gewerbegericht*), which strongly advocated the establishment of a municipal employment bureau in that city. Although the plan was not carried out at the time, it met with the warmest approval the following year at the meeting of the Social Congress at Frankfort, where it was advocated both by workingmen and capitalists. The plan suggested there formed the basis of the various municipal offices which sprang up in rapid succession in all parts of the empire. In South Germany, especially, the movement met with success. In Würtemberg, Bavaria, Hesse, Baden, and Prussia one city after another proceeded with the establishment of public bureaus. It is impossible to say how many such offices exist at present in Germany, as no authoritative list has been published and the number is large and steadily growing. Dr. Freund, superintendent of the Invalid and Old Age Pension Office at Berlin, estimated the number in 1899 at about 114.[1]

The fundamental principle of the public offices is equal representation : employers and employees are both represented in the management in equal proportion and with equal powers. In general, the administration is connected with the Trade Council (*Gewerbegericht*), and a city official is the chairman of the governing board. These offices are, of course, free to all applicants of any trade or occupation. The organization and administration of the Munich office — which is admittedly the best managed and which has served as a model for many of the others — will serve to illustrate the general features common to them all.[2] The ultimate oversight of this office resides in the city magistrate; but its immediate control rests in the hands of an elective board of seven, of whom three are employers and three employees, the chairman of the Trade Council being *ex officio* chairman of the board. The office has a men's division, where three assistants are employed, and a women's division, where there are also three assistants. It receives applications for every sort of employment, and during the year 1898 secured positions for over 32,000 persons. The total expenses of the office, which are borne by the city of Munich, amounted to only about $3650, of which $500 went for rent. The work of the office is administered with typical German thoroughness. Applicants for employment are divided into classes according to occupation, — thirty-two classes for men and ten for women, — each class having a separate and detailed list. Every applicant is required to fill out a statistical blank, giving occupation, name, and so on, and is given a card with his number. If a suitable position is open, he is sent immediately, or notified by post, to go to the prospective employer, to whom he hands a postal card addressed to the employment bureau; this card legitimatizes him

[1] Freund, Arbeitsnachweise, Berlin, 1899, p. 13.

[2] Die Einrichtung von Arbeitsnachweisen und Arbeitsnachweis-Verbänden. Verhandlungen der ersten deutschen Arbeitsnachweis-Konferenz, Karlsruhe, 1897, Berlin, 1898, p. 42.

and the employer is supposed to fill it out and send it back. The applicant is also required to report the result of his application to the bureau. By this system and by frequent use of the post the bureau seems to have been successful in keeping track of all positions filled. Owing to the German system of police oversight, and particularly to the compulsory use by domestic servants of registration books in which their places and terms of service are all noted, less time is devoted to looking up references than in similar bureaus in the United States. The name of an applicant is kept on the books as long as two months. After the expiration of that period the application must be renewed.

Although the Munich office was not established until 1895, it has served as a model for most of the later offices, much as the Ohio agencies have in this country. In the smaller towns the administration is, of course, much more simple and direct. The development of the separate offices had not proceeded very far, however, before the need was felt of a more centralized system by means of which the various offices could be brought into closer touch with one another. The matter was first agitated by the Würtemberg government, and soon after by Bavaria, Baden, Hesse, and Prussia; and although the movement is as yet only in the experimental stage, it has been fairly well developed in these states. In Baden, for instance, reports are sent in by the other offices to the Karlsruhe office, which acts as a central clearing house, sending out again immediately the reports of each office to every other office. Each office is then in a position to send applicants to fill openings in other places or to request help from the district where there is a surplus. In Würtemberg the Stuttgart office acts as the central agent, sending out reports of all vacancies twice a week, not only to all the other employment offices but to every town of more than 3000 inhabitants and to all institutions which maintain employment features. In Düsseldorf a slightly different method is used. Instead of letting one of the employment offices act as clearing house for the others, an independent central bureau has been established, whose sole duty it is to act as agent between the various offices. Some sort of centralized system has been found so necessary for the best results that a closer union between the different states by means of the establishment of an imperial central bureau has been advocated. While such a move is very unlikely in the near future, the necessary bond of union has been created by the formation (February 4, 1898) of the Association of German Employment Offices, whose first meeting was held in Munich in September, 1898. Its objects are the creation of a deeper interest in the work and establishment of employment offices, and the collection of uniform statistics.[1] At the time of its formation sixty-eight bureaus were enrolled as members, of which thirty were municipal, eight provincial, and the rest philanthropic free institutions. A monthly journal, *Der Arbeitsmarkt*, has also been published in Berlin by Dr. Jastrow, who seeks to tabulate and utilize these statistics to determine accurately the fluctuations of the labor market.

The majority of the public employment offices in Germany are municipal; but many of them are aided by the state, especially in south Germany. Frequently, too, grants have been made by state, province, or municipality to employment offices maintained by joint boards of employers and employees, while no attempts have been made to share in the administration. In fact, like so many of the German social-reform movements, the initiative and support for this one seem to have come largely from the government.

It is difficult to say what the attitude of the labor unions or their members is towards the public employment offices, as opinions in these circles are widely divided.[2] Those workingmen who see in the agencies only a weapon in the struggle with capital oppose their establishment, as they fear that they will be used to their disadvantage. And, in fact, the tone of the discussion in the Munich Conference on the subject of "What can the

[1] The stenographic report of the proceedings of this meeting has been published as a supplement to No. 11 of *Sociale Praxis*, and also separately as Schriften des Verbandes deutscher Arbeitsnachweise, No. 1, Berlin, 1899.

[2] Calwer, *loc. cit.*, p. 7.

Employment Bureaus do to secure Laborers for the Agricultural Districts?" seemed to lend color to that idea.[1] On the other hand, the attitude of the organized employers is also largely hostile to the extension of the public offices.[2] It is only fair to say, however, that extreme opposition is not often shown except by the agrarian members.

One of the most disputed points and one which was most strongly insisted on by the labor unions at the beginning of the movement for public employment offices was the attitude of the office during a strike. The unions demanded that no help should be furnished to an establishment or industry while a strike was in progress. This more extreme position has not been strictly adhered to, and at a preliminary conference held at Karlsruhe in 1897 the representatives of the labor unions declared that they would be satisfied to have the offices continue their activity during a strike, if the officials would only acquaint all applicants with the fact that a strike was in progress.[3] Among the different offices the practice varies in this regard. In Stuttgart the office continues its work without interruption; in Strasburg the governing commission decides whether to stop or not; the same is true of Mainz, Treves, and a number of other cities; Cologne discontinues the work of the office during a strike; in Breslau and Frankfort no rules for the conduct of the offices at such a time have been formulated. It may safely be said that the fear on this point was largely groundless, and that it makes no practical difference as to the outcome of a strike whether the employment office ceases its activities or not. So many other factors enter that the existence of such an agency and its attitude can have very little effect one way or the other.

In spite of some antagonisms and difficulties at first, the German free public employment offices have met with decided success. Their number has grown from a dozen in 1894 to over one hundred in 1899, while the extent of their activity

[1] Verhandlungen der Münchener Konferenz, pp. 6 ff.

[2] Weigert, *loc. cit.*, p. 33.

[3] Verhandlungen der Karlsruhe Konferenz, p. 69.

has more than kept pace with their growth in numbers. The positions secured for applicants numbered about 190,000 in 1896 in all the "free" bureaus, while by 1898 they amounted to over 250,000.[1] One noticeable fact is shown by the statistics of the German agencies, which points to a high degree of success, — the relatively small number of women applicants. Of the men for whom positions were secured by far the larger part belonged, of course, to the class of unskilled labor; but the more skilled trades and occupations were also well represented.

It will at once be seen that, though the movement is a more recent one, it has proceeded farther in Germany than in the United States, and has met with a much greater degree of success. Aside from the undoubted advantages which the German offices possess in the concentration of the population and the smallness of the area that they have to deal with, there seems to be no doubt that such institutions find a more favorable reception on the continent of Europe than in this country. The differences in industrial conditions, indeed, are so great that probably little is to be learned from German experience which will materially aid us in the United States in solving the problem of finding work for the unemployed by means of free employment offices.

E. L. BOGART.

[1] Weigert, *loc. cit.*, pp. 70–75; Jastrow, in Arbeitsmarkt, 1898.

INDEX

ALSO BY WALTER ISAACSON

Leonardo da Vinci

The Innovators: How a Group of Hackers, Geniuses, and Geeks Created the Digital Revolution

Steve Jobs

American Sketches

Einstein: His Life and Universe

Benjamin Franklin: An American Life

Kissinger: A Biography

The Wise Men: Six Friends and the World They Made (with Evan Thomas)

Pro and Con

THE CODE BREAKER

Jennifer Doudna, Gene Editing, and
the Future of the Human Race

WALTER
ISAACSON

Simon & Schuster
NEW YORK LONDON TORONTO SYDNEY NEW DELHI

Simon & Schuster
1230 Avenue of the Americas
New York, NY 10020

First Simon & Schuster hardcover edition March 2021

Manufactured in the United States of America

1 3 5 7 9 10 8 6 4 2

Library of Congress Cataloging-in-Publication Data

ISBN 978-1-9821-1585-2
ISBN 978-1-9821-1587-6 (ebook)

CONTENTS

Part Three: Gene Editing

Part Four: CRISPR in Action

Part Five: Public Scientist

Part Six: CRISPR Babies

Part Seven: The Moral Questions

Part Eight: Dispatches from the Front

Part Nine: Coronavirus

To the memory of Alice Mayhew and Carolyn Reidy.

What a joy it was to see them smile.

INTRODUCTION

Into the Breach

Jennifer Doudna couldn't sleep. Berkeley, the university where she was a superstar for her role in inventing the gene-editing technology known as CRISPR, had just shut down its campus because of the fast-spreading coronavirus pandemic. Against her better judgment, she had driven her son, Andy, a high school senior, to the train station so he could go to Fresno for a robot-building competition. Now, at 2 a.m., she roused her husband and insisted that they retrieve him before the start of the match, when more than twelve hundred kids would be gathering in an indoor convention center. They pulled on their clothes, got in the car, found an open gas station, and made the three-hour drive. Andy, an only child, was not happy to see them, but they convinced him to pack up and come home. As they pulled out of the parking lot, Andy got a text from the team: "Robotics match cancelled! All kids to leave immediately!"[1]

This was the moment, Doudna recalls, that she realized her world, and the world of science, had changed. The government was fumbling its response to COVID, so it was time for professors and graduate students, clutching their test tubes and raising their pipettes high, to rush into the breach. The next day—Friday, March 13, 2020—she led a meeting of her Berkeley colleagues and other scientists in the Bay Area to discuss what roles they might play.

A dozen of them made their way across the abandoned Berkeley campus and converged on the sleek stone-and-glass building that housed her lab. The chairs in the ground-floor conference room were clustered together, so the first thing they did was move them six feet apart. Then they turned on a video system so that fifty other researchers from nearby universities could join by Zoom. As she stood in front of the room to rally them, Doudna displayed an intensity that she usually kept masked by a calm façade. "This is not something that academics typically do," she told them. "We need to step up."[2]

It was fitting that a virus-fighting team would be led by a CRISPR pioneer. The gene-editing tool that Doudna and others developed in 2012 is based on a virus-fighting trick used by bacteria, which have been battling viruses for more than a billion years. In their DNA, bacteria develop clustered repeated sequences, known as CRISPRs, that can remember and then destroy viruses that attack them. In other words, it's an immune system that can adapt itself to fight each new wave of viruses—just what we humans need in an era that has been plagued, as if we were still in the Middle Ages, by repeated viral epidemics.

Always prepared and methodical, Doudna (pronounced DOWD-nuh) presented slides that suggested ways they might take on the coronavirus. She led by listening. Although she had become a science celebrity, people felt comfortable engaging with her. She had mastered the art of being tightly scheduled while still finding the time to connect with people emotionally.

The first team that Doudna assembled was given the job of creating a coronavirus testing lab. One of the leaders she tapped was a postdoc named Jennifer Hamilton who, a few months earlier, had spent a day teaching me to use CRISPR to edit human genes. I was pleased, but also a bit unnerved, to see how easy it was. Even I could do it!

Another team was given the mission of developing new types of coronavirus tests based on CRISPR. It helped that Doudna liked commercial enterprises. Three years earlier, she and two of her graduate students had started a company to use CRISPR as a tool for detecting viral diseases.

In launching an effort to find new tests to detect the coronavirus, Doudna was opening another front in her fierce but fruitful struggle with a cross-country competitor. Feng Zhang, a charming young China-born and Iowa-raised researcher at the Broad Institute of MIT and Harvard, had been her rival in the 2012 race to turn CRISPR into a gene-editing tool, and ever since then they had been locked in an intense competition to make scientific discoveries and form CRISPR-based companies. Now, with the outbreak of the pandemic, they would engage in another race, this one spurred not by the pursuit of patents but by a desire to do good.

Doudna settled on ten projects. She suggested leaders for each and told the others to sort themselves into the teams. They should pair up with someone who would perform the same functions, so that there could be a battlefield promotion system: if any of them were struck by the virus, there would be someone to step in and continue their work. It was the last time they would meet in person. From then on the teams would collaborate by Zoom and Slack.

"I'd like everyone to get started soon," she said. "Really soon."

"Don't worry," one of the participants assured her. "Nobody's got any travel plans."

What none of the participants discussed was a longer-range prospect: using CRISPR to engineer inheritable edits in humans that would make our children, and all of our descendants, less vulnerable to virus infections. These genetic improvements could permanently alter the human race.

"That's in the realm of science fiction," Doudna said dismissively when I raised the topic after the meeting. Yes, I agreed, it's a bit like *Brave New World* or *Gattaca*. But as with any good science fiction, elements have already come true. In November 2018, a young Chinese scientist who had been to some of Doudna's gene-editing conferences used CRISPR to edit embryos and remove a gene that produces a receptor for HIV, the virus that causes AIDS. It led to the birth of twin girls, the world's first "designer babies."

There was an immediate outburst of awe and then shock. Arms flailed, committees convened. After more than three billion years of evolution of life on this planet, one species (us) had developed the talent and temerity to grab control of its own genetic future. There was a sense that we had crossed the threshold into a whole new age, perhaps a brave new world, like when Adam and Eve bit into the apple or Prometheus snatched fire from the gods.

Our newfound ability to make edits to our genes raises some fascinating questions. Should we edit our species to make us less susceptible to deadly viruses? What a wonderful boon that would be! Right? Should we use gene editing to eliminate dreaded disorders, such as Huntington's, sickle-cell anemia, and cystic fibrosis? That sounds good, too. And what about deafness or blindness? Or being short? Or depressed? Hmmm . . . How should we think about that? A few decades from now, if it becomes possible and safe, should we allow parents to enhance the IQ and muscles of their kids? Should we let them decide eye color? Skin color? Height?

Whoa! Let's pause for a moment before we slide all of the way down this slippery slope. What might that do to the diversity of our societies? If we are no longer subject to a random natural lottery when it comes to our endowments, will it weaken our feelings of empathy and acceptance? If these offerings at the genetic supermarket aren't free (and they won't be), will that greatly increase inequality—and indeed encode it permanently in the human race? Given these issues, should such decisions be left solely to individuals, or should society as a whole have some say? Perhaps we should develop some rules.

By "we" I mean *we*. All of us, including you and me. Figuring out if and when to edit our genes will be one of the most consequential questions of the twenty-first century, so I thought it would be useful to understand how it's done. Likewise, recurring waves of virus epidemics make it important to understand the life sciences. There's a joy that springs from fathoming how something works, especially when that something is ourselves. Doudna relished that joy, and so can we. That's what this book is about.

The invention of CRISPR and the plague of COVID will hasten our transition to the third great revolution of modern times. These revolutions arose from the discovery, beginning just over a century ago, of the three fundamental kernels of our existence: the atom, the bit, and the gene.

The first half of the twentieth century, beginning with Albert Einstein's 1905 papers on relativity and quantum theory, featured a revolution driven by physics. In the five decades following his miracle year, his theories led to atom bombs and nuclear power, transistors and spaceships, lasers and radar.

The second half of the twentieth century was an information-technology era, based on the idea that all information could be encoded by binary digits—known as bits—and all logical processes could be performed by circuits with on-off switches. In the 1950s, this led to the development of the microchip, the computer, and the internet. When these three innovations were combined, the digital revolution was born.

Now we have entered a third and even more momentous era, a life-science revolution. Children who study digital coding will be joined by those who study genetic code.

When Doudna was a graduate student in the 1990s, other biologists were racing to map the genes that are coded by our DNA. But she became more interested in DNA's less-celebrated sibling, RNA. It's the molecule that actually does the work in a cell by copying some of the instructions coded by the DNA and using them to build proteins. Her quest to understand RNA led her to that most fundamental question: How did life begin? She studied RNA molecules that could replicate themselves, which raised the possibility that in the stew of chemicals on this planet four billion years ago they started to reproduce even before DNA came into being.

As a biochemist at Berkeley studying the molecules of life, she focused on figuring out their structure. If you're a detective, the most basic clues in a biological whodunit come from discovering how a molecule's twists and folds determine the way it interacts with other molecules. In Doudna's case, that meant studying the structure of RNA. It was an echo of the work Rosalind Franklin had done with DNA, which was used by James Watson and Francis Crick to discover the double-helix structure of DNA in 1953. As it happens, Watson, a complex figure, would weave in and out of Doudna's life.

Doudna's expertise in RNA led to a call from a biologist at Berkeley who was studying the CRISPR system that bacteria developed in their battle against viruses. Like a lot of basic science discoveries, it turned out to have practical applications. Some were rather ordinary, such as protecting the bacteria in yogurt cultures. But in 2012 Doudna and others figured out a more earth-shattering use: how to turn CRISPR into a tool to edit genes.

CRISPR is now being used to treat sickle-cell anemia, cancers, and blindness. And in 2020, Doudna and her teams began exploring how CRISPR could detect and destroy the coronavirus. "CRISPR evolved in bacteria because of their long-running war against viruses," Doudna says. "We humans don't have time to wait for our own cells to evolve natural resistance to this virus, so we have to use our ingenuity to do that. Isn't it fitting that one of the tools is this ancient bacterial immune system called CRISPR? Nature is beautiful that way." Ah, yes. Remember that phrase: Nature is beautiful. That's another theme of this book.

There are other star players in the field of gene editing. Most of them deserve to be the focus of biographies or perhaps even movies. (The elevator pitch: *A Beautiful Mind* meets *Jurassic Park*.) They play important roles in this book, because I want to show that science is a team sport. But I also want to show the impact that a persistent, sharply inquisitive, stubborn, and edgily competitive player can have. With a smile that sometimes (but not always) masks the wariness in her eyes, Jennifer Doudna turned out to be a great central character. She has the instincts to be collaborative, as any scientist must, but ingrained in her character is a competitive streak, which most great innovators have. With her emotions usually carefully controlled, she wears her star status lightly.

Her life story—as a researcher, Nobel Prize winner, and public policy thinker—connects the CRISPR tale to some larger historical threads, including the role of women in science. Her work also illustrates, as Leonardo da Vinci's did, that the key to innovation is connecting a curiosity about basic science to the practical work of devising tools that can be applied to our lives—moving discoveries from lab bench to bedside.

By telling her story, I hope to give an up-close look at how science works. What actually happens in a lab? To what extent do discoveries depend on individual genius, and to what extent has teamwork become more critical? Has the competition for prizes and patents undermined collaboration?

Most of all, I want to convey the importance of *basic* science, meaning quests that are curiosity-driven rather than application-oriented. Curiosity-driven research into the wonders of nature plants the seeds, sometimes in unpredictable ways, for later innovations.[3] Research about surface-state physics eventually led to the transistor and microchip. Likewise, studies of an astonishing method that bacteria use to fight off viruses eventually led to a gene-editing tool and techniques that humans can use in their own struggle against viruses.

It is a story filled with the biggest of questions, from the origins of life to the future of the human race. And it begins with a sixth-grade girl who loved searching for "sleeping grass" and other fascinating phenomena amid the lava rocks of Hawaii, coming home from school one day and finding on her bed a detective tale about the people who discovered what they proclaimed to be, with only a little exaggeration, "the secret of life."

Part One

The Origins of Life

The Lord God made a garden in the east, in Eden;
and there he put the man he had made.
Out of the ground the Lord God caused to grow
every tree that is beautiful and good for food;
the tree of life also in the midst of the garden,
and the tree of the knowledge of good and evil.

—Genesis 2:8–9

Jennifer in Hilo

Don Hemmes

Ellen, Jennifer, Sarah, Martin, and Dorothy Doudna

CHAPTER 1

Hilo

Haole

Had she grown up in any other part of America, Jennifer Doudna might have felt like a regular kid. But in Hilo, an old town in a volcano-studded region of the Big Island of Hawaii, the fact that she was blond, blue-eyed, and lanky made her feel, she later said, "like I was a complete freak." She was teased by the other kids, especially the boys, because unlike them she had hair on her arms. They called her a "haole," a term that, though not quite as bad as it sounds, was often used as a pejorative for non-natives. It imbedded in her a slight crust of wariness just below the surface of what would later become a genial and charming demeanor.[1]

A tale that became part of the family lore involved one of Jennifer's great-grandmothers. She was part of a family of three brothers and three sisters. Their parents could not afford for all six to go to school, so they decided to send the three girls. One became a teacher in Montana and kept a diary that has been handed down over the generations. It is filled with tales of perseverance, broken bones, working in the family store, and other frontier endeavors. "She was crusty and stubborn and had a pioneering spirit," said Jennifer's sister Sarah, the current generation's keeper of the diary.

Jennifer was likewise one of three sisters, but there were no brothers. As the oldest, she was doted on by her father, Martin Doudna, who sometimes referred to his children as "Jennifer and the girls." She was born February 19, 1964, in Washington, D.C., where her father worked as a speechwriter for the Department of Defense. He yearned to be a professor of American literature, so he moved to Ann Arbor with his wife, a community college teacher named Dorothy, and enrolled at the University of Michigan.

When he earned his doctorate, he applied for fifty jobs and got only one offer, from the University of Hawaii at Hilo. So he borrowed $900 from his wife's retirement fund and moved his family there in August 1971, when Jennifer was seven.

Many creative people—including most of those I have chronicled, such as Leonardo da Vinci, Albert Einstein, Henry Kissinger, and Steve Jobs—grew up feeling alienated from their surroundings. That was the case for Doudna as a young blond girl among the Polynesians in Hilo. "I was really, really alone and isolated at school," she says. In the third grade, she felt so ostracized that she had trouble eating. "I had all sorts of digestive problems that I later realized were stress related. Kids would tease me every day." She retreated into books and developed a defensive layer. "There's an internal part of me they'll never touch," she told herself.

Like many others who have felt like an outsider, she developed a wide-ranging curiosity about how we humans fit into creation. "My formative experience was trying to figure out who I was in the world and how to fit in in some way," she later said.[2]

Fortunately, this sense of alienation did not become too ingrained. Life as a schoolkid got better, she developed a genial spirit, and the scar tissue of early childhood began to fade. It would become inflamed only on rare occasions, when some act—an end run on a patent application, a male business colleague being secretive or misleading—scratched deeply enough.

Blossoming

The improvement began halfway through third grade, when her family moved from the heart of Hilo to a new development of cookie-cutter houses that had been carved into a forested slope further up the flanks of the Mauna Loa volcano. She switched from a large school, with sixty kids per grade, to a smaller one with only twenty. They were studying U.S. history, a subject that made her feel more connected. "It was a turning point," she recalled. She thrived so well that by the time she was in fifth grade, her math and science teacher urged that she skip ahead. So her parents moved her into sixth grade.

That year she finally made a close friend, one she kept throughout her life. Lisa Hinkley (now Lisa Twigg-Smith) was from a classic mixed-race Hawaiian family: part Scottish, Danish, Chinese, and Polynesian. She knew how to handle the bullies. "When someone would call me a f—king haole, I would cringe," Doudna recalled. "But when a bully called Lisa names, she would turn and look right at him and give it right back to him. I decided I wanted to be that way." One day in class the students were asked what they wanted to be when they grew up. Lisa proclaimed that she wanted to be a skydiver. "I thought, 'That is so cool.' I couldn't imagine answering that. She was very bold in a way that I wasn't, and I decided to try to be bold as well."

Doudna and Hinkley spent their afternoons riding bikes and hiking through sugarcane fields. The biology was lush and diverse: moss and mushrooms, peach and arenga palms. They found meadows filled with lava rocks covered in ferns. In the lava-flow caves there lived a species of spider with no eyes. How, Doudna wondered, did it come to be? She was also intrigued by a thorny vine called hilahila or "sleeping grass" because its fernlike leaves curl up when touched. "I asked myself," she recalls, "'What causes the leaves to close when you touch them?'"[3]

We all see nature's wonders every day, whether it be a plant that moves or a sunset that reaches with pink fingers into a sky of deep blue. The key to true curiosity is pausing to ponder the causes. What makes a sky blue or a sunset pink or a leaf of sleeping grass curl?

Doudna soon found someone who could help answer such questions. Her parents were friends with a biology professor named Don Hemmes, and they would all go on nature walks together. "We took excursions to Waipio Valley and other sites on the Big Island to look for mushrooms, which was my scientific interest," Hemmes recalls. After photographing the fungi, he would pull out his reference books and show Doudna how to identify them. He also collected microscopic shells from the beach, and he would work with her to categorize them so they could try to figure out how they evolved.

Her father bought her a horse, a chestnut gelding named Mokihana, after a Hawaiian tree with a fragrant fruit. She joined the soccer team, playing halfback, a position that was hard to fill on her team because it required a runner with long legs and lots of stamina. "That's a good analogy to how I've approached my work," she said. "I've looked for opportunities where I can fill a niche where there aren't too many other people with the same skill sets."

Math was her favorite class because working through proofs reminded her of detective work. She also had a happy and passionate high school biology teacher, Marlene Hapai, who was wonderful at communicating the joy of discovery. "She taught us that science was about a process of figuring things out," Doudna says.

Although she began doing well academically, she did not feel that there were high expectations in her small school. "I didn't get the sense that the teachers really expected very much of me," she said. She had an interesting immune response: the lack of challenges made her feel free to take more chances. "I decided you just have to go for it, because what the hell," she recalled. "It made me more willing to take on risks, which is something I later did in science when I chose projects to pursue."

Her father was the one person who pushed her. He saw his oldest daughter as his kindred spirit in the family, the intellectual who was bound for college and an academic career. "I always felt like I was the son that he wanted to have," she says. "I was treated a bit differently than my sisters."

James Watson's The Double Helix

Doudna's father was a voracious reader who would check out a stack of books from the local library each Saturday and finish them by the following weekend. His favorite writers were Emerson and Thoreau, but as Jennifer was growing up he became more aware that the books he assigned to his class were mostly by men. So he added Doris Lessing, Anne Tyler, and Joan Didion to his syllabus.

Often he would bring home a book, either from the library or the local secondhand bookstore, for her to read. And that is how a used paperback copy of James Watson's *The Double Helix* ended up on her bed one day when she was in sixth grade, waiting for her when she got home from school.

She put the book aside, thinking it was a detective tale. When she finally got around to reading it on a rainy Saturday afternoon, she discovered that she was right, in a sense. As she sped through the pages, she became enthralled with what was an intensely personal detective drama, filled with vividly portrayed characters, about ambition and competition in the pursuit of nature's inner truths. "When I finished, my father discussed it with me," she recalls. "He liked the story and especially the very personal side of it—the human side of doing that kind of research."

In the book, Watson dramatized (and overdramatized) how as a twenty-four-year-old bumptious biology student from the American Midwest he ended up at Cambridge University in England, bonded with the biochemist Francis Crick, and together won the race to discover the structure of DNA in 1953. Written in the sparky narrative style of a brash American who has mastered the English after-dinner art of being self-deprecating and boastful at the same time, the book manages to smuggle a large dollop of science into a gossipy narrative about the foibles of famous professors, along with the pleasures of flirting, tennis, lab experiments, and afternoon tea.

In addition to the role of lucky naïf that he concocted as his own persona in the book, Watson's other most interesting character is Rosalind Franklin, a structural biologist and crystallographer whose data he used without her permission. Displaying the casual sexism of the 1950s, Watson refers to her condescendingly as "Rosy," a name she never used, and pokes fun at her severe appearance and chilly personality. Yet he also is generous in his respect for her mastery of the complex science and beautiful art of using X-ray diffraction to discover the structure of molecules.

"I guess I noticed she was treated a bit condescendingly, but what mainly struck me was that a woman could be a great scientist," Doudna says. "It may sound a bit crazy. I guess I must have heard about Marie Curie. But reading the book was the first time I really thought about it, and it was an eye-opener. Women could be scientists."[4]

The book also led Doudna to realize something about nature that was at once both logical and awe-inspiring. There were biological mechanisms that governed living things, including the wondrous phenomena that caught her eye when she hiked through the rainforests. "Growing up in Hawaii, I had always liked hunting with my dad for interesting things in nature, like the 'sleeping grass' that curls up when you touch it," she recalls. "The book made me realize you could also hunt for the reasons why nature worked the way it did."

Doudna's career would be shaped by the insight that is at the core of *The Double Helix*: the shape and structure of a chemical molecule determine what biological role it can play. It is an amazing revelation for those who are interested in uncovering the fundamental secrets of life. It is the way that chemistry—the study of how atoms bond to create molecules—becomes biology.

In a larger sense, her career would also be shaped by the realization that she was right when she first saw *The Double Helix* on her bed and thought that it was one of those detective mysteries that she loved. "I have always loved mystery stories," she noted years later. "Maybe that explains my fascination with science, which is humanity's attempt to understand the longest-running mystery we know: the origin and function of the natural world and our place in it."[5]

Even though her school didn't encourage girls to become scientists, she decided that is what she wanted to do. Driven by a passion to understand how nature works and by a competitive desire to turn discoveries into inventions, she would help make what Watson, with his typical grandiosity cloaked in the pretense of humility, would later tell her was the most important biological advance since the double helix.

SIGNET NON-FICTION • Q3770 • 95c

A NATIONAL BESTSELLER! THE INTENSELY HUMAN STORY BEHIND THE MOST SIGNIFICANT BIOLOGICAL DISCOVERY SINCE DARWIN "AN ENORMOUS SUCCESS... A CLASSIC"
—*The New York Review of Books*

The Double Helix

BY NOBEL PRIZE WINNER
JAMES D. WATSON

"A publishing triumph... Clearly a great book"
—*John Fischer*

Darwin

Mendel

CHAPTER 2

The Gene

Darwin

The paths that led Watson and Crick to the discovery of DNA's structure were pioneered a century earlier, in the 1850s, when the English naturalist Charles Darwin published *On the Origin of Species* and Gregor Mendel, an underemployed priest in Brno (now part of the Czech Republic), began breeding peas in the garden of his abbey. The beaks of Darwin's finches and the traits of Mendel's peas gave birth to the idea of the gene, an entity inside of living organisms that carries the code of heredity.[1]

Darwin had originally planned to follow the career path of his father and grandfather, who were distinguished doctors. But he found himself horrified by the sight of blood and the screams of a strapped-down child undergoing surgery. So he quit medical school and began studying to become an Anglican parson, another calling for which he was uniquely unsuited. His true passion, ever since he began collecting specimens at age eight, was to be a naturalist. He got his opportunity in 1831 when, at age twenty-two, he was offered the chance to ride as the gentleman collector on a round-the-world voyage of the privately funded brig-sloop HMS *Beagle*.[2]

In 1835, four years into the five-year journey, the *Beagle* explored a dozen or so tiny islands of the Galápagos, off the Pacific coast of South America. There Darwin collected carcasses of what he recorded as finches, blackbirds, grosbeaks, mockingbirds, and wrens. But two years later, after he returned to England, he was informed by the ornithologist John Gould that the birds were, in fact, different species of finches. Darwin began to formulate the theory that they had all evolved from a common ancestor.

He knew that horses and cows near his childhood home in rural England were occasionally born with slight variations, and over the years breeders would select the best to produce herds with more desirable traits. Perhaps nature did the same thing. He called it "natural selection." In certain isolated locales, such as the islands of the Galápagos, he theorized, a few mutations (he used the playful term "sports") would occur in each generation, and a change in conditions might make them more likely to win the competition for scarce food and thus be more likely to reproduce. Suppose a species of finch had a beak suited for eating fruit, but then a drought destroyed the fruit trees; a few random variants with beaks better suited for cracking nuts would thrive. "Under these circumstances, favorable variations would tend to be preserved, and unfavorable ones to be destroyed," he wrote. "The results of this would be the formation of a new species."

Darwin was hesitant to publish his theory because it was so heretical, but competition acted as a spur, as often happens in the history of science. In 1858, Alfred Russel Wallace, a younger naturalist, sent Darwin a draft of a paper that proposed a similar theory. Darwin rushed to get a paper of his own ready for publication, and they agreed that they would present their work on the same day at an upcoming meeting of a prominent scientific society.

Darwin and Wallace had a key trait that is a catalyst for creativity: they had wide-ranging interests and were able to make connections between different disciplines. Both had traveled to exotic places where they observed the variation of species, and both had read "An Essay on the Principle of Population" by Thomas Malthus, an English economist. Malthus argued that the human population was likely to grow faster than the food supply. The resulting overpopulation would lead to famine that would weed out the weaker and poorer people. Darwin and Wallace realized this could be applied to all species and thus lead to a theory of evolution driven by the survival of the fittest. "I happened to read for amusement Malthus on population, and . . . it at once struck me that under these circumstances favorable variations would tend to be preserved and unfavorable ones to be destroyed," Darwin recalled. As the science fiction writer and biochemistry professor Isaac Asimov later noted concerning the genesis of evolutionary theory, "What you needed was someone who studied species, read Malthus, and had the ability to make a cross-connection."[3]

The realization that species evolve through mutations and natural selection left a big question to be answered: What was the mechanism? How could a beneficial variation in the beak of a finch or the neck of a giraffe occur, and then how could it get passed along to future generations? Darwin thought that organisms might have tiny particles that contained hereditary information, and he speculated that the information from a male and female blended together in an embryo. But he soon realized, as did others, that this would mean that any new beneficial trait would be diluted over generations rather than be passed along intact.

Darwin had in his personal library a copy of an obscure scientific journal that contained an article, written in 1866, with the answer. But he never got around to reading it, nor did almost any other scientist at the time.

Mendel

The author was Gregor Mendel, a short, plump monk born in 1822 whose parents were German-speaking farmers in Moravia, then part of the Austrian Empire. He was better at puttering around the garden of the abbey in Brno than being a parish priest; he spoke little Czech and was too shy to be a good pastor. So he decided to become a math and science teacher. Unfortunately, he repeatedly failed his qualifying exams, even after studying at the University of Vienna. His performance on one biology exam was especially dreadful.[4]

With little else to do after his final failure at passing the exams, Mendel retreated to the abbey garden to pursue what had become his obsessive interest in breeding peas. In previous years, he had concentrated on creating purebreds. His plants had seven traits that came in two variations: yellow or green seeds, white or violet flowers, smooth or wrinkled seeds, and so on. By careful selection, he produced purebred vines that had, for example, only violet flowers or only wrinkled seeds.

The following year he experimented with something new: breeding together plants with differing traits, such as those that had white flowers with those that had violet ones. It was a painstaking task that involved snipping off each of the plant's receptors with forceps and using a tiny brush to transfer pollen.

What his experiments showed was momentous, given what Darwin was writing at the time. There was no blending of traits. Tall plants cross-bred with short ones did not produce medium-size offspring, nor did purple-flowered plants cross-bred with white-flowered ones produce some pale mauve hue. Instead, all the offspring of a tall and a short plant were tall. The offspring from purple flowers crossbred with white flowers produced only purple flowers. Mendel called these the dominant traits; the ones that did not prevail he called recessive.

An even bigger discovery came the following summer, when he produced offspring from his hybrids. Although the first generation of hybrids had displayed only the dominant traits (such as all purple flowers or tall stems), the recessive trait reappeared in the next generation. And his records revealed a pattern: in this second generation, the dominant trait was displayed in three out of four cases, with the recessive trait appearing once. When a plant inherited two dominant versions of the gene or a dominant and a recessive version, it would display the dominant trait. But if it happened to get two recessive versions of the gene, it would display that less common trait.

Science advances are propelled by publicity. The quiet friar Mendel, however, seemed to have been born under a vanishing cap. He presented his paper in 1865, in two monthly installments, to forty farmers and plant-breeders of the Natural Science Society in Brno, which later published it in its annual journal. It was rarely cited between then and 1900, at which point it was rediscovered by scientists performing similar experiments.[5]

The findings of Mendel and these subsequent scientists led to the concept of a unit of heredity, what a Danish botanist named Wilhelm Johannsen in 1905 dubbed a "gene." There was, apparently, some molecule that encoded bits of hereditary information. Painstakingly, over many decades, scientists studied living cells to try to determine what molecule that might be.

Watson and Crick with their DNA model, 1953

Chapter 3

DNA

Scientists initially assumed that genes are carried by proteins. After all, proteins do most of the important tasks in organisms. They eventually figured out, however, that it is another common substance in living cells, nucleic acids, that are the workhorses of heredity. These molecules are composed of a sugar, phosphates, and four substances called bases that are strung together in chains. They come in two varieties: ribonucleic acid (RNA) and a similar molecule that lacks one oxygen atom and thus is called deoxyribonucleic acid (DNA). From an evolutionary perspective, both the simplest coronavirus and the most complex human are essentially protein-wrapped packages that contain and seek to replicate the genetic material encoded by their nucleic acids.

The primary discovery that fingered DNA as the repository of genetic information was made in 1944 by the biochemist Oswald Avery and his colleagues at Rockefeller University in New York. They extracted DNA from a strain of bacteria, mixed it with another strain, and showed that the DNA transmitted inheritable transformations.

The next step in solving the mystery of life was figuring out how DNA did it. That required deciphering the clue that is fundamental to all of nature's mysteries. Determining the exact structure of

DNA—how all the atoms fit together and what shape resulted—could explain how it worked. It was a task that required mixing three disciplines that had emerged in the twentieth century: genetics, biochemistry, and structural biology.

James Watson

As a middle-class Chicago boy breezing through public school, James Watson was wickedly smart and cheeky. This ingrained in him a tendency to be intellectually provocative, which would later serve him well as a scientist but less so as a public figure. Throughout his life, his rapid-fire mumbling of unfinished sentences would convey his impatience and inability to filter his impulsive notions. He later said that one of the most important lessons his parents taught him was "Hypocrisy in search of social acceptance erodes your self-respect." He learned it too well. From his childhood into his nineties, he was brutally outspoken in his assertions, both right and wrong, which made him sometimes socially unacceptable but never lacking in self-respect.[1]

His passion growing up was bird-watching, and when he won three war bonds on the radio show *Quiz Kids* he used them to buy a pair of Bausch and Lomb binoculars. He would rise before dawn to go with his father to Jackson Park, spend two hours seeking rare warblers, and then take the trolley to the Lab School, a cauldron of whiz kids.

At the University of Chicago, which he entered at fifteen, he planned to indulge his love of birds, and his aversion to chemistry, by becoming an ornithologist. But in his senior year he read a review of *What Is Life?*, in which the quantum physicist Erwin Schrödinger turned his attention to biology to argue that discovering the molecular structures of a gene would show how it hands down hereditary information through generations. Watson checked the book out of the library the next morning and was thenceforth obsessed with understanding the gene.

With modest grades, he was rejected when he applied to study for a doctorate at Caltech and was not offered a stipend by Harvard.[2] So he went to Indiana University, which had built, partly by recruiting

Jews who were having trouble getting tenure on the East Coast, one of the nation's best genetic departments, starring the future Nobel Prize winner Hermann Muller and the Italian émigré Salvador Luria.

With Luria as his PhD advisor, Watson studied viruses. These tiny packets of genetic material are essentially lifeless on their own, but when they invade a living cell, they hijack its machinery and multiply themselves. The easiest of these viruses to study are the ones that attack bacteria, and they were dubbed (remember the term, for it will reappear when we discuss the discovery of CRISPR) "phages," which was short for "bacteriophages," meaning bacteria-eaters.

Watson joined Luria's international circle of biologists known as the Phage Group. "Luria positively abhorred most chemists, especially the competitive variety out of the jungles of New York City," said Watson. But Luria soon realized that figuring out phages would require chemistry. So he helped Watson get a postdoctoral fellowship to study the subject in Copenhagen.

Bored and unable to understand the mumbling chemist who was supervising his studies, Watson took a break from Copenhagen in the spring of 1951 to attend a meeting in Naples on the molecules found in living cells. Most of the presentations went over his head, but he found himself fascinated by a lecture by Maurice Wilkins, a biochemist at King's College London.

Wilkins specialized in crystallography and X-ray diffraction. In other words, he took a liquid that was saturated with molecules, allowed it to cool, and purified the crystals that formed. Then he tried to figure out the structure of those crystals. If you shine a light on an object from different angles, you can figure out its structure by studying the shadows it casts. X-ray crystallographers do something similar: they shine an X-ray on a crystal from many different angles and record the shadows and diffraction patterns. In the slide that Wilkins showed at the end of his Naples speech, that technique had been used on DNA.

"Suddenly I was excited about chemistry," Watson recalled. "I knew that genes could crystallize; hence they must have a regular structure that could be solved in a straightforward fashion." For the next couple of days, Watson stalked Wilkins with the hope of cadging an invitation to join his lab, but to no avail.

Francis Crick

Instead, Watson was able, in the fall of 1951, to become a postdoctoral student at Cambridge University's Cavendish Laboratory, which was directed by the pioneering crystallographer Sir Lawrence Bragg, who more than thirty years earlier had become, and still is, the youngest person to win a Nobel Prize in science.[3] He and his father, with whom he shared the prize, discovered the basic mathematical law of how crystals diffract X-rays.

At the Cavendish Lab, Watson met Francis Crick, forming one of history's most powerful bonds between two scientists. A biochemical theorist who had served in World War II, Crick had reached the ripe age of thirty-six without having secured his PhD. Nevertheless, he was sure enough of his instincts, and careless enough about Cambridge manners, that he was unable to refrain from correcting his colleagues' sloppy thinking and then crowing about it. As Watson memorably put it in the opening sentence of *The Double Helix*, "I have never seen Francis Crick in a modest mood." It was a line that could likewise have been written of Watson, and they admired each other's immodesty more than their colleagues did. "A youthful arrogance, a ruthlessness, and an impatience with sloppy thinking came naturally to both of us," Crick recalled.

Crick shared Watson's belief that discovering the structure of DNA would provide the key to the mysteries of heredity. Soon they were lunching together on shepherd's pie and talking volubly at the Eagle, a well-worn pub near the labs. Crick had a boisterous laugh and booming voice, which drove Sir Lawrence to distraction. So Watson and Crick were assigned to a pale brick room of their own.

"They were complementary strands, interlocked by irreverence, zaniness, and fiery brilliance," the writer-physician Siddhartha Mukherjee noted. "They despised authority but craved its affirmation. They found the scientific establishment ridiculous and plodding, yet they knew how to insinuate themselves into it. They imagined themselves quintessential outsiders, yet felt most comfortable sitting in the inner quadrangles of Cambridge colleges. They were self-appointed jesters in a court of fools."[4]

The Caltech biochemist Linus Pauling had just rocked the scientific world, and paved the way for his first Nobel Prize, by figuring out the structure of proteins using a combination of X-ray crystallography, his understanding of the quantum mechanics of chemical bonds, and Tinkertoy model building. Over their lunches at the Eagle, Watson and Crick plotted how to use the same tricks to beat Pauling in the race to discover the structure of DNA. They even had the tool shop of the Cavendish Lab cut tin plates and copper wires to represent the atoms and other components for the desktop model they planned to tinker with until they got all the elements and bonds correct.

One obstacle was that they would be treading on the territory of Maurice Wilkins, the King's College London biochemist whose X-ray photograph of a DNA crystal had piqued Watson's interest in Naples. "The English sense of fair play would not allow Francis to move in on Maurice's problem," Watson wrote. "In France, where fair play obviously did not exist, these problems would not have arisen. The States also would not have permitted such a situation to develop."

Wilkins, for his part, seemed in no rush to beat Pauling. He was in an awkward internal struggle, both dramatized and trivialized in Watson's book, with a brilliant new colleague who in 1951 had come to work at King's College London: Rosalind Franklin, a thirty-one-year-old English biochemist who had learned X-ray diffraction techniques while studying in Paris.

She had been lured to King's College with the understanding that she would lead a team studying DNA. Wilkins, who was four years older and already studying DNA, was under the impression that she was coming as a junior colleague who would help him with X-ray diffraction. This resulted in a combustible situation. Within months they were barely speaking to each other. The sexist structure at King's helped keep them apart: there were two faculty lounges, one for men and the other for women, the latter unbearably dingy and the former a venue for elegant lunches.

Franklin was a focused scientist, sensibly dressed. As a result she ran afoul of English academia's fondness for eccentrics and its tendency to look at women through a sexual lens, attitudes apparent in Watson's descriptions of her. "Though her features were strong, she was not unattractive and might have been quite stunning had she taken even a mild interest in clothes," he wrote. "This she did not. There was never lipstick to contrast with her straight black hair, while at the age of thirty-one her dresses showed all the imagination of English bluestocking adolescents."

Franklin refused to share her X-ray diffraction pictures with Wilkins, or anyone else, but in November 1951 she scheduled a lecture to summarize her latest findings. Wilkins invited Watson to take the train down from Cambridge. "She spoke to an audience of about fifteen in a quick, nervous style," he recalled. "There was not a trace of warmth or frivolity in her words. And yet I could not regard her as totally uninteresting. Momentarily I wondered how she would look if she took off her glasses and did something novel with her hair. Then, however, my main concern was her description of the crystalline X-ray diffraction pattern."

Watson briefed Crick the next morning. He had not taken notes, which annoyed Crick, and thus was vague about many key points, particularly the water content that Franklin had found in her DNA samples. Nevertheless, Crick started scribbling diagrams, declaring that Franklin's data indicated a structure of two, three, or four strands twisted in a helix. He thought that, by playing with different models, they might soon discover the answer. Within a week they had what they thought was a solution, even though it meant that some of the atoms were crushed together a little too close: three strands swirled in the middle, and the four bases jutted outward from this backbone.

In a fit of hubris, they invited Wilkins and Franklin to come up to Cambridge and take a look. The two arrived the next morning and, with little small talk, Crick began to display the triple-helix structure. Franklin immediately saw that it was flawed. "You're wrong for the following reasons," she said, her words ripping like those of an exasperated teacher.

She insisted that her pictures of DNA did not show that the molecule was helical. On that point she would turn out to be wrong. But her other two objections were correct: the twisting backbones had to be on the outside, not inside, and the proposed model did not contain enough water. "At this stage the embarrassing fact came out that my recollection of the water content of Rosy's DNA samples could not be right," Watson drily noted. Wilkins, momentarily bonding with Franklin, told her that if they left for the station right away, they could make the 3:40 train back to London, which they did.

Not only were Watson and Crick embarrassed; they were put in a penalty box. Word came down from Sir Lawrence that they were to stop working on DNA. Their model-building components were packed up and sent to Wilkins and Franklin in London.

Adding to Watson's dismay was the news that Linus Pauling was coming over from Caltech to lecture in England, which would likely catalyze his own attempt to solve the structure of DNA. Fortunately, the U.S. State Department came to the rescue. In the weirdness engendered by red-baiting and McCarthyism, Pauling was stopped at the airport in New York and had his passport confiscated because he had been spouting enough pacifist opinions that the FBI thought he might be a threat to the country if allowed to travel. So he never got the chance to discuss the crystallography work done in England, thus helping the U.S. lose the race to figure out DNA.

Watson and Crick were able to monitor some of Pauling's progress through his son Peter, who was a young student in their Cambridge lab. Watson found him amiable and fun. "The conversation could dwell on the comparative virtues of girls from England, the Continent, and California," he recalled. But one day in December 1952, young Pauling wandered into the lab, put his feet up on a desk, and dropped the news that Watson had been dreading. In his hand was a letter from his father in which he mentioned that he had come up with a structure for DNA and was about to publish it.

Linus Pauling's paper arrived in Cambridge in early February. Peter got a copy first and sauntered into the lab to tell Watson and Crick that his father's solution was similar to the one they had tried: a three-chain helix with a backbone in the center. Watson grabbed the paper from Peter's coat pocket and began to read. "At once I felt something was not right," he recalled. "I could not pinpoint the mistake, however, until I looked at the illustrations for several minutes."

Watson realized that some of the atomic connections in Pauling's proposed model would not be stable. As he discussed it with Crick and others in the lab, they became convinced that Pauling had made a big "blooper." They got so excited they quit work early that afternoon to dash off to the Eagle. "The moment its doors opened for the evening, we were there to drink a toast to the Pauling failure," Watson said. "Instead of sherry, I let Francis buy me a whiskey."

"The secret of life"

They knew they could no longer waste time or continue to honor the edict that they defer to Wilkins and Franklin. So Watson took the train down to London one afternoon to see them, carrying his early copy of Pauling's paper. Wilkins was out when he arrived, so he ambled uninvited into the lab of Franklin, who was bending over a light box measuring the latest of her ever-sharper X-ray images of DNA. She gave him an angry look, but he launched into a summary of Pauling's paper.

For a few moments they argued about whether DNA was likely to be a helix, with Franklin still dubious. "Interrupting her harangue, I asserted that the simplest form for any regular polymeric molecule was a helix," Watson recalled. "Rosy by then was hardly able to control her temper, and her voice rose as she told me that the stupidity of my remarks would be obvious if I would stop blubbering and look at her X-ray evidence."

The conversation spiraled downward, with Watson pointing out, correctly but impolitely, that as a good experimentalist Franklin would be more successful if she knew how to collaborate with theorists.

"Suddenly Rosy came from behind the lab bench that separated us and began moving toward me. Fearing that in her hot anger she might strike me, I grabbed up the Pauling manuscript and hastily retreated."

Just as the confrontation climaxed, Wilkins walked by and whisked Watson off to have some tea and calm down. He confided that Franklin had taken some pictures of a wet form of DNA that provided new evidence of its structure. He then went into an adjacent room and retrieved a print of what became known as "photograph 51." Wilkins had gotten hold of the picture validly: he was the PhD advisor of the student who had worked with Franklin to take it. Less proper was showing it to Watson, who recorded some of the key parameters and took them back to Cambridge to share with Crick. The photograph indicated that Franklin had been correct in arguing that the backbone strands of the structure were on the outside, like the strands of a spiral staircase, rather than inside of the molecule, but she was wrong in resisting the possibility that DNA was a helix. "The black cross of reflections which dominated the picture could arise only from a helical structure," Watson immediately saw. A study of Franklin's notes shows that even after Watson's visit she was still many steps away from discerning the DNA structure.[5]

Rosalind Franklin

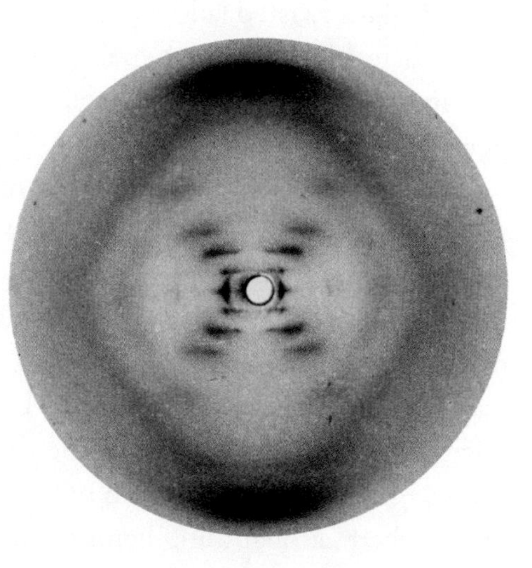

"Photograph 51"

In the unheated train car back to Cambridge, Watson sketched ideas in the margins of his copy of *The Times*. He had to climb over the back gate into his residential college, which had locked up for the night. The next morning, when he went into the Cavendish lab, he encountered Sir Lawrence Bragg, who had demanded that he and Crick steer clear of DNA. But confronted with Watson's excited summary of what he had learned, and hearing of his desire to get back to model-building, Sir Lawrence gave his assent. Watson rushed down the stairs to the machine shop to set them to work on making a new set of components.

Watson and Crick soon got more of Franklin's data. She had submitted to Britain's Medical Research Council a report on her work, and a member of the council shared it with them. Although Watson and Crick had not exactly stolen Franklin's findings, they had appropriated her work without her permission.

By then Watson and Crick had a pretty good idea of DNA's structure. It had two sugar-phosphate strands that twisted and spiraled to form a double-stranded helix. Protruding from these were the four bases in DNA: adenine, thymine, guanine, and cytosine, now commonly known by the letters A, T, G, and C. They came to agree with Franklin that the backbones were on the outside and the bases pointed inward, like a twisted ladder or spiral staircase. As Watson later admitted in a feeble attempt at graciousness, "Her past uncompromising statements on this matter thus reflected first-rate science, not the outpourings of a misguided feminist."

They originally assumed that the bases would each be paired with themselves, for example, a rung that was made up of an adenine bonded to another adenine. But one day Watson, using some cardboard models of bases that he cut out himself, began playing with different pairings. "Suddenly I became aware that an adenine-thymine pair held together by two hydrogen bonds was identical in shape to a guanine-cytosine pair held together by at least two hydrogen bonds." He was lucky to work in a lab of scientists with different specialties; one of them, a quantum chemist, confirmed that adenine would attract thymine and guanine would attract cytosine.

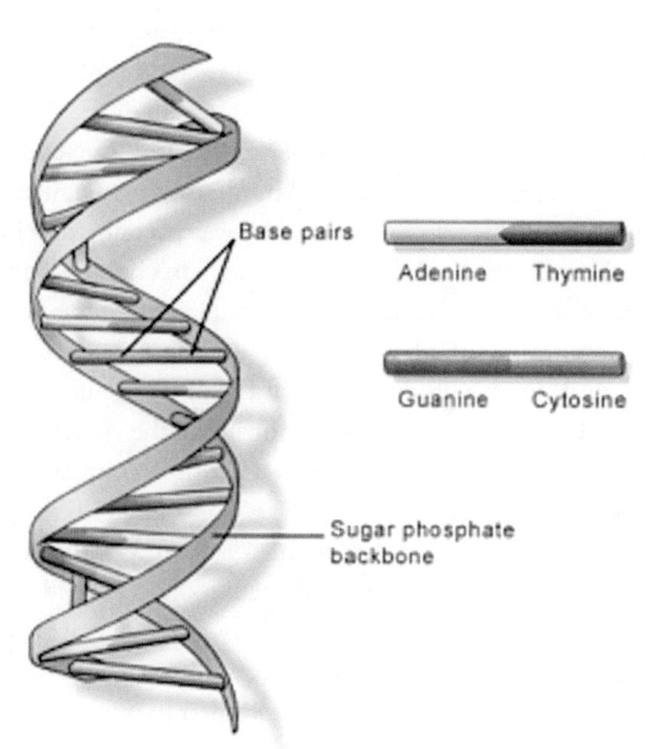

U.S. National Library of Medicine

There was an exciting consequence of this structure: when the two strands split apart, they could perfectly replicate, because any half-rung would attract its natural partner. In other words, such a structure would permit the molecule to replicate itself and pass along the information encoded in its sequences.

Watson returned to the machine shop to prod them to speed up production of the four types of bases for the model. By this point the machinists were infused with his excitement, and they finished soldering the shiny metal plates in a couple of hours. With all the parts now on hand, it took Watson only an hour to arrange them so that the atoms comported with the X-ray data and the laws of chemical bonds.

In Watson's memorable and only slightly hyperbolic phrase in *The Double Helix*, "Francis winged into the Eagle to tell everyone within hearing distance that we had found the secret of life." The solution was too beautiful not to be true. The structure was perfect for the molecule's function. It could carry a code that it could replicate.

Watson and Crick finished their paper on the last weekend of March 1953. It was a mere 975 words, typed by Watson's sister, who was persuaded to do so by his argument that "she was participating in perhaps the most famous event in biology since Darwin's book." Crick wanted to include an expanded section on the implications for heredity, but Watson convinced him that a shorter ending would actually carry more punch. Thus was produced one of the most significant sentences in science: "It has not escaped our notice that the specific pairing we have postulated immediately suggests a possible copying mechanism for the genetic material."

The Nobel Prize was awarded in 1962 to Watson, Crick, and Wilkins. Franklin was not eligible because she had died in 1958, at age thirty-seven, of ovarian cancer, likely caused by her exposure to radiation. If she had survived, the Nobel committee would have faced an awkward situation: each prize can be awarded to only three winners.

Two revolutions coincided in the 1950s. Mathematicians, including Claude Shannon and Alan Turing, showed that all information could be encoded by binary digits, known as bits. This led to a digital revolution powered by circuits with on-off switches that processed information. Simultaneously, Watson and Crick discovered how instructions for building every cell in every form of life were encoded by the four-letter sequences of DNA. Thus was born an information age based on digital coding (0100110111001 . . .) and genetic coding (ACTGGTAGATTACA . . .). The flow of history is accelerated when two rivers converge.

CHAPTER 4

The Education of a Biochemist

Girls do science

Jennifer Doudna would later meet James Watson, work with him on occasion, and be exposed to all of his personal complexity. In some ways he would be like an intellectual godfather, at least until he began saying things that seemed to emanate from the dark side of the Force. (As Chancellor Palpatine said to Anakin Skywalker, "The dark side of the Force is a pathway to many abilities that some consider to be unnatural.")

But her reactions when she first read his book as a sixth-grader were far simpler. It sparked the realization that it was possible to peel back the layers of nature's beauty and discover, as she says, "how and why things worked at the most fundamental and inner level." Life was made up of molecules. The chemical components and structure of these molecules governed what they would do.

The book also sparked the feeling that science could be fun. All of the previous science books she read had "pictures of emotionless men wearing lab coats and glasses." But *The Double Helix* painted a more vibrant picture. "It made me realize that science can be very exciting, like being on a trail of a cool mystery and you're getting a clue here and a clue there. And then you put the pieces together." The tale of Watson

In the lab at Pomona College

and Crick and Franklin was one of competition and collaboration, of letting data dance with theory, and of being in a race with rival labs. All of that resonated with her as a kid, and it would continue to do so throughout her career.[1]

In high school Doudna got a chance to do the standard biology experiments involving DNA, including one that involved breaking apart salmon sperm cells and stirring their gooey contents with a glass rod. She was inspired by an energetic chemistry teacher and by a woman who gave a lecture on the biochemical reasons that cells become cancerous. "It reinforced my realization that women could be scientists."

There was a thread that wove together her childhood curiosity about the eyeless spiders in the lava tubes, the sleeping grass that curled when you touched it, and the human cells that became cancerous: they were all connected to the detective story of the double helix.

She decided that she wanted to study chemistry at college, but like many female scientists of the time, she met resistance. When she explained her college goals to her school's guidance counselor, an older Japanese American man with traditional attitudes, he began to grunt, "No, no, no." She paused and looked at him. "Girls don't do science," he asserted. He discouraged her from even taking the College Board chemistry test. "Do you really know what that is, what that test is for?" he asked her.

"It hurt me," Doudna recalled, but it also stiffened her resolve. "Yes I will do it," she remembers telling herself. "I will show you. If I want to do science, I am going to do it." She applied to Pomona College in California, which had a good program in chemistry and biochemistry, was admitted, and enrolled in the fall of 1981.

Pomona

At first she was unhappy. Having skipped a grade in school, she was now only seventeen. "I was suddenly a small fish in a very big pond," she recalled, "and I doubted I had what it took." She was homesick and, once again, felt out of place. Many of her classmates came from wealthy Southern California families and had their own cars, while she was on a scholarship and worked part time to pay her living expenses. In those days, it was expensive to phone home. "My parents didn't have a lot of money so they told me to call collect, but only once a month."

Having willed herself to major in chemistry, she began to doubt she could handle it. Perhaps her high school counselor had been right. Her general chemistry class had two hundred students, most of whom had gotten a 5 on the AP chemistry test. "It made me question whether I'd set my sights on something that was just not achievable by me," she said. Because of her competitive streak, the field had little appeal if she was going to be just a mediocre student. "I thought, 'I don't want to become a chemist if I'm not going to have a shot at being at the top.'"

She thought about changing her major to French. "I went to talk to my French teacher about that, and she asked what I was majoring in." When Doudna replied that it was chemistry, the teacher told her to stick with it. "She was really insistent. She said 'If you major in chemistry you'll be able to do all sorts of things. If you major in French you will be able to be a French teacher.'"[2]

Her outlook brightened the summer after her freshman year when she got a job working in the lab of her family's friend Don Hemmes, the University of Hawaii biology professor who had taken her on nature walks. He was using electron microscopy to investigate the movement of chemicals inside cells. "Jennifer was fascinated by the ability to look inside cells and study what all the small particles were doing," he recalled.[3]

Hemmes was also studying the evolution of tiny shells. An active scuba diver, he would scoop up samples of the smallest ones, almost microscopic in size, and his students would help him embed them in resin and slice thin sections for analysis under an electron microscope. "He taught us how to use various kinds of chemicals to stain the samples differently, so we could look at shell development," explained Doudna. She kept a lab notebook for the first time.[4]

In chemistry class at college, most of the experiments were

conducted by following a recipe. There was a rigid protocol and a right answer. "The work in Don's lab wasn't like that," she said. "Unlike in class, we didn't know the answer we were supposed to get." It gave her a taste of the thrill of discovery. It also helped her see what it would be like to be part of the community of scientists, making advances and piecing them together to discover the ways that nature worked.

When she returned to Pomona in the fall, she made friends, fit in better, and became more confident in her ability to do chemistry. As part of her work-study program, she had a series of jobs in the college chemistry labs. Most did not engage her because they did not explore how chemistry intersected with biology. But that changed after her junior year, when she got a summer position in the lab of her advisor Sharon Panasenko, a biochemistry professor. "It was more challenging for women biochemists at universities back then, and I admired her not only for being a good scientist but also for being a role model."[5]

Panasenko was studying a topic that aligned with Doudna's interest in the mechanisms of living cells: how some bacteria found in soil are able to communicate so that they can join together when they are starved for nutrients. They form a commune called a "fruiting body." Millions of the bacteria figure out how to aggregate by sending out chemical signals. Panasenko enlisted Doudna to help figure out how those chemical signals worked.

"I have to warn you," Panasenko told her, "that a technician in my lab has been working on growing these bacteria for six months, and he hasn't been able to make it work." Doudna began trying to grow the bacteria in large baking pans rather than the usual Petri dishes. One night she put her preparations in the incubator. "I came in the next day, and when I peeled back the foil on the baking dish that lacked nutrients, I was stunned to see these beautiful structures!" They looked like little footballs. She had succeeded where the other technician had failed. "It was an incredible moment, and it made me think I could do science."

The experiments yielded strong enough results that Panasenko was able to publish a research paper in the *Journal of Bacteriology*, in which she acknowledged Doudna as one of four lab assistants "whose preliminary observations made significant contributions to this project." It was the first time Doudna's name appeared in a scientific journal.[6]

Harvard

When it came time to go to graduate school, she did not initially consider Harvard, despite being the top student in her physical chemistry class. But her father pushed her to apply. "Come on, Dad," she pleaded, "I will never get in." To which he replied, "You certainly won't get in if you don't apply." She did get in, and Harvard even offered her a generous stipend.

She spent part of the summer traveling in Europe on the money she had saved from her work-study program at Pomona. When her trip ended in July 1985, she went right to Harvard so that she could begin working before classes started. Like other universities, Harvard required graduate chemistry students to work each semester in the lab of a different professor. The goal of these rotations was to allow students to learn different techniques and then select a lab for their dissertation research.

Doudna called Roberto Kolter, who was head of the graduate studies program, to ask if she could begin her rotations in his lab. A young Spanish specialist in bacteria, he had a big smile, an elegant sweep of hair, wireless glasses, and a bouncy style of talking. His lab was international, with many of the researchers from Spain or Latin America, and Doudna was struck by how young and politically active they were. "I had been highly influenced by the media's presentation of scientists as old white men, and I thought that's who I would be interacting with at Harvard. That wasn't my experience at all at the Kolter Lab." Her ensuing career, from CRISPR to coronavirus, would reflect the global nature of modern science.

Kolter assigned Doudna to study how bacteria make molecules that are toxic to other bacteria. She was responsible for cloning (making an exact DNA copy of) genes from the bacteria and testing their functions. She thought of a novel way to set up the process, but Kolter declared it wouldn't work. Doudna was stubborn and went ahead with her idea. "I did it my way and got the clone," she told him. He was surprised but supportive. It was a step in overcoming the insecurity that lurked inside her.

Doudna eventually decided to do her dissertation work in the lab of Jack Szostak, an intellectually versatile Harvard biologist who was studying DNA in yeast. A Canadian American of Polish descent, Szostak was one of the young geniuses then in Harvard's Department of Molecular Biology. Even though he was managing a lab, Szostak was still working as a bench scientist, so Doudna got to watch him perform experiments, hear his thought process, and admire the way he took risks. The key aspect of his intellect, she realized, was his ability to make unexpected connections between different fields.

Her experiments gave her a glimpse of how basic science can be turned into applied science. Yeast cells are very efficient at taking up pieces of DNA and integrating them into their genetic makeup. So she worked on a way to make use of this fact. She engineered strands of DNA that ended with a sequence that matched a sequence in the yeast. With a little electric shock, she opened up tiny passageways in the cell wall of the yeast, allowing the DNA that she made to wriggle inside. It then recombined into the yeast's DNA. She had made a tool that could edit the genes of yeast.

Craig Venter and Francis Collins

CHAPTER 5

The Human Genome

James and Rufus Watson

In 1986, when Doudna was working in Jack Szostak's lab, a massive international science collaboration was being hatched.[1] It was called the Human Genome Project, and its goal was to figure out the sequence of the three billion base pairs in our DNA and map the more than twenty thousand genes that these base pairs encode.

One of the many roots of the Human Genome Project involved Doudna's childhood hero James Watson and his son Rufus. The provocative author of *The Double Helix* was the director of Cold Spring Harbor Laboratory, a haven for biomedical research and seminars on a 110-acre wooded campus on the north shore of Long Island. Founded in 1890, it has a history of important research. It was there in the 1940s that Salvador Luria and Max Delbrück led a study group on phages that included the young Watson. But it is also haunted by more controversial ghosts. From 1904 until 1939, under director Charles Davenport, it served as a center for eugenics, producing studies asserting that different races and ethnic groups had genetic differences in such traits as intelligence and criminality.[2] By the end of Watson's tenure as director there from 1968 to 2007, his own pronouncements on race and genetics would revive these ghosts.

In addition to being a research center, Cold Spring Harbor hosts around thirty meetings a year on selected topics. In 1986, Watson decided to launch an annual series titled "The Biology of Genomes." The agenda for the first year's meeting was to plan the Human Genome Project.

On the day the meeting began, Watson made a shocking announcement to the gathered scientists. His son Rufus had broken out of a psychiatric hospital, where he had been committed after trying to break a window and jump to his death from the World Trade Center. He was now missing, and Watson was leaving to help find him.

Born in 1970, Rufus had the lean face, tousled hair, and lopsided grin of his father. He was also very bright. "I was very pleased," Watson says, "because for a while he would go bird-watching with me, and we had some relationship." Bird-watching was something that Watson had done with his own father as a smart, skinny kid in Chicago. But when Rufus was young, he began to show signs of not being able to interact well with people, and in tenth grade at his boarding school, Exeter, he had a psychotic incident and was sent home. A few days later, he went to the top of the World Trade Center with the plan of ending his life. Doctors diagnosed him as schizophrenic. The elder Watson cried. "I had never seen Jim weep before—or ever since in his life," his wife, Elizabeth, says.[3]

Watson missed most of the Cold Spring Harbor genome meeting, while he and Elizabeth joined the hunt for their son. He was finally found wandering in the woods. Watson's science had intersected with real life. The massive international project to map the human genome would no longer be for him an abstract, academic pursuit. It was personal, and it would ingrain in him a belief, bordering on obsession, in the power of genetics to explain human life. Nature, not nurture, made Rufus the way he was, and it also made different groups of people the way they were.

Or so it appeared to Watson, who saw things through glasses filtered by his DNA discovery and his son's condition. "Rufus is as smart as can be, very perceptive, and can be caring but also intense in his anger," Watson says. "My wife and I hoped when he was young we could set up the right environment for him to succeed. But I soon realized that his troubles lay in his genes. That drove me to lead the Human Genome Project. The only way I could understand our son and help him live at a normal level was to decipher the genome."[4]

The race to sequence

When the Human Genome Project was formally launched in 1990, Watson was anointed its first director. All the major players were men. Watson was eventually succeeded by Francis Collins, who in 2009 became the director of the U.S. National Institutes of Health. Among the whiz kids was the charismatic and driven Eric Lander, a breathtakingly brilliant Brooklyn-bred high school math team captain who did a doctoral dissertation on coding theory as a Rhodes Scholar at Oxford and then decided to become a geneticist at MIT. The most controversial player was the wild and abrasive Craig Venter, who had worked in a U.S. Navy field hospital as a draftee during the Tet Offensive of the Vietnam War, had attempted suicide by swimming out to sea, and then became a biochemist and biotech entrepreneur.

The project began as a collaboration, but as with many tales of discovery and innovation it also became a competition. When Venter found different ways to do the sequencing cheaper and faster than everyone else, he broke away to form a private company, Celera, which sought to profit from patenting its discoveries. Watson enlisted Lander to help reorganize the public effort and speed up its work. Lander bruised some egos, but he was able assure that it could keep pace with Venter's private effort.[5]

In early 2000, as the competition became a public spectacle, President Bill Clinton pushed for a truce between Venter and Collins, who had been sniping at each other in the press. Collins had likened Venter's sequencing to "Cliff's Notes" and "*Mad* magazine"; Venter had ridiculed the government project for costing ten times more to do work at a fraction of the speed. "Fix it—make these guys work together," Clinton told his top science advisor. So Collins and Venter met for pizza and beer to see if they could reach an accord on sharing the credit and agreeing to make public, rather than exploiting for private use, what would soon be the world's most important biological data set.

After a few more private meetings, Clinton was able to host Collins and Venter at a White House ceremony to announce the initial results of the Human Genome Project and the agreement to share credit. James Watson hailed the decision. "The events of the past few weeks have shown that those who work for the public good do not necessarily fall behind those driven by personal gain," he said.

I was editor of *Time* then, and we had been working with Venter for weeks to have exclusive access to his story and feature him on the cover. He was an enticing cover boy, because by then he had used his wealth from Celera to become a flashy yacht-owner, competitive surfer, and party-giver. The week that we were closing the story, I got an unexpected phone call from Vice President Al Gore. He pushed me—very hard and persuasively—to put Francis Collins on the cover as well. Venter resisted. He had been forced to share credit with Collins at a press conference, but he did not want to also share a *Time* cover. He eventually agreed, but at the photo session he could not help ragging on Collins for not being able to keep pace with Celera's sequencing. Collins smiled and said nothing.[6]

"Today we are learning the language in which God created life," President Clinton proclaimed at the White House ceremony featuring Venter, Collins, and Watson. The announcement captured the public imagination. The *New York Times* ran a front-page banner headline, "Genetic Code of Human Life Is Cracked by Scientists." The story, written by the distinguished biology journalist Nicholas Wade, began, "In an achievement that represents a pinnacle of human self-knowledge, two rival groups of scientists said today that they had deciphered the hereditary script, the set of instructions that defines the human organism."[7]

Doudna spent time discussing with Szostak, Church, and others at Harvard whether the $3 billion dedicated to the Human Genome

Project was worth it. Church was skeptical at the time, and remains so. "The three billion dollars didn't buy us much," he says. "We didn't discover anything. None of the technologies survived." Having a map of DNA did not, it turned out, lead to most of the grand medical breakthroughs that had been predicted. More than four thousand disease-causing DNA mutations were found. But no cure sprang forth for even the most simple of single-gene disorders, such as Tay-Sachs, sickle cell, or Huntington's. The men who had sequenced DNA taught us how to read the code of life, but the more important step would be learning how to write that code. This would require a different set of tools, ones that would involve the worker-bee molecule that Doudna found more interesting than DNA.

Jack Szostak

Chapter 6

RNA

The central dogma

Accomplishing the goal of being able to *write* as well as to *read* human genes required a shift in focus from DNA to its less famous sibling that actually carries out its coded instructions. RNA (ribonucleic acid) is a molecule in living cells that is similar to DNA (deoxyribonucleic acid), but it has one more oxygen atom in its sugar-phosphate backbone and a difference in one of its four bases.

DNA may be the world's most famous molecule, so well-known that it appears on magazine covers and is used as a metaphor for traits that are ingrained in a society or organization. But like many famous siblings, DNA doesn't do much work. It mainly stays at home in the nucleus of our cells, not venturing forth. Its primary activity is protecting the information it encodes and occasionally replicating itself. RNA, on the other hand, actually goes out and does real work. Instead of just sitting at home curating information, it makes real products, such as proteins. Pay attention to it. From CRISPR to COVID, it will be the starring molecule in this book and in Doudna's career.

At the time of the Human Genome Project, RNA was seen as mainly a messenger molecule that carries instructions from the DNA that is nestled in the nucleus of the cells. A small segment of DNA that encodes a gene is transcribed into a snippet of RNA, which then travels to the manufacturing region of the cell. There this "messenger RNA" facilitates the assembly of the proper sequence of amino acids to make a specified protein.

These proteins come in many types. Fibrous proteins, for example, form structures such as bones, tissues, muscles, hair, fingernails, tendons, and skin cells. Membrane proteins relay signals within cells. Above all is the most fascinating type of proteins: enzymes. They serve as catalysts. They spark and accelerate and modulate the chemical reactions in all living things. Almost every action that takes place in a cell needs to be catalyzed by an enzyme. Pay attention to enzymes. They will be RNA's costars and dancing partners in this book.

Francis Crick, five years after co-discovering the structure of DNA, came up with a name for this process of genetic information moving from DNA to RNA to the building of proteins. He dubbed it the "central dogma" of biology. He later conceded that "dogma," which implies an unchanging and unquestioned faith, was a poor choice of words.[1] But the word "central" was apt. Even as the dogma was modified, the process remained central to biology.

Ribozymes

One of the first tweaks to the central dogma came when Thomas Cech and Sidney Altman independently discovered that proteins were not the only molecules in the cell that could be enzymes. In work done in the early 1980s that would win them the Nobel Prize, they made the surprising discovery that some forms of RNA could likewise be enzymes. Specifically, they found that some RNA molecules can split themselves by sparking a chemical reaction. They dubbed these catalytic RNAs "ribozymes," a word conjured up by combining "ribonucleic acid" with "enzyme."[2]

Cech and Altman made this discovery by studying introns. Some parts of DNA sequences do not code instructions for how to make proteins. When these sequences are transcribed into RNA molecules, they clog things up. So they have to be sliced out before the RNA can scurry out on its mission to direct the making of proteins. The cut-and-paste process of slicing out these introns and then splicing the useful bits of RNA back together requires a catalyst, and that role is usually performed by a protein enzyme. But Cech and Altman discovered that there were certain RNA introns that were self-splicing!

This had pretty cool implications. If some RNA molecules could store genetic information and also act as a catalyst to spur chemical reactions, they might be more fundamental to the origins of life than DNA, which cannot naturally replicate themselves without the presence of proteins to serve as a catalyst.[3]

RNA rather than DNA

When Doudna's lab rotation ended in the spring of 1986, she asked Jack Szostak if she could stay on and do her doctoral research under him. Szostak agreed—but he added a caveat. He was no longer going to focus on DNA in yeast. While other biochemists were getting excited about sequencing DNA for the Human Genome Project, he had decided to shift his lab's attention to RNA, which he believed might reveal secrets about the biggest of all biological mysteries: the origins of life.

He was intrigued, he told Doudna, by the discoveries that Cech and Altman had made about how certain RNAs had the catalytic powers of enzymes. His goal was to pin down whether these ribozymes could use this power to replicate. "Did this piece of RNA have the chemical chops to copy itself?" he asked her. He suggested that should be the focus of her PhD dissertation.[4]

She found Szostak's enthusiasm infectious and signed up to be the first graduate student in his lab to work on RNA. "When I was taught biology, we learned about the structure and code of DNA, and we learned about how proteins do all the heavy lifting in cells, and RNA was treated as this dull intermediary, sort of a middle manager," she recalls. "I was quite surprised to find that there was this young genius, Jack Szostak, at Harvard who wanted to focus a hundred percent on RNA because he thought that it was the key to understanding the origin of life."

For both Szostak, who was well established, and Doudna, who wasn't, switching to a focus on RNA was risky. "Instead of following the herd doing DNA," Szostak recalled, "we felt we were pioneering something new, exploring a frontier that was a little bit neglected but we all thought was exciting." This was long before RNA was being considered as a technology to interfere with gene expression or deliver edits to human genes. Szostak and Doudna pursued the subject out of pure curiosity about how nature works.

Szostak had a guiding principle: *Never do something that a thousand other people are doing*. That appealed to Doudna. "It was like when I was on the soccer field and wanted to play a position that the other kids didn't," she says. "I learned from Jack that there was more of a risk but also more of a reward if you ventured into a new area."

By this point she knew that the most important clue for understanding a natural phenomenon was to figure out the structure of the molecules involved. That would require her to learn some of the techniques that Watson and Crick and Franklin used to unravel the structure of DNA. If she and Szostak succeeded, it could be a significant step in answering one of the grandest of all biological questions, perhaps *the* grandest: How did life begin?

The origins of life

Szostak's excitement about discovering how life began taught Doudna a second big lesson, in addition to taking risks by moving into new fields: *Ask big questions*. Even though Szostak liked diving into the details of experiments, he was a grand thinker, someone who was constantly pursuing truly profound inquiries. "Why else would you do science?" he asked Doudna. It was an injunction that became one of her own guiding principles.[5]

There are some truly grand questions that our mortal minds may never be able to answer: How did the universe begin? Why is there something rather than nothing? What is consciousness? Others may be wrestled into submission by the end of this century: Is the universe deterministic? Do we have free will? Of the really big ones, the closest to being solved is how life began.

The central dogma of biology requires the presence of DNA, RNA, and proteins. Because it's unlikely that all three of these sprang forth at the exact same time from the primordial stew, a hypothesis arose in the early 1960s—formulated independently by the ubiquitous Francis Crick and others—that there was a simpler precursor system. Crick's hypothesis was that, early on in the history of earth, RNA was able to replicate itself. That leaves the question of where the first RNA came from. Some speculate it came from outer space. But the simpler answer may be that the early earth contained the chemical building blocks of RNA, and it didn't require anything other than natural random mixing to jostle them together. The year that Doudna joined Szostak's lab, biochemist Walter Gilbert dubbed this hypothesis "the RNA world."[6]

An essential quality of living things is that they have a method for creating more organisms akin to themselves: they can reproduce. Therefore, if you want to make the argument that RNA might be the precursor molecule leading to the origin of life, it would help to show how it can replicate itself. This was the project that Szostak and Doudna embarked upon.[7]

Doudna used many tactics to create an RNA enzyme, or ribozyme, that could stitch together little RNA pieces. Eventually, she and Szostak were able to engineer a ribozyme that could splice together a copy of itself. "This reaction demonstrates the feasibility of RNA-catalyzed RNA replications," she and Szostak wrote in a 1998 paper for *Nature*. The biochemist Richard Lifton later called this paper a "technical tour de force."[8] Doudna became a rising star in the rarefied realm of RNA research. That was still a bit of a biological backwater, but over the next two decades the understanding of how little strands of RNA behaved would become increasingly important, both to the field of gene editing and to the fight against coronaviruses.

As a young PhD student, Doudna mastered the special combination of skills that distinguished Szostak and other great scientists: she was good at doing hands-on experiments and also at asking the big questions. She knew that God was in the details but also in the big picture.

"Jennifer was fantastically good at the bench, because she was fast and sharp and could seemingly get anything to work," Szostak says. "But we talked quite a bit about why the really big questions are the important questions."

Doudna also proved herself a team player, which counted a lot for Szostak, who shared that trait with George Church and some other scientists at the Harvard Medical School campus. This was reflected in the number of coauthors she had on most of her papers. In scientific publications, the first author listed is usually the younger researcher most responsible for the hands-on experiments, and the last is the principal investigator or head of the lab. Those listed in the middle are generally ordered by the contributions they made. On one of the important papers that she helped produce for the journal *Science* in 1989, Doudna's name appears in the middle of the list because she was mentoring a lucky Harvard undergraduate who worked in the lab part time, and she felt that the student should be the featured lead author. During her final year in Szostak's lab, her name was on four academic papers in prestigious journals, all describing aspects of how RNA molecules can replicate themselves.[9]

What also stood out for Szostak was Doudna's willingness, even eagerness, to tackle challenges. That became evident near the end of her tenure in Szostak's lab in 1989. She realized that in order to understand the workings of a self-splicing piece of RNA, she would have to fully discern its structure, atom by atom. "At that time, RNA structure was viewed as so difficult that it was maybe impossible to figure out," Szostak recalled. "Hardly anyone was trying anymore."[10]

Meeting James Watson

The first time that Jennifer Doudna made a presentation at a scientific conference, it was at the Cold Spring Harbor Laboratory, and James Watson was, as usual, sitting in the front row as the host. It was the summer of 1987, and he had organized a seminar to discuss "the evolutionary events that may have given rise to the living organisms that now exist on earth."[11] In other words, how did life begin?

The focus of the conference was on the recent discoveries showing that certain RNA molecules could replicate themselves. Because Szostak was unavailable, an invitation went out to Doudna, then only twenty-three, to present the work that she and he were doing on engineering a self-replicating RNA molecule. When she got the letter signed by Watson addressed to "Dear Ms. Doudna" (she was not yet Dr. Doudna), she not only immediately accepted; she had it framed.

The talk she gave, based on a paper she had written with Szostak, was highly technical. "We describe deletions and substitution mutations in the catalytic and substrate domains of the self-splicing intron," she began. That's the type of sentence that excites research biologists, and Watson was intently taking notes. "I was so incredibly nervous that my palms were sweating," she recalls. But at the end, Watson congratulated her, and Tom Cech, whose work on introns had paved the way for Doudna and Szostak's paper, leaned over and whispered, "Good job."[12]

While at the meeting, Doudna took a walk down Bungtown Road, which wanders through the campus. Along the way, she saw a slightly stooped woman walking toward her. It was the biologist Barbara McClintock, who had been a researcher at Cold Spring Harbor for more than forty years and had recently been awarded the Nobel Prize for her discovery of transposons, known as "jumping genes," that can change their position in a genome. Doudna paused, but was too shy to introduce herself. "I felt like I was in the presence of a goddess," she says, still in awe. "Here's this woman who's so famous and so incredibly influential in science acting so unassuming and walking toward her lab thinking about her next experiment. She was what I wanted to be."

Doudna would stay in touch with Watson, attending many of the Cold Spring Harbor meetings he organized. Over the years, he would evolve into an increasingly controversial character because of his unmoored blurtings about racial genetic differences. Doudna generally refrained from letting his behavior diminish her respect for his scientific achievements. "When I saw him, he often would say things he thought were provocative," she says with a slightly defensive laugh.

"That was his way. You know how it is." Despite his frequent public comments about women's looks, beginning with Rosalind Franklin in *The Double Helix*, he was a good mentor to women. "He was very supportive to a close woman friend of mine who was a postdoc," Doudna says. "That influenced my opinion of him."

Chapter 7

Twists and Folds

Structural biology

Ever since she puzzled over the touch-sensitive leaves of the sleeping grass that she found on her walks as a child in Hawaii, Doudna had been passionately curious about the underlying mechanisms of nature. What made the fernlike leaves curl when touched? How did chemical reactions cause biological activity? She learned how to pause, like we all used to do as children, and wonder about how things worked.

The field of biochemistry provided many answers by showing how the chemical molecules in living cells behave. But there was a specialty that looked even deeper into nature: structural biology. Wielding imaging techniques such as X-ray crystallography, which is what Rosalind Franklin used to find evidence of the structure of DNA, structural biologists try to discover the three-dimensional shape of molecules. Linus Pauling worked out the spiral structure of proteins in the early 1950s, which was followed by Watson and Crick's paper on the double-helix structure of DNA.

Doudna realized that she would need to learn more about structural biology if she wanted to truly understand how some RNA molecules could reproduce themselves. "To figure out how these RNA do chemistry," she says, "I needed to know what they looked like." Specifically,

Rising star at Yale

she needed to figure out the folds and twists of the three-dimensional structure of self-splicing RNA. She was aware that such work would be an echo of that done by Franklin on DNA, and the parallel pleased her. "She had a similar kind of question about the chemical structure of a molecule that was at the heart of all of life," Doudna says. "She believed that its structure would provide all sorts of insights."[1]

Doudna also sensed that once you figured out the structure of a ribozyme, it might lead to groundbreaking genetic technologies. The citation for the Nobel Prize that Thomas Cech won with Sidney Altman hinted at what this might be: "A futurist possibility is to correct certain genetic disorders. Such a future use of gene shears will require that we learn more about the molecular mechanisms." *Gene shears*. Yes, the Nobel committee was prescient.

This pursuit meant that it was time to move on from the lab of Jack Szostak, who admitted to not being a visual thinker or expert in structural biology. So in 1991, Doudna considered where she could do her postdoctoral work. There was one obvious choice, the structural biologist who had just shared the Nobel Prize for discovering the catalytic RNA that she and Szostak had been studying: Thomas Cech (pronounced "check") of the University of Colorado in Boulder, who was using X-ray crystallography in order to explore each nook and cranny of the structure of RNA.

Thomas Cech

Doudna already knew Cech. He was the one who whispered "Good job" after her sweaty-palmed lecture at Cold Spring Harbor in the summer of 1987. She had met him again when she took a trip to Colorado that year. "Because we were sort of friendly competitors both racing to make discoveries about the self-splicing introns, I sent him a note," she recalled.

It was a real note, on paper, because email was not yet common. She wrote that she was going to be traveling through Boulder and asked if it would be possible to visit his lab. To her surprise, he quickly got back to her, telephoning one day when she was at work in Szostak's lab.

"Hey, Tom Cech is on the phone for you," the colleague who picked up the phone called out. Her lab mates gave her a curious look, but she just shrugged.

They met in Boulder on a Saturday. Cech had brought his two-year-old daughter to the lab, and he bounced her on his knee as he talked to Doudna, who was completely charmed by both his mind and his fatherly instincts. Their encounter was an example of the mix of competition and collegiality that marks scientific research (and many other endeavors). "I think the reason Tom met with me was that the Szostak Lab was doing work that was potentially competitive but also that there might be opportunities to learn from each other," she says. "And he probably thought it was a way to get some information about what our lab was up to."

After she earned her PhD in 1989, she decided to do her postdoctoral work with Cech. "I realized that if I really wanted to figure out the structure of RNA molecules, my smart move was to go to the very best RNA biochemistry lab," she says. "Who can be better than Tom Cech? This was the lab that had first discovered self-splicing introns."

Tom Griffin

There was one other reason that Doudna decided to go to Boulder for her postdoctoral work. In January 1988 she had married a Harvard Medical School student named Tom Griffin, who was working in a lab next to hers. "He saw in me things I didn't see at the time, including capabilities in science," she says. "He pushed me to be bolder than I would have been."

Griffin, from a military family, loved Colorado. "When we were thinking of where to go when we finished our degrees, he really, really wanted to move to Boulder," says Doudna. "I realized that if we went to Boulder, I could work with Tom Cech." So they moved there in the summer of 1991, and Griffin got a job at a startup biotech company.

At first the marriage worked well enough. Doudna bought a mountain bike, and they would ride along Boulder Creek. She also took up roller-blading and cross-country skiing. But her passion was science, and Griffin didn't have her single-minded focus. Science for him was a nine-to-five endeavor, and he had no aspirations to be an academic researcher. He loved music and books, and he became an early fan of personal computers. Doudna respected his broad range of interests but didn't share them. "I'm someone who's thinking about science all the time," she says. "I'm always focused on what's cooking in the lab, the next experiment, or the bigger question to pursue."

Doudna believes their differences "say something negative about me," though I'm not sure she really believes that, nor do I. People are different in their approaches to their work and passions. She wanted to spend weekends and nights in the lab doing experiments. Not everybody should be that way. But some people should.

After a few years, they decided to go their separate ways and get a divorce. "I was obsessed with what my next experiment was going to be," she says. "He didn't have that same intensity. That just created a critical wedge that was not fixable."

The structure of a ribozyme

Doudna's mission when she arrived at the University of Colorado as a postdoc was to map the intron that Cech had discovered could be a self-splicing piece of RNA, showing all of its atoms, bonds, and shapes. If she succeeded in figuring out its three-dimensional structure, that would help show how its twists and folds could bring the right atoms together to cause chemical reactions and allow the snippet of RNA to replicate itself.

It was a high-risk venture, one that involved going to a region of the playing field where few others wanted to run. At the time there was not much work being done on RNA crystallography, and most people would look at her like she was nuts. But if she succeeded, there would be a huge payoff for science.

During the 1970s, biologists had figured out the structure of a smaller and simpler RNA molecule. But little progress had been made in the twenty years since then because scientists found it difficult to isolate and get images of bigger RNAs. Colleagues told Doudna that getting a good image of a large RNA molecule would, at that time, be a fool's errand. As Cech put it, "If we had asked the National Institutes of Health to fund this project, we would have been laughed out of the room."[2]

The first step was to crystallize the RNA—in other words, convert the liquid RNA molecule into a well-organized solid structure. That was necessary in order to use X-ray crystallography and other imaging techniques to discern its components and shapes.

Helping her was a quiet but cheery graduate student named Jamie Cate. He had been using X-ray crystallography to study the structure of proteins, but when he met Doudna he joined her quest to focus on RNA. "I told him about the project I was working on and he got very interested," she says. "It was really out there. We had no idea what we were going to find." They were pioneering a new field. It was not even clear that RNA molecules would have well-defined structures like proteins do. Unlike Tom Griffin, Cate loved to focus on lab work. He and Doudna would talk every day about how to crystallize the RNA, and soon they were continuing their discussions over coffee and sometimes dinner.

One breakthrough came as a result of the random things that often happen in science: a slight blunder, like the mold that got on Alexander Fleming's Petri dishes and led to the discovery of penicillin. One day a technician was working with Doudna to try to make crystals, and she put the experiment into an incubator that was not working properly. They thought the experiment was spoiled, but when they looked at the samples through a microscope they could see crystals growing. "The crystals had RNA in them and were beautiful," Doudna recalled, "and that was the first breakthrough showing us that to get these crystals we had to elevate the temperature."

Another advance shows the enduring power of being in the same location as other smart people. Tom and Joan Steitz, a husband-and-wife team of Yale biochemists who were studying RNA, were on sabbatical in Boulder for a year. Tom was particularly sociable and liked hanging around the lunchroom of the Cech lab holding a mug of coffee. Doudna mentioned to him one morning that she had been able to get good crystals of the RNA molecule she was researching, but they tended to break down too quickly when they were exposed to X-rays.

Steitz replied that in his Yale lab he had been testing a new technique for cryocooling crystals. They plunged crystals into liquid nitrogen so they would freeze very rapidly. That helped to preserve the structure in the crystals even when they were exposed to X-rays. He arranged for Doudna to fly to Yale and spend time with the researchers in his lab there who were pioneering the technique. It worked beautifully. "At that point we knew that we had crystals that were ordered enough that we would eventually be able to solve the structure," she says.

Yale

Her visit to Tom Steitz's lab at Yale, where innovative techniques and equipment such as cryocoolers were being funded, helped convince Doudna to accept a job there in the fall of 1993 as a tenure-track professor. Not surprisingly, Jamie Cate wanted to accompany her. She contacted the Yale authorities and helped arrange for him to transfer there as a graduate student in her lab. "They required him to retake his qualifying exams," she says, "and as I'm sure you can imagine, he aced them with flying colors."

By using the super-cooling techniques, Doudna and Cate were able to create crystals that diffracted X-rays well. But they were stymied by what is known in crystallography as the "phase problem." X-ray detectors can measure properly only the intensity of a wave but not the phase part of the wave. One way to attack the problem is to introduce a metal ion into a few regions of the crystal. The X-ray diffraction pictures show the position of the metal ions, and that can be used to help calculate the rest of the molecular structure. That had been done with protein molecules, but no one had figured out how to do it with RNA.

Cate solved the problem. He did it by using a molecule called *osmium hexamine*, which has an interesting structure that lends itself to interacting in a few nooks of RNA molecules. As a result, the X-ray diffractions could produce an electron-density map that would provide clues for the structure of an important folded region of the RNA they were studying. They began the process of creating these density maps and then building models of potential structures, just as Watson and Crick had done for DNA.

Her father's farewell

When their work was reaching its climax in the fall of 1995, Doudna got a call from her father. He had been diagnosed with melanoma, and it had metastasized to his brain. He told her that he had only three months to live.

She spent the rest of that fall flying back and forth from New Haven to Hilo, a journey of more than twelve hours. Chunks of time spent at her father's bedside were interspersed with hours on the phone with Cate. Each day, Cate would send her a new electron-density map by fax or email, and they would talk about ways to interpret it. "It was an incredible time of highs and lows and intense emotional swings," she recalls.

Fortunately, her father was genuinely curious about her work, and that made the ordeal less painful. In between periods of pain, he would ask her to explain the latest images she had received. She would walk into his bedroom, and he would be lying there looking at the latest data. Before they could discuss his health, he would begin asking questions. "It would remind me of his scientific curiosity and how he had shared it with me when I was a child," she says.

During a visit that November, which lasted through Thanksgiving, an electron-density map arrived from New Haven that she realized was good enough to nail down the structure of the RNA molecule. She could actually see how the RNA was folded up into an amazing three-dimensional shape. She and Cate had been working on it for more than two years, while countless colleagues had declared what they were doing was impossible, and now the latest data showed that they had triumphed.

Her father was completely bedridden by then and could barely move. But he was lucid. She walked into his bedroom and showed him a color printout she had made from a data file of the latest map.

It looked like a green ribbon that was twisted into a really cool shape. "It looks like green fettuccini," he joked. Then he got serious. "What does it mean?" he asked.

By trying to explain it to him, she was able to clarify her own ideas about what the data meant. They pored over a region on the map that was caused by a cluster of metal ions, and she speculated on the ways that the RNA could be folding around such a cluster. "Maybe there's a core of metals here that helps this RNA to fold up into this type of twist," she suggested.

"Why would that be important?" he asked. She explained that RNA is made up of very few chemicals, so it accomplishes complex tasks based on the different ways it is folded. One of the challenges with RNA is that it's a molecule made of only four chemical building blocks, unlike proteins, which have twenty. "Because there is a lot less chemical complexity to RNA," she says, "the challenge is to think about how does it fold into a unique shape."

The visit clarified how time had deepened her relationship with her father. He took science seriously, and he took her seriously. He was attracted to all the details, but he also sought the bigger picture. She recalled the times she had visited his classroom and seen his excitement at communicating his passions. She also recalled, less happily, the times that she had gotten angry at him because she thought he made snap judgments, some of them prejudiced, about people. Bonds can take different forms, both in chemistry and in life. Sometimes an intellectual bond is the strongest.

When Martin Doudna died a few months later, Jennifer and her mother and sisters went with friends on a hike to scatter his ashes high up in the Waipio Valley near Hilo. The name means "curved water," and the river that winds through its lush wilderness has many gorgeous waterfalls. Among those joining them were Don Hemmes, the biology professor who mentored Jennifer, and her closest childhood friend, Lisa Hinkley Twigg-Smith. "As we released his ashes into the wind," Twigg-Smith recalled, "an endemic hawk known as an 'io, which is associated with the gods, soared overhead."[3]

"It was only after he died that I realized how influential he was in my decision to become a scientist," Doudna says. Among the many gifts that he gave her was a love of the humanities and how it intersects with the sciences. The need for that was becoming clearer to her as research led her into realms that required moral guideposts as well as electron-density maps. "I think my father would have loved to understand CRISPR," Doudna reflected. "He was a humanist, a humanities professor, who also loved science. When I talk about CRISPR's effects on our society, I can hear my father's voice in my head."

Triumph

Her father's death coincided with her first major scientific success. She and Cate, along with their lab colleagues, were able to determine the location of every atom in a self-splicing RNA molecule. Specifically, they showed how the structure of a key domain of the molecule allowed RNA to pack helices together to create its three-dimensional shape. A cluster of metal ions in that domain formed a core around which the structure folded. Just as the double-helix structure of DNA revealed how it could store and transmit genetic information, the structure discovered by Doudna and her team explained how the RNA could be an enzyme and was able to slice, splice, and replicate itself.[4]

When their paper was published, Yale sent out a press release that attracted the notice of a local New Haven television station. After trying to explain what a ribozyme is, the news anchor reported that it had baffled scientists because they had never been able to see its shape. "But now a team led by Yale scientist Jennifer Doudna finally was able to capture a snapshot of the molecule," the anchor proclaimed. The story featured a young, dark-haired Doudna in her lab, showing off a blurry image on her computer screen. "We hope our discovery will provide clues as to how we might be able to modify the ribozyme so that it can repair defective genes," she said. It was a momentous statement, though she didn't think about it much at the time. It would be the beginning of a quest to translate basic science about RNA into a tool that could edit genes.

In another, more sophisticated television report, done by a syndicated science news show, Doudna appeared in a white lab coat using a pipette to put a solution into a test tube. "It's been known for fifteen years that RNA molecules could function like proteins in cells, but nobody knew how that could be, because nobody has really known what RNA molecules look like," she explained. "We have now been able to see how an RNA molecule can form itself into a complicated three-dimensional structure." Asked what the implications could be, she again pointed to what would be her future work: "One possibility is that we might be able to cure or treat people who have genetic defects."[5]

Over the next two decades, many people would contribute to the development of gene-editing technologies. What distinguishes Doudna's tale is that, by the time she entered the field of gene editing, she had already established her reputation and earned distinction in the most basic underlying science: the structure of RNA.

With her husband, Jamie Cate, and son, Andy, in Hawaii, 2003

CHAPTER 8

Berkeley

Going west

In the article that Doudna and her colleagues wrote on their RNA structure discovery, which was published in *Science* in September 1996, her name is listed last, meaning that she was the principal investigator who headed the lab. Jamie Cate's name is listed first because he did the most important experiments.[1] By then they were more than scientific partners; they had become romantically involved. After her divorce was final, they got married in the summer of 2000 at the Melaka Beach Hotel across the Big Island of Hawaii from Hilo. Two years later, they had their only child, Andrew.

By then, Cate had become an assistant professor at MIT, so they were commuting between New Haven and Cambridge. By train it's less than three hours, but for a new couple even that was tiresome, so they decided to see if they could get appointments in the same town.[2]

Yale tried hard to keep Doudna, promoting her to an important professorship. To resolve what is known as the "two-body problem" in academia, it offered Cate a position as well. However, Tom Steitz, the structural biologist who had shown them the techniques of cryocooling, was there doing the same type of research Cate wanted to do, and he felt that would crimp his chance to flourish. "My direct competitor was there," Cate says. "He's a great guy, but it would be hard to be in the same institution."

Harvard offered Doudna a position in the Department of Chemistry and Chemical Biology, which had just been renamed and was growing. She went there as a visiting professor, and on the first day the dean handed her an offer letter for a permanent position. With Cate at MIT, it seemed to be an ideal arrangement. "I was thinking how great it was that I would end up in Boston, back where I was in graduate school and had such a good time," she said.

It is interesting to imagine how her career would have been different if she had stayed at Harvard. Along with MIT and the jointly managed Broad Institute, the university was a cauldron of biotech research, especially in the field of gene engineering. A decade later, she would find herself in a race to develop CRISPR into a gene-editing tool with various Cambridge-based researchers, including Harvard's George Church and the men who would become her bitter rivals, Feng Zhang and Eric Lander of the Broad Institute.

Then she got a call from the University of California at Berkeley. Her first reaction was to deflect any offer, but when she told Cate, he was shocked. "You should call them back," he said. "Berkeley is nice." When he had been a postdoctoral fellow in Santa Cruz, he had often gone up to the Lawrence Berkeley National Laboratory, which was managed by the university, to do experiments at its cyclotron, a particle accelerator.

When they visited the campus, Doudna was still disinclined to move there. But Cate became more enthusiastic. "I'm more of a western guy," he says. "I found Cambridge to be uptight. My director at the time always came to work in a bow tie. I was happier at the thought of being at Berkeley, where the energy level was great." Doudna liked the fact that Berkeley was a public university, and she was easily persuaded. By the summer of 2002, they had moved.

Their choice of Berkeley is a testament to America's investment in public higher education. Its roots stretch back to when Abraham Lincoln, in the middle of the Civil War, thought public education was important enough that he pushed through the Morrill Land-Grant Act of 1862, which used funds from federal land sales to establish new agriculture and mechanical colleges.

Among those was the College of Agricultural, Mining, and Mechanical Arts near Oakland, California, founded in 1866, which two years later merged with the nearby private College of California. It became the University of California, Berkeley, and grew into one of the world's greatest research and learning institutions. In the 1980s, more than half of Berkeley's funding came from the state. However, since then Berkeley, like most other public universities, has faced reductions. When Doudna arrived, state funding accounted for only 30 percent of Berkeley's budget. In 2018, state funding was cut again, and it amounted to less than 14 percent. As a result, Berkeley's undergraduate tuition for a California resident in 2020 was $14,250 per year, more than triple what it was in 2000. Room, board, and other fees raised the total cost to around $36,264. For an out-of-state student, total costs were around $66,000 a year.

RNA interference

Doudna's study of RNA structure led her to a field that would become unexpectedly relevant later in her career: viruses. Specifically, she was interested in how the RNA in some viruses, such as coronaviruses, allow them to hijack the protein-making machinery of cells. During her first semester at Berkeley, in the fall of 2002, there was an outbreak in China of a virus that caused a severe acute respiratory syndrome (SARS). Many viruses are composed of DNA, but SARS was a coronavirus that instead contained RNA. By the time it died out after eighteen months, it had killed close to eight hundred people around the world. It was officially known as SARS-CoV. In 2020, it had to be renamed SARS-CoV-1.

Doudna also became interested in a phenomenon known as RNA interference. Normally, the genes encoded by the DNA in cells dispatch messenger RNAs to direct the building of a protein. RNA interference does just what the name implies: small molecules find a way to mess with these messenger RNAs.

RNA interference was discovered in the 1990s, partly by researchers who were trying to make petunias more purple by juicing up the flower's color genes. But the process ended up suppressing some of the genes, leading to mottled and speckled petunias. Craig Mello and Andrew Fire coined the term "RNA interference" in a 1998 paper and later won the Nobel Prize when they discovered how the phenomenon works in the nematode, a tiny worm.[3]

RNA interference operates by deploying an enzyme known as "Dicer." Dicer snips a long piece of RNA into short fragments. These little fragments can then embark on a search-and-destroy mission: they seek out a messenger RNA molecule that has matching letters, then they use a scissors-like enzyme to chop it up. The genetic information carried by that messenger RNA is thus silenced.

Doudna set about to discover the molecular structure of Dicer. As she had done with self-splicing RNA introns, she used X-ray crystallography to map its twists and folds, which she hoped would show how it worked. Until then, researchers did not know how Dicer was able to cut RNA into precisely the right letter sequences to silence a specific gene. By studying the Dicer structure, Doudna showed that it acted like a ruler that had a clamp at one end, which it used to grab on to a long RNA strand, and a cleaver at the other end, which it used to slice the segment at just the correct length.

Doudna and her team went on to show how a particular domain of the Dicer enzyme could be replaced in order to create tools that would silence other genes. "Perhaps the most exciting finding of this study is that Dicer can be reengineered," their 2006 paper noted.[4] It was a very useful discovery. It permitted researchers to use RNA interference to turn off a wide variety of genes, both to discover what each gene does and to regulate its activity for medical purposes.

In the age of coronaviruses, there is another role that RNA interference may play. Throughout the history of life on our planet, some organisms (though not humans) have evolved ways to use RNA interference to fight off viruses.[5] As Doudna wrote in a scholarly publication back in 2013, researchers hoped to find ways to use RNA interference to protect humans from infections.[6] Two papers published in *Science* that year gave strong evidence that it might work. The hope then was that drugs based on RNA interference might someday be a good option for treating severe viral infections, including those from new coronaviruses.[7]

Doudna's paper on RNA interference appeared in *Science* in January 2006. A few months later, a paper published in a little-known journal described a different virus-fighting mechanism that exists in nature. It was by an obscure Spanish scientist who discovered the mechanism in microorganisms like bacteria, which have a far longer and even more brutal history fighting viruses than we humans do. At first, the handful of scientists studying this system assumed that it worked through RNA interference. They would soon discover that the phenomenon was even more interesting.

Part Two

CRISPR

The scientist does not study nature because it is useful.
He studies it because he takes pleasure in it,
and he takes pleasure in it because it is beautiful.

—Henri Poincaré, *Science and Method*, 1908

Francisco Mojica

Erik Sontheimer and Luciano Marraffini

Chapter 9

Clustered Repeats

Francisco Mojica

When Yoshizumi Ishino was a student at Osaka University in Japan, his PhD research included sequencing a gene in *E. coli* bacteria. It was 1986, and gene sequencing was a laborious process, but he eventually succeeded in determining the 1,038 base pairs of DNA that made up the gene in question. In a long paper on the gene that he published the following year, he noted in the last paragraph an oddity that he did not consider important enough to mention in the paper's abstract. "An unusual structure was found," he wrote. "Five highly homologous sequences of 29 nucleotides were arranged as direct repeats." In other words, he found five segments of DNA that were identical to each other. These repeated sequences, each twenty-nine base pairs long, were sprinkled between normal-looking sequences of DNA, which he called "spacers." Ishino had no idea what these clustered repeats were. In the last line of his paper, he wrote, "The biological significance of these sequences is not known." He didn't pursue the topic.[1]

The first researcher to figure out the function of the repeated sequences was Francisco Mojica, a graduate student at the University of Alicante on the Mediterranean coast of Spain. In 1990, he began working on a PhD dissertation on archaea, which, like bacteria, are single-cell organisms without a nucleus. The archaea he was studying thrive in salt ponds that are ten times saltier than the ocean. He was sequencing regions that he thought might explain its love of salt when he spotted fourteen identical DNA sequences that were repeated at regular intervals. They seemed to be palindromes, meaning they read the same backward and forward.[2]

At first he assumed that he had screwed up the sequencing. "I thought it was a mistake, because sequencing was hard back then," he says with a hearty laugh. But by 1992, when his data kept showing these regularly spaced repeats, Mojica wondered if anyone else had found something similar. Google did not yet exist, nor did online indexes, so he manually sorted through citations for the word "repeat" in a set of *Current Contents*, a printed index of scholarly papers. Because this was in a previous century, when very few publications were online, whenever he found a listing that looked promising, he had to go to the library to find the relevant journal. Eventually he found Ishino's paper.

The *E. coli* bacterium that Ishino studied is a very different organism from Mojica's archaea. So it was surprising that they both had these repeated sequences and spacer segments. This convinced Mojica that the phenomenon must have some important biological purpose. In a paper he published in 1995, he and his thesis advisor dubbed them "tandem repeats," and they guessed, incorrectly, that they might have something to do with cell replication.[3]

After doing two quick postdoctoral stints, one in Salt Lake City and the other at Oxford, Mojica returned in 1997 to the University of Alicante, which was just a few miles from where he was born, and launched a research group to study these mysterious repeated sequences. It was difficult to get funding. "I was told to stop obsessing about repeats, because there were a lot of those type of phenomena in organisms, and mine were probably nothing special," he says.

But he knew that bacteria and archaea have small amounts of genetic material. They cannot afford to waste a lot of it on sequences that have no important function. So he kept trying to figure out the purpose of these clustered repeats. Perhaps they helped shape the

DNA structure or formed loops that proteins could latch on to. Both of those speculations also proved wrong.

The name "CRISPR"

By then, researchers had found these repeated sequences in twenty different species of bacteria and archaea, and many different names for them had sprouted. Mojica became dissatisfied with the name his dissertation advisor had foisted on him, "tandem repeats." The sequences were interspaced, not in tandem. So he renamed them, initially, "short regularly spaced repeats," or SRSR. Though more descriptive, it was an unmemorable name with an unpronounceable acronym.

Mojica had been corresponding with Ruud Jansen of Utrecht University in the Netherlands, who was studying these sequences in tuberculosis bacteria. He had been calling them "direct repeats," but he agreed that they needed to come up with a better name. Mojica was driving home from his lab one evening when he came up with the name CRISPR, for "clustered regularly interspaced short palindromic repeats." Although the clunky phrase was almost impossible to remember, the acronym CRISPR was, indeed, crisp and crispy. It sounded friendly rather than intimidating, though the dropped "e" gave it a futurist sheen. When he got home, he asked his wife what she thought of the name. "It sounds like a great name for a dog," she said. "Crispr, Crispr, come here, pup!" He laughed and decided it would work.

On November 21, 2001, the name was anointed in an email from Jansen in reply to Mojica's suggestion. "Dear Francis," he wrote, "What a great acronym is CRISPR. I feel that every letter that was removed in the alternatives made it less crispy, so I prefer the snappy CRISPR over SRSR and SPIDR."[4]

Jansen formalized the decision in a paper he published in April 2002, which reported his discovery of genes that seemed to be associated with CRISPRs. In most organisms that had CRISPRs, the repeated sequences were flanked by one of these genes, which encoded directions for making an enzyme. He named these "CRISPR-associated," or *Cas*, enzymes. [5]

A virus defense

When Mojica began sequencing the DNA of his salt-loving microbes in 1989, gene sequencing was a slow process. But the Human Genome Project, which was just getting started, eventually spawned new high-speed sequencing methods. By 2003, when Mojica focused on figuring out the role CRISPRs played, the genomes of close to two hundred bacteria had been sequenced (as well as those of humans and mice).

That August, Mojica was on holiday in the beach town of Santa Polo, about twelve miles south of Alicante, staying at the house of his wife's parents. That was not his idea of a good time. "I really do not like sand or being on a beach in the summer when it is hot and crowded with people," he says. "My wife would be lying on the beach getting a suntan, and I would head off and drive up to my lab in Alicante for the day. She had fun on the beach, but I had more fun analyzing sequences from *E. coli* bacteria."[6] Spoken like a dedicated scientist.

What fascinated him were the "spacers," those regions of normal-looking DNA segments that were nestled in between the repeated CRISPR segments. He took the spacer sequences of *E. coli* and ran them through databases. What he found was intriguing: the spacer segments matched sequences that were in viruses that attacked *E. coli*. He found the same thing when he looked at other bacteria with CRISPR sequences; their spacer segments matched those of viruses that attacked that bacteria. "Oh my goodness!" he exclaimed at one point.

One evening, when he was sure about his discovery, he explained it to his wife after he got back to the beach house. "I just discovered something really amazing," he said. "Bacteria have an immune system. They're able to remember what viruses have attacked them in the past." She laughed, admitted she didn't quite understand, but said she believed it must be important because he was so excited. He replied, "In a few years, you'll see this thing that I've just discovered will be written about in newspapers and in history books." That part she did not believe.

What Mojica had stumbled upon was a battlefront in the longest-running, most massive and vicious war on this planet: that between bacteria and the viruses, known as "bacteriophages" or "phages," that attack them. Phages are the largest category of virus in nature. Indeed, phage viruses are by far the most plentiful biological entity on earth. There are 10^{31} of them—a trillion phages for every grain of sand, and more than all organisms (including bacteria) combined. In one milliliter (0.03 ounces) of seawater there can be as many as 900 million of these viruses.[7]

As we humans struggle to fight off novel strains of viruses, it's useful to note that bacteria have been doing this for about three billion years, give or take a few million centuries. Almost from the beginning of life on this planet, there's been an intense arms race between bacteria, which developed elaborate methods of defending against viruses, and the ever-evolving viruses, which sought ways to thwart those defenses.

Mojica found that bacteria with CRISPR spacer sequences seemed to be immune from infection by a virus that had the same sequence. But bacteria without the spacer did get infected. It was a pretty ingenious defense system, but there was something even cooler: it appeared to adapt to new threats. When new viruses came along, the bacteria that survived were able to incorporate some of that virus's DNA and thus create, in its progeny, an acquired immunity to that new virus. Mojica recalls being so overcome by emotion at this realization that he got tears in his eyes.[8] The beauty of nature can sometimes do that to you.

It was an astonishing and elegant discovery, one that would have great repercussions. But Mojica had a ridiculously difficult time getting it published. He submitted a paper to *Nature* in October 2003 entitled "Prokaryotic Repeats Are Involved in an Immunity System." In other words, CRISPR systems were a way that bacteria acquired immunity to viruses. The editors did not even send it out for review. It did not contain, they incorrectly judged, much that wasn't in previous CRISPR papers. They also declared, with more validity, that Mojica had not presented any lab experiments showing how the CRISPR system worked.

Mojica's paper was rejected by two other publications. Finally he was able to get it published in the *Journal of Molecular Evolution*, which was not as prestigious but served to get his findings in a peer-reviewed publication. Even at that journal, Mojica had to pester and prod the slow-moving editors. "I reached out and tried to get in touch with the editors almost every week," he says. "Every week was so terrible, such a nightmare, because I knew we had discovered something really great. And I knew that at some point others would discover it. And I couldn't get them to see how important it was."[9] The journal received the paper in February 2004, did not make a decision until October, and it was not actually published until February 2005, two years after Mojica had come up with his findings.[10]

Mojica says he was driven by his love of the beauties of nature. He had the luxury at Alicante of doing basic research without showing how it might translate into something useful, and he never tried to patent his CRISPR discoveries. "When you work as I do on weird organisms that live in unusual environments, like very salty ponds, your only motivation is curiosity," he says. "It didn't seem likely that our discovery would apply to more normal organisms. But we were wrong."

As is often the case in the history of science, discoveries can have unexpected applications. "When you do curiosity-driven research, you never know what it may someday lead to," Mojica says. "Something that's basic can later have wide consequences." His prediction to his wife that his name would someday be in history books proved to be correct.

Mojica's paper was the beginning of a wave of articles providing evidence that CRISPR was, indeed, an immune system that bacteria adapted whenever they got attacked by a new type of virus. Within a year, Eugene Koonin, a researcher at the U.S. National Center for Biotechnology Information, extended Mojica's theory by showing that the role of the CRISPR-associated enzymes was to grab bits of DNA out of the attacking viruses and insert them into the bacteria's own DNA, sort of like cutting and pasting a mug shot of dangerous viruses.[11] But Koonin and his team got one thing wrong. They speculated that the

CRISPR defense system worked through RNA interference. In other words, they thought that bacteria used the mug shots to find a way to interfere with the messenger RNAs that carry out the instructions encoded by DNA.

Others thought so as well. That is why Jennifer Doudna, Berkeley's leading expert on RNA interference, would end up getting a phone call out of the blue from a colleague who was trying to figure out CRISPR.

Jillian Banfield

CHAPTER 10

The Free Speech Movement Café

Jillian Banfield

In early 2006, shortly after she published her first paper on Dicer, Doudna was in her Berkeley office when she got a call from a Berkeley professor she had heard of but didn't know: Jillian Banfield, a microbiologist who, like Mojica, was interested in tiny organisms found in extreme environments. A gregarious Australian with a wry smile and collaborative nature, Banfield was studying bacteria that her team found in a very salty lake in Australia, a hot geyser in Utah, and the extremely acidic waste draining from a California copper mine into a salt marsh.[1]

When Banfield sequenced the DNA of her bacteria, she kept finding examples of the clustered repeated sequences known as CRISPRs. She was among those who assumed that the CRISPR system worked by using RNA interference. When she typed "RNAi and UC Berkeley" into Google, Doudna's name was the top result, so Banfield gave her a call. "I'm looking for someone at Berkeley," she told Doudna, "who is working on RNA guides, and I did a Google search and your name popped up." They agreed to meet for tea.

Doudna had never heard of CRISPR. In fact, she thought that Banfield was saying "crisper." After hanging up, she did a quick online search and found just a few articles about it. When she got to the point in an article where it said CRISPR stood for "clustered regularly interspaced short palindromic repeats," she decided to wait for Banfield to explain it to her.

They met on a blustery spring day at a stone table in the courtyard of the Free Speech Movement Café, a soup-and-salad hangout at the entrance to Berkeley's undergraduate library. Banfield had printed out the papers by Mojica and Koonin. She realized that, in order to figure out the function of these CRISPR sequences, it made sense to collaborate with a biochemist such as Doudna, who could analyze each component of a mysterious molecule in a laboratory.

When I sat down with the two of them to hear about that meeting, they displayed the same excitement they described feeling back then. They both talked rapidly, especially Banfield, and they finished each other's sentences amid quick laughs. "We are sitting there and drinking tea, and you had a big pile of pages that had all this data of the sequences you had found," Doudna recalled. Banfield, who usually works on her computer and rarely prints out anything, agreed. "I kept showing you the sequences," she recalled. Doudna chimed in, "You were so passionate, and you were talking so fast. You had a lot of data. And I'm thinking, 'She's really, really excited about this.'"[2]

At the café table, Banfield drew a string of diamonds and squares that represented segments of the DNA she had found in her bacteria. The diamonds, she said, all had identical sequences, but the interspersed squares each had unique sequences. "It's like they are diversifying so fast in response to *something*," she told Doudna. "I mean, what was causing these strange clusters of DNA sequences? How did they actually work?"

Until then, CRISPRs had largely been the purview of microbiologists, such as Mojica and Banfield, who studied living organisms. They had come up with elegant theories about CRISPR, some of them correct, but they had not done controlled experiments in test tubes. "At the time, nobody had actually isolated the molecular components of the CRISPR system, tested them in a lab, and figured out their structures," Doudna said. "So the time was right for biochemists and structural biologists like me to jump in."[3]

Chapter 11

Jumping In

Blake Wiedenheft

When Banfield asked her to collaborate on CRISPR, Doudna was initially stymied. She had nobody in her lab to work on it.

Then an unusual candidate walked into her office to interview for a postdoctoral position. Blake Wiedenheft, a charismatic and bear-cub-loveable Montanan with an enthusiasm for the outdoors, had spent most of his academic career, when he wasn't taking time off to pursue wilderness adventures, collecting microorganisms from extreme environments, from Kamchatka in Russia to Yellowstone National Park in his backyard, just like Banfield and Mojica. His letters of reference were not stellar, but he was earnest and passionate about switching his interest from the biology of small organisms to the biology of molecules, and when Doudna asked him what he wanted to work on, he said the magic words: "Have you ever heard of CRISPR?"[1]

Wiedenheft was born in Fort Peck, Montana, population 233, an outpost eighty-one miles from the Canadian border and near nothing else. The son of a fisheries biologist for Montana's Wildlife Department, he ran track, skied, wrestled, and played football in high school.

As an undergraduate at Montana State, he majored in biology, but he spent little time in the lab. Instead, he enjoyed going into nearby

Blake Wiedenheft in Kamchatka, Russia

Yellowstone and collecting microorganisms that can survive in the boiling acid springs there. "It made a huge impression on me," he says, "to scoop up sample organisms from an acid hot spring, bring them back in a thermos, grow them in these artificial hot springs we rigged up in the lab, and then take those samples to the microscope and peer through the lens and see something that has never been seen before. That changed how I imagined life."

Montana State was a perfect university for him, because it allowed him to indulge his love of adventure. "I'm always looking for what's over the next peak," he says.[2] When he graduated, he had no plans to become a research scientist. Instead, like his father, he was interested in fish biology, and he signed up to work on a crabbing vessel in the Bering Sea off Alaska, collecting data for government agencies. He then spent a summer teaching science to young students in Ghana, followed by a stint as a ski patroller in Montana. "I was addicted to adventure."

But during his travels, he would find himself rereading his old biology textbooks at night. His college mentor Mark Young was studying the viruses that attacked the bacteria in Yellowstone's boiling acid springs. "Mark's excitement for understanding how these biological machines work was, literally, infectious."[3] After three years of wandering, Wiedenheft decided there were adventures to be found not only outdoors but in labs. He returned to Montana State as a PhD student under Young, and together they studied how these viruses invade bacteria.[4]

Although Wiedenheft was able to sequence the DNA of the viruses, he found himself wanting more. "Once I started peering at the DNA sequences, I realized they were uninformative," he says. "We had to determine structures, because structures, the folds and shapes, are conserved over a longer evolutionary period than the nucleic acid sequences." In other words, the sequence of letters in the DNA did not reveal how it worked; what was important was how it folded and twisted, which would reveal how it interacted with other molecules.[5]

He decided that he needed to learn structural biology, and there was no place better for that than Doudna's lab at Berkeley.

Wiedenheft is too earnest to be insecure, and that came through when he interviewed with Doudna. "I was coming from a small lab in Montana, and I had enough hubris not to be completely intimidated, though I should have been," he recalls. He had a few subject areas he planned to pitch, but when Doudna showed interest in CRISPR, which was his first passion, he became energized. "I just started yammering and tried to sell myself best I could." He went to the whiteboard and mapped out the CRISPR projects being pursued by other researchers, including John van der Oost and Stan Brouns, a team from the Netherlands he had worked with when they came to Yellowstone to collect microorganisms from the hot springs.

He and Doudna brainstormed about opportunities that her lab might pursue, most notably figuring out the functions of the CRISPR-associated (Cas) enzymes. Doudna was struck by his energy and infectious enthusiasm. For his part, Wiedenheft was impressed that Doudna shared his enthusiasm for CRISPR. "She has a knack for seeing around corners to know what the next big thing is," he says.[6]

Wiedenheft threw himself into his work in Doudna's lab with the joyful passion he displayed as an outdoorsman. He was willing to charge headlong into techniques he had never used before. At lunchtime he would go on a hard-core bike ride, then work through the afternoon and evening still wearing his cycling gear, wandering around the lab in his helmet. He once spent forty-eight hours straight on one experiment, sleeping next to it.

Martin Jinek

Wiedenheft's desire to learn structural biology caused him to latch on to, both intellectually and socially, a postdoc who was the Doudna Lab's expert in crystallography. Martin Jinek (YEE-nik) was born in the Silesian town of Třinec in what was then Czechoslovakia. He studied organic chemistry at Cambridge University and did his doctoral work under the Italian biochemist Elena Conti in Heidelberg. This produced, in addition to an agile scientific outlook, a hybrid accent that featured very precisely pronounced phrases repeatedly interspaced with the interjection "basically."[7]

In Conti's lab, Jinek developed a passion for the star molecule of this book, RNA. "It's such a versatile molecule—it can do catalysis, it can fold into 3D structures," he later told Kevin Davies of the *CRISPR Journal.* "At the same time, it's a carrier of information. It's an all-rounder in the world of biomolecules!"[8] His goal was to work in a lab where he could figure out the structure of complexes that combined RNA and enzymes.[9]

Jinek was good at charting his own path. "He was somebody who could work independently, which has always been important in my lab because I'm not a close hands-on advisor," she says. "I like to hire people who have their own creative ideas and want to work under my guidance and as part of my team, but not with daily direction." She arranged to meet Jinek when she went to Heidelberg for a conference, then enticed him to come to Berkeley and sit down with the members of her lab. She felt it was important that people on her team were comfortable with each new hire.

Jinek's initial work in Doudna's lab focused on how RNA interference works. Researchers had described the process in living cells, but Jinek knew that a full explanation required re-creating the process in a test tube. The *in vitro* experiments allowed him to isolate the enzymes that are essential to interfering with the expression of a gene. He also was able to determine the crystal structure of one particular enzyme, thus showing how it is able to cut up the messenger RNA.[10]

Jinek and Wiedenheft, with their very different backgrounds and personalities, became complementary particles. Jinek was a crystallographer who wanted more experience working with living cells, and Wiedenheft was a microbiologist who wanted to learn crystallography. They took an instant liking to each other. Wiedenheft had a much more playful sense of humor than Jinek, but it was so contagious that Jinek soon acquired it. On one trip they took with other lab members to the Argonne National Laboratory near Chicago, they were working in the huge circular building that houses the Advanced Photon Source, a powerful X-ray machine. It is so large that there are tricycles for researchers to use to get around. At 4 a.m., after working all night, Wiedenheft organized a tricycle race around the entire circuit of the building, which he of course won.[11]

Doudna decided that her lab's goal would be to dissect the CRISPR system into its chemical components and study how each worked. She and Wiedenheft decided to focus first on the CRISPR-associated enzymes.

Cas1

Let's pause for a quick refresher course.

Enzymes are a type of protein. Their main function is to act as a catalyst that sparks chemical reactions in the cells of living organisms, from bacteria to humans. There are more than five thousand biochemical reactions that are catalyzed by enzymes. These include breaking down starches and proteins in the digestive system, causing muscles to contract, sending signals between cells, regulating metabolism, and (most important for this discussion) cutting and splicing DNA and RNA.

By 2008, scientists had discovered a handful of enzymes produced by genes that are adjacent to the CRISPR sequences in a bacteria's DNA. These CRISPR-associated (Cas) enzymes enable the system to cut and paste new memories of viruses that attack the bacteria. They also create short segments of RNA, known as CRISPR RNA (crRNA), that can guide a scissors-like enzyme to a dangerous virus and cut up its genetic material. Presto! That's how the wily bacteria create an adaptive immune system!

The notation system for these enzymes was still in flux in 2009, largely because they were being discovered in different labs. Eventually they were standardized into names such as Cas1, Cas9, Cas12, and Cas13.

Doudna and Wiedenheft decided to focus on what became known as Cas1. It's the only Cas enzyme that appears in all bacteria that have CRISPR systems, which indicates that it performs a fundamental function. Cas1 had another advantage for a lab that was using X-ray crystallography to try to discover how the structure of a molecule determines its functions: it was easy to get it to crystallize.[12]

Wiedenheft was able to isolate the Cas1 gene from bacteria and then clone it. Using a vapor diffusion, he was then able to crystallize it. But he was stymied when he tried to figure out the exact crystal structure because he did not have enough experience in using X-ray crystallography.

Doudna drafted Jinek, who had just finished publishing a paper with her on RNA interference,[13] to help Wiedenheft with the crystallography. Together they went to the particle accelerator at the nearby Lawrence Berkeley National Laboratory, and Jinek helped analyze the data in order to build an atomic model of the Cas1 protein. "In the process, I got infected by Blake's enthusiasm," he recalls. "After that, I decided to stay involved with the CRISPR part of Jennifer's lab."[14]

They discovered that Cas1 has a distinct fold, indicating that it is the mechanism that bacteria use to cleave a snippet of DNA from invading viruses and incorporate it into their CRISPR array, thus being the key to the memory-forming stage of the immune system. In June 2009, they published their discovery in a paper that was the Doudna Lab's initial contribution to the CRISPR field. It was the first explanation of a CRISPR mechanism based on a structural analysis of one of its components.[15]

Rodolphe Barrangou

Philippe Horvath

CHAPTER 12

The Yogurt Makers

Basic research and the linear model of innovation

Historians of science and technology, including myself, often write about what is called the "linear model of innovation." It was propagated by Vannevar Bush, an MIT engineering dean who cofounded Raytheon and during World War II headed the U.S. Office of Scientific Research and Development, which oversaw the invention of radar and the atom bomb. In a 1945 report, "Science, the Endless Frontier," Bush argued that basic curiosity-driven science is the seed corn that eventually leads to new technologies and innovations. "New products and new processes do not appear full-grown," he wrote. "They are founded on new principles and new conceptions, which in turn are painstakingly developed by research in the purest realms of science. Basic research is the pacemaker of technological progress."[1] Based on this report, President Harry Truman launched the National Science Foundation, a government agency that provides funding for basic research, mainly at universities.

There is some truth to the linear model. Basic research in quantum theory and surface-state physics of semiconducting materials led to the development of the transistor. But it wasn't quite that simple or linear. The transistor was developed at Bell Labs, the research organization of the American Telephone and Telegraph Company. It employed many basic science theorists, such as William Shockley and John Bardeen. Even Albert Einstein dropped by. But it also threw them together with practical engineers and pole-climbers who knew how to amplify a phone signal. Added to the mix were business development executives who pushed ways to enable long-distance calls across the continent. All of these players informed and prodded each other.

The story of CRISPR at first seems to accord with the linear model. Basic researchers such as Francisco Mojica pursued an oddity of nature out of pure curiosity, and that seeded the ground for applied technologies such as gene editing and tools to fight coronaviruses. However, as with the transistor, it was not simply a one-way linear progression. Instead, there was an iterative dance among basic scientists, practical inventors, and business leaders.

Science can be the parent of invention. But as Matt Ridley points out in his book *How Innovation Works*, sometimes it's a two-way street. "It is just as often the case that invention is the parent of science: techniques and processes are developed that work, but the understanding of them comes later," he writes. "Steam engines led to the understanding of thermodynamics, not the other way round. Powered flight preceded almost all aerodynamics."[2]

The colorful history of CRISPR provides another great tale about this symbiosis between basic and applied science. And it involves yogurt.

Barrangou and Horvath

As Doudna and her team began working on CRISPR, two young food scientists on different continents were studying CRISPR with the goal of improving ways to make yogurt and cheese. Rodolphe Barrangou in North Carolina and Philippe Horvath in France worked for Danisco, a Danish food ingredient company that makes starter cultures, which initiate and control the fermentation of dairy products.

Starter cultures for yogurt and cheese are made from bacteria, and the greatest threats to the $40 billion global market are viruses that can destroy bacteria. So Danisco was willing to spend a lot of money for research into how bacteria defend themselves against these viruses. It had a valuable asset: a historical record of the DNA sequences of bacteria it had used over the years. And that is how Barrangou and Horvath, who first heard of Mojica's research into CRISPR at a conference, became part of the relationship between basic science and business.

Barrangou was born in Paris, which gave him an enthusiasm for food. He also loved science, and in college he decided to combine his passions. He became the only person I've ever encountered who moved from France to North Carolina in order to learn more about food. He enrolled at North Carolina State in Raleigh and got his master's degree in the science of pickle and sauerkraut fermentation. He went on to get his doctorate there, married a food scientist he met in class, and followed her to Madison, Wisconsin, when she went to work at the Oscar Mayer meat company. Madison is also home to a Danisco unit that produces hundreds of megatons of bacteria cultures for fermented dairy products, including yogurt. Barrangou took a job there as a research director in 2005.[3]

Years before, he had become friends with another French food scientist, Philippe Horvath, who was a researcher at a Danisco laboratory in Dangé-Saint-Romain, a town in central France. Horvath was developing tools to identify the viruses that attack different strains of bacteria, and the two began a long-distance collaboration to research CRISPR.

They would talk by phone two or three times a day in French as they plotted their plans. Their method was to use computational biology to study the CRISPR sequences of bacteria in Danisco's vast database, starting with *Streptococcus thermophilus*, the bacteria that is the great workhorse of the dairy culture industry. They compared the bacteria's CRISPR sequences with the DNA of the viruses that attacked them. The beauty of Danisco's historic collection was that there were bacteria strains from every year since the early 1980s, so they could observe the changes that occurred to them over time.

They noticed that bacteria that had been collected soon after a big virus attack had new spacers with sequences from those viruses, indicating that these had been acquired as a way to repel future attacks. Because the immunity was now part of the bacteria's DNA, it was passed down to all future generations of the bacteria. After one specific comparison done in May 2005, they realized they had nailed it. "We saw there was a hundred-percent match between the CRISPR of the bacterial strain and the sequence of the virus that we knew had attacked it," Barrangou recalls. "That was the eureka moment."[4] It was an important confirmation of the thesis put forth by Francisco Mojica and Eugene Koonin.

They then accomplished something very useful: they showed that they could engineer this immunity by devising and adding their own spacers. The French research facility was not approved for genetic engineering, so Barrangou did that part of the experiments in Wisconsin. "I showed that when you add sequences from the virus into the CRISPR locus, the bacteria develops immunity to that virus," he says.[5] In addition, they proved that CRISPR-associated (Cas) enzymes were critical for acquiring new spacers and warding off attacking viruses. "What I did was knock out two Cas genes," Barrangou recalls. "That wasn't easy to do twelve years ago. One of them was Cas9, and we showed when you knock it out you lose the resistance."

They used these discoveries in August 2005 to apply for and get one of the first patents granted for CRISPR-Cas systems. That year Danisco started using CRISPR to vaccinate its bacterial strains.

Barrangou and Horvath produced a paper for the journal *Science*, which was published in March 2007. "That was a great moment in time," Barrangou says. "Here we were, workers at an unknown Danish company, sending a manuscript on a little-known system in an organism that no scientist cares about. Even to get reviewed was amazing. And we got accepted!"[6]

The CRISPR meetings

The article helped kick interest in CRISPR into a higher orbit. Jillian Banfield, the Berkeley biologist who had enlisted Doudna at the Free Speech Movement Café, immediately called Barrangou. They decided to do what pioneers in emerging fields often do: start an annual conference. The first, organized by Banfield and Blake Wiedenheft, met in late July 2008 in Berkeley's Stanley Hall, where Doudna's lab was. Only thirty-five people attended, including Francisco Mojica, who came from Spain to be a featured speaker.

Long-distance collaborations work well in science—and especially in the CRISPR field, as Barrangou and Horvath showed. But physical proximity can spark more powerful reactions; ideas gel when people have tea at places like the Free Speech Movement Café. "Without those CRISPR conferences, the field would not have moved at the speed it has or be as collaborative," Barrangou says. "The camaraderie would never have existed."

The conference rules were loose and trusting. People could talk informally about data they had not yet published, and the other participants would not take advantage of that. "Small meetings, where unpublished data and ideas can be shared and everyone helps everyone, can change the world," Banfield later noted. Among the first accomplishments was standardizing the lingo and names, including adopting a common designation for the CRISPR-associated proteins. Sylvain Moreau, one of the pioneer participants, called the July meeting "our scientific Christmas party."[7]

Sontheimer and Marraffini

The year of the inaugural conference produced a major advance. Luciano Marraffini and his advisor Erik Sontheimer of Northwestern University in Chicago showed that the target of the CRISPR system was DNA. In other words, CRISPR did not work through RNA interference, which had been the general consensus when Banfield first approached Doudna. Instead, the CRISPR system targeted the DNA of the invading virus.[8]

That had a holy-cow implication. As Marraffini and Sontheimer realized, if the CRISPR system was aimed at the DNA of viruses, then it could possibly be turned into a gene-editing tool. That seminal discovery sparked a new level of interest in CRISPR around the world. "It led to the idea that CRISPR could be fundamentally transformative," Sontheimer says. "If it could target and cut DNA, it would allow you to fix the cause of a genetic problem."[9]

There was still a lot to figure out before that could happen. Marraffini and Sontheimer didn't know precisely how the CRISPR enzyme cut the DNA. It could have done so in a way that was incompatible with genetic editing. Nevertheless, they filed a patent application in September 2008 for the use of CRISPR as a DNA-editing tool. It was rejected, and rightly so. Their guess that it could someday be a gene-editing tool was correct, but it was not yet backed up by experimental evidence. "You can't just patent an idea," Sontheimer admits. "You have to actually have invented what you're claiming." They also applied for a grant from the National Institutes of Health to pursue the possibility of a gene-editing tool. That, too, was rejected. But they were on record as being the first to suggest how CRISPR-Cas systems might be used as gene-editing tools.[10]

Sontheimer and Marraffini had studied CRISPR in living cells, such as those of bacteria. So had the other molecular biologists who published papers on CRISPR that year. But a different approach was required in order to determine the essential components of the system: biochemists working with the molecules *in vitro*, in a test tube. By isolating the components in a test tube, biochemists could explain at the molecular level the discoveries made by microbiologists working *in vivo* and by computational geneticists comparing sequencing data *in silico*.

"When you do experiments *in vivo*, you're never completely sure what's causing things," Marraffini concedes. "We cannot look inside a cell and see how things are working." To understand each component fully, you need to take them out of cells and put them into a test tube, where you control precisely what's included. This was Doudna's specialty, and it was what Blake Wiedenheft and Martin Jinek were pursuing in her lab. "Addressing these questions would require us to move beyond genetics research and take a more biochemical approach," she later wrote, "one that would allow us to isolate the component molecules and study their behavior."[11]

But first, Doudna stutter-stepped onto an odd career detour.

Herbert Boyer and Robert A. Swanson

Chapter 13

Genentech

Restless

In the fall of 2008, just after this spate of CRISPR papers had been published, Jillian Banfield told Doudna she was worried that the most important discoveries had already been made and that perhaps it was time to "move on." Doudna demurred. "I looked at what had been discovered as being the beginning, not the end, of an exciting journey," she recalls. "I knew there was some kind of adaptive immunity going on and wanted to know how it worked."[1]

Yet at that moment, Doudna was personally planning to move on.

She was forty-four, happily married, with a smart and polite seven-year-old son. Yet despite all of her success, or maybe partly because of it, she was having a mild midlife crisis. "I'd been running an academic research lab for fifteen years, and I started to wonder, 'Is there more?'" she recalls. "I wondered if my work was having an impact in the broader sense."

Despite the excitement of being in the forefront of the emerging field of CRISPR, she was becoming restless with basic science. She was eager to do more applied science and translational research, which aims at turning fundamental scientific knowledge into therapies that enhance human health. Even though there were hints that CRISPR could become a gene-editing tool, which would have great practical value, Doudna was feeling the tug to pursue projects that would have a more immediate impact.

At first she considered going to medical school. "I thought I might like to work with actual patients and be involved in clinical trials," she says. She also considered going to business school. Columbia had an executive MBA program that allowed participants to go to class one weekend a month and do the rest of the work online. The travel to and from Berkeley, and also Hawaii, where her mother was ailing, would be grueling, but she seriously considered it.

Then she ran into a former academic colleague who had joined the San Francisco biotech powerhouse Genentech the year before. The company was a poster child for the innovation and profits that can result when basic science meets patent lawyers meet venture capitalists.

Genentech, Inc.

Genentech was spawned in 1972, when Stanford medical professor Stanley Cohen and biochemist Herbert Boyer of the University of California, San Francisco, attended a conference in Honolulu that dealt with recombinant DNA technology, which was Stanford biochemist Paul Berg's discovery of how to splice pieces of DNA from different organisms to create hybrids. At the conference, Boyer gave a talk about his own discovery of an enzyme that could create these hybrids very efficiently. Cohen then spoke about how to clone thousands of identical copies of a piece of DNA by introducing it into *E. coli* bacteria.

Bored and still a bit hungry after their conference dinner one night, they walked to a New York–style deli, with a neon sign reading "Shalom" rather than the usual "Aloha," in a strip mall near Waikiki Beach. Over pastrami sandwiches, they brainstormed how to combine their discoveries to create a method for engineering and manufacturing new genes. They agreed to work together on the idea, and within four months they had spliced together DNA fragments from different organisms and cloned millions of them, giving birth to the field of biotechnology and launching the genetic engineering revolution.[2]

One of Stanford's alert intellectual property lawyers approached them and, to their surprise, offered to help them file a patent application. In 1974 they did, and it was eventually approved. It had not fully occurred to them that one could patent recombinant DNA processes, which are found in nature. It didn't occur to other scientists either, and many were furious—especially Paul Berg, who had made the original breakthroughs on recombinant DNA. He called the claims "dubious, presumptuous, and hubristic."[3]

In late 1975, a year after the Cohen-Boyer patent application was filed, a struggling young wannabe venture capitalist named Robert Swanson started making unsolicited phone calls to scientists who might be interested in starting a genetic engineering company. Swanson had an unbroken record of failure as a venture capitalist. At the time, he was living in a shared apartment, driving a beat-up Datsun, and surviving on cold-cut sandwiches. But he had read up on recombinant DNA and convinced himself that he had finally found a winning horse. As he went down his list of scientists alphabetically, the first one who agreed to meet him was Boyer. (Berg declined.) Swanson went to his office for what was supposed to be a ten-minute meeting, but he and Boyer ended up spending three hours at a neighborhood bar, where they planned a new type of company that would make medicines out of engineered genes. Each agreed to put in $500 to cover the initial legal fees.[4]

Swanson suggested that they call the company HerBob, a recombination of their first names that sounded like an online dating service or down-market beauty parlor. Boyer wisely rejected that and suggested instead that they call it Genentech, a mash-up of "genetic engineering technology." It began making genetically engineered drugs and, in August 1978, blasted into hypergrowth when it won a bet-the-company race to make a synthetic version of insulin to treat diabetes.

Until then, one pound of insulin required eight thousand pounds of pancreas glands ripped from more than twenty-three thousand pigs or cows. Genentech's success with insulin not only changed the lives of diabetics (and a lot of pigs and cows); it lifted the entire biotechnology industry into orbit. A portrait painting of a smiling Boyer appeared on the cover of *Time* with the headline "The Boom in Genetic Engineering." It came out the same week that Prince Charles of England picked Diana to be his princess, an event that, in those more rarefied times for journalism, received only a secondary mention on the magazine's cover.

Genentech's success led to a memorable front page of the *San Francisco Examiner* in October 1980, when the company became the first biotech company to launch an IPO and become publicly traded. Its stock, trading under the symbol GENE, opened at $35 a share and within an hour was selling at $88. "Genentech Jolts Wall Street," the banner front-page headline blared. Right below it was a picture for a totally separate story: a smiling Paul Berg on the telephone learning the news that he had, on that same day, won the Nobel Prize for his discovery of recombinant DNA.[5]

Detour

By the time Genentech began recruiting Doudna in late 2008, the company was worth close to $100 billion. Her former colleague, who was now working on genetically engineering cancer drugs at Genentech, told her that he was loving his new role. His research was much more focused than when he was an academic, and he was working directly on problems that were going to lead to new therapeutics. "So that got me thinking," Doudna says. "Rather than go back to school, maybe I should just go to a place where I could apply my knowledge."

Her first step was to present a couple of seminars at Genentech describing her work. It was a way for her and the Genentech team to sniff each other out. Among those wooing her was Sue Desmond-Hellmann, chief of product development. They had similar personalities, both eager listeners with quick minds and ready smiles. "When I was being recruited there, she and I sat down in her office and [she] told me she would be my mentor if I came to Genentech," Doudna says.

When Doudna decided to accept the job, she was told she could bring some members of her Berkeley team with her. "We were all preparing for the move," recalls Rachel Haurwitz, one of Doudna's doctoral students who, like most of the others, decided to follow her. "We were figuring out what equipment we were going to take and had begun packing it all up."[6]

But as soon as Doudna began working at Genentech, in January 2009, she realized that she had made a mistake. "I felt very quickly in my gut that I was in the wrong place," she says. "It was a visceral response. Every day and night, I felt I had made the wrong decision." She didn't sleep much. She was upset at home. She had trouble carrying out the most basic functions. Her midlife identity crisis was segueing into a mild mental breakdown. She had always been a very measured person, keeping her insecurities and occasional anxieties under wraps and under control. Until now.[7]

Her turmoil climaxed after only a few weeks. On a rainy night in late January, she found herself lying awake in bed. She got up and went outside in her pajamas. "I sat out in the rain in my backyard, getting soaked, and I thought, 'I'm done,'" she recalls. Her husband found her sitting motionless in the rain and coaxed her back inside. She wondered if she was clinically depressed. She knew she wanted to go back to her research lab at Berkeley, but she feared that door had closed.

Her neighbor Michael Marletta, who was chair of the chemistry department at Berkeley, came to her rescue. She called him the next morning and asked him to come over, which he did. She sent Jamie and their son, Andrew, away so she could have an emotional conversation privately. Marletta was immediately struck by how deeply unhappy she looked, and told her so. "I bet you want to come back to Berkeley," he said.

"I think I may have slammed that door," she replied.

"No, you haven't," he reassured her. "I can help you come back."

Instantly, her mood lifted. That night she could sleep again. "I knew that I was going back to where I was meant to be," she says. She returned to her Berkeley lab at the beginning of March, after only two months away.

From this misstep, she became more aware of her passions and skills—and also her weaknesses. She liked being a research scientist in a lab. She was good at brainstorming with people she trusted. She was not good at navigating a corporate environment where the competition was for power and promotions rather than discoveries. "I didn't have the right skill set or passions to work at a big company." But even though her brief stint at Genentech didn't work out, her desire to tie her research to the creation of practical new tools and companies that could commercialize them would drive the next chapter of her life.

CHAPTER 14

The Lab

Recruiting

There are two components to scientific discovery: doing great research and building a lab that does great research. I once asked Steve Jobs what his best product was, thinking he would say the Macintosh or iPhone. Instead he said that creating great products is important, but what's even more important is creating a team that can continually make such products.

Doudna deeply enjoyed being a bench scientist, a researcher who gets to the lab early, puts on latex gloves and a white coat, and begins working with pipettes and Petri dishes. For the first few years after setting up her lab at Berkeley, she was able to work at the bench half her time. "I didn't want to give that up," she says. "I think I was a pretty good experimenter. That's how my mind works. I can see experiments in my mind, especially when I am working myself." But by 2009, after her return from Genentech, Doudna realized that she had to spend more time cultivating her lab rather than her bacterial cultures.

This transition from player to coach happens in many fields. Writers become editors, engineers become managers. When bench scientists become lab heads their new managerial duties include hiring the

Martin Jinek, Rachel Haurwitz, Blake Wiedenheft,
Kaihong Zhou, and Jennifer Doudna

right young researchers, mentoring them, going over their results, suggesting new experiments, and offering up the insights that come from having been there.

Doudna excelled at these tasks. When considering candidates to be doctoral students or postdoctoral researchers in her lab, she made sure that her other team members believed they would fit in. The goal was to find people who were self-directed yet collegial. As her work on CRISPR ramped up, she found two PhD students with the right mix of eagerness and smarts to become core members of her team alongside Blake Wiedenheft and Martin Jinek.

Rachel Haurwitz

As a young girl growing up in Austin, Texas, Rachel Haurwitz was, in her words, "a science nerd." Like Doudna, she became interested in RNA. She made the molecule a focus of her studies as an undergraduate at Harvard, and then she went to Berkeley to pursue a doctorate. Not surprisingly, she was eager to work in Doudna's lab. She joined in 2008 and was soon swept into the CRISPR orbit of Blake Wiedenheft, attracted by his magnetic personality and joyful enthusiasm for odd bacteria. "When I started working with Blake, I had barely heard of CRISPR, so I read all of the papers that had been published in the field," she recalls. "It took me only about two hours. Neither Blake nor I sensed the tiny tip of the iceberg we were standing on."[1]

Haurwitz was at home studying for her PhD qualifying exam in early 2009 when she heard the news that Doudna had decided to cut short her move to Genentech and return to Berkeley. That was fortunate. Haurwitz had been planning to follow her, but she really wanted to stay at Berkeley and do her dissertation on CRISPR working with Wiedenheft. They shared a love both of biochemistry and of the outdoors; Wiedenheft even helped her develop a new training and eating regimen that got her back into running marathons.

Doudna recognized in Haurwitz something of herself: CRISPR was a risky field because it was so new, and that's what made Haurwitz want to jump in. "She loved the fact that it was a novel field, even though some students would be afraid of that," Doudna says. "So I told her, 'Go for it.'"

After Wiedenheft had worked out the structure of Cas1, he decided to do the same for the five other CRISPR-associated proteins that were in the bacteria he was working on. Four of them were easy. But Cas6* was tough to crack, so he enlisted Haurwitz. "He gave me the problem child," she says.

The source of the difficulty turned out to be that the sequencing of the bacteria's genome had been annotated incorrectly in textbooks and databases. "Blake realized that the reason we were having so much trouble was that they got the start wrong," Haurwitz explains. Once they figured out the problem, they were able to make Cas6 in the lab.[2]

The next step was to figure out what it did and how. "I used the two things the Doudna Lab does," explains Haurwitz: "biochemistry to figure out what its function is, and structural biology to figure out what it looks like." The biochemistry experiments revealed that the role of Cas6 is latching on to the long RNAs made by the CRISPR array and slicing them into the shorter CRISPR RNA snippets, which precisely target the DNA of attacking viruses.

The step after that was deciphering the structure of Cas6, which would explain *how* it operates. "At that point neither Blake nor I had the full set of skills to do structural biology by ourselves," Haurwitz says. "So I tapped on the shoulder of Martin Jinek, sitting at the next bench over, and I asked if he would join the project and help show us how to do this."

They found something unusual. Cas6 binds to RNA in a way that textbooks say should not work: it can find just the right sequence in the RNA that has a structural place for it to bind. "None of the other Cas proteins we had seen could do that," she says. The result was that Cas6 would recognize and cut a very precise place and not mess up other RNA.

In their paper, they called it "an unexpected recognition mechanism."

*At the time, it was generally known as Csy4. It eventually became known as Cas6f.

There was an "RNA hairpin" where the Cas6 could interact with just the right sequence. Once again, the twists and folds of a molecule's shape were the key in discovering how it worked.[3]

Sam Sternberg

In early 2008, Sam Sternberg was accepted into many top PhD programs, including Harvard's and MIT's. He decided to go to Berkeley because he had met Doudna and wanted to work with her on RNA structures. But he ended up deferring his enrollment so that he could finish a scientific paper on the work he had been doing as an undergraduate at Columbia.[4]

During that delay, he was surprised to hear about Doudna's abrupt move to Genentech and even more abrupt rebound. Worried about whether he had made the right choice, he sent her an email asking how committed she was to Berkeley. "I didn't trust myself to ask her in person, because I was too nervous," he admits. Doudna sent back a reassuring reply that she was now sure Berkeley was the right place for her. "It was convincing enough that I decided to go through with my plans to study there."[5]

Haurwitz invited Sternberg to a Passover Seder at the apartment she shared with her boyfriend. Unlike at most other Seders, a main topic of conversation was CRISPR. "I kept asking her to tell me more about the experiments she was doing," he says. She showed him a paper that she was writing about Cas enzymes, and he was hooked. "After that, I made it clear to Jennifer that I didn't want to keep working on RNA interference," he says. "I told her I wanted to work instead on this new CRISPR thing."

After Sternberg heard a talk by Columbia professor Eric Greene about single-molecule fluorescence microscopy, he asked Doudna, very tentatively, if he could try applying that method to one of the CRISPR-Cas proteins. "Oh my gosh, yes," she replied. "Absolutely do that." It was the type of risky approach she liked. Her scientific success had always come from connecting small dots to make big pictures, and she worried that Sternberg was tackling only small CRISPR topics.

After praising him for being bright and talented, she was blunt: "Right now you are punching below your weight. You're not taking the kinds of projects that a student like you is capable of. Why else do we do science? We do it to go after big questions and take on risks. If you don't try things, you're never going to have a breakthrough."[6]

Sternberg was convinced. He had asked whether he could go to Columbia for a week to learn more about the technique. "She not only sent me out there for a week to try it out, she ended up paying for me to spend six whole months there," Sternberg later wrote in the acknowledgments of his PhD dissertation. During his six months back at his alma mater, Sternberg figured out how to use the single-molecule fluorescence method to test the behavior of the CRISPR-associated enzymes.[7] The work resulted in two breakthrough papers—coauthored by Sternberg, Columbia's Eric Greene, Jinek, Wiedenheft, and Doudna—that showed for the first time precisely how the CRISPR system's RNA-guided proteins find the right target sequences of an invading virus.[8]

Sternberg grew especially friendly with Wiedenheft, who became a role model. They got a chance to spend an intense week working together in late 2011, when Wiedenheft was writing a review article on CRISPR for *Nature*.[9] They spent days together sitting side by side at a computer arguing over wording and selecting the illustrations to publish. They bonded more closely when they roomed together at a conference in Vancouver. "That was when my own scientific career began to take off," Sternberg says, "because I began thinking about how I could do something bigger that would bring in Blake."[10]

Sternberg and Wiedenheft and Haurwitz sat in a bay of the lab within a few feet of one another. It became a foxhole for biogeeks. When a big experiment was underway, they would have bets on the outcome. "What are we betting?" Blake would ask, and then himself answer, "We're betting a milkshake." The problem was that the Berkeley area had become too hip, or not yet hip enough, to have milkshake shops that were convenient. Still, they would use the milkshake tally to keep score.

The camaraderie in the lab was not an accident: in hiring, Doudna placed as much emphasis on making sure someone was a good fit as she did assessing their research accomplishments. As we walked through her lab one day, I challenged Doudna about this practice. Might it weed out some brilliant misfits, people who will challenge others or disrupt the group thinking, but in a beneficial way? "I've thought about that a little," she says. "I know some people like creative conflict. But I like having in the lab people who work well together."

Leadership

When Ross Wilson, a newly minted PhD from Ohio State, applied to be a postdoctoral fellow in Doudna's lab, Jinek pulled him aside to give him a word of warning. "You have to be self-sufficient," he told Wilson. "If you're not self-motivated, Jennifer is not going to help you much or do the work for you. At times she will seem disengaged. But if you're a self-starter, she will give you the chance to take risks, provide really smart guidance, and be there when you need her."[11]

Doudna's was the only lab where Wilson interviewed in 2010. He was interested in how RNA interacts with enzymes, and he considered her the world's leading expert. When she accepted him, he cried for joy. "I actually did," he says. "It's the only time in my life I've ever done that."

Jinek's cautionary note, he says, was "one hundred percent accurate," but that made her lab an exciting place to work for a self-driven person. "She definitely doesn't hover over you," says Wilson, who now runs his own Berkeley lab aligned with Doudna's, "but when she goes over your experiments and results with you, there are times when she will lower her voice a bit, look you right in the eye, lean in, and say, 'What if you tried . . . ?'" Then she would describe a new approach, a new experiment, or even a big new idea, usually involving some new way of deploying RNA.

One day, for example, Wilson came to her office to show some results about how two molecules that he had crystallized interacted. "If you can disrupt this interaction based on knowing how it works," she said, "maybe we can make that same disruption inside the cell and see how it changes the behavior of the cell." It pushed Wilson to move beyond the test tube and delve into the inner workings of a living cell. "I would never have thought of doing that," he says, "but it worked."

Most mornings when she is in her lab, Doudna schedules a steady stream of her researchers to come present their most recent results. Her questions tend to be Socratic: Have you thought about adding RNA? Can we image that in living cells? "She has a knack for asking the right critical big questions when you're developing your project," says Jinek. They were designed to get her researchers to look up from the details and see the big picture. Why are you doing this? she will ask. What's the point?

Although she takes a hands-off approach during the early stages of a researcher's project, as it gets close to fruition she engages intensely. "Once something exciting emerges or a real discovery is in the works, she senses when it's a big deal and she gets super involved," says Lucas Harrington, one of her former students. "It comes in pulses." That is when Doudna's competitive juices kick in. She doesn't want another lab to beat hers to a discovery. "She might storm into the lab unexpectedly," Harrington says, "and without raising her voice make it clear what things need to be done and be done quickly."

When her lab produced a new discovery, Doudna was tenacious about getting it published. "I've discovered that the journal editors favor people who are aggressive or pushy," she says. "That's not necessarily my nature, but I have become more aggressive when I feel that journal editors are not appreciating that something we did is really important."

Women in science tend to be shy about promoting themselves, and that has serious costs. A study in 2019 of more than six million articles with women as the principal author showed that they are less likely to use self-promotional terms, such as "novel" and "unique" and "unprecedented," to describe their findings. The trend is especially true for articles in the most prestigious journals, which almost by definition feature research that is groundbreaking. In the highest-impact journals that publish the most important cutting-edge research, women are 21 percent less likely to use positive and self-promotional words in describing their work. Partly as a result, their papers are cited approximately 10 percent less frequently.[12]

Doudna does not fall into that trap. At one point in 2011, for example, she and Wiedenheft, along with her Berkeley colleague Eva Nogales, completed a paper on the array of Cas enzymes dubbed CASCADE. It could home in on an exact spot of DNA in the invading virus and then recruit an enzyme to buzz-saw it into hundreds of pieces. They sent it to one of the most prestigious journals, *Nature*, which accepted it. But the editors said it was not an important enough breakthrough to be a featured "article" in the journal, so they wanted to publish it as a "report," which is a notch down in significance. Most of the team was thrilled to have the paper quickly accepted by such an important publication. But Doudna was upset. She argued strongly that it was a big advance and deserved prominent treatment—writing a letter and soliciting supporting letters—but the editors stuck firm. "Most people are jumping up and down if they get a yes from *Nature*," Wiedenheft says. "Jennifer was jumping up and down because she was mad that it was going to be a report, not an article."[13]

Rachel Haurwitz

Chapter 15

Caribou

Bench to bedside

Even though she decided against becoming part of the corporate-science world at Genentech, Doudna retained her desire to translate the basic discoveries about CRISPR into tools that could be useful in medicine. Her opportunity came after Wiedenheft and Haurwitz succeeded in discovering the structure of Cas6.

It was the beginning of a new aspect of her career: looking for ways to turn her CRISPR discoveries into tools that could be useful in medicine. Haurwitz took the idea one more step. If Cas6 could be turned into a medical tool, it could become the basis for a company. "Once we understood how the Cas6 protein worked," she says, "we started to get some ideas on how we might steal it from bacteria and repurpose it for our own uses."[1]

For much of the twentieth century, most new drugs were based on chemical advances. But the launch of Genentech in 1976 shifted the focus of commercialization from chemistry to biotechnology, which involves the manipulation of living cells, often through genetic engineering, to devise new medical treatments. Genentech became the model for commercializing biotech discoveries: scientists and venture capitalists raised capital by divvying up equity stakes, then they entered into agreements with major pharmaceutical companies to license, manufacture, and market some of their discoveries.

Thus did biotech follow the path of digital technology in blurring the lines between academic research and business. This fusion in the digital realm began right after World War II, mainly around Stanford. With prodding from its provost Frederick Terman, Stanford professors were encouraged to turn their discoveries into startups. The companies that sprang out of Stanford included Litton Industries, Varian Associates, and Hewlett-Packard, followed by Sun Microsystems and Google. The process helped turn a valley of apricot orchards into Silicon Valley.

During this period, many other universities, including Harvard and Berkeley, decided it was more appropriate to stick to basic scientific research. Their traditional professors and provosts disdained commercial entanglement. But after envying Stanford's success in the realms of infotech and then biotech, they began to embrace entrepreneurship. Researchers were encouraged to patent their discoveries, partner with venture capitalists, and create businesses. "These companies frequently maintain their links with the universities, working closely with faculty members and postdoctoral candidates on research projects, and sometimes using the university laboratories," Harvard Business School professor Gary Pisano wrote. "In many instances, the founding scientists even retain their faculty posts."[2] This would become Doudna's approach.

Startup

Until then, Doudna had never thought much about commercialization. Money was not then, nor would it be later, a primary motivation in her life. She and Jamie and Andy lived in a spacious but not lavish house in Berkeley, and she never had the desire for a grander one. But she did like the idea of being part of a business, especially one that could have a direct impact on people's health. And unlike Genentech, a startup would have no corporate politics, nor would it drag her away from academia.

Haurwitz likewise felt the allure of business. Although she was good at the lab bench, she realized that she was not cut out to be an academic researcher. So she began taking courses at Berkeley's Haas School of Business. Her favorite was one taught by the venture capitalist Larry Lasky. He split his class into teams of six, half business students and the other half science researchers. Each team built a series of decks for a fictional biotech startup and then spent the semester perfecting how they would pitch it to investors. She also took a class from Jessica Hoover, who had been head of business development at a biotech firm that studied ways to commercialize medical products, including how to secure and license patents.

During Haurwitz's final year in her lab, Doudna asked what she wanted to do next. "Run a biotech company," Haurwitz replied. That would have been an unsurprising response at Stanford, where commercializing research was celebrated, but it was the first time Doudna had heard such an answer at Berkeley, where most PhD students aimed for an academic career.

A few days later, she went into the lab to find Haurwitz. "I've been thinking that maybe we ought to start a company around using Cas6 and some of the other CRISPR enzymes as a tool," she said. With no hesitation, Haurwitz responded, "Of course we should."[3]

So they did. The company was founded in October 2011, and it remained based in Doudna's academic lab for a year while Haurwitz finished her studies. After she got her PhD in the spring of 2012, she became the president and Doudna the chief scientific advisor of the fledgling endeavor.

The idea was that the company, which moved into a low-slung space in a nearby strip mall, would commercialize the patents related to the Cas6 structure and eventually other discoveries to come out of Doudna's lab. Their initial aim was to turn Cas6 into a diagnostic tool that clinics could use to detect the presence of viruses in humans.

The company

By the time Doudna and Haurwitz started their company in 2011, Berkeley had become savvier about encouraging its researchers to be more entrepreneurial. It launched a variety of programs to nurture startups formed by its students and professors. One of them, which was formed in 2000 in partnership with the other University of California campuses in the Bay Area, was the California Institute for Quantitative Biosciences (QB3), which had as its goal "a catalytic partnership between university research and private industry." Doudna and Haurwitz were selected to become participants in QB3's Startup in a Box program, which gave training, legal advice, and banking services to scientist-entrepreneurs who wanted to turn their basic discoveries into commercial ventures.

One day Doudna and Haurwitz took the subway into San Francisco to meet with the lawyer who Startup in a Box enlisted to help them incorporate their new company. When he asked for its name Haurwitz said, "I've been talking to my boyfriend about it, and we think we should call it Caribou." The name is a cut-and-splice mash-up of "Cas" and "ribonucleotides," which are the building blocks of RNA and DNA.

Haurwitz had talents not often found in Silicon Valley entrepreneurs. With her steady personality, she was a naturally good manager. She was down to earth, unflappable, practical, and straightforward. There was no whiff of the combination of ego and insecurity exuded by many startup CEOs. She did not exaggerate or overpromise. That offered many advantages, one of which was that people tended to underestimate her.

On the other hand, she had never been a CEO, so she had some learning to do. That led her to join a local professional development group for young CEOs, the Alliance of Chief Executives, which met for a half-day each month to share problems and solutions. It's hard to imagine Steve Jobs or Mark Zuckerberg joining such a support group, but Haurwitz, like her mentor Doudna, had a self-awareness and humility not usually found among alpha males. Among other things, her Alliance group coached her on how to create a team with different types of expertise.

Today the mere appearance of the word CRISPR in a prospectus is enough to cause venture capitalists to go into heat. But when Doudna and Haurwitz tried to raise money, they had little luck. "At that time, the topic of molecular diagnostics was a turnoff to venture capitalists," Doudna says. "I also feel that there is an anti-female undercurrent, and I was worried that if we took venture money, that Rachel might be pushed out as CEO." None of the venture capitalists they met with was a woman, and this was in 2012. So instead of continuing to seek venture money, they decided to raise what they could from friends and family. Both Doudna and Haurwitz put in their own money.

The triangle

Its bootstrap success may, on the surface, make Caribou Biosciences seem like a poster child for pure free-market capitalism. And there was, nicely, an element of that. But it's important to look deeper and see how, as in so many other companies, from Intel to Google, innovation has been a product of a distinctively American mix of catalysts.

As World War II was ending, the great engineer and public official Vannevar Bush argued that America's innovation engine would require a three-way partnership of government, business, and academia. He was uniquely qualified to envision that triangle, because he had a foot in all three camps. He had been dean of engineering at MIT, a founder of Raytheon, and the chief government science administrator overseeing, among other projects, the building of the atom bomb.[4]

Bush's recommendation was that government should not build big research labs of its own, as it had done with the atomic bomb project, but instead should fund research at universities and corporate labs. This government-business-university partnership produced the great innovations that propelled the U.S. economy in the postwar period, including transistors, microchips, computers, graphical user interfaces, GPS, lasers, the internet, and search engines.

Caribou was an example of this approach. Berkeley, a public university with private philanthropic supporters, housed Doudna's lab and had a partnership with the federally funded Lawrence Berkeley National Laboratory. The amount of federal grants that went from the National Institutes of Health (NIH) to Berkeley to support Doudna's research into CRISPR-Cas systems was $1.3 million.[5] In addition, Caribou itself was able to get a federal grant from the NIH's small business innovation program, which provided $159,000 to the company to create kits to analyze RNA-protein complexes. The program was designed to help innovators turn basic research into commercial products. It kept Caribou alive during the early years, when venture funding was not forthcoming.[6]

There is one other element that is now often added to the academic-government-business triad: philanthropic foundations. In the case of Caribou, that came as a grant from the Bill and Melinda Gates Foundation, which provided $100,000 to fund work on using Cas6 as a tool to diagnose viral infections. "We plan on creating a suite of enzymes that specifically recognize RNA sequences characteristic of viruses including HIV, hepatitis C and influenza," Doudna wrote in her proposal to the foundation. It was a prelude to the funding Doudna would receive from Gates in 2020 to use CRISPR systems to detect coronaviruses.[7]

Chapter 16

Emmanuelle Charpentier

The wanderer

Conferences can have consequences. While attending one in Puerto Rico in the spring of 2011, Doudna had a chance meeting with Emmanuelle Charpentier, an itinerant French biologist who had an alluring mix of mystery and Parisian insouciance. She, too, had been studying CRISPR, and she had homed in on the CRISPR-associated enzyme known as Cas9.

Guarded but engaging, Charpentier was a woman of many cities, many labs, many degrees and postdoc programs, but few roots and commitments, ever willing to pack up her pipettes and move, never showing any outward signs of worry or an instinct for competition. This made her much different from Doudna, which is perhaps why they bonded at first, although mainly in a scientific rather than emotional way. They both had warm smiles that made their protective shells almost, but not totally, invisible.

Charpentier grew up in a leafy suburb on the Seine south of Paris. Her father was in charge of the neighborhood park system, and her mother was the administrative nurse in a psychiatric hospital. One day when Charpentier was twelve, she walked past the Pasteur Institute, the Paris research center specializing in infectious diseases. "I

Emmanuelle Charpentier

am going to work there when I grow up," she told her mother. A few years later, when she had to designate a field for her *baccalauréat* exam, which determines a student's course of study in college, she chose life science.[1]

She also was interested in the arts. She took piano lessons from a neighbor who was a concert musician and pursued ballet with the possibility that she might become a professional dancer, continuing her training well into her twenties. "I would like to have been a ballet dancer, but I finally realized that would be too risky as a career," she says. "I was a few centimeters too short and I had a ligament problem that affected the extension of my right leg."[2]

There were lessons from the arts, she would discover, that applied to science. "Methodology is important in both," she says. "You also must know the basics and master the methods. That requires persistence—repeating experiments and repeating them again, perfecting how to prepare the DNA when you clone a gene, and then doing it over and over again. It's part of the training, just like the hard work of a ballet dancer, repeating all day long the same moves and methods." Also like the arts, once a scientist masters the basic routine, she has to combine it with creativity. "You have to be rigorous and disciplined," Charpentier explains, "but also know when to let yourself loose and blend in a creative approach. I found in biological research the right combination of persistence and creativity."

Fulfilling the prediction she made to her mother, she pursued her graduate studies at the Pasteur Institute, where she learned how bacteria can become resistant to antibiotics. She felt at home in the lab. It was a quiet temple for individual persistence and contemplation. She could be creative and independent as she pursued a path toward her own discoveries. "I began to see myself as a scientist and not just as a student," she says. "I wanted to create knowledge, not just learn it."

Charpentier became a postdoctoral pilgrim, enrolling at Rockefeller University in Manhattan in the lab of the microbiologist Elaine Tuomanen, who was studying how the bacteria that cause pneumonia have DNA sequences that can shift, making the bacteria resistant to antibiotics. On the day she arrived, Charpentier found out that Tuomanen was moving, along with her lab and its postdocs, to the St. Jude Children's Research Hospital in Memphis. There Charpentier worked with Rodger Novak, another postdoc in Tuomanen's lab, and he became for a while a romantic companion and then a business partner. While in Memphis, they coauthored with Tuomanen an important study that showed how antibiotics such as penicillin trigger suicidal enzymes in bacteria that dissolve their cell walls.[3]

Charpentier's peripatetic mind and spirit made her ever ready to move to new towns and new topics, and this was hastened by an unpleasant biological discovery she made in Memphis: Mississippi River mosquitoes love French blood. In addition, she wanted to shift her focus from single-cell microbes such as bacteria and learn about genes in mammals, mainly mice. So she switched to a lab at New York University, where she produced a paper on ways to manipulate mouse genes to regulate hair growth. She also did a third postdoc in which she, along with Novak, focused on the role of small RNA molecules in regulating gene expression in *Streptococcus pyogenes*, a bacteria that causes skin infections and strep throat.[4]

After six years in the U.S., she moved back to Europe in 2002 to become the head of a microbiology and genetics lab at the University of Vienna. But once again she became restless. "People in Vienna knew each other a bit too well," she says, which she clearly regarded as a drawback rather than a benefit. "The dynamics got a bit stuck and the structures became inhibiting." So by the time she met Doudna in 2011, she had left behind most of the researchers in her lab to relocate on her own to Umeå, in northern Sweden. Umeå was no Vienna. Four hundred miles north of Stockholm, the town's 1960s-built university consisted of a cluster of modernist buildings on land that had been a grazing ground for reindeer herders. It was best known for its research on trees. "Yes, it was a risky move," Charpentier agrees, "but it gave me a chance to think."

In the years since she entered the Pasteur Institute in 1992, Charpentier had worked in ten institutions in seven cities in five countries.

Her nomadic life reflected the fact, and reinforced the fact, that she resisted bonds. With no spouse or family, she sought out changing environments and adapted to them without any inhibiting personal ties. "I enjoy the freedom of being on my own, of not depending on partnership," she says. She hated the phrase "work-life balance" because it implied that work competes with life. Her work in the lab and her "passion for science," she says, brought her a "happiness that is as fulfilling as any other passion."

Like the organisms she studied, her need to adapt to new environments kept her innovative. "My instinct to keep moving can be destabilizing, but that can be good," she says. "It assures that you never get stuck." Going from one place to another was her way of repeatedly reconsidering her research and forcing herself to start fresh. "The more one moves, the more one learns to analyze as a new situation and see things that others who have been in the system a long time have not identified."

Moving also made her feel like a bit of a foreigner most of the time, the way the young Jennifer Doudna felt as a child in Hawaii. "It's important to know how to be an outsider," Charpentier says. "You're never completely at home, and that can drive you. It can challenge you not to seek being comfortable." As with so many other observant and creative people, she found that a sense of detachment or slight alienation made her better at figuring out the forces at play. That helped her honor the maxim often preached by Louis Pasteur himself: *Be prepared for the unexpected.*

Partly as a result, Charpentier became one of those scientists who could be both focused and distracted. Though impeccably groomed and casually elegant even when riding a bicycle, she also fit the stereotype of an absent-minded professor. When I traveled to see her in Berlin, where she moved after Umeå, she got to my hotel on her bike a few minutes late. It turned out that she had come that morning from a visit to Munich, and when she was leaving the station she realized that she had left her luggage on the train. Somehow she caught up with the train at its terminal, retrieved her luggage, and then biked to my hotel. As we walked to her nearby lab at the Max Planck Institute for

Infectious Diseases, on the grounds of Charité, the venerable teaching hospital in the middle of Berlin, she pushed her bike purposely down a main artery until, after a few blocks, she realized that she had led us in the wrong direction. The next day, when a friend and I took her to see a show at an art museum, she managed to lose her admission ticket between the box office and the main entrance, and when we went to a serene Japanese restaurant for dinner, she left her phone behind. Yet when we were sitting in her lab office or over a multicourse sushi meal, she could speak for hours with super-intense focus.

tracrRNA

In 2009, the year that Charpentier was uprooting from Vienna and moving to Umeå, the CRISPR crowd had coalesced around Cas9 as being the most interesting of the CRISPR-associated enzymes. Researchers had shown that if you deactivated Cas9 in bacteria, the CRISPR system no longer cut up the invading viruses. They had also established the essential role of another part of the complex: CRISPR RNAs, known as crRNAs. These are the small snippets of RNA that contain some genetic coding from a virus that had attacked the bacteria in the past. This crRNA guides the Cas enzymes to attack that virus when it tries to invade again. These two elements are the core of the CRISPR system: a small snippet of RNA that acts as a guide and an enzyme that acts as scissors.

But there was one additional component of the CRISPR-Cas9 system that played an essential role—or, as it turned out, two roles. It was dubbed a "trans-activating CRISPR RNA," or tracrRNA, pronounced "tracer-RNA." Remember this tiny molecule; it will play an outsized role in our tale. That's because science is most often advanced not by great leaps of discovery but by small steps. And disputes in science are often about who made each one of these steps—and how important each really was. This would turn out to be the case for the discoveries involving tracrRNA.

It turns out that tracrRNA performs two important tasks. First, it facilitates the making of the crRNA, the sequence that carries the memory of a virus that previously attacked the bacteria. Then it serves as a handle to latch on to the invading virus so that the crRNA can target the right spot for the Cas9 enzyme to chop.

The process of uncovering these roles of tracrRNA began in 2010, when Charpentier noticed that the molecule kept appearing in her experiments with bacteria. She couldn't figure out its role, but she realized that it was located in the vicinity of the CRISPR spacers, so she speculated that they were connected. She was able to test this by deleting the tracrRNA in some bacteria. The result was that the crRNAs didn't get produced. Researchers had never quite pinned down how the crRNAs were made inside a bacterial cell. Now Charpentier had a hypothesis: it is this tracrRNA that directs the creation of the short crRNAs.

Charpentier was moving to Sweden at the time. When the researchers in her Vienna lab sent her an email saying they had shown that the absence of tracrRNA meant that crRNA wasn't produced, she spent the night drawing up a long plan of experiments for them to do next. "I became obsessed with this tracrRNA," she says. "I am stubborn. It was important for me to follow up. I said 'We have to go for it! I want someone to look at it.' "[5]

The problem was that there was nobody in her Vienna lab who had the time and inclination to pursue the tracrRNA. That's the drawback of being a wandering professor: you leave your students behind, and they move on to other things.

Charpentier considered doing the experiments herself, even though she was in the midst of a move. But she finally found a volunteer in her Vienna lab: a young student from Bulgaria, studying for a master's degree, named Elitza Deltcheva. "Elitza was very dynamic, and she believed in me," Charpentier says. "She understood what was happening, even though she was just a master's student." She even convinced one of the graduate students, Krzysztof Chylinski, to work with her.

Charpentier's little team discovered that the CRISPR-Cas9 system accomplished its viral-defense mission using only three components: tracrRNA, crRNA, and the Cas9 enzyme. The tracrRNA took long strands of RNA and processed them into the small crRNAs that were targeted at specific sequences in an attacking virus. They prepared a paper for *Nature*, which would be published in March 2011, in which Deltcheva got to be the lead author—and the graduate students who had declined to help were lost to history.[6]

A remaining mystery

Charpentier presented the findings at a CRISPR conference in October 2010 in the Netherlands. She was having trouble getting her paper through the editorial process at *Nature*, and it was risky to go public with work before it was published. But she thought that perhaps one of the paper's reviewers would be in the audience and would be convinced to speed up the process.

She was stressed during her presentation because she had not yet figured out what happened to the tracrRNA after it helped to create a crRNA. Was the work of the tracrRNA done by then? Or did the two little RNAs stick together when it came time to guide the Cas protein to cut up an invading virus? One member of the audience asked her directly, "Do the three elements stay together as a complex?" Charpentier tried to deflect the question. "I tried to laugh and to be very confusing on purpose," she says.

That issue—and what Charpentier knew about it—might seem arcane. But it led to a set of disputes that illuminates how CRISPR researchers—and Doudna in particular—can be very competitive about who deserves credit for each small advance. The fact that the tracrRNA did in fact stick around and play an important role in cleavage would later be among the discoveries published in the seminal 2012 paper that Charpentier would write with Doudna. But to Doudna's annoyance, Charpentier would sometimes imply, years later, that she already knew this fact in 2011.

When I press her, Charpentier admits that her 2011 *Nature* paper did not, in fact, describe the full role of the tracrRNA: "It seemed clear to me that the tracrRNA needed to continue to be associated with the crRNA, but there were some details we didn't fully understand, so we didn't put this in the paper." Instead, she made the decision to save writing about the full tracrRNA function until she could find a convincing way to prove it experimentally.

She had studied the CRISPR system in living cells. To get to the next step would require biochemists who could isolate each chemical component in a test tube and figure out precisely how each one works. That is why she wanted to meet Doudna, who was scheduled to speak at the March 2011 conference of the American Society for Microbiology in Puerto Rico. "I knew we were both going to attend," she says, "and I put in my mind that I would find a chance to talk to her."

Puerto Rico, March 2011

When Jennifer Doudna walked into the coffee shop of the hotel in Puerto Rico on the second afternoon of the conference, Emmanuelle Charpentier was at a table in the corner sitting by herself, as she often liked to do, looking far more elegant than the other patrons. Doudna was with her friend John van der Oost, the Dutch CRISPR researcher, who pointed Charpentier out and offered to introduce her. "That would be great," replied Doudna. "I've read her paper."[7]

Doudna found Charpentier to be charming: just a hint of shyness, or feigned shyness, along with an engaging sense of humor and very stylish aura. "I was instantly struck by her intensity but also her sly humor," Doudna says. "I immediately liked her." They chatted for a few minutes and then Charpentier suggested they get together for a more serious discussion. "I've been thinking of contacting you about a collaboration," she said.

The next day they had lunch, followed by a stroll along the cobblestone streets of old San Juan. When the discussion turned to Cas9, Charpentier became excited. "We have to figure out exactly how it works," she urged Doudna. "What's the exact mechanism it uses to cut DNA?"

Charpentier was taken by Doudna's seriousness and attention to detail. "I think it's going to be fun to work with you," she told her. Doudna was similarly moved by Charpentier's intensity. "Somehow, just the way she said that it would be fun to work with me made a chill run down my back," she recalls. The other enticement was that it was just the sort of detective tale that gave Doudna a sense of purpose: the hunt for the key to one of life's basic mysteries.

Right before Doudna left for Puerto Rico, she had a career-counseling conversation with Martin Jinek, the postdoc in her lab who had been working on the structures of Cas1 and Cas6. He was having doubts, which turned out to be unwarranted, about whether he would be successful as an academic researcher, and had thought about becoming an editor at a medical journal instead. But he decided against it. "I think I'm going to be in your lab about one more year," he told her. "What would you like me to work on?" He was especially interested in finding a CRISPR project of his own, he said.

So when Doudna heard Charpentier's pitch, she thought it would be a perfect project for Jinek. "I've got a wonderful biochemist who's also a structural biologist," she told Charpentier.[8] They agreed that they would connect Jinek with the postdoc in Charpentier's lab who had worked on her earlier Cas9 paper, Krzysztof Chylinski, a Polish-born molecular biologist who had stayed in Vienna when she moved to Umeå. Together this foursome would make one of the most important advances in modern science.

Chapter 17

CRISPR-Cas9

Success

When Doudna returned to Berkeley, she and Jinek began a series of Skype calls with Charpentier in Umeå and Chylinski in Vienna to plot a strategy for figuring out the mechanisms of CRISPR-Cas9. The collaboration was like a model United Nations: a Berkeley professor from Hawaii, her postdoc from the Czech Republic, a Parisian professor working in Sweden, and her Polish-born postdoc working in Vienna.

"It became a twenty-four-hour operation," Jinek recalls. "I would do an experiment at the end of my day, I would send an email to Vienna, and Krzysztof would read it as soon as he got up in the morning." Then there would be a Skype call, and they would decide what the next step should be. "Krzysztof would execute that experiment during the day and send me the results while I was asleep, so that when I woke up and opened my inbox there would be an update."[1]

At first, Charpentier and Doudna would join the Skype calls only once or twice a month. But the pace picked up in July 2011, when Charpentier and Chylinski flew to Berkeley for the fast-growing annual CRISPR conference. Even though they had bonded over Skype, it was the first time that Jinek had personally met Chylinski, a lanky

Emmanuelle Charpentier, Jennifer Doudna, Martin Jinek, and Krzysztof Chylinski at Berkeley in 2012

researcher with an affable personality and an eagerness to be involved in turning basic research into a tool.[2]

In-person meetings can produce ideas in ways that conference calls and Zoom meetings can't. That had happened in Puerto Rico, and it did so again when the four researchers got together for the first time in Berkeley. There they were able to brainstorm a strategy for figuring out exactly what molecules were necessary for a CRISPR system to cut DNA. Physical meetings are especially useful when a project is in an early phase. "There's nothing like sitting in a room with people and seeing their reactions to things and having a chance to bat around ideas face to face," Doudna says. "That's been a cornerstone to every collaboration that we've had, even those where we are conducting a lot of the work by electronic communication."

Jinek and Chylinski were initially unable to make CRISPR-Cas9 chop up the DNA of a virus in a test tube. They had been trying to make it work with just two components: the Cas9 enzyme and the crRNA. In theory the crRNA would guide the Cas9 enzyme to the virus target, which would then get chopped up. But it didn't work. Something was missing. "It was extremely puzzling to us," Jinek recalls.

This is when the tracrRNA reenters our tale. In her 2011 paper Charpentier showed that tracrRNA was required for producing the crRNA guide. She later said that she suspected it played an even larger, ongoing role, though that possibility had not been part of their initial round of experiments. When those experiments failed, Chylinski decided to throw tracrRNA into his test-tube mix.

It worked: the three-component complex reliably chomped up the target DNA. Jinek immediately told Doudna the news: "Without the tracrRNA, the crRNA guide does not bind to the Cas9 enzyme." After that breakthrough, Doudna and Charpentier became more involved in the daily work. Clearly they were heading to an important discovery: determining the essential components of a CRISPR gene-cutting system.

Night after night, Chylinski and Jinek would ping-pong results back and forth, each adding a tiny bit of the puzzle, with Charpentier and Doudna joining the increasingly frequent strategy calls. They were able to discover the precise mechanisms of each of the three essential components of the CRISPR-Cas9 complex. The crRNA contained a twenty-letter sequence that acted as a set of coordinates to guide the complex to a piece of DNA with a similar sequence. The tracrRNA, which had helped create this crRNA, now had the additional role of acting like a scaffold that held the other components in just the right place when they glommed on to the target DNA. Then the Cas9 enzyme began slicing away.

One evening, right after a key experiment had produced positive results, Doudna was at home cooking spaghetti. The swirls in the boiling water reminded her of the salmon sperm she had studied under a microscope back in high school when learning about DNA, and she started to laugh. Her son, Andy, who was nine, asked her why. "We found this protein, an enzyme called Cas9," she explained. "It can be programmed to find viruses and cut them up. It's so incredible." Andy kept asking how it worked. Over billions of years, she explained, bacteria evolved this totally weird and astonishing way to protect themselves against viruses. And it was adaptable; every time a new virus emerged, it learned how to recognize it and beat it back. He was fascinated. "It was a double joy," she recalled, "a moment of fundamental discovery of something that is so cool, and being able to share it with my son and explaining it in a manner where he can get it." Curiosity can be beautiful that way.[3]

A gene editing tool

This amazing little system, it quickly became clear, had a truly momentous potential application: the crRNA guide could be modified to target any DNA sequence you might wish to cut. It was programmable. It could become an editing tool.

The study of CRISPR would become a vivid example of the call-and-response duet between basic science and translational medicine. At the beginning it was driven by the pure curiosity of microbe-hunters

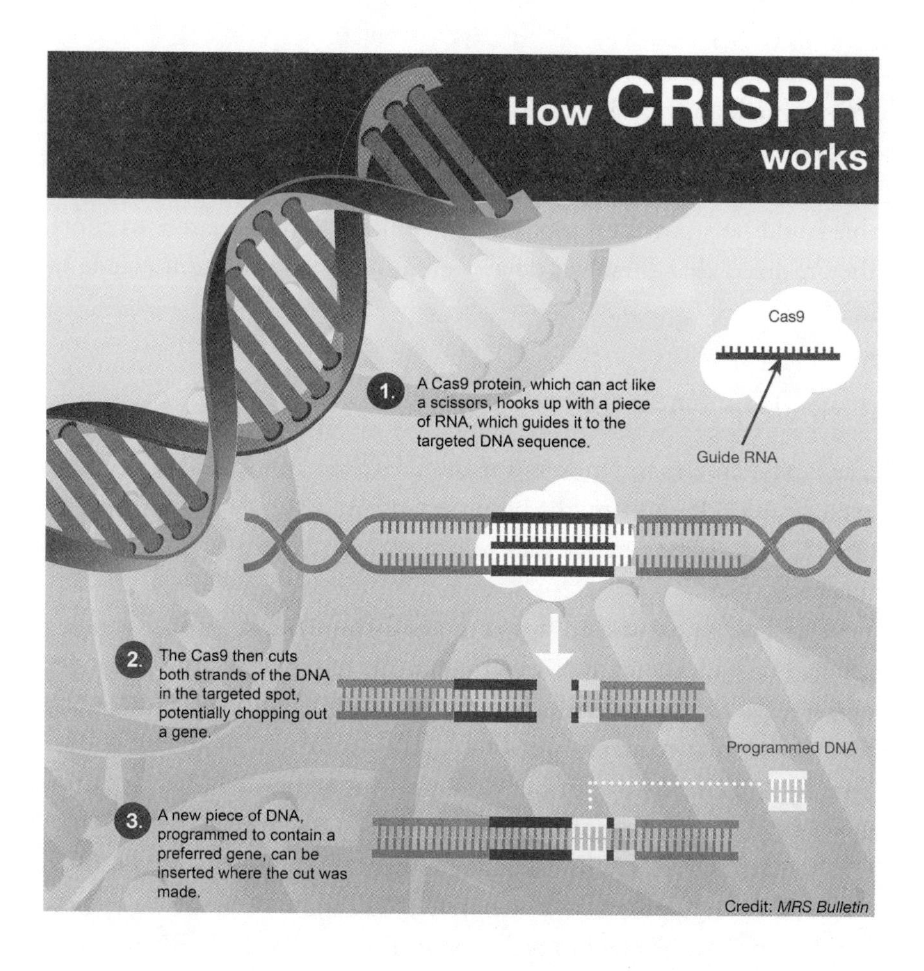

who wanted to explain an oddity they had stumbled upon when sequencing the DNA of offbeat bacteria. Then it was studied in an effort to protect the bacteria in yogurt cultures from attacking viruses. That led to a basic discovery about the fundamental workings of biology. Now a biochemical analysis was pointing the way to the invention of a tool with potential practical uses. “Once we figured out the components of the CRISPR-Cas9 assembly, we realized that we could program it on our own,” Doudna says. “In other words, we could add a different crRNA and get it to cut any different DNA sequence we chose.”

In the history of science, there are few real eureka moments, but this came pretty close. “It wasn’t just some gradual process where it slowly dawned on us," Doudna says. "It was an oh-my-God moment." When Jinek showed Doudna his data demonstrating that you could program Cas9 with different guide RNAs to cut DNA wherever you desired, they actually paused and looked at each other. "Oh my God, this could be a powerful tool for gene editing," she declared. In short, they realized that they had developed a means to rewrite the code of life.[4]

A single-guide RNA

The next step was to figure out if the CRISPR system could be made even simpler. If so, it might become not just a gene-editing tool but one that would be much easier to program and cheaper than existing methods.

One day, Jinek walked down the hall from the lab into Doudna's office. He had been experimenting to determine the minimum requirements for the crRNA that served as a guide and the tracrRNA that clamped it to the target DNA. They were standing at a whiteboard propped in front of her desk, and he was sketching out a diagram of the structure of the two small RNAs. Which parts of the crRNA and tracrRNA, he asked, were essential for cutting up DNA in a test tube? "It appeared that the system had some flexibility as to how long the two RNAs had to be," he says. Each of the little RNAs could be truncated a bit and still function. Doudna had a profound understanding about the structure of RNA and an almost childlike joy in figuring out the ways it worked. As they brainstormed, it became clear to them that they could link the two RNAs together, fusing the tail of one to the head of the other in a way that would keep the combined molecule functional.

Their goal was to engineer a single RNA molecule that would have the guide information on one end and the binding handle on the other. That would create what they ended up calling a "single-guide RNA" (sgRNA). They paused for a moment and looked at each other, then Doudna said, "Wow." As she recalls, "It was one of those moments in science that just comes to you. I had this chill and these little hairs on my neck standing up. In that moment, the two of us realized that this curiosity-driven, fun project had this powerful implication that could change the direction of the project profoundly." It's a fitting scene to imagine: the behavior of a little molecule being able to get the little hairs on Doudna's neck to stand up.

Doudna urged Jinek to begin work right away on fusing these two RNA molecules to work as a single guide for Cas9, and he hastened back down the hall to place an order with a company for the necessary RNA molecules. He also discussed the idea with Chylinski, and they quickly designed a series of experiments. Once they had figured out what parts of the two RNAs could be deleted and how they could be connected, it took only three weeks to make a single-guide RNA that worked.

It was immediately obvious that this single guide would make CRISPR-Cas9 an even more versatile, easy-to-use, and reprogrammable tool for gene editing. What made the single-guide system particularly significant—from both a scientific and an intellectual property standpoint—was that it was an actual human-made invention, not merely a discovery of a natural phenomenon.

So far Doudna's collaboration with Charpentier had produced two significant advances. The first was the discovery that the tracrRNA played an essential role not just in creating the crRNA guide but, more important, holding it together with the Cas9 enzyme and binding it all to the target DNA for the cutting process. The second was the invention of a way to fuse these two RNAs into a single-guide RNA. By studying a phenomenon that evolution had taken a billion or so years to perfect in bacteria, they turned nature's miracle into a tool for humans.

On the day that she and Jinek brainstormed how to engineer a single-guide RNA, Doudna explained the idea to her husband over dinner. Realizing that it would have implications for a possible patent on gene-editing technology, he told her that she needed to have it written up fully in the lab notebook and witnessed. So Jinek went back to the lab that night and wrote a detailed description of their concept.

It was close to 9 p.m., but Sam Sternberg and Rachel Haurwitz were still there. Lab notebooks have witness signature lines at the bottom of each page in order to document important advances, and Jinek asked both of them to sign. Sternberg had never been asked to do that before, so he realized that it was a historic evening.[5]

Chapter 18

Science, 2012

When it came time to write a scholarly paper describing CRISPR-Cas9, Doudna and her teammates used the same round-the-clock collaborative methods they had employed in their experiments. The manuscript was shared in Dropbox, with each of their changes tracked in real time. Jinek and Doudna worked during the day in California, handed things off with a late-night Skype call as dawn was breaking in Europe, and then Charpentier and Chylinski would take the lead for the next twelve hours. Because the sun never set in Umeå during the spring, Charpentier announced she could work any hour of the day. "You can't really sleep much when it's light all the time," she says, "and you're never really tired in those months, so I was on duty at any time."[1]

On June 8, 2012, Doudna hit the Send button on her computer to submit the manuscript to the editors of the journal *Science*. It listed six authors: Martin Jinek, Krzysztof Chylinski, Ines Fonfara, Michael Hauer, Jennifer Doudna, and Emmanuelle Charpentier. An asterisk next to the names of Jinek and Chylinski noted that they had contributed equally. Doudna and Charpentier were listed last because they were the principal investigators leading the labs.[2]

The 3,500-word paper went into great detail on how the crRNA

and the tracrRNA worked to bind the Cas9 protein onto the target DNA. It also showed how the structure of two Cas9 domains determined how each cut one of the DNA strands at a specific location. Finally, it described how they were able to fuse the crRNA and tracrRNA to engineer a single-guide RNA. This system, the authors noted, could be used to edit genes.

When the editors of *Science* received the paper, they were excited. Although many of the activities of CRISPR-Cas9 in living cells had been described before, it was the first time researchers had isolated the essential components of the system and discovered their biochemical mechanisms. In addition, the paper contained a potentially useful invention: the single-guide RNA.

At Doudna's urging, the editors fast-tracked the review process. She knew that other papers on CRISPR-Cas9, including one from a Lithuanian researcher (more on him in a moment), were already circulating, and she wanted to make sure that her team was the first to publish. The editors at *Science* had their own competitive motivation: they didn't want to be scooped by a rival journal. They asked CRISPR pioneer Erik Sontheimer to be one of the reviewers and told him he would have to get his comments back in two days, an unusually fast turnaround. He declined the assignment because he was doing his own work on the topic, but the journal's editors were able to find others to review the paper quickly.

The reviewer comments contained only a few requests for clarification. There was one significant issue that they did not raise. The experiments looked at the CRISPR-Cas9 system of *Streptococcus pyogenes*, a common bacteria that can cause strep throat. Like all bacteria, it is a single-cell organism without a nucleus. But the paper suggested that the CRISPR-Cas9 system could be useful for gene editing in humans. Charpentier thought that would prompt some questions. "I was thinking that the reviewers would ask if there was any evidence that it worked in human cells," she recalls. "But they never raised that, even after the conclusion I wrote saying that it would be an alternative to existing gene-editing methods."[3]

The *Science* editors approved the revisions and formally accepted the paper on Wednesday, June 20, 2012, just as participants were gathering in Berkeley for the annual CRISPR conference. Charpentier had arrived from Umeå and Chylinski from Vienna a few days early so they could be together for the final proofreading and edits. "Krzysztof arrived jet-lagged," Charpentier recalled, "but that was not the case for me because I had been in Umeå where it had been light all the time and I hadn't been sleeping in a rhythm."[4]

They gathered in Doudna's seventh-floor office and watched on her computer as the final PDF files and graphics were uploaded into the journal's online system. "The four of us were sitting in the office watching the status indicators for the uploads," Jinek recalls, "and there was a lot of excitement when the last one reached one hundred percent."

Once the final revisions were submitted, Doudna and Charpentier sat together, just the two of them, in Doudna's office. It had been only fourteen months since they had first met in Puerto Rico. As Charpentier admired the view of the late afternoon sun setting over San Francisco Bay, Doudna spoke of how pleasant it had been collaborating with her. "It was a glorious moment when we finally got to share in person the joy of discovery and also some personal confidences," Doudna recalled. "We got to take a breath and talk about how hard we'd worked together across thousands of miles."

When the talk turned to the future, Charpentier indicated she was interested in returning to a focus on the basic science of microbes rather than making tools for gene editing, and she confided that she was ready to move labs again, probably to the Max Planck Institute in Berlin. Doudna asked, somewhat teasingly, whether she would ever want to settle down, get married, have children. "She said she didn't want that," Doudna recalled. "She said she enjoyed being alone and treasured her private time and was not looking for that kind of companionship."

That evening, Doudna organized a celebratory dinner at Chez Panisse, the Berkeley restaurant where chef Alice Waters pioneered farm-to-table cuisine. Not yet a celebrity outside the rarefied realms of science, Doudna was unable to get a reservation at the fancier downstairs dining room, but she got a long table at the more casual upstairs café. They ordered champagne and toasted what they knew would be a new era in biology. "We felt like we were at the beginning of this intense time when the science was all coming to fruition, and we were thinking about what the implications were," Doudna recalls. Jinek and Chylinski left before dessert. They had to work that night on the slides for the presentation they would make at the conference the next day. On their walk back to the lab, in the last glow of twilight, Chylinski indulged in a cigarette.

Virginijus Šikšnys

Krzysztof Chylinski

Martin Jinek

CHAPTER 19

Dueling Presentations

Virginijus Šikšnys

Virginijus Šikšnys of Vilnius University in Lithuania is a mild-mannered biochemist with wire-rimmed glasses and a shy smile. He studied organic chemistry at Vilnius, got his doctorate at Moscow State University, then returned to his native Lithuania. He became intrigued by CRISPR when he read the 2007 paper by the Danisco yogurt researchers Rodolphe Barrangou and Philippe Horvath showing that CRISPR was a weapon that bacteria acquired in their struggle to fight off viruses.

By February 2012, he had produced a paper, with Barrangou and Horvath as secondary authors, that described how, in a CRISPR system, a Cas9 enzyme was guided by a crRNA to cut up an invading virus. He sent it off to the journal *Cell,* which summarily rejected it. In fact, the journal did not deem the paper interesting enough to send out for peer review. "Even more frustrating, we sent it to *Cell Reports*, which is kind of a sister journal to *Cell*," Šikšnys says. "They rejected it too."[1]

So his next attempt was to send it to *PNAS*, the publication of the U.S. National Academy of Sciences. One expedited path to be accepted by *PNAS* is for a research paper to be approved by a member of that academy. On May 21, 2012, Barrangou decided to send an abstract of the article to the member who was most familiar with the field: Jennifer Doudna.

Doudna was just finishing her paper with Charpentier, so she recused herself. She read only the abstract, not the full paper. But reading the abstract was enough for her to learn that Šikšnys had discovered many of the mechanisms of how, as the abstract said, "DNA cleavage is executed by Cas9." The abstract also declared that this could lead to a method for editing DNA: "These findings pave the way for engineering of universal programmable RNA-guided DNA endonucleases."[2]

The fact that Doudna subsequently hurried to push her own team's paper into print would cause a small controversy, or at least a few raised eyebrows, among some members of the CRISPR crowd. "You should look at the timing of Jennifer's patent filing and the submission of her paper to *Science*," Barrangou told me. At first glance, it can look suspicious. Doudna got Šikšnys's abstract on May 21, and she and her colleagues filed a patent application on May 25 and submitted their paper to *Science* on June 8.

In fact, the Doudna team's patent application and paper had been in the works well before she got Šikšnys's abstract. Barrangou emphasizes he is not accusing Doudna of doing anything wrong. "It was not improper or even unusual," he says. "It's not like she stole anything. We sent it to her. We can't blame her. This is how science is accelerated, when you know that it's a competitive situation. It gives you an impetus to push the process."[3] As it turned out, Doudna remained friendly with both Barrangou and Šikšnys. Their mix of competition and cooperation were part of a process they all understood.

There was, however, one rival who did question Doudna's haste: Eric Lander, director of the Broad Institute at MIT and Harvard. "She tells the *Science* editors that they have competition, she races the paper in, and *Science* rushes the reviewers," he says. "The whole thing gets done in three weeks, and so she scoops the Lithuanians."[4]

I find Lander's implied criticism of Doudna interesting, even a bit amusing, because he is one of the most cheerfully competitive people I know. The fact that he and Doudna are both very comfortable with being competitive has, I suspect, made their rivalry more intense. But I also think it meant that they understood each other, in the way that the two rivals in C. P. Snow's novel *The Masters* were able to understand each other better than any outsider could. Lander told me over dinner one night that he had the emails Doudna sent to the editors of *Science* that proved she pushed them to hurry her 2012 paper into print after she saw an abstract of Šikšnys's paper. When I ask Doudna about this, she readily agrees that she told the editors of *Science* there was a paper being submitted to a competing journal and requested that the reviewers accelerate their process. "So what?" she says. "Ask Eric if he's ever done that." So the next time I have dinner with Lander, I tell him that Doudna wanted me to ask him that question. He pauses, laughs, and then merrily concedes, "Of course I have. It's how science works. This is completely normal behavior."[5]

Šikšnys presents

Barrangou was one of the organizers of the June 2012 CRISPR conference in Berkeley, the one that Charpentier and Chylinski had flown over to attend, and he invited Šikšnys to present his work there. This set the stage for a face-off between the two teams that were racing to describe the CRISPR-Cas9 mechanisms.

Both Šikšnys and the Doudna-Charpentier team were scheduled to present their work on the afternoon of Thursday, June 21, the day after Doudna uploaded the final version of the *Science* article and went with her colleagues to celebrate at Chez Panisse. Barrangou had decided, even though Šikšnys's work had not yet been accepted for publication, that he should present first, followed immediately by the presentation of the Doudna-Charpentier team.

In the annals of history, the priority had been sealed: the Doudna-Charpentier paper had already been accepted by *Science* and would be published online June 28, while Šikšnys would not get published until September 4. Nevertheless, Barrangou's decision to let Šikšnys be the first to present at the Berkeley conference had the potential to give him a small claim to some of the glory—if his research turned out to match or exceed that of the Doudna-Charpentier team. "I was in charge of the order of speakers," Barrangou says. "I got a request from someone in Jennifer's lab to move their talk to before Virginijus. I rejected that. Virginijus had sent his paper to me first, back in February when we were trying to get it published in *Cell*, and I thought it would be fair for Virginijus to present first."[6]

So just after lunch on Thursday, June 21, Virginijus Šikšnys gave a slide presentation, based on his unpublished paper, in the seventy-eight-seat ground-floor auditorium of Berkeley's new Li Ka Shing Center, where the conference was being held. "We isolated the Cas9-crRNA complex and demonstrated that *in vitro* it generates a double-strand break at specific sites in target DNA molecules," he announced. He went on to say that this system could someday become a gene-editing tool.

There were, however, some gaps in the Šikšnys paper and presentation. Most notably, he spoke of the "Cas9-crRNA complex" and made no mention of the role of tracrRNA in the gene-cutting process. Although he described the tracrRNA role in creating the crRNA, he did not realize that it was necessary for this molecule to stick around in order to bind crRNA and Cas9 onto the DNA site targeted for destruction.[7]

For Doudna, this meant that Šikšnys had failed to discover the essential role played by the tracrRNA. "If you don't know that the tracrRNA is required for DNA cutting," she later said, "there is no way you could implement it as a technology. You haven't defined what the components are to get it to work."

There was competitive tension in the air, and Doudna was intent on making sure that Šikšnys's lapse involving the role of tracrRNA was highlighted. She was seated in the third row of the auditorium, and as soon as Šikšnys finished she raised her hand. Does your data, she asked, show the role of the tracrRNA in the cleaving process?

At first Šikšnys did not engage on the point directly, so Doudna kept pressing him to clarify. He did not try to refute her. "I remember there was a hint of debate in the discussion that followed Jennifer's question, and she was very firm in making her voice heard that the tracrRNA was an essential part that was overlooked in the work that Virginijus presented," says Sam Sternberg. "He did not disagree, but neither was there a full admission that he had missed it." Charpentier was likewise surprised. After all, she had written about part of the tracrRNA role in 2011. "What I don't understand is why Šikšnys, after reading my 2011 paper, did not look further into the role of tracrRNA," she says.[8]

To be fair, Šikšnys deserves a lot of credit, which I hope I've given him, for making many of the biochemical findings at about the same time as Doudna and Charpentier. Perhaps I have put a bit too much focus on the role of the tiny tracrRNA, both because I'm writing the book from Doudna's vantage point and because she emphasized it in many of our interviews. But I actually do think it's important. In explaining the amazing mechanisms of life, little things matter. And very little things matter a lot. Showing precisely the essential role of the two snippets of RNA—the tracrRNA and the crRNA—was key to understanding fully how CRISPR-Cas9 could be a gene-editing tool and how the two RNAs could be fused together to create a simple single guide to the right gene target.

Wow

Immediately after Šikšnys finished, it was time for Doudna and Charpentier to deliver what most attendees by then knew was a set of big breakthroughs. The two sat next to each other in the audience, having decided that the presentation would be made by the postdocs who had done most of the hands-on experiments, Jinek and Chylinski.[9]

When the presentation was about to begin, two Berkeley biology professors walked in with some of their postdocs and students. Doudna had been talking to them about collaborating on getting CRISPR-Cas9 to work in humans, but most of the other participants did not know who they were. Sternberg guessed they were patent lawyers. Their appearance heightened the sense of drama. "I remember people being surprised as a dozen or so unknown people filed in,"

Doudna says. "It was sort of a heads-up that something special was about to happen."

Jinek and Chylinski tried to make their presentation fun. They had prepared the slides so that they could take turns explaining each of the experiments they had done, and they had practiced twice before their appearance. The audience was small, informal, and friendly. Nevertheless, it was very clear they were nervous, especially Jinek. "Martin was very stressed, which made me stressed for him," Doudna says.

There was no need to be nervous. The presentation was a triumph. Sylvain Moineau, a CRISPR pioneer at the University of Laval in Quebec, stood up and said, "Wow!" Others hurriedly emailed and texted their lab colleagues back home.

Barrangou, the Danisco researcher who had been a collaborator on Šikšnys's paper, later said that, as soon as he heard the presentation, he knew that Doudna and Charpentier had taken the field to a whole new level. "Jennifer's paper was clearly so much better than ours," he admits. "It wasn't close. It was the tipping point that moved the CRISPR field from an idiosyncratic interesting microbial-world feature to a technology. So Virginijus and I, we had no hard feelings whatsoever."

One especially informed reaction, a mix of excitement and envy, came from Erik Sontheimer. He had been among the first to predict that CRISPR would become a gene-editing tool. When Jinek and Chylinski finished their presentation, he raised his hand to ask a question: How could the single-guide technology be used for gene editing in eukaryotic cells, meaning ones that had a nucleus? More specifically, would it work in human cells? They suggested it could be adapted, just as many previous molecular technologies had been. After the discussion, Sontheimer, a gentle and old-school type of scientist, turned to Doudna, who was sitting two rows behind him, and mouthed the words "Let's talk." During the next break, they ducked out to meet in a hallway.

"I felt comfortable talking to her because, even though we were going to try to do similar things, I knew she was trustworthy," Sontheimer says. "I told her that I was trying to make CRISPR work in yeast. She said she wanted to keep talking, because adapting CRISPR for eukaryotic cells was going to happen fast."

That evening, Doudna took a walk into downtown Berkeley to eat at a sushi restaurant with three of the researchers who had been, and would continue to be, both colleagues and competitors: Erik Sontheimer and the two men whose paper had just been overshadowed by hers, Rodolphe Barrangou and Virginijus Šikšnys. Rather than being upset that they had been scooped, Barrangou said he realized that they had been bested fairly. In fact, as they were walking down the hill to the restaurant, he asked Doudna whether he and Šikšnys might do well to withdraw their paper that was still pending publication. She smiled. "No, Rodolphe, your paper will be fine," she said. "Don't withdraw it. It makes its own contribution, just like we all try to do."

At the dinner, the four shared where each of their labs might go from there. "It was all very warm, despite the potential for awkwardness," Sontheimer says. "Just a very exciting dinner at a very exciting time when we were all just recognizing how important this was going to be."

The Doudna-Charpentier paper, published online on June 28, 2012, galvanized an entire new field of biotechnology: making CRISPR work in the editing of human genes. "We all knew we were going to be in a big race to do this in human cells," says Sontheimer. "It was an idea whose time had come, and it was going to be a sprint to get there first."

PART THREE

Gene Editing

How beauteous mankind is!
O brave new world,
That has such people in't!

—William Shakespeare, *The Tempest*

CHAPTER 20

A Human Tool

Gene therapies

The road to engineering human genes began in 1972 when Professor Paul Berg of Stanford discovered a way to take a bit of the DNA of a virus found in monkeys and splice it to the DNA of a totally different virus. Presto! He had manufactured what he dubbed "recombinant DNA." Herbert Boyer and Stanley Cohen discovered ways to make these artificial genes more efficiently and then clone millions of copies of them. Thus the science of genetic engineering—and the business of biotechnology—was launched.

It took another fifteen years before scientists began to deliver engineered DNA into the cells of humans. The goal was similar to creating a drug. There was no attempt to change the DNA of the patient; it was not gene *editing*. Instead, gene therapy involved delivering into the patient's cells some DNA that had been engineered to counteract the faulty gene that caused the disease.

The first trial came in 1990 on a four-year-old girl with a genetic mutation that crippled her immune system and left her at risk for infection. Doctors found a way to get functioning copies of the missing gene into the T cells of her blood system. The T cells were removed from her body, given the missing gene, and then reintroduced into her body. This led to a dramatic improvement of her immune system and allowed her to live a healthy life.

The field of gene therapy initially showed modest success, but soon there were setbacks. In 1999, a clinical trial in Philadelphia came to a halt when a young man died due to a massive immune response caused by the virus transporting the therapeutic gene. In the early 2000s, a gene therapy procedure for an immune-deficiency disease inadvertently triggered a cancer-causing gene that led to five patients developing leukemia. Tragedies such as these froze for at least a decade most of the clinical trials, but incremental improvements in gene therapies would lay the groundwork for the more ambitious field of gene editing.

Gene editing

Instead of treating genetic problems through gene therapy, some medical researchers began looking for ways to fix the problems at their source. The goal was to *edit* the flawed sequences of DNA in the relevant cells of the patient. Thus was born the endeavor called gene editing.

Harvard professor Jack Szostak, Doudna's thesis advisor, discovered in the 1980s one of the keys to editing a gene: causing a break in both strands of the DNA double helix, known as a double-strand break. When this happens, neither strand can serve as a template to repair the other. So the genome repairs itself in one of two ways. The first is called "nonhomologous end-joining." ("Homologous" comes from the Greek word for "matching.") In such cases, the DNA is repaired by simply stitching two ends together without trying to find a matching sequence. This can be a sloppy process resulting in unwanted inserts and deletions of genetic material. A more precise process, "homology-directed repair," occurs when the cut DNA finds a suitable replacement template nearby. The cell will usually copy and insert the available homologous sequence where the double-strand breaks occurred.

The invention of gene editing required two steps. First, researchers had to find the right enzyme that could cut a double-strand break in DNA. Then they had to find a guide that would navigate the enzyme to the precise target in the cell's DNA where they wanted to make the cut.

The enzymes that can cut DNA or RNA are called "nucleases." In order to build a system for gene editing, researchers needed a nuclease that could be instructed to cut any sequence that the researchers chose to target. By 2000, they had found a tool to do this. The FokI enzyme, which is found in some soil and pond bacteria, has two domains: one that serves as scissors that can cut DNA and another that serves as a guide telling it where to go. These domains can be separated, and the first can be reprogrammed to go anywhere the researchers want.[1]

Researchers were able to devise proteins that could serve as a guide to get the cutting domain to a targeted DNA sequence. One system, zinc-finger nucleases (ZFNs), came from fusing the cutting domain with a protein that has little fingers shaped by the presence of a zinc ion, which allow it to grasp on to a specified DNA sequence. A similar but even more reliable method, known as TALENs (transcription activator–like effector nucleases), came from fusing the cutting domain with a protein that could guide it to longer DNA sequences.

Just when TALENs were being perfected, CRISPR came along. It was somewhat similar: it had a cutting enzyme, which was Cas9, and a guide that led the enzyme to cut a targeted spot on a DNA strand. But in the CRISPR system, the guide was not a protein but a snippet of RNA. This had a big advantage. With ZFNs and TALENs, you had to construct a new protein guide every time you wanted to target a different genetic sequence to cut; it was difficult and time consuming. But with CRISPR you merely had to fiddle with the genetic sequence of the RNA guide. A good student could do it quickly in a lab.

There was one question, which was either a big one or a trivial one, depending on your perspective and your side in the patent wars that would later erupt. The CRISPR systems worked in bacteria and archaea, which are single-cell organisms that have no nucleus. But that left the question: Would they work in cells that *do* have a nucleus, especially multicell organisms such as plants, animals, you, and me?

As a result, the Doudna-Charpentier paper in June 2012 set off a furious sprint in many labs around the world, including Doudna's, to prove that CRISPR-Cas9 could work in human cells. That triumph was accomplished in five places in about six months. This rather quick success could be taken as evidence, as Doudna and her colleagues would later argue, that making CRISPR-Cas9 work in human cells was an easy and obvious step that was not a separate invention. Or it could be used to argue, as Doudna's competitors have, that it was a major inventive step that came after a fiercely competitive race.

On that question would hang patents and prizes.

Chapter 21

The Race

Competition drives discovery. Doudna calls it "the fire that stokes the engine," and it certainly stoked hers. Ever since she was a child, she was not embarrassed to appear ambitious, but she knew how to balance this by being collegial and forthright. She had learned about the importance of competition from reading *The Double Helix*, which describes how the perceived footsteps of Linus Pauling were a catalyst for James Watson and Francis Crick. "Healthy rivalries," she later wrote, "have fueled many of humankind's greatest discoveries."[1]

Scientists are mainly motivated by the joy that comes from understanding nature, but most will admit that they are also driven by the rewards, both psychic and substantive, of being the first to make a discovery: papers published, patents granted, prizes won, and peers impressed. Like any human (is it an evolutionary trait?), they want credit for their accomplishments, payoff for their labor, acclaim from the public, and prize ribbons placed around their necks. That's why they work late into the night, hire publicists and patent attorneys, and even invite writers (like me) into their labs.

Competition gets a bad rap.[2] It's blamed for discouraging collaboration, constricting the sharing of data, and encouraging people to

keep intellectual property proprietary rather than allowing it to be free and open for common use. But the benefits of competition are great. If it hastens the discovery of a way to fix muscular dystrophy, prevent AIDS, or detect cancer, fewer people will die early deaths. To take an example relevant to these days, the Japanese bacteriologist Kitasato Shibasaburō and his Swiss rival Alexandre Yersin both rushed to Hong Kong in 1894 to investigate the pneumonic plague epidemic and, working with different methods, discovered the responsible bacteria within days of each other.

There was one competition in Doudna's life that stands out for becoming heated and then bitter: the race in 2012 to show how CRISPR could edit the genes of humans. It may not be up there with Charles Darwin and Alfred Russel Wallace converging on the idea of evolution or Newton and Leibniz disputing who first figured out calculus. But it is our contemporary counterpart to the race between Pauling and the team of Watson and Crick to discover the structure of DNA.

Doudna entered this competition handicapped by not having a team of collaborators who were experts in working with human cells. Her lab did not specialize in such experiments; its researchers were mainly biochemists comfortable working with molecules in test tubes. So Doudna ended up struggling to keep pace in what turned out to be a six-month frenzied competition.

There were many labs around the world that engaged in this race, but the primary drama—emotionally and personally as well as scientifically—involved three players. All were competitive in their own way, but they were very different in how comfortable they were with their competitiveness:

- Feng Zhang of the Broad Institute of MIT and Harvard. Although as competitive as any star researcher, he was blessed with a cheery sweetness that made him uncomfortable displaying that trait. With deep values imbued by his mother, he had a natural humility that often masked his equally natural ambition. It was as if he had dual cores, one competitive and one beatific, that coexisted quite comfortably. He had a warm smile that rarely left his face except in those moments when the talk turned to competition—or the importance of Doudna's achievements—at which point his lips would continue to smile, but his eyes no longer joined in. He tended to be shy of the limelight, but he was pushed by his mentor Eric Lander, the brilliant and sparky mathematician-turned-scientist who directed the Broad Institute, to compete for credit as well as for discoveries.

- George Church of Harvard, Doudna's longtime friend, who considered himself, at least for a while, to be Zhang's mentor and academic advisor. Both on the surface and as deep as my eye can discern, he was the least competitive of them all. A Santa-bearded vegan who wants to use genetic engineering to bring back the woolly mammoth, he was driven by a playful and earnest curiosity.
- And finally there was Doudna, who was not only competitive but also comfortable with her competitiveness. It was one of the reasons a certain coolness developed between her and Charpentier, who expressed some amusement and a bit of disdain for Doudna's drive for credit. "She is sometimes stressed about credit, which made her seem insecure or not fully grateful for her success," Charpentier says. "I am French and not as worked up, so I was always telling her, 'Surf on the good wave.'" But when pressed, Charpentier admits that the competitiveness that Doudna exhibits is the force that drives most scientific pioneers, and thus science itself. "If it were not for competitive people like Jennifer, our world would not be as good," she says. "Because what drives people to do good things is recognition."[3]

CHAPTER 22

Feng Zhang

Des Moines

When I first approached Feng Zhang to ask if I could spend some time with him, I was nervous. I had told him that I was doing a book focused on Jennifer Doudna, his rival, and I thought he would be put off, perhaps would even push back.

Instead, when I visited him at his lab at the Broad Institute near MIT, with its high windows offering views of the Charles River and the spires of Harvard, he was exceedingly gracious, as he was at our subsequent conversations, lunches, and dinners. I could not tell whether his geniality was genuine or arose from an assessment that it would lead to his being portrayed better in my book. But the more time I spent with him, the more I became convinced that it was the former.

Zhang's journey, which is worthy of a book of its own, is one of those classic immigration tales that has made America great. He was born in 1981 in Shijiazhuang, an industrial city of 4.3 million people southwest of Beijing. His mother taught computer science, his father was a university administrator. The streets of the city were festooned with China's customary banners of exhortations, most notably those touting the patriotic duty to study science. Zhang was sold. "I grew up

playing with robot kits and fascinated by anything to do with science," he recalls.[1]

In 1991, when Zhang was ten, his mother came to the United States as a visiting scholar at the University of Dubuque, a gem nestled in an architecturally rich Iowa city along the Mississippi River. One day she visited a local school, where she marveled at the computer lab and the lack of emphasis on rote memorization. Like any loving parent, she imagined it through the eyes of her child. "She thought I would enjoy being in such a lab and school, so she decided to stay and bring me over," Zhang recalls. She got a job at a paper company in Des Moines and with her H-1B visa was able to bring her son to America the next year.

His father soon followed, but he never learned English well, so Zhang's mother became the driving force in the family. She was the one who pioneered the path to America, got a job, made friends at work, and volunteered to set up computers at local charities. Because of her, and because of the hospitality gene ingrained in heartland towns, the family always had invitations to neighbors' houses for Thanksgiving and other holidays.

"My mother always told me to keep my head down and not be arrogant," Zhang says. She bestowed upon him the gift of easygoing humility, which he wore lightly. But she also instilled in him an ambition to be innovative and never passive. "She pushed me to make things, even on a computer, rather than play with things that other people had made." Years later, as I was writing this book, Zhang's mother had moved in part time with him and his wife in Boston to help take care of their two young kids. As he talks about her while picking at a hamburger in a Cambridge seafood restaurant, Zhang lowers his head and pauses for a moment. "I'm sure going to miss her when she's gone," he says in a very soft voice.

At first Zhang seemed likely to follow the path of so many supersmart kids in the 1990s and become a computer geek. When he got his first computer (a PC, not a Mac) at age twelve, he learned to take it apart and use the components to build other computers. He also became a wizard at using open-source Linux operating system software.

So his mother sent him to computer camp and, just to make sure he was wired for success, debate camp as well. It was the type of enhancement that privileged parents can do even without gene editing.

Instead of pursuing computer science, however, Zhang became a forerunner of what will, I think, soon be common among aspiring geeks: his interests shifted from digital tech to biotech. Computer code was something his parents and their generation did. He became more interested in genetic code.

Zhang's path to biology began with his Des Moines middle school's Gifted and Talented Program, which included a Saturday enrichment class in molecular biology.[2] "Until then, I didn't know much about biology and didn't find it interesting, because in seventh grade all they did was give you a tray with a frog and tell you to dissect it and identify the heart," he recalls. "It was all memorization and not very challenging." In the Saturday enrichment class, the focus was on DNA and how RNA carried out its instructions, with an emphasis on the role played in this process by enzymes, those protein molecules that act as catalysts to spark actions in a cell. "My teacher loved enzymes," Zhang says. "He told me that whenever you face a tough question in biology, just say 'Enzymes.' It's the correct answer to most questions in biology."

They did a lot of hands-on experiments, including one that transformed bacteria to make them resistant to antibiotics. They also watched the 1993 movie *Jurassic Park*, in which scientists bring dinosaurs back from extinction by combining their DNA with that of frogs. "I was excited to discover that animals could be a programmable system," he says. "That meant human genetic coding could be programmable as well." It was more exciting than Linux.

With his corn-fed eagerness to learn and discover, Zhang became an example of the impact that gifted and talented programs can have on turning American kids into world-class scientists. The U.S. Department of Education had just published, in 1993, a study called "A Case for Developing America's Talent," which led to funding for local school districts "to challenge our top performing students to greater heights." Those were the days when people took very seriously, even if it meant spending tax dollars, the aim of creating a world-class education system, one that would keep America the world leader in innovation. In Des Moines, this included a program called STING (Science/Technology Investigations: The Next Generation), which tapped a small group of talented and motivated students to do original projects and work at local hospitals or research institutions.

Zhang's Saturday teacher helped him get selected to spend his afternoons and free time at the gene therapy lab of Methodist Hospital in Des Moines. As a high school student, he worked under a psychologically intense but very personable molecular biologist named John Levy, who explained over tea each day the work he was doing and assigned Zhang to increasingly more sophisticated experiments. On some days Zhang would arrive right after school and work until eight in the evening. "My dear mother would drive each day to pick me up and then sit in the parking lot until I was finished," he says.

His first major experiment involved a fundamental tool in molecular biology: a gene from jellyfish that produces green fluorescent protein, which glows when exposed to ultraviolet light and thus can be used as a marker in cell experiments. Levy first made sure Zhang understood its fundamental natural purpose. Sketching on a piece of paper as he sipped tea, he explained why a jellyfish might need that fluorescent protein as it moved up and down layers of the ocean during different phases of its life cycle. "He drew it in a way that you could just picture the jellyfish and the ocean and nature's wonders."

Levy "held my hand," Zhang recalls, "as I did my first experiment." It involved putting the gene for green fluorescent protein into human melanoma (skin cancer) cells. It was a simple but exciting example of genetic engineering: he had inserted a gene from one organism (a jellyfish) into the cells of another (a human), and he could see the proof of his success when the bluish-green glow emanated from the manipulated cells. "I was so excited that I began to shout, 'It's glowing!'" He had reengineered a human gene.

Zhang spent the next few months studying whether the green fluorescent protein, which absorbs ultraviolet light when it glows, could protect the human cell's DNA from the damage that can be caused by exposure. It worked. "I was using the jellyfish's GFP as a sunscreen to protect human DNA from ultraviolet light damage," he says.

The second science project he did with Levy was to deconstruct HIV, the virus that causes AIDS, and examine how each of the components worked. Part of the goal of the Des Moines enrichment programs was to help students do projects to compete in the Intel Science Search, a national competition. Zhang's virus experiment won him third place, which carried a hefty $50,000 prize. He used it to help pay his tuition when he got into Harvard in 2000.

Harvard and Stanford

Zhang was at Harvard at the same time as Mark Zuckerberg, and it's interesting to speculate on which of them will end up having the most impact on the world. It's a proxy for the larger question, which future historians will answer, of whether the digital revolution or the life-science revolution will end up being the more important.

Majoring in both chemistry and physics, Zhang initially did research with Don Wiley, a crystallographer who was a master at determining the structure of complex molecules. "I don't understand anything in biology unless I know what it looks like," he liked to say, a credo worthy of all structural biologists, from Watson and Crick to Doudna. But in November of Zhang's sophomore year, Wiley mysteriously disappeared one night while attending a conference at St. Jude's Children's Hospital in Memphis, leaving his rental car on a bridge. His body was later found in the river.

That year Zhang also had to help a close friend in his class who was spiraling into major depression. The friend would be sitting in their room studying, and then suddenly he would get hit by an anxiety or depressive attack and not be able to get up or move. "I had heard of depression, but I thought it was like having a bad day and you had to barrel through," Zhang says. "Growing up in my family, I mistakenly thought that psychiatric disease was when someone just wasn't being strong enough." Zhang would sit with his friend to help him avoid suicide. (The student took time off and recovered.) The experience caused Zhang to turn his attention to researching treatments for mental illness.

So when he went to Stanford for graduate school, he asked to join the lab of Karl Deisseroth, a psychiatrist and neuroscientist who was developing ways to make the workings of the brain and its nerve cells, known as neurons, more visible. Along with another graduate student, they pioneered the field of optogenetics, which uses light to stimulate neurons in the brain. That allowed them to map different circuits in the brain and gain insights about how they functioned or malfunctioned.

Zhang focused on inserting light-sensitive proteins into the neurons—an echo of his high school work inserting green fluorescent protein into skin cells. His method was to use viruses as a delivery mechanism. For one demonstration, he inserted these proteins, which become activated when light hits them, into the part of a mouse brain that controls its movement. By using light pulses, the researchers could trigger the neurons and cause the mice to walk in circles.[3]

Zhang faced a challenge. It was difficult to insert the gene for the light-sensitive proteins into the exact right location of the DNA of the brain cell. Indeed, the entire field of genetic engineering was hampered by the lack of simple molecular tools for cutting and pasting desired genes into strands of DNA inside a cell. So after he got his doctorate in 2009, Zhang took a postdoc position at Harvard and began researching the gene-editing tools that were available at the time, such as TALENs.

At Harvard, Zhang focused on ways to make TALENs more versatile so that they could be programmed to target different gene sequences.[4] It was difficult; TALENs are hard to engineer and re-engineer. Fortunately, he was working in the most exciting lab at Harvard Medical School, which was run by a professor who was beloved for embracing new ideas, sometimes wildly, and who fostered a jovial atmosphere that encouraged exploration: Doudna's longtime friend, the avuncular and bushy-bearded George Church, one of the contemporary legends of biology and a scientific celebrity. He became for Zhang, as he did for almost all of his students, a loving and beloved mentor—until the day Church believed that Zhang had betrayed him.

Chapter 23

George Church

Tall and gangly, George Church looks like, and actually is, both a gentle giant and a mad scientist. He is one of those iconic characters who is equally charismatic on Stephen Colbert's TV show and in his bustling Boston lab amid a gaggle of adoring researchers. Always calm and genial, he has the amused demeanor of a time traveler who is eager to get back to the future. With his wild-man beard and halo of hair, he looks like a cross between Charles Darwin and a woolly mammoth, an extinct species that he wants, perhaps out of a vague sense of kinship, to resurrect using CRISPR.[1]

Although he is personable and charming, Church has the literalness often found in successful scientists and geeks. At one point we were discussing some decision that Doudna had made, and I asked him whether he thought it had been necessary. "Necessary?" he replied. "Nothing is necessary. Even breathing is not necessary. You can even stop breathing if you really want to." When I joked that he had taken me too literally, he remarked that one reason he is a good scientist, and also thought of as a bit of a madman, is that he questions the necessity of any premise. He then wandered off into a discourse on free will (which he doesn't believe humans have) until I was able to get him back on track talking about his career.

Born in 1954, he grew up in the marshy exurbs of Clearwater, on Florida's Gulf Coast near Tampa, where his mother went through three husbands. As a result, George had many last names and different schools, which made him feel, he says, "like a real outsider." His birth father had been a pilot at nearby MacDill Air Force Base and a barefoot water-ski champion who was in the Water Ski Hall of Fame. "But he couldn't hold a job, and my mother moved on," Church explains.

The young Church was fascinated by science. In those days when parents were less overprotective, his mother let him roam alone in the marshes and mudflats near Tampa Bay, hunting for snakes and insects. He would crawl through the high swamp grass collecting specimens. One day he found an odd caterpillar that looked like a "submarine with legs" and put it in his jar. The next day he discovered, to his astonishment, that it had transformed into a dragonfly, a metamorphosis that is truly one of nature's thrilling everyday miracles. "That helped set me on my path to be a biologist," he says.

When he came home in the evening, mud on his boots, he would dive into the books his mother provided, including a set of *Collier's Encyclopedia* and a twenty-five-volume series of vibrantly illustrated nature books from Time-Life. Because he was mildly dyslexic, he had trouble reading but could absorb information from pictures. "It made me a more visual person. I could imagine 3-D objects, and by visualizing the structure I could understand how things worked."

When George was nine, his mother married a physician named Gaylord Church, who adopted George and gave him a permanent surname. His new stepfather had a bulging medical bag that George loved to rummage through. He was particularly fascinated by the hypodermic needle, which his stepfather used liberally to administer painkillers and feel-good hormones to his patients and to himself. He taught George how to use the instruments and would sometimes take him on house calls. At a Harvard Square pub over a soybean burger, Church chuckles as he recalls this odd childhood. "My father would let me give his women patients hormone shots, and they loved him for it," he says, "and he let me give him shots of Demerol. I later realized he was addicted to painkillers."

Using the ingredients in his stepfather's medicine bag, Church began to perform experiments. One involved thyroid hormones that his stepfather supplied to grateful patients who complained of fatigue or depression. At age thirteen, Church put some hormones in the water of a group of tadpoles, leaving another group in untreated water. The first group grew faster. "It was my first true biology experiment, with a control set and all," he recalls.

When his mother drove him in her Buick up to the 1964 World's Fair in New York, he became tantalized by the future. It made him feel impatient about being stranded in the present. "I wanted to get to the future, I felt that's where I belonged, and that's when I realized that it was something I had to help create," he says. As the science writer Ben Mezrich noted of Church, "Later in life, he would return to this moment as the instant when he first started to think of himself as a sort of time traveler. Deep down, he started to believe that he was from the far future, and had somehow been left in the past. It was his task in life to try to get back, to try to shift the world to where he had once been."[2]

Bored in his backwater high school, Church soon became a handful, especially to his stepfather, who had initially indulged him. "He decided he wanted me to go away," Church says, "and my mother realized it was a great opportunity, because he would pay for boarding school." So he was packed off to Phillips Academy in Andover, Massachusetts, America's oldest prep school. The idyllic quads with their Georgian buildings were almost as wondrous as the marshlands of his childhood. He taught himself computer coding, maxed out on all the chemistry courses, and then was given a key to the chemistry lab so he could explore on his own. Among his many triumphs: making flytrap plants grow huge by spiking their water with hormones.

He went on to Duke, where he earned two undergraduate degrees in two years and then skipped ahead into a PhD program. There he stumbled. He became so involved in the lab research of his advisor, which included using crystallography to figure out the three-dimensional structure of different RNA molecules, that he stopped going to classes. After failing two of them, he got a letter from the dean coldly informing him, "You are no longer a candidate for the Doctor of Philosophy degree in the department of Biochemistry at Duke University." He kept the letter as a source of pride, the way others keep their framed diplomas.

He had already been a coauthor of five important papers and was able to talk his way into Harvard Medical School. "It's a mystery why Harvard would accept me after flunking out of Duke," he said in an oral history. "Usually, it's the other way around."[3] There he worked with Nobel laureate Walter Gilbert to develop methods for sequencing DNA, and he was at the initial 1984 retreat sponsored by the Department of Energy that led to the launch of the Human Genome Project. But in a preview of their later disputes, he clashed with Eric Lander, who rejected Church's method for streamlining the sequencing tasks by clonally amplifying the DNA.

Church became a quirky popular celebrity in 2008, when the *New York Times* science writer Nicholas Wade interviewed him about the possibility of using his genetic engineering tools to regenerate the extinct woolly mammoth from frozen hairs found in the Arctic. Not surprisingly, the idea had a playful appeal to Church, born of his days juicing up tadpoles with hormones. He became a public face of the effort, still underway, to take the skin cell from a modern elephant, convert it to its embryonic state, and then modify the genes until they match those sequenced from the woolly mammoth.[4]

When Jennifer Doudna was a PhD student at Harvard in the late 1980s, she admired Church's unconventional style and thinking. "He was a new professor, tall and gangly and already had his big beard, and he was quite the maverick," she says. "He was not afraid of being different, and I liked that." Church recalls being impressed by Doudna's demeanor. "She did stellar work, especially on the structure of RNA," he says. "We shared that esoteric interest."

During the 1980s, Church worked to create new gene-sequencing methods. He became prolific not only as a researcher but as a founder of companies to commercialize the work coming out of his lab. Later he focused on finding new tools for gene editing. So when Doudna and Charpentier's *Science* article describing CRISPR-Cas9 went online in June 2012, Church decided to try to get it to work in humans.

He did the polite thing and sent both of them an email. "I was collegial and tried to find out who was working in the field to see if they would mind if I did so," he recalls. An early riser, he dispatched it just after 4 a.m. one day:

> Jennifer and Emmanuelle,
>
> Just a quick note to say how inspiring and helpful is your CRISPR paper in *Science*.
>
> My group is trying to apply some of the lessons from your study to genome engineering in human stem cells. I'm sure that you have received similar appreciative comments from other labs.
>
> I look forward to staying in contact as things progress.
>
> Best wishes, George

Later that day, Doudna wrote back:

> Hi George,
>
> Thanks for your message. We will be very interested to hear how your experiments progress. And yes, there is a lot of interest in Cas9 at the moment—we are hopeful that it will turn out to be useful for genome editing and regulation in various cell types.
>
> All the best, Jennifer

They followed up with some phone conversations, and Doudna told him that she was likewise working on trying to get CRISPR to work in human cells. It was characteristic of the way Church did science: collegially, with a greater inclination toward cooperation and openness than competition and secrecy. "It was very typical of George," Doudna says. "He is incapable of being devious." The best way to get a person to trust you is for you to trust them. Doudna is a guarded person, but she was always open with Church.

There was one person Church did not think of contacting: Feng Zhang. The reason was, he says, that he had no idea that his former doctoral student was working on CRISPR. "If I had known Feng was working on it, I would have asked him about it," Church says. "But he was very secretive when he suddenly hopped on CRISPR."[5]

Chapter 24

Zhang Tackles CRISPR

Stealth mode

After completing his postdoctoral work in Church's Harvard Medical School lab in Boston, Zhang had moved across the Charles River to the Broad Institute in Cambridge. Ensconced in state-of-the-art lab buildings on the edge of MIT's campus, the Broad was founded in 2004 by the irrepressible Eric Lander with funding (eventually $800 million) from Eli and Edythe Broad. Its mission was to advance the treatment of diseases using the knowledge spawned by the Human Genome Project, on which Lander had been the most prolific gene-sequencer.

A mathematician turned biologist, Lander envisioned the Broad as a place where different disciplines would work together. This required a new type of institution, one that fully integrated biology, chemistry, mathematics, computer science, engineering, and medicine. Lander also forged something even more difficult: a collaboration between MIT and Harvard. By 2020, the Broad community included more than three thousand scientists and engineers. It thrived because Lander is a joyful and intensely committed mentor, cheerleader, and fundraiser for wave after wave of young scientists who gravitated to the Broad. He also is able to connect science to public policy and social

Luciano Marraffini

good; for example, he is spearheading a movement called "Count Me In" that encourages cancer patients to anonymously share their medical information and DNA sequences in a public database that any researcher can access.

When Feng Zhang moved to the Broad in January 2011, he continued the research he had been doing in Church's lab on using TALENs for gene editing. But each new editing project required building new TALENs. "That would sometimes take up to three months," he says. "I began looking for a better way."

That better way would turn out to be CRISPR. A few weeks after his arrival at the Broad, Zhang attended a seminar by a Harvard microbiologist who was studying a species of bacteria. He happened to mention, in passing, that they contained CRISPR sequences with enzymes that could cut the DNA of invading viruses. Zhang had barely heard of CRISPR, but ever since his seventh-grade enrichment class he had learned to perk up at the mention of enzymes. He was particularly interested in those enzymes, known as nucleases, that cut DNA. So he did what any of us would do: he googled CRISPR.

The next day he flew to Miami for a conference on how genes get expressed, but instead of sitting through all the talks he stayed in his hotel room reading the dozen or so major scientific papers on CRISPR that he found online. In particular, he was struck by the one published that previous November by the two yogurt researchers at Danisco, Rodolphe Barrangou and Philippe Horvath, which showed that the CRISPR-Cas systems can cut a double-stranded DNA at a specific target.[1] "The minute I read that paper, I thought this was pretty amazing," Zhang says.

Zhang had a protégé and friend who was still a graduate student in Church's lab: Le Cong, a Beijing-born geek with big glasses whose childhood love of electronics had, like Zhang's, given way to a passion for biology. Also like Zhang, Cong was interested in genetic engineering because he hoped to alleviate the suffering that came from mental disorders, such as schizophrenia and bipolar disease.

Immediately after reading the CRISPR papers in his Miami hotel room, Zhang emailed Cong and suggested that they work together to see if it could become a gene-editing tool in humans, perhaps one that was better than the TALENs they had been using. "Take a look at this," Zhang wrote, including a link to the Barrangou-Horvath paper. "Maybe we can test in mammalian system." Cong agreed, replying, "It should be very cool." A couple of days later, Zhang sent another email. Cong was still a student in Church's lab, and Zhang wanted to make sure that he kept the idea secret, even from his advisor. "Hey let's keep this confidential," he wrote.[2] Although Cong formally remained one of Church's graduate students at Harvard, he followed that injunction and did not tell Church that he was going to work on CRISPR when he moved to the Broad with Zhang.

Zhang's office, hallways, conference rooms, and lab areas have multiple whiteboards, poised to accommodate any spontaneous insights that may strike. It's part of the atmosphere at the Broad. Whiteboarding is like a sport, the way foosball is in less rarefied offices. On one of Zhang's well-used whiteboards, he and Le Cong began listing what they would have to do to get CRISPR-Cas systems to penetrate into the nucleus of human cells. Then they would pull late-nighters in the lab, subsisting on ramen noodles.[3]

Even before they started experimenting, Zhang filed a "Confidential Memorandum of Invention" to the Broad Institute, dated February 13, 2011. "The key concept of this invention is based on the CRISPR found in many microbial organisms," it read. The system, he explained, used snippets of RNA to guide an enzyme to make cuts in DNA at targeted spots. If it could be made to work in humans, Zhang noted, it would be a much more versatile gene-editing tool than ZFNs and TALENs. His memo, which was never publicly shared, concluded by stating that the "invention could be useful for genome modification of microbes, cells, plants, animals."[4]

Zhang's memo did not, despite its title, describe an actual invention. He had just begun to sketch out a research plan, and he had done no experiments nor devised any techniques that reduced his concept to practice. The memo was merely a stake in the ground, the type of thing that researchers sometimes file in case they end up being successful inventing something and need evidence (as would indeed be the case) that they had been working on the idea for a long time.

Zhang seemed to sense from the outset that the race to turn CRISPR into a human gene–editing tool would turn out to be very competitive. He kept his plans secret. He did not share his memorandum of invention, nor did he mention CRISPR in a video he made at the end of 2011 that described the research projects he had been working on. But he began to document each of his experiments and discoveries on dated and witnessed notebook pages.

In this competition to adapt CRISPR into a gene-editing tool in humans, Zhang and Doudna came into the arena from different routes. Zhang had never worked on CRISPR. People in that field would later refer to him as a latecomer and interloper, one who jumped on CRISPR after others had pioneered the field. Instead, his specialty was gene editing, and for him CRISPR was simply another method to get to the same goal, along the lines of ZFNs and TALENs, though much better. For her part, Doudna and her team had never worked on gene editing in living cells. Their focus for five years had been on figuring out the components of CRISPR. As a result, Zhang would end up having some difficulty in sorting out the essential molecules in a CRISPR-Cas9 system, while Doudna's difficulty would be figuring out how to get the system into the nucleus of a human cell.

By early 2012—before Doudna and Charpentier went online in June with their *Science* paper showing the essential three components of the CRISPR-Cas9 system—Zhang had made no documented progress. He and a group of colleagues from the Broad filed an application for funding to pursue gene-editing experiments. "We will engineer the CRISPR system to target Cas enzymes to multiple specific targets in the mammalian genome," Zhang wrote in the application. But he made no claim that he had already accomplished any of the major steps to this goal. Indeed, the grant application indicated that work on mammalian cells was not expected to begin until a few months later.[5]

Also, Zhang had not yet figured out the full role of the pesky tracrRNA. Recall that Charpentier's 2011 paper and the work done by

Šikšnys in 2012 described the work that this molecule did in creating a guide RNA, known as crRNA, that navigates an enzyme to the correct DNA location to cut. However, one of the discoveries reported by Doudna and Charpentier in their 2012 paper was that the tracrRNA has another important role: it needs to stick around in order for the CRISPR system to do the actual cutting of the target RNA. Zhang's grant application indicated that he had not yet discovered this; it spoke only about "a tracrRNA element to facilitate the processing of guide RNAs." One of the illustrations showed only the crRNA and not the tracrRNA being part of the complex with Cas9 to do the cutting. This may seem like a small thing. But it's over such small discoveries, or lack of them, that battles for historic credit are waged.[6]

Marraffini helps

If things had worked out differently, Feng Zhang and Luciano Marraffini might have been a collaboration story as inspiring as that of Doudna and Charpentier. Zhang's tale was pretty wonderful on its own: the eager and competitive Chinese immigrant whiz kid who is nurtured in Iowa and whose unrelenting curiosity makes him a star at Stanford, Harvard, and MIT. But it would have double-stranded nicely with the story of Marraffini, an immigrant from Argentina who in early 2012 collaborated with Zhang.

Marraffini loved studying bacteria, and as a doctoral student at the University of Chicago he became interested in the newly discovered phenomenon of CRISPR. Because his wife had a job as a translator in the court system of Chicago, he wanted to stay in that city, so he got a postdoc position in the lab of Erik Sontheimer at Northwestern University. Sontheimer was then studying RNA interference, as Doudna had done, but he and Marraffini soon realized that the CRISPR system worked in a more powerful manner. That is how they made their important discovery in 2008, that it works by chopping up the DNA of invading viruses.[7]

Marraffini met Doudna the following year when she came to Chicago for a conference. He made a point of sitting at the table next to her. "I really wanted to meet her because of her work on RNA structure, which was extremely hard," he says. "It's one thing to crystallize proteins, but it's far harder to crystallize RNA, and that impressed me." She had just begun working on CRISPR, and they discussed the possibility that he might join her lab. But there was not the right opening for him, so in 2010 he moved to Rockefeller University in Manhattan, where he set up a lab studying CRISPR in bacteria.

At the very beginning of 2012, he got an email from Zhang, whom he didn't know. "Happy new year!" Zhang wrote. "My name is Feng Zhang and I am a researcher at MIT. I read many of your papers on the CRISPR system with great interest, and I was wondering if you would be interested in collaborating to develop the CRISPR system for applications in mammalian cells."[8]

Marraffini did a Google search to learn who Zhang was, as he was still unknown to most of the CRISPR research community. Zhang had sent his email at around 10 p.m., and Marraffini answered about an hour later. "I will be very interested in a collaboration," he wrote, adding that he had been working on a "minimal" system—in other words, one that had been stripped down to just the essential molecules. They agreed to talk by phone the next day. It seemed that this would be the beginning of a beautiful friendship.

Marraffini got the impression that Zhang was stymied and was trying out a variety of Cas proteins. "He was testing not only Cas9 but all the different CRISPR systems, including Cas1, Cas2, Cas3, and Cas10," Marraffini says. "Nothing was working. He was doing things like a chicken without a head." So Marraffini, at least by his own recollection, became the one to push him to focus on Cas9. "I was very sure of Cas9. I was an expert in the field. I realized the other enzymes were going to be too difficult."

After their phone call, Marraffini sent Zhang a list of things they should do. The very first item was to quit including any enzymes other than Cas9.[9] He also sent, by regular mail, a printout of the bacteria's entire CRISPR sequence, covering multiple pages (ATGG-TAGAAAACACTAAATTA . . .). When Marraffini told me the tale, he got up from his desk and printed out pages of the sequence for me. "With all of this data," he told me, "I made Feng realize that he had to use Cas9, and I gave him a roadmap, which he followed."

For a while they collaborated by splitting up the tasks. Zhang would come up with ideas that he hoped would work in humans. Then Marraffini, who specialized in microbes, would test to see if the idea worked in bacteria, an easier experiment. One important case involved adding a nuclear location signal (NLS) that was necessary to get the CRISPR-Cas9 into the nucleus of a human cell. Zhang devised ways to add different nuclear location signals to Cas9, and then Marraffini tested them to see if they worked in bacteria. "If you add an NLS and it stops working in bacteria, then you know it also won't work in humans," he explains.

Marraffini believed that they had a fruitful collaboration going, based on mutual respect, that could lead, if they were successful, to being coauthors on the resulting paper and co-inventors on what might be a lucrative set of patents. For a while, that would indeed be the case.

When did he know it?

The work that Zhang did in early 2012 with Marraffini would not lead to any published results until the beginning of 2013. That would later raise a multimillion-dollar question for prize jurors, patent examiners, and historical chroniclers judging The Great CRISPR Race: What did Zhang know and do before Doudna and Charpentier published their CRISPR-Cas9 *Science* paper online in June 2012?

One person who later reconstructed that history was Eric Lander, Zhang's mentor at the Broad. In a controversial article titled "The Heroes of CRISPR," which I will discuss a little later in this book, Lander would tout Zhang's importance. "By mid-2012," he wrote, Zhang "had a robust three-component system consisting of Cas9 from either *S. pyogenes* or *S. thermophilus*, tracrRNA, and a CRISPR array. Targeting sixteen sites in the human and mouse genomes, he showed that it was possible to mutate genes with high efficiency and accuracy."[10]

Lander offered no proof of this assertion, and Zhang had yet to publish any evidence that he had nailed down experimentally the precise role of all the CRISPR-Cas9 components. "We held back," Zhang says. "I did not realize there was competition."

But then, in June of that year, the Doudna-Charpentier paper was published online. Zhang read it when he got one of the regular email alerts sent out by *Science* magazine, and it prodded him to get moving. "That's when I realized that we have to wrap this up and get published," he says. "I thought to myself, 'We don't want to be scooped on the gene-editing part of this.' That was the bar for me: showing that you could use this for editing in human cells."

Zhang bristles slightly when I ask if he was building on the Charpentier-Doudna discoveries. He had, he insists, been striving for more than a year to turn CRISPR into a gene-editing tool. "I don't look at it as taking the torch from them," he says. He was working in the living cells of mice and humans, not just in a test tube. "Theirs was not a gene-editing paper. It was a biochemistry experiment in a test tube."[11]

To Zhang, "a biochemistry experiment in a test tube" was meant as a disparagement. "Showing that CRISPR-Cas9 cleaves DNA in a test tube is not an advance in terms of gene editing," he says. "In gene editing, you have to know whether or not it cleaves in cells. I always worked directly in cells. Not *in vitro*. Because the environment in cells is different than in the biochemistry environment."

Doudna makes the reverse argument, saying that some of the most important advances in biology come when the molecular components are isolated in a test tube. "What Feng was doing was using the entire Cas9 system, with all the genes and CRISPR array that were a part of it, and expressing that in cells," she says. "They weren't doing biochemistry, so they didn't actually know what the individual components were. They didn't know until our paper came out what was necessary."

They are both right. Cellular biology and biochemistry complement each other. That has been true for many of the important discoveries in genetics, most notably CRISPR, and the need to combine the two approaches was a basis for the collaboration between Charpentier and Doudna.

Zhang insists that his gene-editing ideas were already in hand by the time he read the Doudna-Charpentier paper. He presented notebook pages describing experiments in which he used the three components of a CRISPR-Cas9 system—the crRNA, tracrRNA, and Cas9 enzyme—to make edits in a human cell.[12]

There is, however, evidence that in June 2012 he still had a long way to go. A graduate student from China named Shuailiang Lin worked in Zhang's lab on the CRISPR project for nine months, and he would be listed as a coauthor on the paper Zhang eventually produced. In June 2012, when Lin was about to return to China, he prepared a slide show entitled "Summary of CRISPR Work during Oct. 2011–June 2012." It indicates that Zhang's attempts at gene editing thus far were inconclusive or a failure. "No modification seen," one slide reports. Another shows a different approach and declares, "CRISPR 2.0 fail to induce genome modification." And the final summary slide declares, "Maybe Csn1 [what Cas9 was then called] protein is too big, we tried several methods to target it into nucleus but all failed. . . . Maybe other factors need to be identified." In other words, according to Lin's presentation, Zhang's lab had not been able to get a CRISPR system to cut in human cells by June 2012.[13]

When Zhang was embroiled with Doudna in a patent battle three years later, Shuailiang Lin expanded on his slideshow information in an email to Doudna. "Feng is not only unfair to me, but also to the science history," Lin wrote. "The 15-page declaration of his and Le Cong's luciferase data is mis- and overstated. . . . We did not work it out before seeing your paper, it's really a pity."[14]

The Broad Institute dismissed Lin's email as disingenuous, alleging it was sent in hope of getting a job in Doudna's lab. "There are numerous other examples," the Broad said in a statement, "that make clear that beginning in 2011, Zhang and other members of his lab were actively and successfully engineering a unique CRISPR/Cas9 eukaryotic genome-editing system prior to and independent of what was later published [by Charpentier and Doudna]."[15]

One of Zhang's notebook pages records experiments from the

spring of 2012 that he claims document that he was able to produce results that showed the CRISPR-Cas9 system made edits in human cells. But as is often the case with scientific experiments, the data were open to interpretation. They did not clearly prove that Zhang had succeeded in editing the cells because some of the results indicated otherwise. Dana Carroll, a biochemist at the University of Utah, examined Zhang's notebook pages as an expert witness on behalf of Doudna and her colleagues. He says that Zhang left out some of the conflicting or inconclusive data contained in his notebooks. "Feng cherry-picked the data," he concludes. "They even had data that indicated an editing effect when Cas9 was not included."[16]

There is one other aspect of Zhang's work in early 2012 that seems to have fallen short. It goes back to that issue of the role of the tracrRNA. If you will recall, Charpentier discovered in her 2011 paper that tracrRNA is needed for the creation of the crRNA that serves as a guide for the Cas9 enzyme. But it was not until the Doudna-Charpentier June 2012 paper that it was clear the tracrRNA has the more important role of being part of the binding mechanism that allows Cas9 to cut DNA in the targeted location.

In his January 2012 grant application, Zhang did not describe the full role of the tracrRNA. Likewise, in his notebook pages and declaration describing the work he had done before June 2012, there is no evidence that he appreciated the role the tracrRNA plays in cleaving the targeted DNA. One of the relevant pages, Carroll says, "includes a rather detailed recipe of the components included, and that list does not have anything that suggests that a tracrRNA was included." Zhang's lack of understanding of the role of the tracrRNA, Doudna and her supporters would later say, was the main reason that his experiments were not working well before June 2012.[17]

Zhang himself, in the paper that he and his colleagues eventually published in January 2013, seemed to acknowledge that a full understanding of the role of the tracrRNA did not come until he saw what Doudna and Charpentier had published. He noted that it had "previously been shown" that the tracrRNA was needed to cleave DNA, and he footnoted the Doudna-Charpentier paper at that point. "The reason that Feng knew those two RNAs were required was based on reading our paper," Doudna says. "If you look at Feng's 2013 article, we are cited and we're cited for that reason."

When I ask Zhang about this, he says that he included the footnote as a standard practice, because the Doudna-Charpentier paper was the first to publish on the full role of tracrRNA. But he and the Broad Institute say that he was already experimenting with systems that linked the tracrRNA to the crRNA.[18]

These are murky claims to sort out. For what it's worth, my own assessment is that Zhang was working on using CRISPR for human gene editing beginning in 2011, and by mid-2012 he was focusing on the Cas9 system and showing some success, but not a lot, in getting it to work. However, there is no clear evidence, and certainly no published evidence, that he had fully sorted out the precise components that were essential or that he appreciated the ongoing role of the tracrRNA until after reading the Doudna-Charpentier paper of June 2012.

Zhang was open about one thing he learned from the Doudna-Charpentier paper: the possibility of fusing the crRNA and the tracrRNA into a single-guide RNA that could be programmed to target a desired DNA sequence. "We adapted a chimeric crRNA-tracrRNA hybrid design recently validated in vitro," he later wrote, with a footnote citing the Doudna-Charpentier paper. Marraffini, who was still working with Zhang in June 2012, agrees: "Feng and I began using a single-guide RNA only after we saw Jennifer's paper."

As Zhang points out, the creation of the single guide was a useful but not totally essential invention. The CRISPR-Cas9 system can work with the tracrRNA and crRNA remaining separate rather than fused into a simpler molecule, as Doudna and Charpentier's team had done. The single guide simplifies the system and allows it to be delivered more easily into human cells, but it's not what enables the system to work.[19]

CHAPTER 25

Doudna Joins the Race

"We were not genome editors"

It was surprising that Jennifer Doudna was even a contender in the race to make CRISPR-Cas9 work in humans. She had never experimented with human cells, nor had she ever engineered gene-editing tools such as TALENs. That was also true of her primary researcher, Martin Jinek. "I had a lab full of biochemists and people doing crystallography and that sort of thing," she says. "Whether it was creating cultured human cells or even those of nematode worms, that was not the kind of science my lab was expert in." So it was a testament to her willingness to take risks that she jumped into what she knew would be a crowded race to take their discoveries about CRISPR-Cas9 and turn it into a tool that would work in human cells.

Doudna realized, correctly, that using CRISPR to edit human genes was the next breakthrough waiting to happen. She assumed that other researchers, including Eric Sontheimer and probably people at the Broad, were racing to do it, and she felt a competitive urgency. "After our June paper, I knew we had to speed up, and it wasn't clear that our collaborators had the same commitment," she recalls. "That was a frustration to me. I'm competitive." So she pushed Jinek to work more aggressively. "You need to make this your absolute priority," she

repeatedly told him, "because if Cas9 is a robust technology for human genome editing then the world changes." Jinek worried that it would be difficult. "We were not genome editors, unlike some of the labs that pioneered the method," he says, "so we had to reinvent what others had already done."[1]

Alexandra East

At first, Doudna later admitted, she suffered "many frustrations" in her quest to make CRISPR-Cas9 work in human cells.[2] But as the fall semester of 2012 began—and Zhang was racing to finish his own experiments—she got a lucky break. A new graduate student named Alexandra East, who had experience working with human cells, joined the lab. What made her arrival especially interesting was where she came from: she had received her training and honed her gene-editing skills as a technician at the Broad Institute, working with Feng Zhang and others.

East was able to grow the necessary human cells and then began testing ways to get Cas9 into the nucleus. When she started getting the data from her experiments, she was not sure that they showed evidence of gene editing. Sometimes biology experiments do not have clear results. But Doudna, who had a far better eye for assessing results, saw the experiments as successful. "When she showed me the data, it was immediately clear to me that she had beautiful evidence of genome editing by Cas9 in the human cells," Doudna says. "This is a classic difference between a student who is in training and someone like me who's been doing this for a while. I knew what I was looking for, and when I saw the data she had, it just clicked and I thought, 'Yes, she's got it.' Whereas she was unsure and thought she might have to do the experiments again, I was saying, 'Oh my gosh, this is huge! This is so exciting!' "[3]

To Doudna, this was evidence that getting CRISPR-Cas9 to edit in a human cell was not a difficult leap or a major new invention: "It was very well known how you could tag proteins with nuclear localization signals to get them to go into the nucleus, which is what we did with Cas9. It was also well known how to change the codon usage in a gene so it would be expressed well in mammalian cells versus bacteria, and we did that as well." So she did not feel that it was a great inventive step, even though she was racing to be the first to do it. It merely required adapting methods that others had used in the past, such as with TALENs, to get enzymes into the nucleus of a cell. East had been able to do it in a few months. "It was easy once you knew the components," Doudna says. "A first-year grad student was able to do it."

Doudna felt it was important to publish something as soon as possible. She realized—correctly, as it turned out—that if other labs became the first to show that CRISPR-Cas9 could be ported to human cells, they would claim that to be a major discovery. So she pushed East to firm up her data through repeated experiments. In the meantime, Jinek worked on ways to turn the single-guide RNA that they had devised in test tubes into a guide that could get Cas9 to the right target in a human cell. It was not easy. The single-guide RNA that he had engineered was not, it turned out, quite long enough to work most efficiently on human DNA.

Chapter 26

Photo Finish

Zhang's final lap

When Feng Zhang began to test the idea of using a single-guide RNA, he discovered that the version described in the Doudna-Charpentier paper of June 2012 worked poorly in human cells. So he made a longer version of the single-guide RNA that included a hairpin turn. That made the single guide more efficient.[1]

Zhang's modification showed one difference between doing something in a test tube, like Doudna's team, and doing it in human cells. "Jennifer was probably convinced by the biochemical results that the RNA didn't need that extra chunk," he says. "She thought the short single guide that Jinek had engineered was sufficient, because it worked in a test tube. I knew that biochemistry does not always predict what will actually happen in living cells."

Zhang also did other things to improve the CRISPR-Cas9 system and optimize it so that it would work in human cells. It's sometimes hard to get a large molecule through the membrane surrounding a cell nucleus. Zhang used a technique that involved tagging the Cas9 enzyme with a nuclear localization sequence, which grants a protein access to the otherwise impenetrable cell nucleus.

In addition, he used a well-known technique called "codon optimization" to make the CRISPR-Cas9 system work in human cells. Codons are the three-letter snippets of DNA that provide instructions for the specific arrangement of amino acids, which are the building blocks used to make proteins. A variety of codons can code for the same amino acid. In different organisms, one or another of these alternative codons may work more efficiently. When trying to move a gene-expression system from one organism to another, such as from bacteria to a human, codon optimization switches the codon sequence to the one that works best.

On October 5, 2012, Zhang sent his paper to the editors of *Science*, who accepted it on December 12. Among the authors were Shuailiang Lin, the postdoc who said that Zhang was making little progress until after the Doudna-Charpentier paper appeared, and Luciano Marraffini, who had helped Zhang focus on Cas9 but would later be dropped from his main patent application. After describing their experiments and results, their paper concluded with one of those significant final sentences: "The ability to carry out multiplex genome editing in mammalian cells enables powerful applications across basic science, biotechnology, and medicine."[2]

Zhang vs. Church

For twenty-five years, George Church had been working on various methods to engineer genes. He had trained Feng Zhang and was still nominally the academic advisor of Zhang's lead coauthor, Le Cong. But until the late fall of 2012, he hadn't been told—or thought he hadn't been told—by either of them that they had been working for more than a year on turning CRISPR into a human gene–editing tool.

It was not until November of that year, when Church went to the Broad Institute to give a talk, that he found out that Zhang had submitted a paper to *Science* on using CRISPR-Cas9 in human cells. That was a shock, because Church had just submitted a paper to the same journal on the same topic. He was furious and felt betrayed. He had previously published papers on gene editing with Zhang, and he didn't realize that his former student now considered him a rival rather than a collaborator. "I guess Feng didn't get the full culture of my lab," Church says. "Or maybe he just felt the stakes were so high so he didn't tell me." Although Le Cong had moved to the Broad to work with Zhang, he was still a graduate student at Harvard and Church was still officially his advisor. "It was upsetting and seemed to me a breach of protocol that my own student was doing something he knew would interest me but he kept from me," Church says.

Church raised the issue with the Harvard Medical School's dean for graduate studies, who agreed that it was improper. Eric Lander then accused Church of bullying Le Cong. "I didn't want to make a federal case out of it," Church says. "I didn't think I was bullying him, but Eric did. So I backed off."[3]

In order to sort this out, I shuttled back and forth between the various contending parties, finding myself constantly reminded that memory can be an unreliable guide to history. Zhang insists that he did, in fact, tell Church that he was working on CRISPR in August 2012, when they drove together to the San Francisco airport from a cutting-edge conference, known as Science Foo Camp, held on the Google campus an hour away. Church has narcolepsy, and he admits he could have dropped off to sleep while Zhang was talking. But even if that happened, it does not, at least in Church's opinion, get Zhang off the hook for failing to communicate his plans, since he surely would have noticed that he was getting no response from Church.

Over dinner one night, I ask Lander his view of the dispute. Church's narcolepsy issue is "nonsense," he insists, and he accuses Church of starting his own work on CRISPR only after Zhang told him he was embarked on that task. When I ask Church about this, I think that I can detect his placid face tightening beneath his beard. "That is absurd," he replies. "If my students had told me that they wanted to establish their own name in this, I would have backed off. I had a lot else I could have done."

The quarrel so unsettled Le Cong, who is shy and polite, that he subsequently avoided doing much more work in the CRISPR field. When I tracked him down at Stanford Medical School, where he is focusing his research on immunology and neuroscience, he had just returned from his honeymoon. He told me that he thought he had behaved properly when he withheld from Church the details of what he was doing in Zhang's lab. "The two labs were independent research groups at two institutions," he says. "The principal investigators [Zhang and Church] were responsible for sharing information or materials. This is what we were taught as entering PhD students in our Responsible Conduct of Research class."[4]

When I tell him Cong's version of the story, Church chuckles. He teaches an ethics course at Harvard, and he agrees that the behavior of Zhang and Cong was not unethical. "It was within the norms of science." It did, however, violate the norms he tried to cultivate in his own lab. History would have been a little different, he says, if Zhang and Cong had stayed working for him rather than moving to the Broad. "If they had stayed in my lab, where there was a culture of open behavior, I would have made sure that their relationship with Jennifer was much more collaborative, and there wouldn't have been all the patent battles."

Ingrained in Church's character are instincts that promote reconciliation. Zhang, likewise, avoids conflict. He uses his disarming smile as an effective shield to avoid confrontation. "When one of our grandchildren was born, Feng sent us a colorful play-mat with the alphabet on it," Church says. "He also invites me to his workshops each year. We all move on." Zhang feels likewise. "We hug when we see each other."[5]

Church succeeds

Church and Zhang ended up in a virtual tie in showing how CRISPR-Cas9 could be engineered for use in human cells. Church submitted his paper to *Science* on October 26, three weeks after Zhang sent his. After dealing with referee comments, they were both accepted by the editors on the same date, December 12, and were published online simultaneously on January 3, 2013.

Like Zhang, Church created a version of Cas9 that was codon-optimized and had a nuclear localization sequence. Drawing on (and crediting more generously than Zhang did) the Doudna-Charpentier paper of June 2012, Church also synthesized a single-guide RNA. His version was longer than the one Zhang devised and ended up working even better. In addition, Church provided templates for the homology-directed repair of the DNA after CRISPR-Cas9 had made its double-strand break.

Though their papers differ somewhat, they both came to the same historic conclusion. "Our results establish an RNA-guided editing tool," Church's paper declared.[6]

The editor at *Science* was surprised, and a bit suspicious, that the journal had received two papers on the same topic from researchers who were supposed to be colleagues and collaborators. Was he being gamed? "The editor felt as if Feng and I were doing some kind of double dipping, doing two papers when we should have submitted one," Church recalls. "He required a letter from me saying these papers were actually done without knowledge of each other."

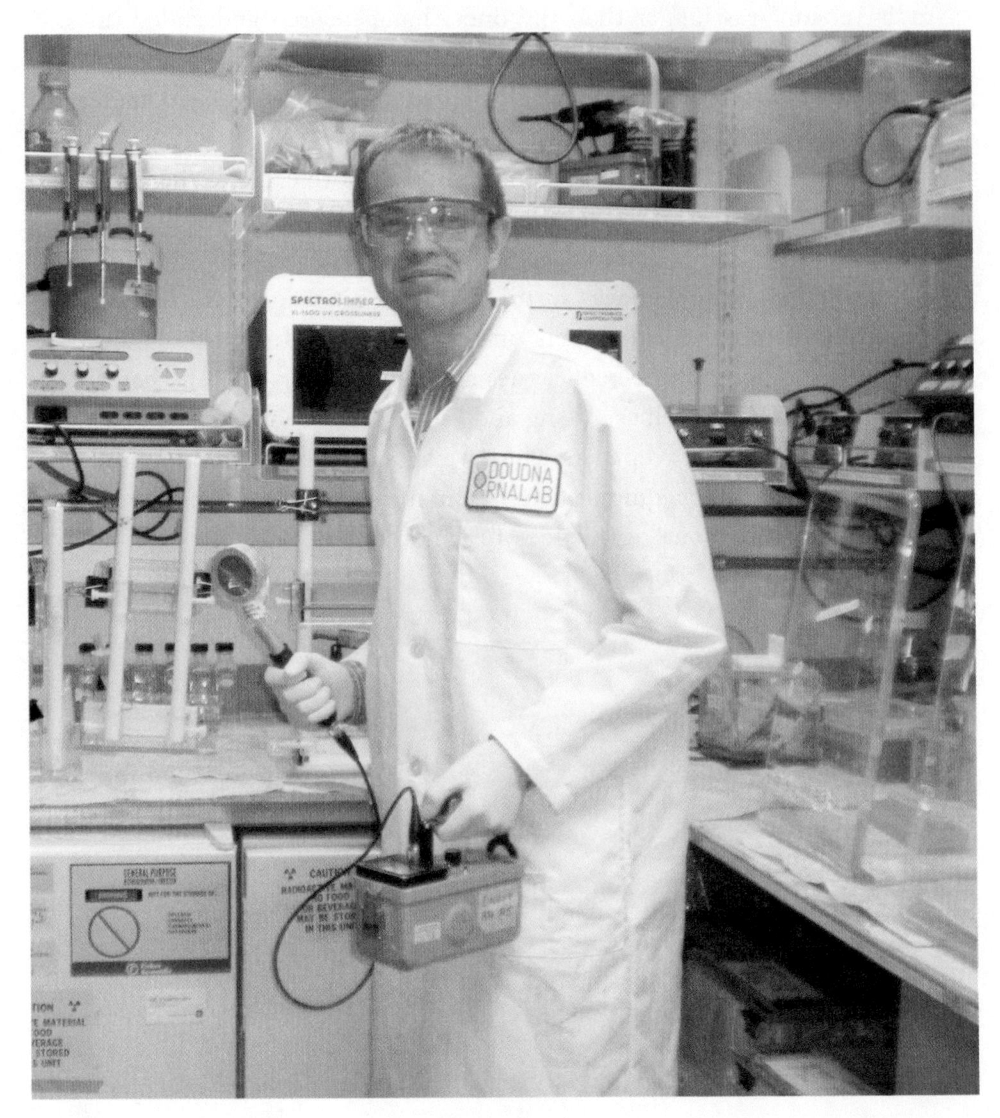

Martin Jinek

Chapter 27

Doudna's Final Sprint

In November 2012, Doudna and her team were pushing hard to pin down the results of their experiments so they could win the race to publish on the use of CRISPR-Cas9 in humans. She didn't know that Church had just submitted a paper to *Science*, and she had barely heard of Feng Zhang, who also had. Then she got a phone call from a colleague. "I hope you're sitting down," the caller said. "CRISPR is turning out to be absolutely spectacular in George Church's hands."[1]

Doudna already knew from Church's email that he was working on CRISPR, and when she heard about his progress in making it work in humans, she gave him a call. He was gracious and explained the experiments he had done and the paper he had submitted. By then, Church had learned about Zhang's work, and he told Doudna that it was slated for publication as well.

Church agreed to send Doudna a copy of his manuscript as soon as the editors at *Science* accepted it. When she received it in early December, she was deflated. Jinek was still doing experiments in her lab, and the data they had were not as extensive as those of Church.

"Should I still go ahead and try to publish my work anyway?" she asked Church. He said yes. "He was very supportive of our work and of us publishing," she says. "I thought he behaved as a great colleague." Whatever experimental data she produced, Church told Doudna, would add to the accumulation of evidence, especially on how best to tailor the RNA guide.

"I felt it was important to keep pushing with our experiments, even if others were already doing the same work," Doudna later told me, "because that would show how easy it was to use Cas9 for human genome editing. It showed that you didn't have to have special expertise to use the technology, and I felt that that was important for people to know." Publishing their work would also help her stake a claim that she had demonstrated CRISPR-Cas9 could work in human cells at approximately the same time as competing labs had.

That meant she needed to get her paper published quickly. So she called a colleague at Berkeley who had recently started an open-access electronic journal, *eLife*, that published papers after less review time than traditional journals such as *Science* and *Nature*. "I talked to him, described the data, and sent him a title," Doudna says. "He said it sounded interesting and he would get it reviewed quickly."

Jinek, however, was reluctant to rush their paper into print. "He's a real perfectionist, and he wanted to have a lot more data, a bigger story," she recalls. "He felt what we had wasn't worth publishing." They had many heated discussions, including one in the Berkeley quad in front of their lab in Stanley Hall.

"Martin, we have to publish this, even if it's not quite the story we wish we could tell," Doudna said. "We have to put out the best story that we can, with the data that we have, because we don't have any more time. These other papers are coming out and we have to publish."

"If we publish this work, we're going to look like amateurs in the genome editing field," Jinek shot back.

"But Martin, we are amateurs, and it's okay," she replied. "I don't think people are going to think badly of us. If we had six more months, we could do a lot more, but I think you will understand better as time goes by that it's incredibly important for us to publish this right now."[2]

Doudna recalls that she "put her foot down," and after a bit more discussion they came to an agreement: Jinek would put together the data and figures for the experiments, but Doudna would have to write the paper.

At the time, she was working on revising a second edition of a textbook on molecular biology she had written with two colleagues.[3] "We hadn't been entirely happy with the first edition, so we rented a house in Carmel to have a two-day powwow on how to revise it," she says. As a result, she found herself in mid-December in Carmel, where it was wickedly cold, in a house that had no working heat. The owners said they would call a repair person, but they couldn't get anyone out there right away. So Doudna and her coauthors huddled around the fireplace as they worked late into the night revising their textbook.

After everyone went to bed at 11 p.m., Doudna stayed up to prepare her CRISPR paper for *eLife*. "I was exhausted and cold and I realized that I had to write the paper then or it wouldn't get written," she says. "So I sat up for three hours in bed, pinching myself to stay awake, and typed out the text of a draft." She sent it off to Jinek, who kept coming back with suggestions. "I didn't tell my textbook coauthors or editors about any of this, so you can imagine the scene where I'm in this freezing cold house trying to talk about this textbook but I'm totally distracted because I knew I had to get the paper written, and Martin kept coming back with revisions." Finally, she cut Jinek off and declared the paper finished. On December 15, she emailed it to *eLife*.

A few days later, she and her husband, Jamie, and their son, Andy, left for a ski vacation in Utah. She spent a lot of her time in their room at the lodge as she negotiated little fixes with Jinek and pushed the *eLife* editor to speed up the reviewing process. Every morning she would check the *Science* magazine website to see if the Church or Zhang paper had been published. The main scholar who was doing the peer review of her paper was in Germany,[4] and Doudna was prodding him by email almost daily.

She was also on the phone with her former collaborator Emmanuelle Charpentier, who was in Umeå, where it was now dark all day. "I was trying to manage my relationship with her, and I didn't want her to feel that we had somehow cut her out of that story, but the reality was that she hadn't participated in the science for the *eLife* paper,"

Doudna says. "So we acknowledged her, but in the end she wasn't a coauthor." Doudna sent her a draft of the manuscript, hoping she would not be upset. "I'm fine," Charpentier responded, without much elaboration. There was a certain frostiness. What Doudna did not quite understand was that, even though Charpentier had not wanted to collaborate on the effort to edit human cells, she felt a little proprietary about the CRISPR-Cas9 system. After all, she was the one who had brought Doudna in on that work when they met in Puerto Rico.[5]

When the peer-review coordinator in Germany finally got back with comments, he asked for a few additional experiments. "A few of the mutated targets must be sequenced, just to demonstrate that the expected types of mutations are present," he wrote. Doudna was able to brush him back. Doing the suggested experiments would "require analyses of close to a hundred clones," she replied, which would "be better performed as part of a larger study."[6]

She prevailed, and on January 3, 2013, *eLife* accepted her paper. But she couldn't celebrate. The evening before, she had received, out of the blue, a happy-new-year email that did not portend a happy new year:

From: Feng Zhang
Sent: Wednesday, January 02, 2013 7:36 PM
To: Jennifer Doudna
Subject: CRISPR
Attachments: CRISPR manuscript.pdf

Dear Dr. Doudna,

Greetings from Boston and happy new year!

I am an assistant professor at MIT and have been working on developing applications based on the CRISPR system. I met you briefly during my graduate school interview at Berkeley back in 2004 and have been very inspired by your work since then. Our group in collaboration with Luciano Marraffini at Rockefeller recently completed a set of studies applying the type II CRISPR

> system to carry out genome editing of mammalian cells. The study was recently accepted by *Science* and it will be publishing online tomorrow. I have attached a copy of our paper for your review. The Cas9 system is very powerful and I would love to talk with you sometime. I am sure we have a lot of synergy and perhaps there are things that would be good to collaborate on in the future!
>
> Very best wishes, Feng
> Feng Zhang, Ph.D.
> Core Member, Broad Institute of MIT and Harvard

If Jinek had been less balky, I later ask Doudna, might her paper have been published sooner? Might she have been able to tie, or even beat, Zhang and Church, even though her team had finished their experiments after them? "It would have been tough," Doudna says. "I don't think so. We were still doing experiments right up until the very last minute because Martin, rightfully, wanted to make sure that the data included in the paper had been replicated three times. I wish it had been possible to submit earlier, but it probably wasn't."

Their paper did not have an extended version of the guide RNA, which both Zhang and Church showed worked better in human cells. Unlike Church's paper, theirs also did not include templates for homology-directed repair that would create more reliable DNA edits. However, it did show that a lab specializing in biochemistry could quickly move CRISPR-Cas9 from a test tube to human cells. "We show here that Cas9 can be expressed and localized to the nucleus of human cells," Doudna wrote. "These results demonstrate the feasibility of RNA-programmed genome editing in human cells."[7]

Some great discoveries and inventions—such as Einstein's theories of relativity and the creation of the transistor at Bell Labs—are singular advances. Others—such as the invention of the microchip and the application of CRISPR to editing human cells—were accomplished by many groups at around the same time.

On the same day that Doudna's paper appeared in *eLife*, January 29, 2013, a fourth paper was published online showing that

CRISPR-Cas9 worked in human cells. It was by a South Korean researcher, Jin-Soo Kim, who had been corresponding with Doudna and credited her June 2012 paper for laying the ground for his own work. "Your *Science* paper prompted us to start this project," he had written in a July email.[8] A fifth paper published that day, by Keith Joung of Harvard, showed that CRISPR-Cas9 could genetically engineer the embryos of zebrafish.[9]

Even though Doudna had been beaten by a few weeks by Zhang and Church, the fact that five different papers on CRISPR-Cas9 editing in animal cells all appeared in January 2013 reinforced the argument that this discovery was inevitable after it had been shown that it could work in a test tube. Whether that was a difficult step, as Zhang contends, or an obvious step, as Doudna claims, the idea of using an easily programmed RNA molecule to target specific genes and change them was, for humanity, a momentous step into a new age.

Chapter 28

Forming Companies

Square dances

In December 2012, a few weeks before the multiple papers on CRISPR gene editing were due to be published, Doudna arranged for one of her business associates, Andy May, to meet with George Church at his Harvard lab. An Oxford-educated molecular biologist, May was the scientific advisor at Caribou Biosciences, the biotech company that Doudna had started with Rachel Haurwitz in 2011, and he wanted to explore the business potential for using CRISPR-based gene editing as a medical technology.

Doudna was giving a seminar in San Francisco when May tried to reach her to report on the meeting. "Can we talk later tonight?" she texted back.

"Yes, but I really need to talk to you," he responded.

When she reached him, she was driving back to Berkeley. He began by saying, "Are you sitting down?"

"Yes, of course, I'm driving home," she replied.

"Well, I hope you don't drive off the road," he said, "because I had this incredible meeting with George who says this will be the most amazing discovery. He's changing his entire gene-editing focus to CRISPR."[1]

Rodger Novak, Jennifer Doudna, and Emmanuelle Charpentier

The excitement over the potential of CRISPR provoked all of the major players to begin square dancing, forming groups and swapping partners in the quest to create companies that would commercialize CRISPR for medical applications. Doudna and May decided, at first, to launch a company with Church and, if they could corral them, some of the other CRISPR pioneers. So in January 2013, Haurwitz accompanied May back to Boston for another meeting with Church.

Church's bushy beard and cultivated eccentricities continued to make him a scientific celebrity, and on the day of the meeting that caused him to be distracted. In an interview with the German magazine *Spiegel*, he had offhandedly speculated about the possibility of resurrecting a Neanderthal by implanting its DNA in the egg of a volunteer surrogate mother. Not surprisingly (except perhaps to him), his phone rang nonstop as tabloid reporters jumped on the story.[2] But he finally focused on his meeting, and within an hour they had a plan. They would try to enlist Emmanuelle Charpentier and Feng Zhang, along with a few top venture capitalists, into a grand consortium to commercialize CRISPR.

Charpentier, in the meantime, was working on a potential startup of her own. Earlier in 2012, she had contacted Rodger Novak, her onetime boyfriend and longtime scientific partner, whom she had befriended when they were researchers at Rockefeller University and in Memphis. They had remained close personal friends, and he had by then joined the pharmaceutical company Sanofi in Paris.

"What do you think about CRISPR?" she asked him.

"What are you talking about?" he replied.

But once he studied her data and consulted with some of his colleagues at Sanofi, he realized it would make sense to launch a business around it. So he called a close friend who was a venture capitalist, Shaun Foy, and they decided to discuss the prospect by going on a surfing trip (even though neither of them knew how to surf) off the northern part of Vancouver Island. A month later, after he had done some more due diligence, Foy called Novak and said they needed to launch a company as soon as possible. "You have to quit your job," he told Novak, who eventually did.[3]

In the hope of getting all of the main players to coalesce, a brunch meeting was scheduled in February 2013 at The Blue Room, a once trendy restaurant with zinc-topped tables nestled in a renovated brick factory near MIT. It was located in Kendall Square in Cambridge, an epicenter of institutions that turn basic science into profitable applications: corporate research centers such as those of Novartis and Biogen and Microsoft, nonprofit institutes such as the Broad and the Whitehead, and a few federal funding agencies such as the National Transportation Systems Center.

Invited to the brunch were Doudna, Charpentier, Church, and Zhang. At the last minute Zhang canceled, but Church urged that they forge ahead without him. "We need to start a company because there is so much we can do with this," he said. "It's so powerful."

"How big do you think it is?" Doudna asked him.

"Well, Jennifer, all that I can tell you is that there is a tidal wave coming," he replied.[4]

Doudna wanted to work with Charpentier, even though they had been drifting apart scientifically. "I spent many hours on the phone with her trying to convince her to come along as a cofounder of what I was doing with George," Doudna says. "But she really did not want to work with some of the folks in Boston. I think she didn't trust them, and in the end I think she was right. But I didn't see that at the time. I was trying to give people the benefit of the doubt."

Church was not as eager to have Charpentier on board. "I became somewhat wary about joining forces with her," he says. "One of the reasons we didn't go in with her was because her boyfriend wanted to be CEO. We just felt that was a nonstarter. You needed to have a process by which you pick the CEO. I was willing to go with it. I tend to be accommodating. But Jennifer laid out the reasons against it, and I said, 'Yeah, you're right.'" (In fact, by then, Novak and Charpentier were no longer romantically involved.)[5]

Andy May had the same negative reaction when Doudna arranged for him to meet with Novak and Foy. "They came in pretty heavy-handed," May says of Charpentier's two business partners. "Their initial approach was that we should get out of the way and let them take care of it."[6]

To be fair, both Novak and Foy had been involved in businesses and knew what they were doing. So along with Charpentier, they broke off discussions with the Doudna-Church group and instead founded a company of their own, CRISPR Therapeutics, initially based in Switzerland but later also in Cambridge, Massachusetts. "It was extremely easy to access money then, especially if you were called CRISPR," Novak says.[7]

For a while in 2013, it seemed as if Doudna and Zhang, despite their rivalry, might become business allies or partners. After he missed the February 2013 brunch at The Blue Room, Zhang sent Doudna an email asking if she might like to collaborate on topics related to the brain, which had long been one of his interests. "I remember sitting at my desk here at my kitchen in Berkeley, seeing him on Skype," she says.

He came out to San Francisco for a conference that spring and met Doudna at the Claremont Hotel in Berkeley. "I went to see her because I thought it was important to have some common alliance around the intellectual property so that you could make this a clean field for people to practice," Zhang says. His idea was that Berkeley's intellectual property and potential patents would be put into a pool with the Broad's, which would make it easy for users to license the CRISPR-Cas9 system. Zhang thought Doudna liked the idea, so Lander phoned her to see if they could establish the framework for such a patent pool. "The next day Eric told me that my trip was productive," Zhang says, "and he thought we had cemented the alliance."

But Doudna had qualms. "I just didn't get a good feeling from Feng," she recalls. "He was not forthright. He was being cagey about when they had actually filed for patents. It didn't sit well with me."

So she decided to give an exclusive license of her intellectual property, which Berkeley managed in coordination with Charpentier, to her existing firm, Caribou Biosciences, and not do an alliance with the Broad. Zhang says that he thinks Doudna "has difficulty trusting people," so she relied too heavily on her former student and Caribou cofounder Haurwitz. "Rachel is a nice person and smart, but not the right person to be the CEO of such a company," he says. "Someone much more seasoned in terms of being able to develop the technology is really important."

The decision not to pool the CRISPR-Cas9 intellectual property would pave the way for an epic patent battle. It also would end up hampering the easy and widespread licensing of the technology. "I think in retrospect, if I had to do it over again, I would have licensed it differently," Doudna says. "When you have a platform technology like CRISPR, it's probably a better idea to license it in a way that offers it as broadly as possible." She had no expertise with intellectual property, and she was at a university that didn't have much either. "It was kind of like the blind leading the blind," she says.

Editas Medicine

Although she did not want to put her intellectual property into a pool with the Broad's, Doudna was still open to becoming a partner in a CRISPR-focused company that would license both her potential patents and those of the Broad. So throughout the spring and summer of 2013, she traveled many times to Boston to dance with a rotating cast of investors and scientists, including Church and Zhang, who were trying to put together companies.

On one trip in early June, she went jogging one evening along the Charles River by Harvard, remembering her days there studying RNA under Jack Szostak. Back then she never thought that her research would lead to commercial ventures. It was not part of the ethos at Harvard. Now Harvard had changed, and so had she. If she wanted to have a direct impact on people, she realized that forming companies would be the best way to translate the basic science of CRISPR into clinical applications.

As the negotiations dragged on through the summer, the stress of figuring out how to form a company began to wear her down. So did flying between San Francisco and Boston every few weeks. Particularly difficult was having to choose between working with Charpentier or with Church and Zhang. "I couldn't tell what the right decision was," she admits. "A couple of people in Berkeley, colleagues that I trusted and had started companies in the past, were telling me to definitely work with the people in Boston, because they were better at business."

Until then, she had rarely gotten sick. But now, in the summer of 2013, she found herself being hit with waves of pain and fever. Her joints locked up in the morning, and sometimes she could barely move. She went to a few doctors, who speculated that she might have a rare virus or perhaps an autoimmune condition.

The problems receded after a month, but then they recurred on a trip to Disneyland with her son late in the summer. "It was just the two of us, and each morning I'd wake up in our hotel and everything was hurting," she recalls. "I didn't want to wake up Andy, so I would go in the bathroom, close the door, and get on the phone with these people in Boston." The stress of the situation, she realized, was affecting her physically.[8]

Nevertheless, she was able to reach an agreement with the Boston-men by the end of the summer. A group coalesced with Doudna, Zhang, and Church at its core. Some Boston-based investment firms—Third Rock Ventures, Polaris Partners, and Flagship Ventures—provided commitments for more than $40 million in initial funding. The group decided to have five scientific founders, so they added two top Harvard biologists who had been working on CRISPR, Keith Joung and David Liu. "It seemed like the five of us were pretty much a dream team," says Church. Their board included representatives from each of the three major investment firms along with some distinguished scientists. There was general consensus about most members, but Church did end up vetoing the selection of Eric Lander.

In September 2013, Gengine, Inc. was founded. Two months later, it changed its name to Editas Medicine. "We have the ability to essentially target any gene," said Kevin Bitterman, a principal at Polaris Partners who served as the interim president for the first few months.

"And we have in our crosshairs any diseases with a genetic component. We can go in and fix the error."[9]

Doudna quits

After only a few months, Doudna's discomfort and stress began to resurface. She sensed that her partners, especially Zhang, were doing things behind her back, and her qualms worsened at a January 2014 medical conference hosted in San Francisco by J.P. Morgan. Zhang came out from Boston with some of the management team from Editas, and they invited Doudna to a couple of meetings with potential investors. She got bad vibes as soon as she walked in. "I could immediately tell from Feng's behavior and body language that something had changed," she says. "He wasn't collegial anymore."

As she watched from a corner, the men at the meeting clustered around Zhang and treated him as the principal. He was introduced as "the inventor" of CRISPR gene editing. Doudna was treated as a secondary player, one of the scientific advisors. "I was being cut out," she says. "There were things involving the intellectual property and I wasn't being kept informed. There was something afoot."

Then she was hit with a surprising piece of news, one that made her understand why she had the queasy sense that Zhang was keeping her in the dark. On April 15, 2014, she received an email from a reporter asking for her reaction to the news that Zhang and the Broad had just been granted a patent for the use of CRISPR-Cas9 as an editing tool. Doudna and Charpentier still had a patent application pending, but Zhang and the Broad, who had put in their own application later, had paid to have their decision fast-tracked. Suddenly it became clear, to Doudna at least, that Zhang and Lander were trying to relegate her and Charpentier to minor players—both in history and in any commercial use of CRISPR-Cas9.

It dawned on Doudna that this was why Zhang and many of the others folks at Editas had seemed secretive with her. The finance people in Boston had been positioning Zhang as the inventor. "They've known about this for months," she said to herself, "and now this patent has been issued and they're trying to completely cut me out and stab me in the back."

It wasn't just Zhang, she felt. It was the gang of men who dominated the biotech and finance world of Boston. "All the Boston people were all so interconnected," she says. "Eric Lander was on an advisory board for Third Rock Ventures, and there was equity going back to the Broad from Editas, and there's licensing agreements that can make them tons of money as long as Feng is seen as the inventor." The episode made her physically ill.

In addition, she was exhausted. She had been flying to Boston once a month for meetings at Editas. "It was brutal. I'd buy an economy class ticket, sit straight up for five hours, and then get in at seven in the morning. I'd go to the United Club, take a shower, change my clothes, go to Editas, have our meetings, and then I'd often go to Church's lab to talk about science. Then I would jump on a six p.m. flight back to California."

So she decided to quit.

She talked to a lawyer about how to extract herself from the agreement she had signed. It took a little time, but by June they had drafted an email to the CEO of Editas saying that she was resigning. They finalized the text over the phone when she was at a meeting in Germany. "Okay, it's ready to go," the lawyer told her after they wrestled with a few final changes. It was evening in Germany and afternoon in Boston when she hit the Send button. "I wondered how many minutes it would be until my phone would ring," she says. "It was less than five minutes, and it was the Editas CEO calling."

"No, no, you can't go, you can't leave," he said. "What's wrong? Why are you doing this?"

"You know what you did to me," she replied. "I'm done. I'm not going to work with people I can't trust, people who stab you in the back. You stabbed me in the back."

The Editas CEO denied being involved in Zhang's patent filings. "Look," Doudna replied, "you may be right or you may be wrong, but either way I can't be part of this company anymore. I'm done."

"What about all your stock?" he asked.

"I don't care," she shot back. "You don't understand. I'm not doing it for the money. And if you think I'm doing it for the money, you don't understand me at all."

When Doudna recounted the episode to me, it was the first time I had heard her so angry. Her steady tone had disappeared. "He claimed he didn't know what I was talking about, and it was ridiculous. It was bullshit. It was all a bunch of lies. And I could be wrong, Walter, but that was my feeling about it."

All of the founders of the company, including Zhang, sent her emails that day asking her to reconsider. They offered to make amends and do whatever was possible to heal the rift. But she refused.

"I'm done," she emailed back.

Immediately, she felt better. "It suddenly seemed like this big weight came off my shoulders."

When she explained the situation to Church, he suggested that, if she wanted, he would consider quitting as well. "I had had a phone call with George at his house on a Sunday," she says. "He vaguely offered to step down, but then he decided not to, and that was his decision."

I ask Church whether Doudna was right to mistrust the other founders. "They were conspiring behind her back, filing for patents without telling her," he agrees. But he says that Doudna should not have been surprised. Zhang was acting in his self-interest. "He probably had lawyers telling him what to do and say," says Church. "I try to understand why people do things." Everyone's actions, including those of Zhang and Lander, could have been predicted, he believes. "Everyone did what I would have expected them to do."

So why didn't he quit? I ask. He explains that it was not logical to be surprised by their behavior, so it was not logical to quit because of it. "I almost left with her, but then I thought, what would that accomplish? It would reward them by giving them the rest of the profits. I always advise people to stay calm. After I thought about it for a while, I decided it was better to be a little calm. I wanted to see a company succeed."

Shortly after she left Editas, Doudna was at a conference where she explained what happened to Charpentier. "Oh, that's interesting," Charpentier responded. "Would you like to get involved with CRISPR Therapeutics?" That was the company that she had founded with Novak.

"You know, it's like getting a divorce," Doudna replied. "I'm not sure I want to get involved again right away. I'm kind of done with companies now."

Within a few months, she decided that she would be most comfortable working with her trusted partner and former student Rachel Haurwitz, with whom she had started Caribou Biosciences in 2011. Caribou had created a spinoff called Intellia, with the mission of commercializing CRISPR-Cas9 tools. "I became very interested in Intellia, because the Caribou team was launching it with the academic scientists I most liked and trusted and respected," Doudna says. These included three great CRISPR pioneers, Rodolphe Barrangou, Erik Sontheimer, and Zhang's former collaborator Luciano Marraffini. They were all brilliant but had an even more important trait: "They were the people who do good science but are more importantly honorable straight-shooters."[10]

As a result, the pioneers of CRISPR-Cas9 ended up in three competing companies: CRISPR Therapeutics, founded by Charpentier and Novak; Editas Medicine, which included Zhang and Church and Doudna until she resigned; and Intellia Therapeutics, founded by Doudna, Barrangou, Sontheimer, Marraffini, and Haurwitz.

CHAPTER 29

Mon Amie

Drifting apart

Doudna's decision to go with a competing company reflected, and perhaps contributed to, the slight coolness that had developed between her and Charpentier. She had tried hard to maintain their relationship. For example, when they first started working together, one of their goals was to crystallize Cas9 and determine its exact structure. After Doudna and her lab succeeded in doing so in late 2013, she asked Charpentier if she wanted to be a coauthor on the resulting journal article. Charpentier, feeling it was a project she had brought to the Doudna Lab, responded that she would like that. This annoyed Jinek, but Doudna went along. "I was really trying to bend over backwards to be generous to her," she says, "and, frankly, I wanted to maintain our scientific and personal relationship."[1]

Partly as a way to keep their scientific partnership intact, Doudna suggested to Charpentier that they coauthor a review article for *Science* in 2014. Unlike a "research article," which is a featured paper on a new discovery, a "review article" is a survey of recent advances on a particular topic. Theirs was titled "The New Frontier of Genome Engineering with CRISPR-Cas9."[2] Doudna wrote a draft, and Charpentier made some edits. It helped to paper over, so to speak, any rift that might be developing between them.

Nevertheless, they began drifting apart. Rather than join Doudna in the quest to find ways to use CRISPR-Cas9 in humans, Charpentier told her that she planned to focus on fruit flies and bacteria. "I like basic research more than looking for tools," she says.[3] There was another underlying reason for the strain: from Doudna's perspective, she was an equal co-discoverer of the CRISPR-Cas9 system, but Charpentier viewed CRISPR-Cas9 as her own project, one that she had brought Doudna into late in the game. At times she spoke of it as "my work" and referred to Doudna as if she were a secondary collaborator. Now Doudna was basking in the limelight, giving interviews and making plans to pursue new CRISPR-Cas9 studies.

Doudna never quite understood Charpentier's proprietary feelings and couldn't figure out how to deal with the coolness that was evident beneath her warm and insouciant manner. She kept suggesting ways they could work together, and Charpentier would reply, "That sounds great." But then nothing would happen. "I wanted to continue collaborating, and Emmanuelle clearly didn't," Doudna says with sadness in her voice. "She never came out and said that to me. We just drifted apart." Eventually, Doudna became frustrated. "I came to feel that it was a passive-aggressive way of interacting," she says. "It was frustrating and it was hurtful."

Part of their problem was the different levels of comfort each had with publicity. When they met at awards ceremonies or conferences, the interactions could be awkward, especially at photo sessions where Charpentier exuded a subtly condescending and amused attitude when the limelight focused on Doudna. Eric Lander, Doudna's occasional antagonist at the Broad Institute, told me that when he talked to Charpentier she expressed resentment at the publicity Doudna got.

Rodger Novak saw Doudna as an American comfortable with acclaim, and his friend Charpentier, whose reputation he protected, as a more properly reticent Parisian. He pushed Charpentier to do more interviews and even get training in how to deal with the media. "It's just a different style of an individual not being on the West Coast but being European, a French person, who focuses more on science than on media hype," he later said.[4]

That is not fully accurate. Although she was comfortable with being a public figure and flattered by recognition, Doudna was not, in fact, someone who actively sought celebrity. She made a point of trying to share the limelight and prizes with Charpentier. Rodolphe Barrangou puts more of the blame on Charpentier. "Emmanuelle makes people feel uncomfortable, even when it comes time to pose for pictures or to be in a green room before a public appearance," he says. "It's baffling to me her lack of desire to share credit with others. I watch Jennifer try to share the light and even overcompensate, but Emmanuelle will seem slightly recalcitrant and resistant."[5]

Their difference in style was reflected in many ways, including their musical tastes. At one of the award ceremonies they attended together, they each got to choose the song that would play when they went onstage. Doudna chose Billie Holiday's bluesy rendition of "On the Sunny Side of the Street." Charpentier selected a technopunk piece from the French electronica duo Daft Punk.[6]

One substantive issue that came between them is one that historians know all too well. Almost every person in any saga tends to remember their own role as being a little more important than the other players see it. That's true in our own lives. We recall vividly the brilliance of our own contributions to a discussion; we're a bit hazier when recalling the contributions of others, or we tend to minimize their significance. As Charpentier views the CRISPR narrative, she was the one who first worked on Cas9, identified its components, and then brought Doudna into the project.

Take, for example, the pesky little issue that keeps cropping up in this tale of the ongoing role of tracrRNA, which not only helps to create the crRNA that guides to a targeted gene but then also, as Doudna and Charpentier revealed in their 2012 paper, sticks around to help the CRISPR-Cas9 complex cleave the targeted DNA. After they published the paper, Charpentier would occasionally suggest that she knew about the ongoing role of tracrRNA back in 2011, before she started collaborating with Doudna.

This began to annoy Doudna. "If you look at talks that she's given recently and the slides she has shown, my opinion is that she's been coached by lawyers and is trying to present the work as if they already knew that the tracrRNA was important for Cas9's function before we started our collaboration, and I think that's disingenuous, it's untrue," Doudna says. "I don't know whether that was her doing or coaching by lawyers, but I think she kind of tried to blur the line between what she did in her 2011 paper and what was figured out much later."[7]

When I ask Charpentier over dinner about the coolness that has developed between them, she is circumspect. She knows, after all, that I am writing a book with Doudna as the central character, and she has never tried to persuade me to shift my focus. With a dash of indifference, she admits that her March 2011 *Nature* paper did not, in fact, describe the full role of the tracrRNA, but she laughs and adds that Doudna should relax a bit and not be so competitive. "She doesn't need to be so stressed about getting proper credit for the tracrRNA and things," Charpentier says. "I find it unnecessary." She smiles as she describes Doudna's competitive streak, as if she finds that trait both admirable and amusing, but also faintly indecorous.

Their rift was exacerbated in 2017 when Doudna published a book on her CRISPR work, coauthored with Sam Sternberg, that was judicious but tended to use the first person more than Charpentier thought was seemly. "It's written in the first person even though her student did most of the writing," Charpentier says. "He should have been told to write in the third person. I know people who do the prizes and the Swedish mentality. They don't like people to write books too early on." By putting the words "prizes" and "Swedish" in the same sentence, she was referring to the most famous of them all.

Prizes

One force that kept Doudna and Charpentier bonded was scientific prizes. Their chances for winning them were best as a pair. Some carry awards of $1 million or more, but they have an even more important value than the money. They serve as a scorecard that the public, press, and future historians use to decide who deserves the most credit for important advances. Lawyers even cite them in arguments made in patent cases.

Each important science prize is given to a limited number of people (for the Nobel, the maximum is three in each field), so the awards do not reflect the full cast of players who contributed to a discovery. As a result, they can distort history and be a disincentive to collaboration, just like patents.

One of the largest and most glamorous of these awards, the Breakthrough Prize in Life Sciences, was given to Doudna and Charpentier as a pair in November 2014, a few months after Zhang beat them to the first patents. The citation heralded them "for harnessing an ancient mechanism of bacterial immunity into a powerful and general technology for editing genomes."

The prize, which carries a $3 million award for each recipient, had been established a year earlier by the Russian billionaire and early Facebook funder Yuri Milner, along with Sergey Brin of Google, Anne Wojcicki of 23andMe, and Mark Zuckerberg of Facebook. Milner, an ebullient fanboy of scientists, staged a glittering televised award ceremony that infused the glory of science with some of the glamor of Hollywood. The 2014 black-tie event, cohosted by *Vanity Fair*, was held in a spacecraft hangar at NASA's Ames Research Center in Mountain View, California, in the heart of Silicon Valley. The emcees included actors Seth MacFarlane, Kate Beckinsale, Cameron Diaz, and Benedict Cumberbatch. Christina Aguilera performed her hit "Beautiful."

Doudna and Charpentier, wearing elegant floor-length black gowns, were presented the prize by Cameron Diaz and Dick Costolo, then the CEO of Twitter. Doudna took the microphone first and paid tribute to the "puzzle-solving process that is science." Charpentier, with a puckish air, then turned to Diaz, who early in her career was a star in the television show *Charlie's Angels*. "We make three powerful women," Charpentier said, gesturing to Diaz and Doudna, and then turning to the bald and bespectacled Costolo added, "I was wondering if you were Charlie."

In the audience was Eric Lander, who had been a prizewinner the year before and had thus been given the duty to telephone Doudna and Charpentier to say they had won. As the director of the Broad Institute and Zhang's mentor, he was zealously engaged in the battle against them for CRISPR kudos. But he had formed a slight bond with Charpentier, or thought he had, by sharing what he believed was her resentment about the acclaim Doudna was garnering. At first, Doudna was nominated for the Breakthrough Prize on her own, Lander told me. But he was able to persuade the prize jury that Doudna's contributions were not as significant as those of Charpentier, Zhang, and the microbiologists who had originally discovered CRISPR in bacteria. "I got the people to understand that Jennifer is probably prize-worthy, but not for CRISPR but for her work on the structure of RNA," he says. "CRISPR was an ensemble act with a lot of people, and Jennifer's contribution was not the most important."

He was not able to prevail in having the prize go to Zhang, but he did help make sure that Charpentier was selected along with Doudna. He also thought that he had an understanding that Zhang would win the following year. When that didn't happen, he would blame Doudna for blocking it.[8]

The Breakthrough Prizes are limited to two winners in each field. The Gairdner Award in biomedical science, given by a Canadian foundation, is more expansive: it honors up to five researchers. That meant that when the foundation decided in 2016 to honor those who developed CRISPR, a broader array of scientists was represented: Doudna and Charpentier were joined by Zhang and the two Danisco yogurt researchers, Horvath and Barrangou. It also meant that some very important players were left out, including Francisco Mojica, Erik Sontheimer, Luciano Marraffini, Sylvain Moineau, Virginijus Šikšnys, and George Church.

Doudna was upset by the exclusion of her friend Church, so she did two things. She donated her prize money, about $100,000, to the Personal Genetics Education Project, which Church had set up with his wife, Ting Wu, a Harvard molecular biology professor. The project encourages people, especially young students, to understand their genes. She also invited them to the ceremony. She was doubtful Church would accept. After all, he had been left out of the honors and, perhaps more significant, was resistant to wearing a tuxedo. But in his gracious manner, Church did show up, impeccably dressed, with his wife. "I'd like to take this opportunity to celebrate the work of two people who have inspired me for a very long time, George Church and Ting Wu," Doudna said, and then she pointedly noted Church's "huge impact on the gene-editing field, including adapting the CRISPR-Cas system for gene editing in mammalian cells."[9]

Doudna and Charpentier completed a hat trick by winning a third major award in 2018, the Kavli Prize. Named after Fred Kavli, an American entrepreneur born in Norway, it carries many of the trappings of the Nobel Prize: there's a glamorous ceremony and for each recipient $1 million and a gold medal stamped with a bust of the prize's founder. The award can go to three scientists, and the committee chose to add Virginijus Šikšnys, a fitting recognition that had until then eluded the shy Lithuanian. "We dreamed of rewriting the language of life itself, and with the discovery of CRISPR we found a new powerful writing tool," said Norwegian actor Heidi Ruud Ellingsen, who cohosted the ceremony with the American actor and science geek Alan Alda. Doudna wore a short black dress, Charpentier a long one, and Šikšnys a sharp gray suit that looked as if it had been bought for the occasion. After being handed their medals by King Harald V of Norway, they bowed slightly amid a fanfare of trumpets.

Eric Lander

CHAPTER 30

The Heroes of CRISPR

Lander's tale

In the spring of 2015, while Emmanuelle Charpentier was visiting America, she had lunch with Eric Lander in his office at the Broad Institute. In his recollection, she was "in a funk" and resentful of some of the acclaim that Doudna was getting. "It became very clear to me that she is pissed at Jennifer," Lander recalls. "She believed that the credit was going to her more than to the microbiologists," such as Francisco Mojica, Rodolphe Barrangou, Philippe Horvath, and herself, who had originally figured out how CRISPR works in bacteria.

Perhaps Lander was right, or perhaps he was in part projecting his own resentments and stoking ones that Charpentier only vaguely felt. Lander is a persuasive personality who is good at getting people to agree with him. When I ask Charpentier about Lander's recollection, she gives a wry smile and suggests, with a tiny shrug, that the feelings were more Lander's than hers. Nevertheless, there was probably some truth to Lander's perceptions of her feelings. "She was subtle and French about it," he recalls.

His lunch conversation with Charpentier, Lander says, was the origin of what would become a detailed, vibrant, well-reported, and controversial journal article on the history of CRISPR. "After talking to

Emmanuelle, I decided to pull the thread and look back at the origins of CRISPR and give credit to the people who had done the original work but weren't getting the acclaim," he says. "I have this streak in me that I defend the underdog. I was brought up in Brooklyn."

I asked him whether he might have had other motivations as well, including a desire to downplay the role of Doudna and Charpentier, who were pitted against his protégé Feng Zhang for patents and prizes. For someone who is so feisty, Lander can also be laudably self-aware. He answers by referring to Michael Frayn's play *Copenhagen*, which applied the uncertainty principle to the motives of Werner Heisenberg when he visited Niels Bohr early in World War II and discussed the possibility of making an atom bomb. "Like the play *Copenhagen*, I cannot be sure of my own motivations," Lander says. "You don't know your own motives." Wow, I think.[1]

One of the appealing things about Lander is that he is merrily and jubilantly competitive, pushing Zhang to claim his credit, then driving the lawsuits to protect Zhang's patents. His bristly moustache and enthusiastic eyes are at all times expressive, conveying every changing emotion in a way that would delight a poker opponent. His relentless drive and passion to persuade—he reminds me of the late diplomat Richard Holbrooke—made him infuriating to rivals, but it also made him a hard-charging and effective team leader and institution builder. His paper on the history of CRISPR was an example of all of these instincts.

After months of reading all the scientific papers and interviewing many of the participants by phone, Lander published "The Heroes of CRISPR" in the journal *Cell* in January 2016.[2] At eight thousand words, it was vividly written and factually correct in its details. But it provoked a firestorm of responses from outraged critics who charged that it was skewed, in ways both subtle and heavy-handed, to tout the contributions of Zhang and minimize those of Doudna. It was history weaponized.

Lander's narrative began with Francisco Mojica and went through the other players I've discussed in this book, mixing personal color with scientific explanations of each step in the development of CRISPR. He described and praised the work of Charpentier in discovering the tracrRNA, but instead of then showing how she and Doudna went on to figure out the exact role of each component in 2012, he provided a long description of the work of the Lithuanian Šikšnys and his difficulty in getting published.

When Lander got to Doudna, he was pleasant enough. He called her "a world-renowned structural biologist and RNA expert," but he breezed by the work she did with Charpentier in just one paragraph out of the article's sixty-seven. Not surprisingly, Zhang was accorded a more lavish account. After stressing how difficult it was to move CRISPR-Cas9 from bacteria to human cells, Lander described in some detail, but without citing evidence, the work Zhang was doing in early 2012. As for Doudna's January 2013 paper showing the system working in human cells, published three weeks after Zhang's, Lander dismissed it in a sentence that included the dagger-like accusation "with assistance from Church."

The main theme of Lander's essay was important and correct. "Scientific breakthroughs are rarely eureka moments," he concluded. "They are typically ensemble acts, played out over a decade or more, in which the cast becomes part of something greater than what any one of them could do alone." Yet the article clearly had another thrust, one that was done with a velvet glove but was nonetheless an unmistakable diminishment of Doudna. Oddly for an academic journal, *Cell* did not disclose that Lander's Broad Institute was competing for patents with Doudna and her colleagues.

Doudna decided to be muted in her public reaction. She simply posted a comment online stating, "The description of my lab's research and our interactions with other investigators is factually incorrect, was not checked by the author, and was not agreed to by me prior to publication." Charpentier was similarly upset. "I regret that the description of me and my collaborators' contributions is incomplete and inaccurate," she posted.

Church was more specific in his criticisms. He pointed out that he, not Zhang, first demonstrated the use in human cells of an extended guide RNA that ended up working the best. He also disputed the assertions that Doudna had taken information from the preprint he had sent her.

Backlash

Doudna's friends rallied to her cause with a fury that would have impressed a Twitter mob. In fact, it included a Twitter mob.

The most vibrant and viral responses came from one of Doudna's high-octane colleagues at Berkeley, genetics professor Michael Eisen. "There is something mesmerizing about an evil genius at the height of their craft, and Eric Lander is an evil genius at the height of his craft," he wrote and posted publicly a few days after the article appeared. He called the piece "at once so evil and yet so brilliant that I find it hard not to stand in awe even as I picture him cackling loudly in his Kendall Square lair, giant laser weapon behind him poised to destroy Berkeley if we don't hand over our patents."

Eisen, who was upfront about the fact that he was Doudna's partisan friend, charged that Lander's piece was "an ingenious strategy" to promote the Broad and denigrate Doudna under the veneer of a historical perspective. "The piece is an elaborate lie that organizes and twists history with no other purpose than to achieve Lander's goals—to win Zhang a Nobel Prize and the Broad an insanely lucrative patent. It is, in its crucial moments, so disconnected from reality that it is hard to fathom how someone so brilliant could have written it."[3] I think that is not fair or true. My own view is that Lander may have been guilty of zeal as a mentor and a zest for spinning, but not dishonesty.

Other, more dispassionate scientists joined the criticism of Lander, with flames erupting on venues ranging from the scientific discussion board *PubPeer* to Twitter.[4] "'Shitstorm' would be one term of art for the reaction in the genome community to a commentary in *Cell* by Eric Lander," wrote Nathaniel Comfort, a professor of the history of medicine at Johns Hopkins. Comfort called Lander's piece "Whig history," suggesting that it was crafted in order "to use history as a political tool." He even created a Twitter hashtag, #Landergate, that became a rallying spot for those who thought Lander was insidiously slagging competitors of the Broad.[5]

In the influential *MIT Technology Review*, Antonio Regalado focused on Lander's assertions, not backed up with any citations, that Zhang had made great progress on developing CRISPR-Cas9 tools a year before the Doudna-Charpentier 2012 paper was published. "Zhang's discoveries weren't published at the time, and so they are not part of the official scientific record," Regalado wrote. "But they're very important if Broad wants to hold onto its patents. . . . No wonder, then, that Lander might like to see them described for the first time in an important journal such as *Cell*. I think that was a little Machiavellian on the part of Lander."[6]

Women scientists and writers, aware of the injustice done to Rosalind Franklin in some of the histories of DNA, were especially incensed at Lander, whose alpha-male style had never endeared him to feminists even though he has a laudable history of supporting women scientists. "His write-up serves as yet another instance of a woman being written out of scientific history," Ruth Reader, a science journalist, wrote in *Mic*. "This helps explain the urgency behind the backlash to Lander's report: Here again, a male leader appears to be usurping credit (and therefore financial gain) for a discovery that was the work of many." An article on *Jezebel*, which describes itself cheekily as "a supposedly feminist website," was headlined "How One Man Tried to Write Women Out of CRISPR, the Biggest Biotech Innovation in Decades." In it Joanna Rothkopf wrote, "The crediting issue evokes that of Rosalind Franklin."[7]

The flare-up against Lander, which occurred while he was on a trip to Antarctica and could not easily respond, became so newsworthy that mainstream publications covered it. Stephen Hall in *Scientific American* called it "the most entertaining food fight in science in years," and asked, "Why would such a shrewd and strategic thinker like Lander tempt such a public backlash by writing such a cleverly slanted history?" Hall quoted Church as saying of Lander, "The only person that could hurt him was himself," and then merrily declaring, "And you thought scientists couldn't talk smack."[8]

Lander responded by criticizing Doudna for not providing more input on the piece when he emailed her some passages right before it went to press. "I received input about the development of CRISPR from more than a dozen scientists around the world," Lander wrote in an email to Tracy Vence of *The Scientist*. "Dr. Doudna was the only one who declined, which is unfortunate. Nonetheless, I fully respect her decision not to share her perspective."[9] That final gauze-cloaked zinger was quintessential Lander.

The article helped to draw the battle lines in the CRISPR war. Doudna's admirers at Harvard, led by Church and her PhD advisor, Jack Szostak, were infuriated. "It's just an awful, awful, piece of writing," Szostak tells me. "Eric wants the credit for the genetic editing revolution to go to Feng Zhang and him, and not Jennifer. So he just totally belittled her contribution in a way that seems just pure animus."[10]

Even within his own institution, Lander's piece raised hackles. After several members of the staff questioned him about it, he sent them an email addressed "Dear Broadies." It was unapologetic. "The essay aims to describe the whole group of extraordinary scientists (many at the early stages of their careers) who took risks and made critical discoveries," he wrote. "I'm very proud of the essay and its messages about science."[11]

A couple of months after publication, as the controversy still simmered, I got enlisted as a peripheral player. Christine Heenan, who was then vice president of communications at Harvard, was asked by Lander to help smooth things over. I had known Eric for a long time, and I was (and am) one of his alloyed admirers. So Heenan asked me to host a discussion with him for the press and scientific community at the Washington headquarters of the Aspen Institute, where I worked. Her goal was to tamp down the controversy by getting Lander to say that he hadn't meant to minimize Doudna's contributions to the CRISPR field. Lander tried to do what Heenan urged, albeit not in a way that could be described as valiantly. "My intention is not to diminish anybody," he said, adding that Doudna was "a spectacular scientist." That was about it. When he was pressed by the *Washington Post*'s Joel Achenbach, he insisted that his article was factual and did not underplay Doudna's accomplishments. I caught Heenan's eye, and she shrugged.[12]

Eldora Ellison

CHAPTER 31

Patents

"Useful arts"

Ever since the Republic of Venice in 1474 passed a statute giving the inventors of "any new and ingenious device" the exclusive right to profit from it for ten years, people have been wrestling over patents. In the United States, they are enshrined in Article 1 of the Constitution: "The Congress shall have power to . . . promote the progress of science and useful arts by securing for limited times to authors and inventors the exclusive right to their respective writings and discoveries." A year after ratification, Congress passed an act that allowed patents on "any useful art, manufacture, engine, machine, or device, or any improvement thereon not before known."

As courts came to realize, it's complicated to apply such concepts, even to things as simple as a doorknob. In the 1850 case *Hotchkiss v. Greenwood*, which involved a patent application for the manufacture of doorknobs out of porcelain rather than wood, the U.S. Supreme Court began the process of defining what was "obvious" and "non-obvious" in assessing whether an invention was "not before known." Deciding on patents was particularly difficult when it involved biological processes. Nevertheless, biological patents have a long history. In 1873, for example, the French biologist Louis Pasteur was awarded the first known patent for a microorganism: a method for making "yeast free from organic germs of disease." Thus we have pasteurized milk, juice, and wine.

The modern biotechnology industry was born a century later, when a Stanford attorney approached Stanley Cohen and Herbert Boyer and convinced them to file for a patent on the method they had discovered for manufacturing new genes using recombinant DNA. Many scientists, including Paul Berg, the discoverer of recombinant DNA, were horrified at the idea of patenting a biological process, but the royalties that flowed to the inventors and their universities quickly made biotech patents popular. Stanford, for example, made $225 million in twenty-five years by granting hundreds of biotech companies non-exclusive licenses to the Cohen-Boyer patents.

Two major milestones occurred in 1980. The U.S. Supreme Court ruled in favor of a genetic engineer who had derived a strain of bacteria capable of eating crude oil, which made it useful in cleaning up oil spills. His application had been rejected by the Patent Office on the theory that you could not patent a living thing. But the Supreme Court ruled, in a 5–4 decision written by Chief Justice Warren Burger, that "a live, human-made micro-organism is patentable" if it is "a product of human ingenuity."[1]

Also that year, Congress passed the Bayh-Dole Act, which made it easier for universities to benefit from patents, even if the research was funded by the government. Until then, universities often were required to assign the rights to their inventions to the federal agencies that had funded them. Some academics feel that the Bayh-Dole Act cheats the public out of the proceeds from inventions funded with taxpayer money and distorts the way universities work. "Encouraged by a small number of patents that made huge sums, universities developed massive infrastructure to profit from their researchers," argues Michael Eisen, Doudna's colleague at Berkeley. He believes that the government should put all work funded by federal dollars into the public domain. "We all would benefit returning academic science to its roots in basic discovery oriented research. We see with CRISPR the toxic effects of turning academic institutions into money hungry hawkers of intellectual property."[2]

That's an appealing argument, but I believe that, on balance, American science has benefited from the current mix of federal funding and commercial incentives. To turn a basic scientific discovery into a tool or a drug can cost billions of dollars. Unless there is a way to recoup that, there won't be as much investment in research.[3] The development of CRISPR and the therapies it led to are a good example.

CRISPR patents

Doudna did not know much about patents. Little of her previous work had practical application. When she and Charpentier were finishing their June 2012 paper, she reached out to the woman at Berkeley in charge of intellectual property, who set her up with a lawyer.

For research professors in the U.S., the patents to their inventions are usually assigned to the academic institution, in Doudna's case Berkeley, with the inventors having a lot of say over how it will be licensed and taking a portion (in most universities about one-third) of the royalties. In Sweden, where Charpentier was then based, the patent goes directly to the inventor. So Doudna's application was filed jointly by Berkeley, Charpentier personally, and the University of Vienna, where Chylinski was based. Shortly after 7 p.m. on May 25, 2012, just as they were finishing their paper for *Science*, they filed their provisional patent application and used a credit card to pay the $155 fee for processing. It did not occur to them to spend a little extra to have the application expedited.[4]

The 168-page application, which included diagrams and experimental data, described CRISPR-Cas9 and made more than 124 claims for ways that the system could be used. All of the data in the application were from experiments done with bacteria. However, it mentioned delivery methods that could work in human cells, and it made the claim that the patent should cover the use of CRISPR as an editing tool in all forms of life.

As I noted earlier, Zhang and the Broad submitted their own patent application in December 2012, when his paper about editing in humans was accepted by *Science*.[5] It specifically described a process for using CRISPR in *human* cells. Unlike Berkeley, the Broad made use of a neat little provision in the patent process: it paid a small additional fee and agreed to a few conditions in order to expedite consideration under what was known as an Accelerated Examination Request or, more poetically, a Petition to Make Special.[6]

Initially, the Patent Office did not grant Zhang's application, asking for more information. Zhang responded by supplying a written declaration. In it, he made an allegation that infuriated Doudna. He pointed out that Church had sent her a preprint of his paper, and he implied that she used his data in her patent application. "I respectfully question the origin of the example," Zhang said. In one of their legal filings, Zhang and the Broad asserted, "It was only after the Church laboratory shared unpublished data that Dr. Doudna's laboratory reported they were able to adapt a CRISPR-Cas9 system" for use in human cells.

Doudna was outraged at Zhang's declaration because it implied that she had plagiarized Church's data. She called Church at his home on a Sunday afternoon, and he shared her anger at what his former student had alleged. "I'm happy to go public and say you didn't improperly use my data," Church told her. She had been polite to include a sentence about him in her acknowledgments, and it was "outrageous," he later told me, that Zhang would turn that small act of collegiality against her.[7]

Marraffini dropped

As Zhang was waiting for a ruling on his patent applications, he and the Broad did something unusual: they dropped the name of his collaborator Luciano Marraffini from the main application. The somewhat mystifying tale is a sad example of the distorting effects that patent law can have on scientific collaboration. It's also a tale of competitiveness, perhaps even greed, overwhelming kindness, and collegiality.

Marraffini is the soft-spoken Argentinian-born bacteriologist at Rockefeller University who collaborated with Zhang beginning in early 2012 and was a coauthor on his *Science* paper. When Zhang initially filed for his patents, Marraffini was listed as one of the co-inventors.[8]

A year later, Marraffini was called into the office of the president of Rockefeller and told, to his shock and profound sadness, that Zhang and the Broad had decided to narrow some of the patent applications and focus one of them only on the process of making CRISPR-Cas9 work in human cells. Marraffini did not contribute enough to that work to deserve being on the patent, the Broad unilaterally decided, so they were dropping him.

"Feng Zhang didn't even have the politeness to tell me directly," Marraffini says, shaking his head, still looking shocked and sad after six years. "I'm a reasonable guy. If they said my contribution was not worth an equal share, I would have accepted a smaller share. But they didn't even tell me." What particularly pains him is that he views the story of his work with Zhang as an inspiring American tale: two young rising stars who were immigrants, one from China and the other from Argentina, joining forces to show how CRISPR could be used in humans.[9]

When I ask Zhang about this, he likewise speaks quietly and sorrowfully, as if he's the one who is hurt. "I focused on Cas9 from the beginning," he insists when I ask if Marraffini should get some credit for getting him to concentrate on that enzyme. It may have been ungenerous to take Marraffini off the patent, but in Zhang's mind it was not unwarranted. Therein lies one of the problem with patents: they prod people to be less generous in sharing credit.[10]

Conflict

The Patent Office decided to grant Zhang's patent application on April 15, 2014, even though Doudna's application* was still being considered.[11] When she heard, she called Andy May, her business associate,

*I am using shorthand when I refer to the applications. When I talk about Doudna's, I am referring to the ones she did jointly with Charpentier, Berkeley, and the University of Vienna. Likewise, when I talk about Zhang's applications, I am referring to the ones he did with the Broad, MIT, and Harvard.

who was driving. "I remember pulling over in the car and taking the call and getting this blast," he says. "'How did this happen?' she asked. 'How did we get beaten?' She was livid, absolutely livid."[12]

Doudna's application was still languishing at the Patent Office. That raised a question: What happens if you apply for a patent and, before the decision gets made, another person is granted a similar patent? Under U.S. law, you have a year to request an "interference" hearing. So in April 2015, Doudna filed a claim that Zhang's patents should be disallowed because they interfered with the patent applications that she had previously submitted.[13]

Specifically, Doudna submitted a 114-page "Suggestion of Interference" detailing why some of Zhang's claims were "not patentably distinct" from her own pending claims. Even though her team's experiments had involved bacteria, she argued that their patent application "specifically states" that the system can be applied in "all organisms" and provides "detailed descriptions of numerous steps that could be taken to apply the system" to humans.[14] Zhang argued in his response declaration that Doudna's application "did NOT [emphasis in the original] have the features required for Cas9 binding and DNA target site recognition in a human cell."[15]

Thus the battle lines were drawn. Doudna and her colleagues had identified the essential components of CRISPR-Cas9 and engineered a technique to make it work using components from bacterial cells. Their contention was that it was then "obvious" how it would work in a human cell. Zhang and the Broad Institute countered that it was *not* obvious that the system would work in humans. It required another inventive step to make it work, and Zhang had beaten Doudna to it. In order to resolve this issue, the patent examiners in December 2015 launched an "interference proceeding" to be decided by a panel of three patent judges.

When Doudna's lawyers asserted it was "obvious" that a system that worked in bacteria would also work in humans, they were using a term of art. In patent law, the term "obvious" refers to a specific legal concept. Courts have declared that the "criterion for determination of obviousness is whether the prior art would have suggested to a person of ordinary skill in the art that this process would have a reasonable likelihood of success."[16] In other words, you don't deserve a new patent if you merely modified a prior invention in a way that was so obvious that a person with ordinary skill in the field could have done the same with a reasonable likelihood of success. Unfortunately, phrases such as "person of ordinary skill" and "reasonable likelihood of success" are fuzzy when applied to biology, where experiments are less predictable than in other forms of engineering. Unexpected things happen when you start fiddling with the innards of living cells.[17]

The trial

It took a full year for all the briefs, declarations, and motions to be filed, after which a hearing was held in December 2016 before a three-judge panel at the Patent and Trademark Office in Alexandria, Virginia. With its blond-wood dais and simple tables, the hearing room looks like a sleepy county traffic court. But on the day of the trial, a hundred journalists, lawyers, investors, and biotech fans, most of them bespectacled and looking a bit nerdy, began lining up at 5:45 a.m. to get seats.[18]

Zhang's lawyer opened the hearing by stating that the key issue was "whether the use of CRISPR in eukaryotic cells was obvious" after the Doudna-Charpentier 2012 article.[19] To make the case that it was not, he put up a series of posters with statements made earlier by Doudna and her team. The first was from an interview Doudna gave to a Berkeley Chemistry Department magazine: "Our 2012 paper was a big success, but there was a problem. We weren't sure if CRISPR-Cas9 would work in plant and animal cells."[20]

Zhang's lawyer then put up a quote that was not merely an offhand comment but a statement that Doudna and Martin Jinek made in the *eLife* paper that they had rushed into publication in January 2013. Their earlier paper had "suggested the exciting possibility" that the CRISPR system could be used for editing human genes, they wrote, but then they added, "However, it was not known whether such a bacterial system would function in eukaryotic cells." As Zhang's lawyer told the court, "These comments at the time belie this idea that this was all obvious."

Doudna's lawyers rebutted that her comments were simply the mark of a careful scientist. This did not impress the lead judge, Deborah Katz. "Are there any statements," she asked Doudna's lawyer, "in which anybody said they did believe it would work?" The best the lawyer could do was point to Doudna's statement that it was "a real possibility."

Fearing that he was playing a losing hand, Doudna's lawyer shifted the argument. Five labs had made the system work in eukaryotic cells within six months of the publication of the Doudna-Charpentier discovery, he said, which was an indication of how "obvious" such a step was. He displayed a chart showing that they all used well-known methods. "There's no special sauce here," he told the judge. "These labs would not have embarked on this quest unless they had a reasonable expectation of success."[21]

The three-judge panel ended up siding with Zhang and the Broad. "Broad has persuaded us that the parties claim patentably distinct subject matter," the judges declared in February 2017. "The evidence shows that the invention of such systems in eukaryotic cells would not have been obvious."[22]

Doudna's side appealed to the federal courts, beginning a process that took another nineteen months. In September 2018, the U.S. Court of Appeals for the Federal Circuit upheld the ruling of the patent board.[23] Zhang was entitled to his patent; it did not interfere with Doudna and Charpentier's application.

But as happens with many complex intellectual property cases, these rulings did not end the case or give Zhang a total victory. Because there was "no interference" between the two sets of applications, they could be considered separately, which meant that it was still possible that the Doudna-Charpentier application would be granted as well.

Patent priority dispute, 2020

That is what happened. In the final two sentences of its 2018 decision affirming Zhang's patent, the U.S. Court of Appeals had emphasized a significant point. "This case is about the scope of two sets of applied-for claims and whether those claims are patentably distinct," the judge wrote. "It is not a ruling on the validity of either set of claims." In other words, there was no "interference" between the patents granted to Zhang and the pending ones that had been applied for by Doudna and Charpentier. They could be considered as two distinct inventions, and it was possible that *both* could deserve patents or that the Doudna-Charpentier ones would take priority.

Of course such a result would be messy and somewhat paradoxical. If both sets of patents got granted and then seemed to overlap, that would fly in the face of the decision that there was no interference between them. But sometimes life, and in particular life inside of cells and courtrooms, can be paradoxical.

In early 2019, the U.S. Patent Office granted fifteen patents based on the applications that Doudna and Charpentier had filed in 2012. By then, Doudna had hired a new lead attorney, Eldora Ellison, who had blazed an educational path that was tailor-made for the age of biotech. She earned her undergraduate degree at Haverford in biology, then a doctorate at Cornell in biochemistry and cell biology, and finally a law degree at Georgetown. I often suggest to my students that they consider studying both biology and business, as Rachel Haurwitz did, or biology and law, as Ellison did.

When she analyzed the case for me over breakfast, Ellison was able to explain the nuances of both the biology and the law, and she readily cited from memory arcane footnotes in various scientific articles and court decisions. I came to the conclusion that Ellison would be great on the Supreme Court, which nowadays could use at least one justice who understands biology and technology.[24]

Ellison was able to prod the Patent Office in June 2019 to launch a new case.[25] Unlike the first case, which looked only at whether Zhang's patents interfered with the ones that Doudna had applied for, this new case would involve adjudicating the fundamental issue: which side had made the key discoveries first. This new "priority dispute" would attempt to pinpoint, using notebooks and other evidence, precisely when each applicant had invented CRISPR-Cas9 as an editing tool.

In a May 2020 hearing, done by phone because of the coronavirus closures, Zhang's lawyer argued that the issue had already been decided: it was not "obvious" that the CRISPR-Cas9 system discovered by Doudna and Charpentier in 2012 would work in human cells, and therefore Zhang was entitled to a patent for being the first to show how it would. Ellison responded that the legal issues in the new case were not the same. The patent that was granted to Doudna and Charpentier was for the use of CRISPR-Cas9 in all organisms, from bacteria to humans. The question, she said, was whether their patent application from 2012 contained enough evidence to show they had discovered this. She contended that even though their experimental data came from using bacterial components in a test tube, their patent application, when considered in its entirety, described how to use the system in any organism.[26] By late 2020, the case was still dragging along.

In Europe, there was initially a similar situation: Doudna and Charpentier were granted a patent, and then Zhang was also given one.[27] But at that point Zhang's dispute with Marraffini popped up again. After Zhang's applications were revised and Marraffini's name dropped, the European patent court ruled that Zhang could not use the date of his original application as his "priority date." As a result, other patent applications were deemed to have an earlier priority date, and the court revoked Zhang's patent. "Feng's European patent was nullified because of the way he took me off," Marraffini says.[28] By 2020, Doudna and Charpentier had been awarded the major patents also in Britain, China, Japan, Australia, New Zealand, and Mexico.

Were all of these patent battles worth it? Would Doudna and Zhang have been better off coming to a deal rather than battling in court? In retrospect, Doudna's business partner Andy May thinks so. "We would have saved a lot of time and money around all of the legal arguments if we had managed to come together," he says.[29]

To an unnecessary extent, the prolonged fight was driven by emotions and resentments. Instead, Doudna and Zhang could have followed the example of Jack Kilby of Texas Instruments and Robert

Noyce of Intel who, after five years of wrangling, agreed to share the patent rights for the microchip by cross-licensing their intellectual property to each other and splitting the royalties, which helped the microchip business grow exponentially and define a new age of technology. Unlike the CRISPR contestants, Noyce and Kilby obeyed an all-important business maxim: *Don't fight over divvying up the proceeds until you finish robbing the stagecoach.*

PART FOUR

CRISPR in Action

If ever man fell ill, there was no defense
—no healing food, no ointment, nor any drink—
but for lack of medicine they wasted away,
until I showed them how to mix soothing remedies.

—Prometheus, in Aeschylus's *Prometheus Bound*

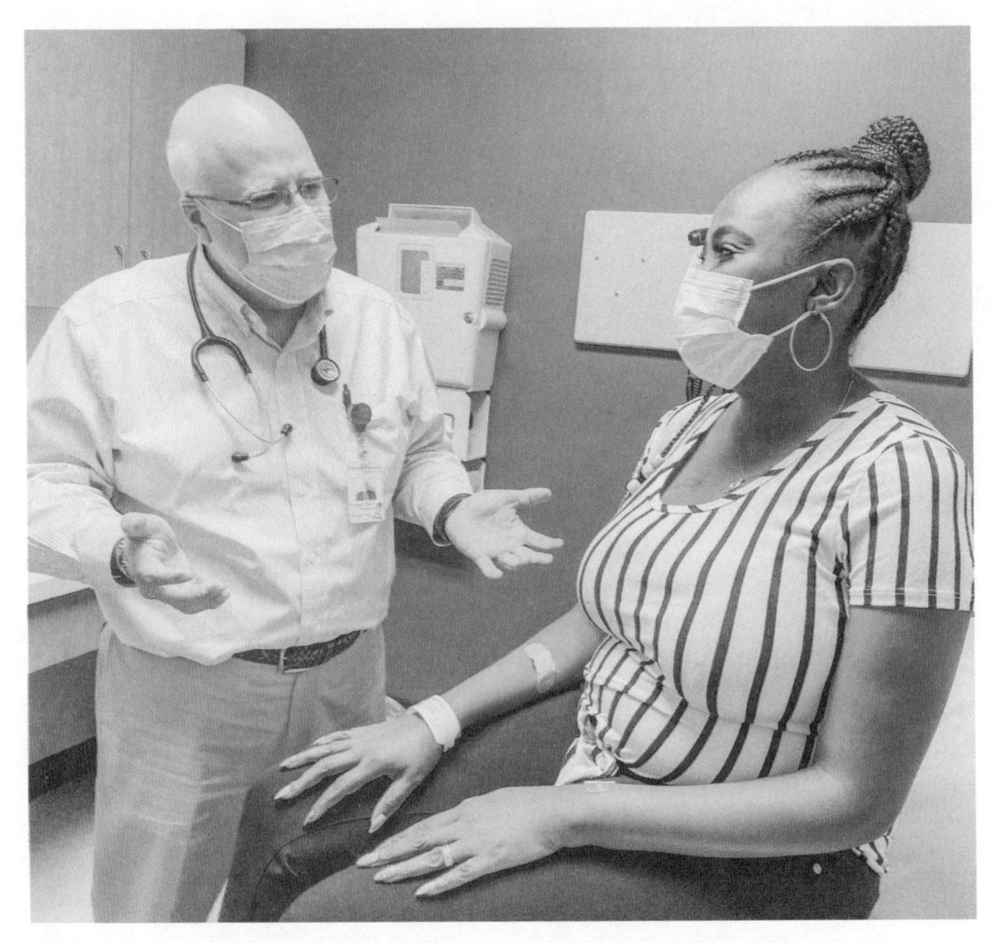

Dr. Haydar Frangoul of the Sarah Cannon Research Institute in Nashville with Victoria Gray

Chapter 32

Therapies

Sickle cell

In July 2019, a doctor at a Nashville hospital plunged the needle of a large syringe into the arm of a thirty-four-year-old African American woman from a small town in central Mississippi and infused her with stem cells that had been extracted from her blood and edited using CRISPR-Cas9. They were now being reinserted in an attempt to cure her of the sickle-cell disease that had plagued her with debilitating pain since she was a baby. Thus did Victoria Gray, a mother of four children, become the first person in the United States to be treated with a CRISPR gene-editing tool. The clinical trial was led by CRISPR Therapeutics, the company formed by Emmanuelle Charpentier. When Gray was injected, her heart rate shot up and for a while she had trouble breathing. "There was a little scary, tough moment for me," she told NPR reporter Rob Stein, who was allowed to follow her treatment. "After that, I cried. But it was happy tears."[1]

Much of the attention paid to CRISPR these days involves its potential to make inheritable (germline) edits in humans that will be passed along to all the cells of all of our future descendants and have the potential to alter our species. These edits are done in reproductive cells or early-stage embryos. This is what occurred with the CRISPR baby twins in China in 2018, and it is the controversial topic that I will discuss later in this book. But in this chapter I'm going to focus on what will be, at least for now, the most common and welcome uses of CRISPR: cases like that of Victoria Gray, in which CRISPR is used to edit some, but not all, of the body (somatic) cells of a patient and make changes that will *not* be inherited. This can be done by taking the cells out of the patient, editing them, and returning them (*ex vivo*) or by delivering the CRISPR editing tool into cells inside of the patient (*in vivo*).

Sickle-cell anemia is one of the best candidates for *ex vivo* gene editing because it involves blood cells that can be easily extracted and returned. The disease is caused by a mutation in a single letter out of more than three billion base pairs of a person's DNA, which causes a kink in the hemoglobin protein. A normal version of hemoglobin protein forms round and smooth blood cells, able to move easily through our vessels and carry oxygen from our lungs to the rest of our body. But the kinked hemoglobin protein forms long fibers that contort the red blood cells, which causes them to clump together and crumple into the shape of a sickle. Oxygen does not get to tissues and organs, causing severe pain and, in most cases, death by age fifty. Sickle-cell disease afflicts more than four million people worldwide, about 80 percent of them in sub-Saharan Africa, and about ninety thousand people in the U.S., mainly African Americans.

The simplicity of the genetic glitch and the severity of the syndrome make it a perfect candidate for gene editing. In the case of Victoria Gray, doctors extracted stem cells from her own blood and edited them, using CRISPR, to activate a gene that produces a type of blood cell that is normally made only during the fetal stage of life. That fetal-stage hemoglobin is healthy, so if the genetic modification works, patients can start producing their own good blood.

A few months after she was injected with her edited cells, Gray drove up to the Nashville hospital to see if the therapy was working. She was optimistic. Ever since she got the edited cells, she hadn't needed to get donor transfusions or had any attacks of pain. A nurse inserted a needle and drew multiple tubes of blood. After a nervous wait, her doctor came in to give her the news. "I am super-excited about your results today," he said. "There are signs that you are starting to make fetal hemoglobin, which is very exciting for us." About half of her blood was now fetal hemoglobin with healthy cells.

In June 2020, Gray got some even more exciting news: the treatment seemed to be lasting. After nine months, she still had not suffered any sickle-cell pain attacks, nor did she need any further blood transfusions. Tests showed that 81 percent of her bone marrow cells were producing the good fetal hemoglobin, meaning that the gene edits were sustained.[2] "High school graduations, college graduations, weddings, grandkids—I thought I wouldn't see none of that," she said after getting the news. "Now I'll be there to help my daughters pick out their wedding dresses."[3] It was an amazing milestone: CRISPR had apparently cured a genetic disease in humans. In Berlin, Charpentier listened to a recording of Gray's emotional NPR interview. "It was pretty amazing to realize as I heard her," she says, "that the little baby I helped to create, CRISPR editing, means that she will no longer suffer."[4]

Affordability

Applications of CRISPR such as this are likely to be lifesavers. They are also sure to be expensive. In fact, the treatment of a single patient could cost $1 million or more, at least initially. So the prospect of CRISPR doing great good is matched by its potential to bankrupt the healthcare system.

Doudna began to focus on this problem after a discussion that she had with a group of U.S. senators in December 2018. The meeting at the Capitol was held a few weeks after the announcement that twin "CRISPR babies" had been born in China with inheritable edits, and Doudna expected it to focus on that headline-making news. At first it did. But to her surprise, the discussion quickly shifted from the perils of inheritable gene-editing to the promise of using gene editing to treat diseases.

Doudna told the senators that CRISPR was on the verge of creating a cure for sickle-cell disease, which got them to perk up, but they immediately peppered her with questions about the cost. "We have 100,000 people in the U.S. affected by sickle cell," one senator pointed out. "How are we going to afford that if it's $1 million per patient? That just breaks the bank."

Doudna decided that making sickle-cell treatments affordable should become a mission of her Innovative Genomics Institute. "The Senate hearing was, for me, a watershed moment," she says. "I'd been thinking a lot about costs before that, but not in a focused way." When she arrived back at Berkeley, she convened a series of meetings of her team to discuss how to make wide access to sickle-cell treatments a new core part of their mission.[5]

The public-private partnership that led to the availability of the polio vaccine became an inspiration. She reached out to the Gates Foundation and the National Institutes of Health, which announced a partnership for a Cure Sickle Cell Initiative funded with $200 million.[6] The primary scientific goal of the initiative is to find a method to edit the sickle-cell mutation inside of a patient without needing to extract bone marrow. One possibility is to inject into the patient's blood a gene-editing molecule with an address label that directs it right to the cells in the bone marrow. The difficult part will be to find the right delivery mechanism, such as a virus-like particle, that won't trigger the patient's immune system.

If the initiative is successful, it will not only cure a lot of people of a dreadful disease; it will advance the cause of health justice. Most sickle-cell patients in the world are Africans or African Americans. These are populations that have been historically underserved by the medical community. Even though the genetic cause of sickle-cell disease has been understood for longer than any similar disorder, new treatments have lagged behind. For example, the fight against cystic fibrosis, which affects primarily white Americans and Europeans, has received eight times more funding from government, charities, and foundations. The great promise of gene editing is that it will transform medicine. The peril is that it will widen the healthcare divide between rich and poor. Doudna's sickle-cell initiative is designed to find ways to avoid that.

Cancer

In addition to treating blood disorders, such as sickle-cell anemia, CRISPR has been used to fight cancer. China has been the pioneer in this field, and it is two or three years ahead of the United States in devising treatments and getting them into clinical trials.[7]

The first person to be treated was a lung-cancer patient in Chengdu, a city of 14 million in the western Chinese province of Sichuan. In October 2016, a team removed from the patient's blood some of his T-cells, which are the white blood cells that help fight off diseases and confer immunity. The doctors then used CRISPR-Cas9 to disable a gene that produces a protein, known as PD-1, which stops the cell's immune response. Cancer cells sometimes trigger the PD-1 response, thus protecting themselves from the immune system. By using CRISPR to edit the gene, the patient's T-cells become more effective in killing the cancer cells. Within a year, China had seven clinical trials using this technique.[8]

"I think this is going to trigger 'Sputnik 2.0,' a biomedical duel on progress between China and the United States," said Carl June, a noted cancer researcher at the University of Pennsylvania who at the time was still struggling to get regulatory approval for a similar clinical trial. He and his colleagues were finally able to get their trial underway and reported preliminary results in 2020. Their method, used in three late-stage cancer patients, was more sophisticated than the one used in China. They knocked out the PD-1 gene and also inserted into the T cells a gene that targeted the patients' tumors.

Although the patients were not cured, the trials showed that the technique was safe. Doudna and one of her postdoctoral students published an article in *Science* explaining the Penn results. "Until now, it has been unknown whether CRISPR-Cas9–edited T cells would be tolerated and thrive once reinfused into a human," they wrote. "The findings represent an important advance in the therapeutic application of gene editing."[9]

CRISPR is also being used as a detection tool to identify precisely what type of cancer a patient has. Mammoth Biosciences, a company that Doudna founded with two of her graduate students, is designing diagnostic tools based on CRISPR that can be used on tumors to identify quickly and easily the DNA sequences associated with different types of cancers. Then precision treatments can be tailored for each patient.[10]

Blindness

The third use of CRISPR editing that was underway by 2020 was to cure a form of congenital blindness. In this case the procedure was performed *in vivo*—inside the patient's body—because eye cells cannot be extracted and returned the way blood and bone marrow cells can. The clinical trials were conducted in partnership with Editas Medicine, the company founded by Zhang and others.

The goal was to treat Leber congenital amaurosis, a common cause of childhood blindness. Those with the condition have a mutation in the gene that makes light-receptor cells in their eye. It causes a critical protein to be shortened, so that the light that hits the cells is not converted into nerve signals.[11]

The first use of the treatment occurred in March 2020, just before coronavirus shut down most clinics, at the Casey Eye Institute in Portland, Oregon. In the hour-long procedure, doctors used a tiny hair-width tube to inject three drops of fluid containing CRISPR-Cas9 into the lining that contains light-sensing cells directly beneath the retina of the patient's eyes. A tailored virus was used as the delivery vehicle to transport the CRISPR-Cas9 into the targeted cells. If the cells are edited as planned, the fix will be permanent, because unlike blood cells, the cells of the eye do not divide and replenish themselves.[12]

Coming soon

Work is also underway on some more ambitious uses of CRISPR gene editing that could make us less vulnerable to pandemics, cancers, Alzheimer's, and other diseases. For example, a gene known as *P53* encodes for a protein that suppresses the growth of cancerous tumors.

It helps the body respond to damaged DNA and prevents cancerous cells from dividing. Humans tend to have one copy of this gene, and cancers proliferate if something goes wrong with it. Elephants have twenty copies of this gene, and they almost never get cancer. Researchers are currently exploring ways to add an extra *P53* gene into humans. Likewise, the gene *APOE4* raises the risk of the devastating disease of Alzheimer's. Researchers are looking for ways to convert it into a benign version of the gene.

Another gene, *PCSK9*, encodes for an enzyme that facilitates the creation of LDL, the "bad" cholesterol. Some people have a mutated copy of the gene that leads to very low levels of this cholesterol, which results in an 88 percent reduction in risk for coronary heart disease. Before he decided to edit the gene for HIV receptors in the CRISPR babies he created, He Jiankui was studying ways to use CRISPR to make germline edits in the *PCSK9* gene of embryos to produce designer babies with far less risk of having heart disease.[13]

At the beginning of 2020, there were two dozen clinical trials for various uses of CRISPR-Cas9 in the pipeline. They included potential treatments for angioedema (a hereditary disease that causes severe swelling), acute myeloid leukemia, super-high cholesterol, and male pattern baldness.[14] In March of that year, however, most academic research labs were temporarily shut down because of the coronavirus pandemic. An exception was made for labs that were engaged in fighting the virus. Many CRISPR researchers, Doudna foremost among them, would shift their focus to creating detection tools and treatments for the disease, some of them making use of the tricks they had learned from studying how bacteria developed an immune response to ward off new viruses.

Josiah Zayner

CHAPTER 33

Biohacking

Wearing a black T-shirt and tight white jeans, Josiah Zayner stood in front of a roomful of biotechnologists at the Global Synthetic Biology Summit in San Francisco in 2017 and launched into a pitch about a do-it-yourself "frog genetic engineering kit" that he made in his garage. Available online for $299, it allowed users to cause a frog's muscles to double in size in a month by injecting CRISPR-edited DNA that turned off the gene that produces myostatin, a protein that inhibits muscle growth once an animal has reached its mature size.

It would also work on humans, Zayner said, flashing a conspiratorial smile. You could grow bigger muscles.

There was some nervous laughter and then a few shouts of encouragement. "What's holding you back?" someone hollered.

Zayner, a serious scientist wrapped in the persona of a rebel, took a swig of Scotch from a leather-covered hip flask. "Are you suggesting I should try it?" he responded.

There were more murmurs, a few gasps and laughs, then some more encouragement. Zayner reached into a medicine bag, pulled out a syringe, filled it from a vial of the edited DNA, and proclaimed, "All right, let's do it!" Sticking the needle into his left forearm, he winced a bit and then plunged the liquid into his veins. "This will modify my muscle genes to give me bigger muscles," he proclaimed.

There was scattered applause. He took another swig of Scotch from his hip flask. "I will let you know how it works out," he said.[1]

Zayner, with his bleached-blond forelock and ten piercings in each ear, thus became the poster boy for a new breed of biohacker, the spirited band of renegade researchers and merry hobbyists who want to democratize biology through citizen science and bring its power to the people. While conventional researchers worry about patents, biohackers want to keep the bio-frontier free of royalties, regulations, and restraints, similar to the way digital hackers felt about the cyber-frontier. In most cases, the biohackers are, like Zayner, accomplished scientists who forgo working at universities or corporations and instead become the rogue wizards of a rarefied part of the do-it-yourself maker's movement. In the drama of CRISPR, Zayner plays the role of one of Shakespeare's wise fools, such as Puck in *A Midsummer Night's Dream*, who speaks truth under the guise of showmanship, pokes fun at the pretensions of the high-minded, and pushes us forward by pointing out what fools these mortals be.

As a teenager, Zayner worked as a programmer for Motorola's cell phone network, but he got laid off when the tech bubble burst in 2000, so he decided to go to college. He earned his bachelor's degree in plant biology from Southern Illinois University and a doctorate in molecular biophysics at the University of Chicago, where he studied how light-activated proteins work. Instead of doing traditional postdoc studies, he wrote about using synthetic biology to help colonize Mars and found himself recruited to work for NASA. But he was not cut out for a hierarchical organization, so he quit to pursue the freedom of being a biohacker.

Before getting into CRISPR, Zayner tried a variety of synthetic biology experiments, including on himself. To treat his gastrointestinal problems, he performed a fecal transplant (don't ask) to transform his gut's microbiome. He did the procedure in a hotel room with two filmmakers documenting the scene, and (in case you really do want to know how it works) it became a short documentary called *Gut Hack* that can be found online.[2]

Zayner now runs from his garage an online biohacking supply store, The ODIN, which creates and sells "kits and tools that allow anyone to make unique and usable organisms at home or in a lab." Among its products, in addition to the frog-muscle kit, are a "DIY bacterial gene engineering CRISPR kit" ($169) and a "genetic engineering home lab kit" ($1,999).

Soon after Zayner started his business in 2016, he got an email from Harvard's George Church. "I like the stuff you're doing," Church wrote. They chatted, eventually met, and Church became the "business and scientific advisor" to The ODIN. "I think George is a collector of interesting people," Zayner says, correctly.[3]

Most of the biologists who work in academic labs are contemptuous of what they see as Zayner's shoddy methods. "Josiah's stunts demonstrate a reckless pursuit of publicity and a lack of scientific understanding," says Kevin Doxzen, who works in Doudna's lab. "Encouraging curiosity and inquiry within the public is a valuable pursuit, but selling kits that suggest you can engineer frogs in your kitchen, human cells in your living room, or bacteria in your garage attempts to simplify a technology that isn't simple. It saddens me to imagine high school teachers spending their shrinking budgets on kits that simply don't work." Zayner dismisses such criticism as coming from academic scientists trying to protect their priesthood. "We put the DNA sequences and all of our data and methods for our kits online for everyone to judge."[4]

The impromptu CRISPR procedure Zayner performed on himself at the San Francisco conference did not have a noticeable effect on the muscles of his somewhat scrawny body. That would have taken a prolonged series of treatments. But it did have an effect on the world of CRISPR regulation. By being the first person to try to edit his own DNA, he showed that the gene genie would someday be out of the bottle, which he insisted was a good thing.

Zayner wants to make the genetic engineering revolution as open and crowdsourced as the early digital revolution was, when coders like Linus Torvalds created the open-source operating system Linux and hackers like Steve Wozniak gathered at the Homebrew Computer Club and talked about liberating computers from the exclusive control of corporations and government institutions. Genetic engineering, he insists, is no harder than computer engineering. "I almost failed out of high school," he says, "but I was able to learn how to do this stuff." His dream is that millions of people around the world will take up amateur bioengineering. "We now all have this ability to program life," he says. "If millions of people took it up, that would immediately change medicine and agriculture, contributing so much to the world. By demonstrating how easy CRISPR is, I want to inspire people to do that."

Isn't it dangerous, I ask, for everyone to have access to this technology? "No, it's fucking exciting," he counters. "No great technology has flourished until people had complete access to it." He has a point. What truly caused the digital age to blossom was when computers became *personal*. It happened in the mid-1970s with the advent of the Altair and the Apple II, devices that democratized control of computing power. First hackers and then the rest of us got to play with our own computers and produce digital content. The digital revolution was kicked into an even higher orbit in the early 2000s with the birth of the smartphone. As Zayner says, "Once we have people doing biotechnology at home, like we did with computer programming, so many amazing things will be contributed."[5]

Zayner will probably have his way. CRISPR technology is on the verge of becoming easy enough that it will not be confined to well-regulated labs. It will also be advanced by rebels and rogues on the far edge of the frontier. In this way it may follow the path of the digital revolution, much of which, from Linux to Wikipedia, was driven by crowdsourcing. In the digital realm, there isn't a clear line separating amateur from professional coders. The same might soon be true of bioengineers.

Despite the dangers, there could be benefits if biotech followed this route. During a pandemic, it would be useful if societies could tap the biological wisdom and innovation of crowds. At the very least, it would be good to have citizens who could test themselves and their neighbors at home. Contact tracing and data collection could be crowdsourced. Today, there is a sharp line dividing officially sanctioned biologists from do-it-yourself hackers, but Josiah Zayner is dedicated to changing that. CRISPR and COVID could help him blur those lines.

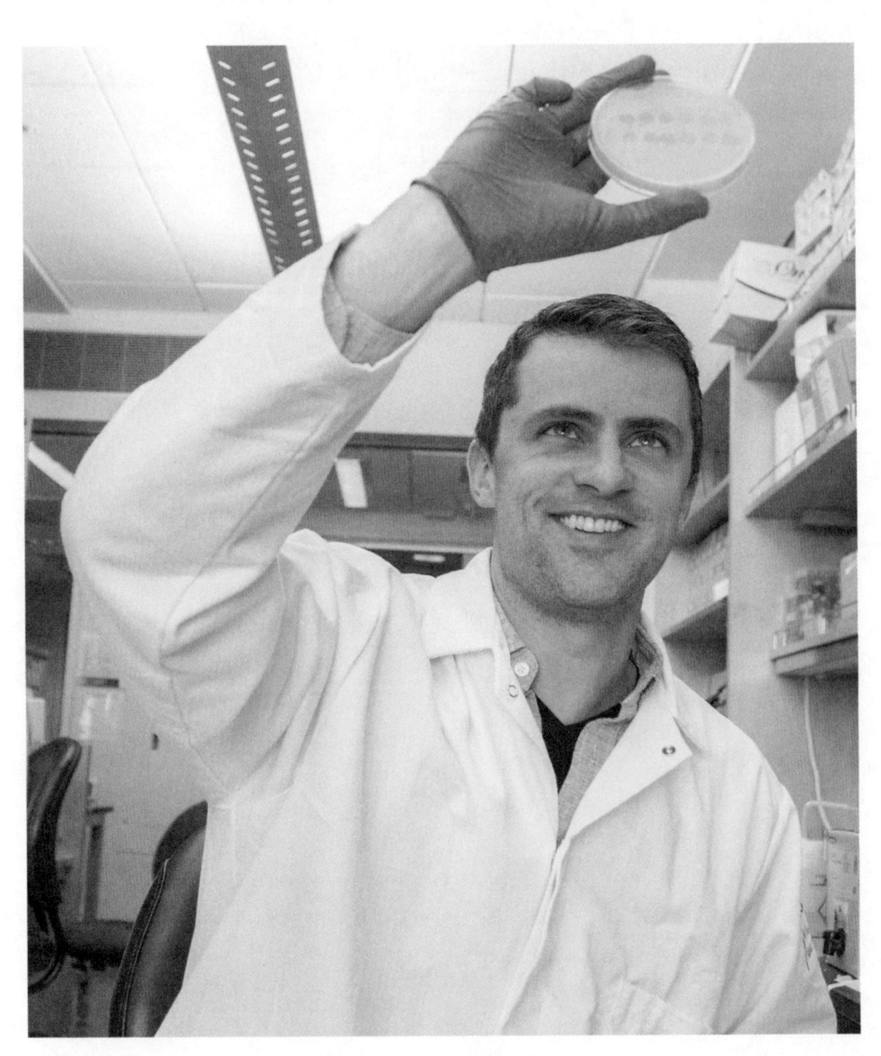

Joseph Bondy-Denomy

CHAPTER 34

DARPA and Anti-CRISPR

Threat assessment

The possibility that CRISPR would be used by hackers or terrorists or foreign adversaries began to worry Doudna. She raised these concerns when she attended a 2014 conference where a researcher described how a virus could be engineered to carry CRISPR components into mice and edit a gene so that the mice would get lung cancer. A chill went through her. A tweak or a mistake in the guide could easily make it work in human lungs. At another conference a year later, she questioned a graduate student who had coauthored an article with Feng Zhang describing a similar CRISPR experiment that caused cancer in mice. These and other experiences led her to join an effort funded by the U.S. Defense Department to find ways to protect against the misuse of CRISPR.[1]

Ever since Cesare Borgia hired Leonardo da Vinci, military spending has driven innovation. This became true for CRISPR in 2016 when James Clapper, the U.S. Director of National Intelligence, issued the agency's annual "Worldwide Threat Assessment" and it included for the first time "genome editing" as a potential weapon of mass destruction. As a result, the Defense Advanced Research Projects Agency (DARPA), which is the Pentagon's well-funded research arm, launched a program called Safe Genes to support ways to defend against genetically engineered weapons. It dispensed $65 million worth of grants, making the military the largest single source of money for CRISPR research.[2]

The initial DARPA grants went to seven teams. George Church at Harvard received one to study the reversal of mutations that come from exposure to radiation. Kevin Esvelt at MIT was tapped to study gene drives, which can accelerate a genetic change through a population of organisms such as mosquitoes and mice. Amit Choudhary of Harvard Medical School got funding to develop ways to switch on and off genome editing.[3]

Doudna's grants, which would eventually total $3.3 million, covered a variety of projects, including looking for ways to block a CRISPR editing system. The goal was to create tools that, as the announcement put it, "might someday be capable of disabling weapons employing CRISPR." It sounded like the plot of a paperback thriller: terrorists or enemy states unleash a CRISPR system that can edit organisms, such as mosquitoes, to be super-destructive, and Dr. Doudna in a white lab coat has to rush in to save us.[4]

Doudna assigned the project to two young postdoctoral students who had just joined her lab, Kyle Watters and Gavin Knott. They focused on a method that some viruses use to disable the CRISPR systems of the bacteria they are attacking. In other words, bacteria developed CRISPR systems to ward off viruses, but then the viruses developed a way to shut down those defenses. It was an arms race the Pentagon could understand: missiles being countered by defense systems being countered by anti–defense systems. The newly discovered systems were dubbed "anti-CRISPRs."

Anti-CRISPR

Anti-CRISPRs were discovered in late 2012, just as Doudna and Zhang were racing to turn CRISPR-Cas9 into a human gene–editing tool, by a doctoral student at the University of Toronto, Joe Bondy-Denomy. He stumbled upon the discovery by trying something that should not have worked: he attempted to infect some bacteria with a virus that should have been defeated by the bacteria's CRISPR system. In a handful of cases, the attacking viruses survived.

At first he assumed he had botched the experiments. Then a thought occurred to him: perhaps the wily viruses had developed a way to disarm the bacteria's CRISPR defenses. That turned out to be right. The viruses had been able to infiltrate the bacteria's DNA with a little sequence that sabotaged their CRISPR system.[5]

His anti-CRISPRs didn't seem to work on CRISPR-Cas9, so the discovery got little attention at first. But in 2016, he and April Pawluk, who had worked with him on the original paper, identified anti-CRISPRs that disabled the Cas9 enzyme. That opened the floodgates for other researchers to join the hunt, and soon more than fifty anti-CRISPR proteins had been discovered. By then Bondy-Denomy had become a professor at the University of California, San Francisco, and he collaborated with Doudna's lab to show that the anti-CRISPRs could be delivered into human cells to modulate or stop CRISPR-Cas9 editing.[6]

It was a basic science discovery about the wonders of nature, showing how the amazing arms race between bacteria and viruses evolved. And once again, it became an example of basic science leading to useful tools. The anti-CRISPRs could be engineered to regulate gene-editing systems. That would be useful for medical applications that needed to time-limit a CRISPR edit, and they could be used as a defense against systems created by terrorists or malevolent enemies. Anti-CRISPRs could also be used to shut off gene drives, the CRISPR systems that are designed to make a genetic change that spreads rapidly through a fast-breeding population such as mosquitoes.[7]

Doudna was successful in delivering on the projects for DARPA, and her Innovative Genomics Institute at Berkeley was able over the next few years to receive grants for new research topics. Like Church's lab at Harvard, it was asked to study how to use CRISPR to protect against nuclear radiation. The leader of that $9.5 million project was Fyodor Urnov, who was an undergraduate at Moscow State University during the Chernobyl disaster. The mission was to save soldiers and civilians exposed to a nuclear attack or disaster.[8]

The labs that received Safe Genes grants gathered once a year with Renee Wegrzyn, the program manager of DARPA's Biological Technologies Office. Doudna went to one meeting in San Diego in 2018 and was impressed by how good Wegrzyn was at promoting collaboration among the labs that received military funding, just as DARPA had done in the 1960s when it was creating what became the internet. She was also struck by the incongruity of the conference. "We were eating outside in the beautiful weather under swaying palm trees," she says, "and we were talking about radiation sickness and genome editing being used to create weapons of mass destruction."[9]

Enlisting our hacker

On February 26, 2020, just as the COVID-19 plague was taking hold in America, a group of U.S. Army generals, Defense Department officials, and biotechnology executives walked past an imposing statue of a seated Albert Einstein and into a ground-floor room of the stately marble headquarters of the National Academy of Sciences in Washington, D.C. They were there to attend the conference, The Bio-Revolution and Its Implications for Army Combat Capabilities, sponsored by the army's Research and Technology Program. Among the fifty or so participants were some distinguished scientists, most notably George Church, as well as one outlier: Josiah Zayner, the biohacker with multiple ear piercings who had injected himself with a CRISPR-edited gene at a San Francisco synthetic biology conference.

"The building was nice, but the cafeteria was shit," Zayner says. And the conference? "It was really boring. A bunch of people who didn't really know what they were talking about." At one point, he scribbled in his notes, "Speaker sounds like she has taken Xanax."

Zayner likes being irreverent, and despite what he says, I got the feeling that he actually enjoyed the conference. He was not initially scheduled to give a talk, but he made such an impression that he was called on to speak impromptu. The military officials had been complaining that they had trouble recruiting quality scientists. "You need to open up your labs and maybe start a biohacker space to interact with the people more," Zayner told them. He pointed out that the military had done that with computer hackers. Government labs staffed by the do-it-yourself biology community, he said, could come up with solutions the military could use.

Some of the other speakers bought into the idea that the military should enlist help from, as they put it, "non-traditional communities." As one official said, "citizen science" can be tapped to improve the military's ability to identify threats. One of the industry scientists took note of the novel coronavirus spreading out of China, which was still a few days away from causing national alarm. They should imagine a world, he said, where such viral pandemics were common; in such situations, it could be useful to enlist citizen-scientists to figure out ways to deploy real-time detection methods and crowdsource the collection and analysis of data. It was an important point, one that Zayner and the biohacker community had been trying to make.

By the end of the meeting, Zayner was pleasantly surprised by the desire of officials to enlist the hacker community in the effort to deploy CRISPR to fight pandemics and to protect soldiers. "Everyone staring at me and surprised I came," he jotted in his notebook. Then, a little bit later: "People coming up to me thanking me for coming."[10]

PART FIVE

Public Scientist

This was a new room, rich with hope, terrible with strange danger.
A dim folk memory had preserved the story of a greater advance:
"the winged hound of Zeus" tearing from Prometheus' liver the
price of fire. Was the world ready for the new step forward?
Certainly, it will change the world. You have to make laws to fit it.
And if plain people did not understand and control it, who would?

—Excerpted from James Agee's cover story, "Atomic Age," on the dropping of the atom bomb, *Time*, August 20, 1945

James Watson and Sydney Brenner at Asilomar

Herbert Boyer and Paul Berg at Asilomar

Chapter 35

Rules of the Road

Utopians vs. bioconservatives

For decades the idea of creating engineered humans belonged to the realm of science fiction. Three classic works warned of what might happen if we snatched this fire from the gods. Mary Shelley's 1818 novel, *Frankenstein; or, The Modern Prometheus*, was a cautionary tale about a scientist who engineers a humanlike creation. In H. G. Wells's *The Time Machine*, published in 1895, a traveler to the future discovers that humans have evolved into two species, a leisure class of Eloi and a working class of Morlocks. Aldous Huxley's *Brave New World*, published in 1932, describes a similarly dystopian future in which genetic modification produces an elite class of leaders with enhanced intellectual and physical traits. In the first chapter, a worker gives a tour of a baby hatchery:

> "We decant our babies as socialized human beings, as Alphas or Epsilons, as future sewage workers or future . . ." He was going to say "future World controllers," but correcting himself, said "future Directors of Hatcheries."

The idea of engineering humans moved from the realm of science fiction to the realm of science in the 1960s. Researchers began to crack the genetic code by figuring out the role played by some of the sequences of our DNA. And the discovery of how to cut and paste DNA from different organisms launched the field of genetic engineering.

The first reaction to these breakthroughs, especially among scientists, was an optimism that bordered on hubris. "We have become the latter-day Prometheus," biologist Robert Sinsheimer declared, with no sign that he understood the Greek myth. "Soon we shall have the power consciously to alter our inheritance, our very nature." He dismissed those who found this prospect troubling. Because the decisions about our genetic future would be guided by individual choice, he argued, this new eugenics would be morally different from the discredited eugenics of the first half of the twentieth century. "We should have the potential to create new genes and new qualities yet undreamed," he exulted. "This is a cosmic event."[1]

The geneticist Bentley Glass, in his address on becoming president of the American Association for the Advancement of Science in 1970, argued that the ethical problem was not that people would embrace these new genetic technologies but that they might reject them. "The right that must become paramount is the right of every child to be born with a sound physical and mental constitution," he said. "No parents will have a right to burden society with a malformed or a mentally incompetent child."[2]

Joseph Fletcher, a professor of medical ethics at the University of Virginia and lapsed Episcopal minister, agreed that genetic engineering could be considered a duty rather than ethically problematic. "Producing our children by 'sexual roulette' without pre-conceptive and uterine control, simply taking pot luck, is irresponsible, now that we can be genetically selective," he wrote in a 1974 book, *The Ethics of Genetic Control*. "As we learn to direct mutations medically, we should do so. Not to control when we can is immoral."[3]

Opposing this biotech utopianism was a group of theologians, technoskeptics, and bioconservatives who became influential in the 1970s. Princeton professor of Christian ethics Paul Ramsey, a prominent Protestant theologian, published *Fabricated Man: The Ethics of Genetic Control*. It is a turgid book with one vivid sentence: "Men ought not to play God before they learn to be men."[4] The social theorist Jeremy Rifkin, dubbed by *Time* America's "foremost opponent of genetic engineering," coauthored a book titled *Who Should Play God?* "Once, all of this could be dismissed as science fiction, the mad ravings of a Dr. Frankenstein," he wrote. "No more. We are not in the Brave New World yet, but we are well along the road."[5]

Even though human gene–editing technologies had not yet been devised, the battle lines had thus been defined. It became the mission of many of the scientists to find a middle ground rather than let the issue become politically polarized.

Asilomar

In the summer of 1972, Paul Berg, who had just published his seminal paper on how to make recombinant DNA, went to the ancient clifftop village of Erice on the coast of Sicily to lead a seminar on the new biotechnologies. The graduate students who attended were shocked by what he described, and they peppered him with questions about the ethical dangers of genetic engineering, especially the modification of humans. Berg had not focused on such questions, and he agreed to hold an informal discussion one evening on the ramparts of the old Norman-era castle overlooking the Straits of Sicily. Under a full moon, eighty students and researchers drank beer and wrestled with the ethical issues. The questions they asked were basic but hard for Berg to answer: What if we could genetically engineer height or eye color? What about intelligence? Would we do that? Should we? Francis Crick, the co-discoverer of DNA's double-helix structure, was there, but he stayed silent as he sipped his beer.[6]

The discussions led Berg to convene a group of biologists in January 1973 at the Asilomar conference center on the California coast near Monterey. Known as "Asilomar I" because it launched a process that would culminate two years later at the same conference site, the meeting focused mainly on lab safety issues. It was followed in April by a conference organized by the National Academies of Science at MIT, which discussed how to prevent the creation of recombinant

DNA organisms that could be dangerous. The more the participants discussed it, the less sure they became that any method would be foolproof. So they issued a letter—which was signed by Berg, James Watson, Herbert Boyer, and others—calling for a "moratorium" on the creation of recombinant DNA until safety guidelines could be formulated.[7]

This led to a memorable gathering that would become famous in the annals of scientists attempting to regulate their own field: the four-day Asilomar conference of February 1975. As the migration of monarch butterflies dappled the sky, 150 biologists and doctors and lawyers from around the world, plus a few journalists who agreed to turn off their tape recorders if the discussion got too heated, gathered to walk the dunes, sit at conference tables, and debate what restraints should be put on new genetic engineering technologies. "Their discussions suggest both the vitality of small boys with new chemistry sets and the electricity of back yard gossip," Michael Rogers of *Rolling Stone* wrote in a piece aptly titled "The Pandora's Box Conference."[8]

One of the primary organizers was a soft-spoken but gently commanding MIT biology professor named David Baltimore, who that year would win the Nobel Prize for his work showing that viruses containing RNA, such as coronaviruses, can insert their genetic material into the DNA of a host cell through a process known as "reverse transcription." In other words, the RNA can be transcribed into DNA, thus modifying the central dogma of biology, which states that genetic information travels in only one direction, from DNA to RNA. Baltimore would go on to become president of Rockefeller University and then Caltech, and his half-century career as a respected leader of policy councils would become a model for Doudna's own public involvement.

After Baltimore set the stage by explaining why the meeting had been convened, Berg described the science that was at issue: recombinant DNA technology made it "ridiculously simple" to combine DNA from different organisms and create new genes. Soon after he had published his discovery, Berg told the group, he started to get calls from researchers asking him to send them material so they could do their own experiments. When he asked the callers what they wanted to do, Berg recalls, "we'd get a description of some kind of horror experiment." He began to fear that some mad scientist would create a new microbe that could threaten the planet, like what Michael Crichton described in his 1969 bio-thriller, *The Andromeda Strain*.

During the policy debates, Berg insisted that the risks of using recombinant DNA to create new organisms were so hard to calculate that such research should be banned. Others found that position absurd. And Baltimore, as he would generally do throughout his career, sought to find a middle ground. He argued for restricting the use of recombinant DNA to viruses that had been "crippled" so that they could not spread.[9]

James Watson, true to form, played the cranky contrarian throughout. "They had worked themselves into a level of hysteria," he later told me. "I was for researchers doing whatever they wanted." At one point he got into a nasty clash with Berg, whose disciplined demeanor was a stark contrast to Watson's impetuousness. The argument got so heated that Berg threatened to sue Watson. "You have signed a letter saying there is a potential risk to this line of work," Berg reminded him, referring to their letter from the year before. "For you to now say you're not willing to institute any procedures which would protect the staff of Cold Spring Harbor, where you're the director, I could bring a suit against you for being irresponsible, and I will."

As the bickering among the elders intensified, some of the younger attendees sneaked out to the beach to smoke dope. By the evening before the conference was scheduled to end, no consensus had been reached. But a panel of lawyers helped spur the scientists by warning that their institutions would likely be held liable if anyone in any lab ever got infected with recombinant DNA. The university responsible might then have to shut down.

Later that night, Berg and Baltimore stayed up with a few colleagues eating takeout Chinese food in a beachside cabana. Using a blackboard they had commandeered, they spent hours trying to write a statement. Around 5 a.m., just before the sun rose, they emerged with a draft.

"The new techniques, which permit combination of genetic information from very different organisms, place us in an arena of biology with many unknowns," they wrote. "It is this ignorance that has compelled us to conclude that it would be wise to exercise considerable caution in performing this research." Then they described in detail the type of safeguards and restrictions that would be put on experiments.

Baltimore made copies of their provisional statement in time to have it distributed at the 8:30 a.m. session, at which point Berg took on the task of herding the scientists to support it. Someone insisted they vote on each paragraph. Berg knew that would be a disaster, and he vetoed the idea. But he did yield to the eminent molecular biologist Sydney Brenner, who asked for an up-or-down vote on the central recommendation being proposed: that the moratorium on genetic engineering research be lifted and that it should proceed with certain safeguards. "The pause is over," Brenner said. The room agreed. A few hours later, just as the bell rang for the final lunch, Berg asked for a vote on the document as a whole, which included detailed safety provisions that labs would have to follow. Most hands went up in favor. Ignoring those who still clamored to speak, he then asked if there were any opposed. Only four or five hands were raised, including that of Watson, who thought all the safeguards were silly.[10]

The conference had two goals: guarding against the hazards that could come from creating new forms of genes and guarding against the threat that politicians would ban genetic engineering altogether. On both fronts, the Asilomar process was successful. They were able to chart "a prudent path forward," an approach that Baltimore and Doudna would later replicate in the debates over CRISPR gene editing.

The restrictions agreed to at Asilomar were accepted by universities and funding agencies worldwide. "This unique conference marked the beginning of an exceptional era for science and for the public discussion of science policy," Berg wrote thirty years later. "We gained the public's trust, for it was the very scientists who were most involved in the work and had every incentive to be left free to pursue their dream that called attention to the risks inherent in the experiments they were doing. Restrictive national legislation was avoided."[11]

Others were less willing to join the mutual back-patting. Erwin Chargaff, a brilliant biochemist who had made key discoveries about the structure of DNA, looked back on the event as a charade. "At this Council of Asilomar there congregated the molecular bishops and church fathers from all over the world, in order to condemn the heresies of which they themselves had been the first and the principal perpetrators," he said. "This was probably the first time in history that the incendiaries formed their own fire brigade."[12]

Berg was right that Asilomar was a great success. It paved the way for genetic engineering to become a booming field. But Chargaff's mocking assessment pointed to another lasting legacy. Asilomar became notable for what the scientists did *not* discuss there. Their focus was on safety. None of them addressed the big ethical question, the one that Berg had stayed up late discussing in Sicily: How far should we go if and when methods of engineering our genes turned out to be safe?

Splicing Life, *1982*

Asilomar's lack of focus on ethical issues bothered many religious leaders. That prompted a letter to President Jimmy Carter signed by the heads of three major religious organizations: the National Council of Churches, the Synagogue Council of America, and the U.S. Catholic Conference. "We are rapidly moving into a new era of fundamental danger triggered by the rapid growth of genetic engineering," they wrote. "Who shall determine how human good is best served when new life forms are being engineered?"[13]

These decisions should not be left to scientists, the trio argued. "There will always be those who believe it appropriate to 'correct' our mental and social structures by genetic means. This becomes more dangerous when the basic tools to do so are finally at hand. Those who would play God will be tempted as never before."

Carter responded by appointing a presidential commission to study the issue. It came back in late 1982 with a 106-page report titled

Splicing Life that ended up being inconclusive mush. It merely called for further dialogue to reach societal consensus. "A goal of this Report is to stimulate thoughtful, long-term discussion—not preempt it with conclusions that would, of necessity, be premature."[14]

The commission's report did raise two concerns that were prescient. The first was a fear that genetic engineering was leading to increased corporate involvement in university research. Universities had historically focused on basic research and the open exchange of ideas, and the report warned, "These goals may run headlong into those of industry—the development of marketable products and techniques through applied research by maintaining a competitive posture, protecting trade secrets, and seeking patent protection."

The second concern was that genetic engineering would increase inequality. New biotech procedures would be expensive, so people who were born into privilege would likely get the most benefits. That could widen, and genetically encode, existing inequalities. "The possibilities presented by gene therapy and gene surgery may in fact call into question a central element of democratic political theory and practice: the commitment to equality of opportunity."

Preimplantation genetic diagnosis and Gattaca

After the development of recombinant DNA in the 1970s, the next big bioengineering advance—and set of ethical issues—came in the 1990s. It resulted from the confluence of two innovations: *in vitro* fertilization (the first test-tube baby, Louise Brown, was born in 1978) combined with genetic sequencing technology. This led, in 1990, to the first use of what became known as preimplantation genetic diagnosis.[15]

Preimplantation diagnosis involves fertilizing an egg with sperm in a Petri dish, doing tests on the resulting embryos* to determine their

*I use the word "embryo" in the broad sense. The single-cell organism resulting from a fertilized egg is a zygote. When the zygote divides to become a collection of cells that can implant in the wall of the uterus, it is called a blastocyst. About four weeks later, after the development of an amniotic sac, it becomes an embryo. After eleven weeks, it is usually referred to as a fetus.

genetic characteristics, and then implanting into a woman's womb the embryo with the most desired traits. It allows parents to choose the gender of their child and avoid having a child who carries a genetic disease or some other attribute the parents find undesirable.

The potential of such genetic screening and selection entered the popular imagination through the 1997 film *Gattaca* (the title is made up of the letters of the four DNA bases), starring Ethan Hawke and Uma Thurman. It tells of a future in which genetic selection is regularly used to ensure that children are enhanced with the best hereditary traits.

To promote the movie, the studio took out advertisements in newspapers that appeared as if they were for a real gene-editing clinic. Headlined "Children Made to Order," the ad read, "At Gattaca, it is now possible to engineer your offspring. Here's a checklist to help you decide what traits to pass on to your newborn." The list included gender, stature, eye color, skin color, weight, addictive susceptibility, criminal aggressive tendencies, musical ability, athletic prowess, and intellect. The final choice was "None of the above." The ad advises of that option, "For religious or other reasons, you may have reservations about genetically engineering your child. We respectfully invite you to reconsider. From where we sit, the human race could use a little improving."

At the bottom of the ad was a toll-free telephone number, which led to a recording offering callers three options: "Press one if you'd like to take the steps to ensure that your offspring is disease-free. Press two if you'd like to enhance intellectual and physical traits. Press three if you don't want to tamper with your kid's genetic makeup." Within two days, the toll-free number had received fifty thousand calls, but the studio, alas, did not track how many chose each of the options.

The hero of the movie, played by Hawke, was conceived without the benefits or burdens of preimplantation engineering, and he must battle genetic discrimination in order to fulfill his dream of becoming an astronaut. He is, of course, triumphant, since this is a movie. A particularly interesting scene occurs when his parents decide to make use of gene editing in having their second child. The doctor describes all the traits and enhancements he can engineer: better eyesight, desired eye and skin color, no predisposition toward alcoholism or baldness, and more. "Is it good to leave a few things to chance?" the parents ask. No, the doctor assures them, they are merely giving their prospective child "the best possible start."

That led film critic Roger Ebert to write, "When parents can order 'perfect' babies, will they? Would you take your chances on a throw of the genetic dice, or order up the make and model you wanted? How many people are prepared to buy a car at random from the universe of all available cars? That's how many, I suspect, would opt to have natural children." But then Ebert smartly expressed the worries that were beginning to form at the time: "Everybody will live longer, look better and be healthier in the Gattacan world. But will it be as much fun? Will parents order children who are rebellious, ungainly, eccentric, creative, or a lot smarter than their parents are? Don't you sometimes have the feeling you were born just in time?"[16]

Watson and others at UCLA, 1998

Once again, the irascible old DNA pioneer James Watson sat in the audience loudly mumbling provocative thoughts that he seemed gleefully unable to suppress. This time it was at a gene-editing conference hosted by UCLA professor Gregory Stock in 1998. French Anderson, a leader in using genetic engineering to create drugs, gave a mini-sermon on the need to distinguish between treating diseases, which he proclaimed to be moral, and providing children with genetic enhancements, which he said wasn't. Watson began to snort and stir. "No one really has the guts to say it," he interrupted, "but if we could make better human beings by knowing how to add genes, why shouldn't we do it?"[17]

The title of the gathering was "Engineering the Human Germline," and it focused on the ethics of making genetic edits that would be inherited. These "germline" edits were fundamentally different, medically and morally, from somatic-cell edits that affect only certain cells in an individual patient. The germline was a red line that scientists had been reluctant to cross. "This is the first gathering where people have talked openly about *germline* engineering," Watson said approvingly. "It seems obvious that germline therapy will be much more successful than somatic-cell edits. If we wait for the success of somatic therapy, we'll wait until the sun burns out."

It was absurd, Watson said, to treat the germline as "some great Rubicon and crossing it involved going against natural law." When he was challenged about the need to respect "the sanctity of the human gene pool," he erupted. "Evolution can be just damn cruel, and to say that we've got a perfect genome and there's some sanctity to it is utter silliness." His schizophrenic son, Rufus, was a daily reminder that the genetic lottery could be, as he put it, damn cruel. "The biggest ethical problem we have is not using our knowledge and not having the guts to go ahead and try to help someone," he insisted.[18]

For the most part, Watson was preaching to the choir. The opinions at the UCLA conference ranged from enthusiasm to unbridled enthusiasm for gene editing. When someone suggested that going down that slope might lead to unintended consequences, Watson was unwavering. "I think the slippery slope argument is just crap. Societies thrive when they're optimistic, not pessimistic, and the slippery slope argument sounds like one from a worn-out person who's angry at himself."

Lee Silver, a Princeton biologist, had just published *Remaking Eden*, which became a manifesto for the conference. He had coined the word "reprogenetics" to describe the use of technology to determine which genes a child would inherit. "In a society that values individual freedom above all else, it is hard to find any legitimate basis for restricting the use of reprogenetics," he wrote.[19]

Silver's work was important because it framed the issue as being about individual freedom and liberty in a market-based consumer society. "If democratic societies allow parents to buy environmental advantages for their children, how can they prohibit them from buying genetic advantages?" he prodded. "Americans would respond to any attempt at a ban with the question, 'Why can't I give my child beneficial genes that other children get naturally?' "[20]

Silver's techno-enthusiasm set the tone for what participants viewed as a historic moment. "For the first time we as a species have the ability to self-evolve," Silver told the group. "I mean, this is an incredible concept." He meant the word "incredible" to be a compliment.

As with the Asilomar conference, one of the goals of the UCLA conference was to fend off government regulation. "The main message we need to draw is to keep the state out of any form of genetic decision," Watson argued. The attendees accepted that view. "No state or federal legislation to regulate germline gene therapy should be passed at this time," organizer Gregory Stock wrote in his summation.

Stock went on to write a pro-editing manifesto, *Redesigning Humans: Our Inevitable Genetic Future.* "A key aspect of human nature is our ability to manipulate the world," he argued. "To turn away from germline selection and modification without even exploring them would be to deny our essential nature and perhaps our destiny." He emphasized that politicians should not try to interfere. "Policymakers sometimes mistakenly think that they have a voice about whether germinal technologies will come into being," he wrote. "They do not."[21]

The American enthusiasm for genetic engineering was a sharp contrast to the attitude in Europe, where policymakers and various commissions had increasingly turned against it, both in agriculture and in humans. The most notable expression came from a meeting convened by the Council of Europe in Oviedo, Spain, in 1997. The resulting Oviedo Convention was intended to be a legally binding treaty designed to prohibit the use of biological advances in ways that threatened human dignity. It barred genetic engineering in humans except "for preventive, diagnostic or therapeutic reasons and only where it does not aim to change the genetic make-up of a person's descendants." In other words, no germline editing. Twenty-nine European countries incorporated the Oviedo Convention into their laws, with Britain and Germany being notable holdouts. Even where it was not ratified it helped shape what is still a general consensus in Europe against genetic engineering.[22]

Jesse Gelsinger

The optimism among American researchers about genetic engineering was deflated in September 1999 by a tragedy that happened in Philadelphia to a sweet, handsome, and slightly rebellious eighteen-year-old high school student. Jesse Gelsinger suffered from a mild form of a disease of the liver caused by a simple genetic mutation. It caused his liver to have problems ridding his body of ammonia, which is a by-product of the breakdown of proteins. It usually kills victims as babies, but Gelsinger's milder form meant that he could survive by eating a very low-protein diet and taking thirty-two pills a day.

A team at the University of Pennsylvania was testing a genetic therapy for the disease. Such therapies do not involve actually editing the DNA of the cells inside the body. Instead, genes without the mutation are created in a lab, and then doctors put these good genes into a virus that serves as a delivery mechanism. In Gelsinger's case, the viruses with the good genes were injected into an artery that led into the liver.

It was unlikely that the therapy would help Gelsinger right away, because it was a trial designed to see how the therapy could be used to save babies. But it offered him hope that someday he would be able to eat hot dogs, and in the meantime, some babies would be saved. "What's the worst that can happen to me?" he said to a friend as he was leaving for the Philadelphia hospital. "I die, and it's for the babies."[23]

Unlike the seventeen other humans in the trial, Gelsinger had a massive immune response caused by the virus transporting the therapeutic gene, which resulted in a high fever followed by the breakdown of his kidneys, lungs, and other organs. In four days he was dead. Work on gene therapy ground to a halt. "We were all very much aware of what happened," Doudna recalled. "That made the whole field of gene therapy go away, mostly, for at least a decade. Even the term *gene therapy* became kind of a black label. You didn't want that in your grants. You didn't want to say, 'I'm working on gene therapy.' It sounded terrible."[24]

The Kass Commission, 2003

The debate over genetic engineering at the turn of the century—after the completion of the Human Genome Project and the cloning of Dolly the sheep—led to another U.S. presidential commission, this one created by President George W. Bush in 2003. It was chaired by Leon Kass, a biologist and social philosopher who had first expressed wariness about biotechnology thirty years earlier.

Kass is the most influential of the country's bioconservatives, the ethical traditionalists with a knowledge of biology who urge restraint when dealing with new genetic technologies. The son of secular Jewish immigrants, he earned a biology degree at the University of Chicago, where he was deeply influenced by its "great books" core curriculum. He got a medical degree from Chicago and a PhD in biochemistry from Harvard. With his wife, Amy, he went to Mississippi in 1965 as part of the cadre of civil rights workers registering Blacks to vote, an experience that reinforced his faith in traditional values. "In Mississippi I saw people living in perilous and meager circumstances, many of them illiterate, but sustained by religion, extended family and community attachment," he recalled.[25]

Upon returning to the University of Chicago as a professor, his writings ranged from scientific papers on molecular biology ("The Antibacterial Activity of 3-Decynoyl-N-Acetylcysteamine") to a book on the Hebrew Bible. After reading Huxley's *Brave New World*, he became more interested in "how the scientific project to master nature could, if we are not careful, lead to our dehumanization." Combining his appreciation for both science and the humanities, he began to tackle the issues raised by reproductive technologies such as cloning and *in vitro* fertilization. "I soon shifted my career from doing science to thinking about its human meaning," he wrote, "worrying about upholding our humanity against possible technological degradation."

His first published warning about bioengineering was a letter in *Science* in 1971 criticizing Bentley Glass's contention that "every child has the inalienable right to a sound heritage." Kass declared, "To make good such an 'inalienable right' means converting human reproduction into manufacture." The following year he wrote an essay explaining his wariness about genetic-engineering technologies. "The road to *Brave New World* is paved with sentimentality—yes, even with love and charity," he wrote. "Have we enough sense to turn back?"[26]

In 2001, the Kass Commission included many distinguished conservative or neoconservative thinkers, including Robert George, Mary Ann Glendon, Charles Krauthammer, and James Q. Wilson. Two prominent philosophers proved to be especially influential members. The first was Michael Sandel, a Harvard professor who is the contemporary successor to John Rawls in defining the concept of justice. At the time, he was writing an essay titled "The Case Against Perfection: What's Wrong with Designer Children, Bionic Athletes, and Genetic Engineering," which he published in *The Atlantic* in 2004.[27] The other key thinker was Francis Fukuyama, who in 2000 published *Our Posthuman Future: Consequences of the Biotechnology Revolution*, which was a forceful call for governments to regulate biotechnology.[28]

Not surprisingly, their final 310-page report, *Beyond Therapy*, was thoughtful, vibrantly written, and filled with qualms about genetic engineering. It warned of the dangers of using technology to go beyond merely treating diseases to using it to enhance human capabilities. "There are reasons to wonder whether life will really be better if we turn to biotechnology to fulfill our deepest human desires," the report declared.[29]

Focusing mainly on philosophical rather than safety concerns, the authors discussed what it meant to be human, to pursue happiness, to respect nature's gifts, and to accept the given. It argued the case, or more accurately it preached the case, that going too far to alter what is "natural" was hubristic and endangered our individual essence. "We want better children—but not by turning procreation into manufacture or by altering their brains to gain them an edge over their peers," they wrote. "We want to perform better in the activities of life—but not by becoming mere creatures of our chemists or by turning ourselves into tools designed to win or achieve in inhuman ways." One can almost sense a congregation nodding "Amen" while a few people in the back mutter, "Speak for yourself."

George Daley, Doudna, and David Baltimore at the 2015 international summit

CHAPTER 36

Doudna Steps In

The Hitler nightmare

In the spring of 2014, when the battle to win CRISPR patents and launch gene-editing companies was heating up, Doudna had a dream. More precisely, she had a nightmare. In it, a prominent researcher asked her to meet someone who wanted to learn about gene editing. When she went into the room, she recoiled. Sitting in front of her, with pen and paper ready to take notes, was Adolf Hitler with the face of a pig. "I want to understand the uses and implications of this amazing technology you've developed," he said. Doudna was jolted awake by the nightmare, she recalls. "As I lay in the dark, my heart racing, I couldn't escape the awful premonition with which the dream had left me." She began to have trouble sleeping at night.

Gene-editing technology had enormous power to do good, but the thought of using it to make alterations in humans that would be inherited by all future generations was unnerving. "Have we created a toolbox for future Frankensteins?" she asked herself. Or perhaps even worse, would it be a tool for future Hitlers? "Emmanuelle and I, and our collaborators, had imagined that CRISPR technology could save lives by helping to cure genetic disease," she later wrote. "Yet as I thought about it now, I could scarcely begin to conceive of all of the ways in which our hard work might be perverted."[1]

Happy Healthy Baby

Around that time, Doudna was confronted with an example of how people with good intentions could pave the way for gene editing. Sam Sternberg, one of the researchers on her close-knit CRISPR team, received an email in March 2014 from an aspiring young entrepreneur in San Francisco named Lauren Buchman, who had gotten Sternberg's name from a friend. "Hi, Sam," she wrote. "Nice to meet you by email. I see that you're located just across the Bridge. Any chance I could buy you a coffee and chat a bit about what you're up to?"[2]

"I'd be happy to meet sometime though my schedule is busy," Sternberg replied. "Maybe in the meantime, you could fill me in a bit on what your company is doing."

"I've started a company called Happy Healthy Baby," she explained in her next email. "We've seen a potential of Cas9 to aid in preventing genetic diseases in children conceived through IVF in the future. Ensuring that this is done with the highest level of scientific and ethical standards is first and foremost to us."

Sternberg was surprised but not totally shocked. By that time CRISPR-Cas9 had already been used to edit embryos implanted in monkeys. He was interested in digging a bit deeper into what Buchman's motivations were and how she was thinking about developing this concept, so he agreed to meet her at a Mexican restaurant in Berkeley. There Buchman pitched him on the idea of offering people the chance to use CRISPR to edit their future babies.

She had already registered the domain name HealthyBabies.com. Might he want to be a cofounder? This surprised Sternberg, and not simply because he shared with his lab pal Blake Wiedenheft a good-humored humility. He had no experience editing human cells, much less knowing the first thing about how to implant embryos.

When I first heard about Buchman's concept, I found it disconcerting. But when I tracked her down, I was surprised to find that she was actually quite thoughtful about the moral issues. Her sister was a leukemia survivor and could not, as a result of her treatment, have children. Buchman herself was trying to launch a career and worried about her biological clock running down. "I was a woman in my thirties," she recalls. "And we're all facing the same issue. We want a career and not to be mommy-tracked, and we are starting to deal with fertility clinics."

She knew that *in vitro* fertility clinics could screen for harmful genes before choosing an embryo to implant, but as a thirtysomething woman she also knew that producing a bunch of fertilized embryos was easier said than done. "You may end up producing only one or two embryos," she points out, "so preimplantation genetic screening is not always easy."

That's when she heard about CRISPR and got excited. "The idea that we could treat something in cells seemed so promising and wonderful."

She was sensitive to the social issues. "All tech can be used for good or for bad, but the early movers in new technologies have the opportunity to promote positive and ethical usage," she says. "I wanted to do gene-editing right, and to do it in the open, so there would be an established pattern for ethical procedures for patients who wanted to use it."

Some of the venture capitalists and biotech entrepreneurs she consulted ended up pitching her on weird ideas that freaked her out, such as enlisting biohackers to crowdsource the editing of patients' genes. "The more I heard, the more I thought 'I have to do this,'" she says, "because if I don't, these fringe folks with no regard for the impact or the ethics will take over the field."

Sternberg left the dinner at the Mexican restaurant before dessert. He had no interest in being a cofounder, but he was intrigued enough to agree to visit the company's workspace. "There was never a chance in a million that I was going to get involved, but I was curious," he says. He knew that Doudna was beginning to worry about these sorts of things, so he decided to visit the lab so that he could talk to someone who wanted to be in the driver's seat on the type of CRISPR application that would stir up controversy.

During his visit, Sternberg watched a promotional video for Happy Healthy Baby, filled with animation and stock footage of lab experiments, in which Buchman, sitting in a sunny room with big glass windows, explains the idea of gene-editing babies. He told her that he didn't see any chance that CRISPR would be approved for use on human babies in the U.S. for at least ten years. She replied that the clinics did not have to be in the U.S. There would likely be other countries where the procedure would be allowed, and people who could afford gene-edited babies would be willing to travel.

Sternberg decided not to get involved, but for a while George Church agreed to serve as an unpaid science advisor. "George suggested that I work with sperm cells rather than embryos," Buchman recalls. "He said it might be less controversial or troubling."[3]

Buchman eventually abandoned the venture. "I dug into the use cases, market regulations, and ethics, and it became obvious that I was too early to be working on this," she says. "The science wasn't ready, and society wasn't ready."

When Sternberg described his meetings to Doudna, he told her that Buchman had "a Promethean glint in her eye." Later, he used that phrase in a book he wrote with Doudna, which infuriated Buchman. Had the Happy Healthy Baby pitch occurred a few years earlier, Doudna and Sternberg wrote, they would have dismissed the idea "as pure fantasy" because "there was little chance of anyone pursuing such Frankenstein schemes." But the invention of CRISPR-Cas9 technology had changed that. "Now, we could no longer laugh off this kind of speculation. Making the human genome as easily manipulable as that of a bacterium was, after all, precisely what CRISPR had accomplished."[4]

Napa, January 2015

As a result of her Hitler dream and Sternberg's Happy Healthy Baby story, Doudna decided in the spring of 2014 to become more engaged in the policy discussions about how CRISPR gene-editing tools should be used. At first she considered writing an op-ed for a newspaper, but that did not seem adequate to the challenge. So she harked back forty years earlier to the process that led to the February 1975

Asilomar conference, the one that had come up with the "prudent path forward" guidelines for work on recombinant DNA. She decided that the invention of CRISPR gene-editing tools warranted convening a similar group.

Her first step was to enlist the participation of two of the key organizers of the 1975 Asilomar conference: Paul Berg, who had invented recombinant DNA, and David Baltimore, who had been involved in most of the major policy gatherings, beginning with Asilomar. "I felt that if we could get them both we would have a direct link to Asilomar and a stamp of credibility," she recalls.

Both agreed to participate, and the meeting was set for January 2015 at a resort in Napa Valley about an hour north of San Francisco. Eighteen other top researchers were invited, including Martin Jinek and Sam Sternberg from Doudna's lab. The focus would be on the ethics of making inheritable genetic edits.

At Asilomar the discussions had been mostly about safety, but Doudna made sure that the Napa conference tackled the moral questions: Did the premium that America put on individual liberty require that decisions about gene-editing of babies be left mainly to parents? To what extent would creating gene-edited babies—and abandoning the idea that our genetic endowments came from a random natural lottery—undermine our sense of moral empathy? Was there a danger in decreasing the diversity of the human species? Or, to frame the question from a more bioliberal perspective: If the technology was available to make healthier and better babies, would it be ethically wrong *not* to use it?[5]

A consensus quickly developed that it would be bad to completely ban germline gene editing. The participants wanted to leave the door open. Their objective became similar to that of Asilomar: finding a path forward rather than putting on the brakes. That would become the theme of most subsequent commissions and conferences organized by scientists: it was too early to do germline editing safely, but someday it would happen, and the goal should be to provide prudent guidelines.

David Baltimore warned of a development that made this Napa

meeting different from the Asilomar one forty years earlier. "The big difference today is the creation of the biotechnology industry," he told the group. "In 1975, there were no big biotechnology companies. Today, the public is concerned about commercial development, because there's less oversight." If the participants wanted to prevent a popular backlash against gene editing, he said, they would have to convince people to trust not only white-coated scientists but also commercially driven corporations. That could be a tough sell. Alta Charo, a bioethicist at the University of Wisconsin Law School, pointed out that the close relationship between academic researchers and commercial companies could taint the credibility of the academics. "Financial interests undermine the 'white coat' image of scientists today," she said.

One of the participants brought up the social justice argument. Gene editing would be expensive. Would only the wealthy have access? Baltimore agreed that was a problem, but he argued it was not a cause for banning the technology. "That argument doesn't cut very deep," he said. "That's how everything is. Look at computers. Everything gets cheaper when it gets done wholesale. It's not an argument against moving forward."

During the conference, word began to circulate about some editing experiments on non-viable embryos that were already happening in China. The technology, unlike that of building nuclear weapons, could spread easily and be used not only by responsible researchers but also by rogue doctors and biohackers. "Can we really put the genie back in the bottle?" one participant asked.

The group agreed that the use of CRISPR tools for *non-inheritable* gene editing in somatic cells was a good thing. It could lead to beneficial drugs and treatments. So they decided that it would be useful to agree to some restraints on germline editing in order to prevent a backlash. "We need to create a political safe space by going slow on germline editing so that we can continue working on somatic cell edits," one participant said.

In the end, they decided to call for a temporary halt on germline editing in humans, at least until the safety and social issues could be further understood. "We wanted the scientific community to hit the

Pause button until the societal, ethical, and philosophical implications of germline editing could be properly and thoroughly discussed—ideally at a global level," Doudna says.

Doudna drafted an initial version of the conference report, which she circulated to the other participants. After incorporating their suggestions, she submitted it in March to *Science*. It was titled "A Prudent Path Forward for Genomic Engineering and Germline Gene Modification."[6] Although she was the lead writer, the names of Baltimore and Berg were listed first. The happenstance of alphabetical order caused the two Asilomar pioneers to be at the fore.

The report clearly defined what was meant by "germline editing" and why crossing that threshold would be a major ethical as well as scientific step. "It is now possible to carry out genome modification in fertilized animal eggs or embryos, thereby altering the genetic makeup of every differentiated cell in an organism and so ensuring that the changes will be passed on to the organism's progeny," they wrote. "The possibility of human germline engineering has long been a source of excitement and unease among the general public, especially in light of concerns about initiating a 'slippery slope' from disease-curing applications toward uses with less compelling or even troubling implications."

As Doudna hoped, the journal article got major national attention. The *New York Times* ran a story on page 1 by Nicholas Wade, with a picture of Doudna at her Berkeley desk and the headline "Scientists Seek Ban on Method of Editing the Human Genome."[7] But the headline was misleading. Indeed, in most of the publicity about the Napa report, a key point was missed. Unlike some other scientists at the time,[8] the participants had purposely decided against calling for a ban or moratorium, which can over time become hard to lift. Their goal was to keep open the possibility of germline editing if it was safe and medically necessary. That was why, in the title of the piece, they called for "a prudent path forward," which had become the watchword of many of the scientific conferences on human germline gene editing.

Chinese embryo work, April 2015

During the Napa conference, Doudna heard an unnerving rumor: a group of Chinese scientists had used CRISPR-Cas9 to edit, for the first time, the genes in an early-stage human embryo, which in theory could create inheritable changes. The mitigating factor was that the embryos were not viable. They would not be implanted in a mother's uterus. Nevertheless, if true, the plans of well-intentioned policymakers would once again be disrupted by the zeal of eager researchers.[9]

The Chinese paper had not been published, but its existence had leaked. It had been rejected by the prestigious journals *Science* and *Nature,* and it was being shopped around. It was finally accepted by the somewhat obscure Chinese journal *Protein & Cell*, which published it online on April 18, 2015.

In the article, researchers at a university in Guangzhou described how they used CRISPR-Cas9 in eighty-six non-viable zygotes (precursors to an embryo) to cut out a mutated gene that causes beta thalassemia, a deadly blood disorder like sickle-cell anemia.[10] Although the embryos were never intended to be grown into babies, a line had been toed, if not crossed. For the first time, CRISPR-Cas9 had been used to make potential edits in the human germline, ones that could be inherited by future generations.

After Doudna read the article in her Berkeley office, she stared out at San Francisco Bay feeling, she later recalled, "awestruck and a bit queasy." Other scientists around the world were probably conducting similar experiments with the technology that she and Charpentier had created. That could lead, she realized, to some very unintended consequences. It could also provoke a public backlash. "The technology is not ready for clinical application in the human germline," she replied when a reporter for NPR asked her about the Chinese experiments. "That application of the technology needs to be on hold pending a broader societal discussion of the scientific and ethical issues."[11]

The Napa conference and the Chinese embryo-editing experiments aroused the interest of Congress. Senator Elizabeth Warren hosted a congressional briefing, and Doudna went to Washington to testify with her friend and fellow CRISPR pioneer George Church. The event was so popular that it was standing-room only. More than 150 senators, congressmen, staffers, and agency personnel crammed into the room. Doudna recounted the history of CRISPR, emphasizing that it had begun as pure "curiosity-driven" research about how bacteria fight off viruses. Using it in humans, she explained, required finding ways to get it to the right cells in the body, a task that was easier when the edits were made in early-stage embryos. "But using gene editing in such a way," she warned, "is also much more ethically controversial."[12]

Doudna and Church wrote back-to-back pieces in *Nature* presenting their perspectives on making inheritable gene edits. Although their positions conflicted to some extent, they reinforced the case that scientists were dealing with the issues seriously and did not require new government regulations. "Opinion on the use of human-germline engineering varies widely," Doudna wrote. "In my view, a complete ban might prevent research that could lead to future therapies, and it is also impractical given the widespread accessibility and ease of use of CRISPR-Cas9. Instead, solid agreement on an appropriate middle ground is desirable."[13] Church was more forceful in arguing that research, even in editing the human germline, should continue. "Rather than talk about the possibility of banning alteration of the human germline, we should instead be discussing how to stimulate ways to improve its safety and efficacy," he wrote. "Banning human-germline editing could put a damper on the best medical research and instead drive the practice underground to black markets and uncontrolled medical tourism."[14]

Church's bio-enthusiasm was given a boost in the popular press by one of his Harvard colleagues, the well-known psychology professor Steven Pinker. "The primary moral goal for today's bioethics can be summarized in a single sentence," he wrote in an op-ed for the *Boston Globe*. "Get out of the way." He took a brutal swipe at the entire profession of bioethicists. "A truly ethical bioethics should not bog down research in red tape, moratoria, or threats of prosecution based on nebulous but sweeping principles such as 'dignity,' 'sacredness,' or 'social justice,'" he argued. "The last thing we need is a lobby of so-called ethicists."[15]

The December 2015 International Summit

Following their Napa Valley meeting, Doudna and Baltimore urged the U.S. National Academy of Sciences and its sister organizations around the world to convene a globally representative group to discuss how to prudently regulate human germline editing. More than five hundred scientists, policymakers, and bioethicists—though very few patients or parents of afflicted children—gathered in Washington for three days at the beginning of December 2015 for the first International Summit on Human Gene Editing. In addition to Doudna and Baltimore, there were other CRISPR pioneers, including Feng Zhang, George Church, and Emmanuelle Charpentier. Cohosts included the Chinese Academy of Sciences and Britain's Royal Society.[16]

"We are here as part of a historical process that dates from Darwin and Mendel's work in the nineteenth century," Baltimore said in his opening remarks. "We could be on the cusp of a new era in human history."

A representative from Peking University assured the audience that China had in place safeguards to prevent germline gene editing: "The manipulation of the genes of human gametes, zygotes, or embryos for the purpose of reproduction is prohibited."

Because there were so many participants and journalists, the meeting consisted mainly of canned presentations rather than real debate. Even the conclusions had been pre-cooked. The most important was almost identical to what had been decided at the small Napa meeting at the beginning of the year. Human germline editing should be strongly discouraged until stringent conditions were met, but the words "moratorium" and "ban" were avoided.

Among the conditions the group adopted was that germline editing should not proceed until "there is broad societal consensus about the appropriateness of the proposed application." The need for a "broad societal consensus" was one that would be invoked often in discussions of the ethics of germline editing, as if a mantra. It was a laudable goal. But as the debate over abortion has shown, discussions do not always lead to broad societal consensuses. The organizers from the National Academy of Sciences realized that. Even as they called for public discussion of the issue, they created a twenty-two-person committee of experts to undertake a yearlong study on whether there should be a moratorium on germline DNA edits.

In their final report, issued in February 2017, the group did not call for a ban or a moratorium. Instead, it provided a list of criteria that should be met before germline editing should be allowed, among them: "absence of reasonable alternatives, restriction to preventing a serious disease or condition," and a few others that were not insurmountable in the foreseeable future.[17] Notably, it omitted one key restriction that was in the 2015 international summit report. There was no longer any mention of the need for a "broad societal consensus" before inheritable gene-editing would be permitted. Instead, the 2017 report called only for "broad ongoing participation and input by the public."

Many bioethicists were dismayed, but most scientists, including Baltimore and Doudna, felt that the report had found a sensible middle ground. Those engaged in medical research saw it as providing a yellow light, allowing them to proceed with caution.[18]

In Britain, the Nuffield Council, the nation's most prestigious independent bioethics organization, produced a report in July 2018 that was even more liberal. "Genome editing has the potential to give rise to transformative technologies in the field of human reproduction," it concluded. "So long as heritable genome editing interventions are consistent with the welfare of the future person and with social justice and solidarity, they do not contravene any categorical moral prohibition." The Council even went so far as to diminish the distinction between using gene editing to cure diseases and using it to provide genetic enhancements. "It is possible that genome editing could be used in the future for . . . enhancing senses or abilities," the guide to the report read. The report was seen, correctly, as paving the way for human germline gene editing. The headline in the *Guardian* was "Genetically Modified Babies Given Go Ahead by UK Ethics Body."[19]

Global regulations

Even though the U.S. National Academy of Sciences and Britain's Nuffield Council espoused a liberal approach to germline editing, some restrictions were imposed in both countries. Congress passed a provision barring the Food and Drug Administration from reviewing any treatment "in which a human embryo is intentionally created or modified to include a heritable genetic modification." President Barack Obama's science advisor, John Holdren, declared, "The Administration believes that altering the human germline for clinical purposes is a line that should not be crossed at this time," and the director of the National Institutes of Health, Francis Collins, announced, "The NIH will not fund any use of gene-editing technologies in human embryos."[20] In Britain, likewise, the editing of human embryos was restricted by various regulations. But in neither Britain nor the U.S. was there an absolute and clear law against germline gene editing.

In Russia, there were no laws to prevent the use of gene editing in humans, and President Vladimir Putin in 2017 touted the potential of CRISPR. At a youth festival that year, he spoke of the benefits and dangers of creating genetically engineered humans, such as super-soldiers. "Man has the opportunity to get into the genetic code created by either nature, or as religious people would say, by God," he said. "One may imagine that scientists could create a person with desired features. This may be a mathematical genius, an outstanding musician, but this can also be a soldier, a person who can fight without fear or compassion, mercy or pain."[21]

In China, the policies were more restrictive, or at least so it seemed. Although there were no clear laws explicitly outlawing inheritable genetic editing of human embryos, there were multiple regulations and guidelines that prevented—or were believed to prevent—it. For example, in 2003 the Ministry of Health issued "Technical Norms on Human Assisted Reproduction" that specified, "Genetic manipulation of human gametes, zygotes and embryos for reproductive purposes is prohibited."[22]

China has one of the world's most controlled societies, and few things happen in clinics without the government's knowledge. Duanqing Pei, a respected young stem-cell researcher who is the director general of Guangzhou Institutes of Biomedicine and Health, assured his fellow steering committee members at the international summit in Washington that germline gene editing of embryos would not happen in China.

That is why Pei and his like-minded friends from around the world were so shocked when they arrived in Hong Kong in November 2018 for the Second International Summit on Human Genome Editing and discovered that, despite all of their high-minded deliberations and carefully crafted reports, the human species had suddenly and unexpectedly been thrust into a new era.

Part Six

CRISPR Babies

A new species would bless me as its creator and source; many happy and excellent natures would owe their being to me.

—Mary Shelley, *Frankenstein; or, The Modern Prometheus*, 1818

He Jiankui taking a selfie with Doudna at Cold Spring Harbor Laboratory

Michael Deem

CHAPTER 37

He Jiankui

The eager entrepreneur

He Jiankui, the son of struggling rice farmers, was born in the Orwellian year 1984 and grew up in Xinhua, one of the poorest villages in a rural part of Hunan province in east-central China. The average family income there when he was a boy was $100 a year. His parents were so poor that they could not afford to buy him textbooks, so Jiankui* walked to a village bookstore to read them there. "I grew up in a small farming family," he recalled. "I picked leeches from my legs every day in the summer. I will never forget my roots."[1]

Jiankui's childhood instilled in him a hunger for success and fame, so he heeded the exhortations on the posters and banners at his school that he should dedicate himself to pushing forward the frontier of science. He would indeed end up pushing that frontier, though less by great science than great eagerness.

Spurred by his belief that science was a patriotic pursuit, young Jiankui built a rudimentary physics laboratory at home, where he

*His name, 贺建奎, is transliterated as He Jiankui and pronounced HUH JEE'-an-kway. His family or "last" name is He. Because it is confusing to refer to him as He, I refer to him by his given name, Jiankui.

relentlessly conducted experiments. After doing well in school, he was tapped to go to the University of Science and Technology in Hefei, 575 miles to the east, where he majored in physics.

He applied to four graduate schools in the United States and was accepted by only one of them: Rice University in Houston. Studying under Professor Michael Deem, a genetic engineer who would later become the subject of an ethics investigation, Jiankui became a star at creating computer simulations of biological systems. "Jiankui is a very high-impact student," Deem said. "He has done a fantastic job here at Rice, and I am sure he will be highly successful in his career."

Jiankui and Deem devised a mathematical model for predicting what strains of flu would emerge each year and, in September 2010, coauthored an undistinguished paper on CRISPR that showed how the spacer sequences matching viral DNA are formed.[2] Popular, gregarious, and an eager networker, Jiankui became president of Rice's Chinese Students and Scholars Association and an avid soccer player. "Rice is a place where you can really enjoy graduate school," he told the university magazine. "Outside of the lab, there's a lot to do. Oh, my God, Rice has six soccer fields! That's awesome."[3]

He got his PhD in physics but then decided that the future was in biology. Deem allowed him to go to conferences around the country and provided an introduction to the Stanford bioengineer Stephen Quake, who invited Jiankui to become a postdoc in his lab. Colleagues there remember him as funny and energetic, with a Texas-size passion for entrepreneurship.

Quake had founded a company to commercialize a gene-sequencing technology that he had developed, but it began sliding into bankruptcy. Believing that he could make the process commercially successful in China, Jiankui decided to start a company there. Quake was enthusiastic. "This has a chance to bring the phoenix back from the ashes," he exulted to one of his partners.[4]

China was eager to nurture biotech entrepreneurs. In 2011, it launched an innovative new university, the South University of Science and Technology, in Shenzhen, a booming city of 20 million people bordering on Hong Kong. Responding to a job opening posted on the university's website, Jiankui ended up getting hired there as a biology professor and announced on his blog that he was forming the "He Jiankui and Michael Deem Joint Laboratory."[5]

Chinese officials had designated genetic engineering as critical to the country's economic future and its competition with the U.S., and to that end they launched a variety of initiatives to encourage entrepreneurs and lure back researchers who studied overseas. Jiankui benefited from two of them: the Thousand Talents Recruitment Program and the Shenzhen government's Peacock Initiative.

When he formed his new company to build gene-sequencing machines based on Quake's technology in July 2012, Shenzhen's Peacock Initiative provided an initial round of $156,000 in funding. "Shenzhen's generosity in encouraging startups, especially venture capitalists, which is comparable to Silicon Valley, attracted me," Jiankui later told the *Beijing Review*. "I am not a professor in the traditional sense. I prefer to be a research-type entrepreneur."

Over the next six years, Jiankui's company would receive about $5.7 million in funding from government sources. By 2017, its gene sequencer was on the market and the company, of which Jiankui had a one-third stake, was valued at $313 million. "The development of the device is a major technical breakthrough and will significantly improve cost-effectiveness, speed and quality of gene sequencing," Jiankui said.[6] In a scientific article describing the use of the machine for sequencing genomes, he claimed that the results "show comparable performance to the Illumina," referring to the American company that dominates the market for DNA sequencers.[7]

With his smooth personality and thirst for fame, Jiankui became a minor scientific celebrity in China, where the state-run media was eagerly looking for innovators to tout as role models. The broadcast network CTV ran a series in late 2017 featuring the country's young science entrepreneurs. As inspiring patriotic music played, Jiankui was shown talking about his company's gene sequencer, which the narrator said works better and faster than American versions. "Somebody said we shocked the world with our machine," a smiling Jiankui declared to the camera. "Yes, they're right! I did that—He Jiankui! That's me who did that!"[8]

Jiankui initially used his gene-sequencing technology to diagnose genetic conditions in early-stage human embryos. But in early 2018, he began to discuss the possibility of not only reading human genomes but also editing them. "For billions of years, life progressed according to Darwin's theory of evolution: random mutation in DNA, selection and reproduction," he wrote on his website. "Today, genome sequencing and genome editing provide powerful new tools to control evolution." His goal, he said, was to sequence a human genome for $100, then move on to fixing any problems. "Once the genetic sequence is known, we can use CRISPR-Cas9 to insert, edit or delete the associated gene for a particular trait. By correcting the disease genes, we humans can better live in the fast changing environment."

He did, however, say that he was against using gene editing for some forms of enhancement. "I support gene editing for the treatment and prevention of disease," Jiankui wrote in a post on the social media site WeChat, "but not for enhancement or improving I.Q., which is not beneficial to society."[9]

Networker

He Jiankui's website and social media comments, which were in Chinese, did not garner much attention in the West. But as a promiscuous networker and conference hopper, he was beginning to develop a circle of acquaintances in the American scientific community.

In August 2016, he attended the annual CRISPR conference held at Cold Spring Harbor Laboratory. "The just-concluded Cold Spring Harbor Gene Editing Conference is the top event in this field," he bragged on his blog. "Feng Zhang and Jennifer Doudna and other leading figures attended the event!" Accompanying the post was a selfie Jiankui took with Doudna seated in the auditorium under the oil portrait of James Watson.[10]

A few months later, in January 2017, Jiankui sent Doudna an email.

As he had done with other top CRISPR researchers, he asked to meet with her when he next came to the United States. "I am working on the technology to improve the efficacy and safety of genome editing human embryos in China," he wrote. The email arrived when Doudna was helping to organize a small workshop on "the challenge and opportunity of gene editing." It had been two years since her Napa Valley conference, and the Templeton Foundation, which supports the study of big ethical questions, had provided funding for a series of discussions on CRISPR. Doudna invited twenty scientists and ethicists to a kickoff workshop in Berkeley, but few were from overseas. "We would be delighted to have your participation," she wrote back to Jiankui, who, not surprisingly, was equally delighted to accept.[11]

The meeting opened with a public lecture by George Church in which he spoke of the possible benefits of germline editing, including ones that would augment human capacities. Church showed a slide listing simple gene variations that offer beneficial effects. Among them was a variant of the *CCR5* gene that would make a person less receptive to the HIV virus that causes AIDS.[12]

On his blog, Jiankui wrote about the off-the-record meeting: "A lot of sharp issues caused fierce debates there, and the smell of gunpowder filled the air." Particularly interesting was his interpretation of the report from the international summit on gene editing, which had just come out. He called it a "yellow light for human genetic editing." In other words, instead of reading the report as a call to not proceed with heritable human embryo editing for the time being, he interpreted it as a signal that he could proceed cautiously.[13]

Jiankui's turn to present came on the second day of the meeting. His talk, titled "Safety of Human Gene Embryo Editing," was unimpressive. There was only one interesting part: his description of his work editing the *CCR5* gene, the one that Church had mentioned in his lecture as a potential candidate for future germline editing. Jiankui described how he had edited the gene, which produces a protein that can serve as a receptor for the HIV virus, in mice, monkeys, and nonviable human embryos discarded from fertility clinics.

Other Chinese researchers had already prompted international ethics discussions by using CRISPR to edit *CCR5* genes in non-viable human embryos, so nobody at the conference took much notice. "His talk made no impression on me," Doudna says. "I found him very eager to meet people and be accepted, but he hadn't published anything important, and he didn't seem to be doing any important science." When Jiankui asked Doudna if he could come to her lab as a visiting fellow, she was surprised at his audacity. "I deflected his request," she says. "I had absolutely no interest." What struck Doudna and others at the meeting was that Jiankui did not seem interested in the moral issues involved with making inheritable gene edits to embryos.[14]

Continuing to network and conference-hop, Jiankui returned to Cold Spring Harbor in July 2017 for its annual CRISPR conference. Wearing a striped shirt and with his dark hair youthfully mussed, he gave pretty much the same talk that he had given in Berkeley earlier that year, again eliciting yawns and shrugs. He ended on a cautionary note, with a slide showing a *New York Times* story on Jesse Gelsinger, the young man who died after receiving gene therapy treatments. "A single case of failure may kill the entire field," he concluded. There were three perfunctory questions. No one thought that his experiments had produced any scientific breakthroughs.[15]

Editing babies

In this July 2017 talk at Cold Spring Harbor, Jiankui described editing the *CCR5* gene in discarded, non-viable human embryos. What he did not say was that he had already made plans to edit the gene in viable human embryos with the intent of giving birth to genetically altered babies—in other words, making inheritable germline edits. Four months earlier, he had submitted a medical ethics application to Shenzhen's Harmonicare Women and Children's Hospital. "We plan to use CRISPR-Cas9 to edit the embryo," he wrote. "The edited embryos will be transferred to women and pregnancy will follow." His goal was to allow couples who suffered from AIDS to have babies who would be protected from the HIV virus, as would all of their descendants.

Because there were simpler ways to prevent AIDS infection, such as sperm-washing and screening for healthy embryos before implantation, the procedure was not medically necessary. Nor would it correct a clear genetic disorder; the *CCR5* gene is common and probably has multiple purposes, including helping to protect against West Nile virus. So Jiankui's plan did not meet the guidelines that had been agreed to at multiple international meetings.

But it did offer Jiankui the possibility, or at least he thought so, of achieving a major historical breakthrough and enhancing the glory of Chinese science. "This is going to be a great science and medicine achievement," he wrote in his application, comparing it to "the IVF technology which was awarded the Nobel Prize in 2010." The hospital ethics committee gave its consent unanimously.[16]

There are approximately 1.25 million HIV-positive people in China, a number that is still growing rapidly, and ostracism of victims is widespread. Working with a Beijing-based AIDS advocacy group, Jiankui sought to recruit twenty volunteer couples in which the husband was HIV positive and the wife was HIV negative. More than two hundred couples showed interest.

Two of the selected couples came to Jiankui's lab in Shenzhen one Saturday in June 2017 and, in a meeting that was videotaped, were informed about the proposed clinical trial and asked if they wished to participate. He walked them through the consent form. "As the volunteer, your partner is diagnosed to have AIDS or has been infected with HIV," it said. "This research project will likely help you produce HIV-resistant infants." The two couples agreed to participate, as did five more recruited at other sessions. They produced thirty-one embryos, sixteen of which Jiankui was able to edit. Eleven were implanted into the volunteers unsuccessfully, but by the late spring of 2018 he was able to implant twin embryos into one mother and one embryo into another.[17]

Jiankui's process involved taking sperm from the father, washing the cells to rid them of the HIV virus, and then injecting the sperm into the mother's eggs. This was probably enough to ensure that the resulting fertilized eggs were free of HIV. But his goal was to guarantee that the children would never later be infected. So he injected the fertilized eggs with CRISPR-Cas9 that targeted the *CCR5* gene. They were allowed to grow for five or so days in a Petri dish until they were an early-stage embryo more than two hundred cells large, and then their DNA was sequenced to see if the edits had worked.[18]

His American confidants

During his visits to the U.S. in 2017, Jiankui began hinting at his plans to a few of the American researchers he met, many of whom later expressed regret that they did not try harder to stop him or blow the whistle. Most notably, he confided in William Hurlbut, a neurobiologist and bioethicist at Stanford, who had co-organized the January 2017 Berkeley gathering with Doudna. They had, Hurlbut later told the journal *Stat*, "several long conversations, like four or five hours long, about science and ethics." Hurlbut realized that Jiankui was intent on making embryo edits leading to live births. "I tried to give him a sense of the practical and moral implications," he says, but Jiankui insisted that only "a fringe group" opposed making germline edits. If such edits could be used to avoid a dread disease, Jiankui asked, why would people be against it? Hurlbut viewed Jiankui as "a well-meaning person who wants his efforts to count for good" but who was spurred by a scientific culture "that puts a premium on provocative research, celebrity, national scientific competitiveness, and firsts."[19]

Jiankui also confided his plans to Matthew Porteus, an accomplished and respected stem-cell researcher at Stanford Medical School. "I was stunned and my jaw dropped," Porteus recalls. It turned from a polite conversation about scientific data into a half-hour lecture by Porteus about all the reasons he thought Jiankui's idea was terrible.[20]

"There's no medical need," Porteus said. "It violates all the guidelines. You're jeopardizing the entire field of genetic engineering." He demanded to know if Jiankui had run it by his senior people.

No, Jiankui said.

"You need to talk to these people, the officials in China, before you proceed any further," Porteus warned with rising anger.

At that point Jiankui became very quiet, his face flushed, and then he walked out of the office. "I don't think he was expecting such a negative reaction," Porteus says.

In hindsight, Porteus blames himself for not doing more. "I fear some people think I made an ass out of myself," he says. "I wish that, while he was in my office, I had insisted that we jointly send emails to various senior people in China." But it's unlikely that Jiankui would have permitted Porteus to tell other people. "He thought that if he told people ahead of time, they would try to stop him," Porteus says, "but once he succeeded in producing the first CRISPR babies everyone would recognize it as a great achievement."[21]

Jiankui also confided in Stephen Quake, the Stanford gene-sequencing entrepreneur who had supervised his postdoctoral work and helped him launch the Shenzhen-based company that used Quake's technology. As early as 2016, Jiankui told Quake that he wanted to be the first person to create gene-edited babies. Quake told him it was "a terrible idea," but when Jiankui persisted, Quake suggested that he do it with the proper approvals. "I will take your suggestion that we will get a local ethic approval before we move on to the first genetic edited human baby," Jiankui told Quake in an email, which was later reported by *New York Times* health writer Pam Belluck. "Please keep it in confidential."

"Good News!" Jiankui wrote Quake in April 2018. "The embryo with CCR5 gene edited was transplanted to the women 10 days ago, and today the pregnancy is confirmed!"

"Wow, that's quite an achievement!" Quake replied. "Hopefully she will carry to term."

After an investigation, Stanford cleared Quake, as well as Hurlbut and Porteus, of any wrongdoing. "The review found that the Stanford researchers expressed serious concerns to Dr. He about his work," the university declared. "When Dr. He did not heed their recommendations and proceeded, Stanford researchers urged him to follow proper scientific practices."[22]

The most involved and tainted of Jiankui's American enablers was Michael Deem, his PhD advisor at Rice. In a scene that was captured on videotape, Deem can be seen sitting at the table during the first of Jiankui's sessions where prospective parents were advised about giving their consent to the gene editing of their embryos. "When this couple gave their informed consent," Jiankui later said publicly, "it was observed by this United States professor." Deem spoke to the volunteers through a translator, a member of the Chinese team told *Stat*.

In an interview with the Associated Press, Deem admitted being in China during the meeting. "I met the parents," he said. "I was there for the informed consent of the parents." Deem also defended Jiankui's actions. But he then hired two Houston lawyers who issued a statement claiming that Deem was not involved in the informed-consent process, even though a scene from the video shows him sitting there. The lawyers also claimed, "Michael does not do human research and he did not do human research on this project." That seemed to be contradicted when it was revealed that Deem was a coauthor of the paper Jiankui wrote on his human gene–editing experiments. Rice said that it would launch an investigation, but after two years had not issued a finding. By the end of 2020, Deem's faculty page had been removed from the Rice website, but the university continued to refuse to offer any explanation.[23]

Jiankui's PR campaign

As the Chinese pregnancies progressed in mid-2018, Jiankui knew that his announcement would be earth-shaking news, and he wanted to capitalize on it. The goal of his experiment, after all, was not merely to protect two kids from AIDS. The prospect of achieving fame was also a motivation. So he hired Ryan Ferrell, a respected American public relations executive he had worked with on another project, who found Jiankui's plans to be so exciting that he left his agency and relocated temporarily to Shenzhen.[24]

Ferrell planned a multimedia announcement campaign. It included having Jiankui write an article on the ethics of gene editing for a journal, cooperate with the Associated Press on an exclusive story on the making of the CRISPR babies, and tape five videos that would be released on his website and YouTube. In addition, he would write a scientific piece, coauthored with Rice's Michael Deem, that he would try to publish in a prestigious journal such as *Nature*.

The ethics story, which Jiankui and Ferrell titled "Draft Ethical Principles for Therapeutic Assisted Reproductive Technologies," was intended for a new publication called the *CRISPR Journal*, edited by the CRISPR pioneer Rodolphe Barrangou and the science journalist Kevin Davies. In his draft, Jiankui listed five principles that should be followed when deciding whether to edit human embryos:

> *Mercy for families in need*: For a few families, early gene surgery may be the only viable way to heal a heritable disease and save a child from a lifetime of suffering. . . .
>
> *Only for serious disease, never vanity*: Gene surgery is a serious medical procedure that should never be used for aesthetics, enhancement, or sex selection. . . .
>
> *Respect a child's autonomy*: A life is more than our physical body. . . .
>
> *Genes do not define you*: Our DNA does not predetermine our purpose or what we could achieve. We flourish from our own hard work, nutrition, and support from society and our loved ones. . . .
>
> *Everyone deserves freedom from genetic disease*: Wealth should not determine health.[25]

Instead of following guidelines such as those established by the National Academy of Sciences, Jiankui had crafted a framework that, at least by his thinking, would justify his use of CRISPR to take out the receptor gene for HIV. He was following moral principles that had been propounded, sometimes quite convincingly, by some prominent Western philosophers. For example, Duke professor Allen Buchanan was the staff philosopher for President Reagan's Commission on Medical Ethics, was on the Advisory Council for the National Human Genome Research Institute under President Clinton, and is a fellow of the prestigious Hastings Center. Seven years before Jiankui decided to edit the *CCR5* gene in human embryos, Buchanan had supported the concept in his influential book *Better Than Human*:

> Suppose we learn that some desirable gene or set of genes already exists, but only in a small number of humans. This is precisely the situation for genes that confer resistance to certain strains of HIV-AIDS. If we rely on the "wisdom of nature" or "let nature take its course," this beneficial genotype may or may not spread through the human population. . . . Suppose it were possible to ensure that such beneficial genes spread much more quickly by intentional genetic modification. This could occur by injecting genes into the testicles or, more radically, by inserting them into a large number of human embryos, utilizing in vitro fertilization. We would get the benefits . . . without the carnage.[26]

Buchanan was not alone. At the time of Jiankui's clinical trial, many serious ethical thinkers, and not just gung-ho scientific researchers, had publicly argued, using the *CCR5* gene as a specific example, that gene editing to cure or prevent diseases could be permissible and even desirable.

Ferrell gave an Associated Press team—Marilynn Marchione, Christina Larson, and Emily Wang—exclusive access to Jiankui. They were even allowed to videotape a non-viable human embryo being injected with CRISPR in Jiankui's lab.

With Ferrell's guidance, Jiankui also prepared videos that featured him in his lab speaking directly to the camera. In the first one, he outlined his five ethical principles. "If we can protect a little girl or boy from certain disease, if we can help more loving couples start families, gene surgery is a wholesome development," he said. He also made a distinction between curing disease and making enhancements. "Gene surgery should only be used for treating serious disease. We should not use it for increasing I.Q., improving sports performance or changing skin color. That's not love."[27]

In the second video, he explained why he felt it was "inhuman for parents *not* to protect their children if nature gives us the tools to do so." The third video explained why he had chosen HIV as his first target. The fourth, which was in Chinese and delivered by one of his postdoctoral students, explained the scientific details of how the CRISPR edits were made.[28] They held off making the fifth video until they could announce the live births of the two babies.

Birth

The public relations campaign and release of the YouTube videos was planned for January, when the babies were due to be born. But one evening in early November 2018, Jiankui got a call saying that the mother had gone into labor prematurely. He dashed to the Shenzhen airport to fly to the city where the mother lived, taking some of the students in his lab. She ended up giving birth, after a caesarean section, to two apparently healthy girls, who were named Nana and Lulu.

The births happened so early that Jiankui had not yet submitted the official description of his clinical trial to Chinese authorities. On November 8, after the twins were born, it was finally submitted. It was written in Chinese, and for two weeks it went unnoticed in the West.[29]

He also finished the academic article he had been working on. Titled "Birth of Twins after Genome Editing for HIV Resistance," it was submitted to the prestigious journal *Nature*. It was never published, but the manuscript, a copy of which was given to me by one of the American researchers he sent it to, offers details about his science and glimpses into his mindset.[30] "Genome editing at the embryonic stage has potential to permanently cure disease and confer resistance to pathogenic infections," he wrote. "Here, we report the first birth from human gene editing: twin girls who had undergone CCR5 gene editing as embryos were born normal and healthy in November 2018." In the article, Jiankui defended the ethical value of what he had done. "We anticipate that human embryo genome editing will bring new hope to millions of families seeking healthy babies free from inherited or acquired life-threatening diseases."

Buried in Jiankui's unpublished paper were some disturbing pieces of information. In Lulu, only one of the two relevant chromosomes had been properly modified. "We confirmed Nana's CCR5 gene was edited successfully with frameshift mutations on both alleles and Lulu's was heterozygous," he admitted. In other words, Lulu had different gene versions on her two chromosomes, which meant that her system would still produce some of the CCR5 protein.

In addition, there was evidence that some unwanted off-target edits had been made and also that both embryos had been mosaics, meaning there had been enough cell division before the CRISPR editing was done that some of the resulting cells in the babies were unedited. Despite all of this, Jiankui later said, the parents chose to have both embryos implanted. Kiran Musunuru of the University of Pennsylvania later commented, "The first attempt to hack the code of life and, ostensibly, improve the health of human babies had in fact been a hack job."[31]

The news breaks

In the first few days after the babies were born, Jiankui and his publicist, Ferrell, tried to keep it under wraps until January, when they hoped that *Nature* would publish their scholarly paper. But the news was too explosive to hold. Just before Jiankui was scheduled to arrive at the Second International Summit on Human Genome Editing, to be held in Hong Kong, news of his CRISPR babies leaked.

Antonio Regalado, a reporter at the *MIT Technology Review*, combined a knowledge of science with the news instincts of a scoop-magnet journalist. He was in China in October, and he happened to be invited to a meeting with Jiankui and Ferrell just as they were making plans for the announcement. Although Jiankui did not reveal his secret, he did discuss the *CCR5* gene, and Regalado was a good enough reporter to suspect that something was afoot. By searching on the internet, he discovered the application Jiankui had submitted to the Chinese Clinical Trial Registry. "Exclusive: Chinese Scientists Are Creating CRISPR Babies" was the headline on his story, which went online November 25.[32]

With Regalado's story online, Marchione and her colleagues unleashed a well-balanced story brimming with details. Their lead sentence captured the drama of the moment: "A Chinese researcher claims that he helped make the world's first genetically edited babies—twin girls born this month whose DNA he said he altered with a powerful new tool capable of rewriting the very blueprint of life."[33]

All of the high-minded discussions that ethicists had been having about germline gene editing were suddenly preempted by an ambitious young Chinese scientist who wanted to make history. As with the birth of the first test-tube baby, Louise Brown, and the cloning of Dolly the sheep, the world had entered a new era.

That evening, Jiankui released the videos he had previously made along with a final one in which he made his momentous announcement on YouTube. Speaking calmly but proudly to the camera, he declared:

> Two beautiful little Chinese girls named Lulu and Nana came crying into the world as healthy as any other babies a few weeks ago. The girls are home now with their mom, Grace, and their dad, Mark. Grace started her pregnancy by regular IVF with one difference. Right after we sent her husband's sperm into her egg, we also sent in a little bit of protein and instructions for it to do gene surgery. When Lulu and Nana were just a single cell, this surgery removed the doorway through which HIV enters to infect people. . . . When Mark saw his daughters, the first thing he said was that he never thought he could be a father. Now he has found a reason to live, a reason to walk, a purpose. You see, Mark has HIV. . . . As a father of two girls, I can't think of a gift more beautiful and wholesome for the society than giving another couple a chance to start a loving family.[34]

He Jiankui coming onstage

With Robin Lovell-Badge and Matthew Porteus

Chapter 38

The Hong Kong Summit

On November 23, two days before He Jiankui's news broke, Doudna received an email from him. The subject line was dramatic: "Babies Born."

She was puzzled, then shocked, and then alarmed. "At first I thought it was fake, or maybe he was crazy," she says. "The idea that you would use 'Babies Born' as a subject line for something like this didn't seem real."[1]

He had included the draft of the manuscript he had submitted to *Nature*. When Doudna opened the attachment, she knew the situation was all too real. "It was a Friday, the day after Thanksgiving," she recalls. "I was over in our condo in San Francisco with family members and longtime friends when this email came in like a bolt out of the blue."

Doudna realized that the news would become even more dramatic because of its timing. In three days, five hundred scientists and policymakers were due to converge in Hong Kong for the Second International Summit on Human Genome Editing, the successor to the December 2015 summit in Washington. Doudna was one of the core organizers, along with David Baltimore, and He Jiankui was scheduled to be a speaker.

Doudna and the other organizers had not originally put Jiankui on the list of invited speakers. But they had changed their minds a few weeks earlier when they heard rumors that he had dreams or delusions of editing human embryos. Some on the planning committee felt that involving him in the summit might help dissuade him from crossing the germline.[2]

Upon getting Jiankui's shocking "Babies Born" email, Doudna tracked down Baltimore's cell phone number and reached him as he was leaving to fly to Hong Kong. They agreed that she would change her flight and arrive a day earlier than planned so that they could gather with some of the other organizers and decide what to do.

When she landed at dawn on the morning of Monday, November 26, and turned her phone back on, Doudna saw that Jiankui had been desperately trying to reach her by email. "The nanosecond I landed at the airport, I had just a ton of emails from Jiankui," Doudna told Jon Cohen of *Science*. He was driving to Hong Kong from Shenzhen, and he wanted to meet as soon as possible. "I have to talk to you right now," he emailed. "Things have really gotten out of control."[3]

She did not reply because she wanted to meet first with Baltimore and the other organizers. Soon after she checked into Le Méridien Cyberport hotel, where the conferees were staying, a bellman knocked at her door with a message from Jiankui, saying to call him right away.

She agreed to meet with Jiankui in the hotel lobby, but first she hastily convened some of the organizers in a fourth-floor conference room. Baltimore was already there, sitting with George Daley of Harvard Medical School, Robin Lovell-Badge of London's Francis Crick Institute, Victor Dzau of the U.S. National Academy of Medicine, and bioethicist Alta Charo from the University of Wisconsin. None of them had seen the scientific paper that Jiankui had submitted to *Nature*, so Doudna showed them the copy he had emailed to her. "Our group all scrambled to decide whether Jiankui should be allowed to remain on the conference program," Dzau recalls.

They quickly decided that he should. In fact, they decided it was important not to let him withdraw. They would give him a solo spot on the program and ask him to address the science and methods he used to make the CRISPR babies.

After fifteen minutes, Doudna went down to the lobby to meet Jiankui. She took with her Robin Lovell-Badge, who would be chairing Jiankui's session. The three of them sat on a couch, and Doudna and Lovell-Badge told Jiankui that they wanted his presentation to explain exactly how and why he had proceeded with his experiment.

Jiankui flummoxed them by insisting that he wanted to stick with his original slide presentation and not discuss the CRISPR babies. Lovell-Badge, whose usual hue is an English pale, turned almost white as he listened. Doudna politely pointed out that Jiankui was being ludicrous. He had triggered the most explosive scientific controversy in years, and there was no way he could avoid discussing it. That seemed to surprise Jiankui. "I think that he was oddly naïve as well as glory-seeking," she recalls. "He had intentionally caused an explosion and yet wanted to act like it hadn't happened." They convinced him to have an early dinner with some members of the organizing committee to discuss the issue.[4]

On her way out of the lobby, shaking her head in amazement, Doudna ran into Duanqing Pei, the American-educated stem-cell biologist from China who heads the Guangzhou Institute of Biomedicine and Health. "Have you heard?" Doudna asked him. When she told him the details, he had trouble believing it. Pei and Doudna had become friendly after many conferences, including the 2015 first international summit in Washington, and he had repeatedly told his American colleagues that there were regulations in China against germline editing in humans. "I assured people that, in our system, everything is carefully controlled and licensed, so this type of thing couldn't occur," Pei later told me. He agreed to come to the dinner with Jiankui that evening.[5]

Showdown over dinner

The dinner, a Cantonese buffet in the hotel's fourth-floor restaurant, was tense. When Jiankui arrived, he was defensive, even a bit defiant, about what he had done. He pulled out his laptop to show his data and the DNA sequencing he had performed on the embryos. "We were increasingly horrified," Lovell-Badge recalled. They peppered him with questions: Had there been oversight on his consent process? Why did he believe germline embryo editing was medically necessary? Had he read the guidelines that the international academies of medicine had adopted? "I feel I complied with all those criteria," Jiankui answered. His university and hospital knew all about what he was doing and had approved, he insisted, "and now that they're seeing the negative reaction, they're denying it and hanging me out to dry." When Doudna walked through the reasons why germline editing was not "medically necessary" to prevent HIV infection, Jiankui got very emotional. "Jennifer, you don't understand China," he said. "There's an incredible stigma about being HIV positive, and I wanted to give these people a chance at a normal life and help them have kids when they otherwise might not have."[6]

The dinner became increasingly fraught. After an hour, Jiankui shifted from being plaintive to being angry. He stood up abruptly and tossed some bills on the table. He had been receiving death threats, he said, and now he was going to move to an undisclosed hotel where the press couldn't find him. Doudna chased after him. "I think it's very important that you appear on Wednesday and present your work," she said. "Will you come?" He paused and then agreed to, but he wanted security. He was afraid. Lovell-Badge promised to have Hong Kong University provide police protection.

One reason Jiankui was defiant was that he had thought he would be hailed as a Chinese hero, perhaps even a global one. Indeed, the first Chinese news reports did so. The *People's Daily*, a government organ, ran a story that morning with the headline "The World's First Gene-Edited Babies Genetically Resistant to AIDS Were Born in China," and it called Jiankui's work "a milestone accomplishment China has achieved in the area of gene-editing technologies." But the tide quickly turned as scientists, even in China, began to criticize his actions. Later that evening, the *People's Daily* deleted the story from its website.[7]

After Jiankui left the hotel restaurant, the organizers stayed at the table discussing how to handle the situation. Pei looked at his smartphone and reported that a group of Chinese scientists had put out a statement condemning Jiankui. Pei began translating it for the others at the table. "Direct human experimentation can only be described as crazy," they declared. "This is a huge blow to the global reputation and development of Chinese science, especially in the field of biomedical research." Doudna asked Pei whether the statement had come from the Chinese Academy of Sciences. No, Pei replied, but a group of more than a hundred prestigious Chinese scientists had signed it, which meant that the statement had official blessing.[8]

Doudna and her dinner partners realized that they, as the conference organizers, should put out a statement as well. But they did not want to make it too strong for fear that it would provoke Jiankui to cancel his talk. Truth be told, Doudna admitted, their motives were not merely scientific. The global buzz was huge, eyes were on Hong Kong, and it would be quite a letdown if Jiankui drove back to Shenzhen and they all missed the chance to be part of a historic moment. "We put out a very short statement that was quite bland and got criticism for that," she says, "but we wanted to ensure that he would show up."

As Doudna and her colleagues were having dinner, Jiankui's extensive publicity plan was unfolding: the YouTube videos were released, the AP story he had cooperated with went viral, and the high-minded ethics piece that he wrote was finally published online by the *CRISPR Journal* editors (though they later retracted it). "We were all struck by the fact that he was pretty young and came across as an interesting combination of hubris and remarkable naïveté," Doudna says.[9]

Jiankui's presentation

At high noon on Wednesday, November 28, 2018, it was finally time for He Jiankui to present.[10] Robin Lovell-Badge, the moderator, came to the podium looking nervous. With his sandy blond hair, which his hands kept mussing nervously, and his horn-rimmed glasses, he looked like an even nerdier version of Woody Allen. He also looked haggard. He later told Doudna that he had not slept at all the night before. Reading from his notes, he instructed the audience to be polite, as if he was afraid that the conferees might rush the stage. "Can you please allow him to speak without interruptions," he said, then waved his hand as if wiping a machine and added, "I have the right to cancel the session if there is too much noise or interruption." But the only sounds were from the clicking cameras of the dozens of photographers standing in the back.

Lovell-Badge explained that Jiankui had been scheduled to speak before the news of his CRISPR babies was known. "We didn't know the story that was going to break over the last couple of days," he said. "In fact he sent me the slides he was going to show in this session, and they did not include any of the work he is going to talk about." Then, looking around nervously, he announced, "I would like, if he can hear me, to invite Jiankui He to the stage to present his work."[11]

At first no one appeared. The audience seemed to be holding its breath. "I'm sure people were wondering if he was actually going to appear," Lovell-Badge later recalled. Then, from directly behind Lovell-Badge, who was standing on the right side of the stage, a young Asian man appeared in a dark suit. There was scattered, tentative applause and a bit of confusion. The man fiddled with a laptop to get the right slide up, then adjusted the microphone. The audience members began to laugh nervously as they realized that it was the audiovisual technician. "Look, I don't know where he is," Lovell-Badge said, waving his notebook.

For an eerie thirty-five seconds, which in cases like this is a *very* long time, there was a charged silence in the room, but no movement. Finally, somewhat tentatively, a slight man wearing a striped white shirt and carrying a bulging tan briefcase stepped out from the far side of the stage. In the somewhat formal atmosphere of Hong Kong (Lovell-Badge was wearing a suit), he looked incongruous with his wide-open collar and no jacket or tie. "He looked more like a commuter hurrying to catch the Star Ferry in the Hong Kong humidity than a scientist at the center of a massive international storm," the science editor Kevin Davies later reported.[12] Lovell-Badge, relieved, waved him over and, when Jiankui got to the podium, whispered in his ear, "Please not too long, we need time to ask you questions."

As Jiankui started to speak, a barrage of camera clicks and flashes from the paparazzi drowned him out and seemed to startle him. David Baltimore stood up in the front row, turned to the press section, and berated them. "The clicking of the cameras was so loud that we couldn't hear what was happening onstage," he says. "So I took over the meeting for a moment and got them to stop."[13]

Jiankui glanced around sheepishly, his smooth face making him look even younger than his thirty-four years. "I must apologize that my results leaked unexpectedly, taking away the chance for peer review before being presented to this conference," he began, and then went on, without seeming to be aware of the contradiction, to "thank the Associated Press who we engaged months before the birth of the humans for accurately reporting the study's outcome." Reading slowly from his speech, with little emotion, he described the scourge of HIV infection, the deaths and discrimination that resulted, and how a *CCR5* gene mutation could prevent the infection of babies born to HIV-positive parents.

After twenty minutes of showing slides and discussing his process, it was time for questions. Lovell-Badge invited Matthew Porteus, the Stanford stem-cell biologist who knew Jiankui, onstage to help with the questioning. Instead of asking Jiankui about the huge issue of why he would violate international norms by making germline edits in a human embryo, Lovell-Badge began with a long question, and then another, about the evolutionary history and possible roles of the *CCR5* gene. Porteus followed up with multiple detailed questions about how many couples, eggs, embryos, and researchers were involved in Jiankui's clinical trial. "I was disappointed that the discussion onstage didn't focus on the main issues," Doudna later said.

Finally, the audience was invited to comment and ask questions. Baltimore rose first and went right to the point. After describing the international guidelines that were supposed to be met before any germline editing of humans, he declared, "That has not happened." He called Jiankui's actions "irresponsible," secretive, and not "medically necessary." David Liu, the prominent biochemist at Harvard, spoke next and challenged Jiankui about why he felt embryo editing was warranted in this case. "You could do sperm washing and generate uninfected embryos," Liu said. "What is the unmet medical need for these patients?" Speaking softly, Jiankui responded that he was not just trying to help the twin girls but wanted to find a way "for millions of HIV children" who might someday need protection from being infected with HIV from their parents even after being born. "I have personal experience with people in an AIDS village where thirty percent of villagers were infected, and they have to give up their children to aunts and uncles for fear of infecting them."

"There's a consensus to not allow genome editing on germline cells," a professor at Peking University pointed out. "Why did you choose to cross this red line? And why did you conduct these [procedures] in secret?" When Lovell-Badge took it upon himself to rephrase the question, he asked only about the secrecy part, which Jiankui deflected by describing how he had consulted with a lot of researchers in the U.S., and so he never directly addressed the key historic issue involved. The final question was submitted by a journalist: "If this was going to be your baby, would you have gone ahead with this?" Jiankui's answer: "If it was my baby in this situation, I would have tried it." Then Jiankui picked up his briefcase, exited the stage, and was driven back to Shenzhen.[14]

Sitting in the audience, Doudna began to sweat. "I was feeling a combination of nervous energy and being sick to my stomach," she recalls. Here was the amazing gene-editing tool, CRISPR-Cas9, that she had co-invented, being used to produce, for the first time in history, a genetically designed human being. And it had been done before the safety issues had been clinically tested, the ethical issues resolved, or a social consensus had formed over whether this was the way for science—and for humans—to evolve. "It was quite emotional for me feeling the incredible disappointment and disgust at the way that it had been handled. I was concerned that the race to do this had been motivated not by medical need or by the desire to help people but by a desire for attention and to be first."[15]

The question that she and the other organizers faced was whether they were partly to blame. For years they had been crafting criteria that should be met before there was any editing of humans. But they had stopped short of calling clearly for a moratorium or prescribing a clear process for approval of a trial. Jiankui could claim, as he did, that in his own mind he had followed these criteria.[16]

"Irresponsible"

Later that evening, Doudna went to the bar of the hotel and huddled with a few of her exhausted fellow organizers. Baltimore showed up, and they ordered beer. He believed, more than the others, that there had been a failure by the scientific community to do enough self-regulation. "One thing is clear," he said. "If this guy really did what he claims to have done, this is actually not very hard to do. That's a sobering thought." They decided that they had to issue a statement.[17]

Doudna, Baltimore, Porteus, and five others commandeered a small meeting room and began hammering out a draft. "It was many hours going over line by line and discussing what the point of each sentence was," Porteus recalls. Like the others, he wanted to express strong disapproval of what Jiankui had done and yet avoid using the word "moratorium" or doing anything that might hamper the progress of gene-editing research. "I find the word 'moratorium' not very productive because it doesn't give you a sense of how you move past it," Porteus says. "I know it's a term that appeals to people because it puts a nice dark line that thou shall not cross. But to just say there should be a moratorium cuts off conversation and doesn't allow us to think through how one might get there in a responsible way."

Doudna was tugged in two directions. She was appalled at what Jiankui had done, because it was premature and unnecessary as a medical procedure and a grandstanding act that could spark a backlash against all gene-editing work. Yet she had come to believe, and hope, that CRISPR-Cas9 would prove to be a powerful tool for human well-being, including someday through making germline edits. During the discussion of the draft statement, that became the consensus at the table.[18]

So they decided, once again, to steer a middle course. There was a need for more specific guidelines on when germline gene editing should be done, but it was also important to avoid rhetoric that would lead to national bans and moratoria. "The sense at the meeting was that the technology had advanced to the stage where we need to have a clear pathway to clinical use of gene editing in embryos," Doudna says. In other words, instead of trying to stop any further uses of CRISPR to make gene-edited babies, she wanted to pave the way to making it safer to do so. "To put your head in the sand or say we need a moratorium is just not realistic," she argues. "Instead we should say, 'If you want to move into the clinic with gene editing, these are the specific steps that need to be taken.'"

Doudna was influenced by George Daley, dean of Harvard Medical School, a longtime friend who was part of these deliberations. He strongly believed that CRISPR could be used someday to make inheritable edits; research was then underway at Harvard to study germline edits in sperm that might prevent Alzheimer's. "George appreciates the potential value of human germline editing in embryos and has wanted to maintain the potential for this to be used in the future," Doudna says.[19]

So the statement that Doudna, Baltimore, and the other organizers crafted was very restrained. "At this summit we heard an unexpected and deeply disturbing claim that human embryos had been edited and implanted, resulting in a pregnancy and the birth of twins," they wrote. "The procedure was irresponsible and failed to conform with international norms." But there was no call for a ban or moratorium. Instead, the statement simply said that the safety risks were currently too great to permit germline editing "at this time." It then proceeded to stress, "Germline genome editing could become acceptable in the future if these risks are addressed and if a number of additional criteria are met." The germline was no longer a red line.[20]

Chapter 39

Acceptance

Francis Collins, Doudna, and Senator Richard Durbin at a congressional hearing

Josiah Zayner celebrates

Josiah Zayner, the biohacker who had injected himself with a CRISPR-edited gene a year earlier, was so excited that he stayed up all night watching a livestream of He Jiankui's announcement in Hong Kong. He watched on his laptop in bed with a blanket over his legs and the lights off, with just the glow of the laptop on his face, because his girlfriend was asleep next to him. "I'm just sitting there waiting for him to take the stage, and I got a tingle down my spine and goosebumps knowing that something exciting was about to happen," he says.[1]

When Jiankui described the CRISPR-edited twins he had wrought, Zayner said to himself, "Holy shit!" It was, he felt, not just a scientific achievement but a milestone for the human race. "We did it!" he exulted. "We genetically engineered an embryo! Our humanity has just been changed forever!"

There was no way to go back now, he realized. It was like when Roger Bannister broke the four-minute mile. Now that it had happened, it would happen again. "I view it as one of the most groundbreaking things that's been done in science. In all of human history, we didn't get to decide what genes we have, right? Now we do." And in a personal way, it validated what Zayner felt was his own mission. "For days I was so excited I couldn't sleep, because it affirmed to me why I do what I do, which is to try to make sure that people can push humanity forward."

Push humanity forward? Yes, sometimes it's the rebels who do so. As Zayner speaks, his flat tones and crazy excitement remind me of a day when Steve Jobs sat in his backyard and recited from memory the lines he had helped craft for Apple's "Think Different" commercial about the misfits and rebels and troublemakers who are not fond of rules and have no respect for the status quo. "They push the human race forward," Jobs said. "Because the people who are crazy enough to think they can change the world, are the ones who do."

One reason it would be hard to prevent future CRISPR babies, Zayner later explained in an essay for *Stat*, was that the technology would soon be within the reach of accomplished misfits. "People are already editing human cells using a $150 inverted microscope," he wrote, and online companies like his own sold Cas9 protein and guide RNAs. "The requirements of embryo injection are minimal: a microinjector, micropipette, and microscope. All of these can be purchased on eBay and assembled for a few thousand dollars." Human embryos can be bought from fertility clinics for about $1,000, he said. "You can probably have the embryo transferred to a human by a medical doctor in the U.S. if you don't tell him or her what you've done, or you can do it in another country. . . . So it won't be long until the next human embryo is edited and implanted."[2]

The great thing about germline gene editing, Zayner says, is that it can remove a disease or genetic abnormality permanently from the human race. "Not just cure it in a patient," he says, "but completely remove miserable death-sentence diseases like muscular dystrophy from the future of humanity, forever." He even supports using CRISPR to make enhancements in children. "If I could have my children be less prone to being obese or having genes that make them perform better athletically and stuff, why would I say no?"[3]

For Zayner, the issue is also personal. When I talked to him in mid-2020, he and his partner were trying to conceive a child through *in vitro* fertilization, and they took advantage of preimplantation genetic diagnosis to select the sex of their child. The doctors also screened for a few major genetic diseases, but they would not give Zayner full genome sequences and markers of the prospective embryos. "We don't get to choose the genes that go into our baby, which is crazy," he says. "Instead we let it be done by chance. I think it's okay to choose the genes you want for your children. It's scary and it's going to create *Homo sapiens* version 2.0. But I also think it's really, really, really exciting."

As I start to push back, Zayner stops me cold by citing a personal example of the type of genetic disposition he would like to edit. "I suffer from bipolar disorder," he says. "It's terrible. It inflicts serious issues on my life. I would love to get rid of it." Does he worry, I ask, that eliminating the disorder would change who he is? "People try to make up these lies that it helps you be more creative and all this other bullshit, but it's a disease. It's an illness that causes suffering, a shitload of suffering. And I think we could probably figure out ways to be creative without this disease."

Zayner knows that there are multiple genes that contribute in mysterious ways to psychological disorders, and we don't know enough now to fix them. But in theory, if it could be made to work, he feels that he would want to use germline gene editing to make sure his own children are less likely to suffer. "If I could edit the genes in a way that would reduce the probability that my child would be bipolar, if I could reduce that a little bit for my child, like, how could I not do that? Like, how can I want my child to just grow up and have to suffer like I have? I just don't think I could."

What about less medically needed edits? "Sure, I would make my kids six inches taller and more athletic if I could," he says. "And more attractive. People who are taller and more attractive are more successful, right? What would you want for your child? Obviously for my kids, I would want the world for them." He guesses, correctly, that I grew up in a household with parents who provided me with the best possible education. "Is that any different," he asks, "than wanting to provide a kid with the best genes?"

No backlash

When Doudna returned home from Hong Kong, she found that her teenage son could not understand why there was so much fuss about Jiankui's gene editing. "Andy was very cavalier, which makes me wonder whether future generations will see this as such a big deal," she says. "Maybe they'll see it like IVF, which was very controversial when it first arose." Her parents, she recalls, were shocked when the first test-tube baby was born in 1978. She was fourteen, had just read *The Double Helix*, and remembers discussing with them why they thought creating babies by *in vitro* fertilization was unnatural and felt wrong. "But then it came to be accepted and my parents accepted it—they had friends who could only have kids by IVF and were delighted that the technology existed."[4]

As it turned out, the political and public reaction to the CRISPR babies was in line with Andy's. Two weeks after returning from Hong Kong, Doudna attended that meeting on Capitol Hill with eight senators to discuss gene editing. Such meetings are usually a forum for politicians to express their shock and dismay about something they don't fully understand and then call for more laws and regulations. Quite the opposite occurred at the Senate briefing, which was hosted by Illinois Democrat Dick Durbin and included South Carolina Republican Lindsey Graham, Rhode Island Democrat Jack Reed, Tennessee Republican Lamar Alexander, and Louisiana Republican Bill Cassidy (a doctor). "I was pleased that all of those senators, all of them, were encouraging of the general idea of editing as an important technology," Doudna says. "I was surprised none of them were demanding more regulations. They just wanted to figure out, 'Where do we go from here?'"

Doudna and National Institutes of Health director Francis Collins, who accompanied her, explained that there were already regulations in place to restrict the use of gene editing in embryos. The senators were more interested in trying to understand the value CRISPR might have in medicine and agriculture. Rather than focus on the just-born Chinese CRISPR babies, they asked detailed questions about how CRISPR might work, both in somatic therapies and germline editing, to cure sickle-cell anemia. "They were electrified by the sickle-cell potential, and for other debilitating single-gene diseases such as Huntington's and Tay-Sachs," Doudna recalls. "They talked about what it meant for sustainable health care."[5]

Two international commissions were created to deal with the issue of germline editing. The first was organized by the national science academies that had been part of the process since 2015. The other was convened by the World Health Organization. Doudna feared that having two groups might lead to conflicting messages, thus allowing future He Jiankuis to make their own interpretations of the guidelines. So I met with Victor Dzau, president of the U.S. National Academy of Medicine, and Margaret Hamburg, co-chair of the WHO commission, to see how they would divide up responsibility. "The national academies group is focusing on science," Hamburg said. "The WHO is looking at how to create a global regulatory framework." Even though there will be two reports, Dzau said, it will be better than in the past, when the scientific academies in different countries were creating different guidelines.

Nevertheless, Hamburg conceded that this was unlikely to prevent countries from crafting their own rules. "They have different attitudes and regulatory standards, like they do on genetically modified foods, that reflect their different social values," she explained. That could, unfortunately, lead to genetic tourism. Privileged people who want enhancements will travel to the countries that offer them. She acknowledged that it would be hard for the WHO to police compliance: "This is not like nuclear weapons where you can have guards and padlocks to enforce a security regimen."[6]

The moratorium issue

As the two commissions were getting to work in mid-2019, a public dispute erupted in the scientific community that once again pitted Doudna against the Broad Institute's hard-charging Eric Lander. It was over the use of the word "moratorium," which most scientific committees over the years had avoided.

In some ways the dispute over whether to call for an official moratorium was semantic. The conditions that had been specified for permissible embryo gene editing—that it be safe and "medically necessary"—could not be met for the time being. But some argued that Jiankui's actions showed the need for a clearer and brighter stoplight. Among them were Lander, his protégé Feng Zhang, Paul Berg, Francis Collins, and Doudna's scientific collaborator Emmanuelle Charpentier. "If you use the m-word," Collins explained, "it has a little more clout."[7]

Lander liked being a public intellectual and policy advisor. Articulate, funny, gregarious, and magnetic—at least to those not turned off by his intensity—he was very good at advocating positions and convening groups of earnest chin-strokers. But Doudna suspected that he stirred up the moratorium issue, at least in small part, because she and David Baltimore, rather than the publicity-shy Zhang, had taken the limelight as the foremost public policy thinkers about CRISPR. "Eric and the Broad Institute have a very big bullhorn," she says. "Their call for a moratorium was a way for them to capture a lot of headlines about something they didn't step up to the plate about early on."

Whatever his motives (and I tend to think they were sincere), Lander set about rounding up support for an article to be published in *Nature* titled "Adopt a Moratorium on Heritable Genome Editing." Zhang of course signed up, as did Doudna's erstwhile collaborator Charpentier. So did Berg, whose recombinant DNA discoveries had prompted Asilomar forty-four years earlier. "We call for a global moratorium on all clinical uses of human germline editing—that is, changing heritable DNA (in sperm, eggs or embryos) to make genetically modified children," the article began.[8]

Lander coordinated the essay with his friend Collins, with whom he had worked on the Human Genome Project. "We have to make the clearest possible statement that this is a path we are not ready to go down, not now, and potentially not ever," Collins said in an interview the day the Lander article was released.

Lander emphasized that the issue should not be left to individual choice and the free market. "We're trying to plan the world we're going to leave for our children," he said. "Is it a world where we're deeply thoughtful about medical applications, and we're using it in serious cases, or is it a world where we just have rampant commercial competition?" Zhang made the point that the issues surrounding gene editing needed to be settled by society as a whole and not by individuals. "You can imagine a situation where parents will feel pressure to edit their children because other parents are," he said. "It could further exacerbate inequality. It could create a total mess in society."[9]

"Why is Eric so intent on publicly pushing for a moratorium?" Margaret Hamburg, the co-chair of the World Health Organization group, asked me. It was a sincere question. Lander's reputation was such that even when he did something that seemed straightforward, others suspected his motives. The call for a moratorium, she felt, seemed like showboating; it was unnecessary, since both the WHO and the national academies were already embarked on figuring out proper guidelines rather than calling a halt to germline editing.[10]

Baltimore too expressed puzzlement. Lander had tried to recruit him to sign the letter, but as with the discussion of recombinant DNA forty years earlier at Asilomar, Baltimore was more interested in finding "a prudent path forward" for what could be a lifesaving advance rather than declaring a moratorium that may be difficult to lift once in place. He suspected that Lander might be pushing the moratorium to curry favor with Collins, the director of the National Institutes of Health, which provides a lot of funding for academic labs.

As for Doudna, her opposition to a moratorium became stronger the more that Lander pushed it. "Since germline editing has already been done with the Chinese babies, I think to put out a call for a moratorium at this stage is just unrealistic," she says. "If you call for a moratorium, you effectively take yourself out of the conversation."[11]

Doudna's view prevailed. In September 2020, a two-hundred-page report was issued by the international academies of science commission formed after Jiankui's shocking announcement. It did not call for a moratorium, nor mention that word, even though Lander was one of the eighteen commission members. Instead, it said that heritable human genome editing "might in the future provide a reproductive option" for couples who have genetic diseases. The report noted that making inheritable gene edits was not yet safe and usually not medically necessary, but it came down in favor of "defining a responsible pathway for clinical use of heritable human genome editing"—in other words, continuing to pursue the goal of "a prudent path forward" that was endorsed at the January 2015 Napa Valley conference that Doudna organized.[12]

He Jiankui convicted

Instead of being acclaimed a national hero, as he had fantasized, He Jiankui was put on trial at the end of 2019 in the People's Court of Shenzhen. The proceedings had many elements of a fair trial: he was permitted to have his own attorneys and to speak in his own defense. But the verdict was not in doubt since he had pleaded guilty to the charge of "illegal medical practice." He was sentenced to three years in prison, fined $430,000, and banned for life from working in reproductive science. "In order to pursue fame and profit, [he] deliberately violated the relevant national regulations and crossed the bottom lines of scientific and medical ethics," the court declared.[13]

The official Chinese news report on the trial also revealed that a third CRISPR baby engineered by Jiankui had been born to a second woman. There were no details about the baby nor about the current status of Lulu and Nana, the original CRISPR-edited twins.

When Doudna was asked by the *Wall Street Journal* to comment on the conviction, she was careful to criticize Jiankui's work but not to denounce germline gene editing. The scientific community would have to sort out the safety and ethical issues, she said. "To me, the big question is not will this ever be done again," she said. "I think the answer is yes. The question is when, and the question is how."[14]

Part Seven

The Moral Questions

If scientists don't play God, who will?

—James Watson, to Britain's Parliamentary and Scientific Committee, May 16, 2000

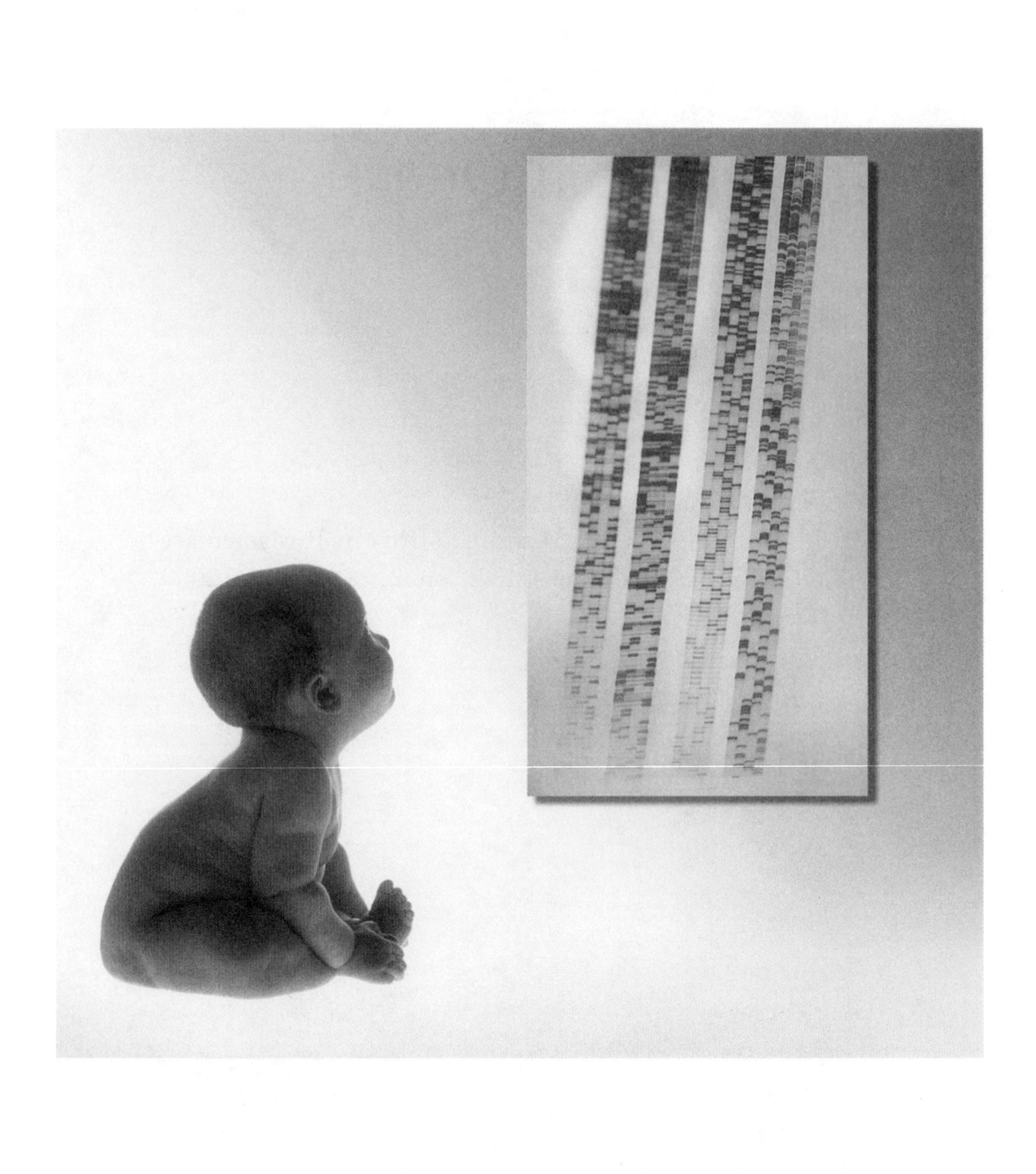

CHAPTER 40

Red Lines

The stakes

When He Jiankui produced the world's first CRISPR babies, with the goal of making them and their descendants immune to an attack by a deadly virus, most responsible scientists expressed outrage. His actions were deemed to be at best premature and at worst abhorrent. But in the wake of the 2020 coronavirus pandemic, the idea of editing our genes to make us immune to virus attacks began to seem a bit less appalling and a bit more appealing. The calls for a moratorium on germline gene editing receded. Just as bacteria have spent millennia evolving ways to develop immunity to viruses, perhaps we humans should use our ingenuity to do the same.

If we could safely edit genes to make our children less susceptible to HIV or coronaviruses, would it be wrong to do so? Or would it be wrong *not* to do so? And what about gene edits for other fixes and enhancements that might be possible in the next few decades? If they turn out to be safe, should governments prevent us from using them?[1]

The issue is one of the most profound we humans have ever faced. For the first time in the evolution of life on this planet, a species has developed the capacity to edit its own genetic makeup. That offers the potential of wondrous benefits, including the elimination of many deadly diseases and debilitating abnormalities. And it will someday offer both the promise and the peril of allowing us, or some of us, to boost our bodies and enhance our babies to have better muscles, minds, memory, and moods.

In the upcoming decades, as we gain more power to hack our own evolution, we will have to wrestle with deep moral and spiritual questions: Is there an inherent goodness to nature? Is there a virtue that arises from accepting what is gifted to us? Does empathy depend on believing that but for the grace of God, or the randomness of the natural lottery, we could have been born with a different set of endowments? Will an emphasis on personal liberty turn the most fundamental aspects of human nature into consumer choices made at a genetic supermarket? Should the rich be able to buy the best genes? Should we leave such decisions to individual choice, or should society come to some consensus about what it will allow?

Then again, are we getting a bit overdramatic with all of this handwringing? Why in the world would we not seize the benefits that will come from ridding our species of dangerous diseases and enhancing the capacities of our children?[2]

The germline as a red line

The primary concern is germline editing, those changes that are done in the DNA of human eggs or sperm or early-stage embryos so that every cell in the resulting children—and all of their descendants—will carry the edited trait. There has already been, and rightly so, general acceptance of what is known as somatic editing, the changes that are made in targeted cells of a living patient and do not affect reproductive cells. If something goes wrong in one of these therapies, it can be disastrous for the patient but not for the species.

Somatic editing can be used on certain types of cells, such as those of the blood, muscles, and eyes. But it is expensive, doesn't work on all cells, and may not be permanent. Germline edits could make a fix in all of the cells of the body. Thus it holds a lot more promise. And a lot more perceived peril.

Until the creation of the first CRISPR babies in 2018, there were two main medical methods for selecting the genetic traits of a child. The first was prenatal testing, which involves performing genetic tests on embryos as they are growing in the womb. Nowadays, such tests can detect Down's syndrome, sex, and dozens of congenital conditions. Parents can decide to abort the embryo if they don't like the traits. In the U.S., a prenatal diagnosis of Down's syndrome results in an abortion approximately two-thirds of the time.[3]

The development of *in vitro* fertilization led to another advance in genetic control: preimplantation genetic diagnosis. Couples can, if they are able, produce multiple fertilized eggs and have them tested in a lab dish, before they get implanted, for genetic characteristics. Do they have the mutations for Huntington's or sickle cell or Tay-Sachs? Or someday we can ask, as happens in the movie *Gattaca*, do they have the desired genes for height, memory, and muscle mass? With preimplantation diagnosis, those fertilized eggs with the parents' desired traits can be implanted and the rest discarded.

Both of these techniques raise some of the same moral issues as germline gene editing. For example, James Watson, the outspoken co-discoverer of DNA, once opined that a woman should have the right to abort a fetus based on any preference or prejudice, including not wanting a child that would be short or dyslexic or gay or female.[4] This caused a lot of people to recoil, understandably. Nevertheless, preimplantation genetic diagnosis is now considered morally acceptable, and parents are generally free to make their own choices about what criteria to use.

The question is whether germline gene editing will someday be considered just another in a long continuum of once controversial biological interventions, such as prenatal or preimplantation screening, that have gradually been accepted. If so, does it make sense to treat germline editing as something distinct, subject to a different set of moral standards?

Call this the continuum conundrum. There are ethicists who are good at making distinctions and those who are good at debunking distinctions. Or to put it another way, there are ethicists who discern lines and others who blur them. The ones who like to blur the lines often go on to pronounce that the lines are so blurry there is no rationale for treating the categories differently.

Take the atom bomb, as an analogy. When Secretary of War Henry Stimson was wrestling with whether to drop it on Japan, some argued that it was an entirely new category of weapon, a line that should not be crossed. Others said it was not fundamentally different, and indeed might be less brutal, than the massive firebombing campaigns that had been waged on Dresden and Tokyo. The latter side prevailed, and the bomb was dropped. Later, however, atomic weaponry came to be seen as being in a distinct category, and it hasn't been used since.

In the case of gene editing, I think the germline is indeed a real line. There may not be a razor-sharp line differentiating it from other biotechnologies, but as Leonardo da Vinci taught us with his *sfumato*, even slightly blurry lines can be definitive. Crossing the germline takes us to a distinct new realm. It involves engineering a genome rather than nurturing one that was produced naturally, and it introduces a change that will be inherited by all future descendants.

Nevertheless, this doesn't mean the germline should never be crossed. It simply means that we can view the germline as a firebreak that gives us a chance to pause, if we decide we ought to, the advance of genetic engineering techniques. The question becomes: Which cases, if any, should cause us to cross this germline?

Treatment vs. enhancement

Another line we might consider, in addition to that between somatic and germline editing, involves the distinction between "treatments" designed to fix dangerous genetic abnormalities and "enhancements" designed to improve human capacities or traits. At first glance, treatments seem easier to justify than enhancements.

But the treatment-vs.-enhancement distinction is a blurry one. Genes might predispose or predetermine certain kids to be short or obese or have attention deficits or be depressive. At what point do genetic modifications to fix such traits cross the line from health treatment to enhancement? What about genetic modifications that help prevent a person from getting HIV or coronavirus or cancer or Alzheimer's? Perhaps for these we need a third category called "preventions" in addition to the ill-defined "treatments" and "enhancements." And to those we might even add a fourth category, called "super-enhancements," which would include giving humans new capabilities that the species has not had before, such as the ability to see infrared light or hear super-high frequencies or avoid the bone, muscle, and memory loss that comes with age.

As you can see, the categories can get complex, and they don't necessarily correlate with what might be desirable and ethical. In order to chart our way through this moral minefield, it may be useful to do some thought experiments.

David Sanchez looks at a CRISPR cure for sickle cell

Chapter 41

Thought Experiments

Huntington's disease

Before our knees jerk and we stumble into hard-and-fast pronouncements—*Somatic editing is fine but inheritable germline edits are bad*; *Treatments are fine but enhancements are bad*—let's explore some specific cases and see what questions they raise.

If ever there was a case for editing a human gene, it would be for getting rid of the mutation that produces the cruel and painful killer known as Huntington's disease. Caused by an abnormal repetition of letters in a DNA sequence, it eventually leads to the death of brain cells. Beginning in middle age, victims start to twitch uncontrollably. They cannot focus. They lose their jobs. Eventually they are unable to walk, then talk, then swallow. Sometimes dementia sets in. It is an agonizing death in very slow motion. And it is devastating for the families—especially the kids, who watch their parent's gruesome decline, face the pity or ridicule of their schoolmates, and eventually learn that they have at least a 50 percent chance of suffering the same fate. One must be a fanatic believer in salvation through suffering to think that any good comes from its existence.[1]

Huntington's is a rare dominant disease; even one copy of the mutation spells doom. Symptoms usually arise only after a person's childbearing years, so its victims often have children before they know they have the genetic disease. Therefore, it's not weeded out by natural selection. The evolutionary process cares little about what happens to us after we have children and get them to a safe age, so there are a whole bunch of middle-aged maladies, including Huntington's and most forms of cancer, that we humans would want to eliminate, even though nature sees no need to.

Fixing Huntington's is not a complex edit. The wild sequence of excess DNA serves no good purpose. So why not edit it out in the germline of afflicted families—and out of our species once and for all?

One argument is that it would be better, where possible, to find an alternative approach to germline gene editing. In most cases—except when both parents have the disease—it might be possible to assure healthy children through preimplantation genetic diagnosis. If the parents can produce enough fertilized eggs, the ones with Huntington's can be weeded out. But producing a lot of viable eggs, as anyone who has been through fertility treatments knows, isn't always easy.

Another alternative is adoption. That, likewise, is not always easy these days. In addition, prospective parents often want to have a genetically related child. Is that a reasonable desire or just vanity?[2] Whatever some ethicists may say, most parents would feel it is reasonable. Millions of years of struggle by organisms, from bacteria to humans, to find ways to pass on their genes show that the impulse to produce genetically related offspring is among the most natural on this planet.

In making a gene edit to eliminate Huntington's, nothing has been altered except the elimination of the horrific mutation. So should it be permissible to do so, especially in cases where preimplantation screening is difficult? Even if we decide to set a high bar for the use of germline editing, it seems (at least to me) that Huntington's is a genetic malady we should try to eliminate from the human race.

If so, what other genetic problems should parents have the right to prevent from being passed along to their babies? Because this slope is slippery, let's take it step by step.

Sickle cell

Sickle-cell anemia is an interesting next case to consider because it raises two complexities, one medical and the other moral. Like Huntington's, sickle cell is caused by a simple mutation. In people who inherit a bad copy of the gene from both parents, the mutation distorts red blood cells, which deliver oxygen to the tissues of the body, into the shape of a sickle. Because these sickled cells die more quickly and have a harder time moving through the body, the disease can lead to fatigue, infections, spasms of pain, and early death. It tends to strike Africans and African Americans.

By 2020, trials were underway for somatic sickle-cell therapies, including the one described earlier involving the Mississippi woman Victoria Gray, who was part of a clinical trial in Nashville. Blood stem cells are removed from patients, edited, and then reinserted into the body. But this is an extraordinarily expensive procedure, not feasible for the more than four million afflicted globally. If the sickle-cell mutation could be fixed in the germline, by editing eggs or sperm or early-stage embryos, that would be a cheaper, one-time cure that would be inherited and could eventually eliminate the disease from our species.

So, does it fall into the same category as Huntington's? Is it a disease that should be eliminated using inheritable edits?

Well, as with many such genes, there's a complexity. People who get a copy of the gene from only one parent do not develop the disease, but they do develop immunity to most forms of malaria. In other words, the gene was (and in some places still is) useful, especially in sub-Saharan Africa. Now that there are treatments for malaria, it's less useful. But it is a reminder, when we think of messing with Mother Nature, that genes may play multiple roles and have evolutionary reasons for existing.

Let's suppose that researchers show that editing out the sickle-cell mutation is safe. Would there then be any reason to prohibit patients from having the gene edited out when they conceive children?

At this point in the discussion, a delightful kid named David Sanchez pops up to add another bit of complexity. He's a plucky, charming, reflective, African American teenager in California who loves to play basketball, except when his sickle-cell anemia causes him to double over in pain. At one point he developed a chest syndrome when the sickled cells blocked the blood to his lungs, and he had to drop out of high school. In a powerful 2019 documentary about CRISPR, *Human Nature*, he is an unlikely star. "My blood just does not like me very much, I guess," he says. "Sometimes you have a little sickle-cell crisis. Sometimes you have a really bad one. But I'm not just going to not play basketball."[3]

Every month, Sanchez's grandmother takes him to Stanford University Children's Hospital, where he gets an infusion of healthy cells from a blood donor. That gives him temporary relief. Matthew Porteus, the gene-editing pioneer at Stanford, has been helping to treat him. At one point he explained to Sanchez that, someday in the future, germline gene editing might eliminate the disease. "Maybe one day with CRISPR," Porteus told him, "they could go in and change the gene in the embryo so that the kid, when it's born, doesn't have sickle cell."

Sanchez's eyes lit up. "I guess that's kind of cool," he said. Then he paused. "But I think that should be up to the kid later." Asked why, he reflected for a moment and then continued slowly. "There's a lot of things that I learned having sickle cell. Because I had it, I learned patience with everyone. I learned how just to be positive."

But would he like to have been born without sickle cell? Again, he pauses. "No, I don't wish that I'd never had it," he says. "I don't think that I would be me if I didn't have sickle cell." Then he bursts into a big and lovely smile. He was born to be in such a documentary.

Not everyone with sickle cell is like David Sanchez. Even David Sanchez may not always be like the David Sanchez in the documentary. Despite what he said on camera, it is hard for me to imagine a kid choosing to have sickle cell rather than not having it. It's even more difficult to imagine parents, especially ones who have themselves endured a life with sickle cell, deciding that they want their kids to have it. After all, Sanchez is enrolled in a program to keep his sickle-cell anemia at bay.

The question gnaws at me, so I arrange to pose some questions to Sanchez.[4] This time his thinking is a bit different than when he was interviewed for the documentary. On complex personal issues like this, our thoughts understandably tend to fluctuate. Would you like to find a way, I ask him, to make sure your children are born without sickle cell? "Yes," he responds. "If that's an option, then of course."

What about the patience and the positive attitude that, as he told the documentary producers, he learned by having sickle cell? "Empathy is something that's really important to humans," he responds. "That is something I learned from sickle cell, and that is something I would really want to convey to my kids if they could be born without sickle cell. But I wouldn't want my kids or others to go through what I went through." The more he learns about CRISPR, the more excited he becomes about how it may cure him and protect his children. But it's complicated.

Character

David Sanchez's wise words bring up a larger question. Challenges and so-called disabilities often build character, teach acceptance, and instill resilience. They may even be correlated to creativity. Take Miles Davis. The pain of sickle cell drove him to drugs and drink. It may have even driven him to his death. It also, however, may have driven him to be the creative artist who could produce *Kind of Blue* and *Bitches Brew*. Would Miles Davis have been Miles Davis without sickle cell?

This is not a new question. Franklin Roosevelt was forged by polio. The challenge transformed his character. Likewise, I knew a guy who was one of the last kids to be touched by polio before Salk and Sabin came up with their vaccines in the late 1950s. He achieved success, I think, partly because of his great depth of character, and he taught all of us about grit and gratitude and humility. My favorite novel, Walker Percy's *The Moviegoer*, tells of the transformative effect the disabled boy Lonnie has on the other characters.

The bioethicist Rosemarie Garland-Thomson, who was born with distorted arms, tells of the friendship circle she has with three other women born with genetic conditions, one blind, one deaf, and one with muscular impairment. "Our genetic conditions gave us a head start in accessing multiple opportunities for expression, creativity, resourcefulness, and relationships—for human flourishing," she writes.[5] Similarly, Jory Fleming is an amazing young man who was born with severe autism as well as other challenging health conditions. He could not cope in class, so he was homeschooled. As he grew older, he taught himself how to deal with the fact that his internal world was different from those of other people. He ended up winning a Rhodes Scholarship to Oxford. In his 2021 memoir, *How to Be Human*, he reflects on whether gene editing should be used, if it becomes feasible, to eliminate some of the causes of autism. "You'd be removing an aspect of the human experience," he writes, "but for what benefit exactly?" Autism, he argues, is a difficult condition to have, but the challenges largely come because the world is not good at accommodating people whose emotional lives are different. Those differences can actually provide a useful perspective for the rest of us, including on how to make decisions that are not unduly influenced by emotion. "Should society change to recognize the benefits of autism instead of just the challenges?" he asks. "Certainly, my experience has been very challenging, and it has been also rewarding. And who knows, hopefully, I'll be able to do something with my life that benefits other people in some way."[6]

It's an interesting dilemma. Once a vaccine was discovered to stop polio, we humans quickly and easily decided to use it to eliminate that disease from our species, even at the risk of allowing future Franklin Roosevelts to remain unforged. Using gene editing to prevent disabilities may make society less diverse and creative. But does this give governments the right to tell parents they can't use such technologies?

Deafness

That raises the question of what attributes should be labeled disabilities. Sharon Duchesneau and Candy McCullough are a lesbian couple who wanted a sperm donor so they could conceive a kid. Both of them are deaf. They consider their deafness to be part of who they are rather than something to be cured, and they wanted a child who would be part of their cultural identity. So they advertised for a sperm donor who was congenitally deaf. They found one, and now they have a deaf child.

A story about the couple in the *Washington Post* caused them to be condemned by some people for inflicting a disability on a child.[7] But they were applauded in the deaf community. Which was the right response? Should they be criticized for making sure their child had a disability, or should they be praised for preserving a subculture that contributes to the diversity and perhaps even the empathy of society? Would it be different if, instead of using a deaf sperm donor, the couple had used preimplantation diagnosis to select an embryo that had the genetic mutation for deafness? What if the embryo was typical, but they edited it to be deaf? Would that be okay? What if they asked a doctor to punch out the child's eardrums after birth?

In some cases when formulating a moral argument, it helps to do a reversal test. The Harvard philosopher Michael Sandel uses this thought experiment: Suppose a parent comes to a doctor and says, "My child is going to be born deaf, but I want you to do something to make her able to hear." The doctor should try, right? But now suppose a parent says, "My child is going to be born able to hear, but I want you to do something to her to make sure she is born deaf." I think most of us would recoil if the doctor agreed. Our natural instinct is to consider deafness a disability.

How do we distinguish between traits that are true disabilities and ones that are disabilities mainly because society is not good at adapting for them? Take the case of the deaf lesbian couple, for example. Some people may consider both the fact that they are deaf and the fact that they are lesbian as disadvantages. What if they wanted a genetic procedure that would make their child more likely to be straight? Suppose they chose the reverse and wanted to make it more likely their child would be gay? (This is a thought experiment. There is no simple gay gene.) Likewise, being born Black in America could be considered a disadvantage. A single gene, *SLC24A5*, has a major influence on determining skin color. What if a set of Black parents considers their race to be a social handicap and wants to edit that gene to produce light-skinned babies?

Such questions prompt us to look at "disabilities" and ask to what extent they are inherently disabling and to what extent the disadvantage is due to our social constructs and prejudices. The disadvantages from being deaf, for a human or any other animal, are very real. In contrast, any disadvantages to being gay or Black are due to social attitudes that can and should be changed. That is why we can make a moral distinction between using genetic techniques to prevent deafness and using these techniques to influence such things as skin color and sexual orientation.

Muscles and sports

Now let's do some thought experiments to see if we might want to cross the blurry line between gene editing that is done to treat true disabilities and gene editing that is done to enhance the traits of our children. The *MSTN* gene produces a protein that curtails the growth of muscles when they reach a normal level. Suppressing the gene takes off the brakes. Researchers have already done this to produce "mighty mice" and cattle with "double muscling." It is what our biohacker Josiah Zayner used to make his kits that produce super-frogs and for the CRISPR he injected into himself.

Among those interested in these types of gene edits, other than cattle breeders, are athletic directors. Pushy parents who want champion children are sure to follow. Especially by using germline editing, they might produce a whole new breed of athletes with bigger bones and stronger muscles.

Add to this mix a rare gene mutation that was discovered in the Olympic champion skier Eero Mäntyranta. Initially accused of doping, he was found to have a gene that increased his number of red blood cells by more than 25 percent, which naturally improved his stamina and ability to use oxygen.

So what do we say to parents who want to use gene editing to produce bigger, more muscular kids with greater stamina? Ones who can run marathons, break tackles, and bend steel with their bare hands? And what does that do to our concept of athletics? Do we go from admiring the diligence of the athlete to admiring instead the wizardry of their genetic engineers? It's easy to put an asterisk next to the home run tallies of José Canseco or Mark McGwire when they admit that they were on steroids. But what do we do if athletes' extra muscles come from genes they were born with? And does it matter if those genes were paid for by their parents rather than bestowed by a random natural lottery?

The role of sports, at least since the first Olympics in 776 BC, is to celebrate two things: natural talent combined with disciplined effort. Enhancements would shift that balance, making human effort less of a component of victory. Therefore the achievement becomes a little less praiseworthy and inspiring. There is a whiff of cheating if an athlete succeeds by obtaining some physical advantages through medical engineering.

But there's a problem with this fairness argument. Most successful athletes have *always* been people who happened to have better athletic genes than the rest of us. Personal effort is a component, but it helps to be born with the genes for good muscles, blood, coordination, and other innate advantages.

For example, almost every champion runner has what is known as the R allele of the *ACTN3* gene. It produces a protein that builds fast-twitch muscle fibers, and it is also associated with improving strength and recovery from muscle injury.[8] Someday it may be possible to edit this variation of the *ACTN3* gene into the DNA of your kids. Would that be unfair? Is it unfair that some kids are born with it naturally? Why is one more unfair than the other?

Height

One way to think through the fairness of using gene editing for physical enhancements is by looking at height. A condition called IMAGe syndrome, which severely curtails size, is caused by a mutation in the

CDKN1C gene. Should it be permissible to genetically edit out this defect so that these kids will grow to an average height? Most of us would think so.

Now let's take the case of parents who just happen to be short. Should they be permitted to edit the genes of their kids so they will grow to average height? If not, what's the moral difference between these two cases?

Suppose there was a genetic edit that could add eight inches to a kid's height. Would it be proper to use it on a boy who would otherwise be under five feet tall to turn him into someone of average height? What about using it on a boy who would otherwise be average height to make him six-foot-five?

A way to wrestle with these questions is by making a distinction between "treatments" and "enhancements." For various traits—height, eyesight, hearing, muscular coordination, and so on—we could use a statistical method to define "typical species functioning." A significant variation below that would be defined as a disability.[9] Using that standard, we might approve of treating a kid who would be less than five feet tall but reject the idea of enhancing a kid who would otherwise be of average height.

By pondering the question of height, we can make another distinction that is useful: the difference between an absolute improvement and a positional improvement. In the first category are enhancements that are beneficial to you even if everyone else gets them. Imagine there was a way to improve your memory or your resistance to virus infections. You'd be better off with it, even if others got the same enhancement. In fact, as the coronavirus pandemic shows, you would be better off *especially* if others had that enhancement as well.

But the advantages of increased height are more positional. Let's call it the standing-on-tiptoes problem. You're in the middle of a crowded room. To see what's going on in the front, you stand on your tiptoes. It works! But then everyone else around you tries it. They all get two inches higher. Then nobody in the room, including you, sees any better than the people in the front row.

Likewise, suppose I'm an average height. If I were enhanced by eight inches, I'd be way taller than most people, and that could be a benefit to me. But if everyone else got the same eight-inch enhancement I did, then I would get no real benefit. The enhancement wouldn't make me or society as a whole better off, especially given the legroom of airline seats these days. The only sure beneficiaries would be carpenters who specialized in raising door frames. So enhanced height is a *positional* good, while enhanced resistance to viruses is an *absolute* good.[10]

That doesn't answer the question of whether we should allow genetic enhancements. But as we grope for a set of principles to include in our moral calculus, the distinction does point to a factor we should consider: favoring enhancements that would benefit all of society over those that would give the recipient a positional advantage.

Super-enhancements and transhumanism

Perhaps some enhancements will gain broad social acceptance. Then what about super-enhancements? Should we ever want to engineer traits and capacities that exceed what any human has ever had? The golfer Tiger Woods had laser surgery to improve his eyesight to be even better than 20/20. Might we want our kids to have super-eyesight? What about adding the capacity to see infrared light or some new color?

DARPA, the Pentagon's research agency, might someday want to create superior soldiers with night vision. They could also imagine an enhancement that allowed human cells to be more resistant to radiation in case of a nuclear attack. Actually, they aren't just imagining that. DARPA already has a project going, in conjunction with Doudna's lab, to study how to create genetically enhanced soldiers.

One odd result of allowing super-enhancements could be that children will become like iPhones: a new version will come out every few years with better features and apps. Will children as they age feel that they are becoming obsolete? That their eyes don't have the cool triple-lens enhancements that are engineered into the latest version of kids?

Fortunately, these are questions we can ask for amusement but not for an answer. It will be up to our grandchildren to figure these out.

Psychological disorders

Two decades after the completion of the Human Genome Project, we still have little understanding of how human psychology is influenced by genetic dispositions. But eventually, we may isolate genes that contribute to a predisposition to schizophrenia, bipolar disorder, severe depression, and other mental challenges.

Then we will have to decide whether we should allow, or perhaps even encourage, parents to make sure that these genes get edited out of their children. Let's pretend to go back in time. If some of the genetic factors predisposing James Watson's son Rufus to schizophrenia could have been edited out, would that have been a good thing? Should we have allowed his parents to make the decision to do that?

Watson has no doubt what the answer should be. "Of course we should use germline therapy to fix things like schizophrenia that nature got horribly wrong," he says. Doing so would lead to a lot less suffering. Schizophrenia, depression, and bipolar disorder can be brutal, often deadly. No one would want to inflict it on a person or on any person's family.

But even if we agree that we want to rid humanity of schizophrenia and similar disorders, we should consider whether there might be some cost to society, even to civilization. Vincent van Gogh had either schizophrenia or bipolar disorder. So did the mathematician John Nash. (And also Charles Manson and John Hinckley.) People with bipolar disorder include Ernest Hemingway, Mariah Carey, Francis Ford Coppola, Carrie Fisher, Graham Greene, Julian Huxley (the eugenicist), Gustav Mahler, Lou Reed, Franz Schubert, Sylvia Plath, Edgar Allan Poe, Jane Pauley, and hundreds of other artists and creators. The number of creative artists with major depressive disorder is in the thousands. A study by schizophrenia-research pioneer Nancy Andreasen of thirty prominent contemporary authors showed that twenty-four had experienced at least one episode of major depression or mood disorder, and twelve were diagnosed with bipolar disorder.[11]

To what extent does dealing with mood swings, fantasies, delusions, compulsions, mania, and deep depression help spur, in some people, creativity and artistry? Is it harder to be a great artist without having some compulsive or even manic traits? Would you cure your own child from being schizophrenic if you knew that, if you didn't, he would become a Vincent van Gogh and transform the world of art? (Don't forget: Van Gogh committed suicide.)

At this point in our deliberations, we have to face the potential conflict between what is desired by the individual versus what is good for human civilization. A reduction in mood disorders would be seen as a benefit by most of the afflicted individuals, parents, and families. They would desire it. But does the issue look different when asked from society's vantage point? As we learn to treat mood disorders with drugs and eventually with genetic editing, will we have more happiness but fewer Hemingways? Do we wish to live in a world in which there are no Van Goghs?

This question of engineering away mood disorders gets to an even more fundamental question: What is the aim or purpose of life? Is it happiness? Contentment? Lack of pain or bad moods? If so, that may be easy. A painless life was engineered by the overlords in *Brave New World*, who made sure the masses had soma, a drug that enhanced their sense of joy and allowed them to avoid discomfort, sadness, or anger. Suppose we could hook our brains to something the philosopher Robert Nozick called an "experience machine," which allowed us to believe that we were hitting home runs and dancing with movie stars and floating in a beautiful bay.[12] It would make us always feel blissful. Would that be desirable?

Or does the good life have aims that are deeper? Should the goal be that each person can flourish, in a more profound fashion, by using talents and traits in a way that is truly fulfilling? If so, that would require authentic experiences, real accomplishments, and true efforts, rather than engineered ones. Does the good life entail making a contribution to our community, society, and civilization? Has evolution encoded such goals into human nature? That might entail sacrifice, pain, mental discomforts, and challenges that we would not always choose.[13]

Smarts

Now let's deal with the final frontier, the one most promising and frightful: the possibility of improving cognitive skills such as memory, focus, information processing, and perhaps even someday the vaguely defined concept of intelligence. Unlike height, cognitive skills are beneficial in more than just a positional way. If everyone were a bit smarter, it probably would make all of us better off. In fact, even if only a portion of the population became smarter, it might benefit everyone in society.

Memory may be the first mental improvement we will be able to engineer, and fortunately it is a less fraught topic than IQ. It has already been improved in mice, such as by enhancing the genes for NMDA receptors in nerve cells. In humans, enhancing those genes could help prevent memory loss in old age, but it could also enhance memory in younger people as well.[14]

Perhaps we will be able to improve our cognitive skills so that we can keep up with the challenges of using our technology wisely. Ah, but there's the rub: *wisely*. Of all the complex components that go into human intelligence, wisdom may be the most elusive. Understanding the genetic components of wisdom may require us to understand consciousness, and I suspect that's not going to happen in this century. In the meantime, we will have to deploy the finite allocation of wisdom that nature has dealt us as we ponder how to use the gene-editing techniques that we've discovered. Ingenuity without wisdom is dangerous.

Chapter 42

Who Should Decide?

The National Academy's video

The tweet was provocative, a bit more provocative than it was intended to be. It read:

> Dream of being stronger? 💪 Or smarter? 🧠 Do you dream of having a top student or star athlete? Or a child free of inheritable #diseases? 👨‍🔬🧬 Can human #GeneEditing eventually make this and more possible?

It was an attempt by the usually staid National Academy of Sciences in October 2019 to spur a "broad public discussion" of gene editing, just like all of those conferences on the topic had recommended. The tweet linked to a quiz and a video explaining germline gene editing.

The video began with five "everyday people" putting sticky notes onto a diagram of a body and fantasizing about what changes they would make in their genes. "I guess I would like to be taller," said one. Other personal desires included: "I would like to change body fat"; "Let's prevent baldness"; "Take away dyslexia."

Doudna was in the video explaining how CRISPR works. Then it showed people discussing the prospect of designing the genes of their future children. "Create the perfect human being?" one man mused. "That's pretty cool!" Said another, "You want the best qualities to be put into your offspring." A woman chimed in, "If I had the chance to choose the best DNA for my child, I would definitely want her to be smart." Others discussed their own health problems, such as attention-deficit disorder and high blood pressure. "I would take that out, for sure," a man said of his heart disease. "I don't want my kids to deal with it."[1]

Bioethicists immediately erupted on Twitter. "What a mistake," tweeted Paul Knoepfler, a cancer researcher and bioethicist at the University of California, Davis. "Who at National Academy of Sciences' media office is behind this bizarre tweet & page it links to that seems troublingly upbeat about human heritable gene editing & to trivialize idea of designer babies?"

Twitter, unsurprisingly, is not the best forum to discuss bioethics. There is a truism about internet comment boards: any discussion descends to shouting "Nazi!" within seven responses. In the case of the gene-editing threads, it was more like by the third response. "Are we still in 1930s Germany?" one person tweeted. Another added, "How did this read in the original German?"[2]

Within a day, the folks at the National Academy of Sciences had sounded retreat. The tweet was deleted and the video pulled off the web. A spokesperson apologized that they had "left the misimpression that the use of genome editing for the 'enhancement' of human traits is permissible or taken lightly."

The brief tempest showed that the bromide of calling for greater societal discussion about the morals of gene editing was easier preached than practiced. It also raised the question of who should get to decide how gene-editing tools should be used. As we saw in the thought experiments in the previous chapter, many of the difficult questions about gene editing involve not just how to decide the issue, but *who* should decide. As is the case with so many policy issues, the desires of an individual might conflict with the good of the community.

The individual or the community?

On most great moral issues, there are two competing perspectives. One emphasizes individual rights, personal liberty, and a deference to personal choice. Stemming from John Locke and other Enlightenment thinkers of the seventeenth century, this tradition recognizes that people will have different beliefs about what is good for their lives, and it argues that the state should give them a lot of liberty to make their own choices, as long as they do not harm others.

The contrasting perspectives are those that view justice and morality through the lens of what is best for the society and perhaps even (in the case of bioengineering and climate policy) the species. Examples include requirements that schoolkids be vaccinated and that people wear masks during a pandemic. The emphasis on societal benefits rather than individual rights can take the form of John Stuart Mill's utilitarianism, which seeks the greatest amount of happiness in a society even if that means trampling on the liberty of some individuals. Or it can take the form of more complex social contract theories, in which moral obligations arise from the agreements we would make to form the society we want to live in.

These contrasting perspectives form the most basic political divide of our times. On the one side are those who wish to maximize individual liberty, minimize regulations and taxes, and keep the state out of our lives as much as possible. On the other side are those who wish to promote the common good, create benefits for all of society, minimize the harm that an untrammeled free market can do to our work and environment, and restrict selfish behaviors that might harm the community and the planet.

The modern foundations for each of these perspectives was expressed in two influential books written fifty years ago: John Rawls's *A Theory of Justice*, which comes down on the side of favoring the good of the community, and Robert Nozick's *Anarchy, State, and Utopia*, which emphasizes the moral foundation for individual liberty.

Rawls seeks to define the rules that we would agree to if we had gathered to make a compact. In order to make sure things are "fair," he said that we should imagine what rules we would make if we didn't know what place we would each end up occupying in society and what natural abilities we would have. He argues that, from behind this "veil of ignorance," people would decide that inequalities should be permitted only to the extent that they result in benefits for all of society, and specifically for the least advantaged. In his book, this leads Rawls to justify genetic engineering only if it does not increase inequality.[3]

Nozick, whose book was a response to that of his Harvard colleague Rawls, likewise imagined how we might emerge from the anarchy of a state of nature. Instead of a complex social contract, he argues that social rules should arise through the voluntary choices of individuals. His guiding principle is that individuals should not be used to promote a social or moral goal devised by others. This leads him to favor a minimalist state that is limited to functions of public safety and enforcement of contracts but avoids most regulations or redistribution efforts. He addresses, in a footnote, the question of genetic engineering, and he takes a libertarian, free-market view. Instead of centralized control and rules set by regulators, he says that there should be "a genetic supermarket." Doctors should accommodate "the individual specifications (within certain moral limits) of prospective parents."[4] Since he wrote his book, the term "genetic supermarket" has become a catchphrase, used by fans and foes, for leaving genetic engineering decisions to individuals and the free market.[5]

Two science fiction books can also help shape our discussion: George Orwell's *1984* and Aldous Huxley's *Brave New World*.[6]

Orwell conjures up an Orwellian world in which information technology is used by "Big Brother," a leader that is always watching you, to centralize power in a super-state and exert control over a cowed populace. Individual freedom and independent thinking are crushed by electronic surveillance and total information control. Orwell was warning about the danger that a Franco or Stalin would someday control information technology and destroy individual freedom.

It didn't happen. When the real 1984 actually rolled around, Apple introduced an easy-to-use personal computer, the Macintosh, and in the words that Steve Jobs wrote for its ad, "you'll see why 1984 won't be like *1984*." That phrase contained a deep truth. Instead of computers becoming an instrument for centralized repression, the combination of the *personal* computer and the decentralized nature of the internet became a way to devolve more power down to each individual, thus unleashing a gusher of free expression and radically democratized media. Perhaps too much so. The dark side of our new information technology is not that it allows government repression of free speech but just the opposite: it permits anyone to spread, with little risk of being held accountable, any idea, conspiracy, lie, hatred, scam, or scheme, with the result that societies become less civil and governable.

The same may be the case for genetic technologies. In his 1932 novel, Huxley warned of a brave new world of centralized government control of reproductive science. Human embryos are created at a "hatchery and conditioning center" and then sorted to be engineered for different social purposes. Those chosen for the "alpha" class are enhanced physically and mentally to become leaders. At the other end of the spectrum, those in the "epsilon" class are bred to become menial laborers and conditioned for a life of induced blissful stupor.

Huxley said that he wrote the book as a reaction to "the current drift toward totalitarian control of everything."[7] But as was the case with information technology, the danger of genetic technology might not be too much *government* control. Instead, it may be too much *individual* control. The excess of the early twentieth-century eugenics movement in America and then the evil of the Nazi program gave a horrid stench to the idea of state-controlled genetic projects. It gave eugenics, which means "good genes," a bad name. Now, however, we may be ushering in a new eugenics—a liberal or libertarian eugenics, one based on free choice and marketed consumerism.

Huxley may have supported this free-market eugenics. He wrote a little-known utopian novel in 1962, *Island*, in which women voluntarily choose to be inseminated by sperm from men with high IQs and artistic talents. "Most married couples feel that it's more moral to take a shot at having a child of superior quality than to run the risk of slavishly reproducing whatever quirks and defects may happen to run in the husband's family," the main character explains.[8]

Free-market eugenics

In our day and age, decisions about genetic editing are likely to be driven, for better or worse, by consumer choice and the persuasive power of marketing. So what's wrong with that? Why shouldn't we leave decisions about gene editing to individuals and parents, just like we do with other reproductive choices? Why do we have to convene ethics conferences, seek a broad societal consensus, and wring our collective hands? Isn't it best to allow the decisions to be made by me and you and other individuals who want the best prospects for our kids and grandkids?[9]

Let's begin by loosening our minds and avoiding a bias for the status quo by asking the most basic question: What's wrong with genetic improvements? If we can do so safely, why shouldn't we prevent abnormalities, diseases, and disabilities? Why not improve our capabilities and create enhancements? "I don't see why eliminating a disability or giving a kid blue eyes or adding fifteen IQ points is truly a threat to public health or to morality," says Doudna's friend George Church, the Harvard geneticist.[10]

In fact, aren't we morally obligated to look after the welfare of our children and of future humans in general? Almost all species share an evolutionary instinct—encoded in the essence of evolution itself—to use whatever wiles they can muster to maximize the chance that their offspring will thrive.

The foremost philosopher advocating this view is Julian Savulescu, a professor of practical ethics at Oxford. He coined the phrase "procreative beneficence" to make the case that it is moral to choose the best genes for your unborn children. Indeed, he argues, it may be immoral *not* to. "Couples should select embryos or fetuses which are most likely to have the best life," he asserts. He even dismissed the concern that this could allow rich people to buy better genes for their children and thereby create a new class (or even subspecies) of enhanced elites. "We should allow selection for non-disease genes even if this maintains or increases social inequality," he writes, specifically citing "genes for intelligence."[11]

To analyze that point of view, let's do another thought experiment. Imagine a world where genetic engineering is determined mainly by individual free choice, with few government regulations and no pesky bioethics panels telling us what's permissible. You go into a fertility clinic and are given, as if at a genetic supermarket, a list of traits you can buy for your children. Would you eliminate serious genetic diseases, such as Huntington's or sickle cell? Of course you would. I personally would also choose that my kids not have genes leading to blindness. How about avoiding below-average height or above-average weight or a low IQ? We would all probably select those options as well. I might even choose a premium-priced option for extra height and muscles and IQ. Now let's say there were, hypothetically, genes that predisposed a child to more likely be straight rather than gay. You're not prejudiced, so you'd likely resist choosing that option, at least initially. But then, assuming no one was judging you, might you rationalize that you wanted your child to avoid discrimination or be a little bit more likely to produce grandchildren for you? And while you were at it, might you throw in blond hair and blue eyes as well?

Whoa!!! Something just went wrong. It really did turn out to be a slippery slope! Without any gates or flags, we might all go barreling down at uncontrollable speed, taking society's diversity and the human genome along with us.

Although this sounds like a scene from *Gattaca*, a real-world version of this baby-designing service—using preimplantation diagnosis—was launched in 2019 by a New Jersey startup, Genomic Prediction. *In vitro* fertilization clinics can send the company genetic samples of prospective babies. The DNA in cells from days-old embryos is sequenced to come up with a statistical estimate of the chances of developing a long list of conditions. Prospective parents can choose which embryo to implant based on the characteristics they want in their child. The embryos can be screened for single-gene disorders such as cystic fibrosis and sickle cell. The tests can also statistically predict multigene conditions, such as diabetes, heart attack risk, hypertension, and, according to the company's promotional material, "intellectual disability" and "height." Within ten years, the founders say, they are likely to be able to make predictions of IQ so that parents can choose to have very smart children.[12]

So now we can see a problem with simply leaving such decisions to individual choice. A liberal or libertarian genetics of individual choice could eventually lead us—just as surely as government-controlled eugenics—to a society with less diversity and deviation from the norm. That might be pleasing to a parent, but we would end up in a society with a lot less creativity, inspiration, and edge. Diversity is good not only for society but for our species. Like any species, our evolution and resilience are strengthened by a bit of randomness in the gene pool.

The problem is that the value of diversity, as our thought experiments showed, can conflict with the value of individual choice. As a society, we may feel that it is profoundly beneficial to the community to have people who are short and tall, gay and straight, placid and tormented, blind and sighted. But what moral right do we have to require another family to forgo a desired genetic intervention simply for the sake of adding to the diversity of society? Would we want the state to require that of us?

One reason to be open to some kind of limit on individual choice is that gene editing could exacerbate inequality and even permanently encode it into our species. Of course, we already tolerate some inequality based on birth and parental choices. We admire parents who read to their kids, make sure they go to good schools, and coach them in soccer. We even accept, perhaps with a roll of the eyes, those who hire SAT tutors and send their kids to computer camp. Many of these confer the advantages of inherited privilege. But the fact that inequality already exists is not an argument to increase or permanently enshrine it.

Permitting parents to buy the best genes for their kids would represent a true quantum leap in inequality. In other words, it won't be just a big leap, but a leap into a new disconnected orbit. After centuries of reducing aristocratic and caste systems based on birth, most societies have embraced a principle of morality that is also a basic premise of democracy: we believe in equal opportunity. The social bond that arises from this "created equal" creed would be severed if we turn financial inequalities into genetic inequalities.

This does not mean that gene editing is inherently bad. But it does argue against allowing it to be part of a free-market bazaar where the rich can buy the best genes and ingrain them into their families.[13]

Restricting individual choice would be difficult to enforce. Various college admissions scandals show us how far some parents will go and what they will pay to give their kids an advantage. Add to that the natural instinct of scientists to pioneer procedures and make discoveries. If a nation imposes too many restrictions, its scientists will move elsewhere and its wealthy parents will seek clinics in some enterprising Caribbean island or foreign haven.

Despite such objections, it's possible to aim for some social consensus on gene editing rather than simply leaving the issue totally to individual choice. There are practices we cannot fully control, from shoplifting to sex trafficking, that are kept to a minimum by a combination of legal sanctions and social shaming. The Food and Drug Administration, for example, regulates new drugs and procedures. Even though some people score drugs for off-label purposes or travel to places for unconventional treatments, FDA restrictions are pretty effective. Our challenge is to figure out what the norms for gene editing should be. Then we can try to find the regulations and social sanctions that will cause most people to follow them.[14]

Playing God

Another reason we might feel uncomfortable with directing our evolution and designing our babies is that we would be "playing God." Like Prometheus snatching fire, we would be usurping a power that properly resides above our pay grade. In so doing, we'd lose a sense of humility about our place in Creation.

The reluctance to play God can also be understood in a more secular way. As one Catholic theologian said at a National Academy of Medicine panel, "When I hear someone say that we shouldn't play God, I'd guess that ninety percent of the time they are atheists." The argument can simply mean that we should not have the hubris to believe that we should fiddle with the awesome, mysterious, delicately interwoven, and beautiful forces of nature. "Evolution has been working toward optimizing the human genome for 3.85 billion years," says NIH director Francis Collins, who is not an atheist. "Do we really think that some small group of human genome tinkerers could do better without all sorts of unintended consequences?"[15]

Our respect for nature and nature's God should, indeed, instill some humility about meddling with our genes. But should it absolutely forbid it? After all, we *Homo sapiens* are part of nature, no less so than bacteria and sharks and butterflies. Through its infinite wisdom or blind stumbling, nature has endowed our species with an ability to edit our own genes. If it's wrong for us to use CRISPR, the reason cannot merely be that it's unnatural. It's just as natural as all of the tricks that bacteria and viruses use.

For all of history, humans (and every other species) have been battling rather than accepting nature's poisoned offerings. Mother Nature has produced massive suffering and distributed it unequally. Thus we devise ways to combat plagues, cure diseases, fix disabilities, and breed better plants, animals, and children.

Darwin wrote about "the clumsy, wasteful, blundering, low, and horridly cruel works of nature." Evolution, he discovered, bears no fingerprints of an intelligent designer or benevolent God. He made a detailed list of things that evolved in a flawed way, including the path of the urinary tract in male mammals, the poor drainage of the sinuses in primates, and the inability of humans to synthesize vitamin C.

These design flaws are not mere exceptions. They are the natural consequence of the way evolution progresses. It stumbles upon and then cobbles together new features, sort of like what happened during the worst eras of Microsoft Office, rather than proceed with a master plan and end product in mind. Evolution's primary guide is reproductive fitness—what traits might cause an organism to reproduce more—which means it permits, and perhaps even encourages, all sorts of plagues, including coronaviruses and cancers, that afflict an organism once its childbearing use is over. This does not mean that, out of respect for nature, we should quit searching for ways to fight against coronaviruses and cancer.[16]

There is, however, a more profound argument against playing God, best articulated by the Harvard philosopher Michael Sandel. If we humans find ways to rig the natural lottery and engineer the genetic endowments of our children, we will be less likely to view our traits as gifts that we accept. That would undermine the empathy that comes from our sense of "there but for the grace of God go I" toward our fellow humans who are less lucky. "What the drive to mastery misses and may even destroy is an appreciation of the gifted character of human powers and achievements," Sandel writes. "To acknowledge the giftedness of life is to recognize that our talents and powers are not wholly our own doing."[17]

Of course I don't fully believe, nor does Sandel, that we must be reverential about the giftedness of all that nature offers us unbidden. Human history has been a quest—a very natural one—to master challenges that happen to us unbidden, be they pandemics or droughts or storms. Few of us would regard Alzheimer's or Huntington's to be a result of giftedness. When we create chemotherapies to fight cancer or vaccines to fight coronaviruses or gene-editing tools to fight birth defects, we are, quite properly, exercising mastery over nature rather than accepting the unbidden as a gift.

But Sandel's argument should nudge us, I think, toward some humility, especially when it comes to trying to design enhancements and perfections for our children. He makes a profound, beautiful, and even spiritual case for eschewing attempts at complete mastery over the unbidden. We can steer a course that avoids a Promethean quest for controlling our endowments while also avoiding complete submission to the vagaries of a lottery. Wisdom involves finding the right balance.

At the Hong Kong summit

CHAPTER 43

Doudna's Ethical Journey

When it became clear that the CRISPR-Cas9 tool that she co-invented could be used for editing human genes, Doudna had a "visceral, knee-jerk reaction." The idea of editing a child's genes, she says, felt unnatural and scary for humanity. "In the early days I was instinctively against it."[1]

Her position began to change at the January 2015 conference on gene editing in Napa Valley that she organized. At one of the sessions, during a heated debate over whether germline editing should ever be allowed, a participant leaned forward and said quietly, "Someday we may consider it unethical *not* to use germline editing to alleviate human suffering."

The idea that germline editing was "unnatural" began to recede in her thinking. All medical advances attempt to correct something that happened "naturally," she realized. "Sometimes nature does things that are downright cruel, and there are many mutations that cause enormous suffering, so the idea that germline editing was unnatural began to carry less weight for me," she says. "I am not sure how to make a sharp distinction in medicine between what is natural and what is unnatural, and I think it's dangerous to use that dichotomy to block something that could alleviate suffering and disability."

Once she became famous for her gene-editing discoveries, she began to hear stories from people who had been affected by genetic diseases and were yearning for science to help. "The ones about kids were especially touching to me as a mother," she recalls. One example sticks in her mind. A woman sent beautiful pictures of her new baby boy, bald and cute, which reminded Doudna of when her own son, Andy, was born. The baby had just been diagnosed with a genetic neurodegenerative disease. His nerve cells would soon start dying and eventually he would be unable to walk, speak, then swallow or eat. He was doomed to die an early and painful death. The note was a wrenching plea for help. "How could you not want to make progress on coming up with ways to prevent such a thing?" Doudna asks. "My heart broke." If gene editing could prevent this in the future, it would be immoral not to pursue it, she decided. She answered all such emails. She wrote the mother back and promised that she and other researchers were working diligently to find therapies and preventions for such genetic conditions. "But I also had to tell her that it would be years before something like gene editing would be potentially useful for her," she says. "I didn't want to mislead her in any way."

After appearing at the World Economic Forum in Davos in January 2016, where she shared her ethical qualms about gene editing, Doudna was pulled aside by another woman on the panel, who described how her sister had been born with a degenerative disease. It affected not only her but the lives and finances of her whole family. "She said if we could have done gene editing to avoid that, everyone in her family would be absolutely in favor of it," Doudna recalls. "She was very emotional about the cruelty of those who would prevent germline editing, and she was on the verge of tears. I found it so touching."

Later that year, a man came to see her at Berkeley. His father and grandfather had died of Huntington's. Three of his sisters had been diagnosed with it and faced a slow, agonizing death. Doudna refrained from asking the man if he was also afflicted. But his visit convinced her that if germline editing became a safe and effective way to eliminate Huntington's, she was in favor. Once you've seen the face of someone with a genetic disease, she says, especially one like Huntington's, it's hard to support why we would refrain from gene editing.

Her thinking was also influenced by long conversations with Janet Rossant, the chief of research at the Hospital for Sick Children in Toronto, and George Daley, dean of the Harvard Medical School. "I realized how we were on the verge of being able to correct disease-causing mutations," she says. "How could you not want to do that?" Why should CRISPR be held to a far higher standard than any other medical procedure?

The evolution in her thinking made her more sympathetic to the view that many gene-editing decisions should be left to individual choice rather than to bureaucrats and ethics panels. "I'm an American, and putting a high priority on personal freedom and choice is part of our culture," she says. "I also think that as a parent I feel that I would want to have that choice to make about my own health or own family's health as these new technologies come along."

However, because there are still huge risks that may be unknown, she feels that CRISPR should be used only when it is medically necessary and there are no good alternatives. "That means we have no reason to be doing it yet," she says. "That's why I had a problem with He Jiankui's use of CRISPR to attempt to achieve immunity to HIV. There were other ways of doing that. It wasn't medically necessary."

One moral issue that continues to loom large for her is inequality, especially if the wealthy are able to buy genetic enhancements for their children. "We could create a gene gap that would get wider with each new generation," she says. "If you think we face inequalities now, imagine what it would be like if society became genetically tiered along economic lines and we transcribed our financial inequality into our genetic code."

By limiting gene edits to those that are truly "medically necessary," she says, we can make it less likely that parents could seek to "enhance" their children, which she feels is morally and socially wrong. The line between medical treatment and enhancement can be blurry, she acknowledges, but it is not totally meaningless. We know the difference between correcting a very harmful gene variant and adding some genetic trait that is not medically necessary. "As long as we are correcting genetic mutations by restoring the 'normal' version of the gene—not inventing some wholly new enhancement not seen in the average human genome—we're likely to be on the safe side."

She is confident that the good that can come from CRISPR will eventually outweigh the dangers. "Science doesn't move backwards, and we can't unlearn this knowledge, so we need to find a prudent path forward," she says, reprising the phrase in the title of the report she wrote after her 2015 Napa Valley meeting. "We've never seen anything like this before. We now have the power to control our genetic future, which is awesome and terrifying. So we must move forward cautiously and with respect for the power we've gained."

Part Eight

Dispatches from the Front

Here's to the crazy ones. The misfits. The rebels. The troublemakers. The round pegs in the square holes. The ones who see things differently. They're not fond of rules. And they have no respect for the status quo. You can quote them, disagree with them, glorify or vilify them. About the only thing you can't do is ignore them. Because they change things. They push the human race forward. And while some may see them as the crazy ones, we see genius. Because the people who are crazy enough to think they can change the world are the ones who do.

—Steve Jobs, Apple's "Think Different" ad, 1997

Samuel Sternberg

Chapter 44

Quebec

Jumping genes

While attending the 2019 CRISPR Conference in Quebec, I am struck by the realization that biology has become the new tech. The meeting has the same vibe as those of the Homebrew Computer Club and the West Coast Computer Faire in the late 1970s, except that the young innovators are buzzing about genetic code rather than computer code. The atmosphere is charged with the catalytic combination of competition and cooperation reminiscent of when Bill Gates and Steve Jobs frequented the early personal computer shows, except this time the rock stars are Jennifer Doudna and Feng Zhang.

The biotech nerds, I realize, are no longer the outsiders. The CRISPR revolution and coronavirus crisis have turned them into the cool kids on the edge, just as happened to the awkward pioneers who once populated the cyber-frontier. As I wandered around reporting dispatches from the front lines of their revolution, I noticed that even as they pursue their new discoveries they feel tugged, sooner than the digital techies did, to engage in a moral reckoning about the new age they are creating.

The buzz in Quebec is about a fascinating breakthrough that reignited the tension between Doudna's realm and that of Zhang. It involves dueling discoveries of an efficient way to add new sequences into DNA. Instead of making a cut in the double-stranded DNA, the newly discovered CRISPR system would insert a new chunk of DNA by harnessing transposons, known as "jumping genes," which are big segments of DNA that can hop from one place to another on chromosomes.

Sam Sternberg, the whip-smart biochemist who studied under Doudna and then was recruited to open his own lab at Columbia, has just published in *Nature* his first major paper as an assistant professor. It describes a CRISPR-guided system that inserts a tailored jumping gene into a desired DNA location. But to Sternberg's surprise, Zhang was able to get a similar paper of his published online in *Science* a few days earlier.[1]

Sternberg seems deflated when he arrives in Quebec, and his friends, including Doudna, are angry. He had submitted his paper to *Nature* on March 15, and word of his discovery began to spread after one of his graduate students gave a talk about it. "Feng then quietly raced to get his paper published first," Martin Jinek tells me at the conference. To Doudna, it was typical of Zhang: "His network of people will tell him about a paper and he will rush ahead."[2]

She and Eric Lander had both conceded to me, when recalling the 2012 race, that rushing a paper into print when you sense competition is fair play. Nevertheless, Zhang's publication on transposons causes resentment. He had submitted his paper to *Science* on May 4, seven weeks after Sternberg had submitted his, but Zhang's was published online on June 6 and Sternberg's did not appear until June 12.

I find it hard to share the Doudna camp's outrage about Zhang. The two papers both involve harnessing jumping genes, but they differ in important ways and each makes a distinctive contribution to the progress of CRISPR. I happened to be visiting Zhang at his Broad Institute lab the day after his paper went online, which was ten days before the Quebec conference, and he described to me the research he had done on transposons. His paper was not a rush job. It had been in the works for a long time. But when he heard footsteps, he pushed *Science* to get it reviewed and online expeditiously—just as Doudna had done with the seminal 2012 paper she coauthored with Charpentier when she heard the footsteps of Virginijus Šikšnys and others.[3]

On the first day of the Quebec conference, Sternberg's friends, including Doudna, both celebrate and commiserate with him in the hotel lobby bar over Romeo's gin, a fragrant Canadian product. His personality is so naturally ebullient that he seems to get over his annoyance by the time he does his presentation the next day, following one given by Zhang. After all, his discovery is an important triumph and step in his career, one not diminished by Zhang's complementary finding. So Sternberg is gracious in his talk. "We heard from Feng earlier today about how CRISPR-Cas12 can mobilize transposable elements," he says. "What I am going to tell you about is a recently published work on type-one systems that work in similar but also different ways to mobilize these bacterial transposons." He makes sure to heap credit on the PhD student in his Columbia lab, Sanne Klompe, who carried out the main experiments.

"Is there any field that is more cutthroat and competitive than biological research?" one of the participants asks me after Zhang and Sternberg give their dueling talks. Well, yes, I think, almost every field can be, from business to journalism. What distinguishes biological research is the collaboration that is woven in. The camaraderie of being rival warriors in a common quest suffuses the Quebec conference. The desire to win prizes and patents tends to create competition, which spurs the pace of discoveries. But equally motivating, I think, is the passion to uncover what Leonardo da Vinci called the "infinite wonders of nature," especially when it comes to something so breathtakingly beautiful as the inner workings of a living cell. "The jumping gene discoveries show just how fun biology is," Doudna says.

Seared bison

When the first day of presentations is over, Doudna and Sternberg go to a casual restaurant in Old Quebec City, but I accept an invitation from Feng Zhang to join him and a small group of his friends for dinner. Not only do I want to hear his perspective, but I also want to check out the inventive new restaurant he has chosen, Chez Boulay, which features crispy seal meatloaf, huge raw scallops, Arctic char, seared bison, and cabbage blood sausage. Our group of a dozen diners includes Kira Makarova of the U.S. National Center for Biotechnology Information, who was a coauthor of Zhang's jumping-gene paper; the CRISPR pioneer Erik Sontheimer, who was Luciano Marraffini's mentor but has stayed above the personal rivalries of the CRISPR world; and April Pawluk, who had been a postdoc in Doudna's lab and was now an editor at *Cell*, a peer-reviewed journal that competes with *Science* and *Nature.* There is a symbiotic relationship between top researchers, who want to make sure their papers get speedy and favorable treatment, and smart journal editors such as Pawluk, who want to publish the most important new discoveries.

Sontheimer orders the wine, which comes from Quebec and is unexpectedly good, and we drink a toast to transposons. When the talk turns from science to the ethical issues hovering over CRISPR, most of the diners agree that, when it's safe and practical, genetic editing—even making inheritable edits in the human germline—ought to be used if necessary to fix bad single-gene mutations, such as Huntington's disease and sickle-cell anemia. But they recoil at the idea of using gene editing for human enhancements, such as trying to give our kids more muscle mass or height or perhaps someday higher IQ and cognitive skills.

The problem is that the distinction is difficult to define and even more difficult to enforce. "There's a blurry line between fixing abnormalities and making enhancements," Zhang says. So I ask him, "What is wrong with making enhancements?" He pauses for a long time. "I just don't like it," he says. "It's messing with nature. And from a longer term population perspective, you may be reducing diversity." He took the famous Harvard course on moral justice taught by the philosopher Michael Sandel, and he has clearly wrestled with these issues in a profound way. But like the rest of us, he hasn't found easy answers.

A looming ethical issue, everyone at the table agrees, is that gene editing could exacerbate, and even encode, inequality in society. "Should rich people be allowed to buy the best genes they can afford?" Sontheimer asks. It is true, of course, that all of society's benefits, including medical ones, are unequally distributed, but creating a marketplace for inheritable genetic enhancements would kick that issue into an entirely new orbit. "Look at what parents are willing to do to get kids in college," Zhang says. "Some people will surely pay for genetic enhancement. In a world in which there are people who don't get access to eyeglasses, it's hard to imagine how we will find a way to have equal access to gene enhancements. Imagine what that will do to our species."

Gavin Knott showing how to edit

CHAPTER 45

I Learn to Edit

Gavin Knott

Now that I had become immersed in the world of CRISPR pioneers, I decided that I should, in my own small way, be initiated into the club. I should learn how to edit DNA using CRISPR.

So I arrange to spend a few days in Doudna's open-space lab amid the dozens of workspaces, cluttered with centrifuges and pipettes and Petri dishes, where her students and postdocs perform their experiments. I want to replicate the major advances I've recounted: using CRISPR-Cas9 to edit DNA in a test tube, like Doudna and Charpentier described in June 2012, and then using it to make an edit in a human cell, as Zhang, Church, Doudna, and others described in January 2013.

For the first, I am helped by Gavin Knott, a young postdoc from western Australia with a trim beard and easygoing manner. As a graduate student, he decided he wanted to find CRISPR-associated enzymes that attack RNA rather than DNA, and he wrote a letter to Doudna proposing that he come to her lab to do that. Doudna's team was already on the case, working with an enzyme known as Cas13. "She had her finger on the pulse much more than I did," Knott says. But she invited him to be a postdoc in her lab anyway. Among other duties, he became part of the group working on the Safe Genes project for DARPA.[1]

When we go into the secure part of the Doudna Lab where experiments are done, I put on my lab coat and goggles, spray my gloved hands to sterilize them, and instantly feel like a pro. Knott takes me to one of the hoods, a tabletop workspace that is partially enclosed by plastic sides and specially ventilated. Just before we begin work, Doudna buzzes through, wearing a white lab coat over jeans and a black Innovative Genetics Institute T-shirt. She briefly checks on the experiments being done by each of her students (and me), before heading off to an all-day strategy retreat with the institute's top researchers.

The experiment that Knott walks me through involves a snippet of DNA that contains a gene that can make bacteria resistant to the antibiotic ampicillin. This is not a good thing, especially if you're a person who's been infected by such bacteria. So Knott concocts for me some Cas9 with a guide RNA that is designed to eliminate the gene. The lab had brewed all of this from scratch. "The Cas9 we need is encoded on a piece of DNA, and anyone who can grow bacteria in a lab can produce large quantities of it," he assures me. My look probably conveys that I'm not sure this is part of my skill set. "Don't worry," he says. "If you don't want to make it all from scratch, you can just buy the Cas9 from companies like IDT on the web. You can even buy the guide RNAs. If you want to edit genes, it's easy to order the components online."

(Later, I go online to see. The IDT website advertises "all of the reagents needed for successful genome editing," with kits designed for delivery into human cells beginning at $95. Over at a site called GeneCopoeia, a Cas9 protein with a nuclear location signal starts at $85.)[2]

Some of the vials that Knott prepared are lined up in an old-fashioned chill box, one that uses ice to keep liquids cool. "This chill box has a significant history," he says, turning it around. On the back is etched the name "Martin." It had been Jinek's before he left to start his own lab at the University of Zurich. "I inherited it," Knott says proudly. I feel part of a historic chain. The experiments we are about to do mirror Jinek's from 2012: taking a piece of DNA and incubating it with the Cas9 and guide RNA to cut it in the desired location. It's sweet to be using his chill box.

Knott walks me through a variety of steps, using pipettes to combine the ingredients and then incubating it for ten minutes. We add a dye to help us visualize the results, and then we are able to create an image of what we had done by using a process called electrophoresis, which puts an electric field through a gel to separate DNA molecules of different sizes. The resulting printout shows bands at different locations along the gel, indicating if and how they were cut by Cas9. "Textbook success!" Knott exclaims as he takes the image off the printer. "Look at the differences in these bands."

On the way out of the lab, I run into Jamie Cate, Doudna's husband, by the elevator, and I show him my printouts. He points to blurry bars at the bottom of two of the columns and asks, "What are those?" I actually know the answer (thanks to Knott's tutorial). "It's the RNA," I say. Later that day, Cate sends out a tweet attached to a picture of Knott and me working at the lab bench, saying, "And Walter Isaacson passed my pop quiz!" For just a moment, until I realize that Knott did all of the real work, I feel like a true gene editor.

Jennifer Hamilton

The next challenge is to edit a gene in a human cell. In other words, I want to take the step that the labs of Zhang and Church and Doudna accomplished at the end of 2012.

For that I team up with another postdoc in Doudna's lab, Jennifer Hamilton, a Seattle native who earned her doctorate in microbiology at Mount Sinai Medical Center in New York City. With her big glasses and even bigger smile, Hamilton radiates enthusiasm for harnessing viruses to deliver gene-editing tools into human cells. When Doudna came to give a talk to the Women in Science group at Mount Sinai in 2016, Hamilton served as her student escort. "I felt instantly a connection with her," Hamilton recalls.

Doudna was then beginning to build the Innovative Genomics Institute at Berkeley, which would bring together researchers from around the Bay Area. Part of its mission was to find ways to deliver CRISPR editing tools into human cells for medical treatments. So she recruited Hamilton. "I had skills in engineering viruses, and I wanted to apply them to figuring out delivery methods for getting CRISPR into humans," Hamilton says.[3] It was a specialty that would prove valuable when the lab took on the coronavirus pandemic and needed to find ways to deliver CRISPR-based treatments into human cells.

When we begin our attempt to edit DNA in a human cell, Hamilton stresses that it is more challenging than doing it in a test tube. The strands of DNA that I had edited the day before with Knott contained only 2.1 kilobases (2,100 pairs of DNA base letters) versus the 6.4 *million* kilobases in the cell we plan to use, which was derived from a human kidney cell. "The challenge with human gene editing," she tells me, "is to get your editing tools past the cell's outer plasma membrane and past its nuclear membrane to get to where the DNA is, and then you also have to get your tools to find the location in the genome."

Hamilton's explanation of our planned procedure seems to support, albeit inadvertently, Zhang's argument that it is not a simple step to move from editing DNA in a tube to editing it in a human cell. However, the fact that I was about to do it could be used, I guess, to make the opposite argument.

Our plan, Hamilton says, is to make a double-strand break at a targeted place in the DNA of the human cell. In addition, we will supply a template so that a new gene will be inserted. The human cell we start with has been engineered to have a gene that creates a fluorescent protein that glows blue. In one of our procedures, we will use CRISPR-Cas9 to cut the gene and thus deactivate it. This means that the cell should no longer glow. In another sample, we will supply a template that the cell will then incorporate, changing three base pairs of the cell's DNA in order to make the fluorescent protein change from blue to green.

The method we use to get the CRISPR-Cas9 and the template into the nucleus of the cell is called nucleofection. It employs electrical pulses to make the cell's membranes more permeable. At the end of the full editing process, I am able to look through a fluorescent microscope and see the results. The control group still glows blue. A group that had been cut with CRISPR-Cas9 but not supplied with a replacement template doesn't glow at all. And finally, there is the group that we had cut and then edited. I look into the microscope and see them glowing green! I have edited—well, Hamilton has actually edited, with me as an eager copilot—a human cell and changed one of its genes.

Before you get too frightened by what I may have wrought, rest assured: we take everything I did, mix it with chlorine bleach, and wash it down a sink. But I did learn how relatively easy the process can be for a student or rogue scientist who has some skill at a lab bench.

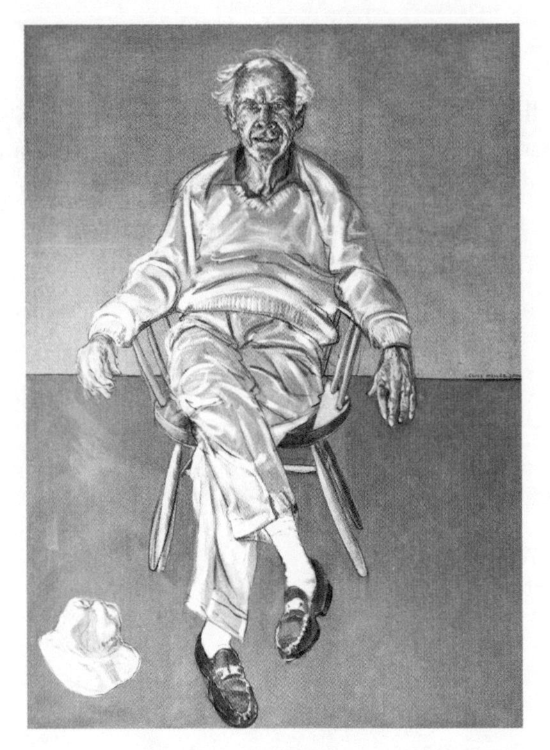

The oil portrait at Cold Spring Harbor, by Lewis Miller

James Watson and his son Rufus in the PBS documentary *Decoding Watson*

CHAPTER 46

Watson Revisited

Intelligence

Cold Spring Harbor Laboratory, where James Watson launched an influential series of annual meetings on the human genome in 1986, decided to add a new series focused on CRISPR gene editing beginning in the fall of 2015. Among the speakers that first year were our four main characters: Jennifer Doudna, Emmanuelle Charpentier, George Church, and Feng Zhang.

Watson attended that initial meeting of the CRISPR group, as he did most meetings at Cold Spring Harbor, and he sat in the front row of the auditorium, underneath a grand oil portrait of himself, to hear Doudna's talk. It was a reprise of her first visit there as a graduate student in the summer of 1987, when Watson also sat up front as she presented, with youthful nervousness, a paper on how some RNAs could replicate themselves. After Doudna's CRISPR talk, he came up to say a few words of praise, just as he had done almost thirty years earlier. It was important, he said, to push the science of making gene edits in humans, including enhancing intelligence. For some in attendance, it felt historic. Stanford biology professor David Kingsley took a picture of Watson and Doudna talking.[1]

But when I show up at the 2019 meeting, Watson is not in his usual seat in the front row. After fifty years, he has been banished from meetings, and the oil portrait of him removed. He is now sentenced to internal exile, living with his wife, Elizabeth, in elegant but tortured isolation at the northern end of the campus in a pale Palladian-style mansion called Ballybung.

His troubles began in 2003, when he marked the fiftieth anniversary of his co-discovery of DNA's structure by giving an interview for a documentary on PBS and the BBC. Genetic engineering should someday be used to "cure" people who have low intelligence, he said. "If you really are stupid, I would call that a disease." It reflected his deep belief, perhaps fostered by pride in his seminal scientific discovery as well as the daily angst of living with his schizophrenic son, Rufus, in the power of DNA to explain human nature. "The lower ten percent who really have difficulty, even in elementary school, what's the cause of it?" Watson asked. "A lot of people would like to say, 'Well, poverty, things like that.' It probably isn't. So I'd like to get rid of that, to help the lower ten percent." As if to make sure that he stoked enough controversy, Watson added that gene-editing could also be used to enhance people's looks. "People say it would be terrible if we made all girls pretty. I think it would be great."[2]

Watson considered himself a political progressive. He supported Democrats from Franklin Roosevelt to Bernie Sanders. His advocacy for gene editing, he insisted, was because he wanted to improve the lot of the less fortunate. But as the Harvard philosopher Michael Sandel noted, "Watson's language contains more than a whiff of the old eugenic sensibility."[3] It was a whiff that was particularly odious wafting from Cold Spring Harbor, given the lab's long history of fomenting that eugenic sensibility.

Watson's comments about intelligence were controversial, but in 2007 he crossed a line by connecting it to race. That year he published another memoir, *Avoid Boring People*, a phrase that he meant to be read in two ways, with "boring" as both a verb and an adjective. Naturally averse, perhaps congenitally so, to boring people, Watson relished mumbling unfiltered and provocative comments, often accompanying them with a windy snort and impish grin. This proved combustible when, as part of the publicity campaign for the book, he gave a series of interviews to Charlotte Hunt-Grubbe, a freelance science journalist who was writing a profile of him for the *Sunday Times* of London. Always unguarded, he was in this case even more so because she was a former student and tennis partner of his who had lived with the Watsons in Cold Spring Harbor for a year.

The result was a languid feature story in which Hunt-Grubbe followed Watson from the library of his house to a local diner to the lawn tennis courts of the Piping Rock Club. After a match, he reflected on his current life. "I'm still thinking," he said, "can we find the genes for mental disease while I'm still alive, and will we have stopped cancer in ten years, and will my tennis serve improve?"[4]

Near the end of her four-thousand-word piece, she offhandedly described him offering some ruminations about race:

> He says that he is "inherently gloomy about the prospect of Africa" because "all our social policies are based on the fact that their intelligence is the same as ours—whereas all the testing says not really, and I know that this hot potato is going to be difficult to address." His hope is that everyone is equal, but he counters that "people who have to deal with black employees find this not true."

The article set off an explosion, and Watson was forced to resign as chancellor of Cold Spring Harbor. But for the time being, he was allowed to wander down the hill from his house at the top of the campus whenever he wanted to attend meetings.

Watson tried to walk his comments back, saying that he was "mortified" about having implied that Africans were "somehow genetically inferior." In a prepared statement released by the lab, he added, "That is not what I meant. More importantly from my point of view, there is no scientific basis for such a belief."[5] There was one problem with his apology: it actually *was* what he meant, and being the type of person he was, he would inevitably have trouble in the future not saying so.

Watson's ninetieth birthday

By the time Watson turned ninety in 2018, the controversy surrounding him seemed to have subsided. His birthday, along with the fiftieth anniversary of his arrival at Cold Spring Harbor Laboratory and his marriage to Elizabeth, was celebrated in the campus auditorium with a concert that featured pianist Emanuel Ax playing Mozart followed by a gala dinner. The benefit raised $750,000 toward an endowed professorship at the laboratory in his honor.

Watson's friends and colleagues tried to sustain a delicate balance. He was honored for being one of the most influential thinkers in modern science, tolerated for being saucy in his writings and conversations, and condemned for his comments on racial intelligence. That balance was sometimes difficult to sustain. A few weeks after the birthday celebration, at a genetics meeting on campus, Eric Lander was asked to make a toast to Watson, who was sitting in the audience. Lander noted that Watson was "flawed," but in his ebullient way added gracious comments about his leadership of the Human Genome Project and for "pushing all of us to explore the frontiers of science for the benefit of humankind."

The toast prompted a backlash, especially on Twitter. Lander, already burned by blasts for minimizing the roles of Doudna and Charpentier in his "Heroes of CRISPR" article, apologized. "I was wrong to toast, and I'm sorry," he wrote in a note to his Broad colleagues that he made public. "I reject his views as despicable. They have no place in science, which must welcome everyone." He added a cryptic comment, which referred to a conversation he once had with Watson about Jewish donors to their respective institutions. "As someone who has been on the receiving end of his abhorrent remarks, I should have been sensitive to the damage caused by recognizing him in any way."[6]

Watson was infuriated by Lander's assertion that it was wrong to be "recognizing him in any way" and the insinuation that he was anti-Semitic. "Lander is regarded as a joke," Watson exploded. "My life has been dominated by, first, my father's love for Jews, and all my good friends in America have been Jewish." He went on to emphasize to me, in a way that would not have mollified his critics, his view that Ashkenazi Jews, who lived for centuries in northern Europe, were genetically more intelligent than other ethnic groups, a point he supported by rattling off those who had won Nobel Prizes.[7]

An American Master

When the *American Masters* series on PBS decided to do a documentary on Watson in 2018, it set out to produce a balanced, intimate, complex, and nuanced look at both his scientific triumphs and his controversial views. He cooperated fully, allowing the cameras to follow him around his elegant home and the Cold Spring Harbor campus. The documentary covered his whole life, including his intellectual bromance with Francis Crick, the controversy over his unauthorized use of Rosalind Franklin's DNA images, and his late-career quest to find genetic treatments for cancer. Most poignant were the scenes of him with his wife and their son Rufus, still living at home at age forty-eight while coping with schizophrenia.[8]

It also dealt with the controversy over his remarks on race. Joseph Graves, the first African American to get a PhD in evolutionary biology, gave a studied rebuttal to those views. "We know a great deal about human genetic variation and how it is apportioned around the world," he said, "and there is absolutely no evidence that there are genetic differences that favor intelligence in any sub-population of human beings." Then the interviewer gave Watson the opportunity to—almost prodded him to—renounce or abandon some of his previous controversial statements.

He didn't. Caught close up on camera, he seemed to pause and even tremble slightly like an aged schoolkid who was unable to say what he was supposed to. It was as if he was congenitally incapable of sugarcoating his thoughts or biting his tongue. "I would like for them to have changed, that there be new knowledge that says that your nurture is much more important than nature," he said as the cameras rolled. "But I haven't seen any knowledge. And there's a difference on the average between blacks and whites on I.Q. tests. I would say the difference is, it's genetic." Later, there was a moment of self-awareness. "It should be no surprise that someone who won the race to find the double helix should think that genes are important."

The documentary aired the first week of January 2019, and Amy Harmon of the *New York Times* wrote a story about his remarks. "James Watson Had a Chance to Salvage His Reputation on Race" was the headline. "He Made Things Worse."[9] She noted that there were complex debates over the relationship between race and IQ, then she quoted Francis Collins, the director of the National Institutes of Health and Watson's successor as head of the Human Genome Project, giving the consensus view. Experts on intelligence, he said, "consider any black-white differences in I.Q. testing to arise primarily from environmental, not genetic, differences."[10]

The board of Cold Spring Harbor Laboratory finally decided it had to cut almost all of its remaining ties to Watson. Calling his comments "reprehensible and unsupported by science," it stripped him of his honorary titles and removed the large and casually elegant oil portrait of him from its main auditorium. He was, however, allowed to remain in his bayfront manor house on the campus.[11]

The Jefferson Conundrum

Watson thus presents historians with what could be called the Jefferson Conundrum: To what extent can you respect a person for great achievements ("We hold these truths") when they are accompanied by reprehensible failings ("are created equal")?

One question raised by the conundrum relates, at least metaphorically, to gene editing. Cutting out a gene for an unwanted trait (sickle-cell anemia or HIV receptivity) might change some existing desirable trait (resistance to malaria or the West Nile virus). The issue is not simply whether we can balance a respect for a person's achievements with a contempt for their flaws. The more complex issue is whether the achievements and the flaws are interwoven. If Steve Jobs had been kinder and gentler, would he have had the passion that allowed him to bend reality and push people to realize their full potential? Did Watson have a congenital tendency to be heretical and provocative, and did that help him push the frontiers of science when he was right and lead him into a dark abyss of prejudice when he was wrong?

I believe that people's flaws cannot be excused by saying they are interwoven with their greatness. But Watson is an important part of the story I am writing—this book begins with Doudna picking up his seminal *The Double Helix* and deciding to become a biochemist—and his views on genetics and human enhancement are an undercurrent of the policy debates over gene editing. So I decide to go visit him right before the summer 2019 CRISPR meeting at Cold Spring Harbor.

A visit with Watson

I have known James Watson since the early 1990s, when I was at *Time* before he was so controversial, and we covered his work on the Human Genome Project, commissioned essays by him, and selected him for our list of the hundred most influential people of the twentieth century. At the 1999 dinner celebrating what we called "the *Time* 100," I asked him to give a toast to the late Linus Pauling, whom he had beaten in the race to discover the structure of DNA. "Failure hovers uncomfortably close to greatness," he said of Pauling. "What matters now are his perfections, not his past imperfections."[12] Perhaps people may say that of Watson someday, but in 2019 he was an outcast.

When I arrive at his house on the Cold Spring Harbor campus, Watson settles into a chintz-covered armchair looking very frail. A few months earlier, he had come back from a trip to China and, with no car provided by the lab to pick him up at the airport, had driven himself in the dark. He ended up veering off the road and into the bay by his home, leading to a long hospitalization. But his mind is still sharp and he is still focused on deploying CRISPR in an equitable way. "If it's only used to solve the problems and desires of the top ten percent, that will be horrible," he says. "We have evolved more and more in the past few decades into an inequitable society, and this would make it much worse."[13]

One step that might help a little, he suggests, is to not allow patents for genetic engineering techniques. There would still likely be a lot of funding for finding safe ways to fix maladies that are devastating, such as Huntington's and sickle-cell anemia. But if there were no patents, there might be less payoff for racing to be the first to devise methods of enhancements, and those that did get invented might be cheaper and more widely available if anyone could copy them. "I would accept some slowdown in the science in return for making it more equitable," he says.

When he made an assertion he knew might shock, he gave his short snort of a laugh and grinned like a scamp who's just done something naughty. "I think my blunt and contrary nature helps my science, because I don't simply accept things just because other people believe it," he says. "My strength is not that I am smarter, it's that I'm more willing to offend the crowd." Sometimes, he admits, he has been "too honest" in order to push an idea. "You have to exaggerate."

Was that the case, I ask, with his comments on race and intelligence? As is his nature, he is able to seem regretful but not repentant. "The PBS documentary on me was actually very good, but I wish they didn't emphasize my old comments on race," he replies. "I don't say anything publicly about that anymore."

But then, as if compelled, he starts to veer off into that realm again. "I couldn't deny what I believed," he tells me. He begins talking about various historical measurements of IQ, the effect of climate, and what he had been taught as an undergraduate at the University of Chicago by Louis Leon Thurstone about factor analysis in intelligence.

Why, I ask him, does he feel the need to say such things? "I haven't given one interview on race since I talked to that girl from the *Sunday Times*," he says. "She had lived in Africa and knew. The only time I repeated it was to this television interviewer, because I couldn't help myself." I suggest that he could help himself if he wanted to. "I always follow my father's advice of saying the truth," he replies. "Someone has to say the truth."

But it's not the truth. Most experts, I tell him, say your views are wrong.

He doesn't engage, so I ask him what other advice his father gave him. "Always be kind," he answers.

Has he heeded that advice?

"I wish I had been better on that one," he admits. "I wish I had worked harder on always being kind."

He badly wanted to be in the audience again for the annual CRISPR meeting at Cold Spring Harbor, which was a week later, but the lab was unwilling to lift its ban. So he requested that I bring Doudna up the hill from the meeting so he could talk to her.

Rufus

Sitting in the kitchen during my visit with Watson was his son Rufus. He didn't join us, but he was listening to every word.

As a boy, Rufus looked like his father did when young: lanky, tousled hair, an easy grin, and an angular face often slightly tilted as if in curiosity. Like father, like son. Heritage and breeding. But now Rufus was in his late forties, pudgy and somewhat disheveled. He has lost the ability to laugh casually. He is acutely aware of his own condition—and also of his father's. Volatile, sensitive, brilliant, disheveled, unfiltered, prone to spouting off, brutally candid, attentive to every conversation, and also gentle—these are all traits that mark Rufus's schizophrenia. To a different degree and in some form, each and every one of these traits can be ascribed to his father as well. Perhaps, someday, the deciphering of the human genome will be able to explain that. Or maybe it won't.

"My dad will say, 'My son Rufus, he's bright but he's mentally ill,'" Rufus told the *American Masters* interviewer. "Whereas I think of it as the opposite. I think I'm dim but not mentally ill." He feels that he has let his father down. "It wasn't until I became aware of how dim I was that I thought this was strange, because my dad's not dim," he says. "Then I thought that I'm a burden on my parents because he's successful, and he deserves to have a successful child. He's worked hard, and if you believe in karma he should have earned himself a successful son."[14]

At one point during my conversations with James Watson, when he veers toward the issue of race, Rufus bursts in from the kitchen shouting. "If you are going to let him say these things, then I am going to have to ask you to leave." Watson merely shrugs and says nothing to his son, but he quits talking about race.[15]

I can sense the intense protectiveness that Rufus feels toward his father. These outbursts also reveal in him a wisdom that his father often lacks. "My dad's statements might make him out to be a bigot and discriminatory," he once said. "They just represent his rather narrow interpretation of genetic destiny." He's right. In many ways he is wiser than his father.[16]

CHAPTER 47

Doudna Pays a Visit

Careful conversation

As Watson requested, I ask Doudna if she would be willing to visit him during the meeting he was barred from attending. When the two of us enter his house, he asks to see the conference book with the abstracts of the scientific papers being presented. I am reluctant to show it to him because the cover of the book is Rosalind Franklin's "photograph 51" X-ray diffraction image that helped Watson discover the structure of DNA. But he seems amused rather than upset. "Ah, that picture, it will always haunt me," he says, then pauses and smiles his impish grin. "But she never figured out it was a helix."[1]

Watson, wearing a peach-colored sweater in the sun-dappled sitting room, points out some of the art he has collected over the years. Tellingly, his most prominent pieces are modernist and abstract depictions of human faces contorted in emotion. These include paintings and drawings by John Graham, André Derain, Wifredo Lam, Duilio Barnabé, Paul Klee, Henry Moore, and Joan Miró, as well as a drawing of Watson's own slightly contorted and emotionally pensive face by David Hockney. Classical music plays in the background. Elizabeth Watson sits in the corner reading a book, and Rufus hovers out of sight in the kitchen, listening. Everyone tries to be careful in the conversation—even Watson, for the most part.

Doudna talking with James Watson under his portrait

"The reason that CRISPR is the most important discovery since DNA's structure," he tells Doudna, "is that it not only describes the world, as we did with the double helix, but makes it easy to change the world." He and Doudna discuss the Watsons' other son, Duncan, who lives in Berkeley near Doudna. "We were just there visiting him," Watson says. "The students at Berkeley are the pits, they are so progressive. These progressive kids are even dumber than Republicans." Elizabeth chimes in to change the subject.

Doudna reminisces about the first meeting Watson had convened on genome editing at Cold Spring Harbor five years earlier, and how he had asked her a question from the audience. "I was enthusiastic about the use of it," he says. "People who cannot think well enough will be able to be made immensely better." Elizabeth again chimes in on a different topic.

The complexity of human life

It was a short visit, and as we walk back down the hill from Watson's home, I ask Doudna her thoughts. "I was thinking back to when I was twelve and began reading the dog-eared copy of *The Double Helix*," she says. "It would have been wild to know that years later I would be visiting with him in his home having that conversation."

She doesn't say much else that day, but the visit resonated. Over the next few months, we would return to it in our conversations. "It was a poignant and sad visit," she says. "He is clearly someone who has had a huge impact on biology and genetics, but he's expressing views that are quite abhorrent."

She admits that she had mixed feelings about agreeing to go to see him. "But I agreed to because of his influence on biology and on my own life. Here's a person who had this incredible career, and had this potential to be a real figure of respect in the field, and it was all squandered because of these views that he holds. Some people may say you shouldn't have met with him. But for me it's not so simple."

Doudna recalls one aspect of her father's personality that used to upset her. Martin Doudna tended to categorize people as good or bad, with little respect for the shadings that most people contain. "He had people that he revered and thought were wonderful and they could do no wrong, and then he had people who were horrible and he disagreed with them on everything, and they could do no right." Reacting to that, Doudna worked hard to see people in all of their complexity. "I felt like the world is kind of grayscale. There are people who have great qualities, but they also have flaws."

I mention "mosaic," a term often used in biology. "That's a better description than grayscale," she says. "And frankly that's true for all of us. All of us, if we're honest with ourselves, know that we have things that we're great at and things that we're not so great at."

That indirect admission that we all have our flaws intrigued me. I tried to tease more out of her, asking how that applied to herself. "If I have a regret, it's that I don't really feel proud of the way I, in some cases, interacted with my dad," she responds. "I got frustrated with him because he viewed people with a black-and-white lens."

Does that influence, I ask, how she tries to view James Watson? "I don't want to do what my father did and come to simple judgments," she answers. "I try to grapple with people who do great things, but who I also completely disagree with on some things." Watson is a prime example, she says. "He has said some really bad things, but every time I see him, I am brought back to that day when I read *The Double Helix* and first started thinking, 'Gee, I wonder if I could do that kind of science someday.' "[2]

Part Nine

Coronavirus

I have no idea what's awaiting me, or what will happen when this all ends. For the moment I know this: there are sick people and they need curing.

—Albert Camus, *The Plague*, 1947

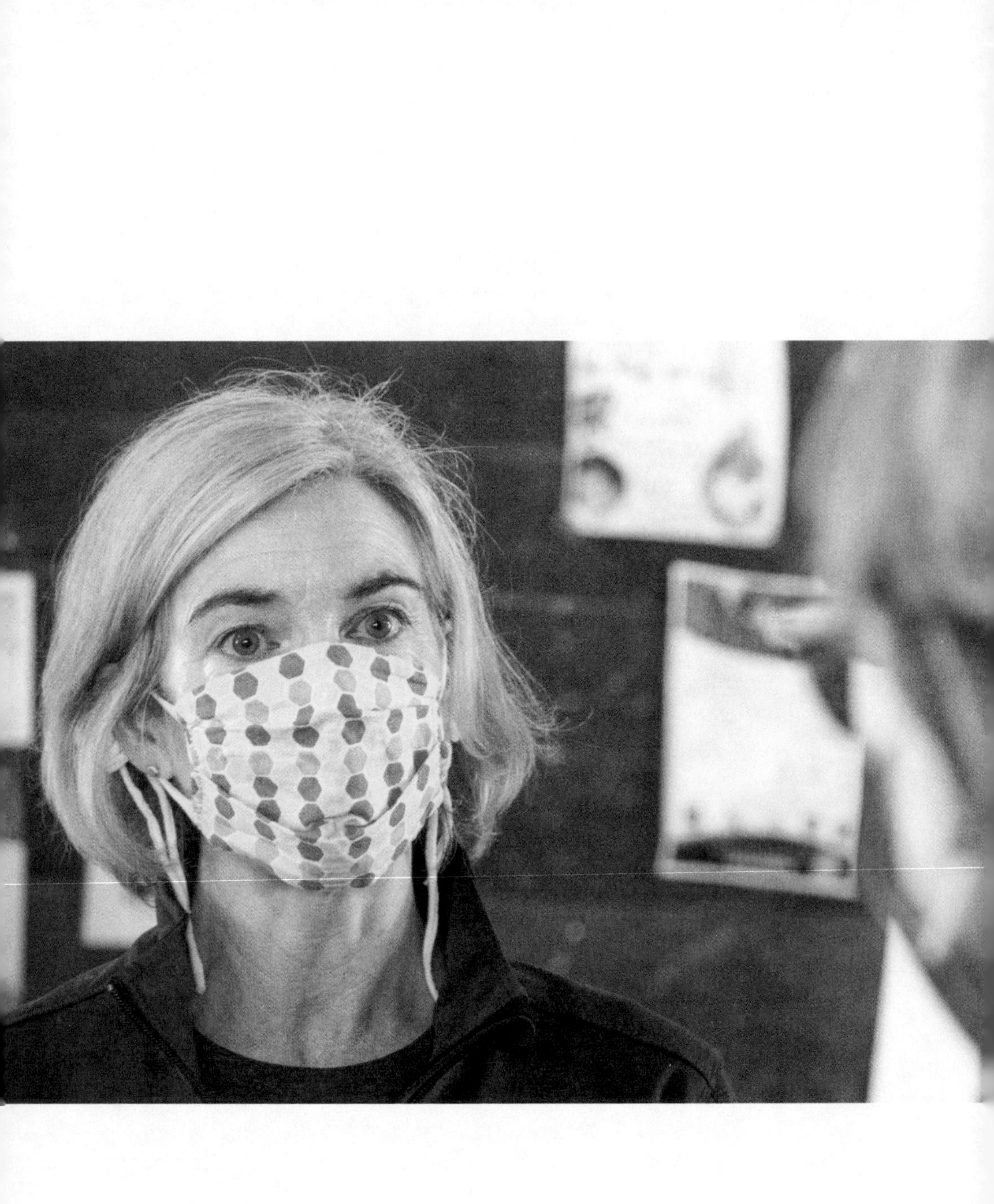

Chapter 48

Call to Arms

Innovative Genomics Institute

At the end of February 2020, Doudna was scheduled to travel from Berkeley to Houston for a seminar. Life in the United States had not yet been disrupted by the looming coronavirus pandemic. There had been no officially reported deaths. But red flags were flying. There were already 2,835 deaths in China, and the stock market was beginning to take notice. The Dow fell more than a thousand points on February 27. "I was nervous," Doudna recalls. "I talked with Jamie about whether or not to go. But at the time everyone I knew was carrying on as usual, and so I went to Houston." She took with her a supply of hand wipes.

When she returned, she began thinking about what she and her colleagues should be doing to fight the pandemic. Having turned CRISPR into a gene-editing tool, she had a profound feel for the molecular mechanisms that could be used by humans to detect and destroy viruses. More important, she had become a maestro of collaboration. It became clear to her that battling coronavirus would require putting together teams that spanned many specialties.

Fortunately, she had a base from which she could build such an effort. She had become the executive director of the Innovative Genomics Institute (IGI), a joint research partnership between Berkeley and the University of California, San Francisco, with a spacious five-story modern building on the northwest corner of the Berkeley campus. (It was originally going to be called the Center for Genetic Engineering, but the university began to worry that the name might unnerve people.)[1] One of the institute's core principles is to foster collaboration between different fields, which is why its building houses plant scientists, microbial researchers, and biomedical specialists. Among the researchers who have their labs in the facility are her husband, Jamie; her original CRISPR collaborator Jillian Banfield; her former postdoc Ross Wilson; and the biochemist Dave Savage, who was using CRISPR to improve how bacteria in ponds convert carbon from the atmosphere into organic compounds.[2]

Doudna had been talking to Savage, whose office is next to hers, for almost a year about launching some project at IGI that would become a model for cross-disciplinary teamwork. One genesis for the plan came from her son, Andy, who had a summer internship at a local biotech company. His day there began with a check-in where leaders from different divisions shared what they were doing to further the company's projects. Hearing this, Doudna had laughed and told Andy she couldn't imagine running an academic lab that way. "Why not?" he asked. She explained that academic researchers get comfortable in their silos and too protective of their independence. It started a long-running conversation in their house about teams, innovation, and how to create a work environment that stimulates creativity.

She kicked around ideas with Savage in late 2019 at a Japanese noodle house in Berkeley. How could you combine, she asked, the best features of a corporate team culture with academic autonomy? They wondered if it would be possible to find a project that would coalesce researchers from a variety of labs around a single goal. They nicknamed the idea "Wigits," for Workshop for IGI Team Science, and they joked that they would all join hands and build wigits together.

When they floated the idea at one of the institute's Friday happy hours, it met with enthusiasm from some of the students but not from most of the professors. "In industry everyone focuses on achieving agreed-upon common goals," says Gavin Knott, one of the students eager to see this happen. "But in academia, everyone functions in their own bubble. We all work on our own research interests and we collaborate only when it's necessary." So with no source of funding and little faculty enthusiasm, the idea remained in limbo.[3]

Then coronavirus came along. Savage's students had been texting him to ask what Berkeley was doing to address the crisis, and he realized it could be the focus of the type of team approach they had discussed. When he wandered into Doudna's office with the idea, he found that she had been thinking along the same lines.

They agreed that she should call a meeting of their IGI colleagues and other Bay Area associates who might be interested in joining a coronavirus effort. That meeting, which is the one described in the introduction of this book, was at 2 p.m. on Friday, March 13—the day after Doudna and her husband made their predawn drive to Fresno to retrieve their son from his robotics competition.

SARS-CoV-2

The rapidly spreading new coronavirus had by then been given an official name: severe acute respiratory syndrome coronavirus 2, or SARS-CoV-2. It was so named because it was similar in its symptoms to the SARS coronavirus that spread out of China in 2003, infecting more than eight thousand people worldwide. The disease caused by the new virus was named COVID-19.

Viruses are deceptively simple little capsules of bad news.* They are just a tiny bit of genetic material, either DNA or RNA, inside a protein shell. When they worm their way into a cell of an organism, they can hijack its machinery in order to replicate themselves. In the case of coronaviruses, the genetic material is RNA, Doudna's specialty. In SARS-CoV-2, the RNA is about 29,900 base letters long, compared to more than three billion in human DNA. The viral sequence provides the code for making a mere twenty-nine proteins.[4]

Here is a sample snippet of the letters in the coronavirus's RNA: CCUCGGCGGGCACGUAGUGUAGCUAGUCAAUCCAU-

*Yes, the world is filled with some very useful and necessary viruses, but they are for a different book.

CAUUGCCUACACUAUGUCACUUGGUGCAGAAAAUUC. That sequence is part of a string that codes for making a protein that sits on the outside of the virus shell. The protein looks like a spike, which gives the virus, when viewed through an electron microscope, the appearance of a crown, hence *corona*. This spike is like a key that can fit into specific receptors on the surface of human cells. Notably, the first twelve letters of the sequence above allow the spike to bind very tightly to one specific receptor on human cells. This evolution of this short sequence explains how the virus could have jumped from bats to other animals to us.

For the SARS-CoV-2 coronavirus, the human receptor is a protein known as ACE2. It plays a role that is similar to the one played for HIV by the CCR5 protein, which the rogue Chinese doctor He Jiankui edited out of his CRISPR twins. Because the ACE2 protein has functions other than just being a receptor, it's probably not a good idea to try to edit it out of our species.

The new coronavirus jumped into humans sometime in late 2019. The first officially certified death was reported on January 9, 2020. Also on that day, Chinese researchers publicly posted the full genetic sequence of the virus. Using cryo-electron microscopy, which fires electrons at proteins that have been frozen in a liquid, structural biologists were able to create a precise model, atom by atom and twist by twist, of the coronavirus and its spikes. With the sequencing information and structural data in hand, molecular biologists began racing to find treatments and vaccines that would block the ability of the virus to latch on to human cells.[5]

The order of battle

The March 13 meeting that Doudna summoned drew far more participants than she and Savage expected. A dozen key lab leaders and students gathered that Friday afternoon in the ground-floor conference room of the IGI building just as the rest of the campus was being locked down. Another fifty researchers from the Bay Area joined by Zoom. "Without planning it or imagining how it would come about," Doudna says, "our idea from the noodle house became reality."[6]

As Doudna discovered, there is an advantage to being part of large organizations such as UC Berkeley and the IGI. Innovation often happens in garages and dorm rooms, but it is sustained by institutions. An infrastructure is needed to handle the logistics required for complex projects. This is especially true during a pandemic. "Having the IGI in place was incredibly useful," Doudna says, "because there were teams of people who could help with things like writing proposals, setting up Slack channels, sending out group emails, arranging Zoom meetings, and coordinating equipment."

Berkeley's legal team came up with a policy for sharing discoveries freely with other coronavirus researchers while protecting the underlying intellectual property. At one of the first meetings, a university lawyer laid out a template for royalty-free licensing. "We will allow non-exclusive no-fee licensing of any of the work that's coming out of this effort," she said. "We still want to file for patent protection for anything discovered, but then we will make it available for this purpose." Doudna had a slide presentation on this for the group's second Zoom meeting, held on March 18. She summarized its message succinctly: "It's not about making money here."

By the time of this second meeting, Doudna also had a slide listing ten projects they had decided to pursue, with the names of the team leaders. Some of the planned tasks made use of the latest CRISPR technology, including developing a CRISPR-based diagnostic test and finding ways to deliver safely into the lungs a CRISPR-based system that could target and destroy the genetic material of the virus.

When the ideas first started rolling in, one of the wise hands in the room, a professor named Robert Tjian, had interjected a note of clarity. "Let's split this in two parts," he said. There are new things we could try to invent, "but first there's the fire-on-my-ass problem." There was a pause for a moment, then he explained. They had to deal with the urgent need for public testing before they could sit at their lab benches and come up with biotechnologies for the future. So the first team Doudna launched was given the mission of converting a space on the ground floor of the building, near where they were seated, into a state-of-the-art, high-speed, automated coronavirus testing lab.

Fyodor Urnov getting the first test samples from Dori Tieu of the Berkeley Fire Department as Dirk Hockemeyer watches

CHAPTER 49

Testing

America's failure

The first official guidance to local health officials in the U.S. about testing for the new coronavirus came in a conference call on January 15, 2020, led by Stephen Lindstrom, a microbiologist at the Centers for Disease Control (CDC). The CDC had developed a test for the new coronavirus, he said, but it could not make it available to state health departments until the Food and Drug Administration (FDA) approved it. That should be soon, Lindstrom promised, but until then, doctors would have to send samples to the CDC in Atlanta for testing.

The next day, a Seattle doctor sent the CDC a nose-swab sample from a thirty-five-year-old man who had returned from a visit to Wuhan and come down with flu-like symptoms. He became the first person in the U.S. to test positive.[1]

On January 31, Health and Human Services Secretary Alex Azar, whose department oversees the FDA, declared a public health emergency. The declaration gave the FDA the right to speed up approvals for coronavirus tests. But it had a weird unintended consequence. In normal circumstances, hospitals and university labs can devise their own tests to use at their facilities, as long as they do not market them. But a declaration of a public health emergency imposes the requirement that such tests not be used until they get an "emergency use authorization." The intent is to avoid the use of unproven tests during a health crisis. As a result, Azar's declaration triggered new restrictions on academic labs and hospitals. That would have been fine if the CDC's test was widely available. But the FDA had still not approved it.

That approval finally came on February 4, and the next day the CDC began sending test kits to state and local labs. The way the test works, or was supposed to work, is that a long swab is inserted into the back of a patient's nasal passage. The lab uses some of the chemical mixtures in the kit to extract any RNA that is in the mucus. The RNA is then "reverse-transcribed" to turn it into DNA. The DNA strands are amplified into millions of copies using a well-known process called a polymerase chain reaction (PCR), which most college biology students learn how to do.

The PCR process was invented in 1983 by Kary Mullis, a chemist at a biotech company. Driving in his car one night, Mullis crafted a way to tag a sequence of DNA and use enzymes to duplicate it through repeated cycles of heating and cooling known as thermocycling. "Beginning with a single molecule of the DNA, the PCR can generate 100 billion similar molecules in an afternoon," he wrote.[2] These days the process is usually done using a machine the size of a microwave that raises and lowers the temperature of the mixture. If the genetic material of the coronavirus is present in the mucus, the PCR process amplifies it so that it can be detected.

When state health officials received the test kits from the CDC, they set about verifying that they worked by trying them on patient samples that were already known to be positive or negative. "Early on Feb. 8, one of the first CDC test kits arrived in a Federal Express package at a public health laboratory on the east side of Manhattan," the *Washington Post* reported. "For hours, lab technicians struggled to verify that the test worked." When they ran the tests on samples known to contain the virus, they got a positive result. That was good. Unfortunately, when they ran the test on purified water, they also got a positive result. One of the chemical compounds in the CDC test kits was defective. It had been contaminated during the manufacturing process. "Oh, shit," said Jennifer Rakeman, an assistant commissioner of the city's health department. "What are we going to do now?"[3]

Adding to the disgrace was the fact that the World Health Organization had delivered 250,000 diagnostic tests that worked just fine to countries around the world. The U.S. could have gotten some of those tests or replicated them, but it had refused.

A university steps in

The University of Washington, at the epicenter of one of the first COVID outbreaks in the U.S., was the first to rush into this minefield. At the beginning of January, after seeing the reports from China, Alex Greninger, a round-faced young assistant director of the virology lab at the university's medical center, talked to his boss, Keith Jerome, about developing their own test. "We're probably going to be wasting some money on this," Jerome said. "It's probably not going to come over here. But you've got to be ready."[4]

Within two weeks, Greninger had a working test, which, under normal regulations, they could use in their own hospital system. But then HHS Secretary Azar issued his emergency declaration, which made regulations more strict. So Greninger submitted a formal application to the FDA for an "Emergency Use Authorization." It took him close to one hundred hours to fill out all of the forms. Then came an astonishing bureaucratic snafu. He got a response from the FDA on February 20 informing him that, in addition to sending his application electronically, he had to mail in a printed copy along with a copy burned onto a compact disc (remember what those were?) to FDA headquarters in Maryland. In an email he wrote to a friend that day describing the FDA's bizarre approach, Greninger vented, "Repeat after me, emergency."

A few days later, the FDA responded by requiring him to do more trials to see if the test he was using inadvertently detected the MERS and SARS viruses, even though they had been dormant for years and he had no samples of those viruses to test. When he called the CDC to see if he could get a sample of the old SARS virus, it refused. "That's when I thought, 'Huh, maybe the FDA and the CDC haven't talked about this at all,'" Greninger told reporter Julia Ioffe. "I realized, Oh, wow, this is going to take a while."[5]

Others had similar problems. The Mayo Clinic had created a crisis team to deal with the pandemic. Of its fifteen members, five were tasked to deal full time with the FDA's paperwork requirements. By late February, there were dozens of hospitals and academic labs, including at Stanford and the Broad Institute of MIT and Harvard, that had developed testing capabilities, but none had managed to win FDA authorization.

At that point Anthony Fauci, the National Institutes of Health infectious disease chief who had become a national superstar, stepped in. On February 27, he spoke to HHS Secretary Azar's chief of staff, Brian Harrison, and urged that the FDA allow universities, hospitals, and private testing services to start using their own tests while waiting for Emergency Use Authorizations. Harrison held a conference call with the relevant agencies and told them, using strong language, that before the end of the meeting they had to come up with such a plan.[6]

The FDA finally relented on Saturday, February 29, and announced that it would allow non-government labs to use their own tests as they waited to get Emergency Use Authorizations. That Monday, Greninger's lab tested thirty patients. Within a few weeks, it would be testing more than 2,500 a day.

Eric Lander's Broad Institute also jumped into the fray. Deborah Hung, the codirector of the Broad's infectious diseases program, also worked as a physician at Brigham and Women's Hospital in Boston. On the evening of March 9, when confirmed cases of COVID in the state had risen to forty-one, it struck her how bad the virus was going to be. She called her colleague Stacey Gabriel, the director of the Broad Institute's genomics sequencing facility, which is a few blocks from the Broad headquarters in a former warehouse that stored beer and popcorn for Fenway Park. Could she turn the lab into a facility for testing for the coronavirus? Gabriel said yes, then called Lander to see if that was okay. Lander was, as always, eager to deploy science in the public interest and rightly proud of the teammates he had assembled who shared that instinct. "The call was kind of irrelevant," Lander says. "I of course said yes, but she was going to do it anyway, as well she should." The lab went into full operation on March 24, receiving samples from hospitals across the Boston area.[7] With the failure of the Trump administration to carry out widespread testing, university research labs began taking on a role that has normally been performed by the government.

Enrique Lin Shiao and Jennifer Hamilton

Chapter 50

The Berkeley Lab

The volunteer army

When Doudna and her colleagues at Berkeley's Innovative Genomics Institute decided at their March 13 meeting to focus on building their own coronavirus testing lab, there was a discussion about what technology to use. Should it be the cumbersome but reliable process of amplifying the genetic material from test swabs using a polymerase chain reaction (PCR), as described earlier? Or should they try to invent a new type of test, one that used CRISPR technology to directly detect the RNA of the virus?

They decided to do both, but they would initially scramble to do the first approach. "We need to walk before we run," Doudna said at the conclusion of the discussion. "Let's use current technology right away, then we can innovate."[1] By having its own testing lab, the IGI would have the data and patient samples to try out new approaches.

After the meeting, the institute sent out a tweet:

> Innovative Genomics Institute @igisci: We are working as hard as possible to establish clinical #COVID19 testing capability at @UCBerkeley campus. We will update this page often to ask for reagents, equipment, and volunteers.

Within two days, more than 860 people had responded and the volunteer list had to be cut off.

The team that Doudna put together reflected the diversity of her lab and of the biotech field in general. To command the operation, she turned to Fyodor Urnov, a gene-editing wizard who had been leading IGI's efforts to develop affordable methods to cure sickle-cell anemia.

Born in 1968 in the heart of Moscow, Urnov learned English from his mother, Julia Palievsky, who was a professor, and his father, Dmitry Urnov, a distinguished literary critic and Shakespeare scholar, William Faulkner fan, and biographer of Daniel Defoe. I asked Fyodor whether the coronavirus had led him to ask his father, who now lives near him in Berkeley, about Defoe's 1722 book, *A Journal of the Plague Year*. "Yes," he said, "I'm going to get him to give me and our daughter who lives in Paris a Zoom lecture on the book."[2]

Like Doudna, Urnov read Watson's *The Double Helix* when he was about thirteen and decided to become a biologist. "Jennifer and I joke about the fact that we both read *The Double Helix* at about the same age," he says. "For all of Watson's shortcomings as a human being, which are substantial, he produced a ripping good yarn that makes the hunt for the mechanisms of life seem very exciting."

At eighteen, Urnov, a bit of a rebel, was drafted into the Soviet military and his head shaved. "I survived unscathed," he says, after which he left for the United States. "In August of 1990, I found myself landing in Boston's Logan Airport, having been accepted to Brown, and a year later my mom got a Fulbright to be a visiting scholar at the University of Virginia." Soon he was happily pursuing his doctorate at Brown, buried in test tubes. "I realized that I was not going back to Russia."

Urnov is among those researchers comfortable with having one foot in academia and the other in industry. For sixteen years, while teaching at Berkeley, he was a team leader at Sangamo Therapeutics, which translates scientific discoveries into medical treatments. His Russian roots and literary parentage instilled in him a dramatic flair, which he earnestly combines with a passion for America's can-do spirit. When he got the assignment from Doudna to lead the lab, he sent around a quote from Tolkien's *Lord of the Rings*:

> "I wish it need not have happened in my time," said Frodo.
>
> "So do I," said Gandalf, "and so do all who live to see such times. But that is not for them to decide. All we have to decide is what to do with the time that is given us."

One of his two scientific field marshals was Jennifer Hamilton, the Doudna protégée who a year earlier had spent a day teaching me to edit a human gene using CRISPR. She grew up in Seattle, studied biochemistry and genetics at the University of Washington, and then worked as a lab technician while listening to the podcast *This Week in Virology*. She did her doctorate at Mount Sinai Medical Center in New York, where she turned viruses and virus-like particles into mechanisms for delivering medical treatments, and then joined Doudna's lab as a postdoc. At the 2019 Cold Spring Harbor conference, Doudna watched proudly when Hamilton presented her research on using virus-like particles to deliver CRISPR-Cas9 gene-editing tools into humans.

When the coronavirus crisis hit in early March, Hamilton told Doudna that she wanted to get involved like people at her University of Washington alma mater were. So Doudna tapped her to lead the technical development of the lab. "It felt like a call to arms," Hamilton says. "I simply had to say yes." She never dreamed that her dexterity at optimizing RNA extraction would turn out to be an urgent skill in a global crisis. The real-world deployment also gave her and her fellow academics a taste of the type of project-oriented teamwork that is common in the business world. "It's the first time that I've been a part of a scientific team where so many people with different talents have coalesced around a common goal."[3]

Working with Hamilton to get the testing lab running was Enrique Lin Shiao, born and raised in Costa Rica, the son of Taiwanese immigrants who left everything behind to start over in a very new place. The cloning of Dolly the sheep in 1996 sparked his interest in genetics. After high school, he got a scholarship to the Technical University of Munich, where he researched how to fold DNA into different shapes to build nanotech biology tools. From there he went to Cambridge University to study how DNA folding is important for cell function. For his doctorate, he went to the University of Pennsylvania, where he figured out how non-coding regions of our genome, previously described as "junk DNA," could play a role in disease progression. In other words, like Feng Zhang, Enrique Lin Shiao was a typical American success story from when the nation was a magnet for diverse global talent.

As a postdoc researcher in Doudna's lab, Lin Shiao worked on ways to make new gene-editing tools that could cut and paste long DNA sequences. While sheltering at home in March 2020, he was scrolling through his Twitter feed and saw the tweet from his IGI colleagues seeking volunteers for the planned testing lab. "They were asking for experience in RNA extraction and PCR, which are techniques I routinely perform in the lab," he says. "The next day I got an email from Jennifer asking if I would be interested in co-leading the technical efforts, and I immediately agreed."[4]

The lab

The IGI was fortunate that there was a 2,500-square-foot space on the building's ground floor that was being converted into a gene-editing lab. Doudna's team began moving in new machines and boxes filled with chemicals to turn the space into a coronavirus testing facility. A lab-building project that normally would take months was done in days.[5]

They begged and borrowed and commandeered supplies from labs across campus. One day, when they were ready to start an experiment, they realized that they did not have the right plates to run in one of the PCR machines. Lin Shiao and others went through all the labs in the IGI building and then in two nearby buildings until they found some. "Since campus was largely closed, it felt like a giant scavenger hunt," he says. "Every day felt a bit like a roller coaster, where we discovered a new problem early in the morning, got worried, and then figured it out by the end of the day."

The lab spent about $550,000 on equipment and supplies.[6] One key machine was a contraption to automate the task of extracting the RNA in patient samples. The Hamilton STARlet uses robotic pipettes to suck small amounts from each patient sample and put them onto plates the size of an iPhone with ninety-six little wells. The trays are moved into the chamber of the machine, where each of the samples is doused with reagents to extract the RNA. Using a barcode, the machines keep track of the patient information from each sample, making sure to follow privacy guidelines. It was a new experience for academic researchers. "Usually for bench scientists like ourselves we feel our impact is a bit indirect and it comes in the long term," Lin Shiao says. "This feels so direct and immediate."[7]

Hamilton's grandfather had been an engineer on the NASA Apollo rocket launches, and one day her team paused to watch a clip someone had posted on their Slack channel from the movie *Apollo 13* where the engineers have to figure out how to make a "square peg fit in a round hole" in order to save the astronauts. "Every day we've been facing challenges, but we're solving these problems as they come up because we know that time is short," Hamilton says. "This experience has made me wonder if this is what it was like for my grandfather working at NASA in the 1960s." It was a fitting analogy. COVID and CRISPR were helping to make human cells the next frontier.

Doudna had to figure out what legal liability the university might incur by testing outsiders. That was a process that would normally have taken the lawyers weeks of hand-wringing, so Doudna called the president of the University of California system, Janet Napolitano, a former Homeland Security secretary. In twelve hours, Napolitano had given her approval and brought the system's legal bureaucracy in line. Urnov notes that it was useful to roll out Doudna as a big gun on such occasions. "I jokingly call her the USS *Jennifer Doudna*," he says.

With federal testing still in disarray and commercial labs taking more than a week to return results, there was huge demand for Berkeley's testing. The town's health officer, Lisa Hernandez, asked Urnov for five thousand tests, some of which would be done on the area's poor and homeless. The fire chief, David Brannigan, told Urnov that thirty of his firefighters were quarantined because they couldn't get test results. Doudna and Urnov promised to accommodate them all.

"Thank you, IGI"

The first major challenge for the new lab was making sure that their COVID tests were accurate. Doudna brought a special eye to this task, since she had been an expert at deciphering readouts involving RNA ever since she was a graduate student. As the results came in, researchers would share them on a Zoom screen and then watch online as Doudna leaned forward and looked intensely at the images of inverted blue triangles, green triangles, and squares indicating data points. Sometimes she would just sit and stare, not moving, as others held their breath. "Yes, that looks good," she said during one session as she pointed a cursor to a part of an RNA detection test. Then her expression changed for all on Zoom to see as she pointed to another place and muttered, "Nope, nope, nope."

Finally, early in April, she looked at the latest data that Lin Shiao had gathered and pronounced it "awesome." The tests were ready to go live.

On Monday, April 6, at 8 a.m., a fire department van pulled up to the door of the IGI and an officer named Dori Tieu delivered a box filled with samples. Urnov, wearing white gloves and a blue mask, accepted the Styrofoam cooler as his colleague Dirk Hockemeyer watched. They promised that they would have results the next morning.

As they were making the final preparations to get the lab into operation, Urnov went to get a takeout meal for his parents, who live nearby. When he arrived back at the IGI building, he saw a sheet of paper taped to the big glass door. On it was written, "Thank you, IGI! Sincerely, the people of Berkeley and the World."

Fyodor Urnov's reflection as he photographs the note

Janice Chen and Lucas Harrington

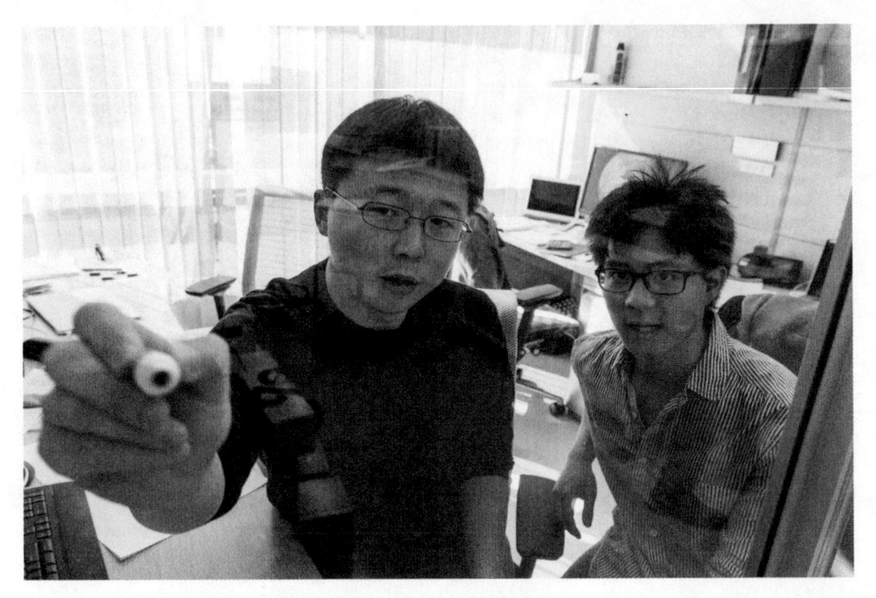

Feng Zhang with Patrick Hsu

Chapter 51

Mammoth and Sherlock

CRISPR as a detection tool

At the March 13 meeting that Doudna convened to address the coronavirus, she decided that a top priority was to create a high-speed conventional PCR testing lab. But during the discussion, Fyodor Urnov suggested that they also consider a more innovative idea: using CRISPR to detect the RNA of the coronavirus, similar to how bacteria use CRISPR to detect attacking viruses.

"There's a paper that just came out on that," a participant interjected.

Urnov showed a slight flash of impatience and interrupted, for he knew the paper well. "Yes, from Janice Chen, formerly of the Doudna Lab."

There were actually two similar papers that had just come out. One was from former members of the Doudna Lab who had formed a company to use CRISPR as a detection tool. The other, not surprisingly, sprang from Feng Zhang of the Broad Institute. Once again, the two realms were competing. This time, however, it was not a race to patent methods for editing human genes. In this new race, the goal was to help save humanity from the novel coronavirus, and their discoveries were being shared for free.

Cas12 and Mammoth

Back in 2017, Janice Chen and Lucas Harrington were doctoral students working in Doudna's lab exploring newly discovered CRISPR-associated enzymes. Specifically, they were analyzing one that became known as Cas12a, which had a special property. It could be targeted, like Cas9, to find and cut a specified sequence of DNA. But it didn't stop there. Once it cleaved the double-stranded DNA target, it went into an indiscriminate cutting frenzy, chopping up any single-stranded DNA that was nearby. "We started to see this very weird behavior," Harrington says.[1]

Over breakfast one day, Doudna's husband, Jamie Cate, suggested that this property could be harnessed to create a diagnostic tool. Chen and Harrington had the same idea. They combined a CRISPR-Cas12 system with a "reporter" molecule, which was a fluorescent signal connected to a bit of DNA. When the CRISPR-Cas12 system found a targeted sequence of DNA, it would also chop up the reporter molecules and cause a glowing signal. The result was a diagnostic tool that could detect whether the patient had a particular virus or bacteria or cancer. Chen and Harrington dubbed it the "DNA endonuclease targeted CRISPR trans reporter," a very clunky phrase that was crafted in order to create the CRISPR-like acronym DETECTR.

When Chen, Harrington, and Doudna submitted their findings in an article to *Science* in November 2017, the editors requested that they write more about how to turn the discovery into a diagnostic test. Even the traditional scientific journals were now showing greater interest in connecting basic science to potential applications. "If a journal tells you to do something like that," Harrington says, "you start working on it very hard." So over Christmas break of 2017, he and Chen collaborated with a researcher at UC San Francisco to show how their CRISPR-Cas12 tool could detect human papillomavirus (HPV), a sexually transmitted infection. "We were going back and forth with a giant piece of lab equipment in an Uber, testing different patient samples," he says.

Doudna prodded *Science* to expedite publication as part of its fast-track program. They resubmitted their article in January 2018 with the data the editors had requested showing that DETECTR detected HPV infections; it was accepted, and a version went online in February.

Ever since Watson and Crick ended their famous DNA paper by saying, "It has not escaped our notice that the specific pairing we have postulated immediately suggests a possible copying mechanism for the genetic material," it has become standard to end journal papers with an understated but important forward-looking sentence. Chen, Harrington, and Doudna ended their paper by saying that the CRISPR-Cas12 system "offers a new strategy to improve the speed, sensitivity and specificity of nucleic acid detection for point-of-care diagnostic applications." In other words, it might be used to create a simple test to detect virus infections quickly, at home or in a hospital.[2]

Even though Harrington and Chen had not yet gotten their doctorates, Doudna encouraged them to form a company. She was now a strong believer that basic research should be combined with translational research, moving discoveries from bench to bedside. "A lot of other technologies that we had discovered were bought as a defensive strategy by big companies that then didn't develop them," Harrington says. "So that motivated us to start our own company." Mammoth Biosciences launched officially in April 2018 with Doudna as chair of its scientific advisory board.

Cas13 and SHERLOCK

As was often the case, Doudna and her team were in a competition with her cross-country rival, the Broad Institute's Feng Zhang. Working with the CRISPR pioneer Eugene Koonin of the NIH, Zhang had used computational biology to sort through the genomes of thousands of microbes, and in October 2015 they reported on their discovery of many new CRISPR-associated enzymes. In addition to the previously known Cas9 and Cas12 enzymes that target DNA, Zhang and Koonin found a class of enzymes that target RNA.[3] They became known as Cas13.

Cas13 had the same odd trait as Cas12: when it found its target, it went into a cutting frenzy. The Cas13 not only cut its targeted RNA, it then proceeded to cut up any other nearby RNA.

At first Zhang assumed this was a mistake. "We thought that Cas13 would cleave the RNA just the way that Cas9 cleaved DNA," he says. "But whenever we did a reaction with Cas13, the RNA got shredded in many different places." He asked his lab team whether they were sure they had been purifying the enzyme correctly; maybe it was contaminated. They painstakingly eliminated all possible sources of contamination, but the indiscriminate cleavage kept happening. Zhang speculated that it was an evolutionary method to have the cell commit suicide if it got too infected by an invading virus, thus preventing the virus from spreading as fast.[4]

Doudna's lab then contributed to the study of precisely how Cas13 works. In a paper in October 2016, Doudna and her coauthors—including her husband, Jamie Cate, and Alexandra East-Seletsky, the graduate student who had done some of the key 2012 experiments on CRISPR in human cells—explained the different functions that Cas13 performs, including being able to indiscriminately chop up thousands of other nearby RNAs once it reaches its target. This promiscuous chopping makes it possible to use Cas13 with fluorescent reporters (as was done with Cas12) to be a detection tool for a specified RNA sequence, such as that of a coronavirus.[5]

Zhang and his colleagues at the Broad were able to create such a detection tool in April 2017, which they named "specific high sensitivity enzymatic reporter unlocking," which was reverse-engineered (though not very well) to produce the acronym SHERLOCK. The game was afoot! They showed that SHERLOCK could detect specific strains of Zika and Dengue viruses.[6] Over the next year, they made a version that combined Cas13 and Cas12 to detect multiple targets in one reaction. Then they were able to simplify the system and make it possible for the detection to be reported on paper lateral flow strips, similar to pregnancy tests.[7]

Zhang decided to start a diagnostics company to commercialize SHERLOCK, just like Chen and Harrington had launched Mammoth. Zhang's cofounders included the two graduate students who were the lead authors on many of the papers from his lab describing CRISPR-Cas13: Omar Abudayyeh and Jonathan Gootenberg. Gootenberg recalls that they almost decided not to publish a paper when they first discovered the tendency of Cas13 to go into a frenzy of indiscriminate RNA cutting. It seemed like a useless quirk of nature. But once Zhang figured out how to harness that quirk to create a virus-detection technology, Gootenberg realized how discoveries in basic science can turn out to have unexpected real-world applications. "You know, nature's got a ton of amazing secrets in it," he says.[8]

It took a while to get Sherlock Biosciences funded and launched because Zhang and his two graduate students did not want profit to be the main goal of the company. They wanted the technologies to be affordable in the developing world. So the company was structured in a way that allowed it to profit on its innovations while still taking a nonprofit approach in places where there was great need.

Unlike the Doudna-Zhang competition for the patents, the one involving diagnostic companies was not very contentious. Both sides knew that the technologies had enormous potential to do good. Whenever there was a new epidemic, Mammoth and Sherlock could quickly reprogram their diagnostic tools to target the novel virus and produce testing kits. The Broad team, for example, sent a team with SHERLOCK to Nigeria in 2019 to help detect victims of an outbreak of Lassa fever, a virus in the same family as Ebola.[9]

At the time, using CRISPR as a diagnostic tool seemed to be a worthy endeavor, though not a particularly exciting one. It did not get as much buzz as using CRISPR to treat diseases or edit human genes. But then, at the beginning of 2020, the world suddenly changed. The ability to quickly detect an attacking virus became critical. And the best way to do it faster and cheaper than the conventional PCR tests, which required a lot of mixing steps and temperature cycles, was to deploy RNA-guided enzymes that had been programmed to detect the genetic material of the virus—in other words, adapt the CRISPR system that bacteria had been deploying for millions of years.

Feng Zhang (*top left*) with Omar Abudayyeh (*top right*) and Jonathan Gootenberg (*middle right*) at a Zoom meeting on COVID detection

CHAPTER 52

Coronavirus Tests

Feng Zhang

In early January 2020, Feng Zhang started getting emails about coronavirus written in Chinese. Some were from Chinese academics he had met, but he also got an unexpected one from the science officer at China's consulate in New York City. "Even though you are American and not living in China," it said, "this is really a problem that's important for humanity." It quoted an old Chinese saying: *When one place is in trouble, assistance comes from all quarters*. "So we hope that you can think about it and see what you can do," the email urged.[1]

Zhang knew little about the novel coronavirus other than what he had read in a *New York Times* article describing the situation in Wuhan, but the emails "gave me a sense of urgency about the situation," he says. This was especially true of the exchange he had with the Chinese consulate. "I usually don't have any interactions from them," says Zhang, who had immigrated to Iowa with his parents when he was eleven.

I asked him whether Chinese authorities think of him as a Chinese scientist. "Yeah, probably," he says after a pause. "I think they probably think of all Chinese people as Chinese. But that's irrelevant because the world is so connected now, especially in a pandemic."

Zhang decided to reconfigure the SHERLOCK detection tool so that it could test for the new coronavirus. Unfortunately, he didn't have anyone in his lab to handle the necessary experiments. So he resolved to go to his bench and do the experiments himself. He also enlisted his two former graduate students, Omar Abudayyeh and Jonathan Gootenberg. They had moved on to open their own lab at MIT's McGovern Institute, a block from the Broad, and they agreed to collaborate with him again.

Zhang did not initially have access to samples of the coronavirus from human patients, so he made a synthetic version of it. Using the SHERLOCK process, he and his team devised a detection test that took only three steps and could be done in an hour without fancy equipment. All it required was a small device to keep the temperature constant while the genetic material from the samples was amplified through a chemical process that was simpler than PCR. The results could be read using a paper dipstick.

On February 14, well before most of the U.S. had focused on the novel coronavirus, Zhang's lab posted a white paper describing the test and inviting any lab to use or adapt the process freely. "Today we are sharing a research protocol for SHERLOCK-based COVID-19 #coronavirus detection, and hope it will help others who are working to combat the outbreak," Zhang tweeted. "We will continue to update this as we make further progress."[2]

The company he had founded, Sherlock Biosciences, quickly began work on turning the process into a commercial testing device that could be used in hospitals and doctors' offices. When the CEO, Rahul Dhanda, told his team that he wanted the company to focus on COVID, the researchers literally swung their chairs back to their workbenches to take on the mission. "When we say a pivot, there was a literal pivot of chairs at the same time there was a pivot of the company towards a new goal," he says. By the end of 2020, the company was working with manufacturing partners to turn out small machines that could be used to get results in less than an hour.[3]

Chen and Harrington

Around the time that Zhang began working on his coronavirus test, Janice Chen got a call from a researcher on the scientific advisory board of the company she had founded with Doudna and Lucas Harrington, Mammoth Biosciences. "What do you think about developing a CRISPR-based diagnostic to detect the SARS-CoV-2 virus?" he asked. She agreed that they should try. As a result, she and Harrington became part of yet another cross-country competition between Doudna's circle and Zhang's.[4]

Within two weeks, the Mammoth team was able to reconfigure its CRISPR-based DETECTR tool so that it would detect SARS-CoV-2. One benefit of collaborating with UC San Francisco, which has its own hospital, was that they could test on real human samples, drawn from thirty-six COVID patients, unlike the Broad, which initially had to use synthetic viruses.

The Mammoth test relied on the CRISPR-associated enzyme that Chen and Harrington had studied in Doudna's lab, Cas12, which targets DNA. That would seem to make it less suited than SHERLOCK's Cas13, which targets RNA, the genetic material of the coronavirus. However, both detection techniques need to convert the RNA of the coronavirus into DNA in order for it to be amplified. In the SHERLOCK test, it has to be transcribed back into RNA to be detected, thus adding a small step to the process.

Chen and Harrington rushed to get a white paper online with the details of their Mammoth test. In many ways it was similar to the SHERLOCK process. All that was necessary was a heating block, the reagents, and paper flow strips to give a readout of the results. Like Zhang, the Mammoth team decided to put what they had devised into the public domain, to be shared freely.

On February 14, while they were preparing to put their white paper online, Chen and Harrington saw a message pop up on the Slack channel they were using. Someone posted the tweet that Zhang had just sent out announcing that he had just published his white paper on how to use the SHERLOCK protocol for detecting the coronavirus.

"We were like, 'Oh, shoot'" Chen recalls of that Friday afternoon. But after a few minutes, they realized that having both papers appear was a good thing. They appended a postscript to the paper they were just about to post. "While we were preparing this whitepaper, another protocol for SARS-CoV-2 detection using CRISPR diagnostics (SHERLOCK, v.20200214) was published," it said. They then included a useful chart comparing the workflows of the two techniques.[5]

Zhang was gracious, though it was easy for him to be since he had beaten the Mammoth team by a day. "Check out the resource provided by Mammoth," he tweeted, including a link to its white paper. "Glad that scientists are working together and sharing openly. #coronavirus."

That tweet reflected a welcome new trend in the CRISPR world. The passionate competition for patents and prizes had led to secrecy about research and the formation of competing CRISPR companies. But the urgency that Doudna and Zhang and their colleagues felt about defeating the coronavirus pushed them to be more open and willing to share their work. Competition was still an important, and useful, part of the equation. There continued to be a race between Doudna's world and Zhang's to publish papers and make advances on the new COVID tests. "I'm not going to sugarcoat it," Doudna says. "There's definitely competition going on. It makes people feel an urgency to move ahead or, if they don't, other people are going to get to something first." But coronavirus made the rivalry less cutthroat, because patents were not a paramount concern. "The awesomely good thing about this terrible situation is that all the intellectual property questions have been put aside, and everyone's really intent on just finding solutions," says Chen. "People are focused on getting something out there that works, rather than on the business aspect of it."

At-home tests

The CRISPR-based tests developed by Mammoth and Sherlock are cheaper and faster than conventional PCR tests. They also have an advantage over antigen tests, such as the one developed by Abbott Labs that was approved in August of the plague year. The CRISPR-based tests can detect the presence of the RNA of a virus as soon as a person has been infected. But the antigen tests, which detect the presence of proteins that exist on the surface of the virus, are most accurate only after a patient has become highly infectious to others.

The ultimate goal for all of these methods was to create a CRISPR-based coronavirus test that would be like a home pregnancy test: cheap, disposable, fast, and simple, which you could buy at the corner drugstore and use in the privacy of your bathroom.

Harrington and Chen of the Mammoth team unveiled their concept for such a device in May 2020 and announced a partnership with the London-based multinational pharmaceutical company GlaxoSmithKline (maker of Excedrin and Tums) to manufacture it. It would provide accurate results in twenty minutes and require no special equipment.

Likewise, Zhang's lab that same month developed a way to simplify the SHERLOCK detection system, which originally required two steps, into a process that required just a single-step reaction. The only equipment necessary was a pot to keep the system heated at a steady 140 degrees Fahrenheit. Zhang named it STOP, for SHERLOCK Testing in One Pot.[6] "Let me show you what it will look like," Zhang says to me with his boyish enthusiasm as he shares slides and renderings on a Zoom call. "You just put a nasal or saliva sample into this cartridge, slide it into the device, break one blister to release a solution that will extract the virus RNA, and then break another blister that will release some freeze-dried CRISPR for a reaction in the amplification chamber."

Zhang named the device STOP-COVID. But the platform can be easily adapted to detect any virus. "That's why we chose the STOP name, which can be paired with any target," he says. "We could create a STOP-flu or a STOP-HIV or have many detection targets on the same platform. The device is agnostic about what virus it's looking for."[7]

Mammoth has the same vision of making it easy to reprogram its own tool to detect any new virus that comes along. "The beauty of CRISPR is that once you have the platform, then it's just a matter of reconfiguring your chemistry to detect a different virus," Chen explains. "It can be used for the next pandemic or any virus. It can also be used against any bacteria or anything that has a genetic sequence, even cancer."[8]

Biology hits home

The development of home testing kits has a potential impact beyond the fight against COVID: bringing biology into the home, the way that personal computers in the 1970s brought digital products and services—and an awareness of microchips and software code—into people's daily lives and consciousness.

Personal computers and then smartphones became platforms on which waves of innovators could build neat products. In addition, they helped make the digital revolution into something *personal*, which caused people to develop some understanding of the technology.

When Zhang was growing up, his parents emphasized that he should use his computer as a tool to build things on. After his attention turned from microchips to microbes, he wondered why biology did not have the same involvement in people's daily lives as computers did. There were no simple biology devices or platforms that innovators could build things on or that people could use in their homes. "As I was doing molecular biology experiments, I thought, 'This is so cool and it's so robust, but why hasn't it impacted people's lives in ways that a software app does?' "

He was still asking that question when he got to graduate school. "Can you think of how we can bring molecular biology into the kitchen or into people's homes?" he would ask his classmates. As he was working on developing his at-home CRISPR tests for viruses, he realized that they could be the way to do that. Home testing kits could become the platform, operating system, and form factor that will allow us to weave the wonders of molecular biology more into our daily lives.

Developers and entrepreneurs may someday be able to use CRISPR-based home testing kits as platforms on which to build a variety of biomedical apps: virus detection, disease diagnosis, cancer screening, nutritional analyses, microbiome assessments, and genetic tests. "We can get people in their homes to check if they have the flu or just a cold," says Zhang. "If their kids have a sore throat, they can determine if it's strep throat." In the process, it might give us all a deeper appreciation for how molecular biology works. The inner workings of molecules may remain, for most people, as mysterious as those of microchips, but at least all of us will be a bit more aware of the beauty and power of both.

Dariia Dantseva, Josiah Zayner, and David Ishee injecting their own vaccine

CHAPTER 53

Vaccines

My shot

"Look me in the eyes," the doctor ordered, staring at me from behind her plastic face guard. Her eyes were vividly blue, almost as blue as her hospital mask. Yet after a moment, I started to turn to the doctor on my left, who was jabbing a long needle deep into the muscle of my upper arm. "No!" the first doctor snapped. "Look at me!"

Then she explained. Because I was part of a double-blind clinical trial of an experimental COVID vaccine,[1] they had to make sure that I didn't get any clues about whether I was being injected with a real dose or merely a placebo made of saline solution. Would I really be able to tell just by looking at the syringe? "Probably not," she answered, "but we want to be careful."

It was early August of the plague year, and I had enlisted as a participant in the clinical trial for the COVID vaccine that was being developed by Pfizer with the German company BioNTech. It was a new type of vaccine that had never before been deployed. Instead of delivering deactivated components of the targeted virus, like traditional vaccines do, it injects into humans a snippet of RNA.

As you know by now, RNA is the strand that runs throughout Doudna's career and this book. In the 1990s, while other scientists were focused on DNA, her Harvard professor Jack Szostak turned her on to its less-celebrated but harder-working sibling that oversaw the making of proteins, acted as a guide for enzymes, could replicate itself, and was probably the root of all life on earth. "I never, ever got over my fascination about how RNA can do so many things," she says when I tell her of my participation in the RNA vaccine trial. "It's the genetic material of the coronavirus and, in a very interesting way, could be the basis for vaccines and cures."[2]

Traditional vaccines

Vaccines work by stimulating a person's immune system. A substance that resembles a dangerous virus (or any other pathogen)* is delivered into a person's body. That substance could be a deactivated version of the virus or a safe fragment of the virus or genetic instructions to make that fragment. This is intended to kick the person's immune system into gear. When it works, the body produces antibodies that will, sometimes for many years, fend off any infection if the real virus ever attacks.

Vaccinations were pioneered in the 1790s by an English doctor named Edward Jenner who noticed that many milkmaids were immune to smallpox. They had all been infected by a form of pox that afflicts cows but is harmless to humans, and Jenner surmised that the cowpox had given the milkmaids immunity to smallpox. So he took some pus from a cowpox blister, rubbed it into scratches he made in the arm of his gardener's eight-year-old son, and then (this was in the days before bioethics panels) exposed the kid to smallpox. He didn't become ill.

Vaccines use a variety of methods to try to stimulate the human immune system. One traditional approach is to inject a weakened and safe (attenuated) version of the virus. These can be good teachers, because they look very much like the real thing. The body responds by

*A "pathogen," commonly referred to as a "germ," is any microorganism that causes disease or infection. The most common are viruses, bacteria, fungi, and protozoa.

making antibodies for fighting them, and the immunity can last a lifetime. Albert Sabin used this approach for the oral polio vaccine in the 1950s, and that's the way we now fend off measles, mumps, rubella, and chicken pox. It takes a long time to develop and cultivate these vaccines (the viruses have to be incubated in chicken eggs), but some companies in 2020 were using this method as a long-term option for attacking COVID.

When Sabin was trying to develop a weakened polio virus for a vaccination, Jonas Salk succeeded with an approach that seemed somewhat safer: using a killed virus. This type of vaccine can still teach a person's immune system how to fight off the live virus. The Beijing-based company Sinovac used this approach to devise an early COVID vaccine.

Another traditional approach is to inject a subunit of the virus, such as one of the proteins that are on the virus's coat. The immune system will then remember these, allowing the body to mount a quick and robust response when it encounters the actual virus. The vaccine against the hepatitis B virus, for example, works this way. Using only a fragment of the virus means that they are safer to inject into a patient and easier to produce, but they are usually not as good at producing long-term immunity. Many companies pursued this approach in the 2020 race for a COVID vaccine by developing ways to introduce into human cells the spike protein that is on the surface of the coronavirus.

Genetic vaccines

The plague year of 2020 is likely to be remembered as the time when these traditional vaccines began to be supplanted by genetic vaccines. Instead of injecting a weakened or partial version of the dangerous virus into humans, these new vaccines deliver a gene or piece of genetic coding that will guide human cells to produce, on their own, components of the virus. The goal is for these components to stimulate the patient's immune system.

One method for doing this is by taking a harmless virus and engineering into it a gene that will make the desired component. As we all now know, viruses are very good at worming their way into human cells. That is why safe viruses can be used as a delivery system, or vector, to transport material into the cells of patients.

This approach led to one of the earliest COVID vaccine candidates, which was developed at the aptly named Jenner Institute of Oxford University. Scientists there genetically reengineered a safe virus—an adenovirus that causes flu in chimpanzees—by editing into it the gene to make the spike protein of the coronavirus. Similar vaccines developed by other companies in 2020 used a human version of the adenovirus. The vaccine created by Johnson & Johnson, for example, used a human adenovirus as the delivery mechanism to carry a gene that codes for making part of the spike protein. But the Oxford team decided that using one from a chimpanzee was better, because patients who previously had cold infections might have an immunity to the human version.

The idea behind both the Oxford and the Johnson & Johnson vaccines was that the reengineered adenovirus would make its way into human cells, where it would cause the cells to make lots of these spike proteins. That in turn would stimulate the person's immune system to make antibodies. As a result, the person's immune system would be primed to respond rapidly if the real coronavirus struck.

The lead researcher at Oxford was Sarah Gilbert.[3] In 1998, when she had triplets who were born prematurely, her husband took time off from his job so that she could return to her lab. In 2014, she worked on developing a vaccine for Middle East respiratory syndrome (MERS), using a chimp adenovirus edited to contain the gene for a spike protein. That epidemic died away before her vaccine could be deployed, but it gave her a head start when COVID struck. She already knew that the chimp adenovirus had successfully delivered into humans the gene for the spike protein of MERS. As soon as the Chinese published the genetic sequence of the new coronavirus in January 2020, she began engineering its spike protein gene into the chimp virus, waking each day at 4 a.m.

By then her triplets were twenty-one, and all were studying biochemistry. They volunteered to be early testers, getting the vaccine and seeing if they developed antibodies. (They did.) Trials in monkeys conducted at a Montana primate center in March also produced promising results.

The Bill and Melinda Gates Foundation provided early funding. Bill Gates also pushed Oxford to team up with a major company that could manufacture and distribute the vaccine if it worked. So Oxford forged a partnership with AstraZeneca, the British-Swedish pharmaceutical company.

DNA vaccines

There is another way to get genetic material into a human cell and cause it to produce the components of a virus that can stimulate the immune system. Instead of engineering the gene for the component into a virus, you can just deliver the genetic code for the component—as DNA or RNA—into human cells. The cells thus become a vaccine-manufacturing facility.

Let's start with DNA vaccines. Although no DNA vaccine had ever been approved before the COVID plague, the concept seemed promising. Researchers at Inovio Pharmaceuticals and a handful of other companies in 2020 created a little circle of DNA that coded for parts of the coronavirus spike protein. The idea was that if it could get inside the nucleus of a cell, the DNA could very efficiently churn out many strands of messenger RNA to go forth and oversee the production of the spike protein parts, which serve to stimulate the immune system. DNA is cheap to produce and do not require dealing with live viruses and incubating them in chicken eggs.

The big challenge facing a DNA vaccine is delivery. How can you get the little ring of engineered DNA not only into a human cell but into the nucleus of the cell? Injecting a lot of the DNA vaccine into a patient's arm will cause some of the DNA to get into cells, but it's not very efficient.

Some of the developers of DNA vaccines, including Inovio, tried to facilitate the delivery into human cells through a method called electroporation, which delivers electrical shock pulses to the patient at the site of the injection. That opens pores in the cell membranes and allows the DNA to get in. The electric pulse guns have lots of tiny needles and are unnerving to behold. It's not hard to see why this technique is unpopular, especially with those on the receiving end.

One of the teams that Doudna organized at the beginning of the coronavirus crisis in March 2020 focused on these delivery challenges facing DNA vaccines. It was led by her former student Ross Wilson, who now runs his own lab down the hall from her at Berkeley, and Alex Marson of the University of California, San Francisco. At one of Doudna's regular Zoom meetings, Wilson showed a slide of the Inovio electric zapper. "They actually shoot the patient in the muscle with one of these guns," he said. "About the only visible advance they've made in ten years is now they have a little plastic thing to hide the tiny needles so they don't frighten the patient as much."

Marson and Wilson devised a way to address the DNA vaccine delivery problem using CRISPR-Cas9. They put together a Cas9 protein, a guide RNA, and a nuclear localization signal that helps the complex get into the nucleus. The result was a "shuttle" that could get the DNA vaccine into cells. The DNA then directs the cells to make coronavirus spike proteins and thus stimulate the immune system to fend off the real coronavirus.[4] It's a brilliant idea that could have uses for many treatments in the future, but it has been difficult to make work. By the beginning of 2021, Wilson and Marson were still trying to prove it could be effective.

RNA vaccines

That leads us back to our favorite molecule, the biochemical star of this book: RNA.

The vaccine that was tested in my clinical trial makes use of the most basic function that RNA performs in the central dogma of biology: serving as a messenger RNA (mRNA) that carries genetic instructions from DNA, which is bunkered inside a cell's nucleus, to the manufacturing region of the cell, where it directs what protein to make. In the case of the COVID vaccine, the mRNA instructs cells to make part of the spike protein that is on the surface of a coronavirus.[5]

RNA vaccines deliver their payloads inside tiny oily capsules, known as lipid nanoparticles, that are injected by a long syringe into the muscles of the upper arm. My muscle hurt for days.

An RNA vaccine has certain advantages over a DNA vaccine. Most notably, the RNA does not need to get into the nucleus of the cell, where DNA is headquartered. The RNA does its work in the outer region of cells, the cytoplasm, which is where proteins are constructed. So an RNA vaccine simply needs to deliver its payload into this outer region.

In 2020, two innovative young pharmaceutical companies produced RNA vaccines for COVID: Moderna, based in Cambridge, Massachusetts, and the German company BioNTech, which formed a partnership with the American company Pfizer. My clinical trial was for BioNTech/Pfizer.

BioNTech was founded in 2008 by the husband-and-wife research team of Uğur Şahin and Özlem Türeci with the goal of creating cancer immunotherapies, which stimulate the immune system to fight cancerous cells. It soon also became a leader in devising medicines that use mRNA as vaccines against viruses. In January 2020, when Şahin read a medical journal article on the new coronavirus in China, he sent an email to the BioNTech board saying that it was wrong to believe that this virus would come and go as easily as MERS and SARS. "This time it is different," he told them.[6]

BioNTech launched what they dubbed Project Lightspeed to devise a vaccine based on RNA sequences that would cause human cells to make versions of the coronavirus's spike protein. Once it looked promising, Şahin called Kathrin Jansen, the head of vaccine research and development at Pfizer. The two companies had been working together since 2018 to develop flu vaccines using mRNA technology, and he asked her whether Pfizer would want to enter a similar partnership for a COVID vaccine. Jansen said she had been about to call and propose the same thing. The deal was signed in March.[7]

By then, a similar RNA vaccine was being developed by Moderna, a much-smaller company with only eight hundred employees. Its chair and cofounder, Noubar Afeyan, a Beirut-born Armenian who immigrated to the United States, became fascinated in 2005 by the prospect that mRNA could be inserted into human cells to direct the production of a desired protein. So he hired some young graduates from the Harvard lab of Jack Szostak, who had been Jennifer Doudna's PhD adviser and turned her on to the wonders of RNA. The company mainly focused on using mRNA to try to develop personalized cancer treatments, but it also had begun experimenting with using the technique to make vaccines against viruses.

In January 2020, Afeyan was celebrating the birthday of one of his daughters at a Cambridge restaurant when he got an urgent text message from the CEO of his company, Stéphane Bancel, in Switzerland. So he stepped outside in the freezing temperature to call him back. Bancel said that he wanted to launch a project to use mRNA to attempt a vaccine against the new coronavirus. At that point, Moderna had twenty drugs in development but none had been approved or even reached the final stage of clinical trials. Afeyan instantly authorized him to start work without waiting for full board approval. Lacking Pfizer's resources, Moderna had to depend on funding from the U.S. government. Anthony Fauci, the government's infectious disease expert, was supportive. "Go for it," he declared. "Whatever it costs, don't worry about it." It took Moderna only two days to create the desired RNA sequences that would produce the spike protein, and thirty-eight days later it shipped the first box of vials to the NIH to begin early-stage trials. Afeyan keeps a picture of that box on his cell phone.

As with CRISPR therapies, a difficult part of the vaccine development was creating the delivery mechanism into the cell. Moderna had been working for ten years to perfect lipid nanoparticles, the tiny synthetic capsules that can carry molecules into a human cell. This gave it one advantage over BioNTech/Pfizer: its particles were more stable and did not have to be stored at extremely low temperatures. Moderna is also using this technology to deliver CRISPR into human cells.[8]

Our biohacker steps in

At this point Josiah Zayner, the garage scientist who injected himself with CRISPR, came back onstage to play Puck again. As others were eagerly awaiting results for the genetic vaccines that went into clinical trials in the summer of 2020, Zayner brought his wise-fool spirit to the battle, enlisting a couple of like-minded biohackers in the cause. His plan was to produce and then inject himself with one of the many potential coronavirus vaccines that were being developed. Then he would see whether (a) he survived and (b) he developed antibodies to protect against COVID. "You can call it a stunt if you want, but it's really about people taking control of science and moving it fucking faster," he told me.[9]

Specifically, he decided to make and test a potential vaccine that had been described that May in a *Science* paper by researchers at Harvard. The vaccine was just beginning human trials.[10] It was a DNA vaccine that included the genetic code for the spike of the coronavirus. The paper described precisely how to make it. With the recipe in hand, Zayner ordered the ingredients and went to work.

From his garage lab in Oakland, just seven miles south of Doudna's at Berkeley, Zayner launched a YouTube streaming course—named Project McAfee, after the anti-virus software—so that others could follow along and perform the experiments on themselves. "Biohackers can be like the test pilots of the modern world by doing the slightly crazy shit that needs to be done," he declared.

He had two copilots. David Ishee is a ponytailed rural Mississippi dog breeder who uses CRISPR to edit the genes of Dalmatians and mastiffs to try to make them healthier, stronger, and in one offbeat experiment glow in the dark. He joined by Skype from a wooden shed in his backyard crammed with lab equipment. When Zayner said that they would be streaming their experiments for the next two months, Ishee took a sip of a Monster energy drink and interjected in his languid honeysuckle-scented drawl, "Or at least until the authorities come for us." Also Skyping in was Dariia Dantseva, a student in Dnipro, Ukraine, who created her country's first biohacking lab. "Ukraine is pretty easy about regulating biohacking, because the state literally does not exist," she says. "I believe that knowledge is not just for the elites, it's for all of us. That's why we do this."

The experiments that Zayner performed through the summer of 2020 were not just a showy stunt, like when he injected CRISPR into his arm at the San Francisco conference. "We could just inject this shit," he said of the DNA vaccine described by the Harvard researchers. "But I don't think anyone would get anything out of that. We want to add a lot more value." Instead, he and his copilots carefully, week after week, did a livestream demonstration to teach people how to make the code for the spike proteins of the coronavirus. That way they could get dozens, perhaps hundreds, of people to test it, thus gathering useful data about its effectiveness. "If a bunch of scrubs like us can do this, hundreds of people could be doing it and moving science forward more quickly," he says. "We want everyone to have the opportunity to create this DNA vaccine and test if it creates antibodies in human cells."

I asked him why he thought a DNA vaccine would work with just a simple injection rather than the electroporation shocks and other techniques that some researchers said were needed to assure that the DNA got into the nucleus of human cells. "We wanted to follow the Harvard paper as closely as possible, and they did not use any special techniques like electroporation," he replied. "DNA is easy to produce, so if some delivery method doubles the efficiency you can get the same results just by doubling or so the amount of DNA you inject."

On Sunday, August 9, the three biohackers appeared together—from California, Mississippi, and Ukraine—in a live video-stream to inject into their arms the vaccines they had been concocting over the past two months. "We three tried to push science forward by showing what people are capable of doing in a do-it-yourself environment," Zayner explained as the video began. "So anyway, here we go! We're doing it!" Then Zayner, wearing a Michael Jordan red tank-top jersey, plunged a long needle into his arm as Dantseva and Ishee followed suit. He offered a bit of reassurance to his audience: "For all of you who signed in to see us die, it's not going to happen."

He was right. They didn't die. They simply winced a lot. And in the end, there was evidence that the vaccine may have worked. Because his experiment did not include any special method for getting the DNA into the nucleus of human cells, the results were not totally clear or convincing. But when he tested his blood in September, streaming it live on the internet for everyone to watch, Zayner found evidence that he had developed neutralizing antibodies to fight the coronavirus. He called it a "mild success," but noted that biology often produces murky results. It gave him a greater appreciation for careful clinical trials.

Some of the scientific researchers I talked to were appalled by what Zayner did. But I found myself rooting for him. If his shadow has offended, think but this and all is mended: *More citizen involvement in science is a good thing*. Genetic coding will never become as crowd-sourced and democratized as software coding, but biology should not remain the exclusive realm of a gospel-guarding priesthood. When Zayner kindly sent me a dose of his homemade vaccine, I decided not to inject it. But I admired him and his two other musketeers for doing so. It made me want to get involved in testing vaccines, though in a more authorized way.[11]

My clinical trial

My own involvement in citizen science was to sign up for a clinical trial of the Pfizer/BioNTech mRNA vaccine. As noted in the opening of this chapter, it was a double-blind study, meaning that neither I nor the researchers were told who got a real vaccine and who got a placebo.

When I volunteered at Ochsner Hospital in New Orleans, I was told that the study could last up to two years. That raised a few questions in my mind. What would happen, I asked the coordinator, if the vaccine got approved before then? She told me that I would then be "unblinded," meaning that they would tell me if I had gotten the placebo and, if so, give me the real vaccine.

What would happen if some other vaccines got approved while our trial was still underway? I could drop out whenever I wanted, she said, and seek to get the approved vaccine. Then I asked a more difficult question: If I dropped out, would I then be unblinded? She paused. She called her supervisor, who paused as well. Finally I was told, "That's not been decided."[12]

So I went to the top. I posed these questions to Francis Collins at the National Institutes of Health, which was overseeing the vaccine studies. (There is an advantage to being a book writer.) "You have asked a question that is currently engaging the members of the Vaccines Working Group in serious debate," he replied. Just a few days earlier, a "consultation report" on this issue had been prepared by the Department of Bioethics at NIH headquarters in Bethesda, Maryland.[13] Even before reading the five-page report, I was impressed and comforted that the NIH had something called a Department of Bioethics.

The report was thoughtful. For a variety of scenarios, the scientific value that could come from continuing a blinded study was balanced against the health of the trial participants. In the case that the vaccine got FDA approval, the advice was: "There will be an obligation to inform participants so that they can decide whether to obtain the vaccine."

After digesting all of this, I decided to quit asking questions and enroll. It might aid the science a little bit, and I would learn first-hand, or first arm, about RNA vaccines. Some people are very skeptical about vaccines and clinical trials. I err on the side of being trusting.

RNA victorious

In December of 2020, with COVID once again resurging throughout much of the world, the two RNA vaccines were the first to be authorized in the United States and became the vanguard of the biotech battle to beat back the pandemic. The plucky little RNA molecule, which had spawned life on our planet and then plagued us in the form of coronaviruses, rode to our rescue. Jennifer Doudna and her colleagues had employed RNA in a tool to edit our genes and then as a method to detect coronaviruses. Now scientists had found a way to enlist RNA's most basic biological function in order to turn our cells into manufacturing plants for the spike protein that would stimulate our immunity to the coronavirus.

Look at the halo of letters—GCACGUAGUGU . . .—on the

cover of this book. It is a snippet of the RNA that creates the part of the spike protein that binds to human cells, and these letters became part of the code used in the new vaccines. Never before had an RNA vaccine been approved for use. But a year after the novel coronavirus was first identified, both Pfizer/BioNTech and Moderna had devised these new genetic vaccines and tested them in large clinical trials, involving people like me, where they proved more than 90 percent effective. When the CEO of Pfizer, Albert Bourla, was informed of the results on a conference call, even he was stunned. "Repeat it," he asked. "Did you say 19 or 90?"[14]

Throughout human history, we have been subjected to wave after wave of viral and bacterial plagues. The first known one was the Babylon flu epidemic around 1200 BC. The plague of Athens in 429 BC killed close to 100,000 people, the Antonine plague in the second century killed ten million, the plague of Justinian in the sixth century killed fifty million, and the Black Death of the fourteenth century took almost 200 million lives, close to half of Europe's population.

The COVID pandemic that killed more than 1.5 million people in 2020 will not be the final plague. However, thanks to the new RNA vaccine technology, our defenses against most future viruses are likely to be immensely faster and more effective. "It was a bad day for viruses," Moderna's chair Afeyan says about the Sunday in November 2020 when he got the first word of the clinical trial results. "There was a sudden shift in the evolutionary balance between what human technology can do and what viruses can do. We may never have a pandemic again."

The invention of easily reprogrammable RNA vaccines was a lightning-fast triumph of human ingenuity, but it was based on decades of curiosity-driven research into one of the most fundamental aspects of life on planet earth: how genes encoded by DNA are transcribed into snippets of RNA that tell cells what proteins to assemble. Likewise, CRISPR gene-editing technology came from understanding the way that bacteria use snippets of RNA to guide enzymes to chop up dangerous viruses. Great inventions come from understanding basic science. Nature is beautiful that way.

Stanley Qi

Nathan and Cameron Myhrvold

Chapter 54

CRISPR Cures

The development of vaccines—both the conventional sort and those employing RNA—would eventually help to beat back the coronavirus pandemic. But they are not a perfect solution. They rely on stimulating a person's immune system, always a risky thing to do. (Most deaths from COVID-19 came from organ inflammation due to unwanted immune-system responses.)[1] As vaccine makers have repeatedly discovered, the multilayered human immune system is very tricky to control. In it lurk mysteries. It contains no simple on-off switches, but instead works through the interaction of complicated molecules that are not easy to calibrate.[2]

The use of antibodies from the blood plasma of recovering patients or made synthetically also helped fight the COVID plague. But these treatments are, likewise, not a perfect long-term solution for each new wave of virus. Convalescent plasma is difficult to harvest from donors in large quantities, and lab-made monoclonal antibodies are hard to manufacture.

The long-range solution to our fight against viruses is the same as the one bacteria found: using CRISPR to guide a scissors-like enzyme to chop up the genetic material of a virus, without having to enlist the patient's immune system. Once again, the circles of scientists around Doudna and Zhang found themselves in competition as they raced to adapt CRISPR to this urgent mission.

Cameron Myhrvold and CARVER

Cameron Myhrvold straddles the world of digital coding and genetic coding, which is not surprising given his heritage and breeding. The lookalike son of Nathan Myhrvold (pronounced MEER-vold), who was the longtime chief technology officer and sparky genius at Microsoft, he has his father's gleeful eyes, chipmunk-cheeked round face, effervescent laugh, and free-range curiosity. People of my generation were awed by his father's brilliance not only in the digital realm but also in fields ranging from food science to asteroid tracking to the speed at which dinosaurs could whip their tails. Cameron shares his father's facility with computer coding, but like many in his generation he focused more on genetic coding and the wonders of biology.

As a Princeton undergraduate, he studied molecular and computational biology, then he got his doctorate from Harvard's Systems, Synthetic, and Quantitative Biology Program, which combines biology and computer science. He loved the intellectual challenge but worried that his work on nano-engineering of organisms was so cutting-edge that it would have little practical impact in the foreseeable future.[3]

So after he got his PhD, he took time off to hike the Colorado Trail. "I was really trying to figure out where to go scientifically," he says. On one leg of his hike, he met a guy who asked him a lot of earnest questions about science. "During that conversation," Myhrvold says, "it became apparent to me that I liked working on problems that were directly relevant to human health."

That led him to decide to become a postdoc in the lab of Pardis Sabeti, a Harvard biologist who uses computer algorithms to explain the evolution of disease. She was born in Tehran and as a child fled with her family to America during the Iranian Revolution. A member of the Broad Institute, she collaborates closely with Feng Zhang. "Joining

Pardis's lab and working with Feng Zhang seemed like a really great way to take on the problem of fighting viruses," Myhrvold says. As a result, Myhrvold became part of the Boston-area orbit around Zhang and eventually a player in its CRISPR star wars with the Berkeley-area orbit of Jennifer Doudna.

While studying for his doctorate at Harvard, Myhrvold became friends with Jonathan Gootenberg and Omar Abudayyeh, the two grad students who worked with Zhang on CRISPR-Cas13. Myhrvold would often kick around ideas with them when he visited Zhang's lab to use its gene-sequencing machine. "That's when I realized, wow, like those two guys were a really special pair," Myhrvold says. "We came up with ways to use Cas13 to detect different RNA sequences, and I thought it would be a really cool opportunity."

When Myhrvold suggested to Sabeti that they should collaborate with Zhang's lab, she was enthusiastic because there was a lot of synergy between the two teams. It resulted in a made-for-the-movies diverse American platoon: Gootenberg, Abudayyeh, Zhang, Myhrvold, Sabeti.

They worked together on Zhang's 2017 paper describing the SHERLOCK system for detecting RNA viruses.[4] The following year, they collaborated on a paper showing how to make the SHERLOCK process even simpler.[5] It appeared in the same issue of *Science* as the paper from Doudna's lab describing the virus-detection tool developed by Chen and Harrington.

In addition to using CRISPR-Cas13 to detect viruses, Myhrvold became interested in turning it into a therapeutic treatment, one that could get rid of viruses. "There are hundreds of viruses that can infect people, but there's only a handful that have available drugs," he says. "That's in part because viruses are so different from each other. What if we could come up with a system that we could program to treat different viruses?"[6]

Most of the viruses that cause human problems, including the coronavirus, have RNA as their genetic material. "They are precisely the type of virus for which you would want a CRISPR enzyme that targets RNA, such as Cas13," he says. So he came up with a way to use CRISPR-Cas13 to do for humans what it does for bacteria: target a dangerous virus and chop it up. Continuing the tradition of reverse-engineering clever acronyms for CRISPR-based inventions, he dubbed the proposed system CARVER, for "Cas13-assisted restriction of viral expression and readout."

In December 2016, shortly after he joined Sabeti's lab as a postdoc, Myhrvold sent her an email reporting on some initial experiments using CARVER to target a virus that causes the symptoms of meningitis or encephalitis. His data showed that it reduced the levels of the virus significantly.[7]

Sabeti was able to get a DARPA grant to study the CARVER system as a way to destroy viruses in humans.[8] Myhrvold and others in her lab did a computer analysis of more than 350 genomes from RNA viruses that infected humans and identified what are known as "conserved sequences," meaning those that are the same in many viruses. These sequences have been preserved unchanged by evolution, and thus are not likely to mutate away anytime soon. His team engineered an arsenal of guide RNAs designed to target these sequences. He then tested Cas13's ability to stop three viruses, including the type that causes severe flu. In cell cultures in a lab, the CARVER system was able too significantly reduce the level of viruses.[9]

Their paper was published online in October 2019. "Our results demonstrate that Cas13 can be harnessed to target a wide range of single-stranded RNA viruses," they wrote. "A programmable antiviral technology would allow for the rapid development of antivirals that can target existing or newly identified pathogens."[10]

A few weeks after the CARVER paper came out, the first cases of COVID-19 were detected in China. "It was one of these moments when you realize the stuff you've been working on for a long time might be a lot more relevant than you thought," Myhrvold says. He started a new computer folder labeled nCov, for "novel coronavirus," since it had not yet been given an official name.

By late January, he and his colleagues had studied the sequence of the coronavirus genome and begun work on CRISPR-based tests for detecting it. The result was a burst of papers in the spring of 2020 for improving CRISPR-based detection technologies for viruses. These included a system known as CARMEN, designed to detect 169 viruses at one time,[11] and a process that combined SHERLOCK's detection capability with an RNA extraction method called HUDSON to create a single-step detection technique he named SHINE.[12] In addition to its CRISPR wizardry, the Broad was a master at devising acronyms.

Myhrvold decided that his time could best be used in developing tools that could detect viruses rather than working on treatments like CARVER, designed to destroy viruses. He was in the process of moving his lab to Princeton, where he had accepted a position beginning in 2021. "I think in the longer term we need treatments," he says, "but I decided that diagnostics were something that we could actually deliver on quickly."

In the West Coast orbit of Jennifer Doudna, however, there was a team that was pushing forward with a coronavirus treatment. Similar to the CARVER system that Myhrvold had invented, it would use CRISPR to seek and destroy viruses.

Stanley Qi and PAC-MAN

Stanley Qi grew up in what he calls a small city in China: Weifang, on the coast about three hundred miles south of Beijing. Its urban core is actually home to more than 2.6 million people, about the same as Chicago, "but that is regarded as small in China," he says. It is bustling with factories but does not have a world-class university, so Qi (pronounced "tshee") went to Tsinghua University in Beijing, where he majored in math and physics. He applied to Berkeley to do graduate work in physics, but he found himself increasingly attracted to biology. "It seemed to have more application for helping the world," he says, "so I decided to switch from physics to bioengineering after my second year at Berkeley."[13]

There he gravitated to the lab of Doudna, who became one of his two advisors. Instead of focusing on gene editing, he developed new ways to use CRISPR to interfere with the expression of genes. "I was surprised at how she spent time to discuss science with me, not on the superficial level but down to the deep level and including key technical details," he says. His interest in viruses increased in 2019 when he was funded (as Myhrvold and Doudna were) by DARPA's program for preparing against pandemics. "We started with a focus on finding a CRISPR method to fight influenza," he says. Then coronavirus struck. In late January 2020, after reading a story about the situation in China, Qi called together his team and shifted his focus from influenza to COVID.

Qi's approach was similar to that pursued by Myhrvold. He wanted to use a guided enzyme to target and then cleave the RNA of the invading virus. Like Zhang and Myhrvold, he decided to use a version of Cas13. The discovery of Cas13a and Cas13b was done at the Broad by Zhang. But another Cas13 variation had been discovered by a brilliant bioengineer in Doudna's orbit, Patrick Hsu, who had experience in both the Broad and Berkeley camps.[14]

Born in Taiwan, Hsu had gotten his undergraduate degree at Berkeley and his doctorate from Harvard, where he worked in the Zhang Lab when Zhang was racing Doudna to make CRISPR work in human cells. Hsu then spent two years as a scientist at Editas, the CRISPR-based company that Zhang had cofounded and Doudna had quit. From there he went to the Salk Institute in Southern California, where he discovered the enzyme that became known as Cas13d. In 2019, he became an assistant professor at Berkeley and one of the team leaders in Doudna's efforts to tackle COVID.

Because of its small size and highly specific targeting capability, the Cas13d that Hsu discovered was chosen by Qi as the best enzyme to target the coronavirus in human lung cells. In the competition to come up with good acronyms, Qi scored high. He dubbed his system PAC-MAN, which he had extracted from "prophylactic antiviral CRISPR in human cells." The name was that of the chomping character in the once popular video game. "I like video games," Qi told *Wired*'s Steven Levy. "The Pac-Man tries to eat cookies, and it is chased by a ghost.

But when it encounters a specific kind of cookie called the power cookie—in our case a CRISPR-Cas13 design—suddenly it turns itself to be so powerful. It can start eating the ghost and start cleaning up the whole battlefield."[15]

Qi and his team tested PAC-MAN on synthesized fragments of the coronavirus. In mid-February, his doctoral student Tim Abbott ran experiments showing that PAC-MAN in a lab setting reduced the amount of the coronavirus by 90 percent. "We demonstrated that Cas13d-based genetic targeting can effectively target and cleave the RNA sequences of SARS-CoV-2 fragments," Qi and his collaborators wrote. "PAC-MAN is a promising strategy to combat not only coronaviruses, including that causing COVID-19, but also a broad range of other viruses."[16]

The paper went online March 14, 2020, the day after Doudna's initial meeting of Bay Area researchers who had enlisted in the coronavirus fight. Qi emailed her a link, and within an hour she had replied, inviting him to join the group and present at their second weekly online meeting. "I told her we needed some resources to develop the PAC-MAN idea, get access to live coronavirus samples, and figure out delivery systems that might get it into the lung cells of patients," he says. "She was super supportive."[17]

Delivery

The concept behind CARVER and PAC-MAN was a brilliant one, although in fairness I should note that bacteria had thought of it more than a billion years ago. The RNA-cleaving Cas13 enzymes could chomp up coronaviruses in human cells. If they could be made to work, CARVER and PAC-MAN would act more efficiently than a vaccine that produces an immune response. By directly targeting the invading virus, these CRISPR-based technologies avoid having to rely on the body's erratic immune response.

The challenge was delivery: How could you get it to the right cells in a human patient and then through the membranes of those cells? That is a very difficult challenge, especially when it involves getting into lung cells, which is why CARVER and PAC-MAN were still not ready for deployment in humans in 2021.

At her March 22 weekly meeting, Doudna introduced Qi and showed a slide describing the group he would lead in their coronavirus war.[18] She teamed him up with researchers in her lab who were working on novel delivery methods, and she worked with him to prepare a white paper pitching the project to potential funders. "We use a variant of CRISPR, Cas13d, to target viral RNA sequences for cleavage and destruction," they wrote. "Our work offers a new strategy that could potentially be used as a genetic vaccine and treatment for COVID-19."[19]

The traditional way to deliver CRISPR and other genetic therapies is by using safe viruses—such as adeno-associated viruses, which don't cause any disease or provoke severe immune responses—as "viral vectors" that can deliver genetic material into cells. Or they can create synthetic virus-like particles to do the delivery, which is the specialty of Jennifer Hamilton and other researchers in Doudna's lab. Another method, electroporation, works by applying an electric field onto a cell's membrane to make it more permeable. All of these approaches have their drawbacks. The small size of viral vectors often limits the types of CRISPR proteins and number of guide RNAs that are deliverable. In search of a safe and effective delivery mechanism, the IGI would need to live up to its name and innovate.

To work with Qi on delivery systems, Doudna put him in touch with Ross Wilson, her former postdoc. Wilson, who now has a lab next to hers at Berkeley, is an expert in new ways to deliver material into the cells of patients. As noted earlier, he is working with Alex Marson to devise a delivery system for a DNA vaccine.[20]

Wilson fears that delivering PAC-MAN or CARVER into cells will be difficult. Qi is nevertheless hopeful that these CRISPR-based therapies can be deployed in the next few years. One method that is proving promising is to encase the CRISPR-Cas13 complex inside of synthetic molecules called lipitoids, which are about the size of a virus. He has been working with the Biological Nanostructures Facility at Lawrence Berkeley National Lab, a sprawling government complex on a hill above Berkeley's campus, to create lipitoids that can deliver PAC-MAN into lung cells.[21]

One way this could work, Qi says, is by delivering PAC-MAN treatments through a nasal spray or some other form of nebulizer. "My son has asthma," he says, "so as a little kid playing football he used a nebulizer as a preventive measure. People use these regularly to prepare the lung to be less allergic if they are exposed to something." The same could be done during a coronavirus pandemic; people could use a nasal spray so that PAC-MAN or another CRISPR-Cas13 prophylactic treatment will protect them.

Once the delivery mechanisms are worked out, CRISPR-based systems such as PAC-MAN and CARVER will be able to treat and protect people without having to activate the body's own immune system, which can be quirky and delicate. They can also be programmed to target essential sequences in the virus's genetic code so they cannot be easily evaded by the virus mutating. And they are simple to reprogram when a new virus emerges.

This concept of reprogramming is also apt in a larger sense. The CRISPR treatments come from reprogramming a system that we humans found in nature. "That gives me hope," Myhrvold says, "that when we face other great medical challenges, we will be able to find other such technologies in nature and put them to use." It is a reminder of the value of curiosity-driven basic research into what Leonardo da Vinci liked to refer to as the infinite wonders of nature. "You never know," Myhrvold says, "when some obscure thing you're studying is going to have important implications for human health." As Doudna likes to put it, "Nature is beautiful that way."

Cold Spring Harbor Laboratory

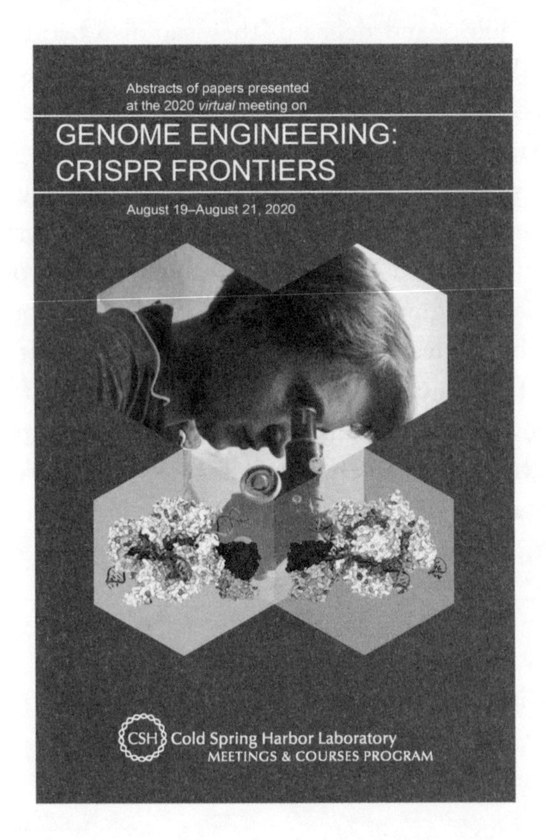

Chapter 55

Cold Spring Harbor Virtual

CRISPR and COVID

The stories of CRISPR and COVID wove together at the Cold Spring Harbor Laboratory's annual CRISPR conference in August 2020. A primary topic was how CRISPR was being used to fight the coronavirus, featuring talks by Jennifer Doudna and Feng Zhang as well as some of the COVID warriors in their rival orbits. Instead of gathering on the rolling campus overlooking an inlet of Long Island Sound, participants convened by Zoom and Slack, looking a bit bleary from months of interacting with boxed faces on their computer screens.

The meeting also wove in another strand of this book. It celebrated the hundredth anniversary of the birth of Rosalind Franklin, whose pioneering work on the structure of DNA inspired Doudna, when she read *The Double Helix* as a young girl, to believe that women could do science. The cover of the meeting's program featured a colorized photograph of Franklin peering into a microscope.

Fyodor Urnov, who directed the COVID testing lab that Doudna created at Berkeley, gave the opening tribute to Franklin. I expected him to deliver it with his usual dramatic flair, but instead he made it, properly, a serious look at her scientific work, including her research into the location of RNA in tobacco mosaic viruses. The only flourish came at the end when he showed a picture of Franklin's empty lab bench after her death. "The best way to honor her is to remember that the structural sexism she faced remains with us today," he said, his voice choking up a bit. "Rosalind is the godmother of gene editing."

Doudna's talk began with a reminder of the natural connection between CRISPR and COVID. "CRISPR is a fabulous way that evolution has dealt with the problem of viral infection," she said. "We can learn from it in this pandemic." Zhang followed with an update on his STOP technology for easy-to-use portable testing machines. As he finished, I sent him a message asking when they would become available at airports and schools, and he texted back seconds later with pictures of the latest prototypes, which had been delivered that week. "We are working hard to make it available this fall," he said. Cameron Myhrvold, speaking animatedly with both hands like his father does, gave a description of how his CARMEN system could be programmed to detect multiple viruses at once. Doudna's former student Janice Chen followed with a presentation about the DETECTR platform that she and Lucas Harrington had created at Mammoth. Patrick Hsu reported on the work being done with Doudna's team to create better methods for amplifying genetic material so it could be detected. And Stanley Qi described how his PAC-MAN system could be used not only to detect coronaviruses but also destroy them.

I was invited to moderate a panel about COVID, and I began by asking Zhang and Doudna about the possibility that the pandemic might create greater public interest in biology. When at-home testing kits become low-cost and easy to use, Zhang replied, they will democratize and decentralize medicine. The most important next steps will be innovations in "microfluidics," which involves channeling tiny amounts of liquid in a device, and then connecting the information to our cell phones. That will allow us all, in the privacy of our homes, to test our saliva and blood for hundreds of medical indicators, monitor our health conditions on our phones, and share the data with doctors and researchers. Doudna added that the pandemic had accelerated the convergence of science with other fields. "The engagement of non-scientists in our work will help achieve an incredibly interesting biotechnology revolution," she predicted. This was molecular biology's moment.

Near the end of the panel, an audience member named Kevin Bishop electronically raised his hand.[1] He worked at the National Institutes of Health and wanted to ask why there were so few African Americans like himself enrolled in the clinical trials for COVID vaccines. That led to a discussion of the distrust Blacks have about medical trials because of historical horrors such as the Tuskegee experiments, in which placebos were given to some sharecroppers suffering from syphilis who thought they were getting real medical treatments. A few of the conference attendees questioned whether it was important to have racial diversity in the COVID vaccine trials. (The consensus: yes, for medical and moral reasons.) Bishop suggested enlisting African American churches and colleges into the effort of enrolling volunteers.

The diversity issue, it struck me, involves far more than just clinical trials. Judging from the list of attendees at the meeting, women are becoming well represented in the field of biological research. But there were very few African Americans, either at the conference or on the benches in the various labs I had visited. In that regard, the new life-sciences revolution resembles, unfortunately, the digital revolution. If there are not efforts at outreach and mentorship, biotechnology will be yet another revolution that leaves most Blacks behind.

CRISPR marches on

The conference presentations on how CRISPR was being deployed to fight COVID were impressive, but equally so were the reports on the discoveries that were pushing CRISPR gene-editing forward. The most important were those made by one of Doudna's co-organizers of the conference, Harvard's soft-spoken superstar David Liu. He has a foot in both the Cambridge and Berkeley camps. After graduating first in his class from Harvard, he got his doctorate from Berkeley and then returned to teach at Harvard, where he became Zhang's colleague at the Broad Institute and cofounder with him of Beam Therapeutics.

With his disarming gentility and friendly intellect, he has remained close to both Doudna and Zhang.

Beginning in 2016, Liu began developing a technique known as "base editing," which can make a precise change in a single letter in DNA without cutting a break in the strands. It's like a very sharp pencil for editing. At the 2019 Cold Spring Harbor meeting, he announced a further advance called "prime editing," in which a guide RNA can carry a long sequence to be edited into a targeted segment of DNA. It requires making only a tiny nick in the DNA rather than a double-strand break. Edits of up to eighty letters are possible.[2] "If CRISPR-Cas9 is like scissors and base editors are like pencils, then you can think of prime editors as like word processors," Liu explained.[3]

Dozens of the presentations at the 2020 meeting involved young researchers who had found clever new ways to use base editing and prime editing. Liu himself described his latest discovery of how to deploy base-editing tools into the energy-producing region of cells.[4] In addition, he was a co-author of a paper that described a user-friendly web app that could be used to design prime-editing experiments.[5] COVID had not slowed the CRISPR revolution.

The importance of base editing was highlighted on the cover of the conference book. Just below the colorized picture of Rosalind Franklin was a beautiful 3-D image of a base editor attached to a purple RNA guide and a blue DNA target. Using some of the structural biology and imaging techniques that Franklin pioneered, the image had been published a month earlier by the labs of Doudna and Liu, with much of the work done by Gavin Knott, the postdoc who had taught me how to edit DNA using CRISPR.[6]

The Blackford Bar

In the dining hall on the Cold Spring Harbor campus, there is a wood-paneled lounge, known as the Blackford Bar, that manages to be both spacious and cozy. Old photographs line the walls, multiple ales and lagers are on tap, TV sets broadcast both scientific lectures and Yankees baseball games, and an outdoor deck overlooks the tranquil harbor. There you can find, on most summer evenings, conference attendees, researchers from nearby lab buildings, and the occasional groundskeeper or campus worker. During previous CRISPR conferences, it was filled with talk of impending discoveries, fanciful ideas, potential job openings, and high and low gossip.

In 2020, the conference organizers tried to re-create the scene with a Slack channel and Zoom room called #virtual-bar. Its purpose, they said, was to "simulate the serendipitous introductions you would've experienced at the Blackford Bar." So I decided to give it a try. About forty others showed up the first night. People introduced themselves in a stilted way, like at a real cocktail reception. Then a moderator broke us into groups of six and sent us to breakout Zoom rooms. After twenty minutes, each breakout session ended, and we were assigned randomly to a different group. Oddly, the format worked rather well when the conversations drilled down on specific scientific questions. There were interesting discussions of such topics as protein synthesis techniques and the hardware being built at Synthego to do automated cell editing. But there was none of the ordinary social chat that lubricates real life and nurtures emotional connections. There was no Yankees game in the background nor sunset to share while sitting on the deck. I left after two rounds.

Cold Spring Harbor Laboratory was founded in 1890 based on a belief in the magic of in-person meetings. The formula is to attract interesting people to an idyllic locale and provide them with opportunities to interact, including at a nice bar. The beauty of nature and the joy that comes from unstructured human engagement is a powerful combination. Even when they don't interact—such as when an awed young Jennifer Doudna passes the aging icon Barbara McClintock on a path through the Cold Spring Harbor campus—people benefit from an atmosphere that is charged in a way that sparks creativity.

One of the transformations wrought by the coronavirus pandemic is that more meetings in the future will be done virtually. It's a shame. If COVID doesn't kill us, Zoom will. As Steve Jobs emphasized when he built a headquarters for Pixar and planned a new Apple campus, new ideas are born out of serendipitous encounters. In-person interactions are especially important in the initial brainstorming of new ideas and the forging of personal bonds. As Aristotle taught, we are a social animal, an instinct that cannot fully be satisfied online.

Nevertheless, there will be an upside to the fact that the coronavirus has expanded how we work together and share ideas. By hastening the Age of Zoom, the pandemic will broaden the horizons of scientific collaboration, allowing it to be even more global and crowdsourced. A walk along the cobblestone streets of San Juan was the catalyst for the collaboration between Doudna and Charpentier, but the technology of Skype and Dropbox allowed them and their two postdocs to work together for six months in three countries to decipher CRISPR-Cas9. Because people have now become comfortable meeting in boxes on a computer screen, teamwork will be more efficient. A balance, I hope, will be struck: the reward for our efficient virtual meetings will be the chance to hang out together in person in places like the campus of Cold Spring Harbor.

Charpentier, remotely

At the end of Doudna's scientific presentation at the conference, a young researcher asked a personal question: "What inspired you to work on CRISPR-Cas9 the very first time?" Doudna paused for a moment, since it was not the type of question that scientific researchers usually ask after a technical presentation. "It started as a wonderful collaboration with Emmanuelle Charpentier," she replied. "I am forever indebted to her for the work we did together."

It was an interesting answer, because a few days earlier Doudna had talked to me about her sorrow that she and Charpentier had drifted apart, personally as well as scientifically. She lamented that she continued to detect a frostiness and asked me if, in my conversations with Charpentier, I had picked up more clues about why. "One of the things I am saddest about in the CRISPR tale is the fact that I really like Emmanuelle, but our relationship fell apart," she said. Doudna had studied French in high school and college, even at one point considering switching her major from chemistry to French. "I always had this fantasy of myself as a French girl, and Emmanuelle in some ways reminded me of that. I just adore her on a certain level. I wish we could have continued to have a wonderful close professional and personal connection and could have enjoyed the science and all of the things that came afterwards as friends."

When she told me this, I suggested that she invite Charpentier to speak at the Cold Spring Harbor virtual conference. Doudna immediately seized on the idea and asked her, through the conference's co-organizer Maria Jasin, to give the tribute to Rosalind Franklin or speak on any other topic. I followed up with Charpentier to encourage her to accept.

She hesitated at first, then replied that she had another meeting to attend remotely during that period. Jasin and Doudna offered to be flexible about the time and date, but Charpentier declined. Sensing her reticence, I tried a different approach: I invited her to join me and Doudna by Zoom the day after the conference for a private chat. I told her that I wanted to include their reminiscences at the end of this book. She surprised me by embracing the idea. She even emailed Doudna to say that she was looking forward to it.

As a result, we met online the Sunday after the conference. I had prepared a list of questions to ask. But as soon as Doudna and Charpentier came online, they began talking to each other and catching up, at first in the slightly stilted manner of people who have not seen each other for a while, and then, after a few minutes, more animatedly. Doudna began referring to Charpentier by her nickname, Manue, and soon they were both laughing. I turned off my video camera so I could leave the screen to them while I just listened.

Doudna talked about how tall her teenage son, Andy, had grown, shared a picture that Martin Jinek had sent of his new baby, and joked about an awards event she and Charpentier did with the American Cancer Society in 2018 at which Joe Biden told them that he did not plan to run for president. Doudna congratulated Charpentier on the success of her CRISPR Therapeutics company in curing sickle-cell anemia in its Nashville trial. "We published our paper in 2012, and here we are in 2020 and someone has already been cured of a disease," Doudna said. Charpentier nodded and laughed. "We can be very happy at how fast things happened," she said.

The talk gradually turned more personal. Charpentier recalled the beginning of their collaboration, when they had lunch at the conference in Puerto Rico, walked the cobblestone streets together, and ended up in a bar for a drink. Many times when you meet another scientist, she said, you know that you could never work with them. But their meeting was the opposite. "I knew we would be good collaborators," she told Doudna. Then they swapped memories about working around the clock by Skype and Dropbox in their six-month race to decode CRISPR-Cas9. Charpentier confessed that she worried whenever she sent Doudna some writing for the paper they produced jointly. "I thought you would have to correct my English," she said. Doudna replied, "Your English is great, and I remember you had to correct some of my own mistakes. It was a lot of fun to write that paper together, because we have different ways of thinking about things."

Finally, when their exchanges began to lag, I turned on my video camera to ask a question. Over the past few years, you've drifted apart, both scientifically and personally, I said. Do you miss the friendship you had?

Charpentier jumped in, eager to explain what had happened. "We were on the road a lot because of the prize ceremonies and other things," she said. "People were overloading our schedule, and we did not have any time to enjoy the in between. So part of the problem was the simple fact that we both became terribly busy." She spoke wistfully of the week they had spent together in Berkeley in June 2012 when they were finishing their paper. "There is this picture of us, with me with a funny haircut, in front of your institute," she said, referring to the picture that is at the beginning of chapter 17 of this book. It was the last time they had been relaxed together, Charpentier said. "After that, it was crazy because of the impact our paper had. We had little time for ourselves."

Charpentier's words made Doudna smile, and she opened up even more. "I enjoyed our friendship as much as doing the science," she said. "I love your delightful manner. I always had this fantasy, ever since I studied French in school, of living in Paris. And Manue, you embodied that for me."

The conversation ended with talk about working together again someday. Charpentier said she had a fellowship to do research in the U.S. Doudna had previously made plans, which COVID scuttled, to spend the Spring 2021 semester on sabbatical at Columbia. They agreed that they should coordinate sabbaticals. "Maybe in the Spring of 2022 in New York," Doudna suggested. "I would very much like that, to be there with you," Charpentier replied. "We could collaborate again."

Celebrating with Andy and Jamie in their kitchen just after the Nobel Prize announcement

CHAPTER 56

The Nobel Prize

"Rewriting the Code of Life"

Doudna was sound asleep when, at 2:53 a.m. on October 9, 2020, she was awakened by the persistent buzz of her cell phone, which she had put on vibrate mode. She was alone in a hotel room in Palo Alto, where she had gone to be part of a small meeting on the biology of aging, the first such in-person event she had attended in the seven months since the onset of the coronavirus crisis. The call was from a reporter for *Nature*. "I hate to bother you so early," she said, "but I wanted your comment on the Nobel."

"Who won?" Doudna asked, sounding slightly irritated.

"You mean you haven't heard?!" the reporter said. "You and Emmanuelle Charpentier!"

Doudna looked at her phone and saw a bunch of missed calls that indeed seemed to have come from Stockholm. After pausing for a moment to absorb the news, she said, "Let me call you back."[1]

The awarding of the 2020 Nobel Prize in Chemistry to Doudna and Charpentier was not a complete surprise, but the recognition came with historic swiftness. Their CRISPR discovery was merely eight years old. The day before, Sir Roger Penrose had shared the Nobel in physics for a discovery about black holes he had made more than fifty years earlier. There was also a sense that this chemistry award was historic. More than just recognizing an achievement, it seemed to herald the advent of a new era. "This year's prize is about rewriting the code of life," the secretary general of the Royal Swedish Academy proclaimed in making the announcement. "These genetic scissors have taken the life sciences into a new epoch."

Also noteworthy was that the prize went only to two people, rather than the usual three. Given the ongoing patent dispute over who first discovered CRISPR as a gene-editing tool, the third slot could have gone to Feng Zhang, although that would have left out George Church, who published similar findings at the same time. In addition, there were many other worthy candidates, including Francisco Mojica, Rodolphe Barrangou, Phillipe Horvath, Eric Sontheimer, Luciano Marraffini, and Virginijus Šikšnys.

There was also the historic significance of the prize going to two women. One could sense a tight smile on the face of Rosalind Franklin's ghost. Although she made the images that helped James Watson and Francis Crick discover the structure of DNA, she became just a minor character in the early histories, and she died before they got their 1962 Nobel Prize. Even if she had lived, it is unlikely she would have displaced Maurice Wilkins as that year's third honoree. Until 2020, only five women, beginning with Marie Curie in 1911, had won a Nobel for chemistry, out of 184 honorees.

When Doudna called the Stockholm number that had been left on her voicemail, she got an answering machine. But after a few minutes, she was able to connect and officially receive the news. After taking a few more calls, including from Martin Jinek and the persistent reporter from *Nature*, she threw her clothes into her bag and jumped in her car for the hourlong drive back to Berkeley. On the way she telephoned Jamie, who said that a communications team from the university was already setting up on their patio. When she arrived home at 4:30 a.m., she texted her neighbors to apologize for the commotion and camera lights.

For a few minutes, she got a chance to celebrate the news over coffee with Jamie and Andy. Then she made a few remarks to the camera team on her patio before heading to Berkeley for a hastily assembled virtual global press conference. On the ride over, she spoke to her colleague Jillian Banfield, who in 2006 had called her out of the blue and asked to meet at the Free Speech Movement Café on campus to discuss some clustered repeated sequences that she kept finding in the DNA of bacteria. "I am so grateful to have you as a collaborator and friend," she told Banfield. "It's been so much fun."

Many of the questions at the press conference focused on how the awards represented a breakthrough for women. "I'm proud of my gender!" Doudna said with a big laugh. "It's great, especially for younger women. For many women there's a feeling that, whatever they do, their work may not be as recognized as it might be if they were a man. I would like to see that change, and this is a step in the right direction." Later, she reflected on her days as a schoolgirl. "I was told more than a few times that girls don't do chemistry or girls don't do science. Fortunately, I ignored that."

As she spoke, Charpentier was holding her own press conference in Berlin, where it was midafternoon. I had reached her a few hours earlier, right after she got the official phone call from Stockholm, and she was unusually emotive. "I had been told that this might someday come," she told me, "but when I received the call I became very moved, very emotional." It took her back, she said, to her early childhood and deciding, while walking past the Pasteur Institute in her native Paris, that she someday would be a scientist. But by the time of her press conference, her emotions were well hidden behind her Mona Lisa smile. Carrying a glass of white wine, she came into the lobby of her institute, posed next to a bust of its namesake, Max Planck, and then answered questions in a way that managed to be both lighthearted and earnest. As happened in Berkeley, most of the focus was on what the award meant for women. "The fact that Jennifer and I were awarded this prize today can provide a very strong message for young girls," she said. "It can show them that women can also be awarded prizes."

That afternoon, their rival Eric Lander sent out a tweet from his perch at the Broad Institute: "Huge congratulations to Drs. Charpentier and Doudna on the @NobelPrize for their contributions to the amazing science of CRISPR! It's exciting to see the endless frontiers of science continue to expand, with big impacts for patients." In public, Doudna reacted graciously. "I'm deeply grateful for the acknowledgment from Eric Lander, and it's an honor to receive his words," she said. Privately, she wondered whether his use of the word "contributions" was a lawyerly way to subtly minimize their Nobel-certified discoveries. More notable to me were his words about "big impacts for patients" in the future. It led me to hope that Zhang and Church and perhaps David Liu will someday win the Nobel Prize for medicine as a companion to the one that Doudna and Charpentier won for chemistry.

Doudna mentioned at her press conference that she was "waving across the ocean" at Charpentier. But she badly wanted to actually talk to her. She texted Charpentier repeatedly throughout the day and left messages on her cell three times. "Please, please call me," Doudna texted at one point. "I won't take much of your time. I just want to say congratulations on the phone to you." Charpentier finally responded, "I'm really, really exhausted, but I promise I'll call you tomorrow." So it wouldn't be until the next morning that they finally connected for a relaxed and rambling chat.

After her press conference, Doudna went to her lab building for a champagne celebration followed by a Zoom party where she was toasted by a hundred or so friends. Mark Zuckerberg and Priscilla Chan, whose foundation was funding some of her work, made a virtual appearance, as did Jillian Banfield and various Berkeley deans and officials. The nicest toast came from Jack Szostak, the Harvard professor who had turned her on to the wonders of RNA back when she was a graduate student. Szostak, who had won a Nobel in medicine in 2009 (jointly with two women), raised a glass of champagne while sitting in the backyard of his stately brick Boston townhouse. "The only thing better than winning a Nobel Prize," he said, "is having one of your students win one."

She and Jamie cooked Spanish omelets for dinner, then Doudna joined her two sisters on a FaceTime call. They talked about how their late parents would have reacted. "I really wish they could have been around," Doudna said. "Mom would have been so emotional, and Dad would have pretended not to be. Instead, he would have made sure he understood the science, then asked me what I planned to do next."

Transformations

By honoring CRISPR, a virus-fighting system found in nature, in the midst of a virus pandemic, the Nobel committee reminded us how curiosity-driven basic research can end up having very practical applications. CRISPR and COVID are speeding our entry into a life-science era. Molecules are becoming the new microchips.

At the height of the coronavirus crisis, Doudna was asked to write a piece for *The Economist* on the social transformations being wrought. "Like many other aspects of life these days, science and its practice seem to be undergoing rapid and perhaps permanent changes," she wrote. "This will be for the better."[2] The public, she predicted, will have more understanding of biology and the scientific method. Elected officials will better appreciate the value of funding basic science. And there will be enduring changes in how scientists collaborate, compete, and communicate.

Before the pandemic, communication and collaboration between academic researchers had become constrained. Universities created large legal teams dedicated to staking a claim to each new discovery, no matter how small, and guarding against any sharing of information that might jeopardize a patent application. "They've turned every interaction scientists have with each other into an intellectual property transaction," says Berkeley biologist Michael Eisen. "Everything I get from or send to a colleague at another academic institution involves a complex legal agreement whose purpose is not to promote science but to protect the university's ability to profit from hypothetical inventions that might arise from scientists doing what we're supposed to do—share our work with each other."[3]

The race to beat COVID was not run by those rules. Instead, led by Doudna and Zhang, most academic labs declared that their discoveries would be made available to anyone fighting the virus. This allowed greater collaboration between researchers and even between countries. The consortium that Doudna put together of labs in the Bay Area could not have coalesced so quickly if they had to worry about intellectual property arrangements. Likewise, scientists around the world contributed to an open database of coronavirus sequences that, by the end of August 2020, had thirty-six thousand entries.[4]

The sense of urgency about COVID also brushed back the gatekeeper role played by expensive, peer-reviewed, paywall-protected scholarly journals such as *Science* and *Nature*. Instead of waiting months for the editors and reviewers to decide whether to publish a paper, researchers at the height of the coronavirus crisis were posting more than a hundred papers a day on preprint servers, such as *medRxiv* and *bioRxiv*, that were free and open and required a minimal review process. This allowed information to be shared in real time, freely, and even be dissected on social media. Despite the potential danger of spreading research that had not been fully vetted, the rapid and open dissemination worked well: it sped up the process of building on each new finding and allowed the public to follow the advance of science as it happened. On some important papers involving coronavirus, publication on the reprint servers led to crowdsourced vetting and wisdom from experts around the world.[5]

George Church says he had long wondered whether there would ever be a biological event that was catalytic enough to bring science into our daily lives. "COVID is it," he says. "Every now and then a meteor hits, and suddenly the mammals are in charge."[6] Most of us someday will have detection devices in our home that will allow us to check for viruses and many other conditions. We will also have wearables with nanopores and molecular transistors that can monitor all of our biological functions, and they will be networked so that they can share information and create a global bio-weather map showing in real time the spread of biological threats. All of this has made biology an even more exciting field of study; in August 2020, applications to medical school had jumped seventeen percent from the previous year.

The academic world will also change, and not just by the rise of more online classes. Instead of being ivory towers, universities will be engaged in tackling real-world problems, from pandemics to climate change. These projects will be cross-disciplinary, breaking down academic silos and the walls between labs, which have traditionally been independent fiefdoms that fiercely guard their autonomy. Fighting the coronavirus required collaboration across disciplines. In that way, it resembled the effort to develop CRISPR, which involved microbe-hunters working with geneticists, structural biologists, biochemists, and computer geeks. It also resembled the way things operate in innovative businesses, where units work together to pursue a specific project or mission. The nature of the scientific threats we face will accelerate this trend toward project-oriented collaborations among disparate labs.

One fundamental aspect of science will remain the same. It has always been a collaboration across generations, from Darwin and Mendel to Watson and Crick to Doudna and Charpentier. "At the end of the day, the discoveries are what endure," Charpentier says. "We are just passing on this planet for a short time. We do our job, and then we leave and others pick up the work."[7]

All of the scientists I write about in this book say that their main motivation is not money, or even glory, but the chance to unlock the mysteries of nature and use those discoveries to make the world a better place. I believe them. And I think that may be one of the most important legacies of the pandemic: reminding scientists of the nobility of their mission. So, too, might it imprint these values on a new generation of students who, as they contemplate their careers, may be more likely to pursue scientific research now that they have seen how exciting and important it can be.

Mardi Gras, 2020

Epilogue

Royal Street, New Orleans, Fall 2020

The Great Pandemic has temporarily receded, and the earth is beginning to heal. I am sitting on my balcony in the French Quarter, and I can again hear music on the street and smell shrimp being boiled at the corner restaurant.

But I know that more viral waves are likely to come, either from the current coronavirus or novel ones in the future, so we need more than just vaccines. Like bacteria, we need a system that can be easily adapted to destroy each new virus. CRISPR could provide that to us, as it does for bacteria. It could also someday be used to fix genetic problems, defeat cancers, enhance our children, and allow us to hack evolution so that we can steer the future of the human race.

I began this journey thinking that biotechnology was the next great scientific revolution, a subject that was filled with awe-inspiring natural wonders, research rivalries, thrilling discoveries, lifesaving triumphs, and creative pioneers such as Jennifer Doudna, Emmanuelle Charpentier, and Feng Zhang. The Year of the Plague made me realize that I was understating the case.

A few weeks ago, I found my old copy of James Watson's *The Double Helix*. Like Doudna, I got the book as a gift from my father when I was in school. It's a first edition with the pale red jacket, and it might be worth something today on eBay except that my sophomoric pencil notes litter the margins, recording and defining words that were new to me, such as "biochemistry."

Reading the book made me, as it made Doudna, want to become a biochemist. Unlike her, I didn't. If I had to do it all over again—pay attention, you students reading this—I would have focused far more on the life sciences, especially if I was coming of age in the twenty-first century. People of my generation became fascinated by personal computers and the web. We made sure our kids learned how to code. Now we will have to make sure they understand the code of life.

One way to do that is for all of us older kids to realize, as the interwoven tales of CRISPR and COVID show, how useful it is to understand the way life works. It's good that some people have strong opinions about the use of GMOs in food, but it would be even better if more of them knew what a genetically modified organism is (and what the yogurt-makers discovered). It's good to have strong opinions about gene engineering in humans, but it's even better if you know what a gene is.

Fathoming the wonders of life is more than merely useful. It is also inspiring and joyful. That is why we humans are lucky that we are endowed with curiosity.

I am reminded of this by a baby lizard that is crawling around the curves of the wrought iron of my balcony and onto a vine, changing color slightly. I become curious: What *causes* the skin to change color? Also, why in heaven's name has this coronavirus plague been followed by such a profusion of lizards? I have to stop myself from conjuring up medieval explanations. I take a quick diversion online to slake my curiosity, and it's a pleasant experience. It reminds me of my favorite note that Leonardo da Vinci scribbled in the margin of one of his crammed notebook pages: "Describe the tongue of the woodpecker." Who wakes up one morning and decides he needs to know what the tongue of a woodpecker looks like? The passionately and playfully curious Leonardo, that's who.

Curiosity is the key trait of the people who have fascinated me, from Benjamin Franklin and Albert Einstein to Steve Jobs and Leonardo da Vinci. Curiosity drove James Watson and the Phage Group, who wanted to understand the viruses that attack bacteria, and the Spanish graduate student Francisco Mojica, who was intrigued by clustered repeated sequences of DNA, and Jennifer Doudna, who wanted to understand what made the sleeping grass curl up when you touched it. And maybe that instinct—curiosity, pure curiosity—is what will save us.

A year ago, after trips to Berkeley and various conferences, I sat on this balcony and tried to process my thoughts about gene editing. My worry then involved the diversity of our species.

I had returned home in time for the funeral of the beloved grande dame of New Orleans, Leah Chase, who died at ninety-six after running a restaurant in the Tremé neighborhood for almost seven decades. With her wooden spoon, she would stir the roux for her shrimp-and-sausage gumbo (one cup of peanut oil and eight tablespoons of flour) until it was the color of café au lait and could bind together the many diverse ingredients. A Creole of color, her restaurant likewise bound together the diversity of New Orleans life, Black and white and Creole.

The French Quarter was hopping that weekend. There was a naked bicycle race that was intended (oddly enough) to promote traffic safety. There were parades and second lines to celebrate the life of Miss Leah and also of Mac Rebennack, the funk musician known as Dr. John. There was the annual Gay Pride Parade and related block parties. And coexisting quite happily was the French Market Creole Tomato Festival, featuring truck farmers and cooks showing off the many varieties of succulent non–genetically modified local tomatoes.

From my balcony, I marveled at the diversity of the passing humanity. There were people short and tall, gay and straight and trans, fat and skinny, light and dark and café au lait. I saw a cluster wearing Gallaudet University T-shirts excitedly using sign language. The supposed promise of CRISPR is that we may someday be able to pick which of these traits we want in our children and in all of our descendants. We could choose for them to be tall and muscular and blond and blue-eyed and not deaf and not—well, pick your preferences.

As I surveyed the scene with all of its natural variety, I pondered how this promise of CRISPR might also be its peril. It took nature millions of years to weave together three billion base pairs of DNA in a complex and occasionally imperfect way to permit all of the wondrous diversity within our species. Are we right to think we can now come along and edit that genome to eliminate what we see as imperfections? Will we lose our diversity? Our humility and empathy? Will we become less flavorful, like our tomatoes?

On Mardi Gras 2020, marchers in the St. Anne parade strutted past our balcony, a few of them dressed as the coronavirus, with bodysuits that mimicked a Corona beer bottle and hoods that made them look like viral rockets. A few weeks later, our shutdown order came. Doreen Ketchens, the beloved clarinetist who plays with her band in front of our corner grocery, gave a farewell-for-now performance to a near-empty sidewalk. She sang a final rendition of "When the Saints Go Marching In," stressing the verse about "when the sun begins to shine."

The mood now is different than it was last year, as are my thoughts on CRISPR. Like our species, my thinking evolves and adapts with changing situations. I now see the promise of CRISPR more clearly than the peril. If we are wise in how we use it, biotechnology can make us more able to fend off viruses, overcome genetic defects, and protect our bodies and minds.

All creatures large and small use whatever tricks they can to survive, and so should we. It's natural. Bacteria came up with a pretty clever virus-fighting technique, but it took them trillions of life cycles to do so. We can't wait that long. We will have to combine our curiosity with our inventiveness to speed up the process.

After millions of centuries during which the evolution of organisms happened "naturally," we humans now have the ability to hack the code of life and engineer our own genetic future. Or, to flummox those who would label gene editing as "unnatural" and "playing God," let's put it another way: Nature and nature's God, in their infinite wisdom, have evolved a species that is able to modify its own genome, and that species happens to be ours.

Like any evolutionary trait, this new ability may help the species thrive and perhaps even produce successor species. Or it may not. It could be one of those evolutionary traits that, as sometimes happens, leads a species down a path that endangers its survival. Evolution is fickle that way.

That's why it works best as a slow process. Every now and then, a rogue or rebel—He Jiankui, Josiah Zayner—will prod us to go faster. But if we are wise, we can pause and decide to proceed with more caution. Slopes are less slippery that way.

To guide us, we will need not only scientists, but humanists. And most important, we will need people who feel comfortable in both worlds, like Jennifer Doudna. This is why it is useful, I think, for all of us to try to understand this new room that we are about to enter, one that seems mysterious but is rich with hope.

Not everything needs to be decided right away. We can begin by asking what type of world we want to leave for our children. Then we can feel our way together, step by step, preferably hand in hand.

ACKNOWLEDGMENTS

I want to thank Jennifer Doudna for her willingness to put up with me. She sat for dozens of interviews, answered my incessant phone calls and emails, allowed me to spend time in her lab, gave me access to a wide variety of meetings, and even let me lurk in her Slack channels. And her husband, Jamie Cate, he put up with me as well, and he also helped.

Feng Zhang was notably gracious. Although the book focuses on his competitor, he cheerfully hosted me in his lab and gave me multiple interviews. I came to like and admire him, just as I do his colleague Eric Lander, who was likewise generous with his time. One of the joys in reporting this book was getting to spend time in Berlin with Emmanuelle Charpentier, who was *charmante*. Although I'm not sure what that means, I know it when I see it, which I hope comes through in these pages. I likewise got a kick out of hanging around George Church, who is a charming (*charmant*?) gentleman disguised as a mad scientist.

Kevin Doxzen of the Innovative Genomics Institute and Spencer Olesky of Tulane were the scientific vetters of this book. They provided very smart comments and corrections. Max Wendell, Benjamin Bernstein, and Ryan Braun of Tulane also chipped in. All of them were wonderful, so please don't blame them for any mistakes that crept in.

I am also grateful to all of the scientists and their fans who spent time with me, provided insights, gave interviews, and checked facts: Noubar Afeyan, Richard Axel, David Baltimore, Jillian Banfield, Cori Bargmann, Rodolphe Barrangou, Joe Bondy-Denomy, Dana Carroll,

Janice Chen, Francis Collins, Kevin Davies, Meredith DeSalazar, Phil Dormitzer, Sarah Doudna, Kevin Doxzen, Victor Dzau, Eldora Ellison, Sarah Goodwin, Margaret Hamburg, Jennifer Hamilton, Lucas Harrington, Rachel Haurwitz, Christine Heenan, Don Hemmes, Megan Hochstrasser, Patrick Hsu, Maria Jasin, Martin Jinek, Elliot Kirschner, Gavin Knott, Eric Lander, Le Cong, Richard Lifton, Enrique Lin Shiao, David Liu, Luciano Marraffini, Alex Marson, Andy May, Sylvain Moineau, Francisco Mojica, Cameron Myhrvold, Rodger Novak, Val Pakaluk, Duanqing Pei, Matthew Porteus, Stanley Qi, Antonio Regalado, Matt Ridley, Dave Savage, Jacob Sherkow, Virginijus Šikšnys, Erik Sontheimer, Sam Sternberg, Jack Szostak, Fyodor Urnov, Elizabeth Watson, James Watson, Jonathan Weissman, Blake Wiedenheft, Ross Wilson, and Josiah Zayner.

As always, I owe deep thanks to Amanda Urban, my agent for forty years now. She manages to be caring and intellectually honest at the same time, which is very bracing. Priscilla Painton and I worked together at *Time* when we were in our salad days and were neighbors when our kids were in their pre-salad ones. Suddenly, she is now my editor. It's sweet the way the world turns. She did a diligent and smart job both restructuring this book at one point and polishing it line by line.

Science is a collaborative effort. So is producing a book. The joy of being with Simon & Schuster is that I get to work with a great team led by the irrepressible and insightful Jonathan Karp, who seemed to read this manuscript many times and kept suggesting improvements. It includes Stephen Bedford, Dana Canedy, Jonathan Evans, Marie Florio, Kimberly Goldstein, Judith Hoover, Ruth Lee-Mui, Hana Park, Julia Prosser, Richard Rhorer, Elise Ringo, and Jackie Seow. Helen Manders and Peppa Mignone at Curtis Brown did a wonderful job working with international publishers. I also want to thank Lindsey Billups, my assistant, who is smart and wise and very sensible. Her help every day was invaluable.

My greatest thanks as always go to my wife, Cathy, who helped with the research, carefully read my drafts, provided sage counsel, and kept me on an even keel (or tried). Our daughter, Betsy, also read the manuscript and made smart suggestions. They are the foundations of my life.

This book was launched by Alice Mayhew, who was the editor of all of my previous books. In our first discussions, I was amazed at how well she knew the science. She was relentless in insisting that I make this book a journey of discovery. She had edited the classic of the genre, Horace Freeland Judson's *The Eighth Day of Creation*, back in 1979, and forty years later she seemed to remember every passage in it. Over the 2019 Christmas holidays, she read the first half of this book and came back with a torrent of joyful comments and insights. But she didn't live to see it finished. Nor did dear Carolyn Reidy, the CEO of Simon & Schuster, who had always been a mentor, guide, and joy to know. One of life's great pleasures was to make Alice and Carolyn smile. If you'd ever seen their smiles, you'd understand. I hope this book would have. I've dedicated it to their memory.

NOTES

Introduction: Into the Breach

1. Author's interview with Jennifer Doudna. The competition was run by First Robotics, a nationwide program created by the irrepressible Segway inventor Dean Kamen.
2. Interviews, audio and video recordings, notes, and slides provided by Jennifer Doudna, Megan Hochstrasser, and Fyodor Urnov; Walter Isaacson, "Ivory Power," *Air Mail*, Apr. 11, 2020.
3. See chapter 12 on the yogurt makers for a fuller discussion of the iterative process that can occur between basic researchers and technological innovation.

Chapter 1: Hilo

1. Author's interviews with Jennifer Doudna and Sarah Doudna. Other sources for this section include *The Life Scientific*, BBC Radio, Sept. 17, 2017; Andrew Pollack, "Jennifer Doudna, a Pioneer Who Helped Simplify Genome Editing," *New York Times*, May 11, 2015; Claudia Dreifus, "The Joy of the Discovery: An Interview with Jennifer Doudna," *New York Review of Books*, Jan. 24, 2019; Jennifer Doudna interview, National Academy of Sciences, Nov. 11, 2004; Jennifer Doudna, "Why Genome Editing Will Change Our Lives," *Financial Times*, Mar. 14, 2018; Laura Kiessling, "A Conversation with Jennifer Doudna," *ACS Chemical Biology Journal*, Feb. 16, 2018; Melissa Marino, "Biography of Jennifer A. Doudna," *PNAS*, Dec. 7, 2004.
2. Dreifus, "The Joy of the Discovery."
3. Author's interviews with Lisa Twigg-Smith, Jennifer Doudna.
4. Author's interviews with Jennifer Doudna, James Watson.
5. Jennifer Doudna, "How COVID-19 Is Spurring Science to Accelerate," *The Economist*, June 5, 2020.

Chapter 2: The Gene

1. This section on the history of genetics and DNA relies on Siddhartha Mukherjee, *The Gene* (Scribner, 2016); Horace Freeland Judson, *The Eighth Day of Creation* (Touchstone, 1979); Alfred Sturtevant, *A History of Genetics* (Cold Spring Harbor, 2001); Elof Axel Carlson, *Mendel's Legacy* (Cold Spring Harbor, 2004).
2. Janet Browne, *Charles Darwin*, vol. 1 (Knopf, 1995) and vol. 2 (Knopf, 2002); Charles Darwin, *The Journey of the Beagle,* originally published 1839; Darwin, *On the Origin of Species*, originally published 1859. Electronic copies of Darwin's books, letters, writings, and journals can be found at Darwin Online, darwin-online.org.uk.

3. Isaac Asimov, "How Do People Get New Ideas," 1959, reprinted in *MIT Technology Review*, Oct. 20, 2014; Steven Johnson, *Where Good Ideas Come From* (Riverhead, 2010), 81; Charles Darwin, *Autobiography*, describing events of October 1838, Darwin Online, darwin-online.org.uk.
4. In addition to Mukherjee, Judson, and Sturtevant, this section on Mendel also draws from Robin Marantz Henig, *The Monk in the Garden* (Houghton Mifflin Harcourt, 2000).
5 Erwin Chargaff, "Preface to a Grammar of Biology," *Science*, May 14, 1971.

Chapter 3: DNA

1. This section draws from my multiple interviews with James Watson over a period of years and from his book *The Double Helix*, originally published by Atheneum in 1968. I used *The Annotated and Illustrated Double Helix*, compiled by Alexander Gann and Jan Witkowski (Simon & Schuster, 2012), which includes the letters describing the DNA model and other supplemental material. This section also draws from James Watson, *Avoid Boring People* (Oxford, 2007); Brenda Maddox, *Rosalind Franklin: The Dark Lady of DNA* (HarperCollins, 2002); Judson, *The Eighth Day*; Mukherjee, *The Gene*; Sturtevant, *A History of Genetics*.
2. Judson says Watson was turned down at Harvard; Watson said to me and in *Avoid Boring People* that he was accepted but not offered a stipend or financing.
3. The youngest person to win a Nobel Prize is now Malala Yousafzai from Pakistan, who won the Peace Prize. She was shot by the Taliban and became a fighter for girls' education.
4. Mukherjee, *The Gene*, 147.
5. Rosalind Franklin, "The DNA Riddle: King's College, London, 1951–1953," Rosalind Franklin Papers, NIH National Library of Medicine, https://profiles.nlm.nih.gov/spotlight/kr/feature/dna; Nicholas Wade, "Was She or Wasn't She?," *The Scientist*, Apr. 2003; Judson, *The Eighth Day*, 99; Maddox, *Rosalind Franklin*, 163; Mukherjee, *The Gene*, 149.

Chapter 4: The Education of a Biochemist

1. Author's interviews with Jennifer Doudna.
2. Author's interviews with Jennifer Doudna.
3. Author's email interviews with Don Hemmes.
4. Author's interviews with Jennifer Doudna; Jennifer A. Doudna and Samuel H. Sternberg, *A Crack in Creation* (Houghton Mifflin, 2017), 58; Kiessling, "A Conversation with Jennifer Doudna"; Pollack, "Jennifer Doudna."
5. Unless otherwise noted, all Jennifer Doudna quotes in this section are from my interviews with her.
6. Sharon Panasenko, "Methylation of Macromolecules during Development in *Myxococcus xanthus*," *Journal of Bacteriology*, Nov. 1985 (submitted July 1985).

Chapter 5: The Human Genome

1. The Department of Energy launched work on sequencing the human genome in 1986. Official funding for the Human Genome Project was in President Reagan's 1988 budget submission. The Department of Energy and the National Institutes of Health signed a memorandum of understanding to formalize the Human Genome Project in 1990.

2. Daniel Okrent, *The Guarded Gate* (Scribner, 2019).
3. "Decoding Watson," directed and produced by Mark Mannucci, *American Masters*, PBS, Jan. 2, 2019.
4. Author's interviews and meetings with James Watson, Elizabeth Watson, and Rufus Watson; Algis Valiunas, "The Evangelist of Molecular Biology," *The New Atlantis*, Summer 2017; James Watson, *A Passion for DNA* (Oxford, 2003); Philip Sherwell, "DNA Father James Watson's 'Holy Grail' Request," *The Telegraph*, May 10, 2009; Nicholas Wade, "Genome of DNA Discoverer Is Deciphered," *New York Times*, June 1, 2007.
5. Author's interviews with George Church, Eric Lander, and James Watson.
6. Frederic Golden and Michael D. Lemonick, "The Race Is Over," and James Watson, "The Double Helix Revisited," *Time*, July 3, 2000; author's conversations with Al Gore, Craig Venter, James Watson, George Church, and Francis Collins.
7. Author's own notes from the White House ceremony; Nicholas Wade, "Genetic Code of Human Life Is Cracked by Scientists," *New York Times*, June 27, 2000.

Chapter 6: RNA

1. Mukherjee, *The Gene*, 250.
2. Jennifer Doudna, "Hammering Out the Shape of a Ribozyme," *Structure*, Dec. 15, 1994.
3. Jennifer Doudna and Thomas Cech, "The Chemical Repertoire of Natural Ribozymes," *Nature*, July 11, 2002.
4. Author's interviews with Jack Szostak and Jennifer Doudna; Jennifer Doudna, "Towards the Design of an RNA Replicase," PhD thesis, Harvard University, May 1989.
5. Author's interviews with Jack Szostak, Jennifer Doudna.
6. Jeremy Murray and Jennifer Doudna, "Creative Catalysis," *Trends in Biochemical Sciences*, Dec. 2001; Tom Cech, "The RNA Worlds in Context," *Cold Spring Harbor Perspectives in Biology*, July 2012; Francis Crick, "The Origin of the Genetic Code," *Journal of Molecular Biology*, Dec. 28, 1968; Carl Woese, *The Genetic Code* (Harper & Row, 1967), 186; Walter Gilbert, "The RNA World," *Nature*, Feb. 20, 1986.
7. Jack Szostak, "Enzymatic Activity of the Conserved Core of a Group I Self-Splicing Intron," *Nature*, July 3, 1986.
8. Author's interviews with Richard Lifton, Jennifer Doudna, Jack Szostak; Greengard Prize citation for Jennifer Doudna, Oct. 2, 2018; Jennifer Doudna and Jack Szostak, "RNA-Catalysed Synthesis of Complementary-Strand RNA," *Nature*, June 15, 1989; J. Doudna, S. Couture, and J. Szostak, "A Multisubunit Ribozyme That Is a Catalyst of and Template for Complementary Strand RNA Synthesis," *Science*, Mar. 29, 1991; J. Doudna, N. Usman, and J. Szostak, "Ribozyme-Catalyzed Primer Extension by Trinucleotides," *Biochemistry*, Mar. 2, 1993.
9. Jayaraj Rajagopal, Jennifer Doudna, and Jack Szostak, "Stereochemical Course of Catalysis by the Tetrahymena Ribozyme," *Science*, May 12, 1989; Doudna and Szostak, "RNA-Catalysed Synthesis of Complementary-Strand RNA"; J. Doudna, B. P. Cormack, and J. Szostak, "RNA Structure, Not Sequence, Determines the 5' Splice-Site Specificity of a Group I Intron," *PNAS*, Oct. 1989; J. Doudna and J. Szostak, "Miniribozymes, Small Derivatives of the sunY Intron, Are Catalytically Active," *Molecular and Cell Biology*, Dec. 1989.
10. Author's interviews with Jack Szostak.
11. Author's interview with James Watson; James Watson et al., "Evolution of Catalytic Function," Cold Spring Harbor Symposium, vol. 52, 1987.

12. Author's interviews with Jennifer Doudna and James Watson; Jennifer Doudna . . . Jack Szostak, et al., "Genetic Dissection of an RNA Enzyme," Cold Spring Harbor Symposium, 1987, p. 173.

Chapter 7: Twists and Folds

1. Author's interviews with Jack Szostak, Jennifer Doudna.
2. Pollack, "Jennifer Doudna."
3. Author's interview with Lisa Twigg-Smith.
4. Jamie Cate . . . Thomas Cech, Jennifer Doudna, et al., "Crystal Structure of a Group I Ribozyme Domain: Principles of RNA Packing," *Science*, Sept. 20, 1996. For the first major step in the Boulder research, see Jennifer Doudna and Thomas Cech, "Self-Assembly of a Group I Intron Active Site from Its Component Tertiary Structural Domains," *RNA*, Mar. 1995.
5. NewsChannel 8 report, "High Tech Shower International," YouTube, May 29, 2018, https://www.youtube.com/watch?v=FxPFLbfrpNk&feature=share.

Chapter 8: Berkeley

1. Cate et al., "Crystal Structure of a Group I Ribozyme Domain."
2. Author's interviews with Jamie Cate, Jennifer Doudna.
3. Andrew Fire . . . Craig Mello, et al., "Potent and Specific Genetic Interference by Double-Stranded RNA in *Caenorhabditis elegans*," *Nature*, Feb. 19, 1998.
4. Author's interviews with Jennifer Doudna, Martin Jinek, Ross Wilson; Ian MacRae, Kaihong Zhou . . . Jennifer Doudna, et al., "Structural Basis for Double-Stranded RNA Processing by Dicer," *Science*, Jan. 13, 2006; Ian MacRae, Kaihong Zhou, and Jennifer Doudna, "Structural Determinants of RNA Recognition and Cleavage by Dicer," *Natural Structural and Molecular Biology*, Oct. 1, 2007; Ross Wilson and Jennifer Doudna, "Molecular Mechanisms of RNA Interference," *Annual Review of Biophysics*, 2013; Martin Jinek and Jennifer Doudna, "A Three-Dimensional View of the Molecular Machinery of RNA Interference," *Nature*, Jan. 22, 2009.
5. Bryan Cullen, "Viruses and RNA Interference: Issues and Controversies," *Journal of Virology*, Nov. 2014.
6. Ross Wilson and Jennifer Doudna, "Molecular Mechanisms of RNA Interference," *Annual Review of Biophysics*, May 2013.
7. Alesia Levanova and Minna Poranen, "RNA Interference as a Prospective Tool for the Control of Human Viral Infections," *Frontiers of Microbiology*, Sept. 11, 2018; Ruth Williams, "Fighting Viruses with RNAi," *The Scientist*, Oct. 10, 2013; Yang Li . . . Shou-Wei Ding, et al., "RNA Interference Functions as an Antiviral Immunity Mechanism in Mammals," *Science*, Oct. 11, 2013; Pierre Maillard . . . Olivier Voinnet, et al., "Antiviral RNA Interference in Mammalian Cells," *Science*, Oct. 11, 2013.

Chapter 9: Clustered Repeats

1. Yoshizumi Ishino . . . Atsuo Nakata, et al., "Nucleotide Sequence of the iap Gene, Responsible for Alkaline Phosphatase Isozyme Conversion in *Escherichia coli*," *Journal of Bacteriology*, Aug. 22, 1987; Yoshizumi Ishino et al., "History of CRISPR-Cas from Encounter with a Mysterious Repeated Sequence to Genome Editing Technology," *Journal of Bacteriology*, Jan. 22, 2018; Carl Zimmer, "Breakthrough DNA Editor Born of Bacteria," *Quanta*, Feb. 6, 2015.
2. Author's interviews with Francisco Mojica. This section also draws from Kevin Davies,

"Crazy about CRISPR: An Interview with Francisco Mojica," *CRISPR Journal*, Feb. 1, 2018; Heidi Ledford, "Five Big Mysteries about CRISPR's Origins," *Nature*, Jan. 12, 2017; Clara Rodríguez Fernández, "Interview with Francis Mojica, the Spanish Scientist Who Discovered CRISPR," *Labiotech*, Apr. 8, 2019; Veronique Greenwood, "The Unbearable Weirdness of CRISPR," *Nautilus*, Mar. 2017; Francisco Mojica and Lluis Montoliu, "On the Origin of CRISPR-Cas Technology," *Trends in Microbiology*, July 8, 2016; Kevin Davies, *Editing Humanity* (Simon & Schuster, 2020).

3. Francesco Mojica . . . Francisco Rodriguez-Valera, et al., "Long Stretches of Short Tandem Repeats Are Present in the Largest Replicons of the Archaea *Haloferax mediterranei* and *Haloferax volcanii* and Could Be Involved in Replicon Partitioning," *Journal of Molecular Microbiology*, July 1995.
4. Email from Ruud Jansen to Francisco Mojica, Nov. 21, 2001.
5. Ruud Jansen . . . Leo Schouls, et al., "Identification of Genes That Are Associated with DNA Repeats in Prokaryotes," *Molecular Biology*, Apr. 25, 2002.
6. Author's interviews with Francisco Mojica.
7. Sanne Klompe and Samuel Sternberg, "Harnessing 'a Billion Years of Experimentation,'" *CRISPR Journal*, Apr. 1, 2018; Eric Keen, "A Century of Phage Research," *Bioessays*, Jan. 2015; Graham Hatfull and Roger Hendrix, "Bacteriophages and Their Genomes," *Current Opinions in Virology*, Oct. 1, 2011.
8. Rodríguez Fernández, "Interview with Francis Mojica"; Greenwood, "The Unbearable Weirdness of CRISPR."
9. Author's interviews with Francisco Mojica; Rodríguez Fernández, "Interview with Francis Mojica"; Davies, "Crazy about CRISPR."
10. Francisco Mojica . . . Elena Soria, et al., "Intervening Sequences of Regularly Spaced Prokaryotic Repeats Derive from Foreign Genetic Elements," *Journal of Molecular Evolution*, Feb. 2005 (received Feb. 6, 2004; accepted Oct. 1, 2004).
11. Kira Makarova . . . Eugene Koonin, et al., "A Putative RNA-Interference-Based Immune System in Prokaryotes," *Biology Direct*, Mar. 16, 2006.

Chapter 10: The Free Speech Movement Café

1. Author's interviews with Jillian Banfield and Jennifer Doudna; Doudna and Sternberg, *A Crack in Creation*, 39; "Deep Surface Biospheres," Banfield Lab page, Berkeley University website.
2. Author's joint interview with Jillian Banfield and Jennifer Doudna.
3. Author's interview with Jennifer Doudna.

Chapter 11: Jumping In

1. Author's interviews with Blake Wiedenheft and Jennifer Doudna.
2. Kathryn Calkins, "Finding Adventure: Blake Wiedenheft's Path to Gene Editing," National Institute of General Medical Sciences, Apr. 11, 2016.
3. Emily Stifler Wolfe, "Insatiable Curiosity: Blake Wiedenheft Is at the Forefront of CRISPR Research," *Montana State University News*, June 6, 2017.
4. Blake Wiedenheft . . . Mark Young, and Trevor Douglas, "An Archaeal Antioxidant: Characterization of a Dps-Like Protein from *Sulfolobus solfataricus*," *PNAS*, July 26, 2005.
5. Author's interview with Blake Wiedenheft.
6. Author's interview with Blake Wiedenheft.
7. Author's interviews with Martin Jinek, Jennifer Doudna.

8. Kevin Davies, "Interview with Martin Jínek," *CRISPR Journal*, Apr. 2020.
9. Author's interview with Martin Jinek.
10. Jinek and Doudna, "A Three-Dimensional View of the Molecular Machinery of RNA Interference"; Martin Jinek, Scott Coyle, and Jennifer A. Doudna, "Coupled 5' Nucleotide Recognition and Processivity in Xrn1-Mediated mRNA Decay," *Molecular Cell*, Mar. 4, 2011.
11. Author's interviews with Blake Wiedenheft, Martin Jinek, Rachel Haurwitz, Jennifer Doudna.
12. Author's interviews with Blake Wiedenheft, Jennifer Doudna; Blake Wiedenheft, Kaihong Zhou, Martin Jinek . . . Jennifer Doudna, et al., "Structural Basis for DNase Activity of a Conserved Protein Implicated in CRISPR-Mediated Genome Defense," *Structure*, June 10, 2009.
13. Jinek and Doudna, "A Three-Dimensional View of the Molecular Machinery of RNA Interference."
14. Author's interviews with Martin Jinek, Blake Wiedenheft, Jennifer Doudna.
15. Wiedenheft et al., "Structural Basis for DNase Activity of a Conserved Protein."

Chapter 12: The Yogurt Makers

1. Vannevar Bush, "Science, the Endless Frontier," Office of Scientific Research and Development, July 25, 1945.
2. Matt Ridley, *How Innovation Works* (Harper Collins, 2020), 282.
3. Author's interviews with Rodolphe Barrangou.
4. Rodolphe Barrangou and Philippe Horvath, "A Decade of Discovery: CRISPR Functions and Applications," *Nature Microbiology*, June 5, 2017; Prashant Nair, "Interview with Rodolphe Barrangou," *PNAS*, July 11, 2017; author's interviews with Rodolphe Barrangou.
5. Author's interviews with Rodolphe Barrangou.
6. Rodolphe Barrangou . . . Sylvain Moineau . . . Philippe Horvath, et al., "CRISPR Provides Acquired Resistance against Viruses in Prokaryotes," *Science*, Mar. 23, 2007 (submitted Nov. 29, 2006; accepted Feb. 16, 2007).
7. Author's interviews with Sylvain Moineau, Jillian Banfield, and Rodolphe Barrangou. Conference agendas 2008–2012 provided by Banfield.
8. Author's interview with Luciano Marraffini.
9. Author's interview with Erik Sontheimer.
10. Author's interviews with Erik Sontheimer, Luciano Marraffini; Luciano Marraffini and Erik Sontheimer, "CRISPR Interference Limits Horizontal Gene Transfer in Staphylococci by Targeting DNA," *Science*, Dec. 19, 2008; Erik Sontheimer and Luciano Marraffini, "Target DNA Interference with crRNA," U.S. Provisional Patent Application 61/009,317, Sept. 23, 2008; Erik Sontheimer, letter of intent, National Institutes of Health, Dec. 29, 2008.
11. Doudna and Sternberg, *A Crack in Creation*, 62.

Chapter 13: Genentech

1. Author's interviews with Jillian Banfield and Jennifer Doudna.
2. Eugene Russo, "The Birth of Biotechnology," *Nature*, Jan. 23, 2003; Mukherjee, *The Gene*, 230.
3. Rajendra Bera, "The Story of the Cohen-Boyer Patents," *Current Science*, Mar. 25, 2009; US Patent 4,237,224 "Process for Producing Biologically Functional Molecular

Chimeras," Stanley Cohen and Herbert Boyer, filed Nov. 4, 1974; Mukherjee, *The Gene*, 237.
4. Mukherjee, *The Gene*, 238.
5. Frederic Golden, "Shaping Life in the Lab," *Time*, Mar. 9, 1981; Laura Fraser, "Cloning Insulin," Genentech corporate history; *San Francisco Examiner* front page, Oct. 14, 1980.
6. Author's interview with Rachel Haurwitz.
7. Author's interview with Jennifer Doudna.

Chapter 14: The Lab

1. Author's interviews with Rachel Haurwitz, Blake Wiedenheft, Jennifer Doudna.
2. Author's interview with Rachel Haurwitz.
3. Rachel Haurwitz, Martin Jinek, Blake Wiedenheft, Kaihong Zhou, and Jennifer Doudna, "Sequence- and Structure-Specific RNA Processing by a CRISPR Endonuclease," *Science*, Sept. 10, 2010.
4. Samuel Sternberg . . . Ruben L. Gonzalez Jr., et al., "Translation Factors Direct Intrinsic Ribosome Dynamics during Translation Termination and Ribosome Recycling," *Nature Structural and Molecular Biology*, July 13, 2009.
5. Author's interviews with Sam Sternberg.
6. Author's interviews with Sam Sternberg, Jennifer Doudna.
7. Author's interviews with Sam Sternberg, Jennifer Doudna; Sam Sternberg, "Mechanism and Engineering of CRISPR-Associated Endonucleases," PhD thesis, University of California, Berkeley, 2014.
8. Samuel Sternberg, . . . and Jennifer Doudna, "DNA Interrogation by the CRISPR RNA-Guided Endonuclease Cas9," *Nature*, Jan. 29, 2014; Sy Redding, Sam Sternberg . . . Blake Wiedenheft, Jennifer Doudna, Eric Greene, et al., "Surveillance and Processing of Foreign DNA by the *Escherichia coli* CRISPR-Cas System," *Cell*, Nov. 5, 2015.
9. Blake Wiedenheft, Samuel H. Sternberg, and Jennifer A. Doudna, "RNA-Guided Genetic Silencing Systems in Bacteria and Archaea," *Nature*, Feb. 14, 2012.
10. Author's interviews with Sam Sternberg.
11. Author's interviews with Ross Wilson, Martin Jinek.
12. Marc Lerchenmueller, Olav Sorenson, and Anupam Jena, "Gender Differences in How Scientists Present the Importance of Their Research," *BMJ*, Dec. 19, 2019; Olga Khazan, "Carry Yourself with the Confidence of a Male Scientist," *Atlantic*, Dec. 17, 2019.
13. Author's interviews with Blake Wiedenheft, Jennifer Doudna; Blake Wiedenheft, Gabriel C. Lander, Kaihong Zhou, Matthijs M. Jore, Stan J. J. Brouns, John van der Oost, Jennifer A. Doudna, and Eva Nogales, "Structures of the RNA-Guided Surveillance Complex from a Bacterial Immune System," *Nature,* Sept. 21, 2011 (received May 7, 2011; accepted July 27, 2011).

Chapter 15: Caribou

1. Author's interview with Jennifer Doudna and Rachel Haurwitz.
2. Gary Pisano, "Can Science Be a Business?," *Harvard Business Review*, Oct. 2006; Saurabh Bhatia, "History, Scope and Development of Biotechnology," *IPO Science*, May 2018.
3. Author's interviews with Rachel Haurwitz, Jennifer Doudna.
4. Bush, "Science, the Endless Frontier."
5. "Sparking Economic Growth," The Science Coalition, April 2017.

6. "Kit for Global RNP Profiling," NIH award 1R43GM105087-01, for Rachel Haurwitz and Caribou Biosciences, Apr. 15, 2013.
7. Author's interviews with Jennifer Doudna, Rachel Haurwitz; Robert Sanders, "Gates Foundation Awards $100,000 Grants for Novel Global Health Research," *Berkeley News*, May 10, 2010.

Chapter 16: Emmanuelle Charpentier

1. Author's interviews with Emmanuelle Charpentier. This chapter also draws from Uta Deffke, "An Artist in Gene Editing," *Max Planck Research Magazine*, Jan. 2016; "Interview with Emmanuelle Charpentier," *FEMS Microbiology Letters*, Feb. 1, 2018; Alison Abbott, "A CRISPR Vision," *Nature*, Apr. 28, 2016; Kevin Davies, "Finding Her Niche: An Interview with Emmanuelle Charpentier," *CRISPR Journal*, Feb. 21, 2019; Margaret Knox, "The Gene Genie," *Scientific American*, Dec. 2014; Jennifer Doudna, "Why Genome Editing Will Change Our Lives," *Financial Times*, Mar. 24, 2018; Martin Jinek, Krzysztof Chylinski, Ines Fonfara, Michael Hauer, Jennifer Doudna, and Emmanuelle Charpentier, "A Programmable Dual-RNA–Guided DNA Endonuclease in Adaptive Bacterial Immunity," *Science*, Aug. 17, 2012.
2. Author's interview with Emmanuelle Charpentier.
3. Author's interviews with Rodger Novak, Emmanuelle Charpentier; Rodger Novak, Emmanuelle Charpentier, Johann S. Braun, and Elaine Tuomanen, "Signal Transduction by a Death Signal Peptide Uncovering the Mechanism of Bacterial Killing by Penicillin," *Molecular Cell*, Jan. 1, 2000.
4. Emmanuelle Charpentier . . . Pamela Cowin, et al., "Plakoglobin Suppresses Epithelial Proliferation and Hair Growth in Vivo," *Journal of Cell Biology*, May 2000; Monika Mangold . . . Rodger Novak, Richard Novick, Emmanuelle Charpentier, et al., "Synthesis of Group A Streptococcal Virulence Factors Is Controlled by a Regulatory RNA Molecule," *Molecular Biology*, Aug. 3, 2004; Davies, "Finding Her Niche"; Philip Hemme, "Fireside Chat with Rodger Novak," *Refresh Berlin*, May 24, 2016, Labiotech .eu.
5. Author's interview with Emmanuelle Charpentier.
6. Elitza Deltcheva, Krzysztof Chylinski . . . Emmanuelle Charpentier, et al., "CRISPR RNA Maturation by Trans-encoded Small RNA and Host Factor RNase III," *Nature*, Mar. 31, 2011.
7. Author's interviews with Emmanuelle Charpentier, Jennifer Doudna, Erik Sontheimer; Doudna and Sternberg, *A Crack in Creation*, 71–73.
8. Author's interviews with Martin Jinek, Jennifer Doudna. See also Kevin Davies, interview with Martin Jinek, *CRISPR Journal*, Apr. 2020.

Chapter 17: CRISPR-Cas9

1. Author's interviews with Martin Jinek, Jennifer Doudna, Emmanuelle Charpentier.
2. Richard Asher, "An Interview with Krzysztof Chylinski," *Pioneers Zero21*, Oct. 2018.
3. Author's interviews with Jennifer Doudna, Emmanuelle Charpentier, Martin Jinek, Ross Wilson.
4. Author's interviews with Jennifer Doudna, Martin Jinek.
5. Author's interviews with Jennifer Doudna, Martin Jinek, Sam Sternberg, Rachel Haurwitz, Ross Wilson.

Chapter 18: Science, *2012*

1. Author's interviews with Jennifer Doudna, Emmanuelle Charpentier, and Martin Jinek.
2. Jinek et al., "A Programmable Dual-RNA–Guided DNA Endonuclease in Adaptive Bacterial Immunity."
3. Author's interview with Emmanuelle Charpentier.
4. Author's interviews with Emmanuelle Charpentier, Jennifer Doudna, Martin Jinek, and Sam Sternberg.

Chapter 19: Dueling Presentations

1. Author's interview with Virginijus Šikšnys.
2. Giedrius Gasiunas, Rodolphe Barrangou, Philippe Horvath, and Virginijus Šikšnys, "Cas9–crRNA Ribonucleoprotein Complex Mediates Specific DNA Cleavage for Adaptive Immunity in Bacteria," *PNAS*, Sept. 25, 2012 (received May 21, 2012; approved Aug. 1; published online Sept. 4).
3. Author's interview with Rodolphe Barrangou.
4. Author's interview with Eric Lander.
5. Author's interviews with Erik Lander, Jennifer Doudna.
6. Author's interview with Rodolphe Barrangou.
7. Virginijus Šikšnys et al., "RNA-Directed Cleavage by the Cas9-crRNA Complex," international patent application WO 2013/142578 Al, priority date Mar. 20, 2012, official filing Mar. 20, 2013, publication Sept. 26, 2013.
8. Author's interviews with Virginijus Šikšnys, Jennifer Doudna, Sam Sternberg, Emmanuelle Charpentier, and Martin Jinek.
9. Author's interviews with Sam Sternberg, Rodolph Barrangou, Erik Sontheimer, Virginijus Šikšnys, Jennifer Doudna, Martin Jinek, and Emmanuelle Charpentier.

Chapter 20: A Human Tool

1. Srinivasan Chandrasegaran and Dana Carroll, "Origins of Programmable Nucleases for Genome Engineering," *Journal of Molecular Biology,* Feb. 27, 2016.

Chapter 21: The Race

1. Author's interviews with Jennifer Doudna; Doudna and Sternberg, *A Crack in Creation*, 242.
2. Ferric C. Fang and Arturo Casadevall, "Is Competition Ruining Science?," *American Society for Microbiology*, Apr. 2015; Melissa Anderson ... Brian Martinson, et al., "The Perverse Effects of Competition on Scientists' Work and Relationships," *Science Engineering Ethics*, Dec. 2007; Matt Ridley, "Two Cheers for Scientific Backbiting," *Wall Street Journal*, July 27, 2012.
3. Author's interview with Emmanuelle Charpentier.

Chapter 22: Feng Zhang

1. Author's interviews with Feng Zhang. This section also draws from Eric Topol, podcast interview with Feng Zhang, Medscape, Mar. 31, 2017; Michael Specter, "The Gene Hackers," *New Yorker*, Nov. 8, 2015; Sharon Begley, "Meet One of the World's Most Groundbreaking Scientists," *Stat*, Nov. 6, 2015.
2. Galen Johnson, "Gifted and Talented Education Grades K–12 Program Evaluation," Des Moines Public Schools, September 1996.

3. Edward Boyden, Feng Zhang, Ernst Bamberg, Georg Nagel, and Karl Deisseroth, "Millisecond-Timescale, Genetically Targeted Optical Control of Neural Activity," *Nature Neuroscience*, Aug. 14, 2005; Alexander Aravanis, Li-Ping Wang, Feng Zhang . . . and Karl Deisseroth, "An Optical Neural Interface: In vivo Control of Rodent Motor Cortex with Integrated Fiberoptic and Optogenetic Technology," *Journal of Neural Engineering*, Sept. 2007.
4. Feng Zhang, Le Cong, Simona Lodato, Sriram Kosuri, George M. Church, and Paola Arlotta, "Efficient Construction of Sequence-Specific TAL Effectors for Modulating Mammalian Transcription," *Nature Biotechnology*, Jan. 19, 2011.

Chapter 23: George Church

1. This section is based on author's interviews and visits with George Church and also Ben Mezrich, *Woolly* (Atria, 2017); Anna Azvolinsky, "Curious George," *The Scientist*, Oct. 1, 2016; Sharon Begley, "George Church Has a Wild Idea to Upend Evolution," *Stat*, May 16, 2016; Prashant Nair, "George Church," *PNAS*, July 24, 2012; Jeneen Interlandi, "The Church of George Church," *Popular Science*, May 27, 2015.
2. Mezrich, *Woolly*, 43.
3. George Church Oral History, National Human Genome Research Institute, July 26, 2017.
4. Nicholas Wade, "Regenerating a Mammoth for $10 Million," *New York Times*, Nov. 19, 2008; Nicholas Wade, "The Wooly Mammoth's Last Stand," *New York Times*, Mar. 2, 2017; Mezrich, *Woolly*.
5. Author's interviews with George Church and Jennifer Doudna.

Chapter 24: Zhang Tackles CRISPR

1. Josiane Garneau . . . Rodolphe Barrangou . . . Philippe Horvath, Alfonso H. Magadán, and Sylvain Moineau, "The CRISPR/Cas Bacterial Immune System Cleaves Bacteriophage and Plasmid DNA," *Nature*, Nov. 3, 2010.
2. Davies, *Editing Humanity*, 80; author's interview with Le Cong.
3. Author's interviews with Eric Lander, Feng Zhang; Begley, "George Church Has a Wild Idea . . ."; Michael Specter, "The Gene Hackers," *New Yorker*, Nov. 8, 2015; Davies, *Editing Humanity*, 82.
4. Feng Zhang, "Confidential Memorandum of Invention," Feb. 13, 2013.
5. David Altshuler, Chad Cowan, Feng Zhang, et al., Grant application 1R01DK097758-01, "Isogenic Human Pluripotent Stem Cell-Based Models of Human Disease Mutations," National Institutes of Health, Jan. 12, 2012.
6. Broad Opposition 3; UC reply 3.
7. Author's interviews with Luciano Marraffini and Erik Sontheimer; Marraffini and Sontheimer, "CRISPR Interference Limits Horizontal Gene Transfer in Staphylococci by Targeting DNA"; Sontheimer and Marraffini, "Target DNA Interference with crRNA," U.S. Provisional Patent Application; Kevin Davies, "Interview with Luciano Marraffini," *CRISPR Journal*, Feb. 2020.
8. Author's interviews with Luciano Marraffini and Feng Zhang; Zhang email to Marraffini, Jan. 2, 2012 (given to me by Marraffini).
9. Marraffini email to Zhang, Jan. 11, 2012.
10. Eric Lander, "The Heroes of CRISPR," *Cell*, Jan. 14, 2016.
11. Author's interviews with Feng Zhang.
12. Feng Zhang, "Declaration in Connection with U.S. Patent Application Serial 14 /0054,414," USPTO, Jan. 30, 2014.

13. Shuailiang Lin, "Summary of CRISPR Work during Oct. 2011–June 2012," Exhibit 14 to Neville Sanjana Declaration, July 23, 2015, UC et al. Reply 3, exhibit 1614, in *Broad v. UC*, Patent Interference 106,048.
14. Shuailiang Lin email to Jennifer Doudna, Feb. 28, 2015.
15. Antonio Regalado, "In CRISPR Fight, Co-Inventor Says Broad Institute Misled Patent Office," *MIT Technology Review*, Aug. 17, 2016.
16. Author's interviews with Dana Carroll; Dana Carroll, "Declaration in Support of Suggestion of Interference," University of California Exhibit 1476, Interference No. 106,048, Apr. 10, 2015.
17. Carroll, "Declaration"; Berkeley et al., "List of Intended Motions," Patent Interference No. 106,115, USPTO, July 30, 2019.
18. Author's interviews with Jennifer Doudna and Feng Zhang; Broad et al., "Contingent Responsive Motion 6" and "Constructive Reduction to Practice by Embodiment 17," USPTO, Patent Interference 106,048, June 22, 2016.
19. Author's interviews with Feng Zhang and Luciano Marraffini. See also Davies, "Interview with Luciano Marraffini."

Chapter 25: Doudna Joins the Race

1. Author's interviews with Martin Jinek and Jennifer Doudna.
2. Melissa Pandika, "Jennifer Doudna, CRISPR Code Killer," *Ozy*, Jan. 7, 2014.
3. Author's interviews with Jennifer Doudna and Martin Jinek.

Chapter 26: Photo Finish

1. Author's interviews with Feng Zhang; Fei Ann Ran, "CRISPR-Cas9," *NABC Report* 26, ed. Alan Eaglesham and Ralph Hardy, Oct. 8, 2014.
2. Le Cong, Fei Ann Ran, David Cox, Shuailiang Lin . . . Luciano Marraffini, and Feng Zhang, "Multiplex Genome Engineering Using CRISPR/Cas Systems," *Science*, Feb. 15, 2013 (received Oct. 5, 2012; accepted Dec. 12; published online Jan. 3, 2013).
3. Author's interviews with George Church, Eric Lander, and Feng Zhang.
4. Author's email interviews with Le Cong.
5. Author's interview with George Church.
6. Prashant Mali . . . George Church, et al., "RNA-Guided Human Genome Engineering via Cas9," *Science*, Feb. 15, 2013 (received Oct. 26, 2012; accepted Dec. 12, 2012; published online Jan. 3, 2013).

Chapter 27: Doudna's Final Sprint

1. Pandika, "Jennifer Doudna, CRISPR Code Killer."
2. Author's interviews with Jennifer Doudna and Martin Jinek.
3. Michael M. Cox, Jennifer Doudna, and Michael O'Donnell, *Molecular Biology: Principles and Practice* (W. H. Freeman, 2011). The first edition cost $195.
4. It was Detlef Weigel, at the Max Planck Institute for Developmental Biology.
5. Author's interviews with Emmanuelle Charpentier and Jennifer Doudna.
6. Detlef Weigel decision letter and Jennifer Doudna author response, *eLife*, Jan. 29, 2013.
7. Martin Jinek, Alexandra East, Aaron Cheng, Steven Lin, Enbo Ma, and Jennifer Doudna, "RNA-Programmed Genome Editing in Human Cells," *eLife*, Jan. 29, 2013 (received Dec. 15, 2012; accepted Jan. 3, 2013).
8. Jin-Soo Kim email to Jennifer Doudna, July 16, 2012; Seung Woo Cho, Sojung Kim, Jong Min Kim, and Jin-Soo Kim, "Targeted Genome Engineering in Human Cells

with the Cas9 RNA-Guided Endonuclease," *Nature Biotechnology*, Mar. 2013 (received Nov. 20, 2012; accepted Jan. 14, 2013; published online Jan. 29, 2013).

9. Woong Y. Hwang . . . Keith Joung, et al., "Efficient Genome Editing in Zebrafish Using a CRISPR-Cas System," *Nature Biotechnology*, Jan. 29, 2013.

Chapter 28: Forming Companies

1. Author's interviews with Andy May, Jennifer Doudna, and Rachel Haurwitz.
2. George Church interview, "Can Neanderthals Be Brought Back from the Dead?," *Spiegel*, Jan. 18, 2013; David Wagner, "How the Viral Neanderthal-Baby Story Turned Real Science into Junk Journalism," *The Atlantic*, Jan. 22, 2013.
3. Author's interview with Rodger Novak; Hemme, "Fireside Chat with Rodger Novak"; Jon Cohen, "Birth of CRISPR Inc.," *Science*, Feb. 17, 2017; author's interviews with Emmanuelle Charpentier.
4. Author's interviews with Jennifer Doudna, George Church, and Emmanuelle Charpentier.
5. Author's interviews with Rodger Novak and Emmanuelle Charpentier.
6. Author's interview with Andy May.
7. Hemme, "Fireside Chat with Rodger Novak."
8. Author's interviews with Jennifer Doudna.
9. Editas Medicine, SEC 10-K filing 2016 and 2019; John Carroll, "Biotech Pioneer in 'Gene Editing' Launches with $43M in VC Cash," *FierceBiotech*, Nov. 25, 2013.
10. Author's interviews with Jennifer Doudna, Rachel Haurwitz, Erik Sontheimer, and Luciano Marraffini.

Chapter 29: Mon Amie

1. Author's interviews with Jennifer Doudna, Emmanuelle Charpentier, and Martin Jinek; Martin Jinek . . . Samuel Sternberg . . . Kaihong Zhou . . . Emmanuelle Charpentier, Eva Nogales, Jennifer A. Doudna, et al., "Structures of Cas9 Endonucleases Reveal RNA-Mediated Conformational Activation," *Science*, Mar. 14, 2014.
2. Jennifer Doudna and Emmanuelle Charpentier, "The New Frontier of Genome Engineering with CRISPR-Cas9," *Science*, Nov. 28, 2014.
3. Author's interviews with Jennifer Doudna and Emmanuelle Charpentier.
4. Hemme, "Fireside Chat with Rodger Novak"; author's interview with Rodger Novak.
5. Author's interview with Rodolphe Barrangou.
6. Davies, *Editing Humanity*, 96.
7. Author's interview with Jennifer Doudna; "CRISPR Timeline," Broad Institute website, broadinstitute.org.
8. Author's interview with Eric Lander; Breakthrough Prize ceremony, Mar. 19, 2015.
9. Author's interviews with Jennifer Doudna, George Church; Gairdner Awards ceremony, Oct. 27, 2016.

Chapter 30: The Heroes of CRISPR

1. Author's interviews with Eric Lander and Emmanuelle Charpentier.
2. Lander, "The Heroes of CRISPR."
3. Michael Eisen, "The Villain of CRISPR," *It Is Not Junk*, Jan. 25, 2016.
4. "Heroes of CRISPR," eighty-four comments, PubPeer, https://pubpeer.com/publications/D400145518C0A557E9A79F7BB20294; Sharon Begley, "Controversial CRISPR History Set Off an Online Firestorm," *Stat*, Jan. 19, 2016.

5. Nathaniel Comfort, "A Whig History of CRISPR," *Genotopia*, Jan. 18, 2016; @nccom fort, "I made a hashtag that became a thing! #Landergate," Twitter, Jan. 27, 2016.
6. Antonio Regalado, "A Scientist's Contested History of CRISPR," *MIT Technology Review*, Jan. 19, 2016.
7. Ruth Reader, "These Women Helped Create CRISPR Gene Editing. So Why Are They Written Out of Its History?," *Mic*, Jan. 22, 2016; Joanna Rothkopf, "How One Man Tried to Write Women Out of CRISPR, the Biggest Biotech Innovation in Decades," *Jezebel*, Jan. 20, 2016.
8. Stephen Hall, "The Embarrassing, Destructive Fight over Biotech's Big Breakthrough," *Scientific American*, Feb. 4, 2016.
9. Tracy Vence, "'Heroes of CRISPR' Disputed," *The Scientist*, Jan. 19, 2016.
10. Author's interview with Jack Szostak.
11. Eric Lander, email to the Broad Institute staff, Jan. 28, 2016.
12. Joel Achenbach, "Eric Lander Talks CRISPR and the Infamous Nobel 'Rule of Three,'" *Washington Post*, Apr. 21, 2016.

Chapter 31: Patents

1. *Diamond v. Chakrabarty*, 447 U.S. 303, U.S. Supreme Court, 1980; Douglas Robinson and Nina Medlock, "*Diamond v. Chakrabarty*: A Retrospective on 25 Years of Biotech Patents," *Intellectual Property & Technology Law Journal*, Oct. 2005.
2. Michael Eisen, "Patents Are Destroying the Soul of Academic Science," *it is NOT junk* (blog), Feb. 20, 2017. See also Alfred Engelberg, "Taxpayers Are Entitled to Reasonable Prices on Federally Funded Drug Discoveries," *Modern Healthcare*, July 18, 2018.
3. Author's interview with Eldora Ellison.
4. Martin Jinek, Jennifer Doudna, Emmanuelle Charpentier, and Krzysztof Chylinski, U.S. Patent Application 61/652,086, "Methods and Compositions, for RNA-Directed Site-Specific DNA Modification," filed May 25, 2012; Jacob Sherkow, "Patent Protection for CRISPR," *Journal of Law and the Biosciences*, Dec. 7, 2017.
5. "CRISPR-Cas Systems and Methods for Altering Expressions of Gene Products," provisional application No. 61/736,527, filed on Dec. 12, 2012, which in 2014 resulted in U.S. Patent No. 8,697,359. This application, later revised, included Luciano Marraffini as well as Feng Zhang, Le Cong, and Shuailiang Lin as inventors.
6. The main patent application and related filings of Zhang/Broad can be found through the U.S. Patent Office as U.S. Provisional Patent Application No. 61/736,527. The Doudna/Charpentier/Berkeley filings are under U.S. Provisional Patent Application No. 61/652,086. A good guide to the patent issues is the work of Jacob Sherkow of New York Law School, which includes "Law, History and Lessons in the CRISPR Patent Conflict," *Nature Biotechnology*, Mar. 2015; "Patents in the Time of CRISPR," *Biochemist*, June 2016; "Inventive Steps: The CRISPR Patent Dispute and Scientific Progress," *EMBO Reports*, May 23, 2017; "Patent Protection for CRISPR."
7. Author's interviews with George Church, Jennifer Doudna, Erik Lander, and Feng Zhang.
8. "CRISPR-Cas Systems and Methods for Altering Expressions of Gene Products," provisional application No. 61/736,527.
9. Author's interviews with Luciano Marraffini.
10. Author's interviews with Feng Zhang and Eric Lander; Lander, "Heroes of CRISPR."
11. U.S. Patent No. 8,697,359.

12. Author's interviews with Andy May and Jennifer Doudna.
13. Provisional patent application U.S. 2012/61652086P and published patent application U.S. 2014/0068797A1 of Doudna et al.; Provisional patent application U.S. 2012 /61736527P (Dec. 12, 2012) and granted patent US 8,697,359 B1 (Apr. 15, 2014) of Zhang et al.
14. "Suggestion of Interference" and "Declaration of Dana Carroll, PhD, in Support of Suggestion of Interference," in re Patent Application of Jennifer Doudna et al., serial no. 2013/842859, U.S. Patent and Trademark Office, Apr. 10 and 13, 2015; Mark Summerfield, "CRISPR—Will This Be the Last Great US Patent Interference?," *Patentology*, July 11, 2015; Jacob Sherkow, "The CRISPR Patent Interference Showdown Is On," Stanford Law School blog, Dec. 29, 2015; Antonio Regalado, "CRISPR Patent Fight Now a Winner-Take-All Match," *MIT Technology Review*, Apr. 15, 2015.
15. Feng Zhang, "Declaration," in re Patent Application of Feng Zhang, Serial no. 2014 /054,414, Jan. 30, 2014, provided privately to the author.
16. *In re Dow Chemical Co.*, 837 F.2d 469, 473 (Fed. Cir. 1988).
17 Jacob Sherkow, "Inventive Steps: The CRISPR Patent Dispute and Scientific Progress," *EMBO Reports*, May 23, 2017; Broad et al. contingent responsive motion 6 for benefit of Broad et al. Application 61/736,527, USPTO, June 22, 2016; University of California et al., Opposition motion 2, Patent Interference case 106,048, USPTO, Aug. 15, 2016 (Opposing Broad's Allegations of No Interference-in-Fact).
18. Alessandra Potenza, "Who Owns CRISPR?," *The Verge*, Dec. 6, 2016; Jacob Sherkow, "Biotech Trial of the Century Could Determine Who Owns CRISPR," *MIT Technology Review*, Dec. 7, 2016; Sharon Begley, "CRISPR Court Hearing Puts University of California on the Defensive," *Stat*, Dec. 6, 2016.
19. Transcript of oral arguments before the patent trial board, Dec. 6, 2016, Patent Interference Case 106,048, U.S. Patent and Trademark Office.
20. Jennifer Doudna interview, *Catalyst*, UC Berkeley College of Chemistry, July 10, 2014.
21. Berkeley substantive motion 4, Patent Interference Case 106,048, May 23, 2016. See also Broad substantive motions 2, 3, and 5.
22. Patent Trial Board Judgment and Decision on Motions, Patent Interference Case 106,048, Feb. 15, 2017.
23. Judge Kimberly Moore, decision, Patent Interference Case 106,048, United States Court of Appeals for the Federal Circuit, Sept. 10, 2018.
24. Author's interviews with Eldora Ellison.
25. Patent Interference No. 106,115, Patent Trial and Appeal Board, June 24, 2019.
26. Oral argument, Patent Interference No. 106,115, Patent Trial and Appeal Board, May 18, 2020.
27. "Methods and Compositions for RNA-Directed Target DNA Modification," European Patent Office, patent EP2800811, granted Apr. 7, 2017; Jef Akst, "UC Berkeley Receives CRISPR Patent in Europe," *The Scientist*, Mar. 24, 2017; Sherkow, "Inventive Steps."
28. Author's interviews with Luciano Marraffini; "Engineering of Systems, Methods, and Optimized Guide Compositions for Sequence Manipulation," European Patent Office, patent EP2771468; Kelly Servick, "Broad Institute Takes a Hit in European CRISPR Patent Struggle," *Science*, Jan. 18, 2018; Rory O'Neill, "EPO Revokes Broad's CRISPR Patent," *Life Sciences Intellectual Property Review*, Jan. 16, 2020.
29. Author's interview with Andy May.

Chapter 32: Therapies

1. Rob Stein, "In a First, Doctors in U.S. Use CRISPR Tool to Treat Patient with Genetic Disorder," *Morning Edition*, NPR, July 29, 2019; Rob Stein, "A Young Mississippi Woman's Journey through a Pioneering Gene-Editing Experiment," *All Things Considered*, NPR, Dec. 25, 2019.
2. "CRISPR Therapeutics and Vertex Announce New Clinical Data," CRISPR Therapeutics, June 12, 2020.
3. Rob Stein, "A Year In, 1st Patient to Get Gene-Editing for Sickle Cell Disease Is Thriving," *Morning Edition*, NPR, June 23, 2020.
4. Author's interview with Emmanuelle Charpentier.
5. Author's interview with Jennifer Doudna.
6. "Proposal for an IGI Sickle Cell Initiative," Innovative Genomics Institute, February 2020.
7. Preetika Rana, Amy Dockser Marcus, and Wenxin Fan, "China, Unhampered by Rules, Races Ahead in Gene-Editing Trials," *Wall Street Journal*, Jan. 21, 2018.
8. David Cyranoski, "CRISPR Gene-Editing Tested in a Person for the First Time," *Nature*, Nov. 15, 2016.
9. Jennifer Hamilton and Jennifer Doudna, "Knocking Out Barriers to Engineered Cell Activity," *Science*, Feb. 6, 2020; Edward Stadtmauer . . . Carl June, et al., "CRISPR-Engineered T Cells in Patients with Refractory Cancer," *Science*, Feb. 6, 2020.
10. "CRISPR Diagnostics in Cancer Treatments," Mammoth Biosciences website, June 11, 2019.
11. "Single Ascending Dose Study in Participants with LCA10," ClinicalTrials.gov, Mar. 13, 2019, identifier: NCT03872479; Morgan Maeder . . . and Haiyan Jiang, "Development of a Gene-Editing Approach to Restore Vision Loss in Leber Congenital Amaurosis Type 10," *Nature*, Jan. 21, 2019.
12. Marilynn Marchione, "Doctors Try 1st CRISPR Editing in the Body for Blindness," AP, Mar. 4, 2020.
13. Sharon Begley, "CRISPR Babies' Lab Asked U.S. Scientist for Help to Disable Cholesterol Gene in Human Embryos," *Stat*, Dec. 4, 2018; Anthony King, "A CRISPR Edit for Heart Disease," *Nature*, Mar. 7, 2018.
14. Matthew Porteus, "A New Class of Medicines through DNA Editing," *New England Journal of Medicine*, Mar. 7, 2019; Sharon Begley, "CRISPR Trackr: Latest Advances," *Stat Plus*.

Chapter 33: Biohacking

1. Josiah Zayner, "DIY Human CRISPR Myostatin Knock-Out," YouTube, Oct. 6, 2017; Sarah Zhang, "Biohacker Regrets Injecting Himself with CRISPR on Live TV," *The Atlantic*, Feb. 20, 2018; Stephanie Lee, "This Guy Says He's the First Person to Attempt Editing His DNA with CRISPR," *BuzzFeed*, Oct. 14, 2017.
2. Kate McLean and Mario Furloni, "Gut Hack," *New York Times* op-doc, Apr. 11, 2017; Arielle Duhaime-Ross, "A Bitter Pill," *The Verge*, May 4, 2016.
3. "About us," The Odin, https://www.the-odin.com/about-us/; author's interviews with Josiah Zayner.
4. Author's interviews with Josiah Zayner and Kevin Doxzen.
5. Author's interview with Josiah Zayner. See also Josiah Zayner, "CRISPR Babies Scientist He Jiankui Should Not Be Villainized," *Stat*, Jan. 2, 2020.

Chapter 34: DARPA and anti-CRISPR

1. Heidi Ledford, "CRISPR, the Disruptor," *Nature*, June 3, 2015. Danilo Maddalo . . . and Andrea Ventura, "In vivo Engineering of Oncogenic Chromosomal Rearrangements with the CRISPR/Cas9 System," *Nature*, Oct. 22, 2014; Sidi Chen, Neville E. Sanjana . . . Feng Zhang, and Phillip A. Sharp, "Genome-wide CRISPR Screen in a Mouse Model of Tumor Growth and Metastasis," *Cell*, Mar. 12, 2015.
2. James Clapper, "Threat Assessment of the U.S. Intelligence Community," Feb. 9, 2016; Antonio Regalado, "The Search for the Kryptonite That Can Stop CRISPR," *MIT Technology Review*, May 2, 2019; Robert Sanders, "Defense Department Pours $65 Million into Making CRISPR Safer," *Berkeley News*, July 19, 2017.
3. Defense Advanced Research Projects Agency, "Building the Safe Genes Toolkit," July 19, 2017.
4. Author's interview with Jennifer Doudna.
5. Author's interview with Joe Bondy-Denomy; Joe Bondy-Denomy, April Pawluk . . . Alan R. Davidson, et al., "Bacteriophage Genes That Inactivate the CRISPR/Cas Bacterial Immune System," *Nature*, Jan. 17, 2013; Elie Dolgin, "Kill Switch for CRISPR Could Make Gene Editing Safer," *Nature*, Jan. 15, 2020.
6. Jiyung Shin . . . Joseph Bondy-Denomy, and Jennifer Doudna, "Disabling Cas9 by an Anti-CRISPR DNA Mimic," *Science Advances*, July 12, 2017.
7. Nicole D. Marino . . . and Joseph Bondy-Denomy, "Anti-CRISPR Protein Applications: Natural Brakes for CRISPR-Cas Technologies," *Nature Methods*, Mar. 16, 2020.
8. Author's interview with Fyodor Urnov; Emily Mullin, "The Defense Department Plans to Build Radiation-Proof CRISPR Soldiers," *One Zero*, Sept. 27, 2019.
9. Author's interviews with Jennifer Doudna and Gavin Knott.
10. Author's interviews with Josiah Zayner.

Chapter 35: Rules of the Road

1. Robert Sinsheimer, "The Prospect of Designed Genetic Change," *Engineering and Science*, Caltech, Apr. 1969.
2. Bentley Glass, Presidential Address to the AAAS, Dec. 28, 1970, *Science*, Jan. 8, 1971.
3. John Fletcher, *The Ethics of Genetic Control: Ending Reproductive Roulette* (Doubleday, 1974), 158.
4. Paul Ramsey, *Fabricated Man* (Yale, 1970), 138.
5. Ted Howard and Jeremy Rifkin, *Who Should Play God?* (Delacorte, 1977), 14; Dick Thompson, "The Most Hated Man in Science," *Time*, Dec. 4, 1989.
6. Shane Crotty, *Ahead of the Curve* (University of California, 2003), 93; Mukherjee, *The Gene*, 225.
7. Paul Berg et al., "Potential Biohazards of Recombinant DNA Molecules, " *Science*, July 26, 1974.
8. Author's interview with David Baltimore; Michael Rogers, "The Pandora's Box Conference," *Rolling Stone*, June 19, 1975; Michael Rogers, *Biohazard* (Random House, 1977); Crotty, *Ahead of the Curve*, 104–8; Mukherjee, *The Gene*, 226–30; Donald S. Fredrickson, "Asilomar and Recombinant DNA: The End of the Beginning," in *Biomedical Politics* (National Academies Press, 1991); Richard Hindmarsh and Herbert Gottweis, "Recombinant Regulation: The Asilomar Legacy 30 Years On," *Science as Culture*, Fall 2005; Daniel Gregorowius, Nikola Biller-Andorno, and Anna Deplazes-Zemp, "The Role of Scientific Self-Regulation for the Control of Genome Editing

in the Human Germline," *EMBO Reports*, Feb. 20, 2017; Jim Kozubek, *Modern Prometheus* (Cambridge, 2016), 124.

9. Author's interviews with James Watson and David Baltimore.
10. Paul Berg et al., "Summary Statement of the Asilomar Conference on Recombinant DNA Molecules," *PNAS*, June 1975.
11. Paul Berg, "Asilomar and Recombinant DNA," *The Scientist*, Mar. 18, 2002.
12. Hindmarsh and Gottweis, "Recombinant Regulation," 301.
13. Claire Randall, Rabbi Bernard Mandelbaum, and Bishop Thomas Kelly, "Message from Three General Secretaries to President Jimmy Carter," June 20, 1980.
14. Morris Abram et al., *Splicing Life*, President's Commission for the Study of Ethical Problems in Medicine and Biomedical and Behavioral Research, Nov. 16, 1982.
15. Alan Handyside et al., "Birth of a Normal Girl after in vitro Fertilization and Preimplantation Diagnostic Testing for Cystic Fibrosis," *New England Journal of Medicine*, Sept. 1992.
16. Roger Ebert, *Gattaca* review, Oct. 24, 1997, rogerebert.com.
17. Gregory Stock and John Campbell, *Engineering the Human Germline* (Oxford, 2000), 73–95; author's interviews with James Watson; Gina Kolata, "Scientists Brace for Changes in Path of Human Evolution," *New York Times*, Mar. 21, 1998.
18. Steve Connor, "Nobel Scientist Happy to 'Play God' with DNA," *The Independent*, May 17, 2000.
19. Lee Silver, *Remaking Eden* (Avon, 1997), 4.
20. Lee Silver, "Reprogenetics: Third Millennium Speculation," *EMBO Reports*, Nov. 15, 2000.
21. Gregory Stock, *Redesigning Humans: Our Inevitable Genetic Future* (Houghton Mifflin, 2002), 170.
22. Council of Europe, "Oviedo Convention and Its Protocols," April 4, 1997.
23. Sheryl Gay Stolberg, "The Biotech Death of Jesse Gelsinger," *New York Times*, Nov. 28, 1999.
24. Meir Rinde, "The Death of Jesse Gelsinger," *Science History Institute*, June 4, 2019.
25. Harvey Flaumenhaft, "The Career of Leon Kass," *Journal of Contemporary Health Law & Policy*, 2004; "Leon Kass," Conversations with Bill Kristol, Dec. 2015, https://conversationswithbillkristol.org/video/leon-kass/.
26. Leon Kass, "What Price the Perfect Baby?," *Science*, July 9, 1971; Leon Kass, "Review of *Fabricated Man* by Paul Ramsey," *Theology Today*, Apr. 1, 1971; Leon Kass, "Making Babies: the New Biology and the Old Morality," *Public Interest*, Winter 1972.
27. Michael Sandel, "The Case against Perfection," *The Atlantic*, Apr. 2004; Michael Sandel, *The Case Against Perfection* (Harvard, 2007).
28. Francis Fukuyama, *Our Posthuman Future* (Farrar, Straus and Giroux, 2000), 10.
29. Leon Kass et al., *Beyond Therapy: Biotechnology and the Pursuit of Happiness*, report of the President's Council on Bioethics, October 2003.

Chapter 36: Doudna Steps In

1. Doudna and Sternberg, *A Crack in Creation*, 198; Michael Specter, "Humans 2.0," *New Yorker*, Nov. 16, 2015; author's interview with Jennifer Doudna.
2. Author's interviews with Sam Sternberg and Lauren Buchman.
3. Author's interviews with George Church and Lauren Buchman.
4. Doudna and Sternberg, *A Crack in Creation*, 199–220; author's interviews with Jennifer Doudna and Sam Sternberg.

5. Author's interviews with David Baltimore, Jennifer Doudna, Sam Sternberg, and Dana Carroll.
6. David Baltimore, et al., "A Prudent Path Forward for Genomic Engineering and Germline Gene Modification," *Science*, Apr. 3, 2015 (published online Mar. 19).
7. Nicholas Wade, "Scientists Seek Ban on Method of Editing the Human Genome," *New York Times*, Mar. 19, 2015.
8. See, for example, Edward Lanphier, Fyodor Urnov, et al., "Don't Edit the Human Germ Line," *Nature*, Mar. 12, 2015.
9. Author's interviews with Jennifer Doudna, Sam Sternberg; Doudna and Sternberg, *A Crack in Creation*, 214ff.
10. Puping Liang . . . Junjiu Huang, et al., "CRISPR/Cas9-Mediated Gene Editing in Human Tripronuclear Zygotes," *Protein & Cell*, May 2015 (published online Apr. 18).
11. Rob Stein, "Critics Lash Out at Chinese Scientists Who Edited DNA in Human Embryos," *Morning Edition*, NPR, April 23, 2015.
12. Author's interviews with Ting Wu, George Church, Jennifer Doudna; Johnny Kung, "Increasing Policymaker's Interest in Genetics," pgEd briefing paper, Dec. 1, 2015.
13. Jennifer Doudna, "Embryo Editing Needs Scrutiny," *Nature*, Dec. 3, 2015.
14. George Church, "Encourage the Innovators," *Nature*, Dec. 3, 2015.
15. Steven Pinker, "A Moral Imperative for Bioethics," *Boston Globe*, Aug. 1, 2015; Paul Knoepfler, Steven Pinker interview, *The Niche*, Aug. 10, 2015.
16. Author's interviews with Jennifer Doudna, David Baltimore, and George Church; *International Summit on Human Gene Editing, Dec. 1–3, 2015* (National Academies Press, 2015); Jef Akst, "Let's Talk Human Engineering," *The Scientist*, Dec. 3, 2015.
17. R. Alto Charo, Richard Hynes, et al., "Human Genome Editing: Scientific, Medical, and Ethical Considerations," report of the National Academies of Sciences, Engineering, Medicine, 2017.
18. Françoise Baylis, *Altered Inheritance: CRISPR and the Ethics of Human Genome Editing* (Harvard, 2019); Jocelyn Kaiser, "U.S. Panel Gives Yellow Light to Human Embryo Editing," *Science*, Feb. 14, 2017; Kelsey Montgomery, "Behind the Scenes of the National Academy of Sciences' Report on Human Genome Editing," *Medical Press*, Feb. 27, 2017.
19. "Genome Editing and Human Reproduction," Nuffield Council on Bioethics, July 2018; Ian Sample, "Genetically Modified Babies Given Go Ahead by UK Ethics Body," *Guardian*, July 17, 2018; Clive Cookson, "Human Gene Editing Morally Permissible, Says Ethics Study," *Financial Times*, July 17, 2018; Donna Dickenson and Marcy Darnovsky, "Did a Permissive Scientific Culture Encourage the 'CRISPR Babies' Experiment?," *Nature Biotechnology*, Mar. 15, 2019.
20. Consolidated Appropriations Act of 2016, Public Law 114-113, Section 749, Dec. 18, 2015; Francis Collins, "Statement on NIH Funding of Research Using Gene-Editing Technologies in Human Embryos," Apr. 28, 2015; John Holdren, "A Note on Genome Editing," May 26, 2015.
21. "Putin said scientists could create Universal Soldier-style supermen," YouTube, Oct. 24, 2017, youtube.com/watch?v=9v3TNGmbArs; "Russia's Parliament Seeks to Create Gene-Edited Babies," *EU Observer*, Sept. 3, 2019; Christina Daumann, "'New Type of Society'," *Asgardia*, Sept. 4, 2019.
22. Achim Rosemann, Li Jiang, and Xinqing Zhang, "The Regulatory and Legal Situation of Human Embryo, Gamete and Germ Line Gene Editing Research and Clinical Applications in the People's Republic of China," Nuffield Council on Bioethics, May

2017; Jing-ru Li, et. al., "Experiments That Led to the First Gene-Edited Babies," *Journal of Zhejiang University Science B*, Jan. 2019.

Chapter 37: He Jiankui

1. This section is based on Xi Xin and Xu Yue, "The Life Track of He Jiankui," *Jiemian News*, Nov. 27, 2018; Jon Cohen, "The Untold Story of the 'Circle of Trust' behind the World's First Gene-Edited Babies," *Science*, Aug. 1, 2019; Sharon Begley and Andrew Joseph, "The CRISPR Shocker," *Stat*, Dec. 17, 2018; Zach Coleman, "The Businesses behind the Doctor Who Manipulated Baby DNA," *Nikkei Asian Review*, Nov. 27, 2018; Zoe Low, "China's Gene Editing Frankenstein," *South China Morning Post*, Nov. 27, 2018; Yangyang Cheng, "Brave New World with Chinese Characteristics," *Bulletin of the Atomic Scientists*, Jan. 13, 2019; He Jiankui, "Draft Ethical Principles," YouTube, Nov. 25, 2018, youtube.com/watch?v=MyNHpMoPkIg; Antonio Regalado, "Chinese Scientists Are Creating CRISPR Babies," *MIT Technology Review*, Nov. 25, 2018; Marilynn Marchione, "Chinese Researcher Claims First Gene-Edited Babies," AP, Nov. 26, 2018; Christina Larson, "Gene-Editing Chinese Scientist Kept Much of His Work Secret," AP, Nov. 27, 2018; Davies, *Editing Humanity*.
2. Jiankui He and Michael W. Deem, "Heterogeneous Diversity of Spacers within CRISPR," *Physical Review Letters*, Sept. 14, 2010.
3. Mike Williams, "He's on a Hot Streak," *Rice News*, Nov. 17, 2010.
4. Cohen, "The Untold Story"; Coleman, "The Businesses behind the Doctor."
5. Davies, *Editing Humanity*, 209.
6. Yuan Yuan, "The Talent Magnet," *Beijing Review*, May 31, 2018.
7. Luyang Zhao . . . Jiankui He, et al., "Resequencing the *Escherichia coli* Genome by GenoCare Single Molecule," bioRxiv, posted online July 13, 2017.
8. Teng Jing Xuan, "CCTV's Glowing 2017 Coverage of Gene-Editing Pariah He Jiankui," *Caixan Global*, Nov. 30, 2018; Rob Schmitz, "Gene-Editing Scientist's Actions Are a Product of Modern China," *All Things Considered*, NPR, Feb. 5, 2019.
9. "Welcome to the Jiankui He Lab," http://sustc-genome.org.cn/people.html (site no longer active); Regalado, "Chinese Scientists Are Creating CRISPR Babies."
10. He Jiankui, "CRISPR Gene Editing Meeting," blog post (in Chinese), Aug. 24, 2016, http://blog.sciencenet.cn/home.php?mod=space&uid=514529&do=blog&id=998292.
11. Cohen, "The Untold Story"; Begley and Joseph, "The CRISPR Shocker"; author's interviews with Jennifer Doudna; Jennifer Doudna and William Hurlbut, "The Challenge and Opportunity of Gene Editing," Templeton Foundation grant 217,398.
12. Davies, *Editing Humanity*, 221; George Church, "Future, Human, Nature: Reading, Writing, Revolution," Innovative Genomics Institute, January 26, 2017, innovativegenomics.org/multimedia-library/george-church-lecture/.
13. He Jiankui, "The Safety of Gene-Editing of Human Embryos to Be Resolved," blog post (in Chinese), Feb. 19, 2017, blog.sciencenet.cn/home.php?mod=space&uid=514529&do=blog&id=1034671.
14. Author's interview with Jennifer Doudna.
15. He Jiankui, "Evaluating the Safety of Germline Genome Editing in Human, Monkey, and Mouse Embryos," Cold Spring Harbor Lab Symposium, July 29, 2017, youtube.com/watch?v=llxNRGMxyCc&t=3s; Regalado, "Chinese Scientists Are Creating CRISPR Babies."
16. Medical Ethics Approval Application Form, HarMoniCare Shenzhen Women's and Children's Hospital, March 7, 2017, theregreview.org/wp-content/uploads/2019/05

/He-Jiankui-Documents-3.pdf; Cohen, "The Untold Story"; Kathy Young, Marilynn Marchione, Emily Wang, et al., "First Gene-Edited Babies Reported in China," YouTube, Nov. 25, 2018, https://www.youtube.com/watch?v=C9V3mqswbv0; Gerry Shih and Carolyn Johnson, "Chinese Genomics Scientist Defends His Gene-Editing Research," *Washington Post*, Nov. 28, 2018.

17. Jiankui He, "Informed Consent, Version: Female 3.0," Mar. 2017, theregreview.org /wp-content/uploads/2019/05/He-Jiankui-Documents-3.pdf; Cohen, "The Untold Story"; Marilynn Marchione, "Chinese Researcher Claims First Gene-Edited Babies," AP, Nov. 26, 2018; Larson, "Gene-Editing Chinese Scientist Kept Much of His Work Secret."
18. Kiran Musunuru, *The Crispr Generation* (BookBaby, 2019).
19. Begley and Joseph, "The CRISPR Shocker." See also Pam Belluck, "How to Stop Rogue Gene-Editing of Human Embryos?," *New York Times*, Jan. 23, 2019; Preetika Rana, "How a Chinese Scientist Broke the Rules to Create the First Gene-Edited Babies," *Wall Street Journal*, May 10, 2019.
20. Author's interviews with Matthew Porteus.
21. Cohen, "The Untold Story"; Begley and Joseph, "The CRISPR Shocker"; Marilyn Marchione and Christina Larson, "Could Anyone Have Stopped Gene-Edited Babies Experiment?," AP, Dec. 2, 2018.
22. Pam Belluck, "Gene-Edited Babies: What a Chinese Scientist Told an American Mentor," *New York Times*, Apr. 14, 2019; "Statement on Fact-Finding Review related to Dr. Jiankui He," *Stanford News*, Apr. 16, 2019. Belluck was the first to publish the emails between He and Quake.
23. He Jiankui, question-and-answer session, the Second International Summit on Human Genome Editing, Hong Kong, Nov. 28, 2018; Cohen, "The Untold Story"; Marchione and Larson, "Could Anyone Have Stopped Gene-Edited Babies Experiment?"; Marchione, "Chinese Researcher Claims First Gene-Edited Babies"; Jane Qiu, "American Scientist Played More Active Role in 'CRISPR Babies' Project Than Previously Known," *Stat*, Jan. 31, 2019; Todd Ackerman, "Lawyers Say Rice Professor Not Involved in Controversial Gene-Edited Babies Research," *Houston Chronicle*, Dec. 13, 2018; decommissioned web page: Rice University, Faculty, https://profiles.rice.edu /faculty/michael-deem; see Michael Deem search on Rice website: https://search.rice .edu/?q=michael+deem&tab=Search.
24. Cohen, "The Untold Story."
25. He Jiankui, Ryan Ferrell, Chen Yuanlin, Qin Jinzhou, and Chen Yangran, "Draft Ethical Principles for Therapeutic Assisted Reproductive Technologies," *CRISPR Journal*, originally published Nov. 26, 2019, but later retracted and removed from the website. See also Henry Greeley, "CRISPR'd Babies," *Journal of Law and the Biosciences*, Aug. 13, 2019.
26. Allen Buchanan, *Better Than Human* (Oxford, 2011), 40, 101.
27. He Jiankui, "Draft Ethical Principles for Therapeutic Assisted Reproductive Technologies."
28. He Jiankui, "Designer Baby Is an Epithet" and "Why We Chose HIV and *CCR5* First," The He Lab, YouTube, Nov. 25, 2018.
29. He Jiankui, "HIV Immune Gene CCR5 Gene Editing in Human Embryos," Chinese Clinical Trial Registry, ChiCTR1800019378, Nov. 8, 2018.
30. Jinzhou Qin . . . Michael W. Deem, Jiankui He, et al., "Birth of Twins after Genome Editing for HIV Resistance," submitted to *Nature* Nov. 2019 (never published; I was given

a copy by an American researcher who received it from He Jiankui); Qiu, "American Scientist Played More Active Role in 'CRISPR Babies' Project Than Previously Known."

31. Greely, "CRISPR'd Babies"; Musunuru, *The Crispr Generation*; author's interview with Dana Carroll.
32. Regalado, "Chinese Scientists Are Creating CRISPR Babies."
33. Marchione, "Chinese Researcher Claims First Gene-Edited Babies"; Larson, "Gene-Editing Chinese Scientist Kept Much of His Work Secret."
34. He Jiankui, "About Lulu and Nana," YouTube, Nov. 25, 2018.

Chapter 38: The Hong Kong Summit

1. Author's interview with Jennifer Doudna.
2. Author's interview with David Baltimore.
3. Cohen, "The Untold Story."
4. Author's interviews with Victor Dzau, David Baltimore, Jennifer Doudna.
5. Author's interviews with Duanqing Pei.
6. Author's interviews with Jennifer Doudna; Robin Lovell-Badge, "CRISPR Babies," *Development*, Feb. 6, 2019.
7. Cached story deleted from the *China's People's Daily*, Nov. 26, 2018, ithome.com/html/discovery/396899.htm.
8. Author's interviews with Duanqing Pei, Jennifer Doudna.
9. Author's interviews with Jennifer Doudna, Victor Dzau.
10. Second International Summit on Genome Editing, University of Hong Kong, Nov. 27–29, 2018.
11. He Jiankui session, the Second International Summit on Human Genome Editing, Hong Kong, Nov. 28, 2018.
12. Davies, *Editing Humanity*, 235.
13. Author's interview with David Baltimore.
14. Author's interview with Matthew Porteus.
15. Author's interviews with Jennifer Doudna.
16. Author's interview with Duanqing Pei.
17. Author's interviews with Jennifer Doudna, David Baltimore.
18. Author's interviews with Matthew Porteus, David Baltimore.
19. Mary Louise Kelly, "Harvard Medical School Dean Weighs In on Ethics of Gene Editing," *All Things Considered*, NPR, Nov. 29, 2018. See also Baylis, *Altered Inheritance*, 140; George Daley, Robin Lovell-Badge, and Julie Steffann, "After the Storm—A Responsible Path for Genome Editing," and R. Alta Charo, "Rogues and Regulation of Germline Editing," *New England Journal of Medicine*, Mar. 7, 2019; David Cyranoski and Heidi Ledford, "How the Genome-Edited Babies Revelation Will Affect Research," *Nature*, Nov. 27, 2018.
20. David Baltimore, et al., "Statement by the Organizing Committee of the Second International Summit on Human Genome Editing," Nov. 29, 2018.

Chapter 39: Acceptance

1. Author's interview with Josiah Zayner.
2. Zayner, "CRISPR Babies Scientist He Jiankui Should Not Be Villainized."
3. Author's interview with Josiah Zayner.
4. Author's interview with Jennifer Doudna and dinner with her and Andrew Doudna Cate.

5. Author's interviews with Jennifer Doudna, Bill Cassidy.
6. Author's interview with Margaret Hamburg and Victor Dzau; Walter Isaacson, "Should the Rich Be Allowed to Buy the Best Genes?," *Air Mail*, July 27, 2019.
7. Belluck, "How to Stop Rogue Gene-Editing of Human Embryos?"
8. Eric S. Lander, et. al., "Adopt a Moratorium on Heritable Genome Editing," *Nature*, Mar. 13, 2019.
9. Ian Sample, "Scientists Call for Global Moratorium on Gene Editing of Embryos," *Guardian*, Mar. 13, 2019; Joel Achenbach, "NIH and Top Scientists Call for Moratorium on Gene-Edited Babies," *Washington Post*, Mar. 13, 2019; Jon Cohen, "New Call to Ban Gene-Edited Babies Divides Biologists," *Science*, Mar. 13, 2019; Francis Collins, "NIH Supports International Moratorium on Clinical Application of Germline Editing," National Institutes of Health statement, Mar. 13, 2019.
10. Author's interview with Margaret Hamburg. See also Sara Reardon, "World Health Organization Panel Weighs In on CRISPR-Babies Debate," *Nature*, Mar. 19, 2019.
11. Author's interview with Jennifer Doudna. For a strong critique of Doudna's argument, see Baylis, *Altered Inheritance*, 163–66.
12. Kay Davies, Richard Lifton, et al., "Heritable Human Genome Editing," International Commission on the Clinical Use of Human Germline Genome Editing, Sept. 3, 2020.
13. "He Jiankui Jailed for Illegal Human Embryo Gene-Editing," Xinhua news agency, Dec. 30, 2019.
14. Philip Wen and Amy Dockser Marcus, "Chinese Scientist Who Gene-Edited Babies Is Sent to Prison," *Wall Street Journal*, Dec. 30, 2019.

Chapter 40: Red Lines

1. This chapter draws on a wealth of writing about the ethics of genetic engineering. These include Françoise Baylis, Michael Sandel, Leon Kass, Francis Fukuyama, Nathaniel Comfort, Jason Scott Robert, Eric Cohen, Bill McKibben, Marcy Darnovsky, Erik Parens, Josephine Johnston, Rosemarie Garland-Thomson, Robert Sparrow, Ronald Dworkin, Jürgen Habermas, Michael Hauskeller, Jonathan Glover, Gregory Stock, John Harris, Maxwell Mehlman, Guy Kahane, Jamie Metzl, Allen Buchanan, Julian Savulescu, Lee Silver, Nick Bostrom, John Harris, Ronald Green, Nicholas Agar, Arthur Caplan, and Hank Greeley. I also drew on the work of the Hastings Center, the Center for Genetics and Society, the Oxford Uehiro Centre for Practical Ethics, and the Nuffield Council on Bioethics.
2. Sandel, *The Case against Perfection*; Robert Sparrow, "Genetically Engineering Humans," *Pharmaceutical Journal*, Sept. 24, 2015; Jamie Metzl, *Hacking Darwin* (Sourcebooks, 2019); Julian Savulescu, Ruud ter Meulen, and Guy Kahane, *Enhancing Human Capacities* (Wiley, 2011).
3. Gert de Graaf, Frank Buckley, and Brian Skotko, "Estimates of the Live Births, Natural Losses, and Elective Terminations with Down Syndrome in the United States," *American Journal of Medical Genetics*, Apr. 2015.
4. Steve Boggan, Glenda Cooper, and Charles Arthur, "Nobel Winner Backs Abortion 'for Any Reason,'" *The Independent*, Feb. 17, 1997.

Chapter 41: Thought Experiments

1. Matt Ridley, *Genome* (Harper Collins, 2000), chapter 4, powerfully describes Huntington's and the work of Nancy Wexler in researching it.
2. Baylis, *Altered Inheritance*, 30; Tina Rulli, "The Ethics of Procreation and Adoption," *Philosophy Compass*, June 6, 2012.

3. Adam Bolt, director, and Elliot Kirschner, executive producer, *Human Nature*, documentary, the Wonder Collaborative, 2019.
4. My questions to David Sanchez and his responses were relayed through the *Human Nature* producer, Meredith DeSalazar.
5. Rosemarie Garland-Thomson, "Welcoming the Unexpected," in Erik Parens and Josephine Johnston, *Human Flourishing in an Age of Gene Editing* (Oxford, 2019); Rosemarie Garland-Thomson, "Human Biodiversity Conservation," *American Journal of Bioethics*, Jan. 2015. See also Ethan Weiss, "Should 'Broken' Genes Be Fixed?" *Stat*, Feb. 21, 2020.
6. Jory Fleming, *How to Be Human* (Simon & Schuster, 2021).
7. Liza Mundy, "A World of Their Own," *Washington Post*, Mar. 31, 2002; Sandel, *The Case against Perfection*; Marion Andrea Schmidt, *Eradicating Deafness?* (Manchester University Press, 2020).
8. Craig Pickering and John Kiely, "ACTN#: More Than Just a Gene for Speed," *Frontiers in Physiology*, Dec. 18, 2017; David Epstein, *The Sports Gene* (Current, 2013); Haran Sivapalan, "Genetics of Marathon Runners," *Fitness Genes*, Sept. 26, 2018.
9. The Americans with Disabilities Act defines a disability as "a physical or mental impairment that substantially limits one or more major life activity."
10. Fred Hirsch, *Social Limits to Growth* (Routledge, 1977); Glenn Cohen, "What (If Anything) Is Wrong with Human Enhancement? What (If Anything) Is Right with It?," *Tulsa Law Review*, Apr. 21, 2014.
11. Nancy Andreasen, "The Relationship between Creativity and Mood Disorders," *Dialogues in Clinical Psychology*, June 2018; Neel Burton, "Hide and Seek: Bipolar Disorder and Creativity," *Psychology Today*, Mar. 19, 2012; Nathaniel Comfort, "Better Babies," *Aeon*, Nov. 17, 2015.
12. Robert Nozick, *Anarchy, State, and Utopia* (Basic Books, 1974).
13. See Erik Parens and Josephine Johnston, eds., *Human Flourishing in an Age of Gene Editing* (Oxford, 2019).
14. Jinping Liu . . . Yan Wu, et al., "The Role of NMDA Receptors in Alzheimer's Disease," *Frontiers in Neuroscience*, Feb. 8, 2019.

Chapter 42: Who Should Decide?

1. National Academy of Sciences, "How Does Human Gene Editing Work?" 2019, https://thesciencebehindit.org/how-does-human-gene-editing-work/, page removed; Marilynn Marchione, "Group Pulls Video That Stirred Talk of Designer Babies," AP, Oct. 2, 2019.
2. Twitter thread, @FrancoiseBaylis, @pknoepfler, @UrnovFyodor, @theNASAcademies, and others, Oct. 1, 2019.
3. John Rawls, *A Theory of Justice* (Harvard, 1971), 266, 92.
4. Nozick, *Anarchy, State and Utopia*, 315n.
5. Colin Gavaghan, *Defending the Genetic Supermarket* (Routledge-Cavendish, 2007); Peter Singer, "Shopping at the Genetic Supermarket," in John Rasko, ed., *The Ethics of Inheritable Genetic Modification* (Cambridge, 2006); Chris Gyngell and Thomas Douglas, "Stocking the Genetic Supermarket," *Bioethics*, May 2015.
6. Fukuyama, *Our Posthuman Future*, chapter 1; George Orwell, *1984* (Harcourt, 1949); Aldous Huxley, *Brave New World* (Harper, 1932).
7. Aldous Huxley, *Brave New World Revisited* (Harper, 1958), 120.
8. Aldous Huxley, *Island* (Harper, 1962), 232; Derek So, "The Use and Misuse of Brave New World in the CRISPR Debate," *CRISPR Journal*, Oct. 2019.

9. Nathaniel Comfort, "Can We Cure Genetic Diseases without Slipping into Eugenics?," *The Nation*, Aug. 3, 2015; Nathaniel Comfort, *The Science of Human Perfection* (Yale, 2012); Mark Frankel, "Inheritable Genetic Modification and a Brave New World," *Hastings Center Report*, Mar. 6, 2012; Arthur Caplan, "What Should the Rules Be?," *Time*, Jan. 14, 2001; Françoise Baylis and Jason Scott Robert, "The Inevitability of Genetic Enhancement Technologies," *Bioethics*, Feb. 2004; Daniel Kevles, "If You Could Design Your Baby's Genes, Would You?," *Politico*, Dec. 9, 2015; Lee M. Silver, "How Reprogenetics Will Transform the American Family," *Hofstra Law Review*, Fall 1999; Jürgen Habermas, *The Future of Human Nature* (Polity, 2003).
10. Author's interview with George Church, and similarly quoted in Rachel Cocker, "We Should Not Fear 'Editing' Embryos to Enhance Human Intelligence," *The Telegraph*, Mar. 16, 2019; Lee Silver, *Remaking Eden* (Morrow, 1997); John Harris, *Enhancing Evolution* (Princeton, 2011); Ronald Green, *Babies by Design* (Yale, 2008).
11. Julian Savulescu, "Procreative Beneficence: Why We Should Select the Best Children," *Bioethics*, Nov. 2001.
12. Antonio Regalado, "The World's First Gattaca Baby Tests Are Finally Here," *MIT Technology Review*, Nov. 8, 2019; Genomic Prediction company website, "Frequently Asked Questions," retrieved July 6, 2020; Hannah Devlin, "IVF Couples Could Be Able to Choose the 'Smartest' Embryo," *Guardian*, May 24, 2019; Nathan Treff . . . and Laurent Tellier, "Preimplantation Genetic Testing for Polygenic Disease Relative Risk Reduction," *Genes*, June 12, 2020; Louis Lello . . . and Stephen Hsu, "Genomic Prediction of 16 Complex Disease Risks," *Nature*, Oct. 25, 2019. In November 2019, *Nature* issued a conflict-of-interest correction saying that some of the authors did not disclose that they were affiliated with the company Genomic Prediction.
13. In addition to the sources cited above, see Laura Hercher, "Designer Babies Aren't Futuristic. They're Already Here," *MIT Technology Review*, Oct. 22, 2018; Ilya Somin, "In Defense of Designer Babies," *Reason*, Nov. 11, 2018.
14. Francis Fukuyama, "Gene Regime," *Foreign Policy*, Mar. 2002.
15. Francis Collins in Patrick Skerrett, "Experts Debate: Are We Playing with Fire When We Edit Human Genes?," *Stat*, Nov. 17, 2016.
16. Russell Powell and Allen Buchanan, "Breaking Evolution's Chains," *Journal of Medical Philosophy*, Feb. 2011; Allen Buchanan, *Better Than Human* (Oxford, 2011); Charles Darwin to J. D. Hooker, July 13, 1856.
17. Sandel, *The Case against Perfection*; Leon Kass, "Ageless Bodies, Happy Souls," *The New Atlantis*, Jan. 2003; Michael Hauskeller, "Human Enhancement and the Giftedness of Life," *Philosophical Papers*, Feb. 26, 2011.

Chapter 43: Doudna's Ethical Journey

1. Author's interviews with Jennifer Doudna; Doudna and Sternberg, *A Crack in Creation*, 222–40; Hannah Devlin, "Jennifer Doudna: 'I Have to Be True to Who I Am as a Scientist,'" *The Observer*, July 2, 2017.

Chapter 44: Quebec

1. Sanne Klompe . . . Samuel Sternberg, et al., "Transposon-Encoded CRISPR-Cas Systems Direct RNA-Guided DNA Integration," *Nature*, July 11, 2019 (received Mar. 15, 2019; accepted June 4; published online June 12); Jonathan Strecker . . . Eugene Koonin, Feng Zhang, et al., "RNA-Guided DNA Insertion with CRISPR-Associated Transposases," *Science*, July 5, 2019 (received May 4, 2019; accepted May 29; published online June 6).

2. Author's interviews with Sam Sternberg, Martin Jinek, Jennifer Doudna, Joe Bondy-Denomy.
3. Author's interviews with Feng Zhang.

Chapter 45: I Learn to Edit

1. Author's interviews with Gavin Knott.
2. "Alt-R CRISPR-Cas9 System: Delivery of Ribonucleoprotein Complexes into HEK-293 Cells Using the Amaxa Nucleofector System," IDTDNA.com; "CRISPR Gene-Editing Tools," GeneCopoeia.com.
3. Author's interviews with Jennifer Hamilton.

Chapter 46: Watson Revisited

1. Author's interviews with James Watson, Jennifer Doudna; "The CRISPR/Cas Revolution," Cold Spring Harbor Laboratory meeting, Sept. 24–27, 2015.
2. David Dugan, producer, *DNA*, documentary, Windfall Films for WNET/PBS and BBC4, 2003; Shaoni Bhattacharya, "Stupidity Should Be Cured, Says DNA Discoverer," *The New Scientist*, Feb. 28, 2003. See also Tom Abate, "Nobel Winner's Theories Raise Uproar in Berkeley," *San Francisco Chronicle*, Nov. 13, 2000.
3. Michael Sandel, "The Case against Perfection," *The Atlantic*, Apr. 2004.
4. Charlotte Hunt-Grubbe, "The Elementary DNA of Dr Watson," *Sunday Times* (London), Oct. 14, 2007; author's interviews with James Watson.
5. Author's interviews with James Watson; Roxanne Khamsi, "James Watson Retires amidst Race Controversy," *The New Scientist*, Oct. 25, 2007.
6. Author's interview with Eric Lander; Sharon Begley, "As Twitter Explodes, Eric Lander Apologizes for Toasting James Watson," *Stat*, May 14, 2018.
7. Author's interviews with James Watson.
8. "Decoding Watson."
9. Amy Harmon, "James Watson Had a Chance to Salvage His Reputation on Race. He Made Things Worse," *New York Times*, Jan. 1, 2019.
10. Harmon, "James Watson Had a Chance to Salvage His Reputation on Race."
11. "Decoding Watson"; Harmon, "James Watson Had a Chance to Salvage His Reputation on Race"; author's interviews with James Watson.
12. James Watson, "An Appreciation of Linus Pauling," *Time* magazine seventy-fifth anniversary dinner, Mar. 3, 1998.
13. Author's interviews with James Watson. I used some of these quotes, as well as other passages, in a piece I wrote, "Should the Rich Be Allowed to Buy the Best Genes?"
14. "Decoding Watson."
15. Author's meetings with James Watson, Rufus Watson, Elizabeth Watson.
16. Malcolm Ritter, "Lab Revokes Honors for Controversial DNA Scientist Watson," AP, Jan. 11, 2019.

Chapter 47: Doudna Pays a Visit

1. Author's visit with James Watson and Jennifer Doudna. The conference book was designed by Megan Hochstrasser, who works in Doudna's lab.
2. Author's interviews with Jennifer Doudna.

Chapter 48: Call to Arms

1. Robert Sanders, "New DNA-Editing Technology Spawns Bold UC Initiative," *Berkeley News*, Mar. 18, 2014; "About Us," Innovative Genomics Institute website, https://

innovativegenomics.org/about-us/. It was relaunched in January 2017 as the Innovative Genomics Institute.
2. Author's interview with Dave Savage; Benjamin Oakes . . . Jennifer Doudna, David Savage, et al., "CRISPR-Cas9 Circular Permutants as Programmable Scaffolds for Genome Modification," *Cell*, Jan 10, 2019.
3. Author's interviews with Dave Savage, Gavin Knott, and Jennifer Doudna.
4. Jonathan Corum and Carl Zimmer, "Bad News Wrapped in Protein: Inside the Coronavirus Genome," *New York Times*, Apr. 3, 2020; GenBank, National Institutes of Health, SARS-CoV-2 Sequences, updated Apr. 14, 2020.
5. Alexander Walls . . . David Veesler, et al., "Structure, Function, and Antigenicity of the SARS-CoV-2 Spike Glycoprotein," *Cell*, Mar. 9, 2020; Qihui Wang . . . and Jianxun Qi, "Structural and Functional Basis of SARS-CoV-2 Entry by Using Human ACE2," *Cell*, May 14, 2020; Francis Collins, "Antibody Points to Possible Weak Spot on Novel Coronavirus," NIH, Apr. 14, 2020; Bonnie Berkowitz, Aaron Steckelberg, and John Muyskens, "What the Structure of the Coronavirus Can Tell Us," *Washington Post*, Mar. 23, 2020.
6. Author's interviews with Megan Hochstrasser, Jennifer Doudna, Dave Savage, and Fyodor Urnov.

Chapter 49: Testing

1. Shawn Boburg, Robert O'Harrow Jr., Neena Satija, and Amy Goldstein, "Inside the Coronavirus Testing Failure," *Washington Post*, Apr. 3, 2020; Robert Baird, "What Went Wrong with Coronavirus Testing in the U.S.," *New Yorker*, Mar. 16, 2020; Michael Shear, Abby Goodnough, Sheila Kaplan, Sheri Fink, Katie Thomas, and Noah Weiland, "The Lost Month: How a Failure to Test Blinded the U.S. to COVID-19," *New York Times*, Mar. 28, 2020.
2. Kary Mullis, "The Unusual Origin of the Polymerase Chain Reaction," *Scientific American*, Apr. 1990.
3. Boburg et al., "Inside the Coronavirus Testing Failure"; David Willman, "Contamination at CDC Lab Delayed Rollout of Coronavirus Tests," *Washington Post*, Apr. 18, 2020.
4. JoNel Aleccia, "How Intrepid Lab Sleuths Ramped Up Tests as Coronavirus Closed In," *Kaiser Health News*, Mar. 16, 2020.
5. Julia Ioffe, "The Infuriating Story of How the Government Stalled Coronavirus Testing," *GQ*, Mar. 16, 2020; Boburg et al., "Inside the Coronavirus Testing Failure." Greninger's email to a friend is in the excellent *Washington Post* reconstruction.
6. Boburg et al., "Inside the Coronavirus Testing Failure"; Patrick Boyle, "Coronavirus Testing: How Academic Medical Labs Are Stepping Up to Fill a Void," *AAMC*, Mar. 12, 2020.
7. Author's interview with Eric Lander; Leah Eisenstadt, "How Broad Institute Converted a Clinical Processing Lab into a Large-Scale COVID-19 Testing Facility in a Matter of Days," *Broad Communications*, Mar. 27, 2020.

Chapter 50: The Berkeley Lab

1. IGI COVID-19 Rapid Response Research meeting, Mar. 13, 2020. I was allowed to attend the meetings of the rapid-response team and its working groups, most of which took place on Zoom with discussion in Slack channels.
2. Author's interviews with Fyodor Urnov. Dmitry Urnov became a professor at Adelphi

University in New York. He is an accomplished horseman who once accompanied three horses on a sea voyage when Nikita Khrushchev wanted to give them as a gift to the American industrialist Cyrus Eaton. He and his wife, Julia Palievsky, wrote *A Kindred Writer: Dickens in Russia*. They are also scholars of William Faulkner.

3. Author's interviews with Jennifer Hamilton; Jennifer Hamilton, "Building a COVID-19 Pop-Up Testing Lab," *CRISPR Journal*, June 2020.
4. Author's interviews with Enrique Lin Shiao.
5. Author's interviews with Fyodor Urnov, Jennifer Doudna, Jennifer Hamilton, Enrique Lin Shiao; Hope Henderson, "IGI Launches Major Automated COVID-19 Diagnostic Testing Initiative," *IGI News*, Mar. 30, 2020; Megan Molteni and Gregory Barber, "How a Crispr Lab Became a Pop-Up COVID Testing Center," *Wired*, Apr. 2, 2020.
6. Innovative Genomics Institute SARS-CoV-2 Testing Consortium, Dirk Hockemeyer, Fyodor Urnov, and Jennifer A. Doudna, "Blueprint for a Pop-up SARS-CoV-2 Testing Lab," *medRxiv*, Apr. 12, 2020.
7. Author's interviews with Fyodor Urnov, Jennifer Hamilton, and Enrique Lin Shiao.

Chapter 51: Mammoth and Sherlock

1. Author's interview with Lucas Harrington and Janice Chen.
2. Janice Chen . . . Lucas B. Harrington . . . Jennifer A. Doudna, et al., "CRISPR-Cas12a Target Binding Unleashes Indiscriminate Single-Stranded DNase Activity," *Science*, Apr. 27, 2018 (received Nov. 29, 2017; accepted Feb. 5, 2018; published online Feb. 15); John Carroll, "CRISPR Legend Jennifer Doudna Helps Some Recent College Grads Launch a Diagnostics Up-start," *Endpoints*, Apr. 26, 2018.
3. Sergey Shmakov, Omar Abudayyeh, Kira S. Makarova . . . Konstantin Severinov, Feng Zhang, and Eugene V. Koonin, "Discovery and Functional Characterization of Diverse Class 2 CRISPR-Cas Systems," *Molecular Cell*, Nov. 5, 2015 (published online Oct. 22, 2015); Omar Abudayyeh, Jonathan Gootenberg . . . Eric Lander, Eugene Koonin, and Feng Zhang, "C2c2 Is a Single-Component Programmable RNA-Guided RNA-Targeting CRISPR Effector," *Science*, Aug. 5, 2016 (published online June 2, 2016).
4. Author's interviews with Feng Zhang.
5. Alexandra East-Seletsky . . . Jamie Cate, Robert Tjian, and Jennifer Doudna, "Two Distinct RNase Activities of CRISPR-C2c2 Enable Guide-RNA Processing and RNA Detection," *Nature*, Oct. 13, 2016. CRISPR-C2c2 was renamed CRISPER-Cas13a.
6. Jonathan Gootenberg, Omar Abudayyeh . . . Cameron Myhrvold . . . Eugene Koonin . . . Feng Zhang et al., "Nucleic Acid Detection with CRISPR-Cas13a/C2c2," *Science*, Apr. 28, 2017.
7. Jonathan Gootenberg, Omar Abudayyeh . . . Feng Zhang, et al., "Multiplexed and Portable Nucleic Acid Detection Platform with Cas13, Cas12a, and Csm6," *Science*, Apr. 27, 2018. See also Abudayyeh et al., "C2c2 Is a Single Component Programmable RNA-Guided RNA-Targeting CRISPR Effector."
8. Author's interview with Feng Zhang; Carey Goldberg, "CRISPR Comes to COVID," WBUR, July 10, 2020.
9. Emily Mullin, "CRISPR Could Be the Future of Disease Diagnosis," *OneZero*, July 25, 2019; Emily Mullin, "CRISPR Pioneer Jennifer Doudna on the Future of Disease Detection," *OneZero*, July 30, 2019; Daniel Chertow, "Next-Generation Diagnostics with CRISPR," *Science*, Apr. 27, 2018; Ann Gronowski "Who or What Is SHERLOCK?," *EJIFCC*, Nov. 2018.

Chapter 52: Coronavirus Tests

1. Author's interviews with Feng Zhang.
2. Feng Zhang, Omar Abudayyeh, and Jonathan Gootenberg, "A Protocol for Detection of COVID-19 Using CRISPR Diagnostics," Broad Institute website, posted Feb. 14, 2020; Carl Zimmer, "With Crispr, a Possible Quick Test for the Coronavirus," *New York Times*, May 5, 2020.
3. Goldberg, "CRISPR Comes to COVID"; "Sherlock Biosciences and Binx Health Announce Global Partnership to Develop First CRISPR-Based Point-of-Care Test for COVID-19," *PR Newswire*, July 1, 2020.
4. Author's interviews with Janice Chen and Lucas Harrington; Jim Daley, "CRISPR Gene Editing May Help Scale Up Coronavirus Testing," *Scientific American*, Apr. 23, 2020; John Cumbers, "With Its Coronavirus Rapid Paper Test Strip, This CRISPR Startup Wants to Help Halt a Pandemic," *Forbes*, Mar. 14, 2020; Lauren Martz, "CRISPR-Based Diagnostics Are Poised to Make an Early Debut amid COVID-19 Outbreak," *Biocentury*, Feb. 28, 2020.
5. James Broughton . . . Charles Chiu, Janice Chen, et al., "A Protocol for Rapid Detection of the 2019 Novel Coronavirus SARS-CoV-2 Using CRISPR Diagnostics: SARS-CoV-2 DETECTR," Mammoth Biosciences website, posted Feb. 15, 2020. The full Mammoth paper with patient data and other details is James Broughton . . . Janice Chen, and Charles Chiu, "CRISPR–Cas12-Based Detection of SARS-CoV-2," *Nature Biotechnology*, Apr. 16, 2020 (received Mar. 5, 2020). See also Eelke Brandsma . . . and Emile van den Akker, "Rapid, Sensitive and Specific SARS Coronavirus-2 Detection: A Multi-center Comparison between Standard qRT-PCR and CRISPR Based DETECTR," *medRxiv*, July 27, 2020.
6. Julia Joung . . . Jonathan S. Gootenberg, Omar O. Abudayyeh, and Feng Zhang, "Point-of-Care Testing for COVID-19 Using SHERLOCK Diagnostics," *medRxiv*, May 5, 2020.
7. Author's interview with Feng Zhang.
8. Author's interview with Janice Chen.

Chapter 53: Vaccines

1. Ochsner Health System, phase 2/3 study by Pfizer Inc. and BioNTech SE of investigational vaccine, BNT162b2, against SARS-CoV-2, beginning July 2020.
2. Author's interview with Jennifer Doudna.
3. Simantini Dey, "Meet Sarah Gilbert," *News18*, July 21, 2020; Stephanie Baker, "Covid Vaccine Front-Runner Is Months Ahead of Her Competition," *Bloomberg BusinessWeek*, July 14, 2020; Clive Cookson, "Sarah Gilbert, the Researcher Leading the Race to a Covid-19 Vaccine," *Financial Times*, July 24, 2020.
4. Author's interviews with Ross Wilson, Alex Marson; IGI white paper seeking funding for DNA vaccine delivery systems, Mar. 2020; Ross Wilson report at IGI COVID-response meeting, June 11, 2020.
5. "A Trial Investigating the Safety and Effects of Four BNT162 Vaccines against COVID-2019 in Healthy Adults," ClinicalTrials.gov, May 2020, identifier: NCT04380701; "BNT162 SARS-CoV-2 Vaccine," *Precision Vaccinations*, Aug. 14, 2020; Mark J. Mulligan . . . Uğur Şahin, Kathrin Jansen, et. al., "Phase 1/2 Study of COVID-19 RNA Vaccine BNT162b1 in Adults," *Nature*, Aug. 12, 2020.
6. Joe Miller, "The Immunologist Racing to Find a Vaccine," *Financial Times*, Mar. 20, 2020.
7. Author's interview with Phil Dormitzer; Matthew Herper, "In the Race for a

COVID-19 Vaccine, Pfizer Turns to a Scientist with a History of Defying Skeptics," *Stat*, Aug. 24, 2020.

8. Author's interviews with Noubar Afeyan, Christine Heenan.
9. Author's interview and emails with Josiah Zayner; Kristen Brown, "One Biohacker's Improbable Bid to Make a DIY Covid-19 Vaccine," *Bloomberg Business Week*, June 25, 2020; Josiah Zayner videos, www.youtube.com/josiahzayner.
10. Jingyou Yu . . . and Dan H. Barouch, "DNA Vaccine Protection against SARS-CoV-2 in Rhesus Macaques," *Science*, May 20, 2020.
11. Author's interviews with Josiah Zayner; Kristen Brown, "Home-Made Vaccine Appeared to Work, but Questions Remain," *Bloomberg BusinessWeek*, Oct. 10, 2020.
12. The Ochsner Health system clinical trial of Pfizer/BioNTech vaccine BNT162b2, led by Julia Garcia-Diaz, director of Clinical Infectious Diseases Research, and Leonardo Seoane, chief academic officer.
13. Author's interview with Francis Collins; "Bioethics Consultation Service Consultation Report," Department of Bioethics, NIH Clinical Center, July 31, 2020.
14. Sharon LaFraniere, Katie Thomas, Noah Weiland, David Gelles, Sheryl Gay Stolberg and Denise Grady, "Politics, Science and the Remarkable Race for a Coronavirus Vaccine," *New York Times*, Nov. 21, 2020; author's interviews with Noubar Afeyan, Moncef Slaoui, Philip Dormitzer, Christine Heenan.

Chapter 54: CRISPR Cures

1. David Dorward . . . and Christopher Lucas, "Tissue-Specific Tolerance in Fatal COVID-19," *medRxiv*, July 2, 2020; Bicheng Zhag . . . and Jun Wan, "Clinical Characteristics of 82 Cases of Death from COVID-19," *Plos One*, July 9, 2020.
2. Ed Yong, "Immunology Is Where Intuition Goes to Die," *The Atlantic*, Aug. 5, 2020.
3. Author's interview with Cameron Myhrvold.
4. Jonathan Gootenberg, Omar Abudayyeh . . . Cameron Myhrvold . . . Eugene Koonin . . . Pardis Sabeti . . . and Feng Zhang, "Nucleic Acid Detection with CRISPR-Cas13a/C2c2," *Science*, Apr. 28, 2017.
5. Cameron Myhrvold, Catherine Freije, Jonathan Gootenberg, Omar Abudayyeh . . . Feng Zhang, and Pardis Sabeti, "Field-Deployable Viral Diagnostics Using CRISPR-Cas13," *Science*, Apr. 27, 2018.
6. Author's interview with Cameron Myhrvold.
7. Cameron Myhrvold to Pardis Sabeti, Dec. 22, 2016.
8. Defense Advanced Research Projects Agency (DARPA) grant D18AC00006.
9. Susanna Hamilton, "CRISPR-Cas13 Developed as Combination Antiviral and Diagnostic System," *Broad Communications*, Oct. 11, 2019.
10. Catherine Freije, Cameron Myhrvold . . . Omar Abudayyeh, Jonathan Gootenberg . . . Feng Zhang, and Pardis Sabeti, "Programmable Inhibition and Detection of RNA Viruses Using Cas13," *Molecular Cell*, Dec. 5, 2019 (received Apr. 16, 2019; revised July 18, 2019; accepted Sept. 6, 2019; published online Oct. 10, 2019); Tanya Lewis, "Scientists Program CRISPR to Fight Viruses in Human Cells," *Scientific American*, Oct. 23, 2019.
11. Cheri Ackerman, Cameron Myhrvold . . . and Pardis C. Sabeti, "Massively Multiplexed Nucleic Acid Detection with Cas13m," *Nature*, Apr. 29, 2020 (received Mar. 20, 2020; accepted Apr. 20, 2020).
12. Jon Arizti-Sanz, Catherine Freije . . . Pardis Sabeti, and Cameron Myhrvold, "Integrated Sample Inactivation, Amplification, and Cas13-Based Detection of SARS-CoV-2," *bioRxiv*, May 28, 2020.

13. Author's interviews with Stanley Qi.
14. Silvana Konermann . . . and Patrick Hsu, "Transcriptome Engineering with RNA-Targeting Type VI-D CRISPR Effectors," *Cell*, Mar. 15, 2018.
15. Steven Levy, "Could CRISPR Be Humanity's Next Virus Killer?," *Wired*, Mar. 10, 2020.
16. Timothy Abbott . . . and Lei [Stanley] Qi, "Development of CRISPR as a Prophylactic Strategy to Combat Novel Coronavirus and Influenza," *bioRxiv*, Mar. 14, 2020.
17. Author's interview with Stanley Qi.
18. IGI weekly Zoom meeting, Mar. 22, 2020; author's interviews with Stanley Qi and Jennifer Doudna.
19. Stanley Qi, Jennifer Doudna, and Ross Wilson, "A White Paper for the Development of Novel COVID-19 Prophylactic and Therapeutics Using CRISPR Technology," unpublished, Apr. 2020.
20. Author's interviews with Ross Wilson; Ross Wilson, "Engineered CRISPR RNPs as Targeted Effectors for Genome Editing of Immune and Stem Cells In Vivo," unpublished, Apr. 2020.
21. Theresa Duque, "Cellular Delivery System Could Be Missing Link in Battle against SARS-CoV-2," *Berkeley Lab News*, June 4, 2020.

Chapter 55: Cold Spring Harbor Virtual

1. Kevin Bishop and others gave me permission to quote them from the meeting.
2. Andrew Anzalone . . . David Liu, et al., "Search-and-Replace Genome Editing without Double-Strand Breaks or Donor DNA," *Nature*, Dec. 5, 2019 (received Aug. 26; accepted Oct. 10; published online Oct. 21).
3. Megan Molteni, "A New Crispr Technique Could Fix Almost All Genetic Diseases," *Wired*, Oct. 21, 2019; Sharon Begley, "New CRISPR Tool Has the Potential to Correct Almost All Disease-Causing DNA Glitches," *Stat*, Oct. 21, 2019; Sharon Begley, "You Had Questions for David Liu," *Stat*, Nov. 6, 2019.
4. Beverly Mok . . . David Liu, et al., "A Bacterial Cytidine Deaminase Toxin Enables CRISPR-Free Mitochondrial Base Editing," *Nature*, July 8, 2020.
5. Jonathan Hsu . . . David Liu, Keith Joung, Lucan Pinello, et al., "PrimeDesign Software for Rapid and Simplified Design of Prime Editing Guide RNAs," *bioRxiv*, May 4, 2020.
6. Audrone Lapinaite, Gavin Knott . . . David Liu, and Jennifer A. Doudna, "DNA Capture by a CRISPR-Cas9–Guided Adenine Base Editor," *Science*, July 31, 2020.

Chapter 56: The Nobel Prize

1. Author's interviews with Heidi Ledford, Jennifer Doudna, Emmanuelle Charpentier.
2. Jennifer Doudna, "How COVID-19 Is Spurring Science to Accelerate," *The Economist*, June 5, 2020. See also Jane Metcalfe, "COVID-19 Is Accelerating Human Transformation—Let's Not Waste It," *Wired*, July 5, 2020.
3. Michael Eisen, "Patents Are Destroying the Soul of Academic Science," *it is NOT junk* (blog), Feb. 20, 2017.
4. "SARS-CoV-2 Sequence Read Archive Submissions," National Center for Biotechnology Information, https://www.ncbi.nlm.nih.gov/sars-cov-2/, n.d.
5. Simine Vazire, "Peer-Reviewed Scientific Journals Don't Really Do Their Job," *Wired*, June 25, 2020.
6. Author's interview with George Church.
7. Author's interview with Emmanuelle Charpentier.

INDEX

Page numbers in *italics* refer to photographs.

IMAGE CREDITS

By page number

Front and back endpaper: Carlos Chavarria/Redux
iv: Brittany Hosea-Small/UC Berkeley
xi (left and right): David Jacobs
xii: Jeff Gilbert/Alamy
2 :(clockwise): Courtesy of Jennifer Doudna; Leah Wyzykowski; courtesy of Jennifer Doudna
10: (left to right): George Richmond/Wikimedia/Public Domain; Wikimedia/Public Domain
16: A. Barrington Brown/Science Photo Library
25 (left to right): Universal History Archive/Universal Images Group/Getty Images; Courtesy Ava Helen and Linus Pauling Papers, Oregon State University Libraries
27: Historic Images/Alamy
30: Courtesy of Jennifer Doudna
36: Natl Human Genome Research Institute
42: Jim Harrison
52: YouTube
62: Courtesy of Jennifer Doudna
70 (top to bottom): Courtesy of BBVA Foundation; courtesy of Luciano Marraffini
78: The Royal Society / CC BY-SA (https://creativecommons.org/licenses/by-sa/3.0)
82: Mark Young
88: (top to bottom): Marc Hall/NC State courtesy of Rodolphe Barrangou; Franklin Institute /YouTube
96: Courtesy of Genetech
104: Roy Kaltschmidt/Lawrence Berkeley National Laboratory
112: Courtesy of Caribou Biosciences
120: Hallbauer & Fioretti/Wikimedia Commons
130: Berkeley Lab
133: MRS Bulletin
138: Miguel Riopa/AFP via Getty Images
142 (clockwise): Edgaras Kurauskas/Vilniaus universitetas; Heribert Corn/courtesy of Krzysztof Chylinski; Michael Tomes/ courtesy of Martin Jinek
152: Andriano_CZ/iStock by Getty Images
158: (top to bottom): Justin Knight/McGovern Institute; Seth Kroll / Wyss Institute at Harvard University; Thermal PR

162: Justin Knight/McGovern Institute
168: Seth Kroll / Wyss Institute at Harvard University
176: Wikimedia Commons
188: Anastasiia Sapon/The New York Times/Redux
196: Courtesy of Martin Jinek
204: Courtesy Rodger Novak
214: BBVA Foundation
222: Casey Atkins, courtesy Broad Institute
230: Courtesy of Sterne, Kessler, Goldstein & Fox P.L.L.C.
244: Amanda Stults, RN, Sarah Cannon Research Institute/The Children's Hos
252: Courtesy of The Odin
258: Susan Merrell/UCSF
266: (top to bottom): National Academy of Sciences, courtesy of Cold Spring Harbor Laboratory; Peter Breining/San Francisco Chronicle via Getty Images
282: Pam Risdom
298: (top to bottom): Courtesy He Jiankui; ABC News/YouTube
314: (top and bottom): Kin Cheung/AP/Shutterstock
325: Courtesy of UCDC
334: Tom & Dee Ann McCarthy/Getty Images
340: Wonder Collaborative
366: Isaac Lawrence/AFP/Getty Images
372: Nabor Godoy
384 (top to bottom): Lewis Miller; PBS
396: Courtesy of Jennifer Doudna
400: Irene Yi / UC Berekely
406: Fyodor Urnov
412: Courtesy of Innovative Genomics Institute
420 (top to bottom): Mammoth Biosciences; Justin Knight/McGovern Institute
426: Omar Abudayyeh
448 (top to bottom): Paul Sakuma; courtesy of Cameron Myhrvold
458 (top to bottom): Wikimedia Commons; Cold Spring Harbor Laboratory Archives
468: Brittany Hosea-Small/UC Berkeley E103
476: Gordon Russell

ABOUT THE AUTHOR

WALTER ISAACSON, a professor of history at Tulane, has been CEO of the Aspen Institute, chair of CNN, and editor of *Time*. He is the author of *Leonardo da Vinci*; *The Innovators*; *Steve Jobs*; *Einstein: His Life and Universe*; *Benjamin Franklin: An American Life*; and *Kissinger: A Biography*, and the coauthor of *The Wise Men: Six Friends and the World They Made*.